20. $\displaystyle\int \frac{du}{u\sqrt{a+bu}} = \begin{cases} \dfrac{1}{\sqrt{a}}\ln\left|\dfrac{\sqrt{a+bu}-\sqrt{a}}{\sqrt{a+bu}+\sqrt{a}}\right| + C & \text{if } a > 0 \\[2ex] \dfrac{2}{\sqrt{-a}}\tan^{-1}\sqrt{\dfrac{a+bu}{-a}} + C & \text{if } a < 0 \end{cases}$

21. $\displaystyle\int \frac{du}{u^n\sqrt{a+bu}} = -\frac{\sqrt{a+bu}}{a(n-1)u^{n-1}} - \frac{b(2n-3)}{2a(n-1)}\int \frac{du}{u^{n-1}\sqrt{a+bu}}$

22. $\displaystyle\int \frac{\sqrt{a+bu}\,du}{u} = 2\sqrt{a+bu} + a\int \frac{du}{u\sqrt{a+bu}}$

23. $\displaystyle\int \frac{\sqrt{a+bu}\,du}{u^n} = -\frac{(a+bu)^{3/2}}{a(n-1)u^{n-1}} - \frac{b(2n-5)}{2a(n-1)}\int \frac{\sqrt{a+bu}\,du}{u^{n-1}}$

Forms Containing $a^2 \pm u^2$

24. $\displaystyle\int \frac{du}{a^2+u^2} = \frac{1}{a}\tan^{-1}\frac{u}{a} + C$

25. $\displaystyle\int \frac{du}{a^2-u^2} = \frac{1}{2a}\ln\left|\frac{u+a}{u-a}\right| + C = \begin{cases} \dfrac{1}{a}\tanh^{-1}\dfrac{u}{a} + C & \text{if } |u| < a \\[2ex] \dfrac{1}{a}\coth^{-1}\dfrac{u}{a} + C & \text{if } |u| > a \end{cases}$

26. $\displaystyle\int \frac{du}{u^2-a^2} = \frac{1}{2a}\ln\left|\frac{u-a}{u+a}\right| + C = \begin{cases} -\dfrac{1}{a}\tanh^{-1}\dfrac{u}{a} + C & \text{if } |u| < a \\[2ex] -\dfrac{1}{a}\coth^{-1}\dfrac{u}{a} + C & \text{if } |u| > a \end{cases}$

Forms Containing $\sqrt{u^2 \pm a^2}$

In formulas 27 through 38, we may replace

$\ln(u + \sqrt{u^2+a^2})$ by $\sinh^{-1}\dfrac{u}{a}$

$\ln|u + \sqrt{u^2-a^2}|$ by $\cosh^{-1}\dfrac{u}{a}$

$\ln\left|\dfrac{a + \sqrt{u^2+a^2}}{u}\right|$ by $\sinh^{-1}\dfrac{a}{u}$

27. $\displaystyle\int \frac{du}{\sqrt{u^2 \pm a^2}} = \ln|u + \sqrt{u^2 \pm a^2}| + C$

28. $\displaystyle\int \sqrt{u^2 \pm a^2}\,du = \frac{u}{2}\sqrt{u^2 \pm a^2} \pm \frac{a^2}{2}\ln|u + \sqrt{u^2 \pm a^2}| + C$

29. $\displaystyle\int u^2\sqrt{u^2 \pm a^2}\,du = \frac{u}{8}(2u^2 \pm a^2)\sqrt{u^2 \pm a^2}$
$\hspace{4cm} - \dfrac{a^4}{8}\ln|u + \sqrt{u^2 \pm a^2}| + C$

30. $\displaystyle\int \frac{\sqrt{u^2 + a^2}\,du}{u} = \sqrt{u^2 + a^2} - a\ln\left|\frac{a + \sqrt{u^2+a^2}}{u}\right| + C$

31. $\displaystyle\int \frac{\sqrt{u^2 - a^2}\,du}{u} = \sqrt{u^2 - a^2} - a\sec^{-1}\left|\frac{u}{a}\right| + C$

32. $\displaystyle\int \frac{\sqrt{u^2 \pm a^2}\,du}{u^2} = -\frac{\sqrt{u^2 \pm a^2}}{u} + \ln|u + \sqrt{u^2 \pm a^2}| + C$

33. $\displaystyle\int \frac{u^2\,du}{\sqrt{u^2 \pm a^2}} = \frac{u}{2}\sqrt{u^2 \pm a^2} - \frac{\pm a^2}{2}\ln|u + \sqrt{u^2 \pm a^2}| + C$

34. $\displaystyle\int \frac{du}{u\sqrt{u^2 + a^2}} = -\frac{1}{a}\ln\left|\frac{a + \sqrt{u^2+a^2}}{u}\right| + C$

35. $\displaystyle\int \frac{du}{u\sqrt{u^2 - a^2}} = \frac{1}{a}\sec^{-1}\left|\frac{u}{a}\right| + C$

36. $\displaystyle\int \frac{du}{u^2\sqrt{u^2 \pm a^2}} = -\frac{\sqrt{u^2 \pm a^2}}{\pm a^2 u} + C$

37. $\displaystyle\int (u^2 \pm a^2)^{3/2}\,du = \frac{u}{8}(2u^2 \pm 5a^2)\sqrt{u^2 \pm a^2}$
$\hspace{4cm} + \dfrac{3a^4}{8}\ln|u + \sqrt{u^2 \pm a^2}| + C$

38. $\displaystyle\int \frac{du}{(u^2 \pm a^2)^{3/2}} = \frac{u}{\pm a^2\sqrt{u^2 \pm a^2}} + C$

Forms Containing $\sqrt{a^2 - u^2}$

39. $\displaystyle\int \frac{du}{\sqrt{a^2-u^2}} = \sin^{-1}\frac{u}{a} + C$

40. $\displaystyle\int \sqrt{a^2-u^2}\,du = \frac{u}{2}\sqrt{a^2-u^2} + \frac{a^2}{2}\sin^{-1}\frac{u}{a} + C$

41. $\displaystyle\int u^2\sqrt{a^2-u^2}\,du = \frac{u}{8}(2u^2 - a^2)\sqrt{a^2-u^2} + \frac{a^4}{8}\sin^{-1}\frac{u}{a} + C$

42. $\displaystyle\int \frac{\sqrt{a^2-u^2}\,du}{u} = \sqrt{a^2-u^2} - a\ln\left|\frac{a + \sqrt{a^2-u^2}}{u}\right| + C$
$\hspace{3cm} = \sqrt{a^2-u^2} - a\cosh^{-1}\frac{a}{u} + C$

43. $\displaystyle\int \frac{\sqrt{a^2-u^2}\,du}{u^2} = -\frac{\sqrt{a^2-u^2}}{u} - \sin^{-1}\frac{u}{a} + C$

(This table is continued on the back endpapers)

THE CALCULUS
WITH ANALYTIC GEOMETRY

THE CALCULUS
WITH ANALYTIC GEOMETRY
third edition

Part I Functions of one variable, plane analytic geometry, and infinite series

Louis Leithold

UNIVERSITY OF SOUTHERN CALIFORNIA

HARPER & ROW, PUBLISHERS
New York, Evanston, San Francisco, London

Sponsoring Editor: George J. Telecki
Project Editor: Karen A. Judd
Designer: Rita Naughton
Production Supervisor: Francis X. Giordano
Compositor: Progressive Typographers
Printer and Binder: Kingsport Press
Art Studio: J & R Technical Services Inc.
Cover and chapter opening art: "Study Light" by Patrick Caulfield

THE CALCULUS WITH ANALYTIC GEOMETRY, Third Edition
Part I: Functions of One Variable, Plane Analytic Geometry, and Infinite Series.
Copyright © 1968, 1972, 1976 by Louis Leithold

Library of Congress Cataloging in Publication Data
Leithold, Louis.
     The calculus, with analytic geometry.

     Includes index.
     CONTENTS: pt. 1.   Functions of one variable,
plane analytic geometry, and infinite series. —pt.
2.   Infinite series, vectors, and functions of
several variables.
     1. Calculus. 2. Geometry, Analytic. I. Title.
QA303.L428 1976   515'.15   75-25981
ISBN 0-06-043948-3 (v. 1)

To Gordon Marc

Contents

Preface

This third edition of THE CALCULUS WITH ANALYTIC GEOMETRY, like the other two, is designed for prospective mathematics majors as well as for students whose primary interest is in engineering, the physical sciences, or nontechnical fields. A knowledge of high-school algebra and geometry is assumed.

The text is available either in one volume or in two parts: Part I consists of the first sixteen chapters, and Part II comprises Chapters 16 through 21 (Chapter 16 on Infinite Series is included in both parts to make the use of the two-volume set more flexible). The material in Part I consists of the differential and integral calculus of functions of a single variable and plane analytic geometry, and it may be covered in a one-year course of nine or ten semester hours or twelve quarter hours. The second part is suitable for a course consisting of five or six semester hours or eight quarter hours. It includes the calculus of several variables and a treatment of vectors in the plane, as well as in three dimensions, with a vector approach to solid analytic geometry.

The objectives of the previous editions have been maintained. I have endeavored to achieve a healthy balance between the presentation of elementary calculus from a rigorous approach and that from the older, intuitive, and computational point of view. Bearing in mind that a textbook should be written for the student, I have attempted to keep the presentation geared to a beginner's experience and maturity and to leave no step unexplained or omitted. I desire that the reader be aware that proofs of theorems are necessary and that these proofs be well motivated and carefully explained so that they are understandable to the student who has achieved an average mastery of the preceding sections of the book. If a theorem is stated without proof, I have generally augmented the discussion by both figures and examples, and in such cases I have always stressed that what is presented is an illustration of the content of the theorem and is not a proof.

Changes in the third edition occur in the first five chapters. The first section of Chapter 1 has been rewritten to give a more detailed exposition of the real-number system. The introduction to analytic geometry in this chapter includes the traditional material on straight lines as well as that of the circle, but a discussion of the parabola is postponed to Chapter 14, The Conic Sections. Functions are now introduced in Chapter 1. I have defined a function as a set of ordered pairs and have used this idea to point up the concept of a function as a correspondence between sets of real numbers.

The treatment of limits and continuity which formerly consisted of ten sections in Chapter 2 is now in two chapters (2 and 4), with the chapter on the derivative placed between them. The concepts of limit and continuity are at the heart of any first course in the calculus. The notion of a limit of a function is first given a step-by-step motivation, which brings the discussion from computing the value of a function near a number, through an intuitive treatment of the limiting process, up to a rigorous epsilon-delta definition. A sequence of examples progressively graded in difficulty is included. All the limit theorems are stated, and some proofs are presented in the text, while other proofs have been outlined in the exercises. In the discussion of continuity, I have used as examples and counterexamples "common, everyday" functions and have avoided those that would have little intuitive meaning.

In Chapter 3, before giving the formal definition of a derivative, I have defined the tangent line to a curve and instantaneous velocity in rectilinear motion in order to demonstrate in advance that the concept of a derivative is of wide application, both geometrical and physical. Theorems on differentiation are proved and illustrated by examples. Application of the derivative to related rates is included.

Additional topics on limits and continuity are given in Chapter 4. Continuity on a closed interval is defined and discussed, followed by the introduction of the Extreme-Value Theorem, which involves such functions. Then the Extreme-Value Theorem is used to find the absolute extrema of functions continuous on a closed interval. Chapter 4 concludes with Rolle's Theorem and the Mean-Value Theorem. Chapter 5 gives additional applications of the derivative, including problems on curve sketching as well as some related to business and economics.

The antiderivative is treated in Chapter 6. I use the term "antidifferentiation" instead of indefinite integration, but the standard notation $\int f(x)\, dx$ is retained so that you are not given a bizarre new notation that would make the reading of standard references difficult. This notation will suggest that some relation must exist between definite integrals, introduced in Chapter 7, and antiderivatives, but I see no harm in this as long as the presentation gives the theoretically proper view of the definite integral as the limit of sums. Exercises involving the evaluation of definite integrals by finding limits of sums are given in Chapter 7 to stress that this is how they are calculated. The introduction of the definite integral follows the definition of the measure of the area under a curve as a limit of sums. Elementary properties of the definite integral are derived and the fundamental theorem of the calculus is proved. It is emphasized that this is a theorem, and an important one, because it provides us with an alternative to computing limits of sums. It is also emphasized that the definite integral is in no sense some special type of antiderivative. In Chapter 8 I have given numerous applications of definite integrals. The presentation highlights not only the manipulative techniques but also the fundamental principles involved. In each application, the definitions of the new terms are intuitively motivated and explained.

The treatment of logarithmic and exponential functions in Chapter 9 is the modern approach. The natural logarithm is defined as an integral, and after the discussion of the inverse of a function, the exponential function is defined as the inverse of the natural logarithmic function. An irrational power of a real number is then defined. The trigonometric functions are defined in Chapter 10 as functions assigning numbers to numbers. The important trigonometric identities are derived and used to obtain the formulas for the derivatives and integrals of these functions. Following are sections on the differentiation and integration of the trigonometric functions as well as of the inverse trigonometric functions.

Chapter 11, on techniques of integration, involves one of the most important computational aspects of the calculus. I have explained the theoretical backgrounds of each different method after an introductory motivation. The mastery of integration techniques depends upon the examples, and I have used as illustrations problems that the student will certainly meet in practice, those which require patience and persistence to solve. The material on the approximation of definite integrals includes the statement of theorems for computing the bounds of the error involved in these approximations. The theorems and the problems that go with them, being self-contained, can be omitted from a course if the instructor so wishes.

A self-contained treatment of hyperbolic functions is in Chapter 12. This chapter may be studied immediately following the discussion of the circular trigonometric functions in Chapter 10, if so desired. The geometric interpretation of the hyperbolic functions is postponed until Chapter 17 because it involves the use of parametric equations.

Polar coordinates and some of their applications are given in Chapter 13. In Chapter 14, conics are treated as a unified subject to stress their natural and close relationship to each other. The parabola is discussed in the first two sections. Then equations of the conics in polar coordinates are treated, and the cartesian equations of the ellipse and the hyperbola are derived from the polar equations. The topics of indeterminate forms, improper integrals, and Taylor's formula, and the computational techniques involved, are presented in Chapter 15.

I have attempted in Chapter 16 to give as complete a treatment of infinite series as is feasible in an elementary calculus text. In addition to the customary computational material, I have included the proof of the equivalence of convergence and boundedness of monotonic sequences based on the completeness property of the real numbers and the proofs of the computational processes involving differentiation and integration of power series.

The first five sections of Chapter 17 on vectors in the plane can be taken up after Chapter 5 if it is desired to introduce vectors earlier in the course. The approach to vectors is modern, and it serves both as an introduction to the viewpoint of linear algebra and to that of classical vector analysis. The applications are to physics and geometry. Chapter 18 treats vectors in three-dimensional space, and, if desired, the topics in the first three sections of this chapter may be studied concurrently with the corresponding topics in Chapter 17.

Limits, continuity, and differentiation of functions of several variables are considered in Chapter 19. The discussion and examples are applied mainly to functions of two and three variables; however, statements of most of the definitions and theorems are extended to functions of n variables.

In Chapter 20, a section on directional derivatives and gradients is followed by a section that shows the application of the gradient to finding an equation of the tangent plane to a surface. Applications of partial derivatives to the solution of extrema problems and an introduction to Lagrange multipliers are presented, as well as a section on applications of partial derivatives in economics. Three sections, new in the third edition, are devoted to line integrals and related topics. The double integral of a function of two variables and the triple integral of a function of three variables, along with some applications to physics, engineering, and geometry, are given in Chapter 21.

New to this edition is a short table of integrals appearing on the front and back endpapers. However, as stated in Chapter 11, you are advised to use a table of integrals only after you have mastered integration.

Louis Leithold

ACKNOWLEDGMENTS

Reviewers of *The Calculus with Analytic Geometry*

Professor William D. Bandes, San Diego Mesa College
Professor Archie D. Brock, East Texas State University
Professor Phillip Clarke, Los Angeles Valley College
Professor Reuben W. Farley, Virginia Commonwealth University
Professor Jacob Golightly, Jacksonville University
Professor Robert K. Goodrich, University of Colorado
Professor Albert Herr, Drexel University
Professor James F. Hurley, University of Connecticut
Professor Gordon L. Miller, Wisconsin State University
Professor William W. Mitchell, Jr., Phoenix College
Professor Roger B. Nelsen, Lewis and Clark College
Professor Robert A. Nowlan, Southern Connecticut State College
Sister Madeleine Rose, Holy Names College
Professor George W. Schultz, St. Petersburg Junior College
Professor Donald R. Sherbert, University of Illinois
Professor John Vadney, Fulton-Montgomery Community College
Professor David Whitman, San Diego State College

Production Staff at Harper & Row

George Telecki, Mathematics Editor
Karen Judd, Project Editor
Rita Naughton, Designer

Assistants for Answers to Exercises

Jacqueline Dewar, Loyola Marymount University
Ken Kast, Logicon, Inc.
Jean Kilmer, West Covina Unified School District

Cover and Chapter Opening Artist

Patrick Caulfield, London, England

To these people and to all the users of the first and second editions who have suggested changes, I express my deep appreciation.

L. L.

1

Real numbers, introduction to analytic geometry, and functions

1.1 SETS, REAL NUMBERS, AND INEQUALITIES

The idea of "set" is used extensively in mathematics and is such a basic concept that it is not given a formal definition. We can say that a *set* is a collection of objects, and the objects in a set are called the *elements* of a set. We may speak of the set of books in the New York Public Library, the set of citizens of the United States, the set of trees in Golden Gate Park, and so on. In calculus, we are concerned with the set of real numbers. Before discussing this set, we introduce some notation and definitions.

We want every set to be *well defined*; that is, there should be some rule or property that enables one to decide whether a given object is or is not an element of a specific set. A pair of braces { } used with words or symbols can describe a set.

If S is the set of natural numbers less than 6, we can write the set S as

$$\{1, 2, 3, 4, 5\}$$

We can also write the set S as

$$\{x, \text{ such that } x \text{ is a natural number less than 6}\}$$

where the symbol "x" is called a "variable." A *variable* is a symbol used to represent any element of a given set. Another way of writing the above set S is to use what is called *set-builder notation*, where a vertical bar is used in place of the words "such that." Using set-builder notation to describe the set S, we have

$$\{x|x \text{ is a natural number less than 6}\}$$

which is read "the set of all x such that x is a natural number less than 6."

The set of natural numbers will be denoted by N. Therefore, we may write the set N as

$$\{1, 2, 3, \ldots\}$$

where the three dots are used to indicate that the list goes on and on with no last number. With set-builder notation the set N may be written as $\{x|x \text{ is a natural number}\}$.

The symbol "$\in$" is used to indicate that a specific element belongs to a set. Hence, we may write $8 \in N$, which is read "8 is an element of N." The notation $a, b \in S$ indicates that both a and b are elements of S. The symbol $\notin$ is read "is not an element of." Thus, we read $\frac{1}{2} \notin N$ as "$\frac{1}{2}$ is not an element of N."

We denote the set of all integers by J. Because every element of N is also an element of J (that is, every natural number is an integer), we say that N is a "subset" of J, written $N \subseteq J$.

1.1.1 Definition The set S is a *subset* of the set T, written $S \subseteq T$, if and only if every element of S is also an element of T. If, in addition, there is at least one element of T

which is not an element of S, then S is a *proper subset* of T, and it is written $S \subset T$.

Observe from the definition that every set is a subset of itself, but a set is *not* a proper subset of itself.

In Definition 1.1.1, the "if and only if" qualification is used to combine two statements: (i) "the set S is a subset of the set T *if* every element of S is also an element of T"; and (ii) "the set S is a subset of set T *only if* every element of S is also an element of T," which is logically equivalent to the statement "if S is a subset of T, then every element of S is also an element of T."

● ILLUSTRATION 1: Let N be the set of natural numbers and let M be the set denoted by $\{x|x$ is a natural number less than 10$\}$. Because every element of M is also an element of N, M is a subset of N and we write $M \subseteq N$. Also, there is at least one element of N which is not an element of M, and so M is a proper subset of N and we may write $M \subset N$. Furthermore, because $\{6\}$ is the set consisting of the number 6, $\{6\} \subset M$, which states that the set consisting of the single element 6 is a proper subset of the set M. We may also write $6 \in M$, which states that the number 6 is an element of the set M.   ●

Consider the set $\{x|2x + 1 = 0,$ and $x \in J\}$. This set contains no elements because there is no integer solution of the equation $2x + 1 = 0$. Such a set is called the "empty set" or the "null set."

1.1.2 Definition   The *empty set* (or *null set*) is the set that contains no elements. The empty set is denoted by the symbol $\varnothing$.

The concept of "subset" may be used to define what is meant by two sets being "equal."

1.1.3 Definition   Two sets A and B are said to be *equal*, written $A = B$, if and only if $A \subseteq B$ and $B \subseteq A$.

Essentially, this definition states that the two sets A and B are equal if and only if every element of A is an element of B and every element of B is an element of A, that is, if the sets A and B have identical elements.

There are two operations on sets that we shall find useful as we proceed. These operations are given in Definitions 1.1.4 and 1.1.5.

1.1.4 Definition   Let A and B be two sets. The *union* of A and B, denoted by $A \cup B$ and read "A union B," is the set of all elements that are in A or in B or in both A and B.

EXAMPLE 1: Let $A = \{2, 4, 6, 8, 10, 12\}$, $B = \{1, 4, 9, 16\}$, and $C = \{2, 10\}$. Find

(a) $A \cup B$ (b) $A \cup C$
(c) $B \cup C$ (d) $A \cup A$

SOLUTION:

(a) $A \cup B = \{1, 2, 4, 6, 8, 9, 10, 12, 16\}$
(b) $A \cup C = \{2, 4, 6, 8, 10, 12\}$
(c) $B \cup C = \{1, 2, 4, 9, 10, 16\}$
(d) $A \cup A = \{2, 4, 6, 8, 10, 12\} = A$

1.1.5 Definition   Let A and B be two sets. The *intersection* of A and B, denoted by $A \cap B$ and read "A intersection B," is the set of all elements that are in both A and B.

EXAMPLE 2: If A, B, and C are the sets defined in Example 1, find

(a) $A \cap B$ (b) $A \cap C$
(c) $B \cap C$ (d) $A \cap A$

SOLUTION:

(a) $A \cap B = \{4\}$ (b) $A \cap C = \{2, 10\}$
(c) $B \cap C = \varnothing$ (d) $A \cap A = \{2, 4, 6, 8, 10, 12\} = A$

The *real number system* consists of a set of elements called *real numbers* and two operations called *addition* and *multiplication*. The set of real numbers is denoted by R^1. The operation of addition is denoted by the symbol "$+$", and the operation of multiplication is denoted by the symbol "$\cdot$". If $a, b \in R^1$, $a + b$ denotes the *sum* of a and b, and $a \cdot b$ (or ab) denotes their *product*.

We now present seven axioms that give laws governing the operations of addition and multiplication on the set R^1. The word *axiom* is used to indicate a formal statement that is assumed to be true without proof.

1.1.6 Axiom
(Closure and Uniqueness Laws)

If $a, b \in R^1$, then $a + b$ is a unique real number, and ab is a unique real number.

1.1.7 Axiom
(Commutative Laws)

If $a, b \in R^1$, then

$$a + b = b + a \quad \text{and} \quad ab = ba$$

1.1.8 Axiom
(Associative Laws)

If $a, b, c \in R^1$, then

$$a + (b + c) = (a + b) + c \quad \text{and} \quad a(bc) = (ab)c$$

1.1.9 Axiom
(Distributive Law)

If $a, b, c \in R^1$, then

$$a(b + c) = ab + ac$$

1.1.10 Axiom
(Existence of Negative Elements)

There exist two distinct real numbers 0 and 1 such that for any real number a,

$$a + 0 = a \quad \text{and} \quad a \cdot 1 = a$$

1.1.11 Axiom
(Existence of Negative or Additive Inverse)

For every real number a, there exists a real number called the *negative of a* (or *additive inverse of a*), denoted by $-a$ (read "the negative of a"), such that

$$a + (-a) = 0$$

1.1.12 Axiom
(Existence of Reciprocal or Multiplicative Inverse)

For every real number a, except 0, there exists a real number called the *reciprocal of a* (or *multiplicative inverse of a*), denoted by a^{-1}, such that

$$a \cdot a^{-1} = 1$$

Axioms 1.1.6 through 1.1.12 are called *field axioms* because if these axioms are satisfied by a set of elements, then the set is called a *field* under the two operations involved. Hence, the set R^1 is a field under addition and multiplication. For the set J of integers, each of the axioms 1.1.6 through 1.1.11 is satisfied, but Axiom 1.1.12 is not satisfied (for instance, the integer 2 has no multiplicative inverse in J). Therefore, the set of integers is not a field under addition and multiplication.

1.1.13 Definition

If $a, b \in R^1$, the operation of *subtraction* assigns to a and b a real number, denoted by $a - b$ (read "a minus b"), called the *difference* of a and b, where

$$a - b = a + (-b) \tag{1}$$

Equality (1) is read "a minus b equals a plus the negative of b."

1.1.14 Definition

If $a, b \in R^1$, and $b \neq 0$, the operation of *division* assigns to a and b a real number, denoted by $a \div b$ (read "a divided by b"), called the *quotient* of a and b, where

$$a \div b = a \cdot b^{-1}$$

Other notations for the quotient of a and b are

$$\frac{a}{b} \quad \text{and} \quad a/b$$

By using the field axioms and Definitions 1.1.13 and 1.1.14, we can derive properties of the real numbers from which follow the familiar algebraic operations as well as the techniques of solving equations, factoring, and so forth. In this book we are not concerned with showing how such properties are derived from the axioms.

Properties that can be shown to be logical consequences of axioms are *theorems*. In the statement of most theorems there are two parts: the "if" part, called the *hypothesis*, and the "then" part, called the *conclusion*. The argument verifying a theorem is a *proof*. A proof consists of showing that the conclusion follows from the assumed truth of the hypothesis.

The concept of a real number being "positive" is given in the following axiom.

1.1.15 Axiom
(Order Axiom)

In the set of real numbers there exists a subset called the *positive numbers* such that

(i) if $a \in R^1$, exactly one of the following three statements holds:
$$a = 0 \qquad a \text{ is positive} \qquad -a \text{ is positive.}$$
(ii) the sum of two positive numbers is positive.
(iii) the product of two positive numbers is positive.

Axiom 1.1.15 is called the order axiom because it enables us to order the elements of the set R^1. In Definitions 1.1.17 and 1.1.18 we use this axiom to define the relations of "greater than" and "less than" on R^1.

The negatives of the elements of the set of positive numbers form the set of "negative" numbers, as given in the following definition.

1.1.16 Definition

The real number a is *negative* if and only if $-a$ is positive.

From Axiom 1.1.15 and Definition 1.1.16 it follows that a real number is either a positive number, a negative number, or zero. Any real number can be classified as a *rational* number or an *irrational* number. A rational number is any number that can be expressed as the ratio of two integers. That is, a rational number is a number of the form p/q, where p and q are integers and $q \neq 0$. The rational numbers consist of the following:

The *integers* (positive, negative, and zero)

$$\ldots, -5, -4, -3, -2, -1, 0, 1, 2, 3, 4, 5, \ldots$$

The positive and negative *fractions* such as

$$\tfrac{2}{7} \qquad -\tfrac{4}{5} \qquad \tfrac{83}{5}$$

The positive and negative *terminating decimals* such as

$$2.36 = \frac{236}{100} \qquad -0.003251 = -\frac{3,251}{1,000,000}$$

The positive and negative *nonterminating repeating decimals* such as

$$0.333\ldots = \tfrac{1}{3} \qquad -0.549549549\ldots = -\tfrac{61}{111}$$

The real numbers which are not rational numbers are called *irrational numbers*. These are positive and negative *nonterminating, nonrepeating* decimals, for example,

$$\sqrt{3} = 1.732\ldots \qquad \pi = 3.14159\ldots \qquad \tan 140° = -0.8391\ldots$$

The field axioms do not imply any ordering of the real numbers. That is, by means of the field axioms alone we cannot state that 1 is less than

2, 2 is less than 3, and so on. However, we have introduced the order axiom (Axiom 1.1.15), and because the set R^1 of real numbers satisfies the order axiom and the field axioms, we say that R^1 is an *ordered field*.

We use the concept of a positive number given in the order axiom to define what we mean by one real number being "less than" another.

1.1.17 Definition   If $a, b \in R^1$, then a *is less than* b (written $a < b$) if and only if $b - a$ is positive.

● ILLUSTRATION 2: (a) $3 < 8$ because $8 - 3 = 5$, and 5 is positive. (b) $-10 < -6$ because $-6 - (-10) = 4$, and 4 is positive.   ●

1.1.18 Definition   If $a, b \in R^1$, then a *is greater than* b (written $a > b$) if and only if b is less than a; with symbols we write

$$a > b \text{ if and only if } b < a$$

1.1.19 Definition   The symbols $\leq$ (" is less than or equal to") and $\geq$ (" is greater than or equal to") are defined as follows:

(i) $a \leq b$ if and only if either $a < b$ or $a = b$.
(ii) $a \geq b$ if and only if either $a > b$ or $a = b$.

The statements $a < b$, $a > b$, $a \leq b$, and $a \geq b$ are called *inequalities*. Some examples are $2 < 7$, $-5 < 6$, $-5 < -4$, $14 > 8$, $2 > -4$, $-3 > -6$, $5 \geq 3$, $-10 \leq -7$. In particular, $a < b$ and $a > b$ are called *strict* inequalities, whereas $a \leq b$ and $a \geq b$ are called *nonstrict* inequalities.

The following theorems can be proved by using 1.1.6 through 1.1.19.

1.1.20 Theorem   (i) $a > 0$ if and only if a is positive.
(ii) $a < 0$ if and only if a is negative.
(iii) $a > 0$ if and only if $-a < 0$.
(iv) $a < 0$ if and only if $-a > 0$.

1.1.21 Theorem   If $a < b$ and $b < c$, then $a < c$.

● ILLUSTRATION 3: $3 < 6$ and $6 < 14$; so $3 < 14$.   ●

1.1.22 Theorem   If $a < b$, then $a + c < b + c$, and $a - c < b - c$ if c is any real number.

● ILLUSTRATION 4: $4 < 7$; so $4 + 5 < 7 + 5$; and $4 - 5 < 7 - 5$.   ●

1.1.23 Theorem   If $a < b$ and $c < d$, then $a + c < b + d$.

● ILLUSTRATION 5: $2 < 6$ and $-3 < 1$; so $2 + (-3) < 6 + 1$. '   ●

1.1.24 Theorem   If $a < b$, and c is any positive number, then $ac < bc$.

● ILLUSTRATION 6: $2 < 5$; so $2 \cdot 4 < 5 \cdot 4$.

1.1.25 Theorem   If $a < b$, and c is any negative number, then $ac > bc$.

● ILLUSTRATION 7: $2 < 5$; so $2(-4) > 5(-4)$.

1.1.26 Theorem   If $0 < a < b$ and $0 < c < d$, then $ac < bd$.

● ILLUSTRATION 8: $0 < 4 < 7$ and $0 < 8 < 9$; so $4(8) < 7(9)$.

Theorem 1.1.24 states that if both members of an inequality are multiplied by a positive number, the direction of the inequality remains unchanged, whereas Theorem 1.1.25 states that if both members of an inequality are multiplied by a negative number, the direction of the inequality is reversed. Theorems 1.1.24 and 1.1.25 also hold for division, because dividing both members of an inequality by a number d is equivalent to multiplying both members by $1/d$.

To illustrate the type of proof that is usually given, we present a proof of Theorem 1.1.23:

By hypothesis $a < b$. Then $b - a$ is positive (by Definition 1.1.17).
By hypothesis $c < d$. Then $d - c$ is positive (by Definition 1.1.17).
Hence, $(b - a) + (d - c)$ is positive (by Axiom 1.1.15(ii)).
Therefore, $(b + d) - (a + c)$ is positive (by Axioms 1.1.8 and 1.1.7
and Definition 1.1.13).
Therefore, $a + c < b + d$ (by Definition 1.1.17).

The following theorems are identical to Theorems 1.1.21 to 1.1.26 except that the direction of the inequality is reversed.

1.1.27 Theorem   If $a > b$ and $b > c$, then $a > c$.

● ILLUSTRATION 9: $8 > 4$ and $4 > -2$; so $8 > -2$.

1.1.28 Theorem   If $a > b$, then $a + c > b + c$, and $a - c > b - c$ if c is any real number.

● ILLUSTRATION 10: $3 > -5$; so $3 - 4 > -5 - 4$.

1.1.29 Theorem   If $a > b$ and $c > d$, then $a + c > b + d$.

● ILLUSTRATION 11: $7 > 2$ and $3 > -5$; so $7 + 3 > 2 + (-5)$.

1.1.30 Theorem   If $a > b$ and if c is any positive number, then $ac > bc$.

● ILLUSTRATION 12: $-3 > -7$; so $(-3)4 > (-7)4$.

1.1.31 Theorem   If $a > b$ and if c is any negative number, then $ac < bc$.

• ILLUSTRATION 13: $-3 > -7$; so $(-3)(-4) < (-7)(-4)$.   •

1.1.32 Theorem   If $a > b > 0$ and $c > d > 0$, then $ac > bd$.

• ILLUSTRATION 14: $4 > 3 > 0$ and $7 > 6 > 0$; so $4(7) > 3(6)$.   •

So far we have required the set R^1 of real numbers to satisfy the field axioms and the order axiom, and we have stated that because of this requirement R^1 is an ordered field. There is one more condition that is imposed upon the set R^1. This condition is called the *axiom of completeness* (Axiom 16.2.5). We defer the statement of this axiom until Section 16.2 because it requires some terminology that is best introduced and discussed later. However, we now give a geometric interpretation to the set of real numbers by associating them with the points on a horizontal line, called an *axis*. The axiom of completeness guarantees that there is a one-to-one correspondence between the set R^1 and the set of points on an axis.

Refer to Figure 1.1.1. A point on the axis is chosen to represent the number 0. This point is called the *origin*. A unit of distance is selected. Then each positive number x is represented by the point at a distance of x units to the right of the origin, and each negative number x is represented by the point at a distance of $-x$ units to the left of the origin (it should be noted that if x is negative, then $-x$ is positive). To each real number there corresponds a unique point on the axis, and with each point on the axis there is associated only one real number; hence, we have a one-to-one correspondence between R^1 and the points on the axis. So the points on the axis are identified with the numbers they represent, and we shall use the same symbol for both the number and the point representing that number on the axis. We identify R^1 with the axis, and we call R^1 the *real number line*.

We see that $a < b$ if and only if the point representing the number a is to the left of the point representing the number b. Similarly, $a > b$ if and only if the point representing a is to the right of the point representing b. For instance, the number 2 is less than the number 5 and the point 2 is to the left of the point 5. We could also write $5 > 2$ and say that the point 5 is to the right of the point 2.

A number x is between a and b if $a < x$ and $x < b$. We can write this as a continued inequality as follows:

$$a < x < b \tag{2}$$

The set of all numbers x satisfying the continued inequality (2) is called an "open interval."

Figure 1.1.1

1.1.33 Definition   The *open interval* from a to b, denoted by (a, b), is defined by

$$(a, b) = \{x \mid a < x < b\}$$

The "closed interval" from a to b is the open interval (a, b) together with the two endpoints a and b.

1.1.34 Definition   The *closed interval* from a to b, denoted by $[a, b]$, is defined by

$$[a, b] = \{x \mid a \leq x \leq b\}$$

Figure 1.1.2

Figure 1.1.2 illustrates the open interval (a, b) and Fig. 1.1.3 illustrates the closed interval $[a, b]$.

The "interval half-open on the left" is the open interval (a, b) together with the right endpoint b.

Figure 1.1.3

1.1.35 Definition   The *interval half-open on the left*, denoted by $(a, b]$, is defined by

$$(a, b] = \{x \mid a < x \leq b\}$$

We define an "interval half-open on the right" in a similar way.

1.1.36 Definition   The *interval half-open on the right*, denoted by $[a, b)$, is defined by

$$[a, b) = \{x \mid a \leq x < b\}$$

Figure 1.1.4

Figure 1.1.4 illustrates the interval $(a, b]$ and Fig. 1.1.5 illustrates the interval $[a, b)$.

We shall use the symbol $+\infty$ ("positive infinity") and the symbol $-\infty$ ("negative infinity"); however, care must be taken not to confuse these symbols with real numbers, for they do not obey the properties of the real numbers

Figure 1.1.5

1.1.37 Definition

(i) $(a, +\infty) = \{x \mid x > a\}$
(ii) $(-\infty, b) = \{x \mid x < b\}$
(iii) $[a, +\infty) = \{x \mid x \geq a\}$
(iv) $(-\infty, b] = \{x \mid x \leq b\}$
(v) $(-\infty, +\infty) = R^1$

Figure 1.1.6

Figure 1.1.6 illustrates the interval $(a, +\infty)$, and Fig. 1.1.7 illustrates the interval $(-\infty, b)$. Note that $(-\infty, +\infty)$ denotes the set of all real numbers.

For each of the intervals (a, b), $[a, b]$, $[a, b)$, and $(a, b]$ the numbers a and b are called the *endpoints* of the interval. The closed interval $[a, b]$ contains both its endpoints, whereas the open interval (a, b) contains neither endpoint. The interval $[a, b)$ contains its left endpoint but not its right one, and the interval $(a, b]$ contains its right endpoint but not its left one. An open interval can be thought of as one which contains none

Figure 1.1.7

of its endpoints, and a closed interval can be regarded as one which contains all of its endpoints. Consequently, the interval $[a, +\infty)$ is considered to be a closed interval because it contains its only endpoint a. Similarly, $(-\infty, b]$ is a closed interval, whereas $(a, +\infty)$ and $(-\infty, b)$ are open. The intervals $[a, b)$ and $(a, b]$ are neither open nor closed. The interval $(-\infty, +\infty)$ has no endpoints, and it is considered both open and closed.

Intervals are used to represent "solution sets" of inequalities in one variable. The *solution set* of such an inequality is the set of all numbers that satisfy the inequality.

EXAMPLE 3: Find the solution set of the inequality

$$2 + 3x < 5x + 8$$

Illustrate it on the real number line.

SOLUTION: If x is a number such that

$$2 + 3x < 5x + 8$$

then

$$2 + 3x - 2 < 5x + 8 - 2 \quad \text{(by Theorem 1.1.22)}$$

or, equivalently,

$$3x < 5x + 6$$

Then, adding $-5x$ to both members of this inequality, we have

$$-2x < 6 \quad \text{(by Theorem 1.1.22)}$$

Dividing on both sides of this inequality by -2 and reversing the direction of the inequality, we obtain

$$x > -3 \quad \text{(by Theorem 1.1.25)}$$

What we have proved is that if

$$2 + 3x < 5x + 8$$

then

$$x > -3$$

Each of the steps is reversible; that is, if we start with

$$x > -3$$

we multiply on each side by -2, reverse the direction of the inequality, and obtain

$$-2x < 6$$

Then we add $5x$ and 2 to both members of the inequality, in which case we get

$$2 + 3x < 5x + 8$$

Figure 1.1.8

Therefore, we can conclude that

$$2 + 3x < 5x + 8 \quad \textit{if and only if} \quad x > -3$$

So the solution set of the given inequality is the interval $(-3, +\infty)$, which is illustrated in Fig. 1.1.8.

EXAMPLE 4: Find the solution set of the inequality

$$4 < 3x - 2 \le 10$$

Illustrate it on the real number line.

Figure 1.1.9

SOLUTION: Adding 2 to each member of the inequality, we obtain

$$6 < 3x \le 12$$

Dividing each member by 3, we get

$$2 < x \le 4$$

Each step is reversible; so the solution set is the interval $(2, 4]$, as is illustrated in Fig. 1.1.9.

EXAMPLE 5: Find the solution set of the inequality

$$\frac{7}{x} > 2$$

Illustrate it on the real number line.

Figure 1.1.10

SOLUTION: We wish to multiply both members of the inequality by x. However, the direction of the inequality that results will depend upon whether x is positive or negative. So we must consider two cases.

Case 1: x is positive; that is, $x > 0$.
  Multiplying on both sides by x, we obtain

$$7 > 2x$$

Dividing on both sides by 2, we get

$$\tfrac{7}{2} > x \quad \text{or, equivalently,} \quad x < \tfrac{7}{2}$$

Therefore, since the above steps are reversible, the solution set of Case 1 is $\{x | x > 0\} \cap \{x | x < \tfrac{7}{2}\}$ or, equivalently, $\{x | 0 < x < \tfrac{7}{2}\}$, which is the interval $(0, \tfrac{7}{2})$.

Case 2: x is negative; that is, $x < 0$.
  Multiplying on both sides by x and reversing the direction of the inequality, we find

$$7 < 2x$$

Dividing on both sides by 2, we have

$$\tfrac{7}{2} < x \quad \text{or, equivalently,} \quad x > \tfrac{7}{2}$$

Again, because the above steps are reversible, the solution set of Case 2 is $\{x | x < 0\} \cap \{x > \tfrac{7}{2}\} = \varnothing$.
  From Cases 1 and 2 we conclude that the solution set of the given inequality is the open interval $(0, \tfrac{7}{2})$, which is illustrated in Fig. 1.1.10.

EXAMPLE 6:   Find the solution set of the inequality

$$\frac{x}{x-3} < 4$$

Illustrate it on the real number line.

Figure 1.1.11

SOLUTION: To multiply both members of the inequality by $x-3$, we must consider two cases, as in Example 5.

Case 1: $x-3 > 0$; that is, $x > 3$.
   Multiplying on both sides of the inequality by $x-3$, we get

$$x < 4x - 12$$

Adding $-4x$ to both members, we obtain

$$-3x < -12$$

Dividing on both sides by -3 and reversing the direction of the inequality, we have

$$x > 4$$

Thus the solution set of Case 1 is $\{x|x > 3\} \cap \{x|x > 4\}$ or, equivalently, $\{x|x > 4\}$, which is the interval $(4, +\infty)$.

Case 2: $x-3 < 0$; that is, $x < 3$.
   Multiplying on both sides by $x-3$ and reversing the direction of the inequality, we have

$$x > 4x - 12$$

or, equivalently,

$$-3x > -12$$

or, equivalently,

$$x < 4$$

Therefore, x must be less than 4 and also less than 3. Thus, the solution set of Case 2 is the interval $(-\infty, 3)$.
   If the solution sets for Cases 1 and 2 are combined, we obtain $(-\infty, 3) \cup (4, +\infty)$, which is illustrated in Fig. 1.1.11.

EXAMPLE 7:   Find the solution set of the inequality

$$(x+3)(x+4) > 0$$

SOLUTION: The inequality will be satisfied when both factors have the same sign, that is, if $x+3 > 0$ and $x+4 > 0$, or if $x+3 < 0$ and $x+4 < 0$. Let us consider the two cases.

Case 1: $x+3 > 0$ and $x+4 > 0$. That is,

$$x > -3 \quad \text{and} \quad x > -4$$

Thus, both inequalities hold if $x > -3$, which is the interval $(-3, +\infty)$.

Case 2: $x+3 < 0$ and $x+4 < 0$. That is,

$$x < -3 \quad \text{and} \quad x < -4$$

Both inequalities hold if $x < -4$, which is the interval $(-\infty, -4)$.
   If we combine the solution sets for Cases 1 and 2, we have $(-\infty, -4) \cup (-3, +\infty)$.

Exercises 1.1

In Exercises 1 through 10, list the elements of the given set if $A = \{0, 2, 4, 6, 8\}$, $B = \{1, 2, 4, 8\}$, $C = \{1, 3, 5, 7, 9\}$, and $D = \{0, 3, 6, 9\}$.

1. $A \cup B$
2. $C \cup D$
3. $A \cap B$
4. $C \cap D$
5. $B \cup D$
6. $A \cup C$
7. $B \cap D$
8. $A \cap C$
9. $(A \cap D) \cup (B \cap C)$
10. $(A \cup B) \cap (C \cup D)$

In Exercises 11 through 32, find the solution set of the given inequality and illustrate the solution on the real number line.

11. $5x + 2 > x - 6$
12. $3 - x < 5 + 3x$
13. $\frac{2}{3}x - \frac{1}{2} < 0$
14. $3x - 5 < \frac{3}{4}x + \frac{1-x}{3}$
15. $13 \geq 2x - 3 \geq 5$
16. $2 \leq 5 - 3x < 11$
17. $2 > -3 - 3x \geq -7$
18. $\frac{5}{x} < \frac{3}{4}$
19. $\frac{4}{x} - 3 > \frac{2}{x} - 7$
20. $\frac{2}{1-x} \leq 1$
21. $x^2 > 4$
22. $x^2 \leq 9$
23. $(x-3)(x+5) > 0$
24. $x^2 - 3x + 2 > 0$
25. $1 - x - 2x^2 \geq 0$
26. $x^2 + 3x + 1 > 0$
27. $4x^2 + 9x < 9$
28. $2x^2 - 6x + 3 < 0$
29. $\frac{1}{x+1} < \frac{2}{3x-1}$
30. $\frac{x+1}{2-x} < \frac{x}{3+x}$
31. $\frac{1}{3x-7} \geq \frac{4}{3-2x}$
32. $x^3 + 1 > x^2 + x$
33. Prove Theorem 1.1.21.
34. Prove Theorem 1.1.22.

35. Prove Theorems 1.1.24 and 1.1.25.

36. If $a > b \geq 0$, prove that $a^2 > b^2$.

37. If a and b are nonnegative numbers, and $a^2 > b^2$, prove that $a > b$.

38. Prove that if $a \geq 0$ and $b \geq 0$, then $a^2 = b^2$ if and only if $a = b$.

39. Prove that if $b > a > 0$ and $c > 0$, then
$$\frac{a+c}{b+c} > \frac{a}{b}$$

40. Prove that if $x < y$, then $x < \frac{1}{2}(x + y) < y$.

1.2 ABSOLUTE VALUE

The concept of the "absolute value" of a number is used in some important definitions in the study of calculus. Furthermore, you will need to work with inequalities involving "absolute value."

1.2.1 Definition   The *absolute value* of x, denoted by $|x|$, is defined by

$$|x| = x \quad \text{if } x > 0$$
$$|x| = -x \quad \text{if } x < 0$$
$$|0| = 0$$

Figure 1.2.1

Thus, the absolute value of a positive number or zero is equal to the number itself. The absolute value of a negative number is the corresponding positive number because the negative of a negative number is positive.

● ILLUSTRATION 1: $|3|=3; |-5|=-(-5)=5; |8-14|=|-6|=-(-6)=6.$ ●

We see from the definition that the absolute value of a number is either a positive number or zero; that is, it is nonnegative.

In terms of geometry, the absolute value of a number x is its distance from 0, without regard to direction. In general, $|a-b|$ is the distance between a and b without regard to direction, that is, without regard to which is the larger number. Refer to Fig. 1.2.1.

We have the following properties of absolute values.

1.2.2 Theorem $|x| < a$ if and only if $-a < x < a$, where $a > 0$.

1.2.3 Corollary $|x| \le a$ if and only if $-a \le x \le a$, where $a > 0$.

1.2.4 Theorem $|x| > a$ if and only if $x > a$ or $x < -a$, where $a > 0$.

1.2.5 Corollary $|x| \ge a$ if and only if $x \ge a$ or $x \le -a$, where $a > 0$.

The proof of a theorem that has an "if and only if" qualification requires two parts, as illustrated in the following proof of Theorem 1.2.2.

PART 1:   Prove that $|x| < a$ if $-a < x < a$, where $a > 0$. Here, we have to consider two cases: $x \ge 0$ and $x < 0$.

Case 1: $x \ge 0$.
    Then $|x| = x$. Because $x < a$, we conclude that $|x| < a$.

Case 2: $x < 0$.
    Then $|x| = -x$. Because $-a < x$, we apply Theorem 1.1.25 and obtain $a > -x$ or, equivalently, $-x < a$. But because $-x = |x|$, we have $|x| < a$.
    In both cases, then,

$$|x| < a \quad \text{if} \quad -a < x < a, \qquad \text{where } a > 0$$

PART 2:   Prove that $|x| < a$ only if $-a < x < a$, where $a > 0$. Here we must show that whenever the inequality $|x| < a$ holds, the inequality $-a < x < a$ also holds. Assume that $|x| < a$ and consider the two cases $x \ge 0$ and $x < 0$.

Case 1: $x \ge 0$.
    Then $|x| = x$. Because $|x| < a$, we conclude that $x < a$. Also, because $a > 0$, it follows from Theorem 1.1.31 that $-a < 0$. Thus, we have $-a < 0 \le x < a$, or $-a < x < a$.

Case 2: $x < 0$.
    Then $|x| = -x$. Because $|x| < a$, we conclude that $-x < a$. Also, be-

cause $x < 0$, it follows from Theorem 1.1.25 that $0 < -x$. Therefore, we have $-a < 0 < -x < a$, or $-a < -x < a$, which by applying Theorem 1.1.25 yields $-a < x < a$.

In both cases,

$$|x| < a \quad \text{only if} \quad -a < x < a, \qquad \text{where } a > 0 \qquad \blacksquare$$

The proof of Theorem 1.2.4 is left as an exercise (see Exercise 27).

The following examples illustrate the solution of equations and inequalities involving absolute values.

EXAMPLE 1:   Solve for x:

$$|3x + 2| = 5.$$

SOLUTION: This equation will be satisfied if either

$$3x + 2 = 5 \quad \text{or} \quad 3x + 2 = -5$$

Considering each equation separately, we have

$$x = 1 \quad \text{and} \quad x = -\tfrac{7}{3}$$

which are the two solutions to the given equation.

EXAMPLE 2:   Solve for x:

$$|2x - 1| = |4x + 3|.$$

SOLUTION: This equation will be satisfied if either

$$2x - 1 = 4x + 3 \quad \text{or} \quad 2x - 1 = -(4x + 3)$$

Solving the first equation, we have $x = -2$; solving the second, we get $x = -\tfrac{1}{3}$, thus giving us two solutions to the original equation.

EXAMPLE 3:   Solve for x:

$$|5x + 4| = -3.$$

SOLUTION: Because the absolute value of a number may never be negative, this equation has no solution.

EXAMPLE 4:   Find the solution set of the inequality

$$|x - 5| < 4$$

Illustrate it on the real number line.

Figure 1.2.2

SOLUTION: If x is a number such that

$$|x - 5| < 4$$

then

$$-4 < x - 5 < 4 \quad \text{(by Theorem 1.2.2)}$$

Adding 5 to each member of the preceding inequality, we obtain

$$1 < x < 9$$

Because each step is reversible, we can conclude that

$$|x - 5| < 4 \quad \text{if and only if} \quad 1 < x < 9$$

So, the solution set of the given inequality is $(1, 9)$, which is illustrated in Fig. 1.2.2.

EXAMPLE 5:   Find the solution set of the inequality

$$\left|\frac{3-2x}{2+x}\right| \le 4$$

SOLUTION: By Corollary 1.2.3, the given inequality is equivalent to

$$-4 \le \frac{3-2x}{2+x} \le 4$$

If we multiply by $2+x$, we must consider two cases, depending upon whether $2+x$ is positive or negative.

Case 1: $2+x > 0$ or $x > -2$.

Then we have

$$-4(2+x) \le 3-2x \le 4(2+x)$$

or, equivalently,

$$-8-4x \le 3-2x \le 8+4x$$

So, if $x > -2$, then also $-8-4x \le 3-2x$ and $3-2x \le 8+4x$. We solve these two inequalities. The first inequality is

$$-8-4x \le 3-2x$$

Adding $2x+8$ to both members gives

$$-2x \le 11$$

Dividing both members by -2 and reversing the inequality sign, we obtain

$$x \ge -\tfrac{11}{2}$$

The second inequality is

$$3-2x \le 8+4x$$

Adding $-4x-3$ to both members gives

$$-6x \le 5$$

Dividing both members by -6 and reversing the inequality sign, we obtain

$$x \ge -\tfrac{5}{6}$$

Therefore, if $x > -2$, then the original inequality holds if and only if $x \ge -\tfrac{11}{2}$ and $x \ge -\tfrac{5}{6}$.

Because all three inequalities $x > -2$, $x \ge -\tfrac{11}{2}$, and $x \ge -\tfrac{5}{6}$ must be satisfied by the same value of x, we have $x \ge -\tfrac{5}{6}$, or the interval $[-\tfrac{5}{6}, +\infty)$.

Case 2: $2+x < 0$ or $x < -2$.

Thus, we have

$$-4(2+x) \ge 3-2x \ge 4(2+x)$$

or, equivalently,

$$-8-4x \ge 3-2x \ge 8+4x$$

Considering the left inequality, we have

$$-8 - 4x \geq 3 - 2x$$

or, equivalently,

$$-2x \geq 11$$

or, equivalently,

$$x \leq -\tfrac{11}{2}$$

From the right inequality we have

$$3 - 2x \geq 8 + 4x$$

or, equivalently,

$$-6x \geq 5$$

or, equivalently,

$$x \leq -\tfrac{5}{6}$$

Therefore, if $x < -2$, the original inequality holds if and only if $x \leq -\tfrac{11}{2}$ and $x \leq -\tfrac{5}{6}$.

Because all three inequalities must be satisfied by the same value of x, we have $x \leq -\tfrac{11}{2}$, or the interval $(-\infty, -\tfrac{11}{2}]$.

Combining the solution sets of Cases 1 and 2, we have as the solution set $(-\infty, -\tfrac{11}{2}] \cup [-\tfrac{5}{6}, +\infty)$.

EXAMPLE 6: Find the solution set of the inequality

$$|3x + 2| > 5$$

SOLUTION: By Theorem 1.2.4, the given inequality is equivalent to

$$3x + 2 > 5 \quad \text{or} \quad 3x + 2 < -5 \tag{1}$$

That is, the given inequality will be satisfied if either of the inequalities in (1) is satisfied.

Considering the first inequality, we have

$$3x + 2 > 5$$

or, equivalently,

$$x > 1$$

Therefore, every number in the interval $(1, +\infty)$ is a solution.

From the second inequality, we have

$$3x + 2 < -5$$

or, equivalently,

$$x < -\tfrac{7}{3}$$

Hence, every number in the interval $(-\infty, -\tfrac{7}{3})$ is a solution.

The solution set of the given inequality is therefore $(-\infty, -\frac{7}{3}) \cup (1, +\infty)$.

You may recall from algebra that the symbol $\sqrt{a}$, where $a \geq 0$, is defined as the unique *nonnegative* number x such that $x^2 = a$. We read $\sqrt{a}$ as "the principal square root of a." For example,

$$\sqrt{4} = 2 \qquad \sqrt{0} = 0 \qquad \sqrt{\tfrac{9}{25}} = \tfrac{3}{5}$$

NOTE: $\sqrt{4} \neq -2$; -2 is a square root of 4, but $\sqrt{4}$ denotes only the *positive* square root of 4.

Because we are concerned only with real numbers in this book, $\sqrt{a}$ is not defined if $a < 0$. From the definition of $\sqrt{a}$, it follows that

$$\sqrt{x^2} = |x|$$

For example, $\sqrt{5^2} = 5$ and $\sqrt{(-3)^2} = 3$.

The following theorems about absolute value will be useful later.

1.2.6 Theorem   If a and b are any numbers, then

$$|ab| = |a| \cdot |b|$$

Expressed in words, this equation states that the absolute value of the product of two numbers is the product of the absolute values of the two numbers.

PROOF:

$$|ab| = \sqrt{(ab)^2}$$
$$= \sqrt{a^2 b^2}$$
$$= \sqrt{a^2} \cdot \sqrt{b^2}$$
$$= |a| \cdot |b|$$

∎

1.2.7 Theorem   If a is any number and b is any number except 0,

$$\left| \frac{a}{b} \right| = \frac{|a|}{|b|}$$

That is, the absolute value of the quotient of two numbers is the quotient of the absolute values of the two numbers.

The proof of Theorem 1.2.7 is left as an exercise (see Exercise 28).

1.2.8 Theorem
The Triangle Inequality

If a and b are any numbers, then

$$|a + b| \leq |a| + |b|$$

PROOF: By Definition 1.2.1, either $a = |a|$ or $a = -|a|$; thus

$$-|a| \le a \le |a| \tag{2}$$

Furthermore,

$$-|b| \le b \le |b| \tag{3}$$

From inequalities (2) and (3) and Theorem 1.1.23, we have

$$-(|a| + |b|) \le a + b \le |a| + |b|$$

Hence, from Corollary 1.2.3, it follows that

$$|a + b| \le |a| + |b| \qquad \blacksquare$$

Theorem 1.2.8 has two important corollaries which we now state and prove.

1.2.9 Corollary   If a and b are any numbers, then

$$|a - b| \le |a| + |b|$$

PROOF: $|a - b| = |a + (-b)| \le |a| + |(-b)| = |a| + |b|$. $\blacksquare$

1.2.10 Corollary   If a and b are any numbers, then

$$|a| - |b| \le |a - b|$$

PROOF: $|a| = |(a - b) + b| \le |a - b| + |b|$; thus, subtracting $|b|$ from both members of the inequality, we have

$$|a| - |b| \le |a - b| \qquad \blacksquare$$

Exercises 1.2

In Exercises 1 through 10, solve for x.

1. $|4x + 3| = 7$

2. $|3x - 8| = 4$

3. $|5 - 2x| = 11$

4. $|4 + 3x| = 1$

5. $|5x - 3| = |3x + 5|$

6. $|x - 2| = |3 - 2x|$

7. $|7x| = 4 - x$

8. $2x + 3 = |4x + 5|$

9. $\left|\dfrac{x + 2}{x - 2}\right| = 5$

10. $\left|\dfrac{3x + 8}{2x - 3}\right| = 4$

In Exercises 11 through 14, find all the values of x for which the number is real.

11. $\sqrt{8x - 5}$

12. $\sqrt{x^2 - 16}$

13. $\sqrt{x^2 - 5x + 4}$

14. $\sqrt{x^2 + 2x - 1}$

In Exercises 15 through 26, find the solution set of the given inequality, and illustrate the solution on the real number line.

15. $|x + 4| < 7$

16. $|2x - 5| < 3$

17. $|3x - 4| \leq 2$

18. $|6 - 2x| \geq 7$

19. $|2x - 5| > 3$

20. $|3 + 2x| < |4 - x|$

21. $|x + 4| \leq |2x - 6|$

22. $|3x| > |6 - 3x|$

23. $|9 - 2x| \geq |4x|$

24. $\left| \dfrac{6 - 5x}{3 + x} \right| \leq \dfrac{1}{2}$

25. $\left| \dfrac{x + 2}{2x - 3} \right| < 4$

26. $\left| \dfrac{5}{2x - 1} \right| \geq \left| \dfrac{1}{x - 2} \right|$

27. Prove Theorem 1.2.4.

28. Prove Theorem 1.2.7.

In Exercises 29 through 32, solve for x and use absolute value bars to write the answer.

29. $\dfrac{x - a}{x + a} > 0$

30. $\dfrac{a - x}{a + x} \geq 0$

31. $\dfrac{x - 2}{x - 4} > \dfrac{x + 2}{x}$

32. $\dfrac{x + 5}{x + 3} < \dfrac{x + 1}{x - 1}$

33. Prove that if a and b are any numbers, then $|a - b| \leq |a| + |b|$. (HINT: Write $a - b$ as $a + (-b)$ and use Theorem 1.2.8.)

34. Prove that if a and b are any numbers, then $|a| - |b| \leq |a - b|$. (HINT: Let $|a| = |(a - b) + b|$, and use Theorem 1.2.8.)

35. What single inequality is equivalent to the following two inequalities: $a > b + c$ and $a > b - c$?

1.3 THE NUMBER PLANE AND GRAPHS OF EQUATIONS

Ordered pairs of real numbers will now be considered. Any two real numbers form a *pair*, and when the order of the pair of real numbers is designated, we call it an *ordered pair of real numbers*. If x is the first real number and y is the second real number, we denote this ordered pair by writing them in parentheses with a comma separating them as (x, y). Note that the ordered pair $(3, 7)$ is different from the ordered pair $(7, 3)$.

1.3.1 Definition   The set of all ordered pairs of real numbers is called the *number plane*, and each ordered pair (x, y) is called a *point* in the number plane. The number plane is denoted by R^2.

Just as we can identify R^1 with points on an axis (a one-dimensional space), we can identify R^2 with points in a geometric plane (a two-dimensional space). The method we use with R^2 is the one attributed to the French mathematician René Descartes (1596–1650), who is credited with the invention of analytic geometry in 1637.

A horizontal line is chosen in the geometric plane and is called the x axis. A vertical line is chosen and is called the y axis. The point of intersection of the x axis and the y axis is called the *origin* and is denoted by the letter O. A unit of length is chosen (usually the unit length on each axis is the same). We establish the positive direction on the x axis to the right of the origin, and the positive direction on the y axis above the origin.

Figure 1.3.1

We now associate an ordered pair of real numbers (x, y) with a point P in the geometric plane. The distance of P from the y axis (considered as positive if P is to the right of the y axis and negative if P is to the left of the y axis) is called the *abscissa* (or *x coordinate*) of P and is denoted by x. The distance of P from the x axis (considered as positive if P is above the x axis and negative if P is below the x axis) is called the *ordinate* (or *y coordinate*) of P and is denoted by y. The abscissa and the ordinate of a point are called the *rectangular cartesian coordinates* of the point. There is a one-to-one correspondence between the points in a geometric plane and R^2; that is, with each point there corresponds a unique ordered pair (x, y), and with each ordered pair (x, y) there is associated only one point. This one-to-one correspondence is called a *rectangular cartesian coordinate system*. Figure 1.3.1 illustrates a rectangular cartesian coordinate system with some points plotted.

The x and y axes are called the *coordinate axes*. They divide the plane into four parts, called *quadrants*. The first quadrant is the one in which the abscissa and the ordinate are both positive, that is, the upper right quadrant. The other quadrants are numbered in the counterclockwise direction, with the fourth, for example, being the lower right quadrant.

Because of the one-to-one correspondence, we identify R^2 with the geometric plane. For this reason we call an ordered pair (x, y) a *point.* Similarly, we refer to a "line" in R^2 as the set of all points corresponding to a line in the geometric plane, and we use other geometric terms for sets of points in R^2.

Consider the equation

$$y = x^2 - 2 \qquad (1)$$

where (x, y) is a point in R^2. We call this an equation in R^2.

By a solution of this equation, we mean an ordered pair of numbers, one for x and one for y, which satisfies the equation. For example, if x is replaced by 3 in Eq. (1), we see that $y = 7$; thus, $x = 3$ and $y = 7$ constitutes a solution of this equation. If any number is substituted for x in the right side of Eq. (1), we obtain a corresponding value for y. It is seen, then, that Eq. (1) has an unlimited number of solutions. Table 1.3.1 gives a few such solutions.

Table 1.3.1

x	0	1	2	3	4	−1	−2	−3	−4
$y = x^2 - 2$	−2	−1	2	7	14	−1	2	7	14

If we plot the points having as coordinates the number pairs (x, y) satisfying Eq. (1), we have a sketch of the graph of the equation. In Fig. 1.3.2 we have plotted points whose coordinates are the number pairs ob-

Figure 1.3.2

tained from Table 1.3.1. These points are connected by a smooth curve. Any point (x, y) on this curve has coordinates satisfying Eq. (1). Also, the coordinates of any point not on this curve do not satisfy the equation. We have the following general definition.

1.3.2 Definition   The *graph of an equation* in R^2 is the set of all points (x, y) in R^2 whose coordinates are numbers satisfying the equation.

We sometimes call the graph of an equation the *locus* of the equation. The graph of an equation in R^2 is also called a *curve*. Unless otherwise stated, an equation with two unknowns, x and y, is considered an equation in R^2.

EXAMPLE 1:   Draw a sketch of the graph of the equation

$$y^2 - x - 2 = 0 \qquad (2)$$

SOLUTION: Solving Eq. (2) for y, we have

$$y = \pm\sqrt{x + 2} \qquad (3)$$

Equations (3) are equivalent to the two equations

$$y = \sqrt{x + 2} \qquad (4)$$

$$y = -\sqrt{x + 2} \qquad (5)$$

The coordinates of all points that satisfy Eq. (3) will satisfy either Eq. (4) or (5), and the coordinates of any point that satisfies either Eq. (4) or (5) will satisfy Eq. (3). Table 1.3.2 gives some of these values of x and y.

Table 1.3.2

x	0	0	1	1	2	2	3	3	−1	−1	−2
y	$\sqrt{2}$	$-\sqrt{2}$	$\sqrt{3}$	$-\sqrt{3}$	2	−2	$\sqrt{5}$	$-\sqrt{5}$	1	−1	0

Note that for any value of $x < -2$ there is no real value for y. Also, for each value of $x > -2$ there are two values for y. A sketch of the graph of Eq. (2) is shown in Fig. 1.3.3. The graph is a *parabola*.

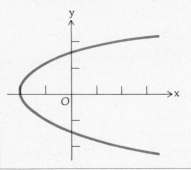

Figure 1.3.3

EXAMPLE 2:   Draw sketches of the graphs of the equations

$$y = \sqrt{x+2} \qquad (6)$$

and

$$y = -\sqrt{x+2}$$

SOLUTION: Equation (6) is the same as Eq. (4). The value of y is nonnegative; hence, the graph of Eq. (6) is the upper half of the graph of Eq. (3). A sketch of this graph is shown in Fig. 1.3.4.

Similarly, the graph of the equation

$$y = -\sqrt{x+2}$$

a sketch of which is shown in Fig. 1.3.5, is the lower half of the parabola of Fig. 1.3.3.

Figure 1.3.4

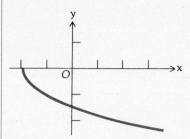

Figure 1.3.5

EXAMPLE 3:   Draw a sketch of the graph of the equation

$$y = |x+3| \qquad (7)$$

SOLUTION: From the definition of the absolute value of a number, we have

$$y = x+3 \quad \text{if} \quad x+3 \geq 0$$

and

$$y = -(x+3) \quad \text{if} \quad x+3 < 0$$

or, equivalently,

$$y = x+3 \quad \text{if} \quad x \geq -3$$

and

$$y = -(x+3) \quad \text{if} \quad x < -3$$

Table 1.3.3 gives some values of x and y satisfying Eq. (7).

Figure 1.3.6

Table 1.3.3

x	0	1	2	3	-1	-2	-3	-4	-5	-6	-7	-8	-9
y	3	4	5	6	2	1	0	1	2	3	4	5	6

A sketch of the graph of Eq. (7) is shown in Fig. 1.3.6.

EXAMPLE 4:   Draw a sketch of the graph of the equation

$$(x - 2y + 3)(y - x^2) = 0 \quad (8)$$

SOLUTION: By the property of real numbers that $ab = 0$ if and only if $a = 0$ or $b = 0$, we have from Eq. (8)

$$x - 2y + 3 = 0 \qquad (9)$$

Figure 1.3.7

and
$$y - x^2 = 0 \tag{10}$$

The coordinates of all points that satisfy Eq. (8) will satisfy either Eq. (9) or Eq. (10), and the coordinates of any point that satisfies either Eq. (9) or (10) will satisfy Eq. (8). Therefore, the graph of Eq. (8) will consist of the graphs of Eqs. (9) and (10). Table 1.3.4 gives some values of x and y satisfying Eq. (9), and Table 1.3.5 gives some values of x and y satisfying Eq. (10). A sketch of the graph of Eq. (8) is shown in Fig. 1.3.7.

Table 1.3.4

x	0	1	2	3	-1	-2	-3	-4	-5
y	$\frac{3}{2}$	2	$\frac{5}{2}$	3	1	$\frac{1}{2}$	0	$-\frac{1}{2}$	-1

Table 1.3.5

x	0	1	2	3	-1	-2	-3
y	0	1	4	9	1	4	9

1.3.3 Definition An *equation of a graph* is an equation which is satisfied by the coordinates of those, and only those, points on the graph.

● ILLUSTRATION 1: In R^2, $y = 8$ is an equation whose graph consists of those points having an ordinate of 8. This is a line which is parallel to the x axis, and 8 units above the x axis. ●

In drawing a sketch of the graph of an equation, it is often helpful to consider properties of *symmetry* of a graph.

1.3.4 Definition Two points P and Q are said to be *symmetric with respect to a line* if and only if the line is the perpendicular bisector of the line segment PQ. Two points P and Q are said to be *symmetric with respect to a third point* if and only if the third point is the midpoint of the line segment PQ.

Figure 1.3.8

● ILLUSTRATION 2: The points $(3, 2)$ and $(3, -2)$ are symmetric with respect to the x axis, the points $(3, 2)$ and $(-3, 2)$ are symmetric with respect to the y axis, and the points $(3, 2)$ and $(-3, -2)$ are symmetric with respect to the origin (see Fig. 1.3.8). ●

In general, the points (x, y) and $(x, -y)$ are symmetric with respect to the x axis, the points (x, y) and $(-x, y)$ are symmetric with respect to the y axis, and the points (x, y) and $(-x, -y)$ are symmetric with respect to the origin.

1.3.5 Definition   The graph of an equation is symmetric with respect to a line l if and only if for every point P on the graph there is a point Q, also on the graph, such that P and Q are symmetric with respect to l. The graph of an equation is symmetric with respect to a point R if and only if for every point P on the graph there is a point S, also on the graph, such that P and S are symmetric with respect to R.

From Definition 1.3.5 it follows that if a point (x, y) is on a graph which is symmetric with respect to the x axis, then the point $(x, -y)$ also must be on the graph. And, if both the points (x, y) and $(x, -y)$ are on the graph, then the graph is symmetric with respect to the x axis. Therefore, the coordinates of the point $(x, -y)$ as well as (x, y) must satisfy an equation of the graph. Hence, we may conclude that the graph of an equation in x and y is symmetric with respect to the x axis if and only if an equivalent equation is obtained when y is replaced by $-y$ in the equation. We have thus proved part (i) in the following theorem. The proofs of parts (ii) and (iii) are similar.

1.3.6 Theorem
(Tests for Symmetry)

The graph of an equation in x and y is

(i) symmetric with respect to the x axis if and only if an equivalent equation is obtained when y is replaced by $-y$ in the equation;
(ii) symmetric with respect to the y axis if and only if an equivalent equation is obtained when x is replaced by $-x$ in the equation;
(iii) symmetric with respect to the origin if and only if an equivalent equation is obtained when x is replaced by $-x$ and y is replaced by $-y$ in the equation.

The graph in Fig. 1.3.2 is symmetric with respect to the y axis, and for Eq. (1) an equivalent equation is obtained when x is replaced by $-x$. In Example 1 we have Eq. (2) for which an equivalent equation is obtained when y is replaced by $-y$, and its graph sketched in Fig. 1.3.3 is symmetric with respect to the x axis. The following example gives a graph which is symmetric with respect to the origin.

EXAMPLE 5:   Draw a sketch of the graph of the equation

$$xy = 1 \qquad (11)$$

SOLUTION: We see that if in Eq. (11) x is replaced by $-x$ and y is replaced by $-y$, an equivalent equation is obtained; hence, by Theorem 1.3.6(iii) the graph is symmetric with respect to the origin. Table 1.3.6 gives some values of x and y satisfying Eq. (11).

Table 1.3.6

x	1	2	3	4	$\frac{1}{2}$	$\frac{1}{3}$	$\frac{1}{4}$	-1	-2	-3	-4	$-\frac{1}{2}$	$-\frac{1}{3}$	$-\frac{1}{4}$
y	1	$\frac{1}{2}$	$\frac{1}{3}$	$\frac{1}{4}$	2	3	4	-1	$-\frac{1}{2}$	$-\frac{1}{3}$	$-\frac{1}{4}$	-2	-3	-4

Figure 1.3.9

From Eq. (11) we obtain $y = 1/x$. We see that as x increases through positive values, y decreases through positive values and gets closer and closer to zero. As x decreases through positive values, y increases through positive values and gets larger and larger. As x increases through negative values (i.e., x takes on the values $-4, -3, -2, -1, -\frac{1}{2}$, etc.), y takes on negative values having larger and larger absolute values. A sketch of the graph is shown in Fig. 1.3.9.

Exercises 1.3

In Exercises 1 through 6, plot the given point P and such of the following points as may apply:
(a) The point Q such that the line through Q and P is perpendicular to the x axis and is bisected by it. Give the coordinates of Q.
(b) The point R such that the line through P and R is perpendicular to and is bisected by the y axis. Give the coordinates of R.
(c) The point S such that the line through P and S is bisected by the origin. Give the coordinates of S.
(d) The point T such that the line through P and T is perpendicular to and is bisected by the 45° line through the origin bisecting the first and third quadrants. Give the coordinates of T.

1. $P(1, -2)$

2. $P(-2, 2)$

3. $P(2, 2)$

4. $P(-2, -2)$

5. $P(-1, -3)$

6. $P(0, -3)$

In Exercises 7 through 28, draw a sketch of the graph of the equation.

7. $y = 2x + 5$

8. $y = 4x - 3$

9. $y = \sqrt{x - 3}$

10. $y = -\sqrt{x - 3}$

11. $y^2 = x - 3$

12. $y = 5$

13. $x = -3$

14. $x = y^2 + 1$

15. $y = |x - 5|$

16. $y = -|x + 2|$

17. $y = |x| - 5$

18. $y = -|x| + 2$

19. $4x^2 + 9y^2 = 36$

20. $4x^2 - 9y^2 = 36$

21. $y = 4x^3$

22. $y^2 = 4x^3$

23. $4x^2 - y^2 = 0$

24. $3x^2 - 13xy - 10y^2 = 0$

25. $4x^2 + y^2 = 0$

26. $(2x + y - 1)(4y + x^2) = 0$

27. $x^4 - 5x^2y + 4y^2 = 0$

28. $(y^2 - x + 2)(y + \sqrt{x - 4}) = 0$

29. Draw a sketch of the graph of each of the following equations:
   (a) $y = \sqrt{2x}$
   (b) $y = -\sqrt{2x}$
   (c) $y^2 = 2x$

30. Draw a sketch of the graph of each of the following equations:
   (a) $y = \sqrt{-2x}$
   (b) $y = -\sqrt{-2x}$
   (c) $y^2 = -2x$

31. Draw a sketch of the graph of each of the following equations:

    (a) $x + 3y = 0$ (b) $x - 3y = 0$ (c) $x^2 - 9y^2 = 0$

32. (a) Write an equation whose graph is the x axis. (b) Write an equation whose graph is the y axis. (c) Write an equation whose graph is the set of all points on either the x axis or the y axis.

33. (a) Write an equation whose graph consists of all points having an abscissa of 4. (b) Write an equation whose graph consists of all points having an ordinate of -3.

34. Prove that a graph that is symmetric with respect to both coordinate axes is also symmetric with respect to the origin.

35. Prove that a graph that is symmetric with respect to any two perpendicular lines is also symmetric with respect to their point of intersection.

1.4 DISTANCE FORMULA AND MIDPOINT FORMULA

If A is the point (x_1, y) and B is the point (x_2, y) (i.e., A and B have the same ordinate but different abscissas), then the directed distance from A to B, denoted by $\overline{AB}$, is defined as $x_2 - x_1$.

• ILLUSTRATION 1: Refer to Fig. 1.4.1(a), (b), and (c).

Figure 1.4.1

If A is the point $(3, 4)$ and B is the point $(9, 4)$, then $\overline{AB} = 9 - 3 = 6$. If A is the point $(-8, 0)$ and B is the point $(6, 0)$, then $\overline{AB} = 6 - (-8) = 14$. If A is the point $(4, 2)$ and B is the point $(1, 2)$, then $\overline{AB} = 1 - 4 = -3$. We see that $\overline{AB}$ is positive if B is to the right of A, and $\overline{AB}$ is negative if B is to the left of A.   •

If C is the point (x, y_1) and D is the point (x, y_2), then the directed distance from C to D, denoted by $\overline{CD}$, is defined as $y_2 - y_1$.

• ILLUSTRATION 2: Refer to Fig. 1.4.2(a) and (b).

If C is the point $(1, -2)$ and D is the point $(1, -8)$, then $\overline{CD} = -8 - (-2) = -6$. If C is the point $(-2, -3)$ and D is the point $(-2, 4)$, then $\overline{CD} = 4 - (-3) = 7$. The number $\overline{CD}$ is positive if D is above C, and $\overline{CD}$ is negative if D is below C.   •

Figure 1.4.2

We consider a directed distance $\overline{AB}$ as the signed distance traveled by a particle that starts at $A(x_1, y)$ and travels to $B(x_2, y)$. In such a case, the abscissa of the particle changes from x_1 to x_2, and we use the notation Δx ("delta x") to denote this change; that is,

$$\Delta x = x_2 - x_1$$

Therefore, $\overline{AB} = \Delta x$.

Figure 1.4.3

It is important to note that the symbol Δx denotes the difference between the abscissa of B and the abscissa of A, and it *does not mean* "delta multiplied by x."

Similarly, if we consider a particle moving along a line parallel to the y axis from a point $C(x, y_1)$ to a point $D(x, y_2)$, then the ordinate of the particle changes from y_1 to y_2. We denote this change by Δy or

$$\Delta y = y_2 - y_1$$

Thus, $\overline{CD} = \Delta y$.

Now let $P_1(x_1, y_1)$ and $P_2(x_2, y_2)$ be any two points in the plane. We wish to obtain a formula for finding the nonnegative distance between these two points. We shall denote this distance by $|\overline{P_1P_2}|$. We use absolute-value bars because we are concerned only with the length, which is a nonnegative number, of the line segment between the two points P_1 and P_2. To derive the formula, we note that $|\overline{P_1P_2}|$ is the length of the hypotenuse of a right triangle P_1MP_2. This is illustrated in Fig. 1.4.3 for P_1 and P_2, both of which are in the first quadrant.

Using the Pythagorean theorem, we have

$$|\overline{P_1P_2}|^2 = |\Delta x|^2 + |\Delta y|^2$$

So

$$|\overline{P_1P_2}| = \sqrt{|\Delta x|^2 + |\Delta y|^2}$$

That is,

$$|\overline{P_1P_2}| = \sqrt{(x_2 - x_1)^2 + (y_2 - y_1)^2} \tag{1}$$

Formula (1) holds for all possible positions of P_1 and P_2 in all four quadrants. The length of the hypotenuse will always be $|\overline{P_1P_2}|$, and the lengths of the two legs will always be $|\Delta x|$ and $|\Delta y|$ (see Exercises 1 and 2). We state this result as a theorem.

1.4.1 Theorem   The undirected distance between the two points $P_1(x_1, y_1)$ and $P_2(x_2, y_2)$ is given by

$$|\overline{P_1P_2}| = \sqrt{(x_2 - x_1)^2 + (y_2 - y_1)^2}$$

EXAMPLE 1: If a point $P(x, y)$ is such that its distance from $A(3, 2)$ is always twice its distance from $B(-4, 1)$, find an equation which the coordinates of P must satisfy.

SOLUTION: From the statement of the problem

$$|\overline{PA}| = 2|\overline{PB}|$$

Using formula (1), we have

$$\sqrt{(x - 3)^2 + (y - 2)^2} = 2\sqrt{(x + 4)^2 + (y - 1)^2}$$

Squaring on both sides, we have

$$x^2 - 6x + 9 + y^2 - 4y + 4 = 4(x^2 + 8x + 16 + y^2 - 2y + 1)$$

or, equivalently,

$$3x^2 + 3y^2 + 38x - 4y + 55 = 0$$

EXAMPLE 2:   Show that the triangle with vertices at $A(-2, 4)$, $B(-5, 1)$, and $C(-6, 5)$ is isosceles.

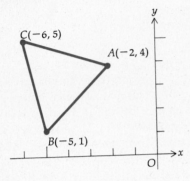

Figure 1.4.4

SOLUTION: The triangle is shown in Fig. 1.4.4.

$$|\overline{BC}| = \sqrt{(-6+5)^2 + (5-1)^2} = \sqrt{1+16} = \sqrt{17}$$
$$|\overline{AC}| = \sqrt{(-6+2)^2 + (5-4)^2} = \sqrt{16+1} = \sqrt{17}$$
$$|\overline{BA}| = \sqrt{(-2+5)^2 + (4-1)^2} = \sqrt{9+9} = 3\sqrt{2}$$

Therefore,

$$|\overline{BC}| = |\overline{AC}|$$

Hence, triangle ABC is isosceles.

EXAMPLE 3:   Prove analytically that the lengths of the diagonals of a rectangle are equal.

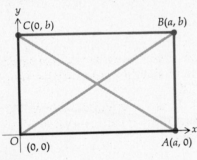

Figure 1.4.5

SOLUTION: Draw a general rectangle. Because we can choose the coordinate axes anywhere in the plane, and because the choice of the position of the axes does not affect the truth of the theorem, we take the origin at one vertex, the x axis along one side, and the y axis along another side. This procedure simplifies the coordinates of the vertices on the two axes. Refer to Fig. 1.4.5.

Now the hypothesis and the conclusion of the theorem can be stated.
Hypothesis: OABC is a rectangle with diagonals OB and AC.
Conclusion: $|\overline{OB}| = |\overline{AC}|$.

PROOF:

$$|\overline{OB}| = \sqrt{(a-0)^2 + (b-0)^2} = \sqrt{a^2 + b^2}$$
$$|\overline{AC}| = \sqrt{(0-a)^2 + (b-0)^2} = \sqrt{a^2 + b^2}$$

Therefore,

$$|\overline{OB}| = |\overline{AC}|$$

Let $P_1(x_1, y_1)$ and $P_2(x_2, y_2)$ be the endpoints of a line segment. We shall denote this line segment by P_1P_2. This is not to be confused with the notation $\overline{P_1P_2}$, which denotes the directed distance from P_1 to P_2. That is, $\overline{P_1P_2}$ denotes a number, whereas P_1P_2 is a line segment. Let $P(x, y)$ be the midpoint of the line segment P_1P_2. Refer to Fig. 1.4.6.

In Fig. 1.4.6 we see that triangles P_1RP and PTP_2 are congruent. Therefore, $|\overline{P_1R}| = |\overline{PT}|$, and so $x - x_1 = x_2 - x$, giving us

$$x = \frac{x_1 + x_2}{2} \tag{2}$$

Similarly, $|\overline{RP}| = |\overline{TP_2}|$. Then $y - y_1 = y_2 - y$, and therefore

$$y = \frac{y_1 + y_2}{2}$$

(3)

Hence, the coordinates of the midpoint of a line segment are, respectively, the average of the abscissas and the average of the ordinates of the endpoints of the line segment.

Figure 1.4.6

In the derivation of formulas (2) and (3) it was assumed that $x_2 > x_1$ and $y_2 > y_1$. The same formulas are obtained by using any orderings of these numbers (see Exercises 3 and 4).

EXAMPLE 4: Prove analytically that the line segments joining the midpoints of the opposite sides of any quadrilateral bisect each other.

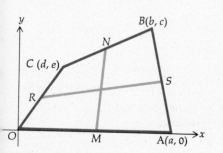

Figure 1.4.7

SOLUTION: Draw a general quadrilateral. Take the origin at one vertex and the x axis along one side. This method simplifies the coordinates of the two vertices on the x axis. See Fig. 1.4.7.

Hypothesis: $OABC$ is a quadrilateral. M is the midpoint of OA, N is the midpoint of CB, R is the midpoint of OC, and S is the midpoint of AB.

Conclusion: MN and RS bisect each other.

PROOF: To prove that two line segments bisect each other, we show that they have the same midpoint. Using formulas (2) and (3), we obtain the coordinates of M, N, R, and S. M is the point $(\frac{1}{2}a, 0)$, N is the point $(\frac{1}{2}(b + d), \frac{1}{2}(c + e))$, R is the point $(\frac{1}{2}d, \frac{1}{2}e)$, and S is the point $(\frac{1}{2}(a + b), \frac{1}{2}c)$.

The abscissa of the midpoint of MN is $\frac{1}{2}[\frac{1}{2}a + \frac{1}{2}(b + d)] = \frac{1}{4}(a + b + d)$.
The ordinate of the midpoint of MN is $\frac{1}{2}[0 + \frac{1}{2}(c + e)] = \frac{1}{4}(c + e)$.
Therefore, the midpoint of MN is the point $(\frac{1}{4}(a + b + d), \frac{1}{4}(c + e))$.
The abscissa of the midpoint of RS is $\frac{1}{2}[\frac{1}{2}d + \frac{1}{2}(a + b)] = \frac{1}{4}(a + b + d)$.
The ordinate of the midpoint of RS is $\frac{1}{2}[\frac{1}{2}e + \frac{1}{2}c] = \frac{1}{4}(c + e)$.
Therefore, the midpoint of RS is the point $(\frac{1}{4}(a + b + d), \frac{1}{4}(c + e))$.
Thus, the midpoint of MN is the same point as the midpoint of RS.
Therefore, MN and RS bisect each other. ■

Exercises 1.4

1. Derive distance formula (1) if P_1 is in the third quadrant and P_2 is in the second quadrant. Draw a figure.

2. Derive distance formula (1) if P_1 is in the second quadrant and P_2 is in the fourth quadrant. Draw a figure.

3. Derive midpoint formulas (2) and (3) if P_1 is in the first quadrant and P_2 is in the third quadrant.

4. Derive midpoint formulas (2) and (3) if $P_1(x_1, y_1)$ and $P_2(x_2, y_2)$ are both in the second quadrant and $x_2 > x_1$ and $y_1 > y_2$.

5. Find the length of the medians of the triangle having vertices $A(2, 3)$, $B(3, -3)$, and $C(-1, -1)$.

6. Find the midpoints of the diagonals of the quadrilateral whose vertices are $(0, 0)$, $(0, 4)$, $(3, 5)$, and $(3, 1)$.

7. Prove that the triangle with vertices $A(3, -6)$, $B(8, -2)$, and $C(-1, -1)$ is a right triangle. Find the area of the triangle. (HINT: Use the converse of the Pythagorean theorem.)

8. Prove that the points $A(6, -13)$, $B(-2, 2)$, $C(13, 10)$, and $D(21, -5)$ are the vertices of a square. Find the length of a diagonal.

9. By using distance formula (1), prove that the points $(-3, 2)$, $(1, -2)$, and $(9, -10)$ lie on a line.

10. If one end of a line segment is the point $(-4, 2)$ and the midpoint is $(3, -1)$, find the coordinates of the other end of the line segment.

11. The abscissa of a point is -6, and its distance from the point $(1, 3)$ is $\sqrt{74}$. Find the ordinate of the point.

12. Determine whether or not the points $(14, 7)$, $(2, 2)$, and $(-4, -1)$ lie on a line by using distance formula (1).

13. If two vertices of an equilateral triangle are $(-4, 3)$ and $(0, 0)$, find the third vertex.

14. Find an equation that must be satisfied by the coordinates of any point that is equidistant from the two points $(-3, 2)$ and $(4, 6)$.

15. Find an equation that must be satisfied by the coordinates of any point whose distance from the point $(5, 3)$ is always two units greater than its distance from the point $(-4, -2)$.

16. Given the two points $A(-3, 4)$ and $B(2, 5)$, find the coordinates of a point P on the line through A and B such that P is (a) twice as far from A as from B, and (b) twice as far from B as from A.

17. Find the coordinates of the three points that divide the line segment from $A(-5, 3)$ to $B(6, 8)$ into four equal parts.

18. If r_1 and r_2 are positive integers, prove that the coordinates of the point $P(x, y)$, which divides the line segment P_1P_2 in the ratio r_1/r_2—that is, $|\overline{P_1P}|/|\overline{P_1P_2}| = r_1/r_2$—are given by

$$x = \frac{(r_2 - r_1)x_1 + r_1x_2}{r_2} \quad \text{and} \quad y = \frac{(r_2 - r_1)y_1 + r_1y_2}{r_2}$$

In Exercises 19 through 23, use the formulas of Exercise 18 to find the coordinates of point P.

19. The point P is on the line segment between points $P_1(1, 3)$ and $P_2(6, 2)$ and is three times as far from P_2 as it is from P_1.

20. The point P is on the line segment between points $P_1(1, 3)$ and $P_2(6, 2)$ and is three times as far from P_1 as it is from P_2.

21. The point P is on the line through P_1 and P_2 and is three times as far from $P_2(6, 2)$ as it is from $P_1(1, 3)$ but is not between P_1 and P_2.

22. The point P is on the line through P_1 and P_2 and is three times as far from $P_1(1, 3)$ as it is from $P_2(6, 2)$ but is not between P_1 and P_2.

23. The point P is on the line through $P_1(-3, 5)$ and $P_2(-1, 2)$ so that $\overline{PP_1} = 4 \cdot \overline{P_1P_2}$.

24. (a) Find an equation whose graph is the circle that is the set of all points that are at a distance of 4 units from the point $(1, 3)$.

25. (a) Find an equation whose graph consists of all points equidistant from the points $(-1, 2)$ and $(3, 4)$. (b) Draw a sketch of the graph of the equation found in (a).

26. Prove analytically that the sum of the squares of the distances of any point from two opposite vertices of any rectangle is equal to the sum of the squares of its distances from the other two vertices.

27. Prove analytically that the line segment joining the midpoints of two opposite sides of any quadrilateral and the line segment joining the midpoints of the diagonals of the quadrilateral bisect each other.

28. Prove analytically that the midpoint of the hypotenuse of any right triangle is equidistant from each of the three vertices.

29. Prove analytically that if the lengths of two of the medians of a triangle are equal, the triangle is isosceles.

1.5 EQUATIONS OF A LINE

Figure 1.5.1

Let l be a nonvertical line and $P_1(x_1, y_1)$ and $P_2(x_2, y_2)$ be any two distinct points on l. Figure 1.5.1 shows such a line. In the figure, R is the point (x_2, y_1), and the points P_1, P_2, and R are vertices of a right triangle; furthermore, $\overline{P_1R} = x_2 - x_1$ and $\overline{RP_2} = y_2 - y_1$. The number $y_2 - y_1$ gives the measure of the change in the ordinate from P_1 to P_2, and it may be positive, negative, or zero. The number $x_2 - x_1$ gives the measure of the change in the abscissa from P_1 to P_2, and it may be positive or negative. The number $x_2 - x_1$ may not be zero because $x_2 \neq x_1$ since the line l is not vertical. For all choices of the points P_1 and P_2 on l, the quotient

$$\frac{y_2 - y_1}{x_2 - x_1}$$

is constant; this quotient is called the "slope" of the line. Following is the formal definition.

1.5.1 Definition

If $P_1(x_1, y_1)$ and $P_2(x_2, y_2)$ are any two distinct points on line l, which is not parallel to the y axis, then the *slope* of l, denoted by m, is given by

$$m = \frac{y_2 - y_1}{x_2 - x_1} \qquad (1)$$

In Eq. (1), $x_2 \neq x_1$ since l is not parallel to the y axis.

The value of m computed from Eq. (1) is independent of the choice of the two points P_1 and P_2 on l. To show this, suppose we choose two different points, $\overline{P_1}(\overline{x_1}, \overline{y_1})$ and $\overline{P_2}(\overline{x_2}, \overline{y_2})$, and compute a number $\overline{m}$ from Eq. (1).

$$\overline{m} = \frac{\overline{y_2} - \overline{y_1}}{\overline{x_2} - \overline{x_1}}$$

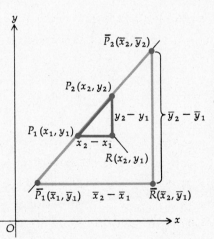

Figure 1.5.2

We shall show that $\overline{m} = m$. Refer to Fig. 1.5.2. Triangles $\overline{P_1}R\overline{P_2}$ and P_1RP_2 are similar, so the lengths of corresponding sides are proportional. Therefore,

$$\frac{\overline{y_2} - \overline{y_1}}{\overline{x_2} - \overline{x_1}} = \frac{y_2 - y_1}{x_2 - x_1}$$

or

$$\overline{m} = m$$

Figure 1.5.3

Figure 1.5.4

Figure 1.5.5

Hence, we conclude that the value of m computed from Eq. (1) is the same number no matter what two points on l are selected.

In Fig. 1.5.2, $x_2 > x_1$, $y_2 > y_1$, $\bar{x}_2 > \bar{x}_1$, and $\bar{y}_2 > \bar{y}_1$. The discussion above is valid for any ordering of these pairs of numbers since Definition 1.5.1 holds for any ordering.

In Sec. 1.4 we defined $\Delta y = y_2 - y_1$ and $\Delta x = x_2 - x_1$. Substituting these values into Eq. (1), we have

$$m = \frac{\Delta y}{\Delta x}$$

Multiplying on both sides of this equation by Δx, we obtain

$$\Delta y = m\,\Delta x \tag{2}$$

It is seen from Eq. (2) that if we consider a particle moving along line l, the change in the ordinate of the particle is proportional to the change in the abscissa, and the constant of proportionality is the slope of the line.

If the slope of a line is positive, then as the abscissa of a point on the line increases, the ordinate increases. Such a line is shown in Fig. 1.5.3. In Fig. 1.5.4, we have a line whose slope is negative. For this line, as the abscissa of a point on the line increases, the ordinate decreases. Note that if the line is parallel to the x axis, then $y_2 = y_1$ and so $m = 0$.

If the line is parallel to the y axis, $x_2 = x_1$; thus, Eq. (1) is meaningless because we cannot divide by zero. This is the reason that lines parallel to the y axis, or vertical lines, are excluded in Definition 1.5.1. We say that a vertical line does not have a slope.

• ILLUSTRATION 1: Let l be the line through the points $P_1(2, 3)$ and $P_2(4, 7)$. The slope of l, by Definition 1.5.1, is given by

$$m = \frac{7 - 3}{4 - 2} = 2$$

Refer to Fig. 1.5.5. If $P(x, y)$ and $Q(x + \Delta x, y + \Delta y)$ are any two points on l, then

$$\frac{\Delta y}{\Delta x} = 2$$

or

$$\Delta y = 2\,\Delta x$$

Thus, if a particle is moving along the line l, the change in the ordinate is twice the change in the abscissa. That is, if the particle is at $P_2(4, 7)$ and the abscissa is increased by one unit, then the ordinate is increased by two units, and the particle is at the point $P_3(5, 9)$. Similarly, if the particle is at $P_1(2, 3)$ and the abscissa is decreased by three units, then the ordinate is decreased by six units, and the particle is at $P_4(-1, -3)$.   •

Since two points $P_1(x_1, y_1)$ and $P_2(x_2, y_2)$ determine a unique line, we should be able to obtain an equation of the line through these two points. Consider $P(x, y)$ any point on the line. We want an equation that is satisfied by x and y if and only if $P(x, y)$ is on the line through $P_1(x_1, y_1)$ and $P_2(x_2, y_2)$. We distinguish two cases.

Case 1: $x_2 = x_1$.

In this case the line through P_1 and P_2 is parallel to the y axis, and all points on this line have the same abscissa. So $P(x, y)$ is any point on the line if and only if

$$x = x_1 \tag{3}$$

Equation (3) is an equation of a line parallel to the y axis. Note that this equation is independent of y; that is, the ordinate may have any value whatsoever, and the point $P(x, y)$ is on the line whenever the abscissa is x_1.

Case 2: $x_2 \neq x_1$.

The slope of the line through P_1 and P_2 is given by

$$m = \frac{y_2 - y_1}{x_2 - x_1} \tag{4}$$

If $P(x, y)$ is any point on the line except (x_1, y_1), the slope is also given by

$$m = \frac{y - y_1}{x - x_1} \tag{5}$$

The point P will be on the line through P_1 and P_2 if and only if the value of m from Eq. (4) is the same as the value of m from Eq. (5), that is, if and only if

$$\frac{y - y_1}{x - x_1} = \frac{y_2 - y_1}{x_2 - x_1}$$

Multiplying on both sides of this equation by $(x - x_1)$, we obtain

$$y - y_1 = \frac{y_2 - y_1}{x_2 - x_1}(x - x_1) \tag{6}$$

Equation (6) is satisfied by the coordinates of P_1 as well as by the coordinates of any other point on the line through P_1 and P_2.

Equation (6) is called the *two-point* form of an equation of the line. It gives an equation of the line if two points on the line are known.

● ILLUSTRATION 2: An equation of the line through the two points $(6, -3)$ and $(-2, 3)$ is

$$y - (-3) = \frac{3 - (-3)}{-2 - 6}(x - 6)$$

$$y + 3 = -\tfrac{3}{4}(x - 6)$$

$$3x + 4y = 6$$

●

If in Eq. (6) we replace $(y_2 - y_1)/(x_2 - x_1)$ by m, we get

$$y - y_1 = m(x - x_1) \qquad (7)$$

Equation (7) is called the *point-slope* form of an equation of the line. It gives an equation of the line if a point $P_1(x_1, y_1)$ on the line and the slope m of the line are known.

● ILLUSTRATION 3: An equation of the line through the point $(-4, -5)$ and having a slope of 2 is

$$y - (-5) = 2[x - (-4)]$$
$$2x - y + 3 = 0$$

●

If we choose the particular point $(0, b)$ (i.e., the point where the line intersects the y axis) for the point (x_1, y_1) in Eq. (7), we have

$$y - b = m(x - 0)$$

or, equivalently,

$$y = mx + b \qquad (8)$$

The number b, which is the ordinate of the point where the line intersects the y axis, is called the y *intercept* of the line. Consequently, Eq. (8) is called the *slope-intercept* form of an equation of the line. This form is especially important because it enables us to find the slope of a line from its equation. It is also important because it expresses the y coordinate explicitly in terms of the x coordinate.

EXAMPLE 1:   Given the line having the equation $3x + 4y = 7$, find the slope of the line.

SOLUTION: Solving the equation for y, we have

$$y = -\tfrac{3}{4}x + \tfrac{7}{4}$$

Comparing this equation with Eq. (8), we see that $m = -\tfrac{3}{4}$ and $b = \tfrac{7}{4}$. Therefore, the slope is $-\tfrac{3}{4}$.

Another form of an equation of a line is the one involving the intercepts of a line. We define the x *intercept* of a line as the abscissa of the point at which the line intersects the x axis. The x intercept is denoted by a. If the x intercept a and the y intercept b are given, we have two points $(a, 0)$ and $(0, b)$ on the line. Applying Eq. (6), the two-point form, we have

$$y - 0 = \frac{b - 0}{0 - a}(x - a)$$

$$-ay = bx - ab$$

$$bx + ay = ab$$

Dividing by ab, if $a \neq 0$ and $b \neq 0$, we obtain

$$\frac{x}{a} + \frac{y}{b} = 1 \tag{9}$$

Equation (9) is called the *intercept* form of an equation of the line. Obviously it does not apply to a line through the origin, because for such a line both a and b are zero.

EXAMPLE 2:   The point (2, 3) bisects that portion of a line which is cut off by the coordinate axes. Find an equation of the line.

Figure 1.5.6

SOLUTION: Refer to Fig. 1.5.6. If a is the x intercept of the line and b is the y intercept of the line, then the point (2, 3) is the midpoint of the line segment joining $(a, 0)$ and $(0, b)$. By the midpoint formulas, we have

$$2 = \frac{a + 0}{2} \quad \text{and} \quad 3 = \frac{0 + b}{2}$$

Then

$$a = 4 \quad \text{and} \quad b = 6$$

The intercept form, Eq. (9), gives us

$$\frac{x}{4} + \frac{y}{6} = 1$$

or, equivalently,

$$3x + 2y = 12$$

1.5.2 Theorem   The graph of the equation

$$Ax + By + C = 0 \tag{10}$$

where A, B, and C are constants and where not both A and B are zero, is a straight line.

PROOF: Consider the two cases $B \neq 0$ and $B = 0$.

Case 1: $B \neq 0$.

Because $B \neq 0$, we divide on both sides of Eq. (10) by B and obtain

$$y = -\frac{A}{B} x - \frac{C}{B} \tag{11}$$

Equation (11) is an equation of a straight line because it is in the slope-intercept form, where $m = -A/B$ and $b = -C/B$.

Case 2: $B = 0$.

Because $B = 0$, we may conclude that $A \neq 0$ and thus have

$$Ax + C = 0$$

or, equivalently,

$$x = -\frac{C}{A}$$

Equation (12) is in the form of Eq. (3), and so the graph is a straight line parallel to the y axis. This completes the proof. ■

Because the graph of Eq. (10) is a straight line, it is called a *linear equation*. Equation (10) is the general equation of the first degree in x and y.

Because two points determine a line, to draw a sketch of the graph of a straight line from its equation we need only determine the coordinates of two points on the line, plot the two points, and then draw the line. Any two points will suffice, but it is usually convenient to plot the two points where the line intersects the two axes (which are given by the intercepts).

EXAMPLE 3: Given line l_1, having the equation $2x - 3y = 12$, and line l_2, having the equation $4x + 3y = 6$, draw a sketch of each of the lines. Then find the coordinates of the point of intersection of l_1 and l_2.

Figure 1.5.7

SOLUTION: To draw a sketch of the graph of l_1, we find the intercepts a and b. In the equation of l_1, we substitute 0 for x and get $b = -4$. In the equation of l_1, we substitute 0 for y and get $a = 6$. Similarly, we obtain the intercepts a and b for l_2, and for l_2 we have $a = \frac{3}{2}$ and $b = 2$. The two lines are plotted in Fig. 1.5.7.

To find the coordinates of the point of intersection of l_1 and l_2, we solve the two equations simultaneously. Because the point must lie on both lines, its coordinates must satisfy both equations. If both equations are put in the slope-intercept form, we have

$$y = \tfrac{2}{3}x - 4 \quad \text{and} \quad y = -\tfrac{4}{3}x + 2$$

Eliminating y gives

$$\tfrac{2}{3}x - 4 = -\tfrac{4}{3}x + 2$$

$$2x - 12 = -4x + 6$$

$$x = 3$$

So

$$y = \tfrac{2}{3}(3) - 4$$

$$= -2$$

Therefore, the point of intersection is $(3, -2)$.

1.5.3 Theorem If l_1 and l_2 are two distinct nonvertical lines having slopes m_1 and m_2, respectively, then l_1 and l_2 are parallel if and only if $m_1 = m_2$.

PROOF: Let an equation of l_1 be $y = m_1x + b_1$, and let an equation of l_2 be $y = m_2x + b_2$. Because there is an "if and only if" qualification, the proof consists of two parts.

PART 1: Prove that l_1 and l_2 are parallel if $m_1 = m_2$.

Assume that l_1 and l_2 are not parallel. Let us show that this assumption leads to a contradiction. If l_1 and l_2 are not parallel, then they intersect. Call this point of intersection $P(x_0, y_0)$. The coordinates of P must satisfy the equations of l_1 and l_2, and so we have

$$y_0 = m_1x_0 + b_1 \quad \text{and} \quad y_0 = m_2x_0 + b_2$$

But $m_1 = m_2$, which gives

$$y_0 = m_1x_0 + b_1 \quad \text{and} \quad y_0 = m_1x_0 + b_2$$

from which it follows that $b_1 = b_2$. Thus, because $m_1 = m_2$ and $b_1 = b_2$, both lines l_1 and l_2 have the same equation, $y = m_1x + b_1$, and so the lines are the same. But this contradicts the hypothesis that l_1 and l_2 are distinct lines. Therefore, our assumption is false. So we conclude that l_1 and l_2 are parallel.

PART 2:   Prove that l_1 and l_2 are parallel only if $m_1 = m_2$. Here we must show that if l_1 and l_2 are parallel, then $m_1 = m_2$.

Assume that $m_1 \neq m_2$. Solving the equations for l_1 and l_2 simultaneously, we get, upon eliminating y,

$$m_1x + b_1 = m_2x + b_2$$

from which it follows that

$$(m_1 - m_2)x = b_2 - b_1$$

Because we have assumed that $m_1 \neq m_2$, this gives

$$x = \frac{b_2 - b_1}{m_1 - m_2}$$

Hence, l_1 and l_2 have a point of intersection, which contradicts the hypothesis that l_1 and l_2 are parallel. So our assumption is false, and therefore $m_1 = m_2$. ∎

In Fig. 1.5.8, the two lines l_1 and l_2 are perpendicular. We state and prove the following theorem on the slopes of two perpendicular lines.

1.5.4 Theorem   If neither line l_1 nor line l_2 is vertical, then l_1 and l_2 are perpendicular if and only if the product of their slopes is -1. That is, if m_1 is the slope of l_1 and m_2 is the slope of l_2, then l_1 and l_2 are perpendicular if and only if $m_1m_2 = -1$.

PROOF:

PART 1:   Prove that l_1 and l_2 are perpendicular only if $m_1m_2 = -1$.

Let L_1 be the line through the origin parallel to l_1 and let L_2 be the line through the origin parallel to l_2. See Fig. 1.5.8. Therefore, by Theorem 1.5.3, the slope of line L_1 is m_1 and the slope of line L_2 is m_2. Because neither

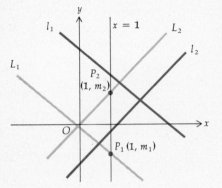

Figure 1.5.8

L_1 nor L_2 is vertical, these two lines intersect the line $x = 1$ at points P_1 and P_2, respectively. The abscissa of both P_1 and P_2 is 1. Let $\bar{y}$ be the ordinate of P_1. Since L_1 contains the points $(0, 0)$ and $(1, \bar{y})$ and its slope is m_1, we have from Definition 1.5.1

$$m_1 = \frac{\bar{y} - 0}{1 - 0}$$

and so $\bar{y} = m_1$. Similarly, the ordinate of P_2 is shown to be m_2.

Applying the Pythagorean theorem to right triangle P_1OP_2, we get

$$|\overline{OP_1}|^2 + |\overline{OP_2}|^2 = |\overline{P_1P_2}|^2 \tag{13}$$

By applying the distance formula, we obtain

$$|\overline{OP_1}|^2 = (1 - 0)^2 + (m_1 - 0)^2 = 1 + m_1{}^2$$

$$|\overline{OP_2}|^2 = (1 - 0)^2 + (m_2 - 0)^2 = 1 + m_2{}^2$$

$$|\overline{P_1P_2}|^2 = (1 - 1)^2 + (m_2 - m_1)^2 = m_2{}^2 - 2m_1m_2 + m_1{}^2$$

Substituting into Eq. (13) gives

$$(1 + m_1{}^2) + (1 + m_2{}^2) = m_2{}^2 - 2m_1m_2 + m_1{}^2$$

$$2 = -2m_1m_2$$

$$m_1m_2 = -1$$

PART 2: Prove that l_1 and l_2 are perpendicular if $m_1m_2 = -1$. Starting with $m_1m_2 = -1$, we can reverse the steps of the proof of Part 1 in order to obtain

$$|\overline{OP_1}|^2 + |\overline{OP_2}|^2 = |\overline{P_1P_2}|^2$$

from which it follows, from the converse of the Pythagorean theorem, that L_1 and L_2 are perpendicular; hence, l_1 and l_2 are perpendicular. ∎

Theorem 1.5.4 states that if two lines are perpendicular and neither one is vertical, the slope of one of the lines is the negative reciprocal of the slope of the other line.

● ILLUSTRATION 4: If line l_1 is perpendicular to line l_2 and the slope of l_1 is $\frac{2}{3}$, then the slope of l_2 must be $-\frac{3}{2}$. ●

EXAMPLE 4: Prove by means of slopes that the four points $A(6, 2)$, $B(8, 6)$, $C(4, 8)$, and $D(2, 4)$ are the vertices of a rectangle.

SOLUTION: See Fig. 1.5.9. Let

$$m_1 = \text{the slope of } AB = \frac{6 - 2}{8 - 6} = 2.$$

$$m_2 = \text{the slope of } BC = \frac{8 - 6}{4 - 8} = -\frac{1}{2}.$$

Figure 1.5.9

$$m_3 = \text{the slope of } DC = \frac{8-4}{4-2} = 2.$$

$$m_4 = \text{the slope of } AD = \frac{4-2}{2-6} = -\frac{1}{2}.$$

Because

$$m_1 = m_3, \ AB \parallel DC.$$

$$m_2 = m_4, \ BC \parallel AD.$$

$$m_1 m_2 = -1, \ AB \perp BC.$$

Therefore, quadrilateral $ABCD$ has opposite sides parallel and two adjacent sides perpendicular, and we conclude that $ABCD$ is a rectangle.

EXAMPLE 5: Given the line l having the equation

$$2x + 3y - 5 = 0$$

find an equation of the line perpendicular to line l and passing through the point $A(-1, 3)$.

SOLUTION: Because the required line is perpendicular to line l, its slope must be the negative reciprocal of the slope of l. We find the slope of l by putting its equation into the slope-intercept form. Solving the given equation for y, we obtain

$$y = -\tfrac{2}{3}x + \tfrac{5}{3}$$

Therefore, the slope of l is $-\tfrac{2}{3}$, and the slope of the required line is $\tfrac{3}{2}$. Because we also know that the required line contains the point $(-1, 3)$, we use the point-slope form, which gives

$$y - 3 = \tfrac{3}{2}(x + 1)$$

$$2y - 6 = 3x + 3$$

$$3x - 2y + 9 = 0$$

Exercises 1.5

In Exercises 1 through 4, find the slope of the line through the given points.

1. $(2, -3)$, $(-4, 3)$

2. $(5, 2)$, $(-2, -3)$

3. $(\tfrac{1}{3}, \tfrac{1}{2})$, $(-\tfrac{5}{6}, \tfrac{2}{3})$

4. $(-2.1, 0.3)$, $(2.3, 1.4)$

In Exercises 5 through 14, find an equation of the line satisfying the given conditions.

5. The slope is 4 and through the point $(2, -3)$.

6. Through the two points $(3, 1)$ and $(-5, 4)$.

7. Through the point $(-3, -4)$ and parallel to the y axis.

8. Through the point $(1, -7)$ and parallel to the x axis.

9. The x intercept is -3, and the y intercept is 4.

10. Through $(1, 4)$ and parallel to the line whose equation is $2x - 5y + 7 = 0$.

11. Through $(-2, -5)$ and having a slope of $\sqrt{3}$.

12. Through the origin and bisecting the angle between the axes in the first and third quadrants.

13. Through the origin and bisecting the angle between the axes in the second and fourth quadrants.

14. The slope is -2, and the x intercept is 4.

15. Find an equation of the line through the points $(1, 3)$ and $(2, -2)$, and put the equation in the intercept form.

16. Find an equation of the line through the points $(3, -5)$ and $(1, -2)$, and put the equation in the slope-intercept form.

17. Show by means of slopes that the points $(-4, -1)$, $(3, \frac{8}{3})$, $(8, -4)$, and $(2, -9)$ are the vertices of a trapezoid.

18. Three consecutive vertices of a parallelogram are $(-4, 1)$, $(2, 3)$, and $(8, 9)$. Find the coordinates of the fourth vertex.

19. For each of the following sets of three points, determine by means of slopes if the points are on a line: (a) $(2, 3)$, $(-4, -7)$, $(5, 8)$; (b) $(-3, 6)$, $(3, 2)$, $(9, -2)$; (c) $(2, -1)$, $(1, 1)$, $(3, 4)$; and (d) $(4, 6)$, $(1, 2)$, $(-5, -4)$.

20. Prove by means of slopes that the three points $A(3, 1)$, $B(6, 0)$, and $C(4, 4)$ are the vertices of a right triangle, and find the area of the triangle.

21. Given the line l having the equation $2y - 3x = 4$ and the point $P(1, -3)$, find (a) an equation of the line through P and perpendicular to l; (b) the shortest distance from P to line l.

22. If A, B, C, and D are constants, show that (a) the lines $Ax + By + C = 0$ and $Ax + By + D = 0$ are parallel and (b) the lines $Ax + By + C = 0$ and $Bx - Ay + D = 0$ are perpendicular.

23. Given the line l, having the equation $Ax + By + C = 0$, $B \neq 0$, find (a) the slope, (b) the y intercept, (c) the x intercept, (d) an equation of the line through the origin perpendicular to l.

24. Find an equation of the line which has equal intercepts and which passes through the point $(8, -6)$.

25. Find equations of the three medians of the triangle having vertices $A(3, -2)$, $B(3, 4)$, and $C(-1, 1)$, and prove that they meet in a point.

26. Find equations of the perpendicular bisectors of the sides of the triangle having vertices $A(-1, -3)$, $B(5, -3)$, and $C(5, 5)$, and prove that they meet in a point.

27. Find an equation of each of the lines through the point $(3, 2)$, which forms with the coordinate axes a triangle of area 12.

28. Let l_1 be the line having the equation $A_1x + B_1y + C_1 = 0$, and let l_2 be the line having the equation $A_2x + B_2y + C_2 = 0$. If l_1 is not parallel to l_2 and if k is any constant, the equation

$$A_1x + B_1y + C_1 + k(A_2x + B_2y + C_2) = 0$$

represents an unlimited number of lines. Prove that each of these lines contains the point of intersection of l_1 and l_2.

29. Given an equation of l_1 is $2x + 3y - 5 = 0$ and an equation of l_2 is $3x + 5y - 8 = 0$, by using Exercise 28 and without finding the coordinates of the point of intersection of l_1 and l_2, find an equation of the line through this point of intersection and (a) passing through the point $(1, 3)$; (b) parallel to the x axis; (c) parallel to the y axis; (d) having slope -2; (e) perpendicular to the line having the equation $2x + y = 7$; (f) forming an isosceles triangle with the coordinate axes.

30. Find an equation of each straight line that is perpendicular to the line having the equation $5x - y = 1$ and that forms with the coordinate axes a triangle having an area of measure 5.

31. Prove analytically that the diagonals of a rhombus are perpendicular.

32. Prove analytically that the line segments joining consecutive midpoints of the sides of any quadrilateral form a parallelogram.

33. Prove analytically that the diagonals of a parallelogram bisect each other.

34. Prove analytically that if the diagonals of a quadrilateral bisect each other, then the quadrilateral is a parallelogram.

1.6 THE CIRCLE The simplest curve that is the graph of a quadratic equation in two variables is the "circle," which we now define.

1.6.1 Definition A *circle* is the set of all points in a plane equidistant from a fixed point. The fixed point is called the *center* of the circle, and the measure of the constant equal distance is called the *radius* of the circle.

1.6.2 Theorem The circle with center at the point $C(h, k)$ and radius r has as an equation

$$(x - h)^2 + (y - k)^2 = r^2 \qquad (1)$$

PROOF: The point $P(x, y)$ lies on the circle if and only if

$$|\overline{PC}| = r$$

that is, if and only if

$$\sqrt{(x - h)^2 + (y - k)^2} = r$$

This is true if and only if

$$(x - h)^2 + (y - k)^2 = r^2$$

which is Eq. (1). Equation (1) is satisfied by the coordinates of those and only those points which lie on the given circle. Hence, (1) is an equation of the circle. ■

From Definition 1.3.2, it follows that the graph of Eq. (1) is the circle with center at (h, k) and radius r.

If the center of the circle is at the origin, then $h = k = 0$; therefore, its equation is $x^2 + y^2 = r^2$.

● ILLUSTRATION 1: Figure 1.6.1 shows the circle with center at $(2, -3)$ and radius equal to 4. For this circle $h = 2$, $k = -3$, and $r = 4$. We obtain an equation of the circle by substituting these values into Eq. (1) and we obtain

$$(x - 2)^2 + [y - (-3)]^2 = 4^2$$

$$(x - 2)^2 + (y + 3)^2 = 16$$

Squaring and then combining terms, we have

$$x^2 - 4x + 4 + y^2 + 6y + 9 = 16$$

$$x^2 + y^2 - 4x + 6y - 3 = 0 \qquad ●$$

Figure 1.6.1

EXAMPLE 1: Given the equation

$$x^2 + y^2 + 6x - 2y - 15 = 0$$

prove that the graph of this equation is a circle, and find its center and radius.

SOLUTION: The given equation may be written as

$$(x^2 + 6x) + (y^2 - 2y) = 15$$

Completing the squares of the terms in parentheses by adding 9 and 1 on both sides of the equation, we have

$$(x^2 + 6x + 9) + (y^2 - 2y + 1) = 15 + 9 + 1$$

$$(x + 3)^2 + (y - 1)^2 = 25$$

Comparing this equation with Eq. (1), we see that this is an equation of a circle with its center at $(-3, 1)$ and a radius of 5.

In Eq. (1), removing parentheses and combining terms gives

$$x^2 + y^2 - 2hx - 2ky + (h^2 + k^2 - r^2) = 0 \tag{2}$$

Equation (2) is of the form

$$x^2 + y^2 + Dx + Ey + F = 0 \tag{3}$$

where $D = -2h$, $E = -2k$, and $F = h^2 + k^2 - r^2$.

Equation (3) is called the *general form* of an equation of a circle, whereas Eq. (1) is called the *center-radius form*. Because every circle has a center and a radius, its equation can be put in the center-radius form, and hence into the general form.

We now consider the question of whether or not the graph of every equation of the form

$$x^2 + y^2 + Dx + Ey + F = 0$$

is a circle. To determine this, we shall attempt to write this equation in the center-radius form. We rewrite the equation as

$$x^2 + y^2 + Dx + Ey = -F$$

and complete the squares of the terms in parentheses by adding $\frac{1}{4}D^2$ and $\frac{1}{4}E^2$ on both sides, thus giving us

$$(x^2 + Dx + \tfrac{1}{4}D^2) + (y^2 + Ey + \tfrac{1}{4}E^2) = -F + \tfrac{1}{4}D^2 + \tfrac{1}{4}E^2$$

or, equivalently,

$$(x + \tfrac{1}{2}D)^2 + (y + \tfrac{1}{2}E)^2 = \tfrac{1}{4}(D^2 + E^2 - 4F) \tag{4}$$

Equation (4) is in the form of Eq. (1) if and only if

$$\tfrac{1}{4}(D^2 + E^2 - 4F) = r^2$$

We now consider three cases, namely, $(D^2 + E^2 - 4F)$ as positive, zero, and negative.

Case 1: $(D^2 + E^2 - 4F) > 0$.

Then $r^2 = \tfrac{1}{4}(D^2 + E^2 - 4F)$, and so Eq. (4) is an equation of a circle having a radius equal to $\tfrac{1}{2}\sqrt{D^2 + E^2 - 4F}$ and its center at $(-\tfrac{1}{2}D, -\tfrac{1}{2}E)$.

Case 2: $D^2 + E^2 - 4F = 0$.

Equation (4) is then of the form

$$(x + \tfrac{1}{2}D)^2 + (y + \tfrac{1}{2}E)^2 = 0 \tag{5}$$

Because the only real values of x and y satisfying Eq. (5) are $x = -\tfrac{1}{2}D$ and $y = -\tfrac{1}{2}E$, the graph is the point $(-\tfrac{1}{2}D, -\tfrac{1}{2}E)$. Comparing Eq. (5) with Eq. (1), we see that $h = -\tfrac{1}{2}D$, $k = -\tfrac{1}{2}E$, and $r = 0$. Thus, this point can be called a *point-circle*.

Case 3: $(D^2 + E^2 - 4F) < 0$.

Then Eq. (4) has a negative number on the right side and the sum of the squares of two real numbers on the left side. There are no real values of x and y that satisfy such an equation; consequently, we say the graph is the empty set.

Before stating the results of these three cases as a theorem, we observe that an equation of the form

$$Ax^2 + Ay^2 + Dx + Ey + F = 0 \qquad \text{where } A \neq 0 \tag{6}$$

can be written in the form of Eq. (3) by dividing by A, thereby obtaining

$$x^2 + y^2 + \frac{D}{A}x + \frac{E}{A}y + \frac{F}{A} = 0$$

Equation (6) is a special case of the general equation of the second degree:

$$Ax^2 + Bxy + Cy^2 + Dx + Ey + F = 0$$

in which the coefficients of x^2 and y^2 are equal and which has no xy term. We have, then, the following theorem.

1.6.3 Theorem   The graph of any second-degree equation in R^2 in x and y, in which the coefficients of x^2 and y^2 are equal and in which there is no xy term, is either a circle, a point-circle, or the empty set.

• ILLUSTRATION 2: The equation

$$2x^2 + 2y^2 + 12x - 8y + 31 = 0$$

is of the form (6), and therefore its graph is either a circle, a point-circle, or the empty set. If the equation is put in the form of Eq. (1), we have

$$x^2 + y^2 + 6x - 4y + \tfrac{31}{2} = 0$$

$$(x^2 + 6x) + (y^2 - 4y) = -\tfrac{31}{2}$$

$$(x^2 + 6x + 9) + (y^2 - 4y + 4) = -\tfrac{31}{2} + 9 + 4$$

$$(x + 3)^2 + (y - 2)^2 = -\tfrac{5}{2}$$

Therefore, the graph is the empty set.   •

EXAMPLE 2: Find an equation of the circle through the three points $A(4, 5)$, $B(3, -2)$, and $C(1, -4)$.

SOLUTION: The general form of an equation of the circle is

$$x^2 + y^2 + Dx + Ey + F = 0$$

Because the three points A, B, and C must lie on the circle, the coordinates of these points must satisfy the equation. So we have

$$16 + 25 + 4D + 5E + F = 0$$
$$9 + 4 + 3D - 2E + F = 0$$
$$1 + 16 + D - 4E + F = 0$$

or, equivalently,

$$4D + 5E + F = -41$$
$$3D - 2E + F = -13$$
$$D - 4E + F = -17$$

Solving these three equations simultaneously, we get

$$D = 7 \qquad E = -5 \qquad F = -44$$

Thus, an equation of the circle is

$$x^2 + y^2 + 7x - 5y - 44 = 0$$

In the following example we have a line which is tangent to a circle. The definition of the tangent line to a general curve at a specific point is given in Sec. 3.1. However, for a circle we use the definition from plane geometry which states that a tangent line at a point P on the circle is the line intersecting the circle at only the point P.

EXAMPLE 3: Find an equation of the circle with its center at the point $C(1, 6)$ and tangent to the line l having the equation $x - y - 1 = 0$.

SOLUTION: See Fig. 1.6.2. Given that $h = 1$ and $k = 6$, if we find r, we can obtain an equation of the circle by using the center-radius form.

Let l_1 be the line through C and the point P, which is the point of tangency of line l with the circle.

$$r = |\overline{PC}|$$

Hence, we must find the coordinates of P. We do this by finding an equation of l_1 and then finding the point of intersection of l_1 with l. Since l_1 is along a diameter of the circle, and l is tangent to the circle, l_1 is perpendicular to l. Because the slope of l is 1, the slope of l_1 is -1. Therefore, using the point-slope form of an equation of a line, we obtain as an equation of l_1

$$y - 6 = -1(x - 1)$$

Figure 1.6.2

or, equivalently,

$$x + y - 7 = 0$$

Solving this equation simultaneously with the given equation of l, namely,

$$x - y - 1 = 0$$

we get $x = 4$ and $y = 3$. Thus, P is the point $(4, 3)$. Therefore,

$$r = |\overline{PC}| = \sqrt{(4-1)^2 + (3-6)^2}$$

or, equivalently,

$$r = \sqrt{18}$$

So, an equation of the circle is

$$(x - 1)^2 + (y - 6)^2 = (\sqrt{18})^2$$

or, equivalently,

$$x^2 + y^2 - 2x - 12y + 19 = 0$$

Exercises 1.6

In Exercises 1 through 4, find an equation of the circle with center at C and radius r. Write the equation in both the center-radius form and the general form.

1. $C(4, -3), r = 5$

2. $C(0, 0), r = 8$

3. $C(-5, -12), r = 3$

4. $C(-1, 1), r = 2$

In Exercises 5 through 10, find an equation of the circle satisfying the given conditions.

5. Center is at $(1, 2)$ and through the point $(3, -1)$.

6. Center is at $(-2, 5)$ and tangent to the line $x = 7$.

7. Center is at $(-3, -5)$ and tangent to the line $12x + 5y - 4 = 0$.

8. Through the three points $(2, 8)$, $(7, 3)$, and $(-2, 0)$.

9. Tangent to the line $3x + y + 2 = 0$ at $(-1, 1)$ and through the point $(3, 5)$.

10. Tangent to the line $3x + 4y - 16 = 0$ at $(4, 1)$ and with a radius of 5. (Two possible circles.)

In Exercises 11 through 14, find the center and radius of each circle, and draw a sketch of the graph.

11. $x^2 + y^2 - 6x - 8y + 9 = 0$

12. $2x^2 + 2y^2 - 2x + 2y + 7 = 0$

13. $3x^2 + 3y^2 + 4y - 7 = 0$

14. $x^2 + y^2 - 10x - 10y + 25 = 0$

In Exercises 15 through 20, determine whether the graph is a circle, a point-circle, or no real locus.

15. $x^2 + y^2 - 2x + 10y + 19 = 0$

16. $4x^2 + 4y^2 + 24x - 4y + 1 = 0$

17. $x^2 + y^2 - 10x + 6y + 36 = 0$

18. $x^2 + y^2 + 2x - 4y + 5 = 0$

19. $36x^2 + 36y^2 - 48x + 36y - 119 = 0$

20. $9x^2 + 9y^2 + 6x - 6y + 5 = 0$

21. Find an equation of the common chord of the two circles $x^2 + y^2 + 4x - 6y - 12 = 0$ and $x^2 + y^2 + 8x - 2y + 8 = 0$. (HINT: If the coordinates of a point satisfy two different equations, then the coordinates also satisfy the difference of the two equations.)

22. Find the points of intersection of the two circles in Exercise 21.

23. Find an equation of the line which is tangent to the circle $x^2 + y^2 - 4x + 6y - 12 = 0$ at the point $(5, 1)$.

24. Find an equation of each of the two lines having slope $-\frac{4}{3}$ which are tangent to the circle $x^2 + y^2 + 2x - 8y - 8 = 0$.

25. From the origin, chords of the circle $x^2 + y^2 + 4x = 0$ are drawn. Prove that the set of midpoints of these chords is a circle.

26. Prove analytically that a line from the center of any circle bisecting any chord is perpendicular to the chord.

27. Prove analytically that an angle inscribed in a semicircle is a right angle.

28. Given the line $y = mx + b$ tangent to the circle $x^2 + y^2 = r^2$, find an equation involving m, b, and r.

1.7 FUNCTIONS AND THEIR GRAPHS

We intuitively consider y to be a function of x if there is some rule by which a unique value is assigned to y by a corresponding value of x. Familiar examples of such relationships are given by equations such as

$$y = 2x^2 + 5 \tag{1}$$

and

$$y = \sqrt{x^2 - 9} \tag{2}$$

It is not necessary that x and y be related by an equation in order for a functional relationship to exist between them, as shown in the following illustration.

● ILLUSTRATION 1: If y is the number of cents in the postage of a domestic First class letter, and if x is the number of ounces in the weight of the letter, then y is a function of x. For this functional relationship, there is no equation involving x and y; however, the relationship between x and y may be given by means of a table, such as Table 1.7.1.   ●

Table 1.7.1

x: number of ounces in the weight of the letter	$0 < x \le 1$	$1 < x \le 2$	$2 < x \le 3$	$3 < x \le 4$	$4 < x \le 5$	$5 < x \le 6$
y: number of cents in first class postage	13	26	39	52	65	78

The formal definition makes the concept of a function precise.

1.7.1 Definition   A *function* is a set of ordered pairs of numbers (x, y) in which no two distinct ordered pairs have the same first number. The set of all possible values of x is called the *domain* of the function, and the set of all possible values of y is called the *range* of the function.

In Definition 1.7.1, the restriction that no two distinct ordered pairs can have the same first number assures us that y is unique for a specific value of x.

Equation (1) defines a function. Let us call this function f. The equation gives the rule by which a unique value of y can be determined whenever x is given; that is, multiply the number x by itself, then multiply that product by 2, and add 5. The function f is the set of all ordered pairs (x, y) such that x and y satisfy Eq. (1), that is,

$$f = \{(x, y)\,|\,y = 2x^2 + 5\}$$

The numbers x and y are called *variables*. Because for the function f values are assigned to x and because the value of y is dependent upon the choice of x, we call x the *independent variable* and y the *dependent variable*. The domain of the function is the set of all possible values of the independent variable, and the range of the function is the set of all possible values of the dependent variable. For the function f under consideration, the domain is the set of all real numbers which can be denoted with interval notation as $(-\infty, +\infty)$. The smallest value that y can assume is 5 (when $x = 0$). The range of f is then the set of all positive numbers greater than or equal to 5, which is $[5, +\infty)$.

● ILLUSTRATION 2: Let g be the function which is the set of all ordered pairs (x, y) defined by Eq. (2); that is,

$$g = \{(x, y)\,|\,y = \sqrt{x^2 - 9}\}$$

Because the numbers are confined to real numbers, y is a function of x only for $x \geq 3$ or $x \leq -3$ (or simply $|x| \geq 3$) because for any x satisfying either of these inequalities a unique value of y is determined. However, if x is in the interval $(-3, 3)$, a square root of a negative number is obtained, and hence no real number y exists. Therefore, we must restrict x, and so

$$g = \{(x, y)\,|\,y = \sqrt{x^2 - 9} \text{ and } |x| \geq 3\}$$

The domain of g is $(-\infty, -3] \cup [3, +\infty)$, and the range of g is $[0, +\infty)$. ●

It should be stressed that in order to have a function there must be *exactly one value* of the dependent variable for a value of the independent variable in the domain of the function.

1.7.2 Definition   If f is a function, then the *graph* of f is the set of all points (x, y) in R^2 for which (x, y) is an ordered pair in f.

Figure 1.7.1

Hence, the graph of a function is a curve which is the set of all points in R^2 whose cartesian coordinates are given by the ordered pairs of numbers (x, y). Because for each value of x in the domain of the function there corresponds a unique value of y, no vertical line can intersect the graph of the function at more than one point.

● ILLUSTRATION 3: Let $f = \{(x, y)|y = \sqrt{5 - x}\}$. A sketch of the graph of f is shown in Fig. 1.7.1. The domain of f is the set of all real numbers less than or equal to 5, which is $(-\infty, 5]$, and the range of f is the set of all nonnegative real numbers, which is $[0, +\infty)$.   ●

● ILLUSTRATION 4: Let g be the function which is the set of all ordered pairs (x, y) such that

$$y = \begin{cases} -3 & \text{if } x \le -1 \\ 1 & \text{if } -1 < x \le 2 \\ 4 & \text{if } 2 < x \end{cases}$$

The domain of g is $(-\infty, +\infty)$, while the range of g consists of the three numbers -3, 1, and 4. A sketch of the graph is shown in Fig. 1.7.2.   ●

Observe in Fig. 1.7.2 that there is a break at $x = -1$ and another at $x = 2$. We say that g is discontinuous at -1 and 2. Continuous and discontinuous functions are considered in Sec. 2.5.

● ILLUSTRATION 5: Consider the set

$$\{(x, y)|x^2 + y^2 = 25\}$$

This set of ordered pairs is not a function because for any x in the interval $(-5, 5)$ there are two ordered pairs having that number as a first element. For example, both $(3, 4)$ and $(3, -4)$ are ordered pairs in the given set. Furthermore, observe that the graph of the given set is a circle with center at the origin and radius 5, and a vertical line having the equation $x = a$ (where $-5 < a < 5$) intersects the circle in two points.   ●

Figure 1.7.2

EXAMPLE 1: Let

$$h = \{(x, y)|y = |x|\}$$

Find the domain and range of h, and draw a sketch of the graph of h.

SOLUTION: The domain of h is $(-\infty, +\infty)$, and the range of h is $[0, +\infty)$. A sketch of the graph of h is shown in Fig. 1.7.3.

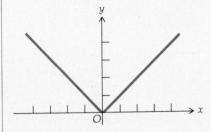

Figure 1.7.3

EXAMPLE 2: Let F be the function which is the set of all ordered pairs (x, y) such that

$$y = \begin{cases} 3x - 2 & \text{if } x < 1 \\ x^2 & \text{if } 1 \le x \end{cases}$$

Find the domain and range of F, and draw a sketch of the graph of F.

SOLUTION: A sketch of the graph of F is shown in Fig. 1.7.4. The domain of F is $(-\infty, +\infty)$, and the range of F is $(-\infty, +\infty)$.

Figure 1.7.4

EXAMPLE 3: Let G be the function which is the set of all ordered pairs (x, y) such that

$$y = \frac{x^2 - 9}{x - 3}$$

Find the domain and range of G, and draw a sketch of the graph of G.

SOLUTION: A sketch of the graph is shown in Fig. 1.7.5. Because a value for y is determined for each value of x except $x = 3$, the domain of G consists of all real numbers except 3. When $x = 3$, both the numerator and denominator are zero, and $0/0$ is undefined.

Factoring the numerator into $(x - 3)(x + 3)$, we obtain

$$y = \frac{(x - 3)(x + 3)}{(x - 3)}$$

or $y = x + 3$, provided that $x \ne 3$. In other words, the function G consists of all ordered pairs (x, y) such that

$$y = x + 3 \quad \text{and} \quad x \ne 3$$

The range of G consists of all real numbers except 6. The graph consists of all points on the line $y = x + 3$ except the point $(3, 6)$.

Figure 1.7.5

EXAMPLE 4: Let H be the function which is the set of all ordered pairs (x, y) such that

$$y = \begin{cases} x + 3 & \text{if } x \neq 3 \\ 2 & \text{if } x = 3 \end{cases}$$

Find the domain and range of H, and draw a sketch of the graph of H.

SOLUTION: A sketch of the graph of this function is shown in Fig. 1.7.6. The graph consists of the point $(3, 2)$ and all points on the line $y = x + 3$ except the point $(3, 6)$. Function H is defined for all values of x, and therefore the domain of H is $(-\infty, +\infty)$. The range of H consists of all real numbers except 6.

Figure 1.7.6

EXAMPLE 5: Let ϕ be the function which is the set of all ordered pairs (x, y) such that

$$y = \frac{(x^2 + 3x - 4)(x^2 - 9)}{(x^2 + x - 12)(x + 3)}$$

Find the domain and range of ϕ, and draw a sketch of the graph of ϕ.

Figure 1.7.7

SOLUTION: A sketch of the graph of this function is shown in Fig. 1.7.7. Factoring the numerator and denominator, we obtain

$$y = \frac{(x + 4)(x - 1)(x - 3)(x + 3)}{(x + 4)(x - 3)(x + 3)}$$

We see that the denominator is zero for $x = -4, -3$, and 3; therefore, ϕ is undefined for these three values of x. For values of $x \neq -4, -3$, or 3, we may divide numerator and denominator by the common factors and obtain

$$y = x - 1 \quad \text{if} \quad x \neq -4, -3, \text{ or } 3$$

Therefore, the domain of ϕ is the set of all real numbers except -4, -3, and 3, and the range of ϕ is the set of all real numbers except those values of $(x - 1)$ obtained by replacing x by $-4, -3$, or 3, that is, all real numbers except $-5, -4$, and 2. The graph of this function is the straight line $y = x - 1$, with the points $(-4, -5)$, $(-3, -4)$, and $(3, 2)$ deleted.

EXAMPLE 6:   Let f be the function which is the set of all ordered pairs (x, y) such that

$$y = \begin{cases} x^2 & \text{if } x \neq 2 \\ 7 & \text{if } x = 2 \end{cases}$$

Find the domain and range of f, and draw a sketch of the graph of f.

SOLUTION: A sketch of the graph of f is shown in Fig. 1.7.8. The graph consists of the point $(2, 7)$ and all points on the parabola $y = x^2$, except the point $(2, 4)$. Function f is defined for all values of x, and so the domain of f is $(-\infty, +\infty)$. The range of f consists of all nonnegative real numbers.

Figure 1.7.8

EXAMPLE 7:   Let h be the function which is the set of all ordered pairs (x, y) such that

$$y = \begin{cases} x - 1 & \text{if } x < 3 \\ 2x + 1 & \text{if } 3 \leq x \end{cases}$$

Find the domain and range of h, and draw a sketch of the graph of h.

SOLUTION: A sketch of the graph of h is shown in Fig. 1.7.9. The domain of h is $(-\infty, +\infty)$. The values of y are either less than 2 or greater than or equal to 7. So the range of h is $(-\infty, 2) \cup [7, +\infty)$ or, equivalently, all real numbers not in $[2, 7)$.

Figure 1.7.9

EXAMPLE 8: Let

$$g = \{(x, y) | y = \sqrt{x(x-2)}\}$$

Find the domain and range of g, and draw a sketch of the graph of g.

Figure 1.7.10

SOLUTION: Because $\sqrt{x(x-2)}$ is not a real number when $x(x-2) < 0$, the domain of g consists of the values of x for which $x(x-2) \geq 0$. This inequality will be satisfied when one of the following two cases holds: $x \geq 0$ and $x - 2 \geq 0$; or $x \leq 0$ and $x - 2 \leq 0$.

Case 1: $x \geq 0$ and $x - 2 \geq 0$.
   That is,

$$x \geq 0 \quad \text{and} \quad x \geq 2$$

Both inequalities hold if $x \geq 2$, which is the interval $[2, +\infty)$.

Case 2: $x \leq 0$ and $x - 2 \leq 0$.
   That is,

$$x \leq 0 \quad \text{and} \quad x \leq 2$$

Both inequalities hold if $x \leq 0$, which is the interval $(-\infty, 0]$.

Combining the solutions for the two cases, we obtain for the domain of g $(-\infty, 0] \cup [2, +\infty)$. The range of g is the interval $[0, +\infty)$. Figure 1.7.10 shows a sketch of the graph of g.

In the next illustration, the symbol $[\![x]\!]$ is used. $[\![x]\!]$ is defined as the greatest integer which is less than or equal to x; that is,

$$[\![x]\!] = n \quad \text{if} \quad n \leq x < n+1 \qquad \text{where } n \text{ is an integer}$$

This function is called the *greatest integer function*. It follows that $[\![1]\!] = 1$, $[\![1.3]\!] = 1$, $[\![\tfrac{1}{2}]\!] = 0$, $[\![-4.2]\!] = -5$, $[\![-8]\!] = -8$, $[\![9.8]\!] = 9$, and so on.

● ILLUSTRATION 6: Let F be the greatest integer function; that is, $F = \{(x, y) | y = [\![x]\!]\}$. A sketch of the graph of F is shown in Fig. 1.7.11. The following values are used to draw the sketch.

$$-5 \leq x < -4 \qquad [\![x]\!] = -5$$
$$-4 \leq x < -3 \qquad [\![x]\!] = -4$$
$$-3 \leq x < -2 \qquad [\![x]\!] = -3$$
$$-2 \leq x < -1 \qquad [\![x]\!] = -2$$
$$-1 \leq x < 0 \qquad [\![x]\!] = -1$$
$$0 \leq x < 1 \qquad [\![x]\!] = 0$$
$$1 \leq x < 2 \qquad [\![x]\!] = 1$$
$$2 \leq x < 3 \qquad [\![x]\!] = 2$$
$$3 \leq x < 4 \qquad [\![x]\!] = 3$$
$$4 \leq x < 5 \qquad [\![x]\!] = 4$$

Figure 1.7.11

The domain of F is the set of all real numbers. The range of F consists of all the integers. •

EXAMPLE 9: Let

$$G = \{(x, y) \mid y = [\![x]\!] - x\}$$

Draw a sketch of the graph of G. State the domain and range of G.

Figure 1.7.12

SOLUTION:

If $0 \le x < 1$, $[\![x]\!] = 0$;   so $G(x) = -x$.
If $1 \le x < 2$, $[\![x]\!] = 1$;   so $G(x) = 1 - x$.
If $2 \le x < 3$, $[\![x]\!] = 2$;   so $G(x) = 2 - x$.
If $-1 \le x < 0$, $[\![x]\!] = -1$;   so $G(x) = -1 - x$.

and so on.

A sketch of the graph is shown in Fig. 1.7.12. The domain of G is the set of all real numbers, and the range of G is $(-1, 0]$.

Exercises 1.7

In Exercises 1 through 10, find the domain and range of the given function, and draw a sketch of the graph of the function.

1. $f = \{(x, y) \mid y = 3x - 1\}$

2. $g = \{(x, y) \mid y = x^2 + 2\}$

3. $F = \{(x, y) \mid y = 3x^2 - 6\}$

4. $G = \{(x, y) \mid y = \sqrt{x + 1}\}$

5. $h = \{(x, y) \mid y = \sqrt{3x - 4}\}$

6. $f = \{(x, y) \mid y = \sqrt{4 - x^2}\}$

7. $g = \{(x, y) \mid y = \sqrt{x^2 - 4}\}$

8. $H = \{(x, y) \mid y = |x - 3|\}$

9. $\phi = \{(x, y) \mid y = |3x + 2|\}$

10. $F = \left\{(x, y) \mid y = \dfrac{4x^2 - 1}{2x + 1}\right\}$

In Exercises 11 through 34, the function is the set of all ordered pairs (x, y) satisfying the given equation. Find the domain and range of the function, and draw a sketch of the graph of the function.

11. $G: y = \begin{cases} -2 & \text{if } x \le 3 \\ 2 & \text{if } 3 < x \end{cases}$

12. $h: y = \begin{cases} -4 & \text{if } x < -2 \\ -1 & \text{if } -2 \le x \le 2 \\ 3 & \text{if } 2 < x \end{cases}$

13. $f: y = \begin{cases} 2x - 1 & \text{if } x \ne 2 \\ 0 & \text{if } x = 2 \end{cases}$

14. $\phi: y = \begin{cases} x + 5 & \text{if } x < -5 \\ \sqrt{25 - x^2} & \text{if } -5 \le x \le 5 \\ x - 5 & \text{if } 5 < x \end{cases}$

15. $H: y = \begin{cases} x^2 - 4 & \text{if } x < 3 \\ 2x - 1 & \text{if } 3 \le x \end{cases}$

16. $g: y = \begin{cases} 6x + 7 & \text{if } x \le -2 \\ 4 - x & \text{if } -2 < x \end{cases}$

17. $F: y = \dfrac{(x + 1)(x^2 + 3x - 10)}{x^2 + 6x + 5}$

18. $G: y = \dfrac{(x^2 + 3x - 4)(x^2 - 5x + 6)}{(x^2 - 3x + 2)(x - 3)}$

19. $f: y = \sqrt{x^2 - 3x - 4}$

20. $h: y = \sqrt{6x^2 - 5x - 4}$

21. $g: y = \dfrac{x^3 - 2x^2}{x - 2}$

22. $f: y = \dfrac{x^3 + 3x^2 + x + 3}{x + 3}$

23. $h: y = \dfrac{x^3 + 5x^2 - 6x - 30}{x + 5}$

24. $F: y = \dfrac{x^4 + x^3 - 9x^2 - 3x + 18}{x^2 + x - 6}$

25. $f: y = |x| + |x - 1|$

26. $g: y = |x| \cdot |x - 1|$

27. $G: y = x - [\![x]\!]$

28. $F: y = [\![x + 2]\!]$

29. $h: y = [\![x^2]\!]$

30. $H: y = |x| + [\![x]\!]$

31. $g: y = \dfrac{[\![x]\!]}{|x|}$

32. $f: y = (x - [\![x]\!])^2$

33. $f: y = 2 + (-1)^n$, where $n = [\![x]\!]$

34. $h: y = \dfrac{|x|}{[\![x]\!]}$

1.8 FUNCTION NOTATION, OPERATIONS ON FUNCTIONS, AND TYPES OF FUNCTIONS

If f is the function having as its domain values of x and as its range values of y, the symbol $f(x)$ (read "f of x") denotes the particular value of y which corresponds to the value of x.

● ILLUSTRATION 1: In Illustration 3 of Sec. 1.7,

$$f = \{(x, y) \mid y = \sqrt{5 - x}\}$$

Thus, we may write $f(x) = \sqrt{5 - x}$. Because when $x = 1$, $\sqrt{5 - x} = 2$, we write $f(1) = 2$. Similarly, $f(-6) = \sqrt{11}$, $f(0) = \sqrt{5}$, and so on. ●

When defining a function, the domain of the independent variable must be given either explicitly or implicitly. For instance, if we are given that f is defined by

$$f(x) = 3x^2 - 5x + 2$$

it is implied that x can be any real number. However, if we are given that f is defined by

$$f(x) = 3x^2 - 5x + 2 \qquad 1 \le x \le 10$$

then the domain of f consists of all real numbers between and including 1 and 10.

Similarly, if g is defined by the equation

$$g(x) = \frac{5x - 2}{x + 4}$$

it is implied that $x \ne -4$, because the quotient is undefined for $x = -4$; hence, the domain of g is the set of all real numbers except -4.

If we are given

$$h(x) = \sqrt{9 - x^2}$$

it is implied that x is in the closed interval $-3 \le x \le 3$, because $\sqrt{9 - x^2}$ is undefined (i.e., not a real number) for $x > 3$ or $x < -3$. So the domain of h is $[-3, +3]$, and the range of h is $[0, 3]$.

EXAMPLE 1: Given that f is the function defined by $f(x) = x^2 + 3x - 4$, find: (a) $f(0)$; (b) $f(2)$; (c) $f(h)$; (d) $f(2h)$; (e) $f(2x)$; (f) $f(x + h)$; (g) $f(x) + f(h)$.

SOLUTION:

(a) $f(0) = 0^2 + 3 \cdot 0 - 4 = -4$
(b) $f(2) = 2^2 + 3 \cdot 2 - 4 = 6$
(c) $f(h) = h^2 + 3h - 4$

(d) $f(2h) = (2h)^2 + 3(2h) - 4 = 4h^2 + 6h - 4$

(e) $f(2x) = (2x)^2 + 3(2x) - 4 = 4x^2 + 6x - 4$

(f) $f(x + h) = (x + h)^2 + 3(x + h) - 4$
$$= x^2 + 2hx + h^2 + 3x + 3h - 4$$
$$= x^2 + (2h + 3)x + (h^2 + 3h - 4)$$

(g) $f(x) + f(h) = (x^2 + 3x - 4) + (h^2 + 3h - 4)$
$$= x^2 + 3x + (h^2 + 3h - 8)$$

EXAMPLE 2: Given

$$g(x) = \sqrt{3x - 1}$$

find

$$\frac{g(x + h) - g(x)}{h} \qquad h \neq 0$$

SOLUTION:

$$\frac{g(x + h) - g(x)}{h} = \frac{\sqrt{3(x + h) - 1} - \sqrt{3x - 1}}{h}$$

$$= \frac{(\sqrt{3x + 3h - 1} - \sqrt{3x - 1})(\sqrt{3x + 3h - 1} + \sqrt{3x - 1})}{h(\sqrt{3x + 3h - 1} + \sqrt{3x - 1})}$$

$$= \frac{(3x + 3h - 1) - (3x - 1)}{h(\sqrt{3x + 3h - 1} + \sqrt{3x - 1})}$$

$$= \frac{3h}{h(\sqrt{3x + 3h - 1} + \sqrt{3x - 1})}$$

$$= \frac{3}{\sqrt{3x + 3h - 1} + \sqrt{3x - 1}}$$

In the second step of this solution, the numerator and denominator were multiplied by the conjugate of the numerator in order to rationalize the numerator, and this gave a common factor of h in the numerator and the denominator.

We now consider operations (i.e., addition, subtraction, multiplication, division) on functions. The functions obtained from these operations—called the sum, the difference, the product, and the quotient of the original functions—are defined as follows.

1.8.1 Definition   Given the two functions f and g:

(i) their *sum*, denoted by $f + g$, is the function defined by $(f + g)(x) = f(x) + g(x)$;

(ii) their *difference*, denoted by $f - g$, is the function defined by $(f - g)(x) = f(x) - g(x)$;

(iii) their *product*, denoted by $f \cdot g$, is the function defined by $(f \cdot g)(x) = f(x) \cdot g(x)$;

(iv) their *quotient*, denoted by f/g, is the function defined by $(f/g)(x) = f(x)/g(x)$.

In each case the *domain* of the resulting function consists of those values of x common to the domains of f and g, with the exception that in case (iv) the values of x for which $g(x) = 0$ are excluded.

EXAMPLE 3:   Given that f is the function defined by $f(x) = \sqrt{x+1}$ and g is the function defined by $g(x) = \sqrt{x-4}$, find: (a) $(f+g)(x)$; (b) $(f-g)(x)$; (c) $(f \cdot g)(x)$; (d) $(f/g)(x)$. In each case, determine the domain of the resulting function.

SOLUTION:

(a) $(f+g)(x) = \sqrt{x+1} + \sqrt{x-4}$
(b) $(f-g)(x) = \sqrt{x+1} - \sqrt{x-4}$
(c) $(f \cdot g)(x) = \sqrt{x+1} \cdot \sqrt{x-4}$

(d) $(f/g)(x) = \dfrac{\sqrt{x+1}}{\sqrt{x-4}}$

The domain of f is $[-1, +\infty)$, and the domain of g is $[4, +\infty)$. So in parts (a), (b), and (c) the domain of the resulting function is $[4, +\infty)$. In part (d) the denominator is zero when $x = 4$; thus, 4 is excluded from the domain, and the domain is therefore $(4, +\infty)$.

To indicate the product of a function f multiplied by itself, or $f \cdot f$, we write f^2. For example, if f is defined by $f(x) = 3x$, then f^2 is the function defined by $f^2(x) = (3x)(3x) = 9x^2$.

In addition to combining two functions by the operations given in Definition 1.8.1, we shall consider the "composite function" of two given functions.

1.8.2 Definition   Given the two functions f and g, the *composite function*, denoted by $f \circ g$, is defined by

$$(f \circ g)(x) = f(g(x))$$

and the domain of $f \circ g$ is the set of all numbers x in the domain of g such that $g(x)$ is in the domain of f.

EXAMPLE 4:   Given that f is defined by $f(x) = \sqrt{x}$ and g is defined by $g(x) = 2x - 3$, find $F(x)$ if $F = f \circ g$, and find the domain of F.

SOLUTION: $F(x) = (f \circ g)(x) = f(g(x))$

$$= f(2x - 3)$$

$$= \sqrt{2x - 3}$$

The domain of g is $(-\infty, +\infty)$, and the domain of f is $[0, +\infty)$. So the domain of F is the set of real numbers for which $2x - 3 \geq 0$ or, equivalently, $[\frac{3}{2}, +\infty)$.

EXAMPLE 5:   Given that f is defined by $f(x) = \sqrt{x}$ and g is defined by $g(x) = x^2 - 1$, find: (a) $f \circ f$; (b) $g \circ g$; (c) $f \circ g$; (d) $g \circ f$. Also find the domain of the composite function in each part.

SOLUTION: The domain of f is $[0, +\infty)$, and the domain of g is $(-\infty, +\infty)$.

(a) $(f \circ f)(x) = f(f(x)) = f(\sqrt{x}) = \sqrt{\sqrt{x}} = \sqrt[4]{x}$
   The domain of $f \circ f$ is $[0, +\infty)$.
(b) $(g \circ g)(x) = g(g(x)) = g(x^2 - 1) = (x^2 - 1)^2 - 1 = x^4 - 2x^2$
   The domain of $g \circ g$ is $(-\infty, +\infty)$.

(c) $(f \circ g)(x) = f(g(x)) = f(x^2 - 1) = \sqrt{x^2 - 1}$

The domain of $f \circ g$ is $(-\infty, -1] \cup [1, +\infty)$ or, equivalently, all x not in $(-1, 1)$.

(d) $(g \circ f)(x) = g(f(x)) = g(\sqrt{x}) = (\sqrt{x})^2 - 1 = x - 1$

The domain of $g \circ f$ is $[0, +\infty)$. Note that even though $x - 1$ is defined for all values of x, the domain of $g \circ f$, by Definition 1.8.2, is the set of all numbers x in the domain of f such that $f(x)$ is in the domain of g.

1.8.3 Definition

(i) A function f is said to be an *even* function if for every x in the domain of f, $f(-x) = f(x)$.

(ii) A function f is said to be an *odd* function if for every x in the domain of f, $f(-x) = -f(x)$.

In both parts (i) and (ii) it is understood that $-x$ is in the domain of f whenever x is.

● ILLUSTRATION 2:

(a) If $f(x) = 3x^4 - 2x^2 + 7$, then $f(-x) = 3(-x)^4 - 2(-x)^2 + 7 = 3x^4 - 2x^2 + 7 = f(x)$. Therefore, f is an even function.

(b) If $g(x) = 2x^5 + 5x^3 - 8x$, then $g(-x) = 2(-x)^5 + 5(-x)^3 - 8(-x) = -2x^5 - 5x^3 + 8x = -(2x^5 + 5x^3 - 8x) = -g(x)$. Thus, g is an odd function.

(c) If $h(x) = 2x^4 + 5x^3 - x^2 + 8$, $h(-x) = 2(-x)^4 + 5(-x)^3 - (-x)^2 + 8 = 2x^4 - 5x^3 - x^2 + 8$. We see that the function h is neither even nor odd.

●

From the definition of an even function and Theorem 1.3.6(ii) it follows that the graph of an even function is symmetric with respect to the y axis. From Theorem 1.3.6(iii) and the definition of an odd function, we see that the graph of an odd function is symmetric with respect to the origin.

If the range of a function f consists of only one number, then f is called a *constant function*. So if $f(x) = c$, and if c is any real number, then f is a constant function and its graph is a straight line parallel to the x axis at a directed distance of c units from the x axis.

If a function f is defined by

$$f(x) = a_0 x^n + a_1 x^{n-1} + a_2 x^{n-2} + \cdots + a_{n-1} x + a_n$$

where n is a nonnegative integer, and $a_0, a_1, \ldots, a_n$ are real numbers $(a_0 \neq 0)$, then f is called a *polynomial function* of degree n. Thus, the function f defined by

$$f(x) = 3x^5 - x^2 + 7x - 1$$

is a polynomial function of degree 5.

If the degree of a polynomial function is 1, then the function is called a *linear function;* if the degree is 2, the function is called a *quadratic function;* and if the degree is 3, the function is called a *cubic function.*

● ILLUSTRATION 3:

The function f defined by $f(x) = 3x + 4$ is a linear function.
The function g defined by $g(x) = 5x^2 - 8x + 1$ is a quadratic function.
The function h defined by $h(x) = 8x^3 - x + 4$ is a cubic function.   ●

If the degree of a polynomial function is zero, the function is a constant function.

The general linear function is defined by

$$f(x) = mx + b$$

where m and b are constants and $m \neq 0$. The graph of this function is a straight line having m as its slope and b as its y intercept.

The particular linear function defined by

$$f(x) = x$$

is called the *identity function.* The general quadratic function is defined by

$$f(x) = ax^2 + bx + c$$

where a, b, and c are constants and $a \neq 0$.

If a function can be expressed as the quotient of two polynomial functions, the function is called a *rational function.* For example, the function f defined by

$$f(x) = \frac{x^3 - x^2 + 5}{x^2 - 9}$$

is a rational function, for which the domain is the set of all real numbers except 3 and -3.

An *algebraic function* is a function formed by a finite number of algebraic operations on the identity function and the constant function. These algebraic operations include addition, subtraction, multiplication, division, raising to powers, and extracting roots. An example of an algebraic function is the function f defined by

$$f(x) = \frac{(x^2 - 3x + 1)^3}{\sqrt{x^4 + 1}}$$

In addition to algebraic functions, *transcendental functions* are considered in elementary calculus. Examples of transcendental functions are trigonometric functions, logarithmic functions, and exponential functions, which are discussed in later chapters.

Exercises 1.8

1. Given $f(x) = 2x^2 + 5x - 3$, find:

   (a) $f(-2)$ (b) $f(-1)$ (c) $f(0)$ (d) $f(3)$

   (e) $f(h + 1)$ (f) $f(2x^2)$ (g) $f(x^2 - 3)$ (h) $f(x + h)$

   (i) $f(x) + f(h)$ (j) $\dfrac{f(x + h) - f(x)}{h}, h \neq 0$

2. Given $g(x) = 3x^2 - 4$, find:

   (a) $g(-4)$ (b) $g(\frac{1}{2})$ (c) $g(x^2)$ (d) $g(3x^2 - 4)$

   (e) $g(x - h)$ (f) $g(x) - g(h)$ (g) $\dfrac{g(x + h) - g(x)}{h}, h \neq 0$

3. Given $F(x) = \sqrt{2x + 3}$, find:

   (a) $F(-1)$ (b) $F(4)$ (c) $F(\frac{1}{2})$

   (d) $F(30)$ (e) $F(2x + 3)$ (f) $\dfrac{F(x + h) - F(x)}{h}, h \neq 0$

4. Given $G(x) = \sqrt{2x^2 + 1}$, find:

   (a) $G(-2)$ (b) $G(0)$ (c) $G(\frac{1}{3})$

   (d) $G(\frac{4}{7})$ (e) $G(2x^2 - 1)$ (f) $\dfrac{G(x + h) - G(x)}{h}, h \neq 0$

5. Given

   $$f(x) = \begin{cases} \dfrac{|x|}{x} & \text{if } x \neq 0 \\ 1 & \text{if } x = 0 \end{cases}$$

   find: (a) $f(1)$; (b) $f(-1)$; (c) $f(4)$; (d) $f(-4)$; (e) $f(-x)$; (f) $f(x + 1)$; (g) $f(x^2)$; (h) $f(-x^2)$.

6. Given $f(t) = \dfrac{|3 + t| - |t| - 3}{t}$ express $f(t)$ without absolute-value bars if (a) $t > 0$; (b) $-3 \leq t < 0$; (c) $t < -3$.

In Exercises 7 through 12, the functions f and g are defined. In each problem define the following functions and determine the domain of the resulting function: (a) $f + g$; (b) $f - g$; (c) $f \cdot g$; (d) f/g; (e) g/f; (f) $f \circ g$; (g) $g \circ f$.

7. $f(x) = x - 5$; $g(x) = x^2 - 1$ 8. $f(x) = \sqrt{x}$; $g(x) = x^2 + 1$ 9. $f(x) = \dfrac{x + 1}{x - 1}$; $g(x) = \dfrac{1}{x}$

10. $f(x) = \sqrt{x - 2}$; $g(x) = \dfrac{1}{x}$ 11. $f(x) = \sqrt{x^2 - 1}$; $g(x) = \sqrt{x - 1}$ 12. $f(x) = |x|$; $g(x) = |x - 3|$

13. For each of the following functions, determine whether f is even, odd, or neither.

   (a) $f(x) = 2x^4 - 3x^2 + 1$ (b) $f(x) = 5x^3 - 7x$ (c) $f(s) = s^2 + 2s + 2$

   (d) $f(x) = x^6 - 1$ (e) $f(t) = 5t^7 + 1$ (f) $f(x) = |x|$

   (g) $f(y) = \dfrac{y^3 - y}{y^2 + 1}$ (h) $f(x) = \dfrac{x - 1}{x + 1}$

14. Prove that if f and g are both odd functions, then $(f + g)$ and $(f - g)$ are also odd functions.

15. Prove that if f and g are both odd functions, then $f \cdot g$ and f/g are both even functions.

16. Prove that any function can be expressed as the sum of an even function and an odd function by writing

$$f(x) = \tfrac{1}{2}[f(x) + f(-x)] + \tfrac{1}{2}[f(x) - f(-x)]$$

and showing that the function having function values $\tfrac{1}{2}[f(x) + f(-x)]$ is an even function and the function having function values $\tfrac{1}{2}[f(x) - f(-x)]$ is an odd function.

17. Use the result of Exercise 16 to express the functions defined by the following equations as the sum of an even function and an odd function: (a) $f(x) = x^2 + 2$; (b) $f(x) = x^3 - 1$; (c) $f(x) = x^4 + x^3 - x + 3$; (d) $f(x) = 1/x$; (e) $f(x) = (x-1)/(x+1)$; (f) $f(x) = |x| + |x - 1|$.

18. There is one function that is both even and odd. What is it?

19. Determine whether the composite function $f \circ g$ is odd or even in each of the following cases: (a) f and g are both even; (b) f and g are both odd; (c) f is even and g is odd; (d) f is odd and g is even.

20. The function g is defined by $g(x) = x^2$. Define a function f such that $(f \circ g)(x) = x$ if (a) $x \geq 0$; (b) $x < 0$.

In Exercises 21 through 34, draw a sketch of the graph of the given function. In Exercises 23 through 34, the function U is the unit step function defined in Exercise 21 and the function sgn is the signum function defined in Exercise 22.

21. U is the function defined by $U(t) = \begin{cases} 0 & \text{if } t < 0 \\ 1 & \text{if } t \geq 0 \end{cases}$

This function U is called the *unit step function*.

22. The *signum function* (or *sign function*), denoted by sgn, is defined by

$$\text{sgn } x = \begin{cases} -1 & \text{if } x < 0 \\ 0 & \text{if } x = 0 \\ 1 & \text{if } x > 0 \end{cases}$$

sgn x is read "signum of x."

23. $f(x) = U(x - 1)$ 24. $g(x) = U(x) - U(x - 1)$

25. $g(x) = \text{sgn}(x + 1) - \text{sgn}(x - 1)$ 26. $f(x) = \text{sgn } x^2 - \text{sgn } x$

27. $h(x) = x \cdot U(x)$ 28. $F(x) = (x + 1) \cdot U(x + 1)$

29. $G(x) = (x + 1) \cdot U(x + 1) - x \cdot U(x)$ 30. $F(x) = x - 2 \text{ sgn } x$

31. $h(x) = \text{sgn } x - U(x)$ 32. $f(x) = \text{sgn } x \cdot U(x + 1)$

33. $g(x) = \text{sgn } x + x \cdot U(x)$ 34. $G(x) = \text{sgn}(U(x))$

35. Find formulas for $(f \circ g)(x)$ if

$$f(x) = \begin{cases} 0 & \text{if } x < 0 \\ 2x & \text{if } 0 \leq x \leq 1 \\ 0 & \text{if } x > 1 \end{cases} \quad \text{and} \quad g(x) = \begin{cases} 1 & \text{if } x < 0 \\ \tfrac{1}{2}x & \text{if } 0 \leq x \leq 1 \\ 1 & \text{if } x > 1 \end{cases}$$

36. Find formulas for $(g \circ f)(x)$ for the functions of Exercise 35.

37. Find formulas for $(f \circ g)(x)$ if

$$f(x) = \begin{cases} 0 & \text{if } x < 0 \\ x^2 & \text{if } 0 \leq x \leq 1 \\ 0 & \text{if } x > 1 \end{cases} \quad \text{and} \quad g(x) = \begin{cases} 1 & \text{if } x < 0 \\ 2x & \text{if } 0 \leq x \leq 1 \\ 1 & \text{if } x > 1 \end{cases}$$

38. If $f(x) = x^2$, find two functions g for which $(f \circ g)(x) = 4x^2 - 12x + 9$.

39. If $f(x) = x^2 + 2x + 2$, find two functions g for which $(f \circ g)(x) = x^2 - 4x + 5$.

Review Exercises (Chapter 1)

In Exercises 1 through 6, find the solution set of the given inequality, and illustrate the solution on the real number line.

1. $8 < 5x + 4 \le 10$

2. $\dfrac{x}{x-1} > \dfrac{1}{4}$

3. $2x^2 + x < 3$

4. $\dfrac{3}{x+4} < \dfrac{2}{x-5}$

5. $|3 + 5x| \le 9$

6. $\left| \dfrac{2 - 3x}{3 + x} \right| \ge \dfrac{1}{4}$

7. Define the following sets of points by either an equation or an inequality: (a) the point circle $(3, -5)$; (b) the set of all points whose distance from the point $(3, -5)$ is less than 4; (c) the set of all points whose distance from the point $(3, -5)$ is at least 5.

8. Prove that the points $(1, -1)$, $(3, 2)$, and $(7, 8)$ are collinear in two ways: (a) by using the distance formula; (b) by using slopes.

9. Find equations of the lines passing through the origin that are tangent to the circle having its center at $(2, 1)$ and a radius of 2.

10. Prove that the quadrilateral having vertices at $(1, 2)$, $(5, -1)$, $(11, 7)$, and $(7, 10)$ is a rectangle.

11. Determine the values of k and h if $3x + ky + 2 = 0$ and $5x - y + h = 0$ are equations of the same line.

12. Show that the triangle with vertices at $(-8, 1)$, $(-1, -6)$ and $(2, 4)$ is isosceles and find its area.

13. Two vertices of a parallelogram are at $(-3, 4)$ and $(2, 3)$ and its center is at $(0, -1)$. Find the other two vertices.

14. Two opposite vertices of a square are at $(3, -4)$ and $(9, -4)$. Find the other two vertices.

15. Determine all values of k for which the graphs of the two equations $x^2 + y^2 = k$ and $x + y = k$ intersect.

16. Prove that if x is any real number, $|x| < x^2 + 1$.

17. Find an equation of the circle circumscribed about the triangle having sides on the lines $x - 3y + 2 = 0, 3x - 2y + 6 = 0$, and $2x + y - 3 = 0$.

18. Find an equation of the circle having as its diameter the common chord of the two circles $x^2 + y^2 + 2x - 2y - 14 = 0$ and $x^2 + y^2 - 4x + 4y - 2 = 0$.

19. Find an equation of the line through the point of intersection of the lines $5x + 6y - 4 = 0$ and $x - 3y + 2 = 0$ and perpendicular to the line $x - 4y - 20 = 0$ without finding the point of intersection of the two lines. (HINT: See Exercise 28 in Exercises 1.5.)

20. The sides of a parallelogram are on the lines $x + 2y - 10 = 0$, $3x - y + 20 = 0$, $x + 2y - 15 = 0$, and $3x - y + 10 = 0$. Find the equations of the diagonals without finding the vertices of the parallelogram. (HINT: See Exercise 28 in Exercises 1.5.)

In Exercises 21 through 24, the function is the set of all ordered pairs (x, y) satisfying the given equation. Find the domain and range of the function, and draw a sketch of the graph of the function.

21. $f: y = \sqrt{2x + 5}$

22. $g: y = \dfrac{x^2 - 16}{x + 4}$

23. h: $y = \dfrac{(x-2)(2x^2 + 11x + 15)}{2x^2 + x - 10}$

24. F: $y = \begin{cases} x + 3 & \text{if } x < -3 \\ \sqrt{9 - x^2} & \text{if } -3 \le x \le 3 \\ x - 3 & \text{if } 3 < x \end{cases}$

In Exercises 25 through 28, for the given functions f and g, define the following functions and determine the domain of the resulting function: (a) $f + g$; (b) $f - g$; (c) $f \cdot g$; (d) f/g; (e) g/f; (f) $f \circ g$; (g) $g \circ f$.

25. $f(x) = x^2 - 4$ and $g(x) = 4x - 3$.

26. $f(x) = \sqrt{x + 2}$ and $g(x) = x^2 + 4$.

27. $f(x) = 1/(x - 3)$ and $g(x) = x/(x + 1)$.

28. $f(x) = \sqrt{x}$ and $g(x) = 1/x^2$.

29. Prove that x sgn $x = |x|$.

30. Prove that the two lines $A_1 x + B_1 y + C_1 = 0$ and $A_2 x + B_2 y + C_2 = 0$ are parallel if and only if $A_1 B_2 - A_2 B_1 = 0$.

31. Prove analytically that the three medians of any triangle meet in a point.

32. Prove analytically that the line segment joining the midpoints of any two sides of a triangle is parallel to the third side and that its length is one-half the length of the third side.

33. Prove analytically that if the diagonals of a rectangle are perpendicular, then the rectangle is a square.

34. Prove analytically that the set of points equidistant from two given points is the perpendicular bisector of the line segment joining the two points.

35. In a triangle the point of intersection of the medians, the point of intersection of the altitudes, and the center of the circumscribed circle are collinear. Find these three points and prove they are collinear for the triangle having vertices at $(2, 8)$, $(5, -1)$, and $(6, 6)$.

2

Limits and continuity

2.1 THE LIMIT OF A FUNCTION

Consider the function f defined by the equation

$$f(x) = \frac{(2x+3)(x-1)}{(x-1)} \tag{1}$$

f is defined for all values of x except $x = 1$. Furthermore, if $x \neq 1$, the numerator and denominator can be divided by $(x-1)$ to obtain

$$f(x) = 2x + 3 \qquad x \neq 1 \tag{2}$$

We shall investigate the function values, $f(x)$, when x is close to 1 but not equal to 1. First, let x take on the values 0, 0.25, 0.50, 0.75, 0.9, 0.99, 0.999, 0.9999, and so on. We are taking values of x closer and closer to 1, but less than 1; in other words, the variable x is approaching 1 through values that are less than 1. We illustrate this in Table 2.1.1. Now, let the variable

Table 2.1.1

x	0	0.25	0.5	0.75	0.9	0.99	0.999	0.9999	0.99999
$f(x) = 2x + 3$ $(x \neq 1)$	3	3.5	4	4.5	4.8	4.98	4.998	4.9998	4.99998

x approach 1, through values that are greater than 1; that is, let x take on the values 2, 1.75, 1.5, 1.25, 1.1, 1.01, 1.001, 1.0001, 1.00001, and so on. Refer to Table 2.1.2.

Table 2.1.2

x	2	1.75	1.5	1.25	1.1	1.01	1.001	1.0001	1.00001
$f(x) = 2x + 3$ $(x \neq 1)$	7	6.5	6.0	5.5	5.2	5.02	5.002	5.0002	5.00002

We see from both tables that as x gets closer and closer to 1, $f(x)$ gets closer and closer to 5; and the closer x is to 1, the closer $f(x)$ is to 5. For instance, from Table 2.1.1, when $x = 0.9$, $f(x) = 4.8$; that is, when x is 0.1 less than 1, $f(x)$ is 0.2 less than 5. When $x = 0.999$, $f(x) = 4.998$; that is, when x is 0.001 less than 1, $f(x)$ is 0.002 less than 5. Furthermore, when $x = 0.9999$, $f(x) = 0.49998$; that is, when x is 0.0001 less than 1, $f(x)$ is 0.0002 less than 5.

Table 2.1.2 shows that when $x = 1.1$, $f(x) = 5.2$, that is, when x is 0.1 greater than 1, $f(x)$ is 0.2 greater than 5. When $x = 1.001$, $f(x) = 5.002$; that is, when x is 0.001 greater than 1, $f(x)$ is 0.002 greater than 5. When $x = 1.0001$, $f(x) = 5.0002$; that is, when x is 0.0001 greater than 1, $f(x)$ is 0.0002 greater than 5.

Therefore, from the two tables, we see that when x differs from 1 by ±0.001 (i.e., $x = 0.999$ or $x = 1.001$), $f(x)$ differs from 5 by ±0.002 [i.e., $f(x) = 4.998$ or $f(x) = 5.002$]. And when x differs from 1 by ±0.0001, $f(x)$ differs from 5 by ±0.0002.

Now, looking at the situation another way, we consider the values of $f(x)$ first. We see that we can make the value of $f(x)$ as close to 5 as we please by taking x close enough to 1. Another way of saying this is that we can make the absolute value of the difference between $f(x)$ and 5 as small as we please by making the absolute value of the difference between x and 1 small enough. That is, $|f(x) - 5|$ can be made as small as we please by making $|x - 1|$ small enough.

A more precise way of noting this is by using two symbols for these small differences. The symbols usually used are ϵ (epsilon) and δ (delta). So we state that $|f(x) - 5|$ will be less than any given positive number ϵ whenever $|x - 1|$ is less than some appropriately chosen positive number δ and $|x - 1| \neq 0$ (since $x \neq 1$). It is important to realize that the size of δ depends on the size of ϵ. Still another way of phrasing this is: Given any positive number ϵ, we can make $|f(x) - 5| < \epsilon$ by taking $|x - 1|$ small enough; that is, there is some sufficiently small positive number δ such that

$$|f(x) - 5| < \epsilon \quad \text{whenever} \quad 0 < |x - 1| < \delta \tag{3}$$

We see from the two tables that $|f(x) - 5| = 0.2$ when $|x - 1| = 0.1$. So, given $\epsilon = 0.2$, we take $\delta = 0.1$ and state that

$$|f(x) - 5| < 0.2 \quad \text{whenever} \quad 0 < |x - 1| < 0.1$$

This is statement (3), with $\epsilon = 0.2$ and $\delta = 0.1$.

Also, $|f(x) - 5| = 0.002$ when $|x - 1| = 0.001$. Hence, if $\epsilon = 0.002$, we take $\delta = 0.001$, and then

$$|f(x) - 5| < 0.002 \quad \text{whenever} \quad 0 < |x - 1| < 0.001$$

This is statement (3), with $\epsilon = 0.002$ and $\delta = 0.001$.

Similarly, if $\epsilon = 0.0002$, we take $\delta = 0.0001$ and state that

$$|f(x) - 5| < 0.0002 \quad \text{whenever} \quad 0 < |x - 1| < 0.0001$$

This is statement (3), with $\epsilon = 0.0002$ and $\delta = 0.0001$.

We could go on and give ϵ any small positive value, and find a suitable value for δ such that $|f(x) - 5|$ will be less than ϵ whenever $|x - 1|$ is less than δ and $x \neq 1$ (or $|x - 1| > 0$). Now, because for any $\epsilon > 0$ we can find a $\delta > 0$ such that $|f(x) - 5| < \epsilon$ whenever $0 < |x - 1| < \delta$, we state that the limit of $f(x)$ as x approaches 1 is equal to 5 or, expressed in symbols,

$$\lim_{x \to 1} f(x) = 5 \tag{4}$$

You will note that we state $0 < |x - 1|$. This condition is imposed because we are concerned only with values of $f(x)$ for x close to 1, but not for $x = 1$. As a matter of fact, this function is not defined for $x = 1$.

Let us see what this means geometrically for the particular function defined by Eq. (1). Figure 2.1.1 illustrates the geometric significance of

Figure 2.1.1

ϵ and δ. We see that $f(x)$ on the vertical axis will lie between $5 - \epsilon$ and $5 + \epsilon$ whenever x on the horizontal axis lies between $1 - \delta$ and $1 + \delta$; or

$$|f(x) - 5| < \epsilon \quad \text{whenever} \quad 0 < |x - 1| < \delta$$

Another way of stating this is that $f(x)$ on the vertical axis can be restricted to lie between $5 - \epsilon$ and $5 + \epsilon$ by restricting x on the horizontal axis to lie between $1 - \delta$ and $1 + \delta$.

Note that the values of ϵ are chosen arbitrarily and can be as small as desired, and that the value of a δ is dependent on the ϵ chosen. We should also point out that the smaller the value of ϵ, the smaller will be the corresponding value of δ.

Summing up for this example, we state that $\lim\limits_{x \to 1} f(x) = 5$ because for any $\epsilon > 0$, however small, there exists a $\delta > 0$ such that

$$|f(x) - 5| < \epsilon \quad \text{whenever} \quad 0 < |x - 1| < \delta$$

We are now in a position to define the limit of a function in general.

2.1.1 Definition   Let f be a function which is defined at every number in some open interval I containing a, except possibly at the number a itself. The *limit of $f(x)$ as x approaches a is L*, written as

$$\lim_{x \to a} f(x) = L \tag{5}$$

if for any $\epsilon > 0$, however small, there exists a $\delta > 0$ such that

$$|f(x) - L| < \epsilon \quad \text{whenever} \quad 0 < |x - a| < \delta \tag{6}$$

In words, Definition 2.1.1 states that the function values $f(x)$ approach a limit L as x approaches a number a if the absolute value of the difference between $f(x)$ and L can be made as small as we please by taking x sufficiently near a, but not equal to a.

It is important to realize that in the above definition nothing is mentioned about the value of the function when $x = a$. That is, it is not necessary that the function be defined for $x = a$ in order for the $\lim\limits_{x \to a} f(x)$ to exist.

In particular, we saw in our example that

$$\lim_{x \to 1} \frac{(2x + 3)(x - 1)}{(x - 1)} = 5$$

but that

$$\frac{(2x + 3)(x - 1)}{(x - 1)}$$

is not defined for $x = 1$. However, the first sentence in Definition 2.1.1 requires that the function of our example be defined at all numbers except 1 in some open interval containing 1.

EXAMPLE 1:   Let the function f be defined by the equation

$$f(x) = 4x - 1$$

Given $\lim\limits_{x \to 3} f(x) = 11$, find a δ for $\epsilon = 0.01$ such that

$$|f(x) - 11| < 0.01$$

whenever

$$0 < |x - 3| < \delta$$

SOLUTION:

$$\begin{aligned}
|f(x) - 11| &= |(4x - 1) - 11| \\
&= |4x - 12| \\
&= 4|x - 3|
\end{aligned}$$

Therefore, we want

$$4|x - 3| < 0.01 \quad \text{whenever} \quad 0 < |x - 3| < \delta$$

or, equivalently,

$$|x - 3| < 0.0025 \quad \text{whenever} \quad 0 < |x - 3| < \delta$$

If we take $\delta = 0.0025$, we have

$$|(4x - 1) - 11| < 0.01 \quad \text{whenever} \quad 0 < |x - 3| < 0.0025 \tag{7}$$

It is important to realize that in this example any positive number less than 0.0025 can be used in place of 0.0025 as the required δ. That is, if $0 < \gamma < 0.0025$ and statement (7) holds, then

$$|(4x - 1) - 11| < 0.01 \quad \text{whenever} \quad 0 < |x - 3| < \gamma \tag{8}$$

because every number x satisfying the inequality $0 < |x - 3| < \gamma$ also satisfies the inequality $0 < |x - 3| < 0.0025$.

The solution of Example 1 consisted of finding a δ for a specific ϵ. If for any ϵ we can find a δ that will work, we shall have established that the value of the limit is 11. We do this in the next example.

EXAMPLE 2:   Using Definition 2.1.1, prove that

$$\lim_{x \to 3} (4x - 1) = 11$$

SOLUTION: We must show that for any $\epsilon > 0$ there exists a $\delta > 0$ such that

$$|(4x - 1) - 11| < \epsilon \quad \text{whenever} \quad 0 < |x - 3| < \delta$$

From Example 1, we note that

$$\begin{aligned}
|(4x - 1) - 11| &= |4x - 12| \\
&= 4|x - 3|
\end{aligned}$$

Therefore, we want

$$4|x - 3| < \epsilon \quad \text{whenever} \quad 0 < |x - 3| < \delta$$

or, equivalently,

$$|x - 3| < \tfrac{1}{4}\epsilon \quad \text{whenever} \quad 0 < |x - 3| < \delta$$

So if we choose $\delta = \tfrac{1}{4}\epsilon$, we have

$$4|x - 3| < 4\delta \quad \text{whenever} \quad 0 < |x - 3| < \delta$$

or, equivalently,

$$4|x-3| < 4 \cdot \tfrac{1}{4}\epsilon \quad \text{whenever} \quad 0 < |x-3| < \delta$$

or, equivalently,

$$4|x-3| < \epsilon \quad \text{whenever} \quad 0 < |x-3| < \delta$$

giving us

$$|(4x-1)-11| < \epsilon \quad \text{whenever} \quad 0 < |x-3| < \delta$$

if $\delta = \tfrac{1}{4}\epsilon$. This proves that $\lim\limits_{x\to 3}(4x-1)=11$.

In particular, if $\epsilon = 0.01$, then we take $\delta = 0.01/4$, or 0.0025, which corresponds to our result in Example 1.

Any positive number $\delta' < \tfrac{1}{4}\epsilon$ can be used in place of $\tfrac{1}{4}\epsilon$ as the required δ in this example.

EXAMPLE 3: **Using Definition 2.1.1, prove that**

$$\lim_{x\to 2} x^2 = 4$$

SOLUTION: We must show that for any $\epsilon > 0$ there exists a $\delta > 0$ such that

$$|x^2-4| < \epsilon \quad \text{whenever} \quad 0 < |x-2| < \delta$$

Factoring, we get

$$|x^2-4| = |x-2| \cdot |x+2|$$

We want to show that $|x^2-4|$ is small when x is close to 2. To do this, we first find an upper bound for the factor $|x+2|$. If x is close to 2, we know that the factor $|x-2|$ is small, and that the factor $|x+2|$ is close to 4. Because we are considering values of x close to 2, we can concern ourselves with only those values of x for which $|x-2| < 1$; that is, we are requiring the δ, for which we are looking, to be less than or equal to 1. The inequality

$$|x-2| < 1$$

is equivalent to

$$-1 < x-2 < 1$$

which is equivalent to

$$1 < x < 3$$

or, equivalently,

$$3 < x+2 < 5$$

This means that if $|x-2| < 1$, then $3 < |x+2| < 5$; therefore, we have

$$|x^2-4| = |x-2| \cdot |x+2| < |x-2| \cdot 5 \quad \text{whenever} \quad |x-2| < 1$$

Now we want

$$|x-2| \cdot 5 < \epsilon \quad \text{or, equivalently,} \quad |x-2| < \tfrac{1}{5}\epsilon$$

Thus, if we choose δ to be the smaller of 1 and $\tfrac{1}{5}\epsilon$, then whenever $|x-2|$

$< \delta$, it follows that $|x - 2| < \frac{1}{5}\epsilon$ and $|x + 2| < 5$ (because this is true when $|x - 2| < 1$) and so $|x^2 - 4| < (\frac{1}{5}\epsilon) \cdot (5)$. Therefore, we conclude that

$$|x^2 - 4| < \epsilon \quad \text{whenever} \quad 0 < |x - 2| < \delta$$

if δ is the smaller of the two numbers 1 and $\frac{1}{5}\epsilon$, which we write as $\delta = \min(1, \frac{1}{5}\epsilon)$.

EXAMPLE 4: Using Definition 2.1.1, prove that

$$\lim_{t \to 7} \frac{8}{t - 3} = 2$$

SOLUTION: We must show that for any $\epsilon > 0$ there exists a $\delta > 0$ such that

$$\left| \frac{8}{t - 3} - 2 \right| < \epsilon \quad \text{whenever} \quad 0 < |t - 7| < \delta$$

Now

$$\left| \frac{8}{t - 3} - 2 \right| = \left| \frac{8 - 2(t - 3)}{t - 3} \right|$$

$$= \left| \frac{14 - 2t}{t - 3} \right|$$

$$= \frac{2 \cdot |7 - t|}{|t - 3|}$$

$$= |t - 7| \cdot \frac{2}{|t - 3|}$$

We wish to show that $|8/(t - 3) - 2|$ is small when t is close to 7. We proceed to find some upper bound for the fraction $2/|t - 3|$. By requiring the δ for which we are looking to be less than or equal to 1, we can say that whenever $|t - 7| < \delta$, then certainly $|t - 7| < 1$. The inequality

$$|t - 7| < 1$$

is equivalent to

$$-1 < t - 7 < 1$$

which is equivalent to

$$3 < t - 3 < 5$$

Thus, if $|t - 7| < 1$, then

$$3 < |t - 3| < 5$$

Therefore, whenever $|t - 7| < 1$, $|t - 3| > 3$, and because we have shown that $|8/(t - 3) - 2| = |t - 7| \cdot 2/|t - 3|$, we have

$$\left| \frac{8}{t - 3} - 2 \right| = |t - 7| \cdot \frac{2}{|t - 3|} < |t - 7| \cdot \frac{2}{3} \quad \text{whenever} \quad |t - 7| < 1$$

We want then $|t - 7| \cdot \frac{2}{3} < \epsilon$ or, equivalently, $|t - 7| < \frac{3}{2}\epsilon$. Consequently, we take δ as the smaller of 1 and $\frac{3}{2}\epsilon$, which assures us that whenever

$|t-7| < \delta$, then $|t-7| < \frac{3}{2}\epsilon$ and $|t-3| > 3$ (because this is true when $|t-7| < 1$). This gives us

$$\left| \frac{8}{t-3} - 2 \right| < |t-7| \cdot \frac{2}{3} < \frac{3}{2} \epsilon \cdot \frac{2}{3}$$

or, equivalently,

$$\left| \frac{8}{t-3} - 2 \right| < \epsilon$$

whenever $0 < |t-7| < \delta$, and where $\delta = \min(1, \frac{3}{2}\epsilon)$. We have therefore proved that $\lim_{t \to 7} [8/(t-3)] = 2$.

The following theorem states that a function cannot approach two different limits at the same time. It is called a *uniqueness theorem* because it guarantees that if the limit of a function exists, it is unique.

2.1.2 Theorem   If $\lim_{x \to a} f(x) = L_1$ and $\lim_{x \to a} f(x) = L_2$, then $L_1 = L_2$.

PROOF: We shall assume that $L_1 \neq L_2$ and show that this assumption leads to a contradiction. Because $\lim_{x \to a} f(x) = L_1$, it follows from Definition 2.1.1 that for any $\epsilon > 0$ there exists a $\delta_1 > 0$ such that

$$|f(x) - L_1| < \epsilon \quad \text{whenever} \quad 0 < |x - a| < \delta_1 \tag{9}$$

Also, because $\lim_{x \to a} f(x) = L_2$, we know that there exists a $\delta_2 > 0$ such that

$$|f(x) - L_2| < \epsilon \quad \text{whenever} \quad 0 < |x - a| < \delta_2 \tag{10}$$

Now, writing $L_1 - L_2$ as $L_1 - f(x) + f(x) - L_2$ and applying the triangle inequality, we have

$$|L_1 - L_2| = |[L_1 - f(x)] + [f(x) - L_2]|$$
$$\leq |L_1 - f(x)| + |f(x) - L_2| \tag{11}$$

So from (9), (10), and (11) we may conclude that for any $\epsilon > 0$ there exists a $\delta_1 > 0$ and a $\delta_2 > 0$ such that

$$|L_1 - L_2| < \epsilon + \epsilon \quad \text{whenever} \quad 0 < |x - a| < \delta_1 \text{ and } 0 < |x - a| < \delta_2 \tag{12}$$

If δ is the smaller of δ_1 and δ_2, then $\delta \leq \delta_1$ and $\delta \leq \delta_2$, and (12) states that for any $\epsilon > 0$ there exists a $\delta > 0$ such that

$$|L_1 - L_2| < 2\epsilon \quad \text{whenever} \quad 0 < |x - a| < \delta \tag{13}$$

However, if we take $\epsilon = \frac{1}{2}|L_1 - L_2|$, then (13) states that there exists a $\delta > 0$ such that

$$|L_1 - L_2| < |L_1 - L_2| \quad \text{whenever} \quad 0 < |x - a| < \delta \tag{14}$$

Because (14) is a contradiction, our assumption is false. So $L_1 = L_2$, and the theorem is proved. ∎

Exercises 2.1

In Exercises 1 through 8, we are given $f(x)$, a, and L, as well as $\lim\limits_{x \to a} f(x) = L$. Determine a number δ for the given ϵ such that $|f(x) - L| < \epsilon$ whenever $0 < |x - a| < \delta$.

1. $\lim\limits_{x \to 3} (2x + 4) = 10$; $\epsilon = 0.01$

2. $\lim\limits_{x \to 2} (4x - 5) = 3$; $\epsilon = 0.001$

3. $\lim\limits_{x \to -1} (3 - 4x) = 7$; $\epsilon = 0.02$

4. $\lim\limits_{x \to -2} (2 + 5x) = -8$; $\epsilon = 0.002$

5. $\lim\limits_{x \to 3} x^2 = 9$; $\epsilon = 0.005$

6. $\lim\limits_{x \to 4} \sqrt{x} = 2$; $\epsilon = 0.005$

7. $\lim\limits_{x \to -2} \dfrac{x^2 - 4}{x + 2} = -4$; $\epsilon = 0.01$

8. $\lim\limits_{x \to 1/3} \dfrac{9x^2 - 1}{3x - 1} = 2$; $\epsilon = 0.01$

In Exercises 9 through 29, establish the limit by using Definition 2.1.1; that is, for any $\epsilon > 0$, find a $\delta > 0$, such that $|f(x) - L| < \epsilon$ whenever $0 < |x - a| < \delta$.

9. $\lim\limits_{x \to 1} (5x - 3) = 2$

10. $\lim\limits_{x \to -2} (7 - 2x) = 11$

11. $\lim\limits_{x \to 3} \dfrac{x^2 - 9}{x - 3} = 6$

12. $\lim\limits_{x \to 4} \dfrac{\sqrt{x} - 2}{x - 4} = \dfrac{1}{4}$

13. $\lim\limits_{x \to 1} x^2 = 1$

14. $\lim\limits_{x \to -3} x^2 = 9$

15. $\lim\limits_{x \to 3} \dfrac{4}{x - 1} = 2$

16. $\lim\limits_{x \to 6} \dfrac{x}{x - 3} = 2$

17. $\lim\limits_{x \to 5} \dfrac{2}{x - 4} = 2$

18. $\lim\limits_{x \to -4} \dfrac{1}{x + 3} = -1$

19. $\lim\limits_{x \to 5} (x^2 - 3x) = 10$

20. $\lim\limits_{x \to 2} (x^2 + 2x - 1) = 7$

21. $\lim\limits_{x \to -3} (5 - x - x^2) = -1$

22. $\lim\limits_{x \to 1/2} \dfrac{3 + 2x}{5 - x} = \dfrac{8}{9}$

23. $\lim\limits_{x \to 4} \sqrt{x + 5} = 3$

24. $\lim\limits_{x \to 1} \dfrac{1}{\sqrt{5 - x}} = \dfrac{1}{2}$

25. Prove that $\lim\limits_{x \to a} x^2 = a^2$ if a is any positive number.

26. Prove that $\lim\limits_{x \to a} x^2 = a^2$ if a is any negative number.

27. Prove that $\lim\limits_{x \to a} \sqrt{x} = \sqrt{a}$ if a is any positive number.

28. Prove that $\lim\limits_{x \to a} \sqrt[3]{x} = \sqrt[3]{a}$. (HINT: $a^3 - b^3 = (a - b)(a^2 + ab + b^2)$.)

29. Prove that if $\lim\limits_{x \to a} f(x)$ exists and is L, then $\lim\limits_{x \to a} |f(x)|$ exists and is $|L|$.

30. Prove that, if $f(x) = g(x)$ for all values of x except $x = a$, then $\lim\limits_{x \to a} f(x) = \lim\limits_{x \to a} g(x)$ if the limits exist.

31. Prove that, if $f(x) = g(x)$ for all values of x except $x = a$, then if $\lim\limits_{x \to a} g(x)$ does not exist, then $\lim\limits_{x \to a} f(x)$ does not exist.

(HINT: Show that the assumption that $\lim\limits_{x \to a} f(x)$ does exist leads to a contradiction.)

2.2 THEOREMS ON LIMITS OF FUNCTIONS

In order to find limits of functions in a straightforward manner, we shall need some theorems. The proofs of the theorems are based on Definition 2.1.1. These theorems, as well as other theorems on limits of functions appearing in later sections of this chapter, will be labeled "limit theorems" and will be so designated as they are presented.

2.2.1 Limit theorem 1   If m and b are any constants,

$$\lim_{x \to a} (mx + b) = ma + b$$

PROOF: To prove this theorem, we use Definition 2.1.1. For any $\epsilon > 0$, we must prove that there exists a $\delta > 0$ such that

$$|(mx + b) - (ma + b)] < \epsilon \quad \text{whenever} \quad 0 < |x - a| < \delta \tag{1}$$

Case 1: $m \neq 0$.

Because $|(mx + b) - (ma + b)| = |mx - ma| = |m| \cdot |x - a|$, we want to find a $\delta > 0$ for any $\epsilon > 0$ such that

$$|m| \cdot |x - a| < \epsilon \quad \text{whenever} \quad 0 < |x - a| < \delta$$

or, because $m \neq 0$,

$$|x - a| < \frac{\epsilon}{|m|} \quad \text{whenever} \quad 0 < |x - a| < \delta \tag{2}$$

Statement (2) will hold if we take $\delta = \epsilon/|m|$, and therefore we conclude that

$$|(mx + b) - (ma + b)| < \epsilon \quad \text{whenever} \quad 0 < |x - a| < \delta \quad \text{if} \quad \delta = \frac{\epsilon}{|m|}$$

This proves the theorem for Case 1.

Case 2: $m = 0$.

If $m = 0$, then $|(mx + b) - (ma + b)| = 0$ for all values of x. So we take δ to be any positive number, and statement (1) holds. This proves the theorem for Case 2.   ∎

● ILLUSTRATION 1: From Limit theorem 1, it follows that

$$\lim_{x \to 2} (3x + 5) = 3 \cdot 2 + 5$$
$$= 11$$

●

2.2.2 Limit theorem 2   If c is a constant, then for any number a,

$$\lim_{x \to a} c = c$$

PROOF: This follows immediately from Limit theorem 1 by taking $m = 0$ and $b = c$.   ∎

2.2.3 Limit theorem 3 $\lim\limits_{x \to a} x = a$

PROOF: This also follows immediately from Limit theorem 1 by taking $m = 1$ and $b = 0$.   ■

● ILLUSTRATION 2: From Limit theorem 2,

$$\lim_{x \to 5} 7 = 7$$

and from Limit theorem 3,

$$\lim_{x \to -6} x = -6$$ ●

2.2.4 Limit theorem 4   If $\lim\limits_{x \to a} f(x) = L$ and $\lim\limits_{x \to a} g(x) = M$, then

$$\lim_{x \to a} [f(x) \pm g(x)] = L \pm M$$

PROOF: We shall prove this theorem using the plus sign. Given

$$\lim_{x \to a} f(x) = L \tag{3}$$

and

$$\lim_{x \to a} g(x) = M \tag{4}$$

we wish to prove that

$$\lim_{x \to a} [f(x) + g(x)] = L + M \tag{5}$$

To prove Eq. (5), we must use Definition 2.1.1; that is, for any $\epsilon > 0$ we must prove that there exists a $\delta > 0$ such that

$$|[f(x) + g(x)] - (L + M)| < \epsilon \quad \text{whenever} \quad 0 < |x - a| < \delta \tag{6}$$

Because we are given Eq. (3), we know from the definition of a limit that for $\frac{1}{2}\epsilon > 0$ there exists a $\delta_1 > 0$ such that

$$|f(x) - L| < \tfrac{1}{2}\epsilon \quad \text{whenever} \quad 0 < |x - a| < \delta_1$$

Similarly, from Eq. (4), for $\frac{1}{2}\epsilon > 0$ there exists a $\delta_2 > 0$ such that

$$|g(x) - M| < \tfrac{1}{2}\epsilon \quad \text{whenever} \quad 0 < |x - a| < \delta_2$$

Now, let δ be the smaller of the two numbers δ_1 and δ_2. Therefore, $\delta \leq \delta_1$ and $\delta \leq \delta_2$. So we can say

$$|f(x) - L| < \tfrac{1}{2}\epsilon \quad \text{whenever} \quad 0 < |x - a| < \delta$$

and

$$|g(x) - M| < \tfrac{1}{2}\epsilon \quad \text{whenever} \quad 0 < |x - a| < \delta$$

Hence, we have

$$|[f(x) + g(x)] - (L + M)| = |(f(x) - L) + (g(x) - M)|$$

$$\leq |f(x) - L| + |g(x) - M|$$

$$< \tfrac{1}{2}\epsilon + \tfrac{1}{2}\epsilon = \epsilon \quad \text{whenever} \quad 0 < |x - a| < \delta$$

In this way, we have obtained statement (6), thereby proving that

$$\lim_{x \to a} [f(x) + g(x)] = L + M$$

The proof of Limit theorem 4 using the minus sign is left as an exercise (see Exercise 24).   ∎

Limit theorem 4 can be extended to any finite number of functions.

2.2.5 Limit theorem 5   If $\lim\limits_{x \to a} f_1(x) = L_1$, $\lim\limits_{x \to a} f_2(x) = L_2$, . . . , and $\lim\limits_{x \to a} f_n(x) = L_n$, then

$$\lim_{x \to a} [f_1(x) \pm f_2(x) \pm \cdots \pm f_n(x)] = L_1 \pm L_2 \pm \cdots \pm L_n$$

This theorem may be proved by applying Limit theorem 4 and mathematical induction (see Exercise 25).

2.2.6 Limit theorem 6   If $\lim\limits_{x \to a} f(x) = L$ and $\lim\limits_{x \to a} g(x) = M$, then

$$\lim_{x \to a} f(x) \cdot g(x) = L \cdot M$$

The proof of this theorem is more sophisticated than those of the preceding theorems, and it is often omitted from a beginning calculus text. We have outlined the proof in Exercises 27 and 28.

● ILLUSTRATION 3: From Limit theorem 3, $\lim\limits_{x \to 3} x = 3$, and from Limit theorem 1, $\lim\limits_{x \to 3} (2x + 1) = 7$. Thus, from Limit theorem 6, we have

$$\lim_{x \to 3} x(2x + 1) = \lim_{x \to 3} x \cdot \lim_{x \to 3} (2x + 1)$$

$$= 3 \cdot 7$$

$$= 21 \qquad\qquad ●$$

Limit theorem 6 also can be extended to any finite number of functions by applying mathematical induction.

2.2.7 Limit theorem 7   If $\lim\limits_{x \to a} f_1(x) = L_1$, $\lim\limits_{x \to a} f_2(x) = L_2$, . . . , and $\lim\limits_{x \to a} f_n(x) = L_n$, then

$$\lim_{x \to a} [f_1(x) f_2(x) \cdots f_n(x)] = L_1 L_2 \cdots L_n$$

The proof is left as an exercise (see Exercise 29).

2.2.8 Limit theorem 8   If $\lim\limits_{x \to a} f(x) = L$ and n is any positive integer, then

$$\lim_{x \to a} [f(x)]^n = L^n$$

The proof follows immediately from Limit theorem 7 by taking

$$f(x) = f_1(x) = f_2(x) = \cdots = f_n(x) \quad \text{and} \quad L = L_1 = L_2 = \cdots = L_n$$

● ILLUSTRATION 4: From Limit theorem 1, $\lim\limits_{x \to -2} (5x + 7) = -3$. Therefore, from Limit theorem 8, it follows that

$$\lim_{x \to -2} (5x + 7)^4 = [\lim_{x \to -2} (5x + 7)]^4$$
$$= (-3)^4$$
$$= 81 \qquad\qquad ●$$

2.2.9 Limit theorem 9   If $\lim\limits_{x \to a} f(x) = L$ and $\lim\limits_{x \to a} g(x) = M$, and $M \neq 0$, then

$$\lim_{x \to a} \frac{f(x)}{g(x)} = \frac{L}{M}$$

The proof, based on Definition 2.1.1, is also frequently omitted from a beginning calculus text. However, a proof is given in Sec. 2.6. Although we are postponing the proof, we apply this theorem when necessary.

● ILLUSTRATION 5: From Limit theorem 3, $\lim\limits_{x \to 4} x = 4$, and from Limit theorem 1, $\lim\limits_{x \to 4} (-7x + 1) = -27$. Therefore, from Limit theorem 9,

$$\lim_{x \to 4} \frac{x}{-7x + 1} = \frac{\lim\limits_{x \to 4} x}{\lim\limits_{x \to 4} (-7x + 1)}$$
$$= \frac{4}{-27}$$
$$= -\frac{4}{27} \qquad\qquad ●$$

2.2.10 Limit theorem 10   If $\lim\limits_{x \to a} f(x) = L$, then

$$\lim_{x \to a} \sqrt[n]{f(x)} = \sqrt[n]{L}$$

if $L > 0$ and n is any positive integer, or if $L \leq 0$ and n is a positive odd integer.

A proof of this theorem is given in Sec. 2.6, and as is the case with the preceding theorem, we apply it when necessary.

● ILLUSTRATION 6: From the result of Illustration 5 and Limit theorem 10, it follows that

$$\lim_{x \to 4} \sqrt[3]{\frac{x}{-7x+1}} = \sqrt[3]{\lim_{x \to 4} \frac{x}{-7x+1}}$$

$$= \sqrt[3]{-\frac{4}{27}}$$

$$= -\frac{\sqrt[3]{4}}{3}$$ ●

Following are some examples illustrating the application of the above theorems. To indicate the limit theorem being used, we use the abbreviation "L.T." followed by the theorem number; for example, "L.T. 2" refers to Limit theorem 2.

EXAMPLE 1: Find

$$\lim_{x \to 3} (x^2 + 7x - 5)$$

and, when applicable, indicate the limit theorems which are being used.

SOLUTION:

$$\lim_{x \to 3} (x^2 + 7x - 5) = \lim_{x \to 3} x^2 + \lim_{x \to 3} 7x - \lim_{x \to 3} 5 \qquad \text{(L.T. 5)}$$

$$= \lim_{x \to 3} x \cdot \lim_{x \to 3} x + \lim_{x \to 3} 7 \cdot \lim_{x \to 3} x - \lim_{x \to 3} 5 \qquad \text{(L.T. 6)}$$

$$= 3 \cdot 3 + 7 \cdot 3 - 5 \qquad \text{(L.T. 3 and L.T. 2)}$$

$$= 9 + 21 - 5$$

$$= 25$$

It is important, at this point, to realize that the limit in Example 1 was evaluated by direct application of the theorems on limits. For the function f defined by $f(x) = x^2 + 7x - 5$, we see that $f(3) = 3^2 + 7 \cdot 3 - 5 = 25$, which is the same as $\lim_{x \to 3} (x^2 + 7x - 5)$. It is not always true that we have $\lim_{x \to a} f(x) = f(a)$ (see Example 4). In Example 1, $\lim_{x \to 3} f(x) = f(3)$ because the function f is continuous at $x = 3$. We discuss the meaning of continuous functions in Sec. 2.6.

EXAMPLE 2: Find

$$\lim_{x \to 2} \sqrt{\frac{x^3 + 2x + 3}{x^2 + 5}}$$

and when applicable indicate the limit theorems being used.

SOLUTION:

$$\lim_{x \to 2} \sqrt{\frac{x^3 + 2x + 3}{x^2 + 5}} = \sqrt{\lim_{x \to 2} \frac{x^3 + 2x + 3}{x^2 + 5}} \qquad \text{(L.T. 10)}$$

$$= \sqrt{\frac{\lim_{x \to 2} (x^3 + 2x + 3)}{\lim_{x \to 2} (x^2 + 5)}} \qquad \text{(L.T. 9)}$$

$$= \sqrt{\frac{\lim_{x \to 2} x^3 + \lim_{x \to 2} 2x + \lim_{x \to 2} 3}{\lim_{x \to 2} x^2 + \lim_{x \to 2} 5}} \qquad \text{(L.T. 5)}$$

$$= \sqrt{\frac{(\lim_{x\to 2} x)^3 + \lim_{x\to 2} 2 \cdot \lim_{x\to 2} x + \lim_{x\to 2} 3}{(\lim_{x\to 2} x)^2 + \lim_{x\to 2} 5}}$$

(L.T. 7 and L.T. 8)

$$= \sqrt{\frac{2^3 + 2 \cdot 2 + 3}{2^2 + 5}}$$

(L.T. 3 and L.T. 2)

$$= \sqrt{\frac{8 + 4 + 3}{9}}$$

$$= \frac{\sqrt{15}}{3}$$

EXAMPLE 3: Find

$$\lim_{x\to 3} \frac{x^3 - 27}{x - 3}$$

and, when applicable, indicate the limit theorems being used.

SOLUTION: Here we have a more difficult problem since Limit theorem 9 cannot be applied to the quotient $(x^3 - 27)/(x - 3)$ because $\lim_{x\to 3} (x - 3) = 0$. However, factoring the numerator, we obtain

$$\frac{x^3 - 27}{x - 3} = \frac{(x - 3)(x^2 + 3x + 9)}{x - 3}$$

This quotient is $(x^2 + 3x + 9)$ if $x \neq 3$ (since if $x \neq 3$ we can divide the numerator and denominator by $(x - 3)$).

When evaluating $\lim_{x\to 3} [(x^3 - 27)/(x - 3)]$, we are considering values of x close to 3, but not equal to 3. Therefore, it is possible to divide the numerator and denominator by $(x - 3)$. The solution to this problem takes the following form:

$$\lim_{x\to 3} \frac{x^3 - 27}{x - 3} = \lim_{x\to 3} \frac{(x - 3)(x^2 + 3x + 9)}{x - 3}$$

$$= \lim_{x\to 3} (x^2 + 3x + 9) \quad \text{dividing numerator and denominator by } (x - 3) \text{ since } x \neq 3$$

$$= \lim_{x\to 3} x^2 + \lim_{x\to 3} (3x + 9) \quad \text{(L.T. 4)}$$

$$= (\lim_{x\to 3} x)^2 + 18 \quad \text{(L.T. 8 and L.T. 1)}$$

$$= 3^2 + 18 \quad \text{(L.T. 3)}$$

$$= 27$$

Note that in Example 3 $(x^3 - 27)/(x - 3)$ is not defined when $x = 3$, but $\lim_{x\to 3} [(x^3 - 27)/(x - 3)]$ exists and is equal to 27.

EXAMPLE 4:   Given that f is the function defined by

$$f(x) = \begin{cases} x - 3 & \text{if } x \neq 4 \\ 5 & \text{if } x = 4 \end{cases}$$

find $\lim\limits_{x \to 4} f(x)$.

SOLUTION: When evaluating $\lim\limits_{x \to 4} f(x)$, we are considering values of x close to 4 but not equal to 4. Thus, we have

$$\lim_{x \to 4} f(x) = \lim_{x \to 4} (x - 3)$$
$$= 1$$

(L.T. 1)

In Example 4 $\lim\limits_{x \to 4} f(x) = 1$ but $f(4) = 5$; therefore, $\lim\limits_{x \to 4} f(x) \neq f(4)$. This is an example of a function which is discontinuous at $x = 4$. In terms of geometry, this means that there is a break in the graph of the function at the point where $x = 4$ (see Fig. 2.2.1). The graph of the function consists of the isolated point (4, 5) and the straight line whose equation is $y = x - 3$, with the point (4, 1) deleted.

There are two limits that we need in order to prove Limit theorems 9 and 10 in Sec. 2.6. They are given in the following two theorems.

Figure 2.2.1

2.2.11 Theorem   If a is any number except zero,

$$\lim_{x \to a} \frac{1}{x} = \frac{1}{a}$$

PROOF: We need to consider two cases: $a > 0$ and $a < 0$. We prove the theorem if $a > 0$ and leave the proof for $a < 0$ as an exercise (see Exercise 30).

So, if a is any positive number, from Definition 2.1.1 we must show that for any $\epsilon > 0$ there exists a $\delta > 0$ such that

$$\left| \frac{1}{x} - \frac{1}{a} \right| < \epsilon \quad \text{whenever} \quad 0 < |x - a| < \delta$$

Now

$$\left| \frac{1}{x} - \frac{1}{a} \right| = \left| \frac{a - x}{ax} \right| = \frac{|x - a|}{|a||x|}$$

and because $a > 0$, we have

$$\left| \frac{1}{x} - \frac{1}{a} \right| = |x - a| \cdot \frac{1}{a|x|}$$

(6)

We proceed to find some upper bound for the fraction $1/a|x|$. If we require the δ for which we are looking to be less than or equal to $\frac{1}{2}a$, then certainly whenever $|x - a| < \delta$, we know $|x - a| < \frac{1}{2}a$. The inequality

$$|x - a| < \tfrac{1}{2}a$$

is equivalent to

$$-\tfrac{1}{2}a < x - a < \tfrac{1}{2}a$$

which is equivalent to

$$\tfrac{1}{2}a < x < \tfrac{3}{2}a$$

or, because $a > 0$,

$$\tfrac{1}{2}a < |x| < \tfrac{3}{2}a$$

Hence, whenever $|x - a| < \tfrac{1}{2}a$, $|x| > \tfrac{1}{2}a$. So from Eq. (6) we have

$$\left|\frac{1}{x} - \frac{1}{a}\right| = |x - a| \cdot \frac{1}{a|x|} < |x - a| \cdot \frac{1}{a \cdot \tfrac{1}{2}a} = |x - a| \cdot \frac{2}{a^2}$$

whenever

$$|x - a| < \tfrac{1}{2}a$$

We want then $|x - a| \cdot (2/a^2) < \epsilon$ or, equivalently, $|x - a| < \tfrac{1}{2}a^2\epsilon$. Hence, we take δ as the smaller of $\tfrac{1}{2}a$ and $\tfrac{1}{2}a^2\epsilon$, which assures us that whenever $|x - a| < \delta$, then $|x - a| < \tfrac{1}{2}a^2\epsilon$ and $|x| > \tfrac{1}{2}a$ (because this is true when $|x - a| < \tfrac{1}{2}a$). This gives us

$$\left|\frac{1}{x} - \frac{1}{a}\right| = |x - a| \cdot \frac{1}{a|x|} < \tfrac{1}{2}a^2\epsilon \cdot \frac{1}{a \cdot \tfrac{1}{2}a}$$

or

$$\left|\frac{1}{x} - \frac{1}{a}\right| < \epsilon$$

whenever $0 < |x - a| < \delta$, and where $\delta = \min(\tfrac{1}{2}a, \tfrac{1}{2}a^2\epsilon)$. Hence, we have proved that $\lim\limits_{x \to a} (1/x) = 1/a$ if a is any positive number.   ∎

The proof of the next theorem makes use of the following formula, where n is any positive integer.

$$a^n - b^n = (a - b)(a^{n-1} + a^{n-2}b + a^{n-3}b^2 + \cdots + a^2b^{n-3} + ab^{n-2} + b^{n-1}) \quad (7)$$

The proof of Eq. (7) follows.

$$a(a^{n-1} + a^{n-2}b + \cdots + ab^{n-2} + b^{n-1}) = a^n + a^{n-1}b + \cdots + a^2b^{n-2} + ab^{n-1} \quad (8)$$

$$b(a^{n-1} + a^{n-2}b + \cdots + ab^{n-2} + b^{n-1}) = a^{n-1}b + \cdots + a^2b^{n-2} + ab^{n-1} + b^n \quad (9)$$

Subtracting terms of Eq. (9) from terms of Eq. (8) gives us Eq. (7).

2.2.12 Theorem   If n is a positive integer, then

$$\lim_{x \to a} \sqrt[n]{x} = \sqrt[n]{a}$$

if either

    (i) a is any positive number

or

    (ii) a is a negative number or zero and n is odd.

PROOF: We prove part (i) and leave the proof of part (ii) as an exercise (see Exercise 31).

Letting a be any positive number and using Definition 2.1.1, we must show that for any $\epsilon > 0$ there exists a $\delta > 0$ such that

$$|\sqrt[n]{x} - \sqrt[n]{a}| < \epsilon \quad \text{whenever} \quad 0 < |x - a| < \delta$$

To express $|\sqrt[n]{x} - \sqrt[n]{a}|$ in terms of $|x - a|$, we use Eq. (7). We have

$$|\sqrt[n]{x} - \sqrt[n]{a}| = \left| \frac{(x^{1/n} - a^{1/n})\left[(x^{1/n})^{n-1} + (x^{1/n})^{n-2}a^{1/n} + \cdots + x^{1/n}(a^{1/n})^{n-2} + (a^{1/n})^{n-1} \right]}{(x^{1/n})^{n-1} + (x^{1/n})^{n-2}a^{1/n} + \cdots + x^{1/n}(a^{1/n})^{n-2} + (a^{1/n})^{n-1}} \right|$$

Applying Eq. (7) to the numerator, we have

$$|\sqrt[n]{x} - \sqrt[n]{a}| = |x - a| \cdot \frac{1}{\left| x^{(n-1)/n} + x^{(n-2)/n}a^{1/n} + \cdots + x^{1/n}a^{(n-2)/n} + a^{(n-1)/n} \right|} \tag{10}$$

We wish to find an upper bound for the fraction on the right side of Eq. (10). If we require the δ for which we are looking to be less than or equal to a, then whenever $|x - a| < \delta$, we know that $|x - a| < a$, which is equivalent to

$$-a < x - a < a$$

or

$$0 < x < 2a$$

So, whenever $|x - a| < a$, then $x > 0$. Therefore, if in the denominator of the fraction on the right side of Eq. (10) the x is replaced by 0, we obtain $1/a^{(n-1)/n}$, which is greater than the fraction appearing in Eq. (10). Hence, whenever $|x - a| < a$, we have

$$|\sqrt[n]{x} - \sqrt[n]{a}| < |x - a| \cdot \frac{1}{a^{(n-1)/n}}$$

We want, then, $|x - a| \cdot 1/a^{(n-1)/n} < \epsilon$ or, equivalently, $|x - a| < a^{(n-1)/n}\epsilon$. Thus, we take δ as the smaller of a and $a^{(n-1)/n}\epsilon$, which assures us that whenever $|x - a| < \delta$, then $|x - a| < a^{(n-1)/n}\epsilon$ and $x > 0$. Therefore,

$$|\sqrt[n]{x} - \sqrt[n]{a}|$$

$$= |x - a| \cdot \frac{1}{\left| x^{(n-1)/n} + x^{(n-2)/n}a^{1/n} + \cdots + x^{1/n}a^{(n-2)/n} + a^{(n-1)/n} \right|}$$

$$< a^{(n-1)/n}\epsilon \cdot \frac{1}{a^{(n-1)/n}}$$

$$= \epsilon$$

whenever $0 < |x - a| < \delta$, where $\delta = \min(a, a^{(n-1)/n}\epsilon)$. We have therefore proved that $\lim\limits_{x \to a} \sqrt[n]{x} = \sqrt[n]{a}$, if a is any positive number. ■

• ILLUSTRATION 7: From part (i) of Theorem 2.2.12 it follows that $\lim\limits_{x \to 5} \sqrt{x} = \sqrt{5}$ and $\lim\limits_{x \to 16} \sqrt[4]{x} = 2$; from part (ii) it follows that $\lim\limits_{x \to -27} \sqrt[3]{x} = -3$. We do not consider a limit such as $\lim\limits_{x \to -4} \sqrt{x}$ because $\sqrt{x}$ is not defined on any open interval containing -4.   •

Exercises 2.2

In Exercises 1 through 17, find the value of the limit, and when applicable indicate the limit theorems being used.

1. $\lim\limits_{x \to 2} (x^2 + 2x - 1)$

2. $\lim\limits_{y \to -1} (y^3 - 2y^2 + 3y - 4)$

3. $\lim\limits_{t \to 2} \dfrac{t^2 - 5}{2t^3 + 6}$

4. $\lim\limits_{x \to -1} \dfrac{2x + 1}{x^2 - 3x + 4}$

5. $\lim\limits_{y \to -2} \dfrac{y^3 + 8}{y + 2}$

6. $\lim\limits_{s \to 1} \dfrac{s^3 - 1}{s - 1}$

7. $\lim\limits_{x \to -3} \dfrac{x^2 + 5x + 6}{x^2 - x - 12}$

8. $\lim\limits_{x \to 4} \dfrac{3x^2 - 17x + 20}{4x^2 - 25x + 36}$

9. $\lim\limits_{r \to 1} \sqrt{\dfrac{8r + 1}{r + 3}}$

10. $\lim\limits_{x \to 2} \sqrt{\dfrac{x^2 + 3x + 4}{x^3 + 1}}$

11. $\lim\limits_{y \to -3} \sqrt{\dfrac{y^2 - 9}{2y^2 + 7y + 3}}$

12. $\lim\limits_{t \to 3/2} \sqrt{\dfrac{8t^3 - 27}{4t^2 - 9}}$

13. $\lim\limits_{x \to 0} \dfrac{\sqrt{x + 2} - \sqrt{2}}{x}$ (HINT: Rationalize the numerator.)

14. $\lim\limits_{t \to 0} \dfrac{2 - \sqrt{4 - t}}{t}$

15. $\lim\limits_{h \to 0} \dfrac{\sqrt[3]{h + 1} - 1}{h}$

16. $\lim\limits_{x \to -2} \dfrac{x^3 - x^2 - x + 10}{x^2 + 3x + 2}$

17. $\lim\limits_{x \to 3} \dfrac{2x^3 - 5x^2 - 2x - 3}{4x^3 - 13x^2 + 4x - 3}$

18. If $f(x) = x^2 + 5x - 3$, show that $\lim\limits_{x \to 2} f(x) = f(2)$.

19. If $F(x) = 2x^3 + 7x - 1$, show that $\lim\limits_{x \to -1} F(x) = F(-1)$.

20. If $g(x) = (x^2 - 4)/(x - 2)$, show that $\lim\limits_{x \to 2} g(x) = 4$ but that $g(2)$ is not defined.

21. If $h(x) = (\sqrt{x + 9} - 3)/x$, show that $\lim\limits_{x \to 0} h(x) = \frac{1}{6}$ but that $h(0)$ is not defined.

22. Given that f is the function defined by

$$f(x) = \begin{cases} 2x - 1 & \text{if } x \neq 2 \\ 1 & \text{if } x = 2 \end{cases}$$

   (a) Find $\lim\limits_{x \to 2} f(x)$, and show that $\lim\limits_{x \to 2} f(x) \neq f(2)$.

   (b) Draw a sketch of the graph of f.

23. Given that f is the function defined by

$$f(x) = \begin{cases} x^2 - 9 & \text{if } x \neq -3 \\ 4 & \text{if } x = -3 \end{cases}$$

   (a) Find $\lim\limits_{x \to -3} f(x)$, and show that $\lim\limits_{x \to -3} f(x) \neq f(-3)$.

   (b) Draw a sketch of the graph of f.

24. Using Definition 2.1.1, prove that if

$$\lim_{x \to a} f(x) = L \quad \text{and} \quad \lim_{x \to a} g(x) = M$$

   then

$$\lim_{x \to a} [f(x) - g(x)] = L - M$$

25. Prove Limit theorem 5 by applying Limit theorem 4 and mathematical induction.

26. Prove that if $\lim\limits_{x \to a} f(x) = L$, then $\lim\limits_{x \to a} (f(x) - L) = 0$.

27. Using Definition 2.1.1, prove that if

$$\lim_{x \to a} f(x) = L \quad \text{and} \quad \lim_{x \to a} g(x) = 0$$

   then

$$\lim_{x \to a} f(x) \cdot g(x) = 0$$

   (HINT: In order to prove that $\lim\limits_{x \to a} f(x) \cdot g(x) = 0$, we must show that for any $\epsilon > 0$ there exists a $\delta > 0$ such that $|f(x) \cdot g(x)| < \epsilon$ whenever $0 < |x - a| < \delta$. First show that there is a $\delta_1 > 0$ such that $|f(x)| < 1 + |L|$ whenever $0 < |x - a| < \delta_1$, by applying Definition 2.1.1 to $\lim\limits_{x \to a} f(x) = L$, with $\epsilon = 1$ and $\delta = \delta_1$, and then use the triangle inequality. Then show that there is a $\delta_2 > 0$ such that $|g(x)| < \epsilon/(1 + |L|)$ whenever $0 < |x - a| < \delta_2$, by applying Definition 2.1.1 to $\lim\limits_{x \to a} g(x) = 0$. By taking δ as the smaller of the two numbers δ_1 and δ_2, the theorem is proved.)

28. Prove Limit theorem 6: If $\lim\limits_{x \to a} f(x) = L$ and $\lim\limits_{x \to a} g(x) = M$, then

$$\lim_{x \to a} [f(x) \cdot g(x)] = L \cdot M$$

   (HINT: Write $f(x) \cdot g(x) = [f(x) - L]g(x) + L[g(x) - M] + L \cdot M$. Apply Limit theorem 5 and the results of Exercises 26 and 27.)

29. Prove Limit theorem 7 by applying Limit theorem 6 and mathematical induction.

30. Prove Theorem 2.2.11 if $a < 0$.

31. Prove Theorem 2.2.12(ii).

2.3 ONE-SIDED LIMITS   When considering $\lim\limits_{x\to a} f(x)$ we are concerned with values of x in an open interval containing a but not at a itself, that is, at values of x close to a and either greater than a or less than a. However, suppose, for example, that we have the function f for which $f(x) = \sqrt{x-4}$. Because $f(x)$ does not exist if $x < 4$, f is not defined on any open interval containing 4. Hence, we cannot consider $\lim\limits_{x\to4} \sqrt{x-4}$. However, if x is restricted to values greater than 4, the value of $\sqrt{x-4}$ can be made as close to 0 as we please by taking x sufficiently close to 4 but greater than 4. In such a case as this, we let x approach 4 from the right and consider the *one-sided limit from the right* or the *right-hand limit*, which we now define.

2.3.1 Definition   Let f be a function which is defined at every number in some open interval (a, c). Then the *limit of $f(x)$, as x approaches a from the right, is L,* written

$$\lim_{x\to a^+} f(x) = L$$

if for any $\epsilon > 0$, however small, there exists a $\delta > 0$ such that

$$|f(x) - L| < \epsilon \quad \text{whenever} \quad 0 < x - a < \delta \tag{1}$$

Note that in statement (1) there are no absolute-value bars around $x - a$ since $x - a > 0$, because $x > a$.

It follows from Definition 2.3.1 that

$$\lim_{x\to4^+} \sqrt{x-4} = 0$$

If when considering the limit of a function the independent variable x is restricted to values less than a number a, we say that x approaches a from the left; the limit is called the *one-sided limit from the left* or the *left-hand limit*.

2.3.2 Definition   Let f be a function which is defined at every number in some open interval (d, a). Then the *limit of $f(x)$, as x approaches a from the left, is L,* written

$$\lim_{x\to a^-} f(x) = L$$

if for any $\epsilon > 0$, however small, there exists a $\delta > 0$ such that

$$|f(x) - L| < \epsilon \quad \text{whenever} \quad -\delta < x - a < 0$$

We can refer to $\lim\limits_{x\to a} f(x)$ as the *two-sided limit*, or the *undirected limit*, to distinguish it from the one-sided limits.

Limit theorems 1–10 given in Sec. 2.2 remain unchanged when "$x \to a$" is replaced by "$x \to a^+$" or "$x \to a^-$."

EXAMPLE 1:   Let f be defined by

$$f(x) = \text{sgn } x = \begin{cases} -1 & \text{if } x < 0 \\ 0 & \text{if } x = 0 \\ 1 & \text{if } 0 < x \end{cases}$$

(a) Draw a sketch of the graph of f. (b) Determine $\lim_{x \to 0^-} f(x)$ if it exists. (c) Determine $\lim_{x \to 0^+} f(x)$ if it exists.

SOLUTION: A sketch of the graph is shown in Fig. 2.3.1. $\lim_{x \to 0^-} f(x) = -1$ since, if x is any number less than 0, $f(x)$ has the value -1. Similarly, $\lim_{x \to 0^+} f(x) = +1$.

Figure 2.3.1

In the above example $\lim_{x \to 0^-} f(x) \neq \lim_{x \to 0^+} f(x)$. Because the left-hand limit and the right-hand limit are not equal, we say that the two-sided limit, $\lim_{x \to 0} f(x)$, does not exist. The concept of the two-sided limit failing to exist because the two one-sided limits are unequal is stated in the following theorem.

2.3.3 Theorem $\lim_{x \to a} f(x)$ exists and is equal to L if and only if $\lim_{x \to a^-} f(x)$ and $\lim_{x \to a^+} f(x)$ both exist and both are equal to L.

The proof of this theorem is left as an exercise (see Exercise 16).

EXAMPLE 2:   Let g be defined by

$$g(x) = \begin{cases} |x| & \text{if } x \neq 0 \\ 2 & \text{if } x = 0 \end{cases}$$

(a) Draw a sketch of the graph of g. (b) Find $\lim_{x \to 0} g(x)$ if it exists.

SOLUTION: A sketch of the graph is shown in Fig. 2.3.2.

$$\lim_{x \to 0^-} g(x) = \lim_{x \to 0^-} (-x) = 0 \quad \text{and} \quad \lim_{x \to 0^+} g(x) = \lim_{x \to 0^+} x = 0$$

Therefore, by Theorem 2.3.2 $\lim_{x \to 0} g(x)$ exists and is equal to 0. Note that $g(0) = 2$, which has no effect on $\lim_{x \to 0} g(x)$.

Figure 2.3.2

EXAMPLE 3: Let h be defined by

$$h(x) = \begin{cases} 4 - x^2 & \text{if } x \leq 1 \\ 2 + x^2 & \text{if } 1 < x \end{cases}$$

(a) Draw a sketch of the graph of h. (b) Find each of the following limits if they exist: $\lim_{x \to 1^-} h(x)$, $\lim_{x \to 1^+} h(x)$, $\lim_{x \to 1} h(x)$.

SOLUTION: A sketch of the graph is shown in Fig. 2.3.3.

$$\lim_{x \to 1^-} h(x) = \lim_{x \to 1^-} (4 - x^2) = 3$$

$$\lim_{x \to 1^+} h(x) = \lim_{x \to 1^+} (2 + x^2) = 3$$

Therefore, by Theorem 2.3.3 $\lim_{x \to 1} h(x)$ exists and is equal to 3. Note that $h(1) = 3$.

Figure 2.3.3

Exercises 2.3

In Exercises 1 through 10, draw a sketch of the graph and find the indicated limit if it exists; if the limit does not exist, give the reason.

1. $f(x) = \begin{cases} 2 & \text{if } x < 1 \\ -1 & \text{if } x = 1 \\ -3 & \text{if } 1 < x \end{cases}$; (a) $\lim_{x \to 1^+} f(x)$; (b) $\lim_{x \to 1^-} f(x)$; (c) $\lim_{x \to 1} f(x)$

2. $g(s) = \begin{cases} s + 3 & \text{if } s \leq -2 \\ 3 - s & \text{if } -2 < s \end{cases}$; (a) $\lim_{s \to -2^+} g(s)$; (b) $\lim_{s \to -2^-} g(s)$; (c) $\lim_{s \to -2} g(s)$

3. $h(x) = \begin{cases} 2x + 1 & \text{if } x < 3 \\ 10 - x & \text{if } 3 \leq x \end{cases}$; (a) $\lim_{x \to 3^+} h(x)$; (b) $\lim_{x \to 3^-} h(x)$; (c) $\lim_{x \to 3} h(x)$

4. $F(x) = \begin{cases} x^2 & \text{if } x \leq 2 \\ 8 - 2x & \text{if } 2 < x \end{cases}$; (a) $\lim_{x \to 2^+} F(x)$; (b) $\lim_{x \to 2^-} F(x)$; (c) $\lim_{x \to 2} F(x)$

5. $f(r) = \begin{cases} 2r + 3 & \text{if } r < 1 \\ 2 & \text{if } r = 1 \\ 7 - 2r & \text{if } 1 < r \end{cases}$; (a) $\lim_{r \to 1^+} f(r)$; (b) $\lim_{r \to 1^-} f(r)$; (c) $\lim_{r \to 1} f(r)$

6. $g(t) = \begin{cases} 3 + t^2 & \text{if } t < -2 \\ 0 & \text{if } t = -2 \\ 11 - t^2 & \text{if } -2 < t \end{cases}$; (a) $\lim_{t \to -2^+} g(t)$; (b) $\lim_{t \to -2^-} g(t)$; (c) $\lim_{t \to -2} g(t)$

7. $F(x) = |x - 5|$; (a) $\lim_{x \to 5^+} F(x)$; (b) $\lim_{x \to 5^-} F(x)$; (c) $\lim_{x \to 5} F(x)$

8. $f(x) = 3 + |2x - 4|$; (a) $\lim_{x \to 2^+} f(x)$; (b) $\lim_{x \to 2^-} f(x)$; (c) $\lim_{x \to 2} f(x)$

9. $f(x) = \dfrac{|x|}{x}$; (a) $\lim_{x \to 0^+} f(x)$; (b) $\lim_{x \to 0^-} f(x)$; (c) $\lim_{x \to 0} f(x)$

10. The absolute value of the signum function (see Exercise 22 in Exercises 1.8).

    (a) $\lim_{x \to 0^+} |\text{sgn } x|$; (b) $\lim_{x \to 0^-} |\text{sgn } x|$; (c) $\lim_{x \to 0} |\text{sgn } x|$.

11. F is the function of Exercise 30 in Exercises 1.8. Find, if they exist:

    (a) $\lim_{x \to 0^+} F(x)$; (b) $\lim_{x \to 0^-} F(x)$; (c) $\lim_{x \to 0} F(x)$.

12. h is the function of Exercise 31 in Exercises 1.8. Find, if they exist: (a) $\lim_{x \to 0^+} h(x)$; (b) $\lim_{x \to 0^-} h(x)$; (c) $\lim_{x \to 0} h(x)$.

13. Find, if they exist: (a) $\lim_{x \to 2^+} [\![x]\!]$; (b) $\lim_{x \to 2^-} [\![x]\!]$; (c) $\lim_{x \to 2} [\![x]\!]$.

14. Let $G(x) = [\![x]\!] + [\![4 - x]\!]$. Draw a sketch of the graph of G. Find, if they exist: (a) $\lim_{x \to 3^+} G(x)$; (b) $\lim_{x \to 3^-} G(x)$; (c) $\lim_{x \to 3} G(x)$.

15. Given

$$f(x) = \begin{cases} x^2 + 3 & \text{if } x \leq 1 \\ x + 1 & \text{if } x > 1 \end{cases} \quad \text{and} \quad g(x) = \begin{cases} x^2 & \text{if } x \leq 1 \\ 2 & \text{if } x > 1 \end{cases}$$

    (a) Show that $\lim_{x \to 1^-} f(x)$ and $\lim_{x \to 1^+} f(x)$ both exist but are not equal, and hence $\lim_{x \to 1} f(x)$ does not exist.
    (b) Show that $\lim_{x \to 1^-} g(x)$ and $\lim_{x \to 1^+} g(x)$ both exist but are not equal, and hence $\lim_{x \to 1} g(x)$ does not exist.
    (c) Find formulas for $f(x) \cdot g(x)$.
    (d) Prove that $\lim_{x \to 1} f(x) \cdot g(x)$ exists by showing that $\lim_{x \to 1^-} f(x) \cdot g(x) = \lim_{x \to 1^+} f(x) \cdot g(x)$.

16. Prove Theorem 2.3.3.

17. Let

$$f(x) = \begin{cases} -1 & \text{if } x < 0 \\ 1 & \text{if } x > 0 \end{cases}$$

Show that $\lim_{x \to 0} f(x)$ does not exist but that $\lim_{x \to 0} |f(x)|$ does exist.

2.4 INFINITE LIMITS

Let f be the function defined by

$$f(x) = \frac{3}{(x - 2)^2}$$

A sketch of the graph of this function is in Fig. 2.4.1.

We investigate the function values of f when x is close to 2. Letting

Figure 2.4.1

x approach 2 from the right, we have the values of $f(x)$ given in Table 2.4.1. From this table we intuitively see that as x gets closer and closer

Table 2.4.1

x	3	$\frac{5}{2}$	$\frac{7}{3}$	$\frac{9}{4}$	$\frac{21}{10}$	$\frac{201}{100}$	$\frac{2001}{1000}$
$f(x) = \dfrac{3}{(x-2)^2}$	3	12	27	48	300	30,000	3,000,000

to 2 through values greater than 2, $f(x)$ increases without bound; in other words, we can make $f(x)$ as large as we please by taking x close enough to 2.

To indicate that $f(x)$ increases without bound as x approaches 2 through values greater than 2, we write

$$\lim_{x \to 2^+} \frac{3}{(x-2)^2} = +\infty$$

If we let x approach 2 from the left, we have the values of $f(x)$ given in Table 2.4.2. We intuitively see from this table that as x gets closer and

Table 2.4.2

x	1	$\frac{3}{2}$	$\frac{5}{3}$	$\frac{7}{4}$	$\frac{19}{10}$	$\frac{199}{100}$	$\frac{1999}{1000}$
$f(x) = \dfrac{3}{(x-2)^2}$	3	12	27	48	300	30,000	3,000,000

closer to 2, through values less than 2, $f(x)$ increases without bound; so we write

$$\lim_{x \to 2^-} \frac{3}{(x-2)^2} = +\infty$$

Therefore, as x approaches 2 from either the right or the left, $f(x)$ increases without bound, and we write

$$\lim_{x \to 2} \frac{3}{(x-2)^2} = +\infty$$

We have the following definition.

2.4.1 Definition   Let f be a function which is defined at every number in some open interval I containing a, except possibly at the number a itself. *As x approaches a, $f(x)$ increases without bound*, which is written

$$\lim_{x \to a} f(x) = +\infty \tag{1}$$

if for any number $N > 0$ there exists a $\delta > 0$ such that $f(x) > N$ whenever $0 < |x - a| < \delta$.

In words, Definition 2.4.1 states that we can make $f(x)$ as large as we please (i.e., greater than any positive number N) by taking x sufficiently close to a.

NOTE: It should be stressed again (as in Sec. 1.1) that $+\infty$ is not a real number; hence, when we write $\lim\limits_{x \to a} f(x) = +\infty$, it does not have the same meaning as $\lim\limits_{x \to a} f(x) = L$, where L is a real number. Equation (1) can be read as "the limit of $f(x)$ as x approaches a is positive infinity." In such a case the limit does not exist, but the symbolism "$+\infty$" indicates the behavior of the function values $f(x)$ as x gets closer and closer to a.

In an analogous manner, we can indicate the behavior of a function whose function values decrease without bound. To lead up to this, we consider the function g defined by the equation

$$g(x) = \frac{-3}{(x - 2)^2}$$

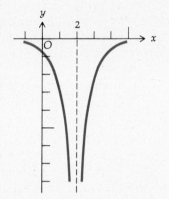

Figure 2.4.2

A sketch of the graph of this function is in Fig. 2.4.2.

The function values given by $g(x) = -3/(x - 2)^2$ are the negatives of the function values given by $f(x) = 3/(x - 2)^2$. So for the function g as x approaches 2, either from the right or the left, $g(x)$ decreases without bound, and we write

$$\lim_{x \to 2} \frac{-3}{(x - 2)^2} = -\infty$$

In general, we have the following definition.

2.4.2 Definition   Let f be a function which is defined at every number in some open interval I containing a, except possibly at the number a itself. *As x approaches a, $f(x)$ decreases without bound,* which is written

$$\lim_{x \to a} f(x) = -\infty \tag{2}$$

if for any number $N < 0$ there exists a $\delta > 0$ such that $f(x) < N$ whenever $0 < |x - a| < \delta$.

NOTE: Equation (2) can be read as "the limit of $f(x)$ as x approaches a is negative infinity," noting again that the limit does not exist and the symbolism "$-\infty$" indicates only the behavior of the function values as x approaches a.

We can consider one-sided limits which are "infinite." In particular, $\lim\limits_{x \to a^+} f(x) = +\infty$ if f is defined at every number in some open interval (a, c) and if for any number $N > 0$ there exists a $\delta > 0$ such that $f(x) > 0$ when-

Figure 2.4.3

ever $0 < x - a < \delta$. Similar definitions can be given if $\lim\limits_{x \to a^-} f(x) = +\infty$, $\lim\limits_{x \to a^+} f(x) = -\infty$, and $\lim\limits_{x \to a^-} f(x) = -\infty$.

Now suppose that h is the function defined by the equation

$$h(x) = \frac{2x}{x - 1} \tag{3}$$

A sketch of the graph of this function is in Fig. 2.4.3. By referring to Figs. 2.4.1, 2.4.2, and 2.4.3, note the difference in the behavior of the function whose graph is sketched in Fig. 2.4.3 from the functions of the other two figures. We see that

$$\lim_{x \to 1^-} \frac{2x}{x - 1} = -\infty$$

and

$$\lim_{x \to 1^+} \frac{2x}{x - 1} = +\infty$$

That is, for the function defined by Eq. (3), as x approaches 1 through values less than 1, the function values decrease without bound, and as x approaches 1 through values greater than 1, the function values increase without bound.

Before giving some examples, we need two limit theorems involving "infinite" limits.

2.4.3 Limit theorem 11 If r is any positive integer, then

(i) $\lim\limits_{x \to 0^+} \dfrac{1}{x^r} = +\infty$

(ii) $\lim\limits_{x \to 0^-} \dfrac{1}{x^r} = \begin{cases} -\infty & \text{if } r \text{ is odd} \\ +\infty & \text{if } r \text{ is even} \end{cases}$

PROOF: We prove part (i). The proof of part (ii) is analogous and is left as an exercise (see Exercise 19). We must show that for any $N > 0$ there exists a $\delta > 0$ such that

$$\frac{1}{x^r} > N \quad \text{whenever} \quad 0 < x < \delta$$

or, equivalently, because $x > 0$ and $N > 0$,

$$x^r < \frac{1}{N} \quad \text{whenever} \quad 0 < x < \delta$$

or, equivalently, since $r > 0$,

$$x < \left(\frac{1}{N}\right)^{1/r} \quad \text{whenever} \quad 0 < x < \delta$$

The above statement holds if $\delta = (1/N)^{1/r}$. We conclude that

$$\frac{1}{x^r} > N \quad \text{whenever} \quad 0 < x < \delta, \text{ if } \delta = \left(\frac{1}{N}\right)^{1/r}$$

∎

● ILLUSTRATION 1: From Limit theorem 11(i), it follows that

$$\lim_{x \to 0^+} \frac{1}{x^3} = +\infty \quad \text{and} \quad \lim_{x \to 0^+} \frac{1}{x^4} = +\infty$$

From Limit theorem 11(ii), we have

$$\lim_{x \to 0^-} \frac{1}{x^3} = -\infty \quad \text{and} \quad \lim_{x \to 0^-} \frac{1}{x^4} = +\infty$$

●

2.4.4 Limit theorem 12 If a is any real number, and if $\lim\limits_{x \to a} f(x) = 0$ and $\lim\limits_{x \to a} g(x) = c$, where c is a constant not equal to 0, then

(i) if $c > 0$ and if $f(x) \to 0$ through positive values of $f(x)$,

$$\lim_{x \to a} \frac{g(x)}{f(x)} = +\infty$$

(ii) if $c > 0$ and if $f(x) \to 0$ through negative values of $f(x)$,

$$\lim_{x \to a} \frac{g(x)}{f(x)} = -\infty$$

(iii) if $c < 0$ and if $f(x) \to 0$ through positive values of $f(x)$,

$$\lim_{x \to a} \frac{g(x)}{f(x)} = -\infty$$

(iv) if $c < 0$ and if $f(x) \to 0$ through negative values of $f(x)$,

$$\lim_{x \to a} \frac{g(x)}{f(x)} = +\infty$$

The theorem is also valid if "$x \to a$" is replaced by "$x \to a^+$" or "$x \to a^-$."

PROOF: We prove part (i) and leave the proofs of the other parts as exercises (see Exercises 20–22). To prove that

$$\lim_{x \to a} \frac{g(x)}{f(x)} = +\infty$$

we must show that for any $N > 0$ there exists a $\delta > 0$ such that

$$\frac{g(x)}{f(x)} > N \quad \text{whenever} \quad 0 < |x - a| < \delta \tag{4}$$

Since $\lim\limits_{x \to a} g(x) = c > 0$, by taking $\epsilon = \tfrac{1}{2}c$ in Definition 2.1.1, it follows that there exists a $\delta_1 > 0$ such that

$$|g(x) - c| < \tfrac{1}{2}c \quad \text{whenever} \quad 0 < |x - a| < \delta_1$$

By applying Theorem 1.2.2 to the above inequality, it follows that there exists a $\delta_1 > 0$ such that

$$-\tfrac{1}{2}c < g(x) - c < \tfrac{1}{2}c \quad \text{whenever} \quad 0 < |x - a| < \delta_1$$

or, equivalently,

$$\tfrac{1}{2}c < g(x) < \tfrac{3}{2}c \quad \text{whenever} \quad 0 < |x - a| < \delta_1$$

So there exists a $\delta_1 > 0$ such that

$$g(x) > \tfrac{1}{2}c \quad \text{whenever} \quad 0 < |x - a| < \delta_1 \tag{5}$$

Now $\lim\limits_{x \to a} f(x) = 0$. Thus, for any $\epsilon > 0$, there exists a $\delta_2 > 0$ such that

$$|f(x)| < \epsilon \quad \text{whenever} \quad 0 < |x - a| < \delta_2$$

Since $f(x)$ is approaching zero through positive values of $f(x)$, we can remove the absolute-value bars around $f(x)$; hence, for any $\epsilon > 0$ there exists a $\delta_2 > 0$ such that

$$f(x) < \epsilon \quad \text{whenever} \quad 0 < |x - a| < \delta_2 \tag{6}$$

From statements (5) and (6) we can conclude that for any $\epsilon > 0$ there exist a $\delta_1 > 0$ and a $\delta_2 > 0$ such that

$$\frac{g(x)}{f(x)} > \frac{\tfrac{1}{2}c}{\epsilon} \quad \text{whenever} \quad 0 < |x - a| < \delta_1 \quad \text{and} \quad 0 < |x - a| < \delta_2$$

Hence, if $\epsilon = c/2N$ and $\delta = \min(\delta_1, \delta_2)$, then

$$\frac{g(x)}{f(x)} > \frac{\tfrac{1}{2}c}{c/2N} = N \quad \text{whenever} \quad 0 < |x - a| < \delta$$

which is statement (4). Hence, part (i) is proved. ∎

EXAMPLE 1: **Find:**

(a) $\lim\limits_{x \to 3^+} \dfrac{x^2 + x + 2}{x^2 - 2x - 3}$

(b) $\lim\limits_{x \to 3^-} \dfrac{x^2 + x + 2}{x^2 - 2x - 3}$

SOLUTION:

(a) $\lim\limits_{x \to 3^+} \dfrac{x^2 + x + 2}{x^2 - 2x - 3} = \lim\limits_{x \to 3^+} \dfrac{x^2 + x + 2}{(x - 3)(x + 1)}$

The limit of the numerator is 14, which can be easily verified.

$$\lim_{x \to 3^+} (x - 3)(x + 1) = \lim_{x \to 3^+} (x - 3) \cdot \lim_{x \to 3^+} (x + 1)$$

$$= 0 \cdot 4 = 0$$

The limit of the denominator is 0, and the denominator is approaching 0 through positive values. Then applying Limit theorem 12(i), we obtain

$$\lim_{x \to 3^+} \frac{x^2 + x + 2}{x^2 - 2x - 3} = +\infty$$

(b) $\lim\limits_{x \to 3^-} \dfrac{x^2 + x + 2}{x^2 - 2x - 3} = \lim\limits_{x \to 3^-} \dfrac{x^2 + x + 2}{(x - 3)(x + 1)}$

As in part (a), the limit of the numerator is 14.

$$\lim_{x \to 3^-} (x - 3)(x + 1) = \lim_{x \to 3^-} (x - 3) \cdot \lim_{x \to 3^-} (x + 1)$$
$$= 0 \cdot 4 = 0$$

In this case, the limit of the denominator is zero, but the denominator is approaching zero through negative values. Applying Limit theorem 12(ii), we have

$$\lim_{x \to 3^-} \frac{x^2 + x + 2}{x^2 - 2x - 3} = -\infty$$

EXAMPLE 2:   Find:

(a) $\lim\limits_{x \to 2^+} \dfrac{\sqrt{x^2 - 4}}{x - 2}$

(b) $\lim\limits_{x \to 2^-} \dfrac{\sqrt{4 - x^2}}{x - 2}$

SOLUTION: (a) Because $x \to 2^+$, $x - 2 > 0$, and so $x - 2 = \sqrt{(x - 2)^2}$. Thus,

$$\lim_{x \to 2^+} \frac{\sqrt{x^2 - 4}}{x - 2} = \lim_{x \to 2^+} \frac{\sqrt{(x - 2)(x + 2)}}{\sqrt{(x - 2)^2}}$$
$$= \lim_{x \to 2^+} \frac{\sqrt{x - 2} \, \sqrt{x + 2}}{\sqrt{x - 2} \, \sqrt{x - 2}}$$
$$= \lim_{x \to 2^+} \frac{\sqrt{x + 2}}{\sqrt{x - 2}}$$

The limit of the numerator is 2. The limit of the denominator is 0, and the denominator is approaching 0 through positive values. Therefore, by Limit theorem 12(i) it follows that

$$\lim_{x \to 2^+} \frac{\sqrt{x^2 - 4}}{x - 2} = +\infty$$

(b) Because $x \to 2^-$, $x - 2 < 0$, and so $x - 2 = -(2 - x) = -\sqrt{(2 - x)^2}$. Therefore,

$$\lim_{x \to 2^-} \frac{\sqrt{4 - x^2}}{x - 2} = \lim_{x \to 2^-} \frac{\sqrt{2 - x} \, \sqrt{2 + x}}{-\sqrt{2 - x} \, \sqrt{2 - x}}$$
$$= \lim_{x \to 2^-} \frac{\sqrt{2 + x}}{-\sqrt{2 - x}}$$

The limit of the numerator is 2. The limit of the denominator is 0, and the denominator is approaching 0 through negative values. Hence, by Limit theorem 12(ii), we have

$$\lim_{x \to 2^-} \frac{\sqrt{4 - x^2}}{x - 2} = -\infty$$

EXAMPLE 3: Find:

$$\lim_{x \to 4^-} \frac{[\![x]\!] - 4}{x - 4}$$

SOLUTION: $\lim_{x \to 4^-} [\![x]\!] = 3$. Therefore, $\lim_{x \to 4^-} ([\![x]\!] - 4) = -1$. Furthermore, $\lim_{x \to 4^-} (x - 4) = 0$, and $x - 4$ is approaching 0 through negative values. Hence, from Limit theorem 12(iv), we have

$$\lim_{x \to 4^-} \frac{[\![x]\!] - 4}{x - 4} = +\infty$$

Remember that because $+\infty$ and $-\infty$ are not numbers, the Limit theorems 1–10 of Sec. 2.2 do not hold for "infinite" limits. However, we do have the following properties regarding such limits. The proofs are left as exercises (see Exercises 23–25).

2.4.5 Theorem (i) If $\lim_{x \to a} f(x) = +\infty$, and $\lim_{x \to a} g(x) = c$, where c is any constant, then

$$\lim_{x \to a} [f(x) + g(x)] = +\infty$$

(ii) If $\lim_{x \to a} f(x) = -\infty$, and $\lim_{x \to a} g(x) = c$, where c is any constant, then

$$\lim_{x \to a} [f(x) + g(x)] = -\infty$$

The theorem is valid if "$x \to a$" is replaced by "$x \to a^+$" or "$x \to a^-$."

● ILLUSTRATION 2: Because $\lim_{x \to 2^+} \dfrac{1}{x - 2} = +\infty$ and $\lim_{x \to 2^+} \dfrac{1}{x + 2} = \dfrac{1}{4}$, it follows from Theorem 2.4.5(i) that

$$\lim_{x \to 2^+} \left[\frac{1}{x - 2} + \frac{1}{x + 2} \right] = +\infty$$

●

2.4.6 Theorem If $\lim_{x \to a} f(x) = +\infty$ and $\lim_{x \to a} g(x) = c$, where c is any constant except 0, then

(i) if $c > 0$, $\lim_{x \to a} f(x) \cdot g(x) = +\infty$.

(ii) if $c < 0$, $\lim_{x \to a} f(x) \cdot g(x) = -\infty$.

The theorem is valid if "$x \to a$" is replaced by "$x \to a^+$" or "$x \to a^-$."

● ILLUSTRATION 3:

$$\lim_{x \to 3} \frac{5}{(x - 3)^2} = +\infty \quad \text{and} \quad \lim_{x \to 3} \frac{x + 4}{x - 4} = -7$$

Therefore, from Theorem 2.4.6(ii), we have

$$\lim_{x \to 3} \left[\frac{5}{(x - 3)^2} \cdot \frac{x + 4}{x - 4} \right] = -\infty$$

●

2.4.7 Theorem   If $\lim\limits_{x \to a} f(x) = -\infty$ and $\lim\limits_{x \to a} g(x) = c$, where c is any constant except 0, then

(i) if $c > 0$, $\lim\limits_{x \to a} f(x) \cdot g(x) = -\infty$.

(ii) if $c < 0$, $\lim\limits_{x \to a} f(x) \cdot g(x) = +\infty$.

The theorem is valid if "$x \to a$" is replaced by "$x \to a^+$" or "$x \to a^-$."

● ILLUSTRATION 4:   In Example 2(b) we showed

$$\lim_{x \to 2^-} \frac{\sqrt{4 - x^2}}{x - 2} = -\infty$$

Furthermore,

$$\lim_{x \to 2^-} \frac{x - 3}{x + 2} = -\frac{1}{4}$$

Thus, from Theorem 2.4.7(ii), it follows that

$$\lim_{x \to 2^-} \left[\frac{\sqrt{4 - x^2}}{x - 2} \cdot \frac{x - 3}{x + 2} \right] = +\infty$$

Exercises 2.4

In Exercises 1 through 14, evaluate the limit.

1. $\lim\limits_{x \to 4^+} \dfrac{x}{x - 4}$

2. $\lim\limits_{x \to 3^-} \dfrac{4x^2}{9 - x^2}$

3. $\lim\limits_{t \to 2^+} \dfrac{t + 2}{t^2 - 4}$

4. $\lim\limits_{t \to 2} \dfrac{t + 2}{(t - 2)^2}$

5. $\lim\limits_{t \to 2} \dfrac{t + 2}{t^2 - 4}$

6. $\lim\limits_{x \to 0^+} \dfrac{\sqrt{3 + x^2}}{x}$

7. $\lim\limits_{x \to 0^-} \dfrac{\sqrt{3 + x^2}}{x}$

8. $\lim\limits_{x \to 0} \dfrac{\sqrt{3 + x^2}}{x^2}$

9. $\lim\limits_{x \to 3^+} \dfrac{\sqrt{x^2 - 9}}{x - 3}$

10. $\lim\limits_{x \to 4^-} \dfrac{\sqrt{16 - x^2}}{x - 4}$

11. $\lim\limits_{x \to 3^-} \dfrac{[\![x]\!] - x}{3 - x}$

12. $\lim\limits_{x \to 1^-} \dfrac{[\![x^2]\!] - 1}{x^2 - 1}$

13. $\lim\limits_{x \to 0^+} \left(\dfrac{1}{x} - \dfrac{1}{x^2} \right)$

14. $\lim\limits_{s \to 2^-} \left(\dfrac{1}{s - 2} - \dfrac{3}{s^2 - 4} \right)$

15. $\lim\limits_{x \to 0^-} \dfrac{2 - 4x^3}{5x^2 + 3x^3}$

16. Prove that $\lim\limits_{x \to 2} \dfrac{3}{(x - 2)^2} = +\infty$ by using Definition 2.4.1.

17. Prove that $\lim\limits_{x \to 4} \dfrac{-2}{(x - 4)^2} = -\infty$ by using Definition 2.4.2.

18. Use Definition 2.4.1 to prove that

$$\lim_{x \to -3} \left| \frac{5 - x}{3 + x} \right| = +\infty$$

19. Prove Theorem 2.4.3(ii). 20. Prove Theorem 2.4.4(ii). 21. Prove Theorem 2.4.4(iii).

22. Prove Theorem 2.4.4(iv). 23. Prove Theorem 2.4.5. 24. Prove Theorem 2.4.6.

25. Prove Theorem 2.4.7.

2.5 CONTINUITY OF A FUNCTION AT A NUMBER

Figure 2.5.1

In Sec. 2.1 we considered the function f defined by the equation

$$f(x) = \frac{(2x+3)(x-1)}{x-1}$$

We noted that f is defined for all values of x except 1. A sketch of the graph consisting of all points on the line $y = 2x + 3$ except $(1, 5)$ is shown in Fig. 2.5.1. There is a break in the graph at the point $(1, 5)$, and we state that the function f is *discontinuous* at the number 1.

If we define $f(1) = 2$, for instance, the function is defined for all values of x, but there is still a break in the graph, and the function is still discontinuous at 1. If we define $f(1) = 5$, however, there is no break in the graph, and the function f is said to be *continuous* at all values of x. We have the following definition.

2.5.1 Definition   The function f is said to be *continuous* at the number a if and only if the following three conditions are satisfied:

    (i) $f(a)$ exists.
    (ii) $\lim\limits_{x \to a} f(x)$ exists.
    (iii) $\lim\limits_{x \to a} f(x) = f(a)$.

If one or more of these three conditions fails to hold at a, the function f is said to be *discontinuous* at a.

We now consider some illustrations of discontinuous functions. In each illustration we draw a sketch of the graph, determine the points where there is a break in the graph, and show which of the three conditions in Definition 2.5.1 fails to hold at each discontinuity.

● ILLUSTRATION 1: Let f be defined as follows:

$$f(x) = \begin{cases} \dfrac{(2x+3)(x-1)}{x-1} & \text{if } x \neq 1 \\ 2 & \text{if } x = 1 \end{cases}$$

A sketch of the graph of this function is given in Fig. 2.5.2. We see that there is a break in the graph at the point where $x = 1$, and so we investi-

Figure 2.5.2

gate there the conditions of Definition 2.5.1.

$f(1) = 2$; therefore, condition (i) is satisfied.

$\lim_{x \to 1} f(x) = 5$; therefore, condition (ii) is satisfied.

$\lim_{x \to 1} f(x) = 5$, but $f(1) = 2$; therefore, condition (iii) is not satisfied.

We conclude that f is discontinuous at 1. •

Note that if in Illustration 1 $f(1)$ is defined to be 5, then $\lim_{x \to 1} f(x) = f(1)$ and f would be continuous at 1.

Figure 2.5.3

• ILLUSTRATION 2: Let f be defined by

$$f(x) = \frac{1}{x - 2}$$

A sketch of the graph of f is given in Fig. 2.5.3. There is a break in the graph at the point where $x = 2$, and so we investigate there the conditions of Definition 2.5.1.

$f(2)$ is not defined; therefore, condition (i) is not satisfied.
We conclude that f is discontinuous at 2. •

• ILLUSTRATION 3: Let g be defined by

$$g(x) = \begin{cases} \dfrac{1}{x - 2} & \text{if } x \neq 2 \\ 3 & \text{if } x = 2 \end{cases}$$

A sketch of the graph of g is shown in Fig. 2.5.4. Investigating the three conditions of Definition 2.5.1 at 2 we have the following.

$g(2) = 3$; therefore, condition (i) is satisfied.

$\lim_{x \to 2^-} g(x) = -\infty$, and $\lim_{x \to 2^+} g(x) = +\infty$; therefore, condition (ii) is not satisfied.

Thus, g is discontinuous at 2. •

Figure 2.5.4

• ILLUSTRATION 4: Let h be defined by

$$h(x) = \begin{cases} 3 + x & \text{if } x \leq 1 \\ 3 - x & \text{if } 1 < x \end{cases}$$

A sketch of the graph of h is shown in Fig. 2.5.5. Because there is a break in the graph at the point where $x = 1$, we investigate the conditions of Definition 2.5.1 at 1. We have the following.

$h(1) = 4$; therefore, condition (i) is satisfied.

$\lim_{x \to 1^-} h(x) = \lim_{x \to 1^-} (3 + x) = 4$

$\lim_{x \to 1^+} h(x) = \lim_{x \to 1^+} (3 - x) = 2$

Figure 2.5.5

Figure 2.5.6

Because $\lim_{x \to 1^-} h(x) \neq \lim_{x \to 1^+} h(x)$, we conclude that $\lim_{x \to 1} h(x)$ does not exist; therefore, condition (ii) fails to hold at 1.

Hence, h is discontinuous at 1.   ●

● ILLUSTRATION 5: Let F be defined by

$$F(x) = \begin{cases} |x - 3| & \text{if } x \neq 3 \\ 2 & \text{if } x = 3 \end{cases}$$

A sketch of the graph of F is shown in Fig. 2.5.6. We investigate the three conditions of Definition 2.5.1 at the point where $x = 3$. We have

$F(3) = 2$; therefore, condition (i) is satisfied.

$\lim_{x \to 3^-} F(x) = 0$ and $\lim_{x \to 3^+} F(x) = 0$. So $\lim_{x \to 3} F(x)$ exists and is 0; therefore, condition (ii) is satisfied.

$\lim_{x \to 3} F(x) = 0$ but $F(3) = 2$; therefore, condition (iii) is not satisfied.

Therefore, F is discontinuous at 3.   ●

It should be apparent that the geometric notion of a break in the graph at a certain point is synonymous with the analytic concept of a function being discontinuous at a certain value of the independent variable.

After Illustration 1 we mentioned that if $f(1)$ had been defined to be 5, then f would be continuous at 1. This illustrates the concept of a *removable discontinuity*. In general, suppose that f is a function which is discontinuous at the number a, but for which $\lim_{x \to a} f(x)$ exists. Then either $f(a) \neq \lim_{x \to a} f(x)$ or else $f(a)$ does not exist. Such a discontinuity is called a removable discontinuity because if f were redefined at a so that $f(a) = \lim_{x \to a} f(x)$, f becomes continuous at a. If the discontinuity is not removable it is called an *essential discontinuity*.

EXAMPLE 1: In each of the Illustrations 1 through 5, determine if the discontinuity is removable or essential.

SOLUTION: In Illustration 1 the function is discontinuous at 1 but $\lim_{x \to 1} f(x) = 5$. By redefining $f(1) = 5$, we have $\lim_{x \to 1} f(x) = f(1)$, and so the discontinuity is removable.

In Illustration 2, the function f is discontinuous at 2. $\lim_{x \to 2} f(x)$ does not exist; hence, the discontinuity is essential.

In Illustration 3, $\lim_{x \to 2} g(x)$ does not exist, and so the discontinuity is essential.

In Illustration 4, the function h is discontinuous because $\lim_{x \to 1} h(x)$ does not exist, and so again the discontinuity is essential.

In Illustration 5, $\lim_{x \to 3} F(x) = 0$, but $F(3) = 2$, and so F is discontinuous at 3. However, if $F(3)$ is redefined to be 0, then the function is continuous at 3, and so the discontinuity is removable.

Exercises 2.5

In Exercises 1 through 22, draw a sketch of the graph of the function; then by observing where there are breaks in the graph, determine the values of the independent variable at which the function is discontinuous and show why Definition 2.5.1 is not satisfied at each discontinuity.

1. $f(x) = \begin{cases} \dfrac{5}{x-4} & \text{if } x \neq 4 \\ 1 & \text{if } x = 4 \end{cases}$

2. $g(x) = \begin{cases} \dfrac{1}{x+2} & \text{if } x \neq -2 \\ 0 & \text{if } x = -2 \end{cases}$

3. $F(x) = \dfrac{x^2 + x - 6}{x + 3}$

4. $h(x) = \dfrac{x^4 - 16}{x^2 - 4}$

5. $g(x) = \begin{cases} \dfrac{x^2 + x - 6}{x + 3} & \text{if } x \neq -3 \\ 1 & \text{if } x = -3 \end{cases}$

6. $f(x) = \dfrac{x^3 - 2x^2 - 11x + 12}{x^2 - 5x + 4}$

7. $h(x) = \dfrac{x + 3}{x^2 + x - 6}$

8. $g(x) = \dfrac{x^2 - 4}{x^4 - 16}$

9. $f(x) = \begin{cases} -1 & \text{if } x < 0 \\ 0 & \text{if } x = 0 \\ x & \text{if } 0 < x \end{cases}$

10. $H(x) = \begin{cases} 1 + x & \text{if } x \leq -2 \\ 2 - x & \text{if } -2 < x \leq 2 \\ 2x - 1 & \text{if } 2 < x \end{cases}$

11. $f(x) = |2x + 5|$

12. $G(x) = \begin{cases} |2x + 5| & \text{if } x \neq -\frac{5}{2} \\ 3 & \text{if } x = -\frac{5}{2} \end{cases}$

13. $f(x) = \dfrac{x - 3}{|x - 3|}$

14. $F(x) = \begin{cases} \dfrac{x - 3}{|x - 3|} & \text{if } x \neq 3 \\ 0 & \text{if } x = 3 \end{cases}$

15. $g(x) = \begin{cases} 2x + 3 & \text{if } x \leq 1 \\ 8 - 3x & \text{if } 1 < x < 2 \\ x + 3 & \text{if } 2 \leq x \end{cases}$

16. $f(x) = \begin{cases} \dfrac{x^2 + x - 2}{x + 2} & \text{if } x \neq -2 \\ -3 & \text{if } x = -2 \end{cases}$

17. The greatest integer function. (See Illustration 6 in Sec. 1.7.)

18. The unit step function. (See Exercise 21 in Exercises 1.8.)

19. The signum function. (See Exercise 22 in Exercises 1.8.)

20. The function of Exercise 24 in Exercises 1.8.

21. The function of Exercise 33 in Exercises 1.8.

22. The function of Exercise 32 in Exercises 1.8.

In Exercises 23 through 30, prove that the function is discontinuous at the number a. Then determine if the discontinuity is removable or essential. If the discontinuity is removable, define $f(a)$ so that the discontinuity is removed.

23. $f(x) = \dfrac{9x^2 - 4}{3x - 2}$; $a = \dfrac{2}{3}$

24. $f(s) = \begin{cases} \dfrac{1}{s + 5} & \text{if } s \neq -5 \\ 0 & \text{if } s = -5 \end{cases}$; $a = -5$

25. $f(x) = \begin{cases} |x - 3| & \text{if } x \neq 3 \\ 2 & \text{if } x = 3 \end{cases}$; $a = 3$

26. $f(x) = \begin{cases} \dfrac{x^2 - 4x + 3}{x - 3} & \text{if } x \neq 3 \\ 5 & \text{if } x = 3 \end{cases}$; $a = 3$

27. $f(x) = \dfrac{\sqrt{2} + \sqrt[3]{x} - 2}{x - 8}$; $a = 8$

28. $f(y) = \dfrac{\sqrt{y + 5} - \sqrt{5}}{y}$; $a = 0$

29. $f(t) = \begin{cases} t^2 - 4 & \text{if } t \leq 2 \\ t & \text{if } t > 2 \end{cases}; \; a = 2$

30. $f(x) = \dfrac{\sqrt[3]{x+1} - 1}{x}; \; a = 0$

31. Let f be the function defined by

$$f(x) = \begin{cases} |x - [\![x]\!]| & \text{if } [\![x]\!] \text{ is even} \\ |x - [\![x+1]\!]| & \text{if } [\![x]\!] \text{ is odd} \end{cases}$$

Draw a sketch of the graph of f. At what numbers is f discontinuous?

2.6 THEOREMS ON CONTINUITY

By applying Definition 2.5.1 and limit theorems, we have the following theorem about functions which are continuous at a number.

2.6.1 Theorem   If f and g are two functions which are continuous at the number a, then

(i) $f + g$ is continuous at a.
(ii) $f - g$ is continuous at a.
(iii) $f \cdot g$ is continuous at a.
(iv) f/g is continuous at a, provided that $g(a) \neq 0$.

To illustrate the kind of proof required for each part of this theorem, we prove part (i):

Because f and g are continuous at a, from Definition 2.5.1 we have

$$\lim_{x \to a} f(x) = f(a) \tag{1}$$

and

$$\lim_{x \to a} g(x) = g(a) \tag{2}$$

Therefore, from Eqs. (1) and (2) and Limit theorem 4, we have

$$\lim_{x \to a} [f(x) + g(x)] = f(a) + g(a) \tag{3}$$

Equation (3) is the condition that $f + g$ is continuous at a, which furnishes the proof of (i).

The proofs of parts (ii), (iii), and (iv) are left as exercises (see Exercises 1–3).

2.6.2 Theorem   A polynomial function is continuous at every number.

To prove this theorem, consider the polynomial function f defined by

$$f(x) = b_0 x^n + b_1 x^{n-1} + b_2 x^{n-2} + \cdots + b_{n-1} x + b_n \qquad b_0 \neq 0$$

where n is a nonnegative integer, and $b_0, b_1, \ldots, b_n$ are real numbers. By successive applications of limit theorems, we can show that if a is any number

$$\lim_{x \to a} f(x) = b_0 a^n + b_1 a^{n-1} + b_2 a^{n-2} + \cdots + b_{n-1} a + b_n$$

from which it follows that

$$\lim_{x \to a} f(x) = f(a)$$

thus establishing the theorem. The details of the proof are left as an exercise (see Exercise 4).

2.6.3 Theorem   A rational function is continuous at every number in its domain.

PROOF: If f is a rational function, it can be expressed as the quotient of two polynomial functions. So f can be defined by

$$f(x) = \frac{g(x)}{h(x)}$$

where g and h are two polynomial functions, and the domain of f consists of all numbers except those for which $h(x) = 0$.

If a is any number in the domain of f, then $h(a) \neq 0$; and so by Limit theorem 9,

$$\lim_{x \to a} f(x) = \frac{\lim\limits_{x \to a} g(x)}{\lim\limits_{x \to a} h(x)} \qquad (4)$$

Because g and h are polynomial functions, by Theorem 2.6.2 they are continuous at a, and so $\lim\limits_{x \to a} g(x) = g(a)$ and $\lim\limits_{x \to a} h(x) = h(a)$. Consequently, from Eq. (4) we have

$$\lim_{x \to a} f(x) = \frac{g(a)}{h(a)}$$

Thus, we can conclude that f is continuous at every number in its domain.   ∎

Definition 2.5.1 states that the function f is continuous at the number a if $f(a)$ exists, if $\lim\limits_{x \to a} f(x)$ exists, and if

$$\lim_{x \to a} f(x) = f(a) \qquad (5)$$

Definition 2.1.1 states that $\lim\limits_{x \to a} f(x) = L$ if for any $\epsilon > 0$ there exists a $\delta > 0$ such that

$$|f(x) - L| < \epsilon \quad \text{whenever} \quad 0 < |x - a| < \delta$$

Applying this definition to Eq. (5), we have $\lim\limits_{x \to a} f(x) = f(a)$ if for any

$\epsilon > 0$ there exists a $\delta > 0$ such that

$$|f(x) - f(a)| < \epsilon \quad \text{whenever} \quad 0 < |x - a| < \delta \tag{6}$$

If f is continuous at a, we know that $f(a)$ exists; thus, in statement (6) it is not necessary that $|x - a| > 0$ because when $x = a$, statement (6) obviously holds. We have, then, the following definition of continuity of a function by using ϵ and δ notation.

2.6.4 Definition   The function f is said to be continuous at the number a if f is defined on some open interval containing a and if for any $\epsilon > 0$ there exists a $\delta > 0$ such that

$$|f(x) - f(a)| < \epsilon \quad \text{whenever} \quad |x - a| < \delta$$

This alternate definition is used in proving the following important theorem regarding the limit of a composite function.

2.6.5 Theorem   If $\lim\limits_{x \to a} g(x) = b$ and if the function f is continuous at b,

$$\lim_{x \to a} (f \circ g)(x) = f(b)$$

or, equivalently,

$$\lim_{x \to a} f(g(x)) = f(\lim_{x \to a} g(x))$$

PROOF: Because f is continuous at b, we have the following statement from Definition 2.6.4. For any $\epsilon_1 > 0$ there exists a $\delta_1 > 0$ such that

$$|f(y) - f(b)| < \epsilon_1 \quad \text{whenever} \quad |y - b| < \delta_1 \tag{7}$$

Because $\lim\limits_{x \to a} g(x) = b$, for any $\delta_1 > 0$ there exists a $\delta_2 > 0$ such that

$$|g(x) - b| < \delta_1 \quad \text{whenever} \quad 0 < |x - a| < \delta_2 \tag{8}$$

Whenever $0 < |x - a| < \delta_2$, we replace y in statement (7) by $g(x)$ and obtain the following: For any $\epsilon_1 > 0$ there exists a $\delta_1 > 0$ such that

$$|f(g(x)) - f(b)| < \epsilon_1 \quad \text{whenever} \quad |g(x) - b| < \delta_1 \tag{9}$$

From statements (9) and (8), we conclude that for any $\epsilon_1 > 0$ there exists a $\delta_2 > 0$ such that

$$|f(g(x)) - f(b)| < \epsilon_1 \quad \text{whenever} \quad 0 < |x - a| < \delta_2$$

from which it follows that

$$\lim_{x \to a} f(g(x)) = f(b)$$

or, equivalently,

$$\lim_{x \to a} f(g(x)) = f(\lim_{x \to a} g(x))$$ ■

An immediate application of Theorem 2.6.5 is in proving Limit theorems 9 and 10, the proofs of which were deferred until now. We restate these theorems and prove them, but before the statement of each theorem a special case is given as an example.

EXAMPLE 1: By using Theorem 2.6.5 and not Limit theorem 9 (limit of a quotient), find

$$\lim_{x \to 2} \frac{4x - 3}{x^2 + 2x + 5}$$

SOLUTION: Let the functions f and g be defined by

$$f(x) = 4x - 3 \quad \text{and} \quad g(x) = x^2 + 2x + 5$$

We consider $f(x)/g(x)$ as the product of $f(x)$ and $1/g(x)$ and use Limit theorem 6 (limit of a product). First of all, though, we must find $\lim_{x \to 2} 1/g(x)$ and this we do by considering $1/g(x)$ as a composite function value.

If h is the function defined by $h(x) = 1/x$, then the composite function $h \circ g$ is the function defined by $h(g(x)) = 1/g(x)$. Now

$$\lim_{x \to 2} g(x) = \lim_{x \to 2} (x^2 + 2x + 5) = 13$$

To use Theorem 2.6.5, h must be continuous at 13, which follows from Theorem 2.2.11. We have, then,

$$\lim_{x \to 2} \frac{1}{x^2 + 2x + 5} = \lim_{x \to 2} \frac{1}{g(x)}$$

$$= \lim_{x \to 2} h(g(x))$$

$$= h(\lim_{x \to 2} g(x)) \quad \text{(by Theorem 2.6.5)}$$

$$= h(13)$$

$$= \tfrac{1}{13}$$

Therefore, by using Limit theorem 6, we have

$$\lim_{x \to 2} \frac{4x - 3}{x^2 + 2x + 5} = \lim_{x \to 2} (4x - 3) \cdot \lim_{x \to 2} \frac{1}{x^2 + 2x + 5}$$

$$= 5 \cdot \tfrac{1}{13}$$

$$= \tfrac{5}{13}$$

Limit theorem 9 $\lim_{x \to a} f(x) = L$ and if $\lim_{x \to a} g(x) = M$ and $M \neq 0$, then

$$\lim_{x \to a} \frac{f(x)}{g(x)} = \frac{L}{M}$$

PROOF: Let h be the function defined by $h(x) = 1/x$. Then the composite function $h \circ g$ is defined by $h(g(x)) = 1/g(x)$. The function h is continuous everywhere except at 0, which follows from Theorem 2.2.11. Hence,

$$\lim_{x \to a} \frac{1}{g(x)} = \lim_{x \to a} h(g(x))$$

$$= h(\lim_{x \to a} g(x)) \quad \text{(by Theorem 2.6.5)}$$

$$= h(M)$$

$$= \frac{1}{M}$$

Applying Limit theorem 6 and the above result, we have

$$\lim_{x \to a} \frac{f(x)}{g(x)} = \lim_{x \to a} f(x) \cdot \lim_{x \to a} \frac{1}{g(x)}$$

$$= L \cdot \frac{1}{M}$$

$$= \frac{L}{M}$$

∎

EXAMPLE 2: By using Theorem 2.6.5 and not Limit theorem 10, find

$$\lim_{x \to 7} \sqrt[4]{3x - 5}$$

SOLUTION: Let the functions f and h be defined by

$$f(x) = 3x - 5 \quad \text{and} \quad h(x) = \sqrt[4]{x}$$

The composite function $h \circ f$ is defined by $h(f(x)) = \sqrt[4]{3x - 5}$. $\lim_{x \to 7} f(x) = \lim_{x \to 7} (3x - 5) = 16$; so, to use Theorem 2.6.5 for the composite function $h \circ f$, h must be continuous at 16, which follows from Theorem 2.2.12(i). The solution, then, is as follows.

$$\lim_{x \to 7} \sqrt[4]{3x - 5} = \lim_{x \to 7} h(f(x))$$

$$= h(\lim_{x \to 7} f(x)) \quad \text{(by Theorem 2.6.5)}$$

$$= h(16)$$

$$= \sqrt[4]{16}$$

$$= 2$$

Limit theorem 10   If $\lim_{x \to a} f(x) = L$, *then*

$$\lim_{x \to a} \sqrt[n]{f(x)} = \sqrt[n]{L}$$

if $L > 0$ and n is any positive integer, or if $L \leq 0$ and n is a positive odd integer.

PROOF: Let h be the function defined by $h(x) = \sqrt[n]{x}$. Then the composite function $h \circ f$ is defined by $h(f(x)) = \sqrt[n]{f(x)}$. From Theorem 2.2.12 it follows that h is continuous at L if $L > 0$ and n is any positive integer or if $L \leq 0$ and n is a positive odd integer. Therefore, we have

$$\lim_{x \to a} \sqrt[n]{f(x)} = \lim_{x \to a} h(f(x))$$

$$= h(\lim_{x \to a} f(x)) \quad \text{(by Theorem 2.6.5)}$$

$$= \sqrt[n]{h(L)}$$

$$= \sqrt[n]{L} \qquad\qquad\qquad ■$$

Another application of Theorem 2.6.5 is in proving that *a continuous function of a continuous function is continuous*. This is now stated as a theorem.

2.6.6 Theorem   If the function g is continuous at a and the function f is continuous at $g(a)$, then the composite function $f \circ g$ is continuous at a.

PROOF: Because g is continuous at a we have

$$\lim_{x \to a} g(x) = g(a) \tag{10}$$

Now f is continuous at $g(a)$; thus, we can apply Theorem 2.6.5 to the composite function $f \circ g$, thereby giving us

$$\lim_{x \to a} (f \circ g)(x) = \lim_{x \to a} f(g(x))$$

$$= f(\lim_{x \to a} g(x))$$

$$= f(g(a)) \quad \text{(by Eq. (10))}$$

$$= (f \circ g)(a)$$

which proves that $f \circ g$ is continuous at a. ■

Theorem 2.6.6 enables us to determine the numbers for which a particular function is continuous. The following example illustrates this.

EXAMPLE 3:   Given

$$h(x) = \sqrt{4 - x^2}$$

determine the values of x for which h is continuous.

SOLUTION: If $g(x) = 4 - x^2$ and $f(x) = \sqrt{x}$, then $h(x) = (f \circ g)(x)$. Because g is a polynomial function, g is continuous everywhere. Furthermore, f is continuous at every positive number. Therefore, by Theorem 2.6.6, h is continuous at every number x for which $g(x) > 0$, that is, when $4 - x^2 > 0$. Hence, h is continuous at every number in the open interval $(-2, 2)$.

In Sec. 4.4 (Continuity on an interval) we extend the concept of continuity to include continuity at an endpoint of a closed interval. We define "right-hand continuity" and "left-hand continuity" and with these definitions we show that the function h of Example 3 is continuous on the closed interval $[-2, 2]$.

Exercises 2.6

1. Prove Theorem 2.6.1(ii).

2. Prove Theorem 2.6.1(iii).

3. Prove Theorem 2.6.1(iv).

4. Prove Theorem 2.6.2, showing step by step which limit theorems are used.

In Exercises 5 through 10, show the application of Theorem 2.6.5 to find the limit.

5. $\lim\limits_{x \to 3} \dfrac{1}{x^2 - 2x + 2}$

6. $\lim\limits_{t \to -1} \dfrac{t + 4}{t - 2}$

7. $\lim\limits_{y \to -4} \sqrt[3]{3y + 4}$

8. $\lim\limits_{x \to 2} \sqrt{x^3 + 1}$

9. $\lim\limits_{x \to 7} \dfrac{x^2 - 4}{\sqrt[4]{x^2 + 5x - 3}}$

10. $\lim\limits_{x \to 3} \dfrac{x + 3}{\sqrt[3]{1 - x^2}}$

In Exercises 11 through 26, determine all values of x for which the given function is continuous. Indicate which theorems you apply.

11. $f(x) = x^2(x + 3)^3$

12. $f(x) = (x - 5)^3(x^2 + 4)^5$

13. $g(x) = \dfrac{x^3 - 1}{x^2 - 4}$

14. $h(x) = \dfrac{x + 2}{x^3 - 7x - 6}$

15. $F(x) = \dfrac{x^2 + 2x - 8}{x^3 + 6x^2 + 5x - 12}$

16. $g(x) = \sqrt{x^2 + 4}$

17. $f(x) = \sqrt{x^2 - 16}$

18. $F(x) = \sqrt{16 - x^2}$

19. $h(x) = \sqrt{\dfrac{x + 4}{x - 4}}$

20. $f(x) = \sqrt{\dfrac{4 - x}{4 + x}}$

21. $f(x) = |x - 5|$

22. $g(x) = |9 - x^2|$

23. $f(x) = x^2(x^{-2} + x^{-1/2})^3$

24. $G(x) = \left(\dfrac{x^2}{x^2 - 4} - \dfrac{1}{x}\right)^{1/3}$

25. $g(x) = [\![\sqrt{1 - x^2}]\!]$

26. $F(x) = 1 - x + [\![x]\!] - [\![1 - x]\!]$

27. Prove that if the function f is continuous at t, then $\lim\limits_{h \to 0} f(t - h) = f(t)$.

28. Prove that if f is continuous at a and g is discontinuous at a, then $f + g$ is discontinuous at a.

29. If
$$f(x) = \begin{cases} -x & \text{if } x < 0 \\ 1 & \text{if } x \geq 0 \end{cases} \quad \text{and} \quad g(x) = \begin{cases} 1 & \text{if } x < 0 \\ x & \text{if } x \geq 0 \end{cases}$$
prove that f and g are both discontinuous at 0 but that the product $f \cdot g$ is continuous at 0.

30. Give an example of two functions that are both discontinuous at a number a, but the sum of the two functions is continuous at a.

31. Give an example to show that the product of two functions f and g may be continuous at a number a where f is continuous at a but g is discontinuous at a.

32. If the function g is continuous at a number a and the function f is discontinuous at a, is it possible for the quotient of the two functions, f/g, to be continuous at a? Prove your answer.

Review Exercises (Chapter 2)

In Exercises 1 through 4, evaluate the limit, and when applicable indicate the limit theorems being used.

1. $\lim\limits_{x \to 2} (3x^2 - 4x + 5)$

2. $\lim\limits_{h \to 1} \dfrac{h^2 - 4}{3h^3 + 6}$

3. $\lim\limits_{t \to 0} \dfrac{\sqrt{9 - t} - 3}{t}$

4. $\lim\limits_{y \to -4} \sqrt{\dfrac{5y + 4}{y - 5}}$

In Exercises 5 through 8, draw a sketch of the graph and discuss the continuity of the function.

5. $f(x) = \sqrt{4x^2 - 9}$

6. $g(x) = \sqrt{\dfrac{x - 3}{4 - x}}$

7. $h(x) = \sqrt{(x - 3)(4 - x)}$

8. $F(x) = \dfrac{|x^2 - 4|}{x + 2}$

In Exercises 9 through 14, establish the limit by using Definition 2.1.1; that is, for any $\epsilon > 0$ find a $\delta > 0$ such that $|f(x) - L| < \epsilon$ whenever $0 < |x - a| < \delta$.

9. $\lim\limits_{x \to -2} (8 - 3x) = 14$

10. $\lim\limits_{x \to 3} (2x^2 - x - 6) = 9$

11. $\lim\limits_{t \to 4} \sqrt{t - 3} = 1$

12. $\lim\limits_{y \to 5} \dfrac{3}{2y - 1} = \dfrac{1}{3}$

13. $\lim\limits_{x \to 3} \dfrac{5 + 3x}{2x + 1} = 2$

14. $\lim\limits_{x \to -2} x^3 = -8$

15. Prove that $\lim\limits_{t \to 2} \sqrt{t^2 - 4} = 0$ by showing that for any $\epsilon > 0$ there exists a $\delta > 0$ such that $\sqrt{t^2 - 4} < \epsilon$ whenever $0 < t - 2 < \delta$.

16. If $f(x) = (|x| - x)/x$, evaluate:

   (a) $\lim\limits_{x \to 0^-} f(x)$; (b) $\lim\limits_{x \to 0^+} f(x)$; (c) $\lim\limits_{x \to 0} f(x)$.

In Exercises 17 through 24, evaluate the limit if it exists.

17. $\lim\limits_{x \to 9} \dfrac{2\sqrt{x} - 6}{x - 9}$

18. $\lim\limits_{s \to 7} \dfrac{5 - \sqrt{4 + 3s}}{7 - s}$

19. $\lim\limits_{x \to -4^+} \dfrac{2x}{16 - x^2}$

20. $\lim\limits_{y \to 5^-} \dfrac{\sqrt{25 - y^2}}{y - 5}$

21. $\lim\limits_{t \to 0} \dfrac{\sqrt[3]{(t + a)^2} - \sqrt[3]{a^2}}{t}$

22. $\lim\limits_{x \to 8} \dfrac{\sqrt{7 + \sqrt[3]{x}} - 3}{x - 8}$

23. $\lim\limits_{x \to 0} \dfrac{\sqrt[4]{x^4 + 1} - \sqrt{x^2 + 1}}{x^2}$

   $\left(\text{HINT: Write } \dfrac{\sqrt[4]{x^4 + 1} - \sqrt{x^2 + 1}}{x^2} = \dfrac{1 - \sqrt{x^2 + 1}}{x^2} + \dfrac{\sqrt[4]{x^4 + 1} - 1}{x^2}. \right)$

24. $\lim\limits_{x \to 1^+} \dfrac{[\![x^2]\!] - [\![x]\!]^2}{x^2 - 1}$

25. Draw a sketch of the graph of f if $f(x) = [\![1 - x^2]\!]$ and $-2 \le x \le 2$. (a) Does $\lim\limits_{x \to 0} f(x)$ exist? (b) Is f continuous at 0?

26. Draw a sketch of the graph of g if $g(x) = (x-1)[\![x]\!]$, and $0 \le x \le 2$.

    (a) Does $\lim\limits_{x \to 1} g(x)$ exist? (b) Is g continuous at 1?

27. Give an example of a function for which $\lim\limits_{x \to 0} |f(x)|$ exists but $\lim\limits_{x \to 0} f(x)$ does not exist.

28. Give an example of a function f that is discontinuous at 1 for which (a) $\lim\limits_{x \to 1} f(x)$ exists but $f(1)$ does not exist; (b) $f(1)$ exists but $\lim\limits_{x \to 1} f(x)$ does not exist; (c) $\lim\limits_{x \to 1} f(x)$ and $f(1)$ both exist but are not equal.

29. Let f be the function defined by
    $$f(x) = \begin{cases} 1 & \text{if } x \text{ is an integer} \\ 0 & \text{if } x \text{ is not an integer} \end{cases}$$
    (a) Draw a sketch of the graph of f. (b) For what values of a does $\lim\limits_{x \to a} f(x)$ exist? (c) At what numbers is f continuous?

30. If the function g is continuous at a and f is continuous at $g(a)$, is the composite function $f \circ g$ continuous at a? Why?

31. (a) Prove that if $\lim\limits_{h \to 0} f(x+h) = f(x)$ then $\lim\limits_{h \to 0} f(x+h) = \lim\limits_{h \to 0} f(x-h)$. (b) Show that the converse of the theorem in (a) is not true by giving an example of a function for which $\lim\limits_{h \to 0} f(x+h) = \lim\limits_{h \to 0} f(x-h)$ but $\lim\limits_{h \to 0} f(x+h) \ne f(x)$.

32. If the domain of f is the set of all real numbers, and f is continuous at 0, prove that if $f(a+b) = f(a) \cdot f(b)$ for all a and b, then f is continuous at every number.

33. If the domain of f is the set of all real numbers and f is continuous at 0, prove that if $f(a+b) = f(a) + f(b)$ for all a and b, then f is continuous at every number.

3

The derivative

3.1 THE TANGENT LINE

Figure 3.1.1

Figure 3.1.2

Many of the important problems in calculus depend on the problem of finding the tangent line to a given curve at a specific point on the curve. If the curve is a circle, we know from plane geometry that the tangent line at a point P on the circle is defined as the line intersecting the circle at only one point P. This definition does not suffice for a curve in general. For example, in Fig. 3.1.1 the line which we wish to be the tangent line to the curve at point P intersects the curve at another point Q.

In this section we arrive at a suitable definition of the tangent line to the graph of a function at a point on the graph. We proceed by considering how we should define the slope of the tangent line at a point, because if we know the slope of a line and a point on the line, the line is determined.

Let the function f be continuous at x_1. We wish to define the slope of the tangent line to the graph of f at $P(x_1, f(x_1))$. Let $Q(x_2, f(x_2))$ be another point on the graph of f such that x_2 is also in I. Draw a line through P and Q. Any line through two points on a curve is called a *secant line;* therefore, the line through P and Q is a secant line. See Fig. 3.1.2. In the figure, Q is to the right of P. However, Q may be on either the right or left side of P.

Let us denote the difference of the abscissas of Q and P by Δx so that

$$\Delta x = x_2 - x_1$$

Δx may be either positive or negative. The slope of the secant line PQ then is given by

$$m_{PQ} = \frac{f(x_2) - f(x_1)}{\Delta x}$$

provided that line PQ is not vertical. Because $x_2 = x_1 + \Delta x$, we can write the above equation as

$$m_{PQ} = \frac{f(x_1 + \Delta x) - f(x_1)}{\Delta x} \tag{1}$$

Now, think of point P as being fixed, and move point Q along the curve toward P; that is, Q approaches P. This is equivalent to stating that Δx approaches zero. As this occurs, the secant line turns about the fixed point P. If this secant line has a limiting position, it is this limiting position which we wish to be the tangent line to the graph at P. So we want the slope of the tangent line to the graph at P to be the limit of m_{PQ} as Δx approaches zero, if this limit exists. If $\lim\limits_{\Delta x \to 0} m_{PQ} = +\infty$ or $-\infty$, then as Δx approaches zero the line PQ approaches the line through P which is parallel to the y axis. In this case we would want the tangent line to the graph at P to be the line $x = x_1$. The preceding discussion leads us to the following definition.

3.1.1 Definition   If the function f is continuous at x_1, then the *tangent line* to the graph of

f at the point $P(x_1, f(x_1))$ is

(i) the line through P having slope $m(x_1)$, given by

$$m(x_1) = \lim_{\Delta x \to 0} \frac{f(x_1 + \Delta x) - f(x_1)}{\Delta x} \qquad (1)$$

if this limit exists;

(ii) the line $x = x_1$ if $\lim\limits_{\Delta x \to 0} \dfrac{f(x_1 + \Delta x) - f(x_1)}{\Delta x} = +\infty$ or $-\infty$

If neither (i) nor (ii) of Definition 3.1.1 holds, then there is no tangent line to the graph of f at the point $P(x_1, f(x_1))$.

EXAMPLE 1: Find the slope of the tangent line to the curve $y = x^2 - 4x + 3$ at the point (x_1, y_1).

SOLUTION: $f(x) = x^2 - 4x + 3$; therefore, $f(x_1) = x_1{}^2 - 4x_1 + 3$, and $f(x_1 + \Delta x) = (x_1 + \Delta x)^2 - 4(x_1 + \Delta x) + 3$. From Eq. (1), we have

$$m(x_1) = \lim_{\Delta x \to 0} \frac{f(x_1 + \Delta x) - f(x_1)}{\Delta x}$$

$$= \lim_{\Delta x \to 0} \frac{[(x_1 + \Delta x)^2 - 4(x_1 + \Delta x) + 3] - [x_1{}^2 - 4x_1 + 3]}{\Delta x}$$

$$= \lim_{\Delta x \to 0} \frac{x_1{}^2 + 2x_1 \Delta x + (\Delta x)^2 - 4x_1 - 4 \Delta x + 3 - x_1{}^2 + 4x_1 - 3}{\Delta x}$$

$$= \lim_{\Delta x \to 0} \frac{2x_1 \Delta x + (\Delta x)^2 - 4 \Delta x}{\Delta x}$$

Because $\Delta x \neq 0$, we can divide the numerator and the denominator by Δx and obtain

$$m(x_1) = \lim_{\Delta x \to 0} (2x_1 + \Delta x - 4)$$

or

$$m(x_1) = 2x_1 - 4 \qquad (2)$$

We now draw a sketch of the graph of the equation in Example 1. We plot some points and a segment of the tangent line at some points. We take values of x arbitrarily and compute the corresponding value of y from the given equation, as well as the value of m from Eq. (2). The results are given in Table 3.1.1, and a sketch of the graph is shown in Fig. 3.1.3. It is important to determine the points where the graph has a horizontal tangent. Because a horizontal line has a slope of zero, these points are found by setting $m(x_1) = 0$ and solving for x_1. Doing this calculation for this example, we have $2x_1 - 4 = 0$, which gives $x_1 = 2$. Therefore, at the point having an abscissa of 2, the tangent line will be parallel to the x axis.

Table 3.1.1

x	y	m
2	-1	0
1	0	-2
0	3	-4
-1	8	-6
3	0	2
4	3	4
5	8	6

Figure 3.1.3

EXAMPLE 2: Find an equation of the tangent line to the curve of Example 1 at the point (4, 3).

SOLUTION: Because the slope of the tangent line at any point (x_1, y_1) is given by

$$m(x_1) = 2x_1 - 4$$

the slope of the tangent line at the point (4, 3) is $m(4) = 2(4) - 4 = 4$. Therefore, an equation of the desired line, if we use the point-slope form, is

$$y - 3 = 4(x - 4)$$

$$4x - y - 13 = 0$$

3.1.2 Definition The *normal line* to a curve at a given point is the line perpendicular to the tangent line at that point.

EXAMPLE 3: Find an equation of the normal line to the curve $y = \sqrt{x - 3}$ which is parallel to the line $6x + 3y - 4 = 0$.

SOLUTION: Let l be the given line. To find the slope of l, we write its equation in the slope-intercept form, which is

$$y = -2x + \tfrac{4}{3}$$

Therefore, the slope of l is -2, and the slope of the desired normal line is also -2 because the two lines are parallel.

To find the slope of the tangent line to the given curve at any point (x_1, y_1), we apply Definition 3.1.1 with $f(x) = \sqrt{x - 3}$, and we have

$$m(x_1) = \lim_{\Delta x \to 0} \frac{\sqrt{x_1 + \Delta x - 3} - \sqrt{x_1 - 3}}{\Delta x}$$

To evaluate this limit, we rationalize the numerator.

$$m(x_1) = \lim_{\Delta x \to 0} \frac{(\sqrt{x_1 + \Delta x - 3} - \sqrt{x_1 - 3})(\sqrt{x_1 + \Delta x - 3} + \sqrt{x_1 - 3})}{\Delta x(\sqrt{x_1 + \Delta x - 3} + \sqrt{x_1 - 3})}$$

$$= \lim_{\Delta x \to 0} \frac{\Delta x}{\Delta x(\sqrt{x_1 + \Delta x - 3} + \sqrt{x_1 - 3})}$$

Dividing numerator and denominator by Δx (since $\Delta x \neq 0$), we obtain

$$m(x_1) = \lim_{\Delta x \to 0} \frac{1}{\sqrt{x_1 + \Delta x - 3} + \sqrt{x_1 - 3}}$$

$$= \frac{1}{2\sqrt{x_1 - 3}}$$

Because the normal line at a point is perpendicular to the tangent line at that point, the product of their slopes is -1. Hence, the slope of the normal line at (x_1, y_1) is given by

$$-2\sqrt{x_1 - 3}$$

As shown above, the slope of the desired line is -2. So we solve the equation

$$-2\sqrt{x_1 - 3} = -2$$

giving us

$$x_1 = 4$$

Therefore, the desired line is the line through point $(4, 1)$ on the curve and has a slope of -2. Using the point-slope form of an equation of a line, we obtain

$$y - 1 = -2(x - 4)$$

$$2x + y - 9 = 0$$

Refer to Fig. 3.1.4, which shows a sketch of the curve together with the line l, the normal line PN at $(4, 1)$, and the tangent line PT at $(4, 1)$.

Figure 3.1.4

Exercises 3.1

In Exercises 1 through 8, find the slope of the tangent line to the graph at the point (x_1, y_1). Make a table of values of x, y, and m at various points on the graph, and include in the table all points where the graph has a horizontal tangent. Draw a sketch of the graph.

1. $y = 9 - x^2$

2. $y = x^2 - 6x + 9$

3. $y = 7 - 6x - x^2$

4. $y = \frac{1}{4}x^2$

5. $y = x^3 - 3x$

6. $y = x^3 - x^2 - x + 10$

7. $y = 4x^3 - 13x^2 + 4x - 3$

8. $y = \sqrt{x + 1}$

In Exercises 9 through 18, find an equation of the tangent line and an equation of the normal line to the given curve at the indicated point. Draw a sketch of the curve together with the resulting tangent line and normal line.

9. $y = x^2 - 4x - 5$; $(-2, 7)$

10. $y = x^2 + 2x + 1$; $(1, 4)$

11. $y = \frac{1}{8}x^3$; $(4, 8)$

12. $y = 2x - x^3$; $(-2, 4)$

13. $y = \sqrt{9 - 4x}$; $(-4, 5)$

14. $y = \sqrt{4x - 3}$; $(3, 3)$

15. $y = \frac{6}{x}$; $(3, 2)$

16. $y = -\frac{8}{\sqrt{x}}$; $(4, -4)$

17. $y = \sqrt[3]{x}$; $(8, 2)$

18. $y = \sqrt[3]{5 - x}$; $(-3, 2)$

19. Find an equation of the tangent line to the curve $y = 2x^2 + 3$ that is parallel to the line $8x - y + 3 = 0$.

20. Find an equation of the normal line to the curve $y = x^3 - 3x$ that is parallel to the line $2x + 18y - 9 = 0$.

21. Find an equation of the tangent line to the curve $y = \sqrt{4x - 3} - 1$ that is perpendicular to the line $x + 2y - 11 = 0$.

22. Find an equation of each line through the point $(3, -2)$ that is tangent to the curve $y = x^2 - 7$.

23. Find an equation of each line through the point $(2, -6)$ that is tangent to the curve $y = 3x^2 - 8$.

24. Prove analytically that there is no line through the point $(1, 2)$ that is tangent to the curve $y = 4 - x^2$.

3.2 INSTANTANEOUS VELOCITY IN RECTILINEAR MOTION

Consider a particle moving along a straight line. Such a motion is called *rectilinear motion.* One direction is chosen arbitrarily as positive, and the opposite direction is negative. For simplicity, we assume that the motion of the particle is along a horizontal line, with distance to the right as positive and distance to the left as negative. Select some point on the line and denote it by the letter O. Let f be the function determining the directed distance of the particle from O at any particular time.

To be more specific, let s feet be the directed distance of the particle from O at t seconds of time. Then f is the function defined by the equation

$$s = f(t) \tag{1}$$

which gives the directed distance from the point O to the particle at a particular instant of time. Equation (1) is called an *equation of motion* of the particle.

● ILLUSTRATION 1: Let

$$s = t^2 + 2t - 3$$

Then, when $t = 0$, $s = -3$; therefore, the particle is 3 ft to the left of point O when $t = 0$. When $t = 1$, $s = 0$; so the particle is at point O at 1 sec. When $t = 2$, $s = 5$; so the particle is 5 ft to the right of point O at 2 sec. When $t = 3$, $s = 12$; so the particle is 12 ft to the right of point O at 3 sec.

Figure 3.2.1 illustrates the various positions of the particle for specific values of t.

Figure 3.2.1

Between the time for $t = 1$ and $t = 3$, the particle moves from the point where $s = 0$ to the point where $s = 12$; thus, in the 2-sec interval the change in the directed distance from O is 12 ft. The average velocity of the particle is the ratio of the change in the directed distance from a fixed point to the change in the time. So the number of feet per second in the average velocity of the particle from $t = 1$ to $t = 3$ is $\frac{12}{2} = 6$. From $t = 0$ to $t = 2$, the change in the directed distance from O of the particle is 8 ft, and so the number of feet per second in the average velocity of the particle in this 2-sec interval is $\frac{8}{2} = 4$.   ●

In Illustration 1, the average velocity of the particle is obviously not constant; and the average velocity supplies no specific information about the motion of the particle at any particular instant. For example, if a person is driving a car a distance of 70 miles in the same direction, and it takes him 2 hr, we say his average velocity in traveling that distance is 35 mi/hr. However, from this information we cannot determine the speedometer reading of the car at any particular time in the 2-hr period. The speedometer reading at a specific time is referred to as the *instantaneous velocity*. The following discussion enables us to arrive at a definition of what is meant by "instantaneous velocity."

Let Eq. (1) define s (the number of feet in the directed distance of the particle from point O) as a function of t (the number of seconds in the time). When $t = t_1$, $s = s_1$. The change in the directed distance from O is $(s - s_1)$ ft over the interval of time $(t - t_1)$ sec, and the number of feet per second in the average velocity of the particle over this interval of time is given by

$$\frac{s - s_1}{t - t_1}$$

or, because $s = f(t)$ and $s_1 = f(t_1)$, the average velocity is found from

$$\frac{f(t) - f(t_1)}{t - t_1}$$

Now the shorter the interval is from t_1 to t, the closer the average velocity will be to what we would intuitively think of as the instantaneous velocity at t_1.

For example, if the speedometer reading of a car as it passes a point P_1 is 40 mi/hr and if a point P is, for instance, 100 ft from P_1, then the average velocity of the car as it travels this 100 ft will very likely be close to 40 mi/hr because the variation of the velocity of the car along this short stretch is probably slight. Now, if the distance from P_1 to P were shortened to 50 ft, the average velocity of the car in this interval would be even closer to the speedometer reading of the car as it passes P_1. We can continue this process, and the speedometer reading at P_1 can be represented as the limit of the average velocity between P_1 and P as P approaches P_1. We have, then, the following definition.

3.2.1 Definition   If f is a function given by the equation

$$s = f(t) \tag{1}$$

and a particle is moving along a straight line so that s is the number of units in the directed distance of the particle from a fixed point on the line at t units of time, then the *instantaneous velocity* of the particle at t_1 units of time is $v(t_1)$ units of velocity where

$$v(t_1) = \lim_{t \to t_1} \frac{f(t) - f(t_1)}{t - t_1} \tag{2}$$

if this limit exists.

Because $t \neq t_1$, we can write

$$t = t_1 + \Delta t \tag{3}$$

and conclude that

$$\text{``}t \to t_1\text{''} \quad \text{is equivalent to} \quad \text{``}\Delta t \to 0\text{''} \tag{4}$$

From Eqs. (2) and (3) and statement (4), we obtain the following expression for $v(t_1)$:

$$v(t_1) = \lim_{\Delta t \to 0} \frac{f(t_1 + \Delta t) - f(t_1)}{\Delta t} \tag{5}$$

if this limit exists.

Formula (5) can be substituted for formula (2) in the definition of instantaneous velocity.

The instantaneous velocity may be either positive or negative, depending on whether the particle is moving along the line in the positive or the negative direction. When the instantaneous velocity is zero, the particle is at rest.

The *speed* of a particle at any time is defined as the absolute value of the instantaneous velocity. Hence, the speed is a nonnegative number. The terms "speed" and "instantaneous velocity" are often confused. It should be noted that the speed indicates only how fast the particle is moving, whereas the instantaneous velocity also tells us the direction of motion.

EXAMPLE 1: A particle is moving along a straight line according to the equation of motion

$$s = 2t^3 - 4t^2 + 2t - 1$$

Determine the intervals of time when the particle is moving to the right and when it is moving to the left. Also determine the instant when the particle reverses its direction.

SOLUTION: $f(t) = 2t^3 - 4t^2 + 2t - 1$.

Applying formula (2) in the definition of the instantaneous velocity of the particle at t_1, we have

$$v(t_1) = \lim_{t \to t_1} \frac{f(t) - f(t_1)}{t - t_1}$$

$$= \lim_{t \to t_1} \frac{(2t^3 - 4t^2 + 2t - 1) - (2t_1^3 - 4t_1^2 + 2t_1 - 1)}{t - t_1}$$

$$= \lim_{t \to t_1} \frac{2(t^3 - t_1^3) - 4(t^2 - t_1^2) + 2(t - t_1)}{t - t_1}$$

$$= \lim_{t \to t_1} \frac{2(t - t_1)[(t^2 + tt_1 + t_1^2) - 2(t + t_1) + 1]}{t - t_1}$$

Dividing the numerator and the denominator by $t - t_1$ (because $t \neq t_1$), we obtain

$$v(t_1) = \lim_{t \to t_1} 2(t^2 + tt_1 + t_1{}^2 - 2t - 2t_1 + 1)$$

$$= 2(t_1{}^2 + t_1{}^2 + t_1{}^2 - 2t_1 - 2t_1 + 1)$$

$$= 2(3t_1{}^2 - 4t_1 + 1)$$

$$= 2(3t_1 - 1)(t_1 - 1)$$

The instantaneous velocity is zero when $t_1 = \frac{1}{3}$ and $t_1 = 1$. Therefore, the particle is at rest at these two times. The particle is moving to the right when $v(t_1)$ is positive, and it is moving to the left when $v(t_1)$ is negative. We determine the sign of $v(t_1)$ for various intervals of t_1, and the results are given in Table 3.2.1.

Table 3.2.1

	$3t_1 - 1$	$t_1 - 1$	Conclusion
$t_1 < \frac{1}{3}$	$-$	$-$	$v(t_1)$ is positive, and the particle is moving to the right
$t_1 = \frac{1}{3}$	0	$-$	$v(t_1)$ is zero, and the particle is changing direction from right to left
$\frac{1}{3} < t_1 < 1$	$+$	$-$	$v(t_1)$ is negative, and the particle is moving to the left
$t_1 = 1$	$+$	0	$v(t_1)$ is zero, and the particle is changing direction from left to right
$1 < t_1$	$+$	$+$	$v(t_1)$ is positive, and the particle is moving to the right

The motion of the particle, indicated in Fig. 3.2.2, is along the horizontal line; however, the behavior of the motion is indicated above the line. The accompanying Table 3.2.2 gives values of s and v for specific values of t.

Figure 3.2.2

Table 3.2.2

t	s	v
-1	-9	16
0	-1	2
$\frac{1}{3}$	$-\frac{19}{27}$	0
1	-1	0
2	3	10

In the above example, $v(t_1)$ can also be found by applying formula (5). (See Exercise 1.)

EXAMPLE 2: A ball is thrown vertically upward from the ground with an initial velocity of 64 ft/sec. If the positive direction of the distance from the starting point is up, the equation of motion is

$$s = -16t^2 + 64t$$

If t is the number of seconds in the time which has elapsed since the ball was thrown, and s is the number of feet in the distance of the ball from the starting point at t sec, find: (a) the instantaneous velocity of the ball at the end of 1 sec; (b) the instantaneous velocity of the ball at the end of 3 sec; (c) how many seconds it takes the ball to reach its highest point; (d) how high the ball will go; (e) the speed of the ball at the end of 1 sec and at the end of 3 sec; (f) how many seconds it takes the ball to reach the ground; (g) the instantaneous velocity of the ball when it reaches the ground. At the end of 1 sec is the ball rising or falling? At the end of 3 sec is the ball rising or falling?

SOLUTION: $v(t_1)$ is the number of feet per second in the instantaneous velocity of the ball at t_1 sec.

$$s = f(t) \qquad \text{where } f(t) = -16t^2 + 64t$$

Applying formula (2), we find that

$$v(t_1) = \lim_{t \to t_1} \frac{f(t) - f(t_1)}{t - t_1}$$

$$= \lim_{t \to t_1} \frac{-16t^2 + 64t - (-16t_1^2 + 64t_1)}{t - t_1}$$

$$= \lim_{t \to t_1} \frac{-16(t^2 - t_1^2) + 64(t - t_1)}{t - t_1}$$

Dividing the numerator and the denominator by $t - t_1$ (because $t \neq t_1$), we obtain

$$v(t_1) = \lim_{t \to t_1} [-16(t + t_1) + 64] = -32t_1 + 64$$

(a) $v(1) = -32(1) + 64 = 32$; so at the end of 1 sec the ball is rising with an instantaneous velocity of 32 ft/sec.

(b) $v(3) = -32(3) + 64 = -32$; so at the end of 3 sec the ball is falling with an instantaneous velocity of -32 ft/sec.

(c) The ball reaches its highest point when the direction of motion changes, that is, when $v(t_1) = 0$. Setting $v(t_1) = 0$, we obtain

$$-32t_1 + 64 = 0$$

Thus,

$$t_1 = 2$$

(d) When $t = 2$, $s = 64$; therefore, the ball reaches a highest point of 64 ft above the starting point.

(e) $|v(t_1)|$ is the number of feet per second in the speed of the ball at t_1 sec.

$$|v(1)| = 32 \quad \text{and} \quad |v(3)| = 32$$

(f) The ball will reach the ground when $s = 0$. Setting $s = 0$, we have $-16t^2 + 64t = 0$, from which we obtain $t = 0$ and $t = 4$. Therefore, the ball will reach the ground in 4 sec.

(g) $v(4) = -64$; when the ball reaches the ground, its instantaneous velocity is -64 ft/sec.

Figure 3.2.3

Table 3.2.3 gives values of s and v for some specific values of t. The motion of the ball is indicated in Fig. 3.2.3. The motion is assumed to be in a straight vertical line, and the behavior of the motion is indicated to the left of the line.

Table 3.2.3

t	s	v
0	0	64
$\frac{1}{2}$	28	48
1	48	32
2	64	0
3	48	-32
$\frac{7}{2}$	28	-48
4	0	-64

Exercises 3.2

1. Apply formula (5) to find $v(t_1)$ for the rectilinear motion in Example 1.

2. Apply formula (5) to find $v(t_1)$ for the rectilinear motion in Example 2.

In Exercises 3 through 8, a particle is moving along a horizontal line according to the given equation of motion, where s ft is the directed distance of the particle from a point O at t sec. Find the instantaneous velocity $v(t_1)$ ft/sec at t_1 sec; and then find $v(t_1)$ for the particular value of t_1 given.

3. $s = 3t^2 + 1$; $t_1 = 3$

4. $s = 8 - t^2$; $t_1 = 5$

5. $s = \sqrt{t + 1}$; $t_1 = 3$

6. $s = \dfrac{1}{4t}$; $t_1 = \dfrac{1}{2}$

7. $s = \dfrac{2}{\sqrt{5t + 6}}$; $t_1 = 2$

8. $s = \sqrt[3]{t + 2}$; $t_1 = 6$

In Exercises 9 through 12, the motion of a particle is along a horizontal line according to the given equation of motion, where s ft is the directed distance of the particle from a point O at t sec. The positive direction is to the right. Determine the intervals of time when the particle is moving to the right and when it is moving to the left. Also determine when the particle reverses its direction. Show the behavior of the motion by a figure similar to Fig. 3.2.2, choosing values of t at random but including the values of t when the particle reverses its direction.

9. $s = t^3 + 3t^2 - 9t + 4$

10. $s = 2t^3 - 3t^2 - 12t + 8$

11. $s = \dfrac{1 + t}{4 + t^2}$

12. $s = \dfrac{t}{1 + t^2}$

13. If an object falls from rest, its equation of motion is $s = -16t^2$, where t is the number of seconds in the time that has elapsed since the object left the starting point, s is the number of feet in the distance of the object from the starting point at t sec, and the positive direction is upward. If a stone is dropped from a building 256 ft high, find: (a) the instantaneous velocity of the stone 1 sec after it is dropped; (b) the instantaneous velocity of the stone 2 sec after it is

dropped; (c) how long it takes the stone to reach the ground; (d) the instantaneous velocity of the stone when it reaches the ground.

14. If a stone is thrown vertically upward from the ground with an initial velocity of 32 ft/sec, the equation of motion is $s = -16t^2 + 32t$, where t sec is the time that has elapsed since the stone was thrown, s ft is the distance of the stone from the starting point at t sec, and the positive direction is upward. Find: (a) the average velocity of the stone during the time interval: $\frac{3}{4} \leq t \leq \frac{5}{4}$; (b) the instantaneous velocity of the stone at $\frac{3}{4}$ sec and at $\frac{5}{4}$ sec; (c) the speed of the stone at $\frac{3}{4}$ sec and at $\frac{5}{4}$ sec; (d) the average velocity of the stone during the time interval: $\frac{1}{2} \leq t \leq \frac{3}{4}$; (e) how many seconds it will take the stone to reach the highest point; (f) how high the stone will go; (g) how many seconds it will take the stone to reach the ground; (h) the instantaneous velocity of the stone when it reaches the ground. Show the behavior of the motion by a figure similar to Fig. 3.2.3.

15. If a ball is given a push so that it has an initial velocity of 24 ft/sec down a certain inclined plane, then $s = 24t + 10t^2$, where s ft is the distance of the ball from the starting point at t sec and the positive direction is down the inclined plane. (a) What is the instantaneous velocity of the ball at t_1 sec? (b) How long does it take for the velocity to increase to 48 ft/sec?

16. A rocket is fired vertically upward, and it is s ft above the ground t sec after being fired, where $s = 560t - 16t^2$ and the positive direction is upward. Find (a) the velocity of the rocket 2 sec after being fired, and (b) how long it takes for the rocket to reach its maximum height.

3.3 THE DERIVATIVE OF A FUNCTION   In Sec. 3.1 the slope of the tangent line to the graph of $y = f(x)$ at the point $(x_1, f(x_1))$ is defined by

$$m(x_1) = \lim_{\Delta x \to 0} \frac{f(x_1 + \Delta x) - f(x_1)}{\Delta x} \tag{1}$$

if this limit exists.

In Sec. 3.2 we learned that if a particle is moving along a straight line so that its directed distance s units from a fixed point at t units of time is given by $s = f(t)$, then if $v(t_1)$ units of velocity is the instantaneous velocity of the particle at t_1 units of time,

$$v(t_1) = \lim_{\Delta t \to 0} \frac{f(t_1 + \Delta t) - f(t_1)}{\Delta t} \tag{2}$$

The limits in formulas (1) and (2) are of the same form. This type of limit occurs in other problems too, and it is given a specific name.

3.3.1 Definition   The *derivative* of the function f is that function, denoted by f', such that its value at any number x in the domain of f is given by

$$f'(x) = \lim_{\Delta x \to 0} \frac{f(x + \Delta x) - f(x)}{\Delta x} \tag{3}$$

if this limit exists. (f' is read "f prime," and $f'(x)$ is read "f prime of x.")

Another symbol that is used instead of $f'(x)$ is $D_x f(x)$, which is read "the derivative of f of x with respect to x."

If $y = f(x)$, then $f'(x)$ is the derivative of y with respect to x, and we use the notation $D_x y$. The notation y' is also used for the derivative of y

with respect to an independent variable, if the independent variable is understood.

If x_1 is a particular number in the domain of f, then

$$f'(x_1) = \lim_{\Delta x \to 0} \frac{f(x_1 + \Delta x) - f(x_1)}{\Delta x} \qquad (4)$$

if this limit exists. Comparing formulas (1) and (4), note that the slope of the tangent line to the graph of $y = f(x)$ at the point $(x_1, f(x_1))$ is precisely the derivative of f evaluated at x_1.

If a particle is moving along a straight line according to the equation of motion $s = f(t)$, then upon comparing formulas (2) and (4), it is seen that $v(t_1)$ in the definition of instantaneous velocity of the particle at t_1 is the derivative of f evaluated at t_1 or, equivalently, the derivative of s with respect to t evaluated at t_1.

EXAMPLE 1:   Given $f(x) = 3x^2 + 12$, find the derivative of f.

SOLUTION: If x is any number in the domain of f, from Eq. (3) we obtain

$$f'(x) = \lim_{\Delta x \to 0} \frac{f(x + \Delta x) - f(x)}{\Delta x}$$

$$= \lim_{\Delta x \to 0} \frac{[3(x + \Delta x)^2 + 12] - (3x^2 + 12)}{\Delta x}$$

$$= \lim_{\Delta x \to 0} \frac{3x^2 + 6x\,\Delta x + 3(\Delta x)^2 + 12 - 3x^2 - 12}{\Delta x}$$

$$= \lim_{\Delta x \to 0} \frac{6x\,\Delta x + 3(\Delta x)^2}{\Delta x} = \lim_{\Delta x \to 0} (6x + 3\,\Delta x)$$

$$= 6x$$

Therefore, the derivative of f is the function f' defined by $f'(x) = 6x$. The domain of f' is the set of all real numbers, which is the same as the domain of f.

In Sec. 3.2 we showed that the limit

$$\lim_{\Delta t \to 0} \frac{f(t_1 + \Delta t) - f(t_1)}{\Delta t}$$

is equivalent to

$$\lim_{t \to t_1} \frac{f(t) - f(t_1)}{t - t_1}$$

Therefore, an alternative formula to (4) for $f'(x_1)$ is given by

$$f'(x_1) = \lim_{x \to x_1} \frac{f(x) - f(x_1)}{x - x_1} \qquad (5)$$

EXAMPLE 2: For the function f of Example 1, find the derivative of f at 2 in three ways: (a) apply formula (4); (b) apply formula (5); (c) substitute 2 for x in the expression for $f'(x)$ in Example 1.

SOLUTION: (a) Applying formula (4), we have

$$f'(2) = \lim_{\Delta x \to 0} \frac{f(2 + \Delta x) - f(2)}{\Delta x}$$

$$= \lim_{\Delta x \to 0} \frac{[3(2 + \Delta x)^2 + 12] - [3(2)^2 + 12]}{\Delta x}$$

$$= \lim_{\Delta x \to 0} \frac{12 + 12\,\Delta x + 3(\Delta x)^2 + 12 - 12 - 12}{\Delta x}$$

$$= \lim_{\Delta x \to 0} \frac{12\,\Delta x + 3(\Delta x)^2}{\Delta x}$$

$$= \lim_{\Delta x \to 0} (12 + 3\,\Delta x)$$

$$= 12$$

(b) From formula (5) we obtain

$$f'(2) = \lim_{x \to 2} \frac{f(x) - f(2)}{x - 2}$$

$$= \lim_{x \to 2} \frac{(3x^2 + 12) - 24}{x - 2}$$

$$= \lim_{x \to 2} \frac{3x^2 - 12}{x - 2}$$

$$= 3 \lim_{x \to 2} \frac{(x - 2)(x + 2)}{x - 2}$$

$$= 3 \lim_{x \to 2} (x + 2)$$

$$= 12$$

(c) Because, from Example 1, $f'(x) = 6x$, we obtain $f'(2) = 12$.

If the function f is given by the equation $y = f(x)$, we can let

$$\Delta y = f(x + \Delta x) - f(x)$$

and write $D_x y$ in place of $f'(x)$, so that from formula (3) we have

$$D_x y = \lim_{\Delta x \to 0} \frac{\Delta y}{\Delta x} \tag{6}$$

A derivative is sometimes indicated by the notation dy/dx. But we avoid this symbolism until we have defined what is meant by dy and dx.

EXAMPLE 3: Given

$$y = \frac{2+x}{3-x}$$

find $D_x y$.

SOLUTION:

$$D_x y = \lim_{\Delta x \to 0} \frac{\Delta y}{\Delta x}$$

$$= \lim_{\Delta x \to 0} \frac{f(x + \Delta x) - f(x)}{\Delta x}$$

$$= \lim_{\Delta x \to 0} \frac{(2 + x + \Delta x)/(3 - x - \Delta x) - (2 + x)/(3 - x)}{\Delta x}$$

$$= \lim_{\Delta x \to 0} \frac{(3 - x)(2 + x + \Delta x) - (2 + x)(3 - x - \Delta x)}{\Delta x(3 - x - \Delta x)(3 - x)}$$

$$= \lim_{\Delta x \to 0} \frac{(6 + x - x^2 + 3\,\Delta x - x\,\Delta x) - (6 + x - x^2 - 2\,\Delta x - x\,\Delta x)}{\Delta x(3 - x - \Delta x)(3 - x)}$$

$$= \lim_{\Delta x \to 0} \frac{5\,\Delta x}{\Delta x(3 - x - \Delta x)(3 - x)}$$

$$= \lim_{\Delta x \to 0} \frac{5}{(3 - x - \Delta x)(3 - x)}$$

$$= \frac{5}{(3 - x)^2}$$

EXAMPLE 4: Given $f(x) = x^{2/3}$, find $f'(x)$.

SOLUTION:

$$f'(x) = \lim_{\Delta x \to 0} \frac{f(x + \Delta x) - f(x)}{\Delta x} = \lim_{\Delta x \to 0} \frac{(x + \Delta x)^{2/3} - x^{2/3}}{\Delta x}$$

We rationalize the numerator in order to obtain a common factor of Δx in the numerator and the denominator; this yields

$$f'(x) = \lim_{\Delta x \to 0} \frac{[(x + \Delta x)^{2/3} - x^{2/3}][(x + \Delta x)^{4/3} + (x + \Delta x)^{2/3}x^{2/3} + x^{4/3}]}{\Delta x[(x + \Delta x)^{4/3} + (x + \Delta x)^{2/3}x^{2/3} + x^{4/3}]}$$

$$= \lim_{\Delta x \to 0} \frac{(x + \Delta x)^2 - x^2}{\Delta x[(x + \Delta x)^{4/3} + (x + \Delta x)^{2/3}x^{2/3} + x^{4/3}]}$$

$$= \lim_{\Delta x \to 0} \frac{x^2 + 2x(\Delta x) + (\Delta x)^2 - x^2}{\Delta x[(x + \Delta x)^{4/3} + (x + \Delta x)^{2/3}x^{2/3} + x^{4/3}]}$$

$$= \lim_{\Delta x \to 0} \frac{2x(\Delta x) + (\Delta x)^2}{\Delta x[(x + \Delta x)^{4/3} + (x + \Delta x)^{2/3}x^{2/3} + x^{4/3}]}$$

$$= \lim_{\Delta x \to 0} \frac{2x + \Delta x}{(x + \Delta x)^{4/3} + (x + \Delta x)^{2/3}x^{2/3} + x^{4/3}}$$

$$= \frac{2x}{x^{4/3} + x^{2/3}x^{2/3} + x^{4/3}}$$

Figure 3.3.1

$$= \frac{2x}{3x^{4/3}}$$

$$= \frac{2}{3x^{1/3}}$$

Note that $f'(0)$ does not exist even though f is continuous at 0. A sketch of the graph of f is shown in Fig. 3.3.1.

If for the function of Example 4 we evaluate

$$\lim_{\Delta x \to 0^+} \frac{f(x_1 + \Delta x) - f(x_1)}{\Delta x} \qquad \text{at } x_1 = 0$$

we have

$$\lim_{\Delta x \to 0^+} \frac{f(0 + \Delta x) - f(0)}{\Delta x} = \lim_{\Delta x \to 0^+} \frac{(\Delta x)^{2/3} - 0}{\Delta x}$$

$$= \lim_{\Delta x \to 0^+} \frac{1}{(\Delta x)^{1/3}}$$

$$= +\infty$$

If we evaluate

$$\lim_{\Delta x \to 0^-} \frac{f(x_1 + \Delta x) - f(x_1)}{\Delta x} \qquad \text{at } x_1 = 0$$

we obtain

$$\lim_{\Delta x \to 0^-} \frac{f(0 + \Delta x) - f(0)}{\Delta x} = -\infty$$

Therefore, we conclude that the tangent line to the graph of f at the origin is the y axis.

Example 4 shows that $f'(x)$ can exist for some values of x in the domain of f but fail to exist for other values of x in the domain of f. We have the following definition.

3.3.2 Definition The function f is said to be *differentiable* at x_1 if $f'(x_1)$ exists.

From Definition 3.3.2 it follows that the function of Example 4 is differentiable at every number except 0.

3.3.3 Definition A function is said to be *differentiable* if it is differentiable at every number in its domain.

Exercises 3.3

In Exercises 1 through 10, find $f'(x)$ for the given function by applying formula (3) of this section.

1. $f(x) = 4x^2 + 5x + 3$ 2. $f(x) = x^3$ 3. $f(x) = \sqrt{x}$

4. $f(x) = \sqrt{3x + 5}$ **5.** $f(x) = \dfrac{1}{x + 1}$ **6.** $f(x) = \sqrt{3x}$

7. $f(x) = \dfrac{1}{x^2} - x$ **8.** $f(x) = \dfrac{3}{1 + x^2}$ **9.** $f(x) = \dfrac{1}{\sqrt{x + 1}}$

10. $f(x) = \sqrt[3]{2x + 3}$

In Exercises 11 through 16, find $f'(a)$ for the given value of a by applying formula (4) of this section.

11. $f(x) = 1 - x^2;\ a = 3$ **12.** $f(x) = \dfrac{4}{5x};\ a = 2$ **13.** $f(x) = \dfrac{2}{x^3};\ a = 6$

14. $f(x) = \dfrac{2}{\sqrt{x}} - 1;\ a = 4$ **15.** $f(x) = \sqrt{x^2 - 9};\ a = 5$ **16.** $f(x) = \dfrac{1}{x} + x + x^2;\ a = -3$

In Exercises 17 through 22, find $f'(a)$ for the given value of a by applying formula (5) of this section.

17. $f(x) = 3x + 2;\ a = -3$ **18.** $f(x) = x^2 - x + 4;\ a = 4$ **19.** $f(x) = 2 - x^3;\ a = -2$

20. $f(x) = \sqrt{1 + 9x};\ a = 7$ **21.** $f(x) = \dfrac{1}{\sqrt{2x + 3}};\ a = 3$ **22.** $f(x) = \dfrac{1}{\sqrt[3]{x}} - x;\ a = -8$

23. Given $f(x) = \sqrt[3]{x - 1}$, find $f'(x)$. Is f differentiable at 1? Draw a sketch of the graph of f.

24. Given $f(x) = \sqrt[3]{(4x - 3)^2}$, find $f'(x)$. Is f differentiable at $\frac{3}{4}$? Draw a sketch of the graph of f.

25. If g is continuous at a and $f(x) = (x - a)g(x)$, find $f'(a)$. (HINT: Use Eq. (5).)

26. Let f be a function whose domain is the set of all real numbers and $f(a + b) = f(a) \cdot f(b)$ for all a and b. Furthermore, suppose that $f(0) = 1$ and $f'(0)$ exists. Prove that $f'(x)$ exists for all x and that $f'(x) = f'(0) \cdot f(x)$.

27. If f is differentiable at a, prove that

$$f'(a) = \lim_{\Delta x \to 0} \frac{f(a + \Delta x) - f(a - \Delta x)}{2\,\Delta x}$$

(HINT: $f(a + \Delta x) - f(a - \Delta x) = f(a + \Delta x) - f(a) + f(a) - f(a - \Delta x)$.)

3.4 DIFFERENTIABILITY AND CONTINUITY

The function of Example 4 of Sec. 3.3 is continuous at the number zero but is not differentiable there. Hence, it may be concluded that continuity of a function at a number does not imply differentiability of the function at that number. However, differentiability *does* imply continuity, which is given by the next theorem.

3.4.1 Theorem If a function f is differentiable at x_1, then f is continuous at x_1.

PROOF: To prove that f is continuous at x_1, we must show that the three conditions of Definition 2.5.1 hold there. That is, we must show that (i) $f(x_1)$ exists; (ii) $\lim\limits_{x \to x_1} f(x)$ exists; and (iii) $\lim\limits_{x \to x_1} f(x) = f(x_1)$.

By hypothesis, f is differentiable at x_1. Therefore, $f'(x_1)$ exists. Because by formula (5) of Sec. 3.3

$$f'(x_1) = \lim_{x \to x_1} \frac{f(x) - f(x_1)}{x - x_1} \tag{1}$$

we conclude that $f(x_1)$ must exist; otherwise, the above limit has no meaning. Therefore, condition (i) holds at x_1. Now, let us consider

$$\lim_{x \to x_1} [f(x) - f(x_1)]$$

We can write

$$\lim_{x \to x_1} [f(x) - f(x_1)] = \lim_{x \to x_1} \left[(x - x_1) \cdot \frac{f(x) - f(x_1)}{x - x_1} \right] \tag{2}$$

Because

$$\lim_{x \to x_1} (x - x_1) = 0 \quad \text{and} \quad \lim_{x \to x_1} \frac{f(x) - f(x_1)}{x - x_1} = f'(x_1)$$

we apply the theorem on the limit of a product (Theorem 2. .6) to the right side of Eq. (2), and we have

$$\lim_{x \to x_1} [f(x) - f(x_1)] = \lim_{x \to x_1} (x - x_1) \cdot \lim_{x \to x_1} \frac{f(x) - f(x_1)}{x - x_1} = 0 \cdot f'(x_1)$$

so that

$$\lim_{x \to x_1} [f(x) - f(x_1)] = 0$$

Then we have

$$\lim_{x \to x_1} f(x) = \lim_{x \to x_1} [f(x) - f(x_1) + f(x_1)]$$

$$= \lim_{x \to x_1} [f(x) - f(x_1)] + \lim_{x \to x_1} f(x_1)$$

$$= 0 + f(x_1)$$

which gives us

$$\lim_{x \to x_1} f(x) = f(x_1) \tag{3}$$

From Eq. (3) we may conclude that conditions (ii) and (iii) for continuity of f at x_1 hold. Therefore, the theorem is proved. ∎

As previously stated, Example 4 of Sec. 3.3 shows that the converse of the above theorem is not true. Before giving an additional example of a function which is continuous at a number but which is not differentiable there, the concept of a *one-sided derivative* is introduced.

3.4.2 Definition If the function f is defined at x_1, then the *derivative from the right* of f at x_1, denoted by $f'_+(x_1)$, is defined by

$$f'_+(x_1) = \lim_{\Delta x \to 0^+} \frac{f(x_1 + \Delta x) - f(x_1)}{\Delta x} \tag{4}$$

or, equivalently,

$$f'_+(x_1) = \lim_{x \to x_1^+} \frac{f(x) - f(x_1)}{x - x_1} \qquad (5)$$

if the limit exists.

3.4.3 Definition   If the function f is defined at x_1, then the *derivative from the left* of f at x_1, denoted by $f'_-(x_1)$, is defined by

$$f'_-(x_1) = \lim_{\Delta x \to 0^-} \frac{f(x_1 + \Delta x) - f(x_1)}{\Delta x} \qquad (6)$$

or, equivalently,

$$f'_-(x_1) = \lim_{x \to x_1^-} \frac{f(x) - f(x_1)}{x - x_1} \qquad (7)$$

if the limit exists.

EXAMPLE 1:   Let f be the function defined by

$$f(x) = \begin{cases} 2x - 1 & \text{if } x < 3 \\ 8 - x & \text{if } 3 \leqslant x \end{cases}$$

(a) Draw a sketch of the graph of f. (b) Prove that f is continuous at 3. (c) Find $f'_-(3)$ and $f'_+(3)$. (d) Is f differentiable at 3?

y

$(3, 5)$

O x

Figure 3.4.1

SOLUTION: (a) A sketch of the graph is shown in Fig. 3.4.1.

(b) To prove that f is continuous at 3, we verify the three conditions for continuity at a number:

(i) $f(3) = 5$

(ii) $\lim_{x \to 3^-} f(x) = \lim_{x \to 3^-} (2x - 1) = 5$

$\lim_{x \to 3^+} f(x) = \lim_{x \to 3^+} (8 - x) = 5$

Therefore,

$\lim_{x \to 3} f(x) = 5$

(iii) $\lim_{x \to 3} f(x) = f(3)$

Because conditions (i), (ii), and (iii) all hold at 3, f is continuous at 3.

(c) $f'_-(3) = \lim_{\Delta x \to 0^-} \dfrac{f(3 + \Delta x) - f(3)}{\Delta x}$

$= \lim_{\Delta x \to 0^-} \dfrac{[2(3 + \Delta x) - 1] - 5}{\Delta x}$

$= \lim_{\Delta x \to 0^-} \dfrac{6 + 2\,\Delta x - 6}{\Delta x}$

$= \lim_{\Delta x \to 0^-} \dfrac{2\,\Delta x}{\Delta x}$

$= \lim_{\Delta x \to 0^-} 2$

$= 2$

$$f'_+(3) = \lim_{\Delta x \to 0^+} \frac{f(3 + \Delta x) - f(3)}{\Delta x}$$

$$= \lim_{\Delta x \to 0^+} \frac{[8 - (3 + \Delta x)] - 5}{\Delta x}$$

$$= \lim_{\Delta x \to 0^+} \frac{8 - 3 - \Delta x - 5}{\Delta x}$$

$$= \lim_{\Delta x \to 0^+} \frac{-\Delta x}{\Delta x}$$

$$= \lim_{\Delta x \to 0^+} (-1)$$

$$= -1$$

(d) Because

$$\lim_{\Delta x \to 0^-} \frac{f(3 + \Delta x) - f(3)}{\Delta x} \neq \lim_{\Delta x \to 0^+} \frac{f(3 + \Delta x) - f(3)}{\Delta x}$$

we conclude that

$$\lim_{\Delta x \to 0} \frac{f(3 + \Delta x) - f(3)}{\Delta x}$$

does not exist. Hence, f is not differentiable at 3. However, the derivative from the left and the derivative from the right both exist at 3.

The function in Example 1 gives us another illustration of a function which is continuous at a number but not differentiable there.

Exercises 3.4

In Exercises 1 through 14, do each of the following: (a) Draw a sketch of the graph of the function; (b) determine if f is continuous at x_1; (c) find $f'_-(x_1)$ and $f'_+(x_1)$ if they exist; (d) determine if f is differentiable at x_1.

1. $f(x) = \begin{cases} x + 2 & \text{if } x \leq -4 \\ -x - 6 & \text{if } x > -4 \end{cases}$

   $x_1 = -4$

2. $f(x) = \begin{cases} 3 - 2x & \text{if } x < 2 \\ 3x - 7 & \text{if } x \geq 2 \end{cases}$

   $x_1 = 2$

3. $f(x) = |x - 3|$; $x_1 = 3$

4. $f(x) = 1 + |x + 2|$; $x_1 = -2$

5. $f(x) = \begin{cases} -1 & \text{if } x < 0 \\ x - 1 & \text{if } x \geq 0 \end{cases}$

   $x_1 = 0$

6. $f(x) = \begin{cases} x & \text{if } x \leq 0 \\ x^2 & \text{if } x > 0 \end{cases}$

   $x_1 = 0$

7. $f(x) = \begin{cases} x^2 & \text{if } x \leq 0 \\ -x^2 & \text{if } x > 0 \end{cases}$

   $x_1 = 0$

8. $f(x) = \begin{cases} x^2 - 4 & \text{if } x < 2 \\ \sqrt{x - 2} & \text{if } x \geq 2 \end{cases}$

   $x_1 = 2$

9. $f(x) = \begin{cases} \sqrt{1-x} & \text{if } x < 1 \\ (1-x)^2 & \text{if } x \geq 1 \end{cases}$
$x_1 = 1$

10. $f(x) = \begin{cases} x^2 & \text{if } x < -1 \\ -1 - 2x & \text{if } x \geq -1 \end{cases}$
$x_1 = -1$

11. $f(x) = \sqrt[3]{x+1}$; $x_1 = -1$

12. $f(x) = (x-2)^{-2}$; $x_1 = 2$

13. $f(x) = \begin{cases} 5 - 6x & \text{if } x \leq 3 \\ -4 - x^2 & \text{if } x > 3 \end{cases}$
$x_1 = 3$

14. $f(x) = \begin{cases} -x^{2/3} & \text{if } x \leq 0 \\ x^{2/3} & \text{if } x > 0 \end{cases}$
$x_1 = 0$

15. Given $f(x) = |x|$, draw a sketch of the graph of f. Prove that f is continuous at 0. Prove that f is not differentiable at 0, but that $f'(x) = |x|/x$ for all $x \neq 0$. (HINT: Let $|x| = \sqrt{x^2}$.)

16. Given $f(x) = \sqrt{9 - x^2}$, prove that neither the derivative from the right at -3 nor the derivative from the left at 3 exist. Draw a sketch of the graph.

17. Given $f(x) = x^{3/2}$, prove that $f'_+(0)$ exists and find its value. Draw a sketch of the graph.

18. Given $f(x) = (1 - x^2)^{3/2}$, prove that $f'(x)$ exists for all values of x in the open interval $(-1, 1)$, and that both $f'_+(-1)$ and $f'_-(1)$ exist. Draw a sketch of the graph of f on $[-1, 1]$.

19. Find the values of a and b so that $f'(1)$ exists if

$$f(x) = \begin{cases} x^2 & \text{if } x < 1 \\ ax + b & \text{if } x \geq 1 \end{cases}$$

20. Given $f(x) = [\![x]\!]$, find $f'(x_1)$ if x_1 is not an integer. Prove by applying Theorem 3.4.1 that $f'(x_1)$ does not exist if x_1 is an integer. If x_1 is an integer, what can you say about $f'_-(x_1)$ and $f'_+(x_1)$?

21. Given $f(x) = (x - 1) [\![x]\!]$. Draw a sketch of the graph of f for x in $[0, 2]$. Find: (a) $f'_-(1)$; (b) $f'_+(1)$; (c) $f'(1)$.

22. Given

$$f(x) = \begin{cases} 0 & \text{if } x \leq 0 \\ x^n & \text{if } x > 0 \end{cases}$$

where n is a positive integer. (a) For what values of n is f differentiable for all values of x? (b) For what values of n is f' continuous for all values of x?

23. Given $f(x) = \text{sgn } x$. (a) Prove that $f'_+(0) = +\infty$ and $f'_-(0) = +\infty$. (b) Prove that $\lim\limits_{x \to 0^+} f'(x) = 0$ and $\lim\limits_{x \to 0^-} f'(x) = 0$.

24. Let the function f be defined by

$$f(x) = \begin{cases} \dfrac{g(x) - g(a)}{x - a} & \text{if } x \neq a \\ g'(a) & \text{if } x = a \end{cases}$$

Prove that if $g'(a)$ exists, f is continuous at a.

3.5 SOME THEOREMS ON DIFFERENTIATION OF ALGEBRAIC FUNCTIONS

The operation of finding the derivative of a function is called *differentiation*, which can be performed by applying Definition 3.3.1. However, because this process is usually rather lengthy, we state and prove some theorems which enable us to find the derivative of certain functions more easily. These theorems are proved by applying Definition 3.3.1. Following the proof of each theorem, we state the corresponding formula of differentiation.

3.5.1 Theorem   If c is a constant and if $f(x) = c$ for all x, then

$$f'(x) = 0$$

PROOF:

$$f'(x) = \lim_{\Delta x \to 0} \frac{f(x + \Delta x) - f(x)}{\Delta x}$$

$$= \lim_{\Delta x \to 0} \frac{c - c}{\Delta x}$$

$$= \lim_{\Delta x \to 0} 0$$

$$= 0 \qquad \blacksquare$$

$$D_x(c) = 0 \tag{1}$$

The derivative of a constant is zero.

● ILLUSTRATION 1: If $f(x) = 5$, then

$$f'(x) = 0$$ ●

3.5.2 Theorem   If n is a positive integer and if $f(x) = x^n$, then

$$f'(x) = nx^{n-1}$$

PROOF:

$$f'(x) = \lim_{\Delta x \to 0} \frac{f(x + \Delta x) - f(x)}{\Delta x}$$

$$= \lim_{\Delta x \to 0} \frac{(x + \Delta x)^n - x^n}{\Delta x}$$

Applying the binomial theorem to $(x + \Delta x)^n$, we have

$$f'(x) = \lim_{\Delta x \to 0} \frac{\left[x^n + nx^{n-1}\,\Delta x + \dfrac{n(n-1)}{2!}\,x^{n-2}(\Delta x)^2 + \cdots + nx(\Delta x)^{n-1} + (\Delta x)^n \right] - x^n}{\Delta x}$$

$$= \lim_{\Delta x \to 0} \frac{nx^{n-1}\,\Delta x + \dfrac{n(n-1)}{2!}\,x^{n-2}(\Delta x)^2 + \cdots + nx(\Delta x)^{n-1} + (\Delta x)^n}{\Delta x}$$

Dividing the numerator and the denominator by Δx, we have

$$f'(x) = \lim_{\Delta x \to 0} \left[nx^{n-1} + \frac{n(n-1)}{2!}\,x^{n-2}(\Delta x) + \cdots + nx(\Delta x)^{n-2} + (\Delta x)^{n-1} \right]$$

Every term, except the first, has a factor of Δx; therefore, every term, except the first, approaches zero as Δx approaches zero. So we obtain

$$f'(x) = nx^{n-1}$$ ∎

$$D_x(x^n) = nx^{n-1}$$ (2)

● ILLUSTRATION 2: (a) If $f(x) = x^8$, then

$$f'(x) = 8x^7$$

(b) If $f(x) = x$, then

$$f'(x) = 1 \cdot x^0$$
$$= 1 \cdot 1$$
$$= 1$$ ●

3.5.3 Theorem   If f is a function, c is a constant, and g is the function defined by

$$g(x) = c \cdot f(x)$$

then if $f'(x)$ exists,

$$g'(x) = c \cdot f'(x)$$

PROOF:

$$g'(x) = \lim_{\Delta x \to 0} \frac{g(x + \Delta x) - g(x)}{\Delta x}$$

$$= \lim_{\Delta x \to 0} \frac{cf(x + \Delta x) - cf(x)}{\Delta x}$$

$$= \lim_{\Delta x \to 0} c \cdot \left[\frac{f(x + \Delta x) - f(x)}{\Delta x} \right]$$

$$= c \cdot \lim_{\Delta x \to 0} \frac{f(x + \Delta x) - f(x)}{\Delta x}$$

$$= cf'(x)$$ ∎

$$D_x[c \cdot f(x)] = c \cdot D_x f(x)$$ (3)

The derivative of a constant times a function is the constant times the derivative of the function if this derivative exists.

By combining Theorems 3.5.2 and 3.5.3 we obtain the following result: If $f(x) = cx^n$, where n is a positive integer and c is a constant,

$$f'(x) = cnx^{n-1}$$

$$D_x(cx^n) = cnx^{n-1}$$ (4)

● ILLUSTRATION 3: If $f(x) = 5x^7$, then

$$f'(x) = 5 \cdot 7x^6$$
$$= 35x^6$$

3.5.4 Theorem   If f and g are functions and if h is the function defined by

$$h(x) = f(x) + g(x)$$

then if $f'(x)$ and $g'(x)$ exist,

$$h'(x) = f'(x) + g'(x)$$

PROOF:

$$h'(x) = \lim_{\Delta x \to 0} \frac{h(x + \Delta x) - h(x)}{\Delta x}$$

$$= \lim_{\Delta x \to 0} \frac{[f(x + \Delta x) + g(x + \Delta x)] - [f(x) + g(x)]}{\Delta x}$$

$$= \lim_{\Delta x \to 0} \frac{[f(x + \Delta x) - f(x)] + [g(x + \Delta x) - g(x)]}{\Delta x}$$

$$= \lim_{\Delta x \to 0} \frac{f(x + \Delta x) - f(x)}{\Delta x} + \lim_{\Delta x \to 0} \frac{g(x + \Delta x) - g(x)}{\Delta x}$$

$$= f'(x) + g'(x) \qquad\blacksquare$$

$$D_x[f(x) + g(x)] = D_x f(x) + D_x g(x) \tag{5}$$

The derivative of the sum of two functions is the sum of their derivatives if these derivatives exist.

The result of the preceding theorem can be extended to any finite number of functions, by mathematical induction, and this is stated as another theorem.

3.5.5 Theorem   The derivative of the sum of a finite number of functions is equal to the sum of their derivatives if these derivatives exist.

From the preceding theorems the derivative of any polynomial function can be found easily.

EXAMPLE 1: Given

$$f(x) = 7x^4 - 2x^3 + 8x + 5$$

find $f'(x)$.

SOLUTION:

$$f'(x) = D_x(7x^4 - 2x^3 + 8x + 5)$$

$$= D_x(7x^4) + D_x(-2x^3) + D_x(8x) + D_x(5)$$

$$= 28x^3 - 6x^2 + 8$$

3.5.6 Theorem   If f and g are functions and if h is the function defined by

$$h(x) = f(x)g(x)$$

then if $f'(x)$ and $g'(x)$ exist,

$$h'(x) = f(x)g'(x) + g(x)f'(x)$$

PROOF:

$$h'(x) = \lim_{\Delta x \to 0} \frac{h(x + \Delta x) - h(x)}{\Delta x}$$

$$= \lim_{\Delta x \to 0} \frac{f(x + \Delta x) \cdot g(x + \Delta x) - f(x) \cdot g(x)}{\Delta x}$$

We subtract and add $f(x + \Delta x) \cdot g(x)$ in the numerator, thereby giving us

$$h'(x) = \lim_{\Delta x \to 0} \frac{f(x+\Delta x) \cdot g(x+\Delta x) - f(x+\Delta x) \cdot g(x) + f(x+\Delta x) \cdot g(x) - f(x) \cdot g(x)}{\Delta x}$$

$$= \lim_{\Delta x \to 0} \left[f(x + \Delta x) \cdot \frac{g(x + \Delta x) - g(x)}{\Delta x} + g(x) \cdot \frac{f(x + \Delta x) - f(x)}{\Delta x} \right]$$

$$= \lim_{\Delta x \to 0} \left[f(x + \Delta x) \cdot \frac{g(x + \Delta x) - g(x)}{\Delta x} \right]$$

$$+ \lim_{\Delta x \to 0} \left[g(x) \cdot \frac{f(x + \Delta x) - f(x)}{\Delta x} \right]$$

$$= \lim_{\Delta x \to 0} f(x + \Delta x) \cdot \lim_{\Delta x \to 0} \frac{g(x + \Delta x) - g(x)}{\Delta x}$$

$$+ \lim_{\Delta x \to 0} g(x) \cdot \lim_{\Delta x \to 0} \frac{f(x + \Delta x) - f(x)}{\Delta x}$$

Because f is differentiable at x, by Theorem 3.4.1, f is continuous at x; therefore, $\lim_{\Delta x \to 0} f(x + \Delta x) = f(x)$. Also,

$$\lim_{\Delta x \to 0} \frac{g(x + \Delta x) - g(x)}{\Delta x} = g'(x)$$

$$\lim_{\Delta x \to 0} \frac{f(x + \Delta x) - f(x)}{\Delta x} = f'(x)$$

and

$$\lim_{\Delta x \to 0} g(x) = g(x)$$

thus giving us

$$h'(x) = f(x)g'(x) + g(x)f'(x) \qquad \blacksquare$$

$$D_x[f(x)g(x)] = f(x) \cdot D_x g(x) + g(x) \cdot D_x f(x) \tag{6}$$

The derivative of the product of two functions is the first function times the derivative of the second function plus the second function times the derivative of the first function if these derivatives exist.

EXAMPLE 2:   Given

$$h(x) = (2x^3 - 4x^2)(3x^5 + x^2)$$

find $h'(x)$.

SOLUTION:

$$h'(x) = (2x^3 - 4x^2)(15x^4 + 2x) + (3x^5 + x^2)(6x^2 - 8x)$$

$$= (30x^7 - 60x^6 + 4x^4 - 8x^3) + (18x^7 - 24x^6 + 6x^4 - 8x^3)$$

$$= 48x^7 - 84x^6 + 10x^4 - 16x^3$$

In Example 2, note that if we multiply first and then perform the differentiation, the same result is obtained. Doing this, we have

$$h(x) = 6x^8 - 12x^7 + 2x^5 - 4x^4$$

Thus,

$$h'(x) = 48x^7 - 84x^6 + 10x^4 - 16x^3$$

3.5.7 Theorem   If f and g are functions and if h is the function defined by

$$h(x) = \frac{f(x)}{g(x)} \qquad \text{where } g(x) \neq 0$$

then if $f'(x)$ and $g'(x)$ exist,

$$h'(x) = \frac{g(x)f'(x) - f(x)g'(x)}{[g(x)]^2}$$

PROOF:

$$h'(x) = \lim_{\Delta x \to 0} \frac{h(x + \Delta x) - h(x)}{\Delta x}$$

$$= \lim_{\Delta x \to 0} \frac{\dfrac{f(x + \Delta x)}{g(x + \Delta x)} - \dfrac{f(x)}{g(x)}}{\Delta x}$$

$$= \lim_{\Delta x \to 0} \frac{f(x + \Delta x) \cdot g(x) - f(x) \cdot g(x + \Delta x)}{\Delta x \cdot g(x) \cdot g(x + \Delta x)}$$

Subtracting and adding $f(x) \cdot g(x)$ in the numerator, we obtain

$$h'(x) = \lim_{\Delta x \to 0} \frac{f(x + \Delta x) \cdot g(x) - f(x) \cdot g(x) - f(x) \cdot g(x + \Delta x) + f(x) \cdot g(x)}{\Delta x \cdot g(x) \cdot g(x + \Delta x)}$$

$$= \lim_{\Delta x \to 0} \frac{\left[g(x) \cdot \dfrac{f(x + \Delta x) - f(x)}{\Delta x} \right] - \left[f(x) \cdot \dfrac{g(x + \Delta x) - g(x)}{\Delta x} \right]}{g(x) \cdot g(x + \Delta x)}$$

$$= \frac{\lim\limits_{\Delta x \to 0} g(x) \cdot \lim\limits_{\Delta x \to 0} \dfrac{f(x + \Delta x) - f(x)}{\Delta x} - \lim\limits_{\Delta x \to 0} f(x) \cdot \lim\limits_{\Delta x \to 0} \dfrac{g(x + \Delta x) - g(x)}{\Delta x}}{\lim\limits_{\Delta x \to 0} g(x) \cdot \lim\limits_{\Delta x \to 0} g(x + \Delta x)}$$

$$= \frac{g(x) \cdot f'(x) - f(x) \cdot g'(x)}{g(x) \cdot g(x)}$$

$$= \frac{g(x) f'(x) - f(x) g'(x)}{[g(x)]^2}$$

■

$$D_x \left[\frac{f(x)}{g(x)} \right] = \frac{g(x) D_x f(x) - f(x) D_x g(x)}{[g(x)]^2} \qquad (7)$$

The derivative of the quotient of two functions is the fraction having as its denominator the square of the original denominator, and as its numerator the denominator times the derivative of the numerator minus the numerator times the derivative of the denominator if these derivatives exist.

EXAMPLE 3: Given

$$h(x) = \frac{2x^3 + 4}{x^2 - 4x + 1}$$

find $h'(x)$.

SOLUTION:

$$h'(x) = \frac{(x^2 - 4x + 1)(6x^2) - (2x^3 + 4)(2x - 4)}{(x^2 - 4x + 1)^2}$$

$$= \frac{6x^4 - 24x^3 + 6x^2 - 4x^4 + 8x^3 - 8x + 16}{(x^2 - 4x + 1)^2}$$

$$= \frac{2x^4 - 16x^3 + 6x^2 - 8x + 16}{(x^2 - 4x + 1)^2}$$

3.5.8 Theorem If $f(x) = x^{-n}$, where $-n$ is a negative integer and $x \neq 0$, then

$$f'(x) = -nx^{-n-1}$$

PROOF: If $-n$ is a negative integer, then n is a positive integer. We write

$$f(x) = \frac{1}{x^n}$$

Applying Theorem 3.5.7, we have

$$f'(x) = \frac{x^n \cdot 0 - 1 \cdot nx^{n-1}}{(x^n)^2} = \frac{-nx^{n-1}}{x^{2n}} = -nx^{n-1-2n}$$

$$= -nx^{-n-1}$$

■

EXAMPLE 4: Given

$$f(x) = \frac{3}{x^5}$$

find $f'(x)$.

SOLUTION: $f(x) = 3x^{-5}$. Hence,

$$f'(x) = 3(-5x^{-6}) = -15x^{-6} = -\frac{15}{x^6}$$

If r is any positive or negative integer it follows from Theorems 3.5.2 and 3.5.8 that

$$D_x(x^r) = rx^{r-1} \qquad (8)$$

and from Theorems 3.5.2, 3.5.3, and 3.5.8 we obtain

$$D_x(cx^r) = crx^{r-1} \qquad (9)$$

Exercises 3.5

In Exercises 1 through 26, differentiate the given function by applying the theorems of this section.

1. $f(x) = x^3 - 3x^2 + 5x - 2$

2. $f(x) = 3x^4 - 5x^2 + 1$

3. $f(x) = \frac{1}{8}x^8 - x^4$

4. $g(x) = x^7 - 2x^5 + 5x^3 - 7x$

5. $F(t) = \frac{1}{4}t^4 - \frac{1}{2}t^2$

6. $H(x) = \frac{1}{3}x^3 - x + 2$

7. $v(r) = \frac{4}{3}\pi r^3$

8. $G(y) = y^{10} + 7y^5 - y^3 + 1$

9. $F(x) = x^2 + 3x + \dfrac{1}{x^2}$

10. $f(x) = x^4 - 5 + x^{-2} + 4x^{-4}$

11. $g(x) = \dfrac{3}{x^2} + \dfrac{5}{x^4}$

12. $H(x) = \dfrac{5}{6x^5}$

13. $f(s) = \sqrt{3}(s^3 - s^2)$

14. $g(x) = (2x^2 + 5)(4x - 1)$

15. $f(x) = (2x^4 - 1)(5x^3 + 6x)$

16. $g(x) = (4x^2 + 3)^2$

17. $H(x) = \dfrac{x^2 + 2x + 1}{x^2 - 2x + 1}$

18. $F(y) = \dfrac{2y + 1}{3y + 4}$

19. $f(x) = \dfrac{x}{x - 1}$

20. $f(x) = (x^2 - 3x + 2)(2x^3 + 1)$

21. $h(x) = \dfrac{5x}{1 + 2x^2}$

22. $g(x) = \dfrac{x^4 - 2x^2 + 5x + 1}{x^4}$

23. $f(x) = \dfrac{x^3 - 8}{x^3 + 8}$

24. $f(x) = \dfrac{x^2 - a^2}{x^2 + a^2}$

25. $f(x) = \dfrac{2x + 1}{x + 5}(3x - 1)$

26. $g(x) = \dfrac{x^3 + 1}{x^2 + 3}(x^2 - 2x^{-1} + 1)$

27. If f, g, and h are functions and if $\phi(x) = f(x) \cdot g(x) \cdot h(x)$, prove that if $f'(x)$, $g'(x)$, and $h'(x)$ exist, $\phi'(x) = f(x) \cdot g(x) \cdot h'(x) + f(x) \cdot g'(x) \cdot h(x) + f'(x) \cdot g(x) \cdot h(x)$. (HINT: Apply Theorem 3.5.6 twice.)

Use the result of Exercise 27 to differentiate the functions in Exercises 28 through 31.

28. $f(x) = (x^2 + 3)(2x - 5)(3x + 2)$

29. $h(x) = (3x + 2)^2(x^2 - 1)$

30. $g(x) = (3x^3 + x^{-3})(x + 3)(x^2 - 5)$

31. $\phi(x) = (2x^2 + x + 1)^3$

32. Find an equation of the tangent line to the curve $y = 8/(x^2 + 4)$ at the point $(2, 1)$.

33. Find an equation of each of the lines through the point $(-1, 2)$ which is a tangent line to the curve $y = (x - 1)/(x + 3)$.

34. Find an equation of each of the tangent lines to the curve $3y = x^3 - 3x^2 + 6x + 4$, which is parallel to the line $2x - y + 3 = 0$.

35. Find an equation of each of the normal lines to the curve $y = x^3 - 4x$ which is parallel to the line $x + 8y - 8 = 0$.

36. An object is moving along a straight line according to the equation of motion $s = 3t/(t^2 + 9)$, with $t \geq 0$, where s ft is the directed distance of the object from the starting point at t sec. (a) What is the instantaneous velocity of the object at t_1 sec? (b) What is the instantaneous velocity at 1 sec? (c) At what time is the instantaneous velocity zero?

3.6 THE DERIVATIVE OF A COMPOSITE FUNCTION

Suppose that y is a function of u and u, in turn, is a function of x. For example, let

$$y = f(u) = u^5 \tag{1}$$

and

$$u = g(x) = 2x^3 - 5x^2 + 4 \tag{2}$$

Equations (1) and (2) together define y as a function of x because if we replace u in (1) by the right side of (2) we have

$$y = h(x) = f(g(x)) = (2x^3 - 5x^2 + 4)^5$$

where h is a composite function which was defined previously (refer to Definition 1.8.2).

We now state and prove a theorem for finding the derivative of a composite function. This theorem is known as the *chain rule*.

3.6.1 Theorem
Chain Rule

If y is a function of u, defined by $y = f(u)$, and $D_u y$ exists, and if u is a function of x, defined by $u = g(x)$, and $D_x u$ exists, then y is a function of x and $D_x y$ exists and is given by

$$D_x y = D_u y \cdot D_x u$$

PROOF: From Eq. (6) of Sec. 3.3, we have

$$D_u y = \lim_{\Delta u \to 0} \frac{\Delta y}{\Delta u}$$

Hence, when $|\Delta u|$ is small (close to zero but not equal to zero) the difference

$$\frac{\Delta y}{\Delta u} - D_u y$$

is numerically small. Denoting the difference by η, we have

$$\eta = \frac{\Delta y}{\Delta u} - D_u y \qquad \text{if } \Delta u \neq 0$$

The above equation defines η as a function of Δu, provided that $\Delta u \neq 0$. Letting $\eta = F(\Delta u)$, we obtain

$$F(\Delta u) = \frac{\Delta y}{\Delta u} - D_u y \qquad \text{if } \Delta u \neq 0 \tag{3}$$

Equation (3) defines $F(\Delta u)$ provided that $\Delta u \neq 0$. In a later part of this proof, we want the function F to be continuous at 0. Thus, we define $F(0)$ to be $\lim_{\Delta u \to 0} F(\Delta u)$. From Eq. (3) we have

$$\lim_{\Delta u \to 0} F(\Delta u) = \lim_{\Delta u \to 0} \frac{\Delta y}{\Delta u} - \lim_{\Delta u \to 0} D_u y$$

$$= D_u y - D_u y$$

$$= 0$$

Hence, we define $F(0) = 0$, and we have

$$F(\Delta u) = \begin{cases} \dfrac{\Delta y}{\Delta u} - D_u y & \text{if } \Delta u \neq 0 \\ 0 & \text{if } \Delta u = 0 \end{cases}$$

Solving Eq. (3) for Δy, we obtain

$$\Delta y = D_u y \cdot \Delta u + \Delta u \cdot F(\Delta u) \qquad \text{if } \Delta u \neq 0 \tag{4}$$

Note that Eq. (4) also holds if $\Delta u = 0$ because we have $\Delta y = 0$ (remember that $\Delta y = f(u + \Delta u) - f(u)$).

Dividing on both sides of Eq. (4) by Δx, where $\Delta x \neq 0$, we obtain

$$\frac{\Delta y}{\Delta x} = D_u y \cdot \frac{\Delta u}{\Delta x} + \frac{\Delta u}{\Delta x} \cdot F(\Delta u)$$

Taking the limit on both sides of the above equation as Δx approaches zero and applying limit theorems, we have

$$\lim_{\Delta x \to 0} \frac{\Delta y}{\Delta x} = \lim_{\Delta x \to 0} D_u y \cdot \lim_{\Delta x \to 0} \frac{\Delta u}{\Delta x} + \lim_{\Delta x \to 0} \frac{\Delta u}{\Delta x} \cdot \lim_{\Delta x \to 0} F(\Delta u)$$

Hence,

$$D_x y = D_u y \cdot D_x u + D_x u \cdot \lim_{\Delta x \to 0} F(\Delta u) \tag{5}$$

We now show that $\lim_{\Delta x \to 0} F(\Delta u) = 0$ by making use of Theorem 2.6.5. We first express Δu as a function of Δx. Because

$$\lim_{\Delta x \to 0} \frac{\Delta u}{\Delta x} = D_x u$$

it follows that when $|\Delta x|$ is small and $\Delta x \neq 0$, $\Delta u / \Delta x$ differs from $D_x u$ by a small number which depends on Δx, which we call $\phi(\Delta x)$. Hence, we write

$$\frac{\Delta u}{\Delta x} = D_x u + \phi(\Delta x) \qquad \text{if } \Delta x \neq 0$$

and multiplying by Δx we obtain

$$\Delta u = D_x u \cdot \Delta x + \phi(\Delta x) \cdot \Delta x \qquad \text{if } \Delta x \neq 0$$

The above equation expresses Δu as a function of Δx. Calling this function G, we have

$$G(\Delta x) = D_x u \cdot \Delta x + \phi(\Delta x) \cdot \Delta x \qquad \text{if } \Delta x \neq 0$$

Hence, $F(\Delta u) = F(G(\Delta x))$, and

$$\lim_{\Delta x \to 0} F(\Delta u) = \lim_{\Delta x \to 0} F(G(\Delta x))$$

Because $\lim_{\Delta x \to 0} G(\Delta x) = 0$ and F is continuous at 0 (remember that we made it so), we can apply Theorem 2.6.5, to the right side of the above equation and we have

$$\lim_{\Delta x \to 0} F(\Delta u) = F(\lim_{\Delta x \to 0} G(\Delta x))$$

$$= F(0)$$

$$= 0$$

So in Eq. (5) if we replace $\lim_{\Delta x \to 0} F(\Delta u)$ by 0, we obtain

$$D_x y = D_u y \cdot D_x u + D_x u \cdot 0$$

Thus,

$$D_x y = D_u y \cdot D_x u \qquad \blacksquare$$

In the following example, we apply the chain rule to the function given at the beginning of this section.

EXAMPLE 1: Given

$$y = (2x^3 - 5x^2 + 4)^5$$

find $D_x y$.

SOLUTION: Considering y as a function of u, where u is a function of x, we have

$$y = u^5 \qquad \text{where } u = 2x^3 - 5x^2 + 4$$

Therefore, from the chain rule,

$$D_x y = D_u y \cdot D_x u = 5u^4(6x^2 - 10x)$$

$$= 5(2x^3 - 5x^2 + 4)^4(6x^2 - 10x)$$

EXAMPLE 2: Given

$$f(x) = \frac{1}{4x^3 + 5x^2 - 7x + 8}$$

find $f'(x)$.

SOLUTION: Write $f(x) = (4x^3 + 5x^2 - 7x + 8)^{-1}$, and apply the chain rule to obtain

$$f'(x) = -1(4x^3 + 5x^2 - 7x + 8)^{-2}(12x^2 + 10x - 7)$$

$$= \frac{-12x^2 - 10x + 7}{(4x^3 + 5x^2 - 7x + 8)^2}$$

EXAMPLE 3: Given

$$f(x) = \left(\frac{2x + 1}{3x - 1}\right)^4$$

find $f'(x)$.

SOLUTION: Applying the chain rule, we have

$$f'(x) = 4\left(\frac{2x + 1}{3x - 1}\right)^3 \frac{(3x - 1)(2) - (2x + 1)(3)}{(3x - 1)^2}$$

$$= \frac{4(2x + 1)^3(-5)}{(3x - 1)^5}$$

$$= -\frac{20(2x + 1)^3}{(3x - 1)^5}$$

EXAMPLE 4:   Given
$$f(x) = (3x^2 + 2)^2(x^2 - 5x)^3$$
find $f'(x)$.

SOLUTION: Consider f as the product of the two functions g and h, where
$$g(x) = (3x^2 + 2)^2 \quad \text{and} \quad h(x) = (x^2 - 5x)^3$$

Using Theorem 3.5.6 for the derivative of the product of two functions, we have
$$f'(x) = g(x)h'(x) + h(x)g'(x)$$

We find $h'(x)$ and $g'(x)$ by the chain rule, thus giving us
$$f'(x) = (3x^2 + 2)^2[3(x^2 - 5x)^2(2x - 5)] + (x^2 - 5x)^3[2(3x^2 + 2)(6x)]$$
$$= 3(3x^2 + 2)(x^2 - 5x)^2[(3x^2 + 2)(2x - 5) + 4x(x^2 - 5x)]$$
$$= 3(3x^2 + 2)(x^2 - 5x)^2[6x^3 - 15x^2 + 4x - 10 + 4x^3 - 20x^2]$$
$$= 3(3x^2 + 2)(x^2 - 5x)^2(10x^3 - 35x^2 + 4x - 10)$$

Exercises 3.6

In Exercises 1 through 20, find the derivative of the given function.

1. $F(x) = (x^2 + 4x - 5)^3$

2. $f(x) = (10 - 5x)^4$

3. $f(t) = (2t^4 - 7t^3 + 2t - 1)^2$

4. $g(r) = (2r^4 + 8r^2 + 1)^5$

5. $f(x) = (x + 4)^{-2}$

6. $H(z) = (z^3 - 3z^2 + 1)^{-3}$

7. $h(u) = (3u^2 + 5)^3(3u - 1)^2$

8. $f(x) = (4x^2 + 7)^2(2x^3 + 1)^4$

9. $g(x) = (2x - 5)^{-1}(4x + 3)^{-2}$

10. $f(x) = (x^2 - 4x^{-2})^2(x^2 + 1)^{-1}$

11. $f(y) = \left(\dfrac{y - 7}{y + 2}\right)^2$

12. $g(t) = \left(\dfrac{2t^2 + 1}{3t^3 + 1}\right)^2$

13. $f(x) = \dfrac{2}{7x^2 + 3x - 1}$

14. $h(x) = \left(\dfrac{x + 4}{2x^2 - 5x + 6}\right)^3$

15. $f(r) = (r^2 + 1)^3(2r + 5)^2$

16. $f(y) = (y + 3)^3(5y + 1)^2(3y^2 - 4)$

17. $f(z) = \dfrac{(z^2 - 5)^3}{(z^2 + 4)^2}$

18. $g(x) = (2x - 9)^2(x^3 + 4x - 5)^3$

19. $G(x) = \dfrac{(4x - 1)^3(x^2 + 2)^4}{(3x^2 + 5)^2}$

20. $F(x) = \dfrac{(5x - 8)^{-2}}{(x^2 + 3)^{-3}}$

21. A particle is moving along a straight line according to the equation of motion $s = [(t^2 - 1)/(t^2 + 1)]^2$, with $t \geq 0$, where s ft is the directed distance of the particle from the origin at t sec. (a) What is the instantaneous velocity of the particle at t_1 sec? (b) What is the instantaneous velocity of the particle at 1 sec? (c) What is the instantaneous velocity at $\frac{3}{2}$ sec?

22. Find an equation of the tangent line to the curve $y = 2/(4 - x)^2$ at each of the following points: $(0, \frac{1}{8})$, $(1, \frac{2}{9})$, $(2, \frac{1}{2})$, $(3, 2)$, $(5, 2)$, $(6, \frac{1}{2})$. Draw a sketch of the graph and segments of the tangent lines at the given points.

23. Find an equation of the normal line to the curve $y = 2/(x^2 - 2x - 4)^2$ at the point $(3, 2)$.

24. Find an equation of the tangent line to the curve $y = (x^2 - 4)^2/(3x - 5)^2$ at the point $(1, \frac{9}{4})$.

25. Given $f(x) = x^3$ and $g(x) = f(x^2)$. Find: (a) $f'(x^2)$; (b) $g'(x)$.

26. Given $f(u) = u^2 + 5u + 5$ and $g(x) = (x + 1)/(x - 1)$. Find the derivative of $f \circ g$ in two ways: (a) by first finding $(f \circ g)(x)$ and then finding $(f \circ g)'(x)$; (b) by using the chain rule.

27. Suppose that f and g are two functions such that (i) $g'(x_1)$ and $f'(g(x_1))$ exist and (ii) for all $x \neq x_1$ in some open interval containing x_1, $g(x) - g(x_1) \neq 0$. Then

$$\frac{(f \circ g)(x) - (f \circ g)(x_1)}{x - x_1} = \frac{(f \circ g)(x) - (f \circ g)(x_1)}{g(x) - g(x_1)} \cdot \frac{g(x) - g(x_1)}{x - x_1} \tag{6}$$

(a) Prove that as $x \to x_1$, $g(x) \to g(x_1)$ and hence that

$$(f \circ g)'(x_1) = f'(g(x_1))g'(x_1)$$

thus simplifying the proof of the chain rule under the additional hypothesis (ii); (b) Show that the proof of the chain rule given in part (a) applies if $f(u) = u^2$ and $g(x) = x^3$, but that it does not apply if $f(u) = u^2$ and $g(x) = \operatorname{sgn} x$.

28. Use the chain rule to prove that (a) the derivative of an even function is an odd function, and (b) the derivative of an odd function is an even function, provided that these derivatives exist.

29. Use the result of Exercise 28(a) to prove that if g is an even function and $g'(x)$ exists, then if $h(x) = (f \circ g)(x)$ and f is differentiable everywhere, $h'(0) = 0$.

30. Suppose that f and g are functions such that $f'(x) = 1/x$ and $f(g(x)) = x$. Prove that if $g'(x)$ exists then $g'(x) = g(x)$.

31. Suppose that y is a function of v, v is a function of u, and u is a function of x, and that the derivatives $D_v y$, $D_u v$, and $D_x u$ all exist. Prove the chain rule for three functions:

$$D_x y = (D_v y)(D_u v)(D_x u)$$

3.7 THE DERIVATIVE OF THE POWER FUNCTION FOR RATIONAL EXPONENTS

The function f defined by

$$f(x) = x^r \tag{1}$$

is called the *power function*. In Sec. 3.5 we obtained the following formula for the derivative of this function when r is a positive or negative integer:

$$f'(x) = rx^{r-1} \tag{2}$$

We now show that this formula holds when r is a rational number, with certain stipulations when $x = 0$.

We first consider $x \neq 0$, and $r = 1/q$, where q is a positive integer. Equation (1) then can be written

$$f(x) = x^{1/q}$$

From Definition 3.3.1, we have

$$f'(x) = \lim_{\Delta x \to 0} \frac{(x + \Delta x)^{1/q} - x^{1/q}}{\Delta x} \tag{3}$$

To evaluate the limit in Eq. (3) we must rationalize the numerator. To do this, we use formula (7) in Sec. 2.2, which is

$$a^n - b^n = (a - b)(a^{n-1} + a^{n-2}b + a^{n-3}b^2 + \cdots + a^2 b^{n-3} + ab^{n-2} + b^{n-1}) \tag{4}$$

So we rationalize the numerator of the fraction in Eq. (3) by applying

Eq. (4), where $a = (x + \Delta x)^{1/q}$, $b = x^{1/q}$, and $n = q$. So we multiply the numerator and denominator by

$$[(x + \Delta x)^{1/q}]^{(q-1)} + [(x + \Delta x)^{1/q}]^{(q-2)}x^{1/q} + \cdots$$
$$+ (x + \Delta x)^{1/q}(x^{1/q})^{(q-2)} + (x^{1/q})^{(q-1)}$$

We have, then, from Eq. (3), $f'(x)$ equals

$$\lim_{\Delta x \to 0} \frac{[(x + \Delta x)^{1/q} - x^{1/q}][(x + \Delta x)^{(q-1)/q} + (x + \Delta x)^{(q-2)/q}x^{1/q} + \cdots + x^{(q-1)/q}]}{\Delta x[(x + \Delta x)^{(q-1)/q} + (x + \Delta x)^{(q-2)/q}x^{1/q} + \cdots + x^{(q-1)/q}]} \tag{5}$$

and now applying Eq. (4) to the numerator we get $(x + \Delta x)^{q/q} - x^{q/q}$, which is Δx. So from (5) we obtain

$$f'(x) = \lim_{\Delta x \to 0} \frac{\Delta x}{\Delta x[(x + \Delta x)^{(q-1)/q} + (x + \Delta x)^{(q-2)/q}x^{1/q} + \cdots + x^{(q-1)/q}]}$$

$$= \lim_{\Delta x \to 0} \frac{1}{(x + \Delta x)^{(q-1)/q} + (x + \Delta x)^{(q-2)/q}x^{1/q} + \cdots + x^{(q-1)/q}}$$

$$= \frac{1}{x^{(q-1)/q} + x^{(q-1)/q} + \cdots + x^{(q-1)/q}}$$

Because there are exactly q terms in the denominator of the above fraction, we have

$$f'(x) = \frac{1}{qx^{1-(1/q)}}$$

or, equivalently,

$$f'(x) = \frac{1}{q} x^{1/q-1} \tag{6}$$

which is formula (2) with $r = 1/q$.

Now, in Eq. (1) with $x \neq 0$, let $r = p/q$, where p is any nonzero integer, and q is any positive integer; that is, r is any rational number except zero. Then Eq. (1) is written as

$$f(x) = x^{p/q}$$

or, equivalently,

$$f(x) = (x^{1/q})^p$$

Because p is either a positive or negative integer, we have, from the chain rule and Theorems 3.5.2 and 3.5.8,

$$f'(x) = p(x^{1/q})^{p-1} \cdot D_x(x^{1/q})$$

Applying formula (6) for $D_x(x^{1/q})$, we get

$$f'(x) = p(x^{1/q})^{p-1} \cdot \frac{1}{q} x^{1/q-1}$$

$$f'(x) = \frac{p}{q} x^{p/q - 1/q + 1/q - 1}$$

$$f'(x) = \frac{p}{q} x^{p/q - 1} \qquad (7)$$

Formula (7) is the same as formula (2) with $r = p/q$.

If $r = 0$, and $x \neq 0$, Eq. (1) becomes $f(x) = x^0 = 1$. In this case $f'(x) = 0$, which can be written as $f'(x) = 0 \cdot x^{0-1}$. Therefore, formula (2) holds if $r = 0$ with $x \neq 0$. We have therefore shown that formula (2) holds when r is any rational number and $x \neq 0$.

Now 0 is in the domain of the power function f if and only if r is a positive number because when $r \leq 0$, $f(0)$ is not defined. Hence, we wish to determine for what positive values of r, $f'(0)$ will be given by formula (2). We must exclude the numbers in the interval $(0, 1]$ because for those values of r, x^{r-1} is not a real number when $x = 0$. Suppose, then, that $r > 1$. By the definition of a derivative

$$f'(0) = \lim_{x \to 0} \frac{x^r - 0^r}{x - 0} = \lim_{x \to 0} x^{r-1}$$

When $r > 1$, $\lim\limits_{x \to 0} x^{r-1}$ exists and equals 0 provided that r is a number such that x^{r-1} is defined on some open interval containing 0. For example, if $r = \frac{3}{2}$, $x^{r-1} = x^{3/2 - 1} = x^{1/2}$, which is not defined on any open interval containing 0 (since $x^{1/2}$ does not exist when $x < 0$). However, if $r = \frac{5}{3}$, $x^{r-1} = x^{5/3 - 1} = x^{2/3}$, which is defined on every open interval containing 0. Hence, we conclude that formula (2) gives the derivative of the power function when $x = 0$ provided that r is a number for which x^{r-1} is defined on some open interval containing 0. Thus, we have proved the following theorem.

3.7.1 Theorem If f is the power function, where r is any rational number (i.e., $f(x) = x^r$), then

$$f'(x) = rx^{r-1}$$

For this formula to give $f'(0)$, r must be a number such that x^{r-1} is defined on some open interval containing 0.

An immediate consequence of Theorem 3.7.1 and the chain rule is the following theorem.

3.7.2 Theorem If f and g are functions such that $f(x) = [g(x)]^r$, where r is any rational number, and if $g'(x)$ exists, then

$$f'(x) = r[g(x)]^{r-1} g'(x)$$

For this formula to give $f'(0)$, r must be a number such that $[g(x)]^{r-1}$ is defined on some open interval containing 0.

EXAMPLE 1:   Given
$$f(x) = 4\sqrt[3]{x^2}$$
find $f'(x)$.

SOLUTION: $f(x) = 4x^{2/3}$.
Applying Theorem 3.7.1, we find

$$f'(x) = 4 \cdot \frac{2}{3} [x^{2/3-1}]$$

$$= \frac{8}{3} x^{-1/3}$$

$$= \frac{8}{3x^{1/3}}$$

$$= \frac{8}{3\sqrt[3]{x}}$$

EXAMPLE 2:   Given
$$h(x) = \sqrt{2x^3 - 4x + 5}$$
find $h'(x)$.

SOLUTION: $h(x) = (2x^3 - 4x + 5)^{1/2}$.
Applying Theorem 3.7.2, we have
$$h'(x) = \tfrac{1}{2}(2x^3 - 4x + 5)^{-1/2}(6x^2 - 4)$$

$$= \frac{3x^2 - 2}{\sqrt{2x^3 - 4x + 5}}$$

EXAMPLE 3:   Given
$$g(x) = \frac{x^3}{\sqrt[3]{3x^2 - 1}}$$
find $g'(x)$.

SOLUTION: Writing the given fraction as a product we have
$$g(x) = x^3(3x^2 - 1)^{-1/3}$$
Using Theorems 3.5.6 and 3.7.2, we have
$$g'(x) = 3x^2(3x^2 - 1)^{-1/3} - \tfrac{1}{3}(3x^2 - 1)^{-4/3}(6x)(x^3)$$
$$= x^2(3x^2 - 1)^{-4/3}[3(3x^2 - 1) - 2x^2]$$
$$= \frac{x^2(7x^2 - 3)}{(3x^2 - 1)^{4/3}}$$

Exercises 3.7

In Exercises 1 through 18, find the derivative of the given function.

1. $f(x) = (3x + 5)^{2/3}$

2. $f(s) = \sqrt{2 - 3s^2}$

3. $g(x) = \sqrt{\dfrac{2x - 5}{3x + 1}}$

4. $h(t) = \dfrac{\sqrt{t - 1}}{\sqrt{t + 1}}$

5. $f(x) = 4x^{1/2} + 5x^{-1/2}$

6. $g(y) = (y^2 + 3)^{1/3}(y^3 - 1)^{1/2}$

7. $F(x) = \sqrt[3]{2x^3 - 5x^2 + x}$

8. $g(x) = \sqrt[3]{(3x^2 + 5x - 1)^2}$

9. $g(t) = \sqrt{2t} + \sqrt{\dfrac{2}{t}}$

10. $f(x) = 3x^{2/3} - 6x^{1/3} + x^{-1/3}$

11. $F(x) = \dfrac{\sqrt{x^2 - 1}}{x}$

12. $G(x) = \dfrac{4x + 6}{\sqrt{x^2 + 3x + 4}}$

13. $h(x) = \dfrac{\sqrt{x-1}}{\sqrt[3]{x+1}}$

14. $f(s) = (s^4 + 3s^2 + 1)^{-2/3}$

15. $f(x) = \sqrt{x^2 - 5\sqrt[3]{x^2 + 3}}$

16. $G(t) = \sqrt{\dfrac{5t+6}{5t-4}}$

17. $f(x) = \sqrt{9 + \sqrt{9-x}}$

18. $g(x) = \sqrt[4]{\dfrac{y^3+1}{y^3-1}}$

19. Find an equation of the tangent line to the curve $y = \sqrt{x^2 + 9}$ at the point $(4, 5)$.

20. Find an equation of the tangent line to the curve $y = (6 - 2x)^{1/3}$ at each of the following points: $(-1, 2)$, $(1, \sqrt[3]{4})$, $(3, 0)$, $(5, -\sqrt[3]{4})$, $(7, -2)$. Draw a sketch of the graph and segments of the tangent lines at the given points.

21. Find an equation of the normal line to the curve $y = x\sqrt{16 + x^2}$ at the origin.

22. Find an equation of the tangent line to the curve $y = 1/\sqrt[3]{7x - 6}$ which is perpendicular to the line $12x - 7y + 2 = 0$.

23. An object is moving along a straight line according to the equation of motion $s = \sqrt{4t^2 + 3}$, with $t \geq 0$. Find the values of t for which the measure of the instantaneous velocity is (a) 0; (b) 1; (c) 2.

24. Given $f(u) = 1/u^2$ and $g(x) = \sqrt{x}/\sqrt{2x^3 - 6x + 1}$, find the derivative of $f \circ g$ in two ways: (a) by first finding $(f \circ g)(x)$ and then finding $(f \circ g)'(x)$; (b) by using the chain rule.

In Exercises 25 through 28, find the derivative of the given function. (HINT: $|a| = \sqrt{a^2}$.)

25. $f(x) = |x^2 - 4|$

26. $g(x) = x|x|$

27. $g(x) = |x|^3$

28. $h(x) = \sqrt[3]{|x| + x}$

29. Suppose $g(x) = |f(x)|$. Prove that if $f'(x)$ and $g'(x)$ exist, then $|g'(x)| = |f'(x)|$.

30. Suppose that $g(x) = \sqrt{9 - x^2}$ and $h(x) = f(g(x))$ where f is differentiable at 3. Prove that $h'(0) = 0$.

31. If g and h are functions and if f is the function defined by

$$f(x) = [g(x)]^r[h(x)]^s$$

where r and s are rational numbers, prove that if $g'(x)$ and $h'(x)$ exist

$$f'(x) = [g(x)]^{r-1}[h(x)]^{s-1}[r \cdot h(x)g'(x) + s \cdot g(x)h'(x)]$$

In Exercises 32 through 35, use the result of Exercise 31 to find the derivative of the given function.

32. $g(x) = (4x + 3)^{1/2}(4 - x^2)^{1/3}$

33. $f(x) = (3x + 2)^4(x^2 - 1)^{2/3}$

34. $f(r) = \left(\dfrac{r+1}{r^2+1}\right)^3 (r^3 + 4)^{1/3}$

35. $F(t) = (t^3 - 2t + 1)^{3/2}(t^2 + t + 5)^{1/3}$

3.8 IMPLICIT DIFFERENTIATION

If $f = \{(x, y) | y = 3x^2 + 5x + 1\}$, then the equation

$$y = 3x^2 + 5x + 1 \tag{1}$$

defines the function f explicitly. However, not all functions are defined explicitly. For example, if we have the equation

$$x^6 - 2x = 3y^6 + y^5 - y^2 \tag{2}$$

we cannot solve for y in terms of x; however, there may exist one or more functions f such that if $y = f(x)$, Eq. (2) is satisfied, that is, such that the equation

$$x^6 - 2x = 3[f(x)]^6 + [f(x)]^5 - [f(x)]^2$$

is true for all values of x in the domain of f. In this case we state that the function f is defined *implicitly* by the given equation.

Using the assumption that Eq. (2) defines y as one or more differentiable functions of x, we can find the derivative of y with respect to x by the process called *implicit differentiation,* which we now do.

The left side of Eq. (2) is a function of x, and the right side is a function of y. Let F be the function defined by the left side of (2), and let G be the function defined by the right side of (2). Thus,

$$F(x) = x^6 - 2x \tag{3}$$

and

$$G(y) = 3y^6 + y^5 - y^2 \tag{4}$$

where y is a function of x, say,

$$y = f(x)$$

So we write Eq. (2) as

$$F(x) = G(f(x)) \tag{5}$$

Equation (5) is satisfied by all values of x in the domain of f for which $G[f(x)]$ exists.

Then for all values of x for which f is differentiable, we have

$$D_x[x^6 - 2x] = D_x[3y^6 + y^5 - y^2] \tag{6}$$

The derivative on the left side of Eq. (6) is easily found, and we have

$$D_x[x^6 - 2x] = 6x^5 - 2 \tag{7}$$

We find the derivative on the right side of Eq. (6) by the chain rule, giving us

$$D_x[3y^6 + y^5 - y^2] = 18y^5 \cdot D_xy + 5y^4 \cdot D_xy - 2y \cdot D_xy \tag{8}$$

Substituting the values from (7) and (8) into (6), we obtain

$$6x^5 - 2 = (18y^5 + 5y^4 - 2y)D_xy$$

Solving for D_xy, we get

$$D_xy = \frac{6x^5 - 2}{18y^5 + 5y^4 - 2y}$$

Equation (2) is a special type of equation involving x and y because it can be written so that all the terms involving x are on one side of the equation and all the terms involving y are on the other side.

In the following illustration we use the method of implicit differentiation to find D_xy from a more general type of equation.

● ILLUSTRATION 1: Consider the equation

$$3x^4y^2 - 7xy^3 = 4 - 8y \qquad (9)$$

and assume that there exist one or more differentiable functions f such that if $y = f(x)$, Eq. (9) is satisfied. Differentiating on both sides of Eq. (9) (bearing in mind that y is one or more differentiable functions of x), and applying the theorems for the derivative of a product, the derivative of a power, and the chain rule, we obtain

$$12x^3y^2 + 3x^4(2yD_xy) - 7y^3 - 7x(3y^2D_xy) = 0 - 8D_xy$$

Solving for D_xy, we have

$$D_xy(6x^4y - 21xy^2 + 8) = 7y^3 - 12x^3y^2$$

$$D_xy = \frac{7y^3 - 12x^3y^2}{6x^4y - 21xy^2 + 8} \qquad ●$$

Remember that we assumed that both Eqs. (2) and (9) define y as one or more differentiable functions of x. It may be that an equation in x and y does not imply the existence of any real-valued function, as is the case for the equation

$$x^2 + y^2 + 4 = 0$$

which is not satisfied by any real values of x and y. Furthermore, it is possible that an equation in x and y may be satisfied by many different functions, some of which are differentiable and some of which are not. A general discussion is beyond the scope of this book, but can be found in an advanced calculus text. In subsequent discussions, when we state that an equation in x and y defines y implicitly as a function of x, we assume that one or more of these functions is differentiable. Example 3, which follows, illustrates the fact that implicit differentiation gives the derivative of every differentiable function defined by the given equation.

EXAMPLE 1: Given

$$(x + y)^2 - (x - y)^2 = x^4 + y^4$$

find D_xy.

SOLUTION: Differentiating implicitly with respect to x, we have

$$2(x + y)(1 + D_xy) - 2(x - y)(1 - D_xy) = 4x^3 + 4y^3D_xy$$

from which we obtain

$$2x + 2y + (2x + 2y)D_xy - 2x + 2y + (2x - 2y)D_xy = 4x^3 + 4y^3D_xy$$

$$D_xy(4x - 4y^3) = 4x^3 - 4y$$

$$D_xy = \frac{x^3 - y}{x - y^3}$$

EXAMPLE 2: Find an equation of the tangent line to the curve $x^3 + y^3 = 9$ at the point $(1, 2)$.

SOLUTION: Differentiating implicitly with respect to x, we obtain

$$3x^2 + 3y^2D_xy = 0$$

Hence,

$$D_x y = -\frac{x^2}{y^2}$$

Therefore, at the point $(1, 2)$, $D_x y = -\frac{1}{4}$. An equation of the tangent line is then

$$y - 2 = -\tfrac{1}{4}(x - 1)$$

EXAMPLE 3:   Given the equation $x^2 + y^2 = 9$, find: (a) $D_x y$ by implicit differentiation; (b) two functions defined by the equation; (c) the derivative of each of the functions obtained in part (b) by explicit differentiation. (d) Verify that the result obtained in part (a) agrees with the results obtained in part (c).

SOLUTION: (a) Differentiating implicitly, we find

$$2x + 2y D_x y = 0 \quad \text{and so} \quad D_x y = -\frac{x}{y}$$

(b) Solving the given equation for y, we obtain

$$y = \sqrt{9 - x^2} \quad \text{and} \quad y = -\sqrt{9 - x^2}$$

Let f_1 be the function for which

$$f_1(x) = \sqrt{9 - x^2}$$

and f_2 be the function for which

$$f_2(x) = -\sqrt{9 - x^2}$$

(c) Because $f_1(x) = (9 - x^2)^{1/2}$, by using the chain rule we obtain

$$f_1'(x) = \tfrac{1}{2}(9 - x^2)^{-1/2}(-2x)$$

$$= -\frac{x}{\sqrt{9 - x^2}}$$

Similarly, we get

$$f_2'(x) = \frac{x}{\sqrt{9 - x^2}}$$

(d) For $y = f_1(x)$, where $f_1(x) = \sqrt{9 - x^2}$, we have from part (c)

$$f_1'(x) = -\frac{x}{\sqrt{9 - x^2}} = -\frac{x}{y}$$

which agrees with the answer in part (a). For $y = f_2(x)$, where $f_2(x) = -\sqrt{9 - x^2}$, we have from part (c)

$$f_2'(x) = \frac{x}{\sqrt{9 - x^2}}$$

$$= -\frac{x}{-\sqrt{9 - x^2}}$$

$$= -\frac{x}{y}$$

which also agrees with the answer in part (a).

Exercises 3.8

In Exercises 1 through 16, find $D_x y$ by implicit differentiation.

1. $x^2 + y^2 = 16$

2. $2x^3 y + 3xy^3 = 5$

3. $x^3 + y^3 = 8xy$

4. $x^2 = \dfrac{x + 2y}{x - 2y}$

5. $\dfrac{1}{x} + \dfrac{1}{y} = 1$

6. $\dfrac{x}{y} - 4y = x$

7. $\sqrt{x} + \sqrt{y} = 4$

8. $y + \sqrt{xy} = 3x^3$

9. $x^2 y^2 = x^2 + y^2$

10. $y\sqrt{2 + 3x} + x\sqrt{1 + y} = x$

11. $(x + y)^2 - (x - y)^2 = x^3 + y^3$

12. $(2x + 3)^4 = 3y^4$

13. $\dfrac{y}{x - y} = 2 + x^2$

14. $\sqrt{y} + \sqrt[3]{y} + \sqrt[4]{y} = x$

15. $\sqrt{xy} + 2x = \sqrt{y}$

16. $x^2 y^3 = x^4 - y^4$

In Exercises 17 through 20, consider y as the independent variable and find $D_y x$.

17. $x^4 + y^4 = 12x^2 y$

18. $y = 2x^3 - 5x$

19. $x^3 y + 2y^4 - x^4 = 0$

20. $y\sqrt{x} - x\sqrt{y} = 9$

21. Find an equation of the tangent line to the curve $16x^4 + y^4 = 32$ at the point $(1, 2)$.

22. There are two lines through the point $(-1, 3)$ which are tangent to the curve

$$x^2 + 4y^2 - 4x - 8y + 3 = 0$$

Find an equation of each of these lines.

23. Prove that the sum of the x and y intercepts of any tangent line to the curve $x^{1/2} + y^{1/2} = k^{1/2}$ is constant and equal to k.

24. If $x^n y^m = (x + y)^{n+m}$, prove that $x \cdot D_x y = y$.

In Exercises 25 through 30, an equation is given. Do the following in each of these problems: (a) Find two functions defined by the equation, and state their domains. (b) Draw a sketch of the graph of each of the functions obtained in part (a). (c) Draw a sketch of the graph of the equation. (d) Find the derivative of each of the functions obtained in part (a) and state the domains of the derivatives. (e) Find $D_x y$ by implicit differentiation from the given equation, and verify that the result so obtained agrees with the results in part (d). (f) Find an equation of each tangent line at the given value of x_1.

25. $y^2 = 4x - 8$; $x_1 = 3$

26. $x^2 + y^2 = 25$; $x_1 = 4$

27. $x^2 - y^2 = 9$; $x_1 = -5$

28. $y^2 - x^2 = 16$; $x_1 = -3$

29. $x^2 + y^2 - 2x - 4y - 4 = 0$; $x_1 = 1$

30. $x^2 + 4y^2 + 6x - 40y + 93 = 0$; $x_1 = -2$

3.9 THE DERIVATIVE AS A RATE OF CHANGE

The concept of velocity in rectilinear motion corresponds to the more general concept of instantaneous rate of change. For example, if a particle is moving along a straight line according to the equation of motion $s = f(t)$, we have seen that the velocity of the particle at t units of time is determined by the derivative of s with respect to t. Because velocity can be interpreted as a rate of change of distance per unit change in time, we see that the derivative of s with respect to t is the rate of change of s per unit change in t.

In a similar way, if a quantity y is a function of a quantity x, we may express the rate of change of y per unit change in x. The discussion is analogous to the discussions of the slope of a tangent line to a graph and the instantaneous velocity of a particle moving along a straight line.

If the functional relationship between y and x is given by

$$y = f(x)$$

and if x changes from the value x_1 to $x_1 + \Delta x$, then y changes from $f(x_1)$ to $f(x_1 + \Delta x)$. So the change in y, which we may denote by Δy, is $f(x_1 + \Delta x) - f(x_1)$ when the change in x is Δx. The average rate of change of y, per unit change in x, as x changes from x_1 to $x_1 + \Delta x$ is then

$$\frac{f(x_1 + \Delta x) - f(x_1)}{\Delta x} = \frac{\Delta y}{\Delta x} \tag{1}$$

If the limit of this quotient exists as $\Delta x \to 0$, this limit is what we intuitively think of as the instantaneous rate of change of y per unit change in x at x_1. Accordingly, we have the following definition.

3.9.1 Definition   If $y = f(x)$, the *instantaneous rate of change of y per unit change in x at x_1* is $f'(x_1)$ or, equivalently, the derivative of y with respect to x at x_1, if it exists there.

The instantaneous rate of change of y per unit change in x may be interpreted as the change in y caused by a change of one unit in x if the rate of change remains constant. To illustrate this geometrically, let $f'(x_1)$ be the instantaneous rate of change of y per unit change in x at x_1. Then if we multiply $f'(x_1)$ by Δx (the change in x), we have the change that would occur in y if the point (x, y) were to move along the tangent line at (x_1, y_1) of the graph of $y = f(x)$. See Fig. 3.9.1. The average rate of change of y per unit change in x is given by the fraction in Eq. (1), and if this is multiplied by Δx, we have

$$\frac{\Delta y}{\Delta x} \cdot \Delta x = \Delta y$$

Figure 3.9.1

which is the actual change in y caused by a change of Δx in x when the point (x, y) moves along the graph.

EXAMPLE 1:   Let V cubic inches be the volume of a cube having an edge of length e inches. Find the average rate of change of the volume per inch change in the length of the edge as e changes from (a) 3.00 to 3.20; (b) 3.00 to 3.10; (c) 3.00 to 3.01. (d) What is the instantaneous rate of change of the volume per inch change in the length of the edge when $e = 3$?

SOLUTION: Because the formula for finding the volume of a cube is $V = e^3$, let f be the function defined by $f(e) = e^3$. Then the average rate of change of V per unit change in e as e changes from e_1 to $e_1 + \Delta e$ is

$$\frac{f(e_1 + \Delta e) - f(e_1)}{\Delta e}$$

(a) $e_1 = 3$, $\Delta e = 0.2$, and $\dfrac{f(3.2) - f(3)}{0.2} = \dfrac{(3.2)^3 - 3^3}{0.2} = \dfrac{5.77}{0.2} = 28.8$

(b) $e_1 = 3$, $\Delta e = 0.1$, and $\dfrac{f(3.1) - f(3)}{0.1} = \dfrac{(3.1)^3 - 3^3}{0.1} = \dfrac{2.79}{0.1} = 27.9$

(c) $e_1 = 3$, $\Delta e = 0.01$, and $\dfrac{f(3.01) - f(3)}{0.01} = \dfrac{(3.01)^3 - 3^3}{0.01} = \dfrac{0.271}{0.01} = 27.1$

In part (a) we see that as the length of the edge of the cube changes from 3.00 inches to 3.20 inches, the change in the volume is 5.77 cubic inches and the average rate of change of the volume is 28.8 cubic inches per inch change in the length of the edge. There are similar interpretations of parts (b) and (c).

(d) The instantaneous rate of change of V per unit change in e at 3 is $f'(3)$.

$$f'(e) = 3e^2$$

Hence,

$$f'(3) = 27$$

Therefore, when the length of the edge of the cube is 3 inches, the instantaneous rate of change of the volume is 27 cubic inches per inch change in the length of the edge.

EXAMPLE 2: The annual gross earnings of a particular corporation t years after January 1, 1974, is p millions of dollars and

$$p = \tfrac{2}{5}t^2 + 2t + 10$$

Find: (a) the rate at which the gross earnings were growing January 1, 1976; (b) the rate at which the gross earnings should be growing January 1, 1980.

SOLUTION: (a) On January 1, 1976, $t = 2$; hence, we find $D_t p$ when $t = 2$.

$$D_t p = \tfrac{4}{5}t + 2 \qquad D_t p \Big]_{t=2} = \tfrac{8}{5} + 2 = 3.6$$

So on January 1, 1976, the gross earnings were growing at the rate of 3.6 million dollars per year.

(b) On January 1, 1980, $t = 6$ and

$$D_t p \Big]_{t=6} = \tfrac{24}{5} + 2 = 6.8$$

Therefore, on January 1, 1980, the gross earnings should be growing at the rate of 6.8 million dollars per year.

The results of Example 2 are meaningful only if they are compared to the actual earnings of the corporation. For example, if on January 1, 1975, it was found that the earnings of the corporation for the year 1974 had been 3 million dollars, then the rate of growth on January 1, 1976, of 3.4 million dollars annually would have been excellent. However, if the earnings in 1974 had been 300 million dollars, then the growth rate on January 1, 1976, would have been very poor. The measure used to compare the rate of change with the amount of the quantity which is being changed is called the *relative rate*.

3.9.2 Definition If $y = f(x)$, the *relative rate of change of y per unit change in x at x_1* is given by $f'(x_1)/f(x_1)$ or, equivalently, $D_x y / y$ evaluated at $x = x_1$.

If the relative rate is multiplied by 100, we have the percent rate of change.

EXAMPLE 3:   Find the relative rate of growth of the gross earnings on January 1, 1976, and January 1, 1980, for the corporation of Example 2.

SOLUTION: (a) When $t = 2$, $p = \frac{2}{5}(4) + 2(2) + 10 = 15.6$. Hence, on January 1, 1976, the relative rate of growth of the corporation's annual gross earnings was

$$\frac{D_t p}{p}\bigg]_{t=2} = \frac{3.6}{15.6} = 0.231 = 23.1\%$$

(b) When $t = 6$, $p = \frac{2}{5}(36) + 2(6) + 10 = 36.4$. Therefore, on January 1, 1980, the relative rate of growth of the corporation's annual gross earnings should be

$$\frac{D_t p}{p}\bigg]_{t=6} = \frac{6.8}{36.4} = 0.187 = 18.7\%$$

Note that the growth rate of 6.8 million dollars for January 1, 1980, is greater than the 3.6 million dollars for January 1, 1976; however, the relative growth rate of 18.7% for January 1, 1980, is less than the relative growth rate of 23.1% for January 1, 1976.

Exercises 3.9

1. If A in.² is the area of a square and s in. is the length of a side of the square, find the average rate of change of A with respect to s as s changes from (a) 4.00 to 4.60; (b) 4.00 to 4.30; (c) 4.00 to 4.10. (d) What is the instantaneous rate of change of A with respect to s when s is 4.00?

2. Suppose a right-circular cylinder has a constant height of 10.00 in. If V in.³ is the volume of the right-circular cylinder, and r in. is the radius of its base, find the average rate of change of V with respect to r as r changes from (a) 5.00 to 5.40; (b) 5.00 to 5.10; (c) 5.00 to 5.01. (d) Find the instantaneous rate of change of V with respect to r when r is 5.00.

3. Let r be the reciprocal of a number n. Find the instantaneous rate of change of r with respect to n and the relative rate of change of r per unit change in n when n is (a) 4 and (b) 10.

4. Let s be the principal square root of a number x. Find the instantaneous rate of change of s with respect to x and the relative rate of change of s per unit change in x when x is (a) 9 and (b) 4.

5. If water is being drained from a swimming pool and V gal is the volume of water in the pool t min after the draining starts, where $V = 250(40 - t)^2$, find (a) the average rate at which the water leaves the pool during the first 5 min, and (b) how fast the water is flowing out of the pool 5 min after the draining starts.

6. The supply equation for a certain kind of pencil is $x = 3p^2 + 2p$ where p cents is the price per pencil when $1000x$ pencils are supplied. (a) Find the average rate of change of the supply per 1 cent change in the price when the price is increased from 10 cents to 11 cents. (b) Find the instantaneous (or marginal) rate of change of the supply per 1 cent change in the price when the price is 10 cents.

7. The profit of a retail store is $100y$ dollars when x dollars are spent daily on advertising and $y = 2500 + 36x - 0.2x^2$. Use the derivative to determine if it would be profitable for the daily advertising budget to be increased if the current daily advertising budget is (a) $60 and (b) $100.

8. A balloon maintains the shape of a sphere as it is being inflated. Find the rate of change of the surface area with respect to the radius at the instant when the radius is 2 in.

9. In an electric circuit, if E volts is the electromotive force, R ohms is the resistance, and I amperes is the current, Ohm's law states that $IR = E$. Assuming that E is constant, show that R decreases at a rate that is proportional to the inverse square of I.

10. Boyle's law for the expansion of a gas is $PV = C$, where P is the number of pounds per square unit of pressure, V is the number of cubic units in the volume of the gas, and C is a constant. Find the instantaneous rate of change of the volume per change of one pound per square unit in the pressure when $P = 4$ and $V = 8$.

11. A bomber is flying parallel to the ground at an altitude of 2 mi and at a speed of $4\frac{1}{2}$ mi/min. If the bomber flies directly over a target, at what rate is the line-of-sight distance between the bomber and the target changing 20 sec later?

12. At 8 A.M. a ship sailing due north at 24 knots (nautical miles per hour) is at a point P. At 10 A.M. a second ship sailing due east at 32 knots is at P. At what rate is the distance between the two ships changing at (a) 9 A.M. and (b) 11 A.M.?

3.10 RELATED RATES

There are many problems concerned with the rate of change of two or more related variables with respect to time, in which it is not necessary to express each of these variables directly as functions of time. For example, suppose that we are given an equation involving the variables x and y, and that both x and y are functions of a third variable t, where t sec denotes time. Then, because the rate of change of x with respect to t and the rate of change of y with respect to t are given by $D_t x$ and $D_t y$, respectively, we differentiate on both sides of the given equation with respect to t by applying the chain rule and proceed as below.

EXAMPLE 1:   A ladder 25 ft long is leaning against a vertical wall. If the bottom of the ladder is pulled horizontally away from the wall at 3 ft/sec, how fast is the top of the ladder sliding down the wall, when the bottom is 15 ft from the wall?

SOLUTION: Let $t =$ the number of seconds in the time that has elapsed since the ladder started to slide down the wall;

$y =$ the number of feet in the distance from the ground to the top of the ladder at t sec;

$x =$ the number of feet in the distance from the bottom of the ladder to the wall at t sec.

See Fig. 3.10.1. Because the bottom of the ladder is pulled horizontally away from the wall at 3 ft/sec, $D_t x = 3$. We wish to find $D_t y$ when $x = 15$. From the Pythagorean theorem, we have

$$y^2 = 625 - x^2 \tag{1}$$

Because x and y are functions of t, we differentiate on both sides of Eq. (1) with respect to t and obtain

$$2y\,D_t y = -2x\,D_t x$$

giving us

$$D_t y = -\frac{x}{y}\,D_t x \tag{2}$$

When $x = 15$, it follows from Eq. (1) that $y = 20$. Because $D_t x = 3$, we

Figure 3.10.1

get from (2)

$$D_t y\bigg]_{y=20} = -\tfrac{15}{20} \cdot 3 = -\tfrac{9}{4}$$

Therefore, the top of the ladder is sliding down the wall at the rate of $2\tfrac{1}{4}$ ft/sec when the bottom is 15 ft from the wall. (The significance of the minus sign is that y is decreasing as t is increasing.)

EXAMPLE 2:   A tank is in the form of an inverted cone, having an altitude of 16 ft and a base radius of 4 ft. Water is flowing into the tank at the rate of 2 ft³/min. How fast is the water level rising when the water is 5 ft deep?

Figure 3.10.2

SOLUTION: Let $t =$ the number of minutes in the time that has elapsed since water started to flow into the tank;

$h =$ the number of feet in the height of the water level at t min;

$r =$ the number of feet in the radius of the surface of the water at t min;

$V =$ the number of cubic feet in the volume of water in the tank at t min.

At any time, the volume of water in the tank may be expressed in terms of the volume of a cone (see Fig. 3.10.2).

$$V = \tfrac{1}{3}\pi r^2 h \tag{3}$$

V, r, and h are all functions of t. Because water is flowing into the tank at the rate of 2 ft³/min, $D_t V = 2$. We wish to find $D_t h$ when $h = 5$. To express r in terms of h, we have from similar triangles

$$\frac{r}{h} = \frac{4}{16} \qquad r = \tfrac{1}{4}h$$

Substituting this value of r into formula (3), we obtain

$$V = \tfrac{1}{3}\pi(\tfrac{1}{4}h)^2(h) \quad \text{or} \quad V = \tfrac{1}{48}\pi h^3 \tag{4}$$

Differentiating on both sides of Eq. (4) with respect to t, we get

$$D_t V = \tfrac{1}{16}\pi h^2\, D_t h$$

Substituting 2 for $D_t V$ and solving for $D_t h$, we obtain

$$D_t h = \frac{32}{\pi h^2}$$

Therefore,

$$D_t h\bigg]_{h=5} = \frac{32}{25\pi}$$

We conclude that the water level is rising at the rate of $32/25\pi$ ft/min when the water is 5 ft deep.

EXAMPLE 3: Two cars, one going due east at the rate of 37.5 mi/hr and the other going due south at the rate of 30.0 mi/hr, are traveling toward an intersection of the two roads. At what rate are the two cars approaching each other at the instant when the first car is 400 ft and the second car is 300 ft from the intersection?

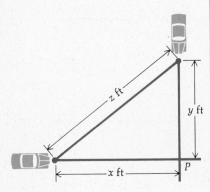

Figure 3.10.3

SOLUTION: Refer to Fig. 3.10.3, where the point P is the intersection of the two roads.

Let $x =$ the number of feet in the distance of the first car from P at t sec;

$y =$ the number of feet in the distance of the second car from P at t sec;

$z =$ the number of feet in the distance between the two cars at t sec.

Because the first car is approaching P at the rate of 37.5 mi/hr $= 37.5 \cdot \frac{22}{15}$ ft/sec $= 55$ ft/sec and because x is decreasing as t is increasing, it follows that $D_t x = -55$. Similarly, because 30 mi/hr $= 30 \cdot \frac{22}{15}$ ft/sec $= 44$ ft/sec, $D_t y = -44$. We wish to find $D_t z$ when $x = 400$ and $y = 300$. From the Pythagorean theorem we have

$$z^2 = x^2 + y^2 \tag{5}$$

Differentiating on both sides of Eq. (5) with respect to t, we obtain

$$2z \, D_t z = 2x \, D_t x + 2y \, D_t y$$

and so

$$D_t z = \frac{x \, D_t x + y \, D_t y}{z} \tag{6}$$

When $x = 400$ and $y = 300$, it follows from Eq. (5) that $z = 500$. In Eq. (6), substituting $D_t x = -55$, $D_t y = -44$, $x = 400$, $y = 300$, and $z = 500$, we get

$$D_t z \bigg]_{z=500} = \frac{(400)(-55) + (300)(-44)}{500} = -70.4$$

Therefore, at the instant in question the cars are approaching each other at the rate of 70.4 ft/sec.

Exercises 3.10

1. A kite is flying at a height of 40 ft. A boy is flying it so that it is moving horizontally at a rate of 3 ft/sec. If the string is taut, at what rate is the string being paid out when the length of the string released is 50 ft?

2. A spherical balloon is being inflated so that its volume is increasing at the rate of 5 ft³/min. At what rate is the diameter increasing when the diameter is 12 ft?

3. A spherical snowball is being made so that its volume is increasing at the rate of 8 ft³/min. Find the rate at which the radius is increasing when the snowball is 4 ft in diameter.

4. Suppose that when the diameter is 6 ft the snowball in Exercise 3 stopped growing and started to melt at the rate of ¼ ft³/min. Find the rate at which the radius is changing when the radius is 2 ft.

5. Sand is being dropped at the rate of 10 ft³/min onto a conical pile. If the height of the pile is always twice the base radius, at what rate is the height increasing when the pile is 8 ft high?

6. A light is hung 15 ft above a straight horizontal path. If a man 6 ft tall is walking away from the light at the rate of 5 ft/sec, how fast is his shadow lengthening?

7. In Exercise 6 at what rate is the tip of the man's shadow moving?

8. A man 6 ft tall is walking toward a building at the rate of 5 ft/sec. If there is a light on the ground 50 ft from the building, how fast is the man's shadow on the building growing shorter when he is 30 ft from the building?

9. A water tank in the form of an inverted cone is being emptied at the rate of 6 ft³/min. The altitude of the cone is 24 ft, and the base radius is 12 ft. Find how fast the water level is lowering when the water is 10 ft deep.

10. A trough is 12 ft long and its ends are in the form of inverted isosceles triangles having an altitude of 3 ft and a base of 3 ft. Water is flowing into the trough at the rate of 2 ft³/min. How fast is the water level rising when the water is 1 ft deep?

11. Boyle's law for the expansion of gas is $PV = C$, where P is the number of pounds per square unit of pressure, V is the number of cubic units of volume of the gas, and C is a constant. At a certain instant the pressure is 3000 lb/ft², the volume is 5 ft³, and the volume is increasing at the rate of 3 ft³/min. Find the rate of change of the pressure at this instant.

12. The adiabatic law (no gain or loss of heat) for the expansion of air is $PV^{1.4} = C$, where P is the number of pounds per square unit of pressure, V is the number of cubic units of volume, and C is a constant. At a specific instant, the pressure is 40 lb/in.² and is increasing at the rate of 8 lb/in.² each second. What is the rate of change of volume at this instant?

13. An automobile traveling at a rate of 30 ft/sec is approaching an intersection. When the automobile is 120 ft from the intersection, a truck traveling at the rate of 40 ft/sec crosses the intersection. The automobile and the truck are on roads that are at right angles to each other. How fast are the automobile and the truck separating 2 sec after the truck leaves the intersection?

14. A man on a dock is pulling in a boat at the rate of 50 ft/min by means of a rope attached to the boat at water level. If the man's hands are 16 ft above the water level, how fast is the boat approaching the dock when the amount of rope out is 20 ft?

15. A ladder 20 ft long is leaning against an embankment inclined 60° to the horizontal. If the bottom of the ladder is being moved horizontally toward the embankment at 1 ft/sec, how fast is the top of the ladder moving when the bottom is 4 ft from the embankment?

16. A horizontal trough is 16 ft long, and its ends are isosceles trapezoids with an altitude of 4 ft, a lower base of 4 ft, and an upper base of 6 ft. Water is being poured into the trough at the rate of 10 ft³/min. How fast is the water level rising when the water is 2 ft deep?

17. In Exercise 16 if the water level is decreasing at the rate of ¼ ft/min when the water is 3 ft deep, at what rate is water being drawn from the trough?

18. Water is being poured at the rate of 8 ft³/min into a tank in the form of a cone. The cone is 20 ft deep and 10 ft in diameter at the top. If there is a leak in the bottom, and the water level is rising at the rate of 1 in./min, when the water is 16 ft deep, how fast is the water leaking?

3.11 DERIVATIVES OF HIGHER ORDER

If f' is the derivative of the function f, then f' is also a function, and it is the *first derivative* of f. It is sometimes referred to as the *first derived function*. If the derivative of f' exists, it is called the *second derivative* of f, or the second derived function, and can be denoted by f'' (read as "f double prime"). Similarly, we define the *third derivative* of f, or the third derived function, as the first derivative of f'' if it exists. We denote the third derivative of f by f''' (read as "f triple prime").

The nth *derivative* of the function f, where n is a positive integer greater than 1, is the first derivative of the $(n-1)$st derivative of f. We denote the nth derivative of f by $f^{(n)}$. Thus, if $f^{(n)}$ denotes the nth derived function, we can denote the function f itself by $f^{(0)}$. Another symbol for the nth derivative of f is $D_x{}^n f$. If the function f is defined by the equation $y = f(x)$, we can denote the nth derivative of f by $D_x{}^n y$.

EXAMPLE 1: Find all the derivatives of the function f defined by

$$f(x) = 8x^4 + 5x^3 - x^2 + 7$$

SOLUTION:

$$f'(x) = 32x^3 + 15x^2 - 2x$$

$$f''(x) = 96x^2 + 30x - 2$$

$$f'''(x) = 192x + 30$$

$$f^{(4)}(x) = 192$$

$$f^{(5)}(x) = 0$$

$$f^{(n)}(x) = 0 \qquad n \geq 5$$

Because $f'(x)$ gives the rate of change of $f(x)$ per unit change in x, $f''(x)$, being the derivative of $f'(x)$, gives the rate of change of $f'(x)$ per unit change in x. The second derivative $f''(x)$ is expressed in units of $f'(x)$ per unit of x, which is units of $f(x)$ per unit of x, per unit of x. For example, in straight-line motion, if $f(t)$ feet is the distance of a particle from the origin at t seconds, then $f'(t)$ feet per second is the velocity of the particle at t seconds, and $f''(t)$ feet per second per second is the instantaneous rate of change of the velocity at t seconds. In physics, the instantaneous rate of change of the velocity is called the *instantaneous acceleration*. Therefore, if a particle is moving along a straight line according to the equation of motion $s = f(t)$, where the instantaneous velocity at t sec is given by v ft/sec and the instantaneous acceleration is given by a ft/sec^2, then a is the first derivative of v with respect to t or, equivalently, the second derivative of s with respect to t; that is,

$$v = D_t s \quad \text{and} \quad a = D_t v = D_t{}^2 s$$

EXAMPLE 2: A particle is moving along a straight line according to the equation of motion

$$s = \frac{1}{2} t^2 + \frac{4t}{t+1}$$

where s ft is the directed distance of the particle from the origin at t sec. If v ft/sec is the instantaneous velocity at t sec and a ft/sec^2 is the instantaneous acceleration at t sec, find t, s, and v when $a = 0$.

SOLUTION:

$$v = D_t s = t + \frac{4}{(t+1)^2}$$

$$a = D_t v = D_t{}^2 s = 1 - \frac{8}{(t+1)^3}$$

Setting $a = 0$, we have

$$\frac{(t+1)^3 - 8}{(t+1)^3} = 0$$

or

$$(t+1)^3 = 8$$

from which the only real value of t is obtained from the principal cube root of 8, so that

$$t + 1 = 2 \quad \text{or} \quad t = 1$$

When $t = 1$

$$s = \frac{1}{2}(1)^2 + \frac{4 \cdot 1}{1 + 1} = 2\frac{1}{2}$$

and

$$v = 1 + \frac{4}{(1 + 1)^2} = 2$$

If (x, y) is any point on the graph of $y = f(x)$, then $D_x y$ gives the slope of the tangent line to the graph at the point (x, y). Thus, $D_x^2 y$ is the rate of change of the slope of the tangent line with respect to x at the point (x, y).

EXAMPLE 3:   Let $m(x)$ be the slope of the tangent line to the curve $y = x^3 - 2x^2 + x$ at the point (x, y). Find the instantaneous rate of change of m per unit change in x at the point $(2, 2)$.

SOLUTION: $m = D_x y = 3x^2 - 4x + 1$.

The instantaneous rate of change of m per unit change in x is given by $D_x m$ or, equivalently, $D_x^2 y$.

$$D_x m = D_x^2 y = 6x - 4$$

At the point $(2, 2)$, $D_x^2 y = 8$. Hence, at the point $(2, 2)$, the change in m is 8 times the change in x.

Further applications of the second derivative are its uses in the second-derivative test for relative extrema (Sec. 5.2) and the sketching of the graph of a function (Secs. 5.4 and 5.5). An important application of other higher-ordered derivatives is to determine infinite series as shown in Chapter 16.

The following example illustrates how the second derivative is found for functions defined implicitly.

EXAMPLE 4:   Given

$$4x^2 + 9y^2 = 36$$

find $D_x^2 y$ by implicit differentiation.

SOLUTION: Differentiating implicitly with respect to x, we have

$$8x + 18y D_x y = 0$$

so that

$$D_x y = -\frac{4x}{9y} \tag{1}$$

To find $D_x^2 y$, we find the derivative of a quotient and keep in mind that y is a function of x. So we have

$$D_x^2 y = \frac{9y(-4) - (-4x)(9\, D_x y)}{81y^2} \tag{2}$$

Substituting the value of $D_x y$ from Eq. (1) into Eq. (2), we get

$$D_x{}^2 y = \frac{-36y + (36x)\dfrac{-4x}{9y}}{81y^2} = \frac{-36y^2 - 16x^2}{81y^3}$$

Thus,

$$D_x{}^2 y = \frac{-4(9y^2 + 4x^2)}{81y^3} \qquad (3)$$

Because any values of x and y satisfying Eq. (3) must also satisfy the original equation, we can replace $(9y^2 + 4x^2)$ by 36 and obtain

$$D_x{}^2 y = \frac{-4(36)}{81y^3} = -\frac{16}{9y^3}$$

Exercises 3.11

In Exercises 1 through 10, find the first and second derivative of the function defined by the given equation.

1. $f(x) = x^5 - 2x^3 + x$

2. $F(x) = 7x^3 - 8x^2$

3. $g(s) = 2s^4 - 4s^3 + 7s - 1$

4. $G(t) = t^3 - t^2 + t$

5. $f(x) = \sqrt{x^2 + 1}$

6. $h(y) = \sqrt[3]{2y^3 + 5}$

7. $F(x) = x^2 \sqrt{x} - 5x$

8. $g(r) = \sqrt{r} + \dfrac{1}{\sqrt{r}}$

9. $G(x) = \dfrac{1}{\sqrt{3 + 2x^2}}$

10. $f(x) = \dfrac{2 - \sqrt{x}}{2 + \sqrt{x}}$

11. Find $D_x{}^3 y$ if $y = x^4 - 2x^2 + x - 5$.

12. Find $D_t{}^3 s$ if $s = \sqrt{4t + 1}$.

13. Find $D_x{}^3 f(x)$ if $f(x) = \dfrac{x}{(1 - x)^2}$.

14. Find $f^{(4)}(x)$ if $f(x) = \dfrac{2}{x - 1}$.

15. Find $D_x{}^4 y$ if $y = x^{7/2} - 2x^{5/2} + x^{1/2}$.

16. Find $D_v{}^3 u$ if $u = v\sqrt{v - 2}$.

17. Given $x^3 + y^3 = 1$, show that $D_x{}^2 y = \dfrac{-2x}{y^5}$.

18. Given $x^{1/2} + y^{1/2} = 2$, show that $D_x{}^2 y = \dfrac{1}{x^{3/2}}$.

19. Given $x^4 + y^4 = a^4$ (a is a constant), find $D_x{}^2 y$ in simplest form.

20. Given $b^2 x^2 - a^2 y^2 = a^2 b^2$ (a and b are constants), find $D_x{}^2 y$ in simplest form.

21. Find the slope of the tangent line at each point of the graph of $y = x^4 + x^3 - 3x^2$ where the rate of change of the slope is zero.

In Exercises 22 and 23, a particle is moving along a straight line according to the given equation of motion, where s ft is the directed distance of the particle from the origin at t sec. If v ft/sec is the velocity and a ft/sec^2 is the acceleration of the particle at t sec, find v and a in terms of t. Also find when the acceleration is zero and the intervals of time when the particle is moving toward the origin and when it is moving away from the origin.

22. $s = t^3 - 9t^2 + 15t$

23. $s = \frac{1}{4}t^4 - 2t^3 + 4t^2$

In Exercises 24 through 27, a particle is moving along a straight line according to the given equation of motion, where s ft is the directed distance of the particle from the origin at t sec. Find the time when the instantaneous acceleration is zero, and then find the directed distance of the particle from the origin and the instantaneous velocity at this instant.

24. $s = 2t^3 - 6t^2 + 3t - 4$, $t \geq 0$

25. $s = \dfrac{125}{16t + 32} - \dfrac{2}{5}t^5$, $t \geq 0$

26. $s = 9t^2 + 2\sqrt{2t + 1}$, $t \geq 0$

27. $s = \frac{4}{3}t^{3/2} + 2t^{1/2}$, $t \geq 0$

In Exercises 28 through 31, find formulas for $f'(x)$ and $f''(x)$ and state the domains of f' and f''.

28. $f(x) = \begin{cases} \dfrac{x^2}{|x|} & \text{if } x \neq 0 \\ 0 & \text{if } x = 0 \end{cases}$

29. $f(x) = \begin{cases} -x^2 & \text{if } x < 0 \\ x^2 & \text{if } x \geq 0 \end{cases}$

30. $f(x) = |x|^3$

31. $f(x) = \begin{cases} \dfrac{x^5}{|x|} & \text{if } x \neq 0 \\ 0 & \text{if } x = 0 \end{cases}$

32. For the function of Exercise 30 find $f'''(x)$ when it exists.

33. For the function of Exercise 31 find $f'''(x)$ when it exists.

34. Show that if $xy = 1$, then $D_x^2 y \cdot D_y^2 x = 4$.

35. If f', g', f'', and g'' exist and if $h = f \circ g$, express $h''(x)$ in terms of the derivatives of f and g.

36. If f and g are two functions such that their first and second derivatives exist and if h is the function defined by $h(x) = f(x) \cdot g(x)$, prove that
$$h''(x) = f(x) \cdot g''(x) + 2f'(x) \cdot g'(x) + f''(x) \cdot g(x)$$

37. If $y = x^n$, where n is any positive integer, prove by mathematical induction that $D_x^n y = n!$

38. If
$$y = \frac{1}{1 - 2x}$$
prove by mathematical induction that
$$D_x^n y = \frac{2^n n!}{(1 - 2x)^{n+1}}$$

Review Exercises (Chapter 3)

In Exercises 1 through 14, find $D_x y$.

1. $y = \dfrac{x^2}{x^3 + a^3}$

2. $y = \dfrac{2x}{\sqrt{x^2 - 9}}$

3. $4x^2 + 4y^2 - y^3 = 0$

4. $y = \sqrt{1 + x} + \sqrt{1 - x}$

5. $y = \left(\sqrt{x} + \dfrac{1}{\sqrt{x}}\right)^3$

6. $y = \dfrac{x^2}{(x + 2)^2(4x - 5)}$

7. $y = \sqrt[3]{\dfrac{x}{x^3 + 1}}$

8. $xy^2 + 2y^3 = x - 2y$

9. $y = \dfrac{1}{x - \sqrt{x^2 - 1}}$

10. $x^{2/3} + y^{2/3} = a^{2/3}$

11. $y = (x^2 - 1)^{3/2}(x^2 - 4)^{1/2}$

12. $y = \dfrac{\sqrt{x^2 + 1} + \sqrt{x^2 - 1}}{\sqrt{x^2 + 1} - \sqrt{x^2 - 1}}$

13. $y = x^2 + [x^3 + (x^4 + x)^2]^3$

14. $y = \dfrac{x\sqrt{3 + 2x}}{4x - 1}$

15. A particle is moving in a straight line according to the equation of motion $s = t^3 - 11t^2 + 24t + 100$ where s ft is the directed distance of the particle from the starting point at t sec. (a) The particle is at the starting point when $t = 0$. For what other values of t is the particle at the starting point? (b) Determine the velocity of the particle at each instant that it is at the starting point, and interpret the sign of the velocity in each case.

16. Find equations of the tangent lines to the curve $y = 2x^3 + 4x^2 - x$ that have the slope $\tfrac{1}{2}$.

17. Find equations of the tangent line and normal line to the curve $2x^3 + 2y^3 - 9xy = 0$ at the point $(2, 1)$.

18. An object is sliding down an inclined plane according to the equation of motion $s = 12t^2 + 6t$ where s ft is the directed distance of the object from the top t sec after starting. (a) Find the velocity 3 sec after the start. (b) Find the initial velocity.

19. Using only the definition of a derivative find $f'(x)$ if $f(x) = \sqrt{4x - 3}$.

20. Using only the definition of a derivative find $f'(5)$ if $f(x) = \sqrt[3]{3x + 1}$.

21. Find $f'(x)$ if $f(x) = (|x + 1| - |x|)^2$.

22. Find $f'(x)$ if $f(x) = x - [\![x]\!]$.

23. Given $f(x) = |x|^3$. (a) Draw a sketch of the graph of f. (b) Find $\lim\limits_{x \to 0} f(x)$ if it exists. (c) Find $f'(0)$ if it exists.

24. Given $f(x) = x^2 \operatorname{sgn} x$. (a) Discuss the differentiability of f. (b) Is f' continuous on its domain?

25. Find $f'(-3)$ if $f(x) = [\![x + \tfrac{1}{2}]\!]\sqrt[3]{9x}$.

26. Find $f'(-3)$ if $f(x) = (|x| - x)\sqrt[3]{9x}$.

27. Prove that the line tangent to the curve $y = -x^4 + 2x^2 + x$ at the point $(1, 2)$ is also tangent to the curve at another point, and find this point.

28. Find an equation of the normal line to the curve $x - y = \sqrt{x + y}$ at the point $(3, 1)$.

29. A ball is thrown vertically upward from the top of a house 112 ft high. Its equation of motion is $s = -16t^2 + 96t$ where s ft is the directed distance of the ball from the starting point at t sec. Find: (a) the instantaneous velocity of the ball at 2 sec; (b) how high the ball will go; (c) how long it takes for the ball to reach the ground; (d) the instantaneous velocity of the ball when it reaches the ground.

30. Prove that the tangent lines to the curves $4y^3 - x^2y - x + 5y = 0$ and $x^4 - 4y^3 + 5x + y = 0$ at the origin are perpendicular.

31. Given
$$f(x) = \begin{cases} ax^2 + b & \text{if } x \le 1 \\ \dfrac{1}{|x|} & \text{if } x > 1 \end{cases}$$

Find the values of a and b so that $f'(1)$ exists.

32. Suppose
$$f(x) = \begin{cases} x^3 & \text{if } x < 1 \\ ax^2 + bx + c & \text{if } x \ge 1 \end{cases}$$

Find the values of a, b, and c so that $f''(1)$ exists.

33. A ship leaves a port at 12 noon and travels due west at 20 knots. At 12 noon the next day, a second ship leaves the same

port and travels northwest at 15 knots. How fast are the two ships separating when the second ship has traveled 90 nautical miles?

34. A particle is moving in a straight line according to the equation of motion $s = \sqrt{a + bt^2}$, where a and b are positive constants. Prove that the measure of the acceleration of the particle is inversely proportional to s^3 for any t.

35. A funnel in the form of a cone is 10 in. across the top and 8 in. deep. Water is flowing into the funnel at the rate of 12 in.^{3}/sec, and out at the rate of 4 in.^{3}/sec. How fast is the surface of the water rising when it is 5 in. deep?

36. As the last car of a train passes under a bridge, an automobile crosses the bridge on a roadway perpendicular to the track and 30 ft above it. The train is traveling at the rate of 80 ft/sec and the automobile is traveling at the rate of 40 ft/sec. How fast are the train and the automobile separating after 2 sec?

37. A particle is moving along the curve $x^2 - y^2 = 9$, and the ordinate of the point of its position is increasing at the rate of 3 units per second. How fast is the abscissa changing at the point $(5, -4)$?

38. Suppose y is the number of workers in the labor force needed to produce x units of a certain commodity, and $x = 4y^2$. If the production of the commodity this year is 250,000 units and the production is increasing at the rate of 18,000 units per year, what is the current rate at which the labor force should be increased?

39. Using Boyle's law for the expansion of gas (Exercise 10 in Exercises 3.9), find the rate of change of the pressure of a certain gas at the instant when the pressure is 8 lb/in.^{2} and the volume in 700 ft^3 if the volume of the gas is increasing at the rate of 3 ft^3/min.

40. If the two functions f and g are differentiable at the number x_1, is the composite function $f \circ g$ necessarily differentiable at x_1? If your answer is yes, prove it. If your answer is no, give a counterexample.

41. Suppose $f(x) = 3x + |x|$ and $g(x) = \frac{3}{4}x - \frac{1}{4}|x|$. Prove that neither $f'(0)$ nor $g'(0)$ exists but that $(f \circ g)'(0)$ does exist.

42. Give an example of two functions f and g for which f is differentiable at $g(0)$, g is not differentiable at 0, and $f \circ g$ is differentiable at 0.

43. Give an example of two functions f and g for which f is not differentiable at $g(0)$, g is differentiable at 0, and $f \circ g$ is differentiable at 0.

44. In Exercise 27 of Exercises 3.3, you are to prove that if f is differentiable at a, then

$$f'(a) = \lim_{\Delta x \to 0} \frac{f(a + \Delta x) - f(a - \Delta x)}{2 \, \Delta x}$$

Show by using the absolute value function that it is possible for the limit in the above equation to exist even though $f'(a)$ does not exist.

45. If $f'(x_1)$ exists, prove that

$$\lim_{x \to x_1} \frac{xf(x_1) - x_1 f(x)}{x - x_1} = f(x_1) - x_1 f'(x_1)$$

46. Let f and g be two functions whose domains are the set of all real numbers. Furthermore, suppose that (i) $g(x) = xf(x) + 1$; (ii) $g(a + b) = g(a) \cdot g(b)$ for all a and b; (iii) $\lim_{x \to 0} f(x) = 1$. Prove that $g'(x) = g(x)$.

47. The remainder theorem of elementary algebra states that if $P(x)$ is a polynomial in x and r is any real number, then there is a polynomial $Q(x)$ such that $P(x) = Q(x)(x - r) + P(r)$. What is $\lim_{x \to r} Q(x)$?

48. Suppose $g(x) = |f(x)|$. If $f^{(n)}(x)$ exists and $f(x) \neq 0$, prove that

$$g^{(n)}(x) = \frac{f(x)}{|f(x)|} f^{(n)}(x)$$

4

Topics on limits, continuity, and the derivative

4.1 LIMITS AT INFINITY

Figure 4.1.1

Consider the function f defined by the equation

$$f(x) = \frac{2x^2}{x^2 + 1}$$

A sketch of the graph of this function is shown in Fig. 4.1.1. Let x take on the values 0, 1, 2, 3, 4, 5, 10, 100, 1000, and so on, allowing x to increase without bound. The corresponding function values are given in Table 4.1.1.

Table 4.1.1

x	0	1	2	3	4	5	10	100	1000
$f(x) = \dfrac{2x^2}{x^2 + 1}$	0	1	$\dfrac{8}{5}$	$\dfrac{18}{10}$	$\dfrac{32}{17}$	$\dfrac{50}{26}$	$\dfrac{200}{101}$	$\dfrac{20{,}000}{10{,}001}$	$\dfrac{2{,}000{,}000}{1{,}000{,}001}$

We see from Table 4.1.1 that as x increases through positive values, the function values $f(x)$ get closer and closer to 2. In particular, when $x = 4$,

$$2 - \frac{2x^2}{x^2 + 1} = 2 - \frac{32}{17} = \frac{2}{17}$$

Therefore, the difference between 2 and $f(x)$ is $\frac{2}{17}$ when $x = 4$. When $x = 100$,

$$2 - \frac{2x^2}{x^2 + 1} = 2 - \frac{20{,}000}{10{,}001} = \frac{2}{10{,}001}$$

Hence, the difference between 2 and $f(x)$ is 2/10,001 when $x = 100$.

Continuing on, we intuitively see that we can make the value of $f(x)$ as close to 2 as we please by taking x large enough. In other words, we can make the difference between 2 and $f(x)$ as small as we please by taking x large enough; or going a step further, for any $\epsilon > 0$, however small, we can find a number $N > 0$ such that $|f(x) - 2| < \epsilon$ whenever $x > N$.

When an independent variable x is increasing without bound through positive values, we write "$x \to +\infty$." From the illustrative example above, then, we can say that

$$\lim_{x \to +\infty} \frac{2x^2}{x^2 + 1} = 2$$

In general, we have the following definition.

4.1.1 Definition   Let f be a function which is defined at every number in some interval $(a, +\infty)$. The *limit of $f(x)$, as x increases without bound, is L*, written

$$\lim_{x \to +\infty} f(x) = L \tag{1}$$

if for any $\epsilon > 0$, however small, there exists a number $N > 0$ such that

$$|f(x) - L| < \epsilon \quad \text{whenever} \quad x > N$$

NOTE: When we write $x \to +\infty$, it does not have the same meaning as, for instance, $x \to 1000$. The symbolism "$x \to +\infty$" indicates the behavior of the variable x. However, we can read Eq. (1) as "the limit of $f(x)$ as x approaches positive infinity is L," bearing in mind this note.

Now let us consider the same function and let x take on the values $0, -1, -2, -3, -4, -5, -10, -100, -1000$, and so on, allowing x to decrease through negative values without bound. Table 4.1.2 gives the corresponding function values of $f(x)$.

Table 4.1.2

x	0	−1	−2	−3	−4	−5	−10	−100	−1000
$f(x) = \dfrac{2x^2}{x^2 + 1}$	0	1	$\dfrac{8}{5}$	$\dfrac{18}{10}$	$\dfrac{32}{17}$	$\dfrac{50}{26}$	$\dfrac{200}{101}$	$\dfrac{20{,}000}{10{,}001}$	$\dfrac{2{,}000{,}000}{1{,}000{,}001}$

Observe that the function values are the same for the negative numbers as for the corresponding positive numbers. So we intuitively see that as x decreases without bound, $f(x)$ approaches 2, and formally we say that for any $\epsilon > 0$, however small, we can find a number $N < 0$ such that $|f(x) - 2| < \epsilon$ whenever $x < N$. Using the symbolism "$x \to -\infty$" to denote that the variable x is decreasing without bound, we write

$$\lim_{x \to -\infty} \frac{2x^2}{x^2 + 1} = 2 \tag{2}$$

In general, we have the following definition.

4.1.2 Definition   Let f be a function which is defined at every number in some interval $(-\infty, a)$. The *limit of $f(x)$, as x decreases without bound, is L,* written

$$\lim_{x \to -\infty} f(x) = L$$

if for any $\epsilon > 0$, however small, there exists a number $N < 0$ such that

$$|f(x) - L| < \epsilon \quad \text{whenever} \quad x < N$$

NOTE: As in the note following Definition 4.1.1, the symbolism "$x \to -\infty$" only indicates the behavior of the variable x, but we can read Eq. (2) as "the limit of $f(x)$ as x approaches negative infinity is L."

Limit theorems 2, 4, 5, 6, 7, 8, 9, and 10 given in Sec. 2.2 and Limit theorems 11 and 12 given in Sec. 2.4 remain unchanged when "$x \to a$" is replaced by $x \to +\infty$ or $x \to -\infty$. We have the following additional limit theorem.

4.1.3 Limit theorem 13   If r is any positive integer, then

$$\text{(i) } \lim_{x \to +\infty} \frac{1}{x^r} = 0 \qquad \text{(ii) } \lim_{x \to -\infty} \frac{1}{x^r} = 0$$

PROOF OF (i): To prove part (i), we must show that Definition 4.1.1 holds for $f(x) = 1/x^r$ and $L = 0$; that is, we must show that for any $\epsilon > 0$ there exists a number $N > 0$ such that

$$\left|\frac{1}{x^r} - 0\right| < \epsilon \quad \text{whenever} \quad x > N$$

or, equivalently,

$$|x|^r > \frac{1}{\epsilon} \quad \text{whenever} \quad x > N$$

or, equivalently, since $r > 0$,

$$|x| > \left(\frac{1}{\epsilon}\right)^{1/r} \quad \text{whenever} \quad x > N$$

In order for the above to hold, take $N = (1/\epsilon)^{1/r}$. Thus, we can conclude that

$$\left|\frac{1}{x^r} - 0\right| < \epsilon \quad \text{whenever} \quad x > N, \text{ if } N = \left(\frac{1}{\epsilon}\right)^{1/r}$$

This proves part (i). ∎

The proof of part (ii) is analogous and is left as an exercise (see Exercise 22).

EXAMPLE 1: Find

$$\lim_{x \to +\infty} \frac{4x - 3}{2x + 5}$$

and when applicable indicate the limit theorems being used.

SOLUTION: To use Limit theorem 13, we divide the numerator and the denominator by x, thus giving us

$$\lim_{x \to +\infty} \frac{4x - 3}{2x + 5} = \lim_{x \to +\infty} \frac{4 - 3/x}{2 + 5/x}$$

$$= \frac{\lim\limits_{x \to +\infty} (4 - 3/x)}{\lim\limits_{x \to +\infty} (2 + 5/x)} \qquad \text{(L.T. 9)}$$

$$= \frac{\lim\limits_{x \to +\infty} 4 - \lim\limits_{x \to +\infty} (3/x)}{\lim\limits_{x \to +\infty} 2 + \lim\limits_{x \to +\infty} (5/x)} \qquad \text{(L.T. 4)}$$

$$= \frac{\lim\limits_{x \to +\infty} 4 - \lim\limits_{x \to +\infty} 3 \cdot \lim\limits_{x \to +\infty} (1/x)}{\lim\limits_{x \to +\infty} 2 + \lim\limits_{x \to +\infty} 5 \cdot \lim\limits_{x \to +\infty} (1/x)} \qquad \text{(L.T. 6)}$$

$$= \frac{4 - 3 \cdot 0}{2 + 5 \cdot 0} \qquad \text{(L.T. 2 and L.T. 13)}$$

$$= 2$$

EXAMPLE 2: Find

$$\lim_{x \to -\infty} \frac{2x^2 - x + 5}{4x^3 - 1}$$

and when applicable indicate the limit theorems being used.

SOLUTION: To use Limit theorem 13, we divide the numerator and the denominator by the highest power of x occurring in either the numerator or denominator, which in this case is x^3. So we have

$$\lim_{x \to -\infty} \frac{2x^2 - x + 5}{4x^3 - 1} = \lim_{x \to -\infty} \frac{2/x - 1/x^2 + 5/x^3}{4 - 1/x^3}$$

$$= \frac{\lim_{x \to -\infty} (2/x - 1/x^2 + 5/x^3)}{\lim_{x \to -\infty} (4 - 1/x^3)} \qquad \text{(L.T. 9)}$$

$$= \frac{\lim_{x \to -\infty} (2/x) - \lim_{x \to -\infty} (1/x^2) + \lim_{x \to -\infty} (5/x^3)}{\lim_{x \to -\infty} 4 - \lim_{x \to -\infty} (1/x^3)} \qquad \text{(L.T. 5)}$$

$$= \frac{\lim_{x \to -\infty} 2 \cdot \lim_{x \to -\infty} (1/x) - \lim_{x \to -\infty} (1/x^2) + \lim_{x \to -\infty} 5 \cdot \lim_{x \to -\infty} (1/x^3)}{\lim_{x \to -\infty} 4 - \lim_{x \to -\infty} (1/x^3)} \qquad \text{(L.T. 6)}$$

$$= \frac{2 \cdot 0 - 0 + 5 \cdot 0}{4 - 0} \qquad \text{(L.T. 2 and L.T. 13)}$$

$$= 0$$

EXAMPLE 3: Find

$$\lim_{x \to +\infty} \frac{3x + 4}{\sqrt{2x^2 - 5}}$$

and when applicable indicate the limit theorems being used.

SOLUTION: We divide the numerator and the denominator of the fraction by x. In the denominator we let $x = \sqrt{x^2}$ since we are considering only positive values of x.

$$\lim_{x \to +\infty} \frac{3x + 4}{\sqrt{2x^2 - 5}} = \lim_{x \to +\infty} \frac{3 + 4/x}{\sqrt{2x^2 - 5}/\sqrt{x^2}}$$

$$= \frac{\lim_{x \to +\infty} (3 + 4/x)}{\lim_{x \to +\infty} \sqrt{2 - 5/x^2}} \qquad \text{(L.T. 9)}$$

$$= \frac{\lim_{x \to +\infty} (3 + 4/x)}{\sqrt{\lim_{x \to +\infty} (2 - 5/x^2)}} \qquad \text{(L.T. 10)}$$

$$= \frac{\lim_{x \to +\infty} 3 + \lim_{x \to +\infty} (4/x)}{\sqrt{\lim_{x \to +\infty} 2 - \lim_{x \to +\infty} (5/x^2)}} \qquad \text{(L.T. 4)}$$

$$= \frac{\lim_{x \to +\infty} 3 + \lim_{x \to +\infty} 4 \cdot \lim_{x \to +\infty} (1/x)}{\sqrt{\lim_{x \to +\infty} 2 - \lim_{x \to +\infty} 5 \cdot \lim_{x \to +\infty} (1/x^2)}} \qquad \text{(L.T. 6)}$$

$$= \frac{3 + 4 \cdot 0}{\sqrt{2 - 5 \cdot 0}} \qquad \text{(L.T. 2 and L.T. 13)}$$

$$= \frac{3}{\sqrt{2}}$$

EXAMPLE 4:   Find

$$\lim_{x \to -\infty} \frac{3x + 4}{\sqrt{2x^2 - 5}}$$

SOLUTION: The function is the same as the one in Example 3; however, since we are considering negative values of x, in this case $\sqrt{x^2} = -x$ or, equivalently, $-\sqrt{x^2} = x$. Hence, in the first step when we divide numerator and denominator by x, we let $x = -\sqrt{x^2}$ in the denominator, and we have

$$\lim_{x \to -\infty} \frac{3x + 4}{\sqrt{2x^2 - 5}} = \lim_{x \to -\infty} \frac{3 + 4/x}{\sqrt{2x^2 - 5}/(-\sqrt{x^2})}$$

$$= \frac{\lim_{x \to -\infty} (3 + 4/x)}{\lim_{x \to -\infty} (-\sqrt{2 - 5/x^2})}$$

$$= \frac{\lim_{x \to -\infty} 3 + \lim_{x \to -\infty} (4/x)}{-\sqrt{\lim_{x \to -\infty} (2 - 5/x^2)}}$$

The remaining steps are similar to those in the solution of Example 3, and in the denominator we obtain $-\sqrt{2}$ instead of $\sqrt{2}$. Hence, the limit is $-3/\sqrt{2}$.

"Infinite" limits at infinity can be considered. There are formal definitions for each of the following.

$$\lim_{x \to +\infty} f(x) = +\infty \qquad \lim_{x \to -\infty} f(x) = +\infty$$

$$\lim_{x \to +\infty} f(x) = -\infty \qquad \lim_{x \to -\infty} f(x) = -\infty$$

For example, $\lim_{x \to +\infty} f(x) = +\infty$ if the function f is defined on some interval $(a, +\infty)$ and if for any number $N > 0$ there exists an $M > 0$ such that $f(x) > N$ whenever $x > M$. The other definitions are left as an exercise (see Exercise 17).

EXAMPLE 5:   Find

$$\lim_{x \to +\infty} \frac{x^2}{x + 1}$$

SOLUTION: Dividing the numerator and the denominator by x^2, we obtain

$$\lim_{x \to +\infty} \frac{x^2}{x + 1} = \lim_{x \to +\infty} \frac{1}{1/x + 1/x^2}$$

Evaluating the limit of the denominator, we have

$$\lim_{x \to +\infty} \left(\frac{1}{x} + \frac{1}{x^2} \right) = \lim_{x \to +\infty} \frac{1}{x} + \lim_{x \to +\infty} \frac{1}{x^2} = 0 + 0 = 0$$

Therefore, the limit of the denominator is 0, and the denominator is approaching 0 through positive values.

The limit of the numerator is 1, and so by Limit theorem 12(i) (2.4.4) it follows that

$$\lim_{x \to +\infty} \frac{x^2}{x + 1} = +\infty$$

EXAMPLE 6: Find

$$\lim_{x \to +\infty} \frac{2x - x^2}{3x + 5}$$

SOLUTION: $\lim_{x \to +\infty} \dfrac{2x - x^2}{3x + 5} = \lim_{x \to +\infty} \dfrac{2/x - 1}{3/x + 5/x^2}$

We consider the limits of the numerator and the denominator separately.

$$\lim_{x \to +\infty} \left(\frac{2}{x} - 1\right) = \lim_{x \to +\infty} \frac{2}{x} - \lim_{x \to +\infty} 1 = 0 - 1 = -1$$

$$\lim_{x \to +\infty} \left(\frac{3}{x} + \frac{5}{x^2}\right) = \lim_{x \to +\infty} \frac{3}{x} + \lim_{x \to +\infty} \frac{5}{x^2} = 0 + 0 = 0$$

Therefore, we have the limit of a quotient in which the limit of the numerator is -1 and the limit of the denominator is 0, where the denominator is approaching 0 through positive values. By Limit theorem 12(iii) it follows that

$$\lim_{x \to +\infty} \frac{2x - x^2}{3x + 5} = -\infty$$

Exercises 4.1

In Exercises 1 through 14, find the limits, and when applicable indicate the limit theorems being used.

1. $\lim_{x \to +\infty} \dfrac{2x + 1}{5x - 2}$

2. $\lim_{s \to +\infty} \dfrac{4s^2 + 3}{2s^2 - 1}$

3. $\lim_{x \to +\infty} \dfrac{x + 4}{3x^2 - 5}$

4. $\lim_{x \to +\infty} \dfrac{x^2 - 2x + 5}{7x^3 + x + 1}$

5. $\lim_{y \to +\infty} \dfrac{\sqrt{y^2 + 4}}{y + 4}$

6. $\lim_{x \to -\infty} \dfrac{\sqrt{x^2 + 4}}{x + 4}$

7. $\lim_{x \to -\infty} \dfrac{4x^3 + 2x^2 - 5}{8x^3 + x + 2}$

8. $\lim_{x \to +\infty} \dfrac{3x^4 - 7x^2 + 2}{2x^4 + 1}$

9. $\lim_{x \to +\infty} (\sqrt{x^2 + 1} - x)$

10. $\lim_{x \to +\infty} (\sqrt{x^2 + x} - x)$

11. $\lim_{x \to -\infty} (\sqrt[3]{x^3 + x} - \sqrt[3]{x^3 + 1})$

12. $\lim_{t \to +\infty} \dfrac{\sqrt{t + \sqrt{t + \sqrt{t}}}}{\sqrt{t + 1}}$

13. $\lim_{y \to +\infty} \dfrac{2y^3 - 4}{5y + 3}$

14. $\lim_{x \to -\infty} \dfrac{5x^3 - 12x + 7}{4x^2 - 1}$

For the functions defined in Exercises 15 and 16, prove that $\lim_{x \to +\infty} f(x) = 1$ by applying Definition 4.1.1; that is, for any $\epsilon > 0$, show that there exists a number $N > 0$ such that $|f(x) - 1| < \epsilon$ whenever $x > N$.

15. $f(x) = \dfrac{x}{x - 1}$

16. $f(x) = \dfrac{x^2 + 2x}{x^2 - 1}$

17. Give a definition for each of the following: (a) $\lim_{x \to +\infty} f(x) = -\infty$; (b) $\lim_{x \to -\infty} f(x) = +\infty$; (c) $\lim_{x \to -\infty} f(x) = -\infty$.

18. Prove that $\lim_{x \to +\infty} (x^2 - 4) = +\infty$ by showing that for any $N > 0$ there exists an $M > 0$ such that $(x^2 - 4) > N$ whenever $x > M$.

19. Prove that $\lim_{x \to +\infty} (6 - x - x^2) = -\infty$ by applying the definition in Exercise 17(a).

20. Prove part (i) of Limit theorem 12 (2.4.4) if "$x \to a$" is replaced by "$x \to +\infty$."

21. Prove that

$$\lim_{x \to -\infty} \frac{8x+3}{2x-1} = 4$$

by showing that for any $\epsilon > 0$ there exists a number $N < 0$ such that

$$\left| \frac{8x+3}{2x-1} - 4 \right| < \epsilon$$

whenever $x < N$.

22. Prove part (ii) of Limit theorem 13 (4.1.3).

23. The function f is defined by

$$f(x) = \lim_{n \to +\infty} \frac{2nx}{1-nx}$$

Draw a sketch of the graph of f. At what values of x is f discontinuous?

4.2 HORIZONTAL AND VERTICAL ASYMPTOTES

An aid in drawing the sketch of the graph of a function is to find, if there are any, the "horizontal and vertical asymptotes" of the graph. Consider the function f defined by

$$f(x) = \frac{1}{(x-a)^2} \tag{1}$$

Figure 4.2.1

A sketch of the graph of f is in Fig. 4.2.1. Any line parallel to and above the x axis will intersect this graph in two points: one point to the left of the line $x = a$ and one point to the right of this line. Thus, for any $k > 0$, no matter how large, the line $y = k$ will intersect the graph of f in two points; the distance of these two points from the line $x = a$ gets smaller and smaller as k gets larger and larger. The line $x = a$ is called a "vertical asymptote" of the graph of f. Following is the definition of a vertical asymptote.

4.2.1 Definition

The line $x = a$ is said to be a *vertical asymptote* of the graph of the function f if at least one of the following statements is true:

(i) $\lim\limits_{x \to a^+} f(x) = +\infty$.

(ii) $\lim\limits_{x \to a^+} f(x) = -\infty$.

(iii) $\lim\limits_{x \to a^-} f(x) = +\infty$.

(iv) $\lim\limits_{x \to a^-} f(x) = -\infty$.

For the function defined by Eq. (1), both parts (i) and (iii) of the above definition are true. If g is the function defined by

$$g(x) = -\frac{1}{(x-a)^2}$$

Figure 4.2.2

then both parts (ii) and (iv) are true, and the line $x = a$ is a vertical asymptote of the graph of g. This is shown in Fig. 4.2.2.

A "horizontal asymptote" of a graph is a line parallel to the x axis.

4.2.2 Definition The line $y = b$ is said to be a *horizontal asymptote* of the graph of the function f if at least one of the following statements is true:

(i) $\lim\limits_{x \to +\infty} f(x) = b$.

(ii) $\lim\limits_{x \to -\infty} f(x) = b$.

EXAMPLE 1: Find the horizontal asymptotes of the graph of the function f defined by

$$f(x) = \frac{x}{\sqrt{x^2 + 1}}$$

and draw a sketch of the graph.

SOLUTION: First we consider $\lim\limits_{x \to +\infty} f(x)$, and we have

$$\lim_{x \to +\infty} f(x) = \lim_{x \to +\infty} \frac{x}{\sqrt{x^2 + 1}}$$

To evaluate this limit we write $x = \sqrt{x^2}$ ($x > 0$, because $x \to +\infty$) and then divide the numerator and the denominator, under the radical sign, by x^2.

$$\lim_{x \to +\infty} \frac{x}{\sqrt{x^2 + 1}} = \lim_{x \to +\infty} \frac{\sqrt{x^2}}{\sqrt{x^2 + 1}}$$

$$= \lim_{x \to +\infty} \sqrt{\frac{1}{1 + 1/x^2}}$$

$$= \sqrt{\frac{1}{1 + \lim\limits_{x \to +\infty} (1/x^2)}}$$

$$= 1$$

Therefore, by Definition 4.2.2(i), the line $y = 1$ is a horizontal asymptote.

Now we consider $\lim\limits_{x \to -\infty} f(x)$; in this case we write $x = -\sqrt{x^2}$ because if $x \to -\infty$, $x < 0$. So we have

$$\lim_{x \to -\infty} f(x) = \lim_{x \to -\infty} \frac{-\sqrt{x^2}}{\sqrt{x^2 + 1}}$$

$$= \lim_{x \to -\infty} -\sqrt{\frac{1}{1 + 1/x^2}}$$

$$= -\sqrt{\frac{1}{1 + \lim\limits_{x \to -\infty} (1/x^2)}}$$

$$= -1$$

Accordingly, by Definition 4.2.2(ii), the line $y = -1$ is a horizontal asymptote. A sketch of the graph is in Fig. 4.2.3.

Figure 4.2.3

EXAMPLE 2: Find the vertical and horizontal asymptotes of the graph of the equation

SOLUTION: Solving the given equation for y, we obtain

$$y = \pm 2 \sqrt{\frac{x}{x - 2}} \qquad (2)$$

$xy^2 - 2y^2 - 4x = 0$, and draw a sketch of the graph.

Figure 4.2.4

Figure 4.2.5

Figure 4.2.6

Equation (2) defines two functions:

$$y = f_1(x) \quad \text{where } f_1 \text{ is defined by} \quad f_1(x) = +2\sqrt{\frac{x}{x-2}}$$

and

$$y = f_2(x) \quad \text{where } f_2 \text{ is defined by} \quad f_2(x) = -2\sqrt{\frac{x}{x-2}}$$

The graph of the given equation is composed of the graphs of the two functions f_1 and f_2. The domains of the two functions consist of those values of x for which $x/(x-2) \geq 0$. By using the result of Example 8, Sec. 1.7, and excluding $x = 2$, we see that the domain of f_1 and f_2 is $(-\infty, 0] \cup (2, +\infty)$.

Now, consider f_1. Because

$$\lim_{x \to 2^+} f_1(x) = \lim_{x \to 2^+} 2\sqrt{\frac{x}{x-2}} = +\infty$$

by Definition 4.2.1(i) the line $x = 2$ is a vertical asymptote of the graph of f_1.

$$\lim_{x \to +\infty} f_1(x) = \lim_{x \to +\infty} 2\sqrt{\frac{x}{x-2}} = \lim_{x \to +\infty} 2\sqrt{\frac{1}{1-2/x}} = 2$$

So by Definition 4.2.2(i) the line $y = 2$ is a horizontal asymptote of the graph of f_1.

Similarly, $\lim_{x \to -\infty} f_1(x) = 2$. A sketch of the graph of f_1 is shown in Fig. 4.2.4.

$$\lim_{x \to 2^+} f_2(x) = \lim_{x \to 2^+} \left[-2\sqrt{\frac{x}{x-2}}\right] = -\infty$$

Hence, by Definition 4.2.1(ii) the line $x = 2$ is a vertical asymptote of the graph of f_2.

$$\lim_{x \to +\infty} f_2(x) = \lim_{x \to +\infty} \left[-2\sqrt{\frac{x}{x-2}}\right] = \lim_{x \to +\infty} \left[-2\sqrt{\frac{1}{1-2/x}}\right] = -2$$

So by Definition 4.2.2(i) the line $y = -2$ is a horizontal asymptote of the graph of f_2.

Also, $\lim_{x \to -\infty} f_2(x) = -2$. A sketch of the graph of f_2 is shown in Fig. 4.2.5.

The graph of the given equation is the union of the graphs of f_1 and f_2, and a sketch is shown in Fig. 4.2.6.

Exercises 4.2

In Exercises 1 through 14, find the horizontal and vertical asymptotes of the graph of the function defined by the given equation, and draw a sketch of the graph.

1. $f(x) = \dfrac{4}{x-5}$

2. $f(x) = \dfrac{-2}{x+3}$

3. $g(x) = \dfrac{-3}{(x+2)^2}$

4. $F(x) = \dfrac{5}{x^2 + 8x + 16}$

5. $f(x) = \dfrac{1}{x^2 + 5x - 6}$

6. $G(x) = \dfrac{2x}{6x^2 + 11x - 10}$

7. $h(x) = \dfrac{4x^2}{x^2 - 9}$

8. $f(x) = \dfrac{x^2}{4 - x^2}$

9. $f(x) = \dfrac{2}{\sqrt{x^2 - 4}}$

10. $g(x) = \dfrac{-1}{\sqrt{x^2 + 5x + 6}}$

11. $F(x) = \dfrac{-3x}{\sqrt{x^2 + 3}}$

12. $h(x) = \dfrac{x}{\sqrt{x^2 - 9}}$

13. $f(x) = \dfrac{4x^2}{\sqrt{x^2 - 2}}$

14. $f(x) = \dfrac{-3x^2}{\sqrt{x^2 + 7x + 10}}$

In Exercises 15 through 21, find the horizontal and vertical asymptotes of the graph of the given equation, and draw a sketch of the graph.

15. $3xy - 2x - 4y - 3 = 0$

16. $2xy + 4x - 3y + 6 = 0$

17. $x^2y^2 - x^2 + 4y^2 = 0$

18. $2xy^2 + 4y^2 - 3x = 0$

19. $(y^2 - 1)(x - 3) = 6$

20. $xy^2 + 3y^2 - 9x = 0$

21. $x^2y + 6xy - x^2 + 2x + 9y + 3 = 0$

4.3 ADDITIONAL THEOREMS ON LIMITS OF FUNCTIONS

We now discuss five theorems which are needed to prove some important theorems in later sections. After the statement of each theorem, a graphical illustration is given.

4.3.1 Theorem If $\lim\limits_{x \to a} f(x)$ exists and is positive, then there is an open interval containing a such that $f(x) > 0$ for every $x \neq a$ in the interval.

• ILLUSTRATION 1: Consider the function f defined by

$$f(x) = \frac{5}{2x - 1}$$

A sketch of the graph of f is in Fig. 4.3.1. Because $\lim\limits_{x \to 3} f(x) = 1$, and $1 > 0$, according to Theorem 4.3.1 there is an open interval containing 3 such that $f(x) > 0$ for every $x \neq 3$ in the interval. Such an interval is $(2, 4)$. Actually, any open interval (a, b) for which $\frac{1}{2} \leq a < 3$ and $b > 3$ will do. •

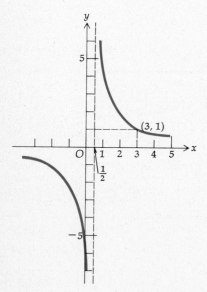

Figure 4.3.1

PROOF OF THEOREM 4.3.1: Let $L = \lim\limits_{x \to a} f(x)$. By hypothesis, $L > 0$. Applying Definition 2.1.1 and taking $\epsilon = \frac{1}{2}L$, we know there is a $\delta > 0$ such that

$$|f(x) - L| < \tfrac{1}{2}L \quad \text{whenever} \quad 0 < |x - a| < \delta \tag{1}$$

Also, $|f(x) - L| < \frac{1}{2}L$ is equivalent to $-\frac{1}{2}L < f(x) - L < \frac{1}{2}L$ (refer to Theorem 1.2.2), which in turn is equivalent to

$$\tfrac{1}{2}L < f(x) < \tfrac{3}{2}L \tag{2}$$

Also, $0 < |x - a| < \delta$ is equivalent to $-\delta < x - a < \delta$ but $x \neq a$, which in turn is equivalent to

$$a - \delta < x < a + \delta \quad \text{but} \quad x \neq a$$

which is equivalent to stating that

$$x \text{ is in the open interval } (a - \delta, a + \delta) \quad \text{but} \quad x \neq a \tag{3}$$

From statements (2) and (3), we can replace (1) by the statement

$$\tfrac{1}{2}L < f(x) < \tfrac{3}{2}L \quad \text{when } x \text{ is in the open interval } (a - \delta, a + \delta) \text{ but } x \neq a$$

Since $L > 0$, we have the conclusion that $f(x) > 0$ for every $x \neq a$ in the open interval $(a - \delta, a + \delta)$. ∎

4.3.2 Theorem If $\lim\limits_{x \to a} f(x)$ exists and is negative, there is an open interval containing a such that $f(x) < 0$ for every $x \neq a$ in the interval.

The proof of this theorem is similar to the proof of Theorem 4.3.1 and is left as an exercise (See Exercise 1).

● ILLUSTRATION 2: Let

$$g(x) = \frac{6 - x}{3 - 2x}$$

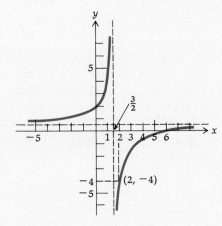

Figure 4.3.2

Figure 4.3.2 shows a sketch of the graph of g. $\lim\limits_{x \to 2} g(x) = -4 < 0$; hence, by Theorem 4.3.2 there is an open interval containing 2 such that $g(x) < 0$ for every $x \neq 2$ in the interval. Such an interval is $(\tfrac{3}{2}, 3)$. Any open interval (a, b) for which $\tfrac{3}{2} \leq a < 2$ and $2 < b \leq 6$ will suffice. ●

The following theorem is sometimes referred to as the *squeeze theorem.*

4.3.3 Theorem Suppose that the functions f, g, and h are defined on some open interval I containing a except possibly at a itself, and that $f(x) \leq g(x) \leq h(x)$ for all x in I for which $x \neq a$. Also suppose that $\lim\limits_{x \to a} f(x)$ and $\lim\limits_{x \to a} h(x)$ both exist and are equal to L. Then $\lim\limits_{x \to a} g(x)$ also exists and is equal to L.

The proof is left as an exercise (see Exercise 2).

● ILLUSTRATION 3: Consider the functions f, g, and h defined by

$$f(x) = -4(x - 2)^2 + 3$$

$$g(x) = \frac{(x - 2)(x^2 - 4x + 7)}{x - 2}$$

$$h(x) = 4(x - 2)^2 + 3$$

The graphs of the functions f and h are parabolas having their vertex at

(2, 3). The graph of g is a parabola with its vertex (2, 3) deleted. Sketches of these graphs are shown in Fig. 4.3.3. The function g is not defined when $x = 2$; however, for all $x \neq 2$, $f(x) \leq g(x) \leq h(x)$. Furthermore, $\lim_{x \to 2} f(x) = 3$ and $\lim_{x \to 2} h(x) = 3$. The hypothesis of Theorem 4.3.3 is therefore satisfied, and it follows that $\lim_{x \to 2} g(x) = 3$. ●

Figure 4.3.3

4.3.4 Theorem   Suppose that the function f is defined on some open interval I containing a, except possibly at a. Also suppose that there is some number M for which there is a $\delta > 0$ such that $f(x) \leq M$ whenever $0 < |x - a| < \delta$. Then, if $\lim_{x \to a} f(x)$ exists and is equal to L, $L \leq M$.

● ILLUSTRATION 4: Figure 4.3.4 shows a sketch of the graph of a function f satisfying the hypothesis of Theorem 4.3.4. From the figure we see that $f(1)$ is not defined, but f is defined on the open interval $(\frac{1}{2}, \frac{3}{2})$ except at 1. Furthermore, $f(x) \leq \frac{9}{4}$ whenever $0 < |x - 1| < \frac{1}{2}$. Thus, we can conclude from Theorem 4.3.4 that if $\lim_{x \to 1} f(x)$ exists and is L, then $L \leq \frac{9}{4}$. From the figure we observe that there is an L and it is 2. ●

PROOF OF THEOREM 4.3.4:   We assume that $M < L$ and show that this as-

Figure 4.3.4

sumption leads to a contradiction. If $M < L$, there is some $\epsilon > 0$ such that $M + \epsilon = L$. Because $\lim\limits_{x \to a} f(x) = L$, there exists a $\delta_1 > 0$ such that

$$|f(x) - L| < \epsilon \quad \text{whenever} \quad 0 < |x - a| < \delta_1$$

which is equivalent to

$$L - \epsilon < f(x) < L + \epsilon \quad \text{whenever} \quad 0 < |x - a| < \delta_1$$

Replace L by $M + \epsilon$; it follows that there exists a $\delta_1 > 0$ such that

$$(M + \epsilon) - \epsilon < f(x) \quad \text{whenever} \quad 0 < |x - a| < \delta_1$$

or, equivalently,

$$M < f(x) \quad \text{whenever} \quad 0 < |x - a| < \delta_1 \tag{4}$$

But, by hypothesis, there is a δ such that

$$f(x) \le M \quad \text{whenever} \quad 0 < |x - a| < \delta \tag{5}$$

Statements (4) and (5) contradict each other. Hence, our assumption that $M < L$ is false. Therefore, $L \le M$. ∎

4.3.5 Theorem Suppose that the function f is defined on some open interval I containing a, except possibly at a. Also suppose that there is some number M for which there is a $\delta > 0$ such that $f(x) \ge M$ whenever $0 < |x - a| < \delta$. Then if $\lim\limits_{x \to a} f(x)$ exists and is equal to L, $L \ge M$.

The proof is left as an exercise (See Exercise 3).

● ILLUSTRATION 5: Figure 4.3.4 also illustrates Theorem 4.3.5. From the figure we see that $f(x) \ge \frac{3}{2}$ whenever $0 < |x - 1| < \frac{1}{2}$; and, because as previously stated, f is defined on the open interval $(\frac{1}{2}, \frac{3}{2})$ except at 1, Theorem 4.3.5 states that if $\lim\limits_{x \to 1} f(x)$ exists and is L, then $L \ge \frac{3}{2}$. ●

Exercises 4.3

1. Prove Theorem 4.3.2.

2. Prove Theorem 4.3.3. (HINT: First show that when $|x - a|$ is sufficiently small, and $\epsilon > 0$, the following inequalities must hold: $L - \epsilon < f(x) < L + \epsilon$, and $L - \epsilon < h(x) < L + \epsilon$.)

3. Prove Theorem 4.3.5.

4. Let f be a function such that $|f(x)| \le x^2$ for all x. Prove that f is differentiable at 0 and that $f'(0) = 0$. (HINT: Use Theorem 4.3.3.)

4.4 CONTINUITY ON AN INTERVAL In Example 3 of Sec. 2.6 we showed that the function h, for which $h(x) = \sqrt{4 - x^2}$, is continuous at every number in the open interval

$(-2, 2)$. Because of this fact, we say that h is continuous on the open interval $(-2, 2)$. Following is the general definition of continuity on an open interval.

4.4.1 Definition A function is said to be *continuous on an open interval* if and only if it is continuous at every number in the open interval.

EXAMPLE 1: If $f(x) = 1/(x - 3)$, on what open intervals is f continuous?

SOLUTION: The function f is continuous at every number except 3. Hence, by Definition 4.4.1, f is continuous on every open interval which does not contain the number 3.

We refer again to the function h for which $h(x) = \sqrt{4 - x^2}$. We know that h is continuous on the open interval $(-2, 2)$. However, because h is not defined on any open interval containing either -2 or 2, we cannot consider $\lim_{x \to -2} h(x)$ or $\lim_{x \to 2} h(x)$. Hence, to discuss the question of the continuity of h on the closed interval $[-2, 2]$, we must extend the concept of continuity to include continuity at an endpoint of a closed interval. We do this by first defining *right-hand continuity* and *left-hand continuity*.

4.4.2 Definition The function f is said to be *continuous from the right at the number a* if and only if the following three conditions are satisfied:

(i) $f(a)$ exists.
(ii) $\lim_{x \to a^+} f(x)$ exists.
(iii) $\lim_{x \to a^+} f(x) = f(a)$.

4.4.3 Definition The function f is said to be *continuous from the left at the number a* if and only if the following three conditions are satisfied:

(i) $f(a)$ exists.
(ii) $\lim_{x \to a^-} f(x)$ exists.
(iii) $\lim_{x \to a^-} f(x) = f(a)$.

4.4.4 Definition A function whose domain includes the closed interval $[a, b]$ is said to be continuous on $[a, b]$ if and only if it is continuous on the open interval (a, b), as well as continuous from the right at a and continuous from the left at b.

EXAMPLE 2: Prove that the function h, for which $h(x) = \sqrt{4 - x^2}$, is continuous on the closed interval $[-2, 2]$.

SOLUTION: The function h is continuous on the open interval $(-2, 2)$ and

$$\lim_{x \to -2^+} \sqrt{4 - x^2} = 0 = h(-2)$$

and

$$\lim_{x \to 2^-} \sqrt{4 - x^2} = 0 = h(2)$$

Thus, by Definition 4.4.4, h is continuous on the closed interval $[-2, 2]$.

4.4.5 Definition

(i) A function whose domain includes the interval half-open on the right $[a, b)$ is said to be continuous on $[a, b)$ if and only if it is continuous on the open interval (a, b) and continuous from the right at a.

(ii) A function whose domain includes the interval half-open on the left $(a, b]$ is said to be continuous on $(a, b]$ if and only if it is continuous on the open interval (a, b) and continuous from the left at b.

EXAMPLE 3:   Given f is the function defined by

$$f(x) = \sqrt{\frac{2 - x}{3 + x}}$$

determine whether f is continuous or discontinuous on each of the following intervals: $(-3, 2)$, $[-3, 2]$, $[-3, 2)$, $(-3, 2]$.

SOLUTION: We first determine the domain of f. The domain of f is the set of all numbers for which $(2 - x)/(3 + x)$ is nonnegative. Thus, any values of x for which the numerator and the denominator of this fraction have opposite signs are excluded from the domain. The numerator changes sign when $x = 2$, and the denominator changes sign when $x = -3$. We make use of Table 4.4.1 to determine when the fraction is positive, negative, zero, or undefined, from which we are able to determine the values of x for which $f(x)$ exists. The domain of f is then the interval half-open on the left $(-3, 2]$. The function f is continuous on the open interval $(-3, 2)$. It is continuous from the left at 2 because

$$\lim_{x \to 2^-} \sqrt{\frac{2 - x}{3 + x}} = 0 = f(2)$$

However, f is not continuous from the right at -3 because

$$\lim_{x \to -3^+} \sqrt{\frac{2 - x}{3 + x}} = +\infty$$

We conclude that f is continuous on $(-3, 2]$ and discontinuous on $[-3, 2]$ and $[-3, 2)$.

Table 4.4.1

	$2 - x$	$3 + x$	$\dfrac{2 - x}{3 + x}$	$f(x)$
$x < -3$	+	−	−	does not exist
$x = -3$	5	0	undefined	does not exist
$-3 < x < 2$	+	+	+	+
$x = 2$	0	5	0	0
$2 < x$	−	+	−	does not exist

EXAMPLE 4: Given $g(x) = [\![x]\!]$ and $1 \leq x \leq 3$. Discuss the continuity of g.

Figure 4.4.1

SOLUTION: Figure 4.4.1 shows a sketch of the graph of g. Suppose that u is any number in $(1, 2)$. Then $[\![u]\!] = 1$, and $\lim_{x \to u} [\![x]\!] = 1$. Hence, if $1 < u < 2$, $\lim_{x \to u} g(x) = g(u)$, and so g is continuous on $(1, 2)$.

$$\lim_{x \to 1^+} g(x) = \lim_{x \to 1^+} [\![x]\!] = 1 = g(1)$$

Therefore, g is continuous from the right at 1. But

$$\lim_{x \to 2^-} g(x) = \lim_{x \to 2^-} [\![x]\!] = 1$$

and $g(2) = 2$. So g is not continuous from the left at 2. The function g is therefore continuous on the interval half-open on the right $[1, 2)$.

Similarly, g is continuous at every number u for which $2 < u < 3$. At 2, g is continuous from the right since $\lim_{x \to 2^+} g(x) = g(2)$, but g is not continuous from the left at 3 because $\lim_{x \to 3^-} g(x) = 2$ and $g(3) = 3$. Hence, g is also continuous on the interval $[2, 3)$.

Exercises 4.4

In Exercises 1 through 16, determine whether the function is continuous or discontinuous on each of the indicated intervals.

1. $f(x) = \dfrac{2}{x+5}$; $(3, 7)$, $[-6, 4]$, $(-\infty, 0)$, $(-5, +\infty)$, $[-5, +\infty)$, $[-10, -5)$.

2. $f(r) = \dfrac{r+3}{r^2-4}$; $(0, 4]$, $(-2, 2)$, $(-\infty, -2]$, $(2, +\infty)$, $[-4, 4]$, $(-2, 2]$.

3. $g(x) = \sqrt{x^2-9}$; $(-\infty, -3)$, $(-\infty, -3]$, $(3, +\infty)$, $[3, +\infty)$, $(-3, 3)$.

4. $f(x) = [\![x]\!]$; $(-\frac{1}{2}, \frac{1}{2})$, $(\frac{1}{4}, \frac{1}{2})$, $(1, 2)$, $[1, 2)$, $(1, 2]$.

5. $f(t) = \dfrac{|t-1|}{t-1}$; $(-\infty, 1)$, $(-\infty, 1]$, $[-1, 1]$, $(-1, +\infty)$, $(1, +\infty)$.

6. $h(x) = \begin{cases} 2x-3 & \text{if } x < -2 \\ x-5 & \text{if } -2 \leq x \leq 1 \\ 3-x & \text{if } 1 < x \end{cases}$; $(-\infty, 1)$, $(-2, +\infty)$, $(-2, 1)$, $[-2, 1)$.

7. $f(x) = \sqrt{4-x^2}$; $(-2, 2)$, $[-2, 2]$, $[-2, 2)$, $(-2, 2]$, $(-\infty, -2]$, $(2, +\infty)$.

8. $f(x) = \sqrt{\dfrac{2+x}{2-x}}$; $(-2, 2)$, $[-2, 2]$, $[-2, 2)$, $(-2, 2]$, $(-\infty, -2)$, $[2, +\infty)$.

9. $F(y) = \dfrac{1}{\sqrt{3+2y-y^2}}$; $(-1, 3)$, $[-1, 3]$, $[-1, 3)$, $(-1, 3]$.

10. $f(x) = \sqrt{3+2x-x^2}$; $(-1, 3)$, $[-1, 3]$, $[-1, 3)$, $(-1, 3]$.

11. $G(x) = \sqrt{\dfrac{9-x^2}{4-x}}$; $(-\infty, -3)$, $(-3, 3)$, $[-3, 3]$, $[-3, 3)$, $[3, 4]$, $(3, 4]$, $[4, +\infty)$, $(4, +\infty)$.

12. $g(x) = \sqrt{\dfrac{2+x}{25-x^2}}$; $(-\infty, -5)$, $(-\infty, -5]$, $[-5, -2]$, $[-2, 5]$, $[-2, 5)$, $(-2, 5]$, $(-2, 5)$, $[5, +\infty)$, $(5, +\infty)$.

In Exercises 13 through 20, determine the intervals on which the given function is continuous.

13. $f(x) = \dfrac{1}{x^2 - 4}$

14. $g(y) = \dfrac{4}{y+1}$

15. $h(x) = \sqrt{x^2 - x - 12}$

16. $F(x) = \sqrt{\dfrac{x-5}{x+6}}$

17. The function of Exercise 25 in Exercises 1.8.

18. The function of Exercise 26 in Exercises 1.8.

19. The function of Exercise 31 in Exercises 1.7.

20. The function of Exercise 34 in Exercises 1.7.

In Exercises 21 through 28, functions f and g are defined. In each exercise define $f \circ g$, and determine all values of x for which $f \circ g$ is continuous.

21. $f(x) = x^3$; $g(x) = \sqrt{x}$

22. $f(x) = x^2$; $g(x) = x^2 - 3$

23. $f(x) = \sqrt{x}$; $g(x) = \dfrac{1}{x-2}$

24. $f(x) = \sqrt{x}$; $g(x) = x + 1$

25. $f(x) = \dfrac{1}{x-2}$; $g(x) = \sqrt{x}$

26. $f(x) = \sqrt[3]{x}$; $g(x) = \sqrt{x+1}$

27. $f(x) = \dfrac{x+1}{x-1}$; $g(x) = \sqrt{x}$

28. $f(x) = \sqrt{x+1}$; $g(x) = \sqrt[3]{x}$

In Exercises 29 through 32, find the values of the constants c and k that make the function continuous on $(-\infty, +\infty)$ and draw a sketch of the graph of the resulting function.

29. $f(x) = \begin{cases} 3x + 7 & \text{if } x \leq 4 \\ kx - 1 & \text{if } 4 < x \end{cases}$

30. $f(x) = \begin{cases} kx - 1 & \text{if } x < 2 \\ kx^2 & \text{if } 2 \leq x \end{cases}$

31. $f(x) = \begin{cases} x & \text{if } x \leq 1 \\ cx + k & \text{if } 1 < x < 4 \\ -2x & \text{if } 4 \leq x \end{cases}$

32. $f(x) = \begin{cases} x + 2c & \text{if } x < -2 \\ 3cx + k & \text{if } -2 \leq x \leq 1 \\ 3x - 2k & \text{if } 1 < x \end{cases}$

33. Given that f is defined by

$$f(x) = \begin{cases} g(x) & \text{if } a \leq x < b \\ h(x) & \text{if } b \leq x \leq c \end{cases}$$

If g is continuous on $[a, b)$, and h is continuous on $[b, c]$, can we conclude that f is continuous on $[a, c]$? If your answer is yes, prove it. If your answer is no, what additional condition or conditions would assure continuity of f on $[a, c]$?

34. If f is the function defined by $f(x) = \sqrt[n]{x^m}$, where m and n are positive integers, prove that f is continuous on the interval $[0, +\infty)$.

4.5 MAXIMUM AND MINIMUM VALUES OF A FUNCTION

We have seen that the geometrical interpretation of the derivative of a function is the slope of the tangent line to the graph of a function at a point. This fact enables us to apply derivatives as an aid in sketching graphs. For example, the derivative may be used to determine at what points the tangent line is horizontal; these are the points where the derivative is zero. Also, the derivative may be used to find the intervals for which the graph of a function lies above the tangent line and the intervals for which the graph lies below the tangent line. Before applying the derivative to draw sketches of graphs, we need some definitions and theorems.

4.5.1 Definition   The function f is said to have a *relative maximum value* at c if there exists an open interval containing c, on which f is defined, such that $f(c) \geq f(x)$ for all x in this interval.

Figures 4.5.1 and 4.5.2 each show a sketch of a portion of the graph of a function having a relative maximum value at c.

Figure 4.5.1

Figure 4.5.2

4.5.2 Definition   The function f is said to have a *relative minimum value* at c if there exists an open interval containing c, on which f is defined, such that $f(c) \leq f(x)$ for all x in this interval.

Figures 4.5.3 and 4.5.4 each show a sketch of a portion of the graph of a function having a relative minimum value at c.

Figure 4.5.3

Figure 4.5.4

If the function f has either a relative maximum or a relative minimum value at c, then f is said to have a *relative extremum* at c. (The plurals of maximum and minimum are maxima and minima; the plural of extremum is extrema.)

The following theorem enables us to locate the possible values of c for which there is a relative extremum.

4.5.3 Theorem   If $f(x)$ exists for all values of x in the open interval (a, b) and if f has a relative extremum at c, where $a < c < b$, then if $f'(c)$ exists, $f'(c) = 0$.

PROOF: The proof will be given for the case when f has a relative minimum value at c.

If $f'(c)$ exists, from formula (5) of Sec. 3.3 we have

$$f'(c) = \lim_{x \to c} \frac{f(x) - f(c)}{x - c} \tag{1}$$

Because f has a relative minimum value at c, by Definition 4.5.2, there exists a $\delta > 0$ such that

$$f(x) - f(c) \geq 0 \qquad \text{whenever } 0 < |x - c| < \delta$$

If x is approaching c from the right, $x - c > 0$, and therefore

$$\frac{f(x) - f(c)}{x - c} \geq 0 \qquad \text{whenever } 0 < x - c < \delta$$

By Theorem 4.3.5, if the limit exists,

$$\lim_{x \to c^+} \frac{f(x) - f(c)}{x - c} \geq 0 \tag{2}$$

Similarly, if x is approaching c from the left, $x - c < 0$, and therefore

$$\frac{f(x) - f(c)}{x - c} \leq 0 \qquad \text{whenever } -\delta < x - c < 0$$

so that by Theorem 4.3.4, if the limit exists,

$$\lim_{x \to c^-} \frac{f(x) - f(c)}{x - c} \leq 0 \tag{3}$$

Because $f'(c)$ exists, the limits in inequalities (2) and (3) must be equal, and both must be equal to $f'(c)$. So from (2) we have

$$f'(c) \geq 0 \tag{4}$$

and from (3),

$$f'(c) \leq 0 \tag{5}$$

Because both (4) and (5) are taken to be true, we conclude that

$$f'(c) = 0$$

which was to be proved.

The proof for the case when f has a relative maximum value at c is similar and is left as an exercise (see Exercise 37). ■

The geometrical interpretation of Theorem 4.5.3 is that if f has a relative extremum at c and if $f'(c)$ exists, then the graph of $y = f(x)$ must have a horizontal tangent line at the point where $x = c$.

If f is a differentiable function, then the only possible values of x for which f can have a relative extremum are those for which $f'(x) = 0$. However, $f'(x)$ can be equal to zero for a specific value of x, and yet f may not have a relative extremum there, as shown in the following illustration.

● ILLUSTRATION 1: Consider the function f defined by

$$f(x) = (x - 1)^3$$

Figure 4.5.5

A sketch of the graph of this function is shown in Fig. 4.5.5. $f'(x) = 3(x - 1)^2$, and so $f'(1) = 0$. However, $f(x) < 0$, if $x < 1$, and $f(x) > 0$, if $x > 1$. So f does not have a relative extremum at 1.   ●

A function f may have a relative extremum at a number and f' may fail to exist there. This situation is shown in Illustration 2.

● ILLUSTRATION 2: Let the function f be defined as follows:

$$f(x) = \begin{cases} 2x - 1 & \text{if } x \le 3 \\ 8 - x & \text{if } 3 < x \end{cases}$$

Figure 4.5.6

A sketch of the graph of this function is shown in Fig. 4.5.6. The function f has a relative maximum value at 3. The derivative from the left at 3 is given by $f'_-(3) = 2$, and the derivative from the right at 3 is given by $f'_+(3) = -1$. Therefore, we conclude that $f'(3)$ does not exist.   ●

Illustration 2 demonstrates why the condition "$f'(c)$ exists" must be included in the hypothesis of Theorem 4.5.3.

In summary, then, if a function f is defined at a number c, a necessary condition for f to have a relative extremum there is that either $f'(c) = 0$ or $f'(c)$ does not exist. But we have noted that this condition is not sufficient.

4.5.4 Definition   If c is a number in the domain of the function f and if either $f'(c) = 0$ or $f'(c)$ does not exist, then c is called a *critical number* of f.

Because of this definition and the previous discussion, we can conclude that a necessary condition for a function to have a relative extremum at a number c is for c to be a critical number.

EXAMPLE 1:   Find the critical numbers of the function f defined by $f(x) = x^{4/3} + 4x^{1/3}$.

SOLUTION: $f'(x) = \dfrac{4}{3} x^{1/3} + \dfrac{4}{3} x^{-2/3} = \dfrac{4}{3} x^{-2/3}(x + 1) = \dfrac{4(x + 1)}{3x^{2/3}}$

$f'(x) = 0$ when $x = -1$, and $f'(x)$ does not exist when $x = 0$. Both -1 and 0 are in the domain of f; therefore, the critical numbers of f are -1 and 0.

We are frequently concerned with a function which is defined on a given interval, and we wish to find the largest or smallest function value on the interval. These intervals can be either closed, open, or closed at one end and open at the other. The greatest function value on an interval is called the "absolute maximum value," and the smallest function value on an interval is called the "absolute minimum value." Following are the precise definitions.

4.5.5 Definition   The function f is said to have an *absolute maximum value on an interval* if there is some number c in the interval such that $f(c) \geq f(x)$ for all x in the interval. In such a case, $f(c)$ is the absolute maximum value of f on the interval.

4.5.6 Definition   The function f is said to have an *absolute minimum value on an interval* if there is some number c in the interval such that $f(c) \leq f(x)$ for all x in the interval. In such a case, $f(c)$ is the absolute minimum value of f on the interval.

An *absolute extremum* of a function on an interval is either an absolute maximum value or an absolute minimum value of the function on the interval. A function may or may not have an absolute extremum on a given interval. In each of the following illustrations, a function and an interval are given, and we determine the absolute extrema of the function on the interval if there are any.

● ILLUSTRATION 3: Suppose f is the function defined by

$$f(x) = 2x$$

A sketch of the graph of f on $[1, 4)$ is shown in Fig. 4.5.7. The function f has an absolute minimum value of 2 on $[1, 4)$. There is no absolute maximum value of f on $[1, 4)$, because $\lim\limits_{x \to 4^-} f(x) = 8$, but $f(x)$ is always less than 8 on the given interval.   ●

● ILLUSTRATION 4: Consider the function f defined by

$$f(x) = -x^2$$

A sketch of the graph of f on $(-3, 2]$ is shown in Fig. 4.5.8. The function f has an absolute maximum value of 0 on $(-3, 2]$. There is no absolute minimum value of f on $(-3, 2]$, because $\lim\limits_{x \to -3^+} f(x) = -9$, but, $f(x)$ is always greater than -9 on the given interval.   ●

● ILLUSTRATION 5: The function f defined by

$$f(x) = \frac{x}{1 - x^2}$$

Figure 4.5.8

Figure 4.5.7

Figure 4.5.9

has neither an absolute maximum value nor an absolute minimum value on $(-1, 1)$. A sketch of the graph of f on $(-1, 1)$ is shown in Fig. 4.5.9. Observe that

$$\lim_{x \to -1^+} f(x) = -\infty \quad \text{and} \quad \lim_{x \to 1^-} f(x) = +\infty \qquad \bullet$$

● ILLUSTRATION 6: Let f be the function defined by

$$f(x) = \begin{cases} x + 1 & \text{if } x < 1 \\ x^2 - 6x + 7 & \text{if } 1 \le x \end{cases}$$

A sketch of the graph of f on $[-5, 4]$ is shown in Fig. 4.5.10. The absolute maximum value of f on $[-5, 4]$ occurs at 1, and $f(1) = 2$; the absolute minimum value of f on $[-5, 4]$ occurs at -5, and $f(-5) = -4$. Note that f has a relative maximum value at 1 and a relative minimum value at 3. Also, note that 1 is a critical number of f because f' does not exist at 1, and 3 is a critical number of f because $f'(3) = 0$. ●

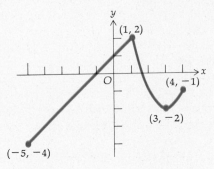

Figure 4.5.10

● ILLUSTRATION 7: The function f defined by

$$f(x) = \frac{1}{x - 3}$$

has neither an absolute maximum value nor an absolute minimum value on $[1, 5]$. See Fig. 4.5.11 for a sketch of the graph of f. $\lim\limits_{x \to 3^-} f(x) = -\infty$; so $f(x)$ can be made less than any negative number by taking $(3 - x) > 0$ and less than a suitable positive δ. Also, $\lim\limits_{x \to 3^+} f(x) = +\infty$; so $f(x)$ can be made greater than any positive number by taking $(x - 3) > 0$ and less than a suitable positive δ.

Figure 4.5.11

We may speak of an absolute extremum of a function when no interval is specified. In such a case we are referring to an absolute extremum of the function on the entire domain of the function.

4.5.7 Definition $f(c)$ is said to be the *absolute maximum value* of the function f if c is in the domain of f and if $f(c) \ge f(x)$ for all values of x in the domain of f.

4.5.8 Definition $f(c)$ is said to be the *absolute minimum value* of the function f if c is in the domain of f and if $f(c) \le f(x)$ for all values of x in the domain of f.

Figure 4.5.12

● ILLUSTRATION 8: The graph of the function f defined by

$$f(x) = x^2 - 4x + 8$$

is a parabola, and a sketch is shown in Fig. 4.5.12. The lowest point of the parabola is at $(2, 4)$, and the parabola opens upward. The function has an absolute minimum value of 4 at 2. There is no absolute maximum value of f. ●

Referring back to Illustrations 3–8, we see that the only case in which there is both an absolute maximum function value and an absolute minimum function value is in Illustration 6, where the function is continuous on the closed interval $[-5, 4]$. In the other illustrations, either we do not have a closed interval or we do not have a continuous function. If a function is continuous on a closed interval, there is a theorem, called the *extreme-value theorem*, which assures us that the function has both an absolute maximum value and an absolute minimum value on the interval. The proof of this theorem is beyond the scope of this book, but we can state it without proof. You are referred to an advanced calculus text for the proof.

4.5.9 Theorem
Extreme-Value Theorem

If the function f is continuous on the closed interval $[a, b]$, then f has an absolute maximum value and an absolute minimum value on $[a, b]$.

An absolute extremum of a function continuous on a closed interval must be either a relative extremum or a function value at an endpoint of the interval. Because a necessary condition for a function to have a relative extremum at a number c is for c to be a critical number, we can determine the absolute maximum value and the absolute minimum value of a continuous function f on a closed interval $[a, b]$ by the following procedure:

(1) find the function values at the critical numbers of f on $[a, b]$;
(2) find the values of $f(a)$ and $f(b)$;
(3) the largest of the values from steps (1) and (2) is the absolute maximum value, and the smallest of the values from steps (1) and (2) is the absolute minimum value.

EXAMPLE 2: Given

$$f(x) = x^3 + x^2 - x + 1$$

find the absolute extrema of f on $[-2, \frac{1}{2}]$.

SOLUTION: Because f is continuous on $[-2, \frac{1}{2}]$, the extreme-value theorem applies. To find the critical numbers of f we first find f':

$$f'(x) = 3x^2 + 2x - 1$$

$f'(x)$ exists for all real numbers, and so the only critical numbers of f will

Figure 4.5.13

be the values of x for which $f'(x) = 0$. Setting $f'(x) = 0$, we have

$$(3x - 1)(x + 1) = 0$$

from which we obtain

$$x = \tfrac{1}{3} \quad \text{and} \quad x = -1$$

The critical numbers of f are -1 and $\tfrac{1}{3}$, and each of these numbers is in the given closed interval $[-2, \tfrac{1}{2}]$. We find the function values at the critical numbers and at the endpoints of the interval, which are given in Table 4.5.1.

The absolute maximum value of f on $[-2, \tfrac{1}{2}]$ is therefore 2, which occurs at -1, and the absolute minimum value of f on $[-2, \tfrac{1}{2}]$ is -1, which occurs at the left endpoint -2. A sketch of the graph of this function on $[-2, \tfrac{1}{2}]$ is shown in Fig. 4.5.13.

Table 4.5.1

x	-2	-1	$\tfrac{1}{3}$	$\tfrac{1}{2}$
$f(x)$	-1	2	$\tfrac{22}{27}$	$\tfrac{7}{8}$

EXAMPLE 3:   Given

$$f(x) = (x - 2)^{2/3}$$

find the absolute extrema of f on $[1, 5]$.

Figure 4.5.14

SOLUTION: Because f is continuous on $[1, 5]$, the extreme-value theorem applies.

$$f'(x) = \frac{2}{3(x - 2)^{1/3}}$$

There is no value of x for which $f'(x) = 0$. However, because $f'(x)$ does not exist at 2, we conclude that 2 is a critical number of f, so that the absolute extrema occur either at 2 or at one of the endpoints of the interval. The function values at these numbers are given in Table 4.5.2.

From the table we conclude that the absolute minimum value of f on $[1, 5]$ is 0, occurring at 2, and the absolute maximum value of f on $[1, 5]$ is $\sqrt[3]{9}$, occurring at 5. A sketch of the graph of this function on $[1, 5]$ is shown in Fig. 4.5.14.

Table 4.5.2

x	1	2	5
$f(x)$	1	0	$\sqrt[3]{9}$

Exercises 4.5

In Exercises 1 through 10, find the critical numbers of the given function.

1. $f(x) = x^3 + 7x^2 - 5x$

2. $f(x) = 2x^3 - 2x^2 - 16x + 1$

3. $f(x) = x^4 + 4x^3 - 2x^2 - 12x$

4. $f(x) = x^{7/3} + x^{4/3} - 3x^{1/3}$

5. $f(x) = x^{6/5} - 12x^{1/5}$

6. $f(x) = x^4 + 11x^3 + 34x^2 + 15x - 2$

7. $f(x) = (x^2 - 4)^{2/3}$

8. $f(x) = (x^3 - 3x^2 + 4)^{1/3}$

9. $f(x) = \dfrac{x}{x^2 - 9}$

10. $f(x) = \dfrac{x + 1}{x^2 - 5x + 4}$

In Exercises 11 through 24, find the absolute extrema of the given function on the given interval, if there are any, and find the values of x at which the absolute extrema occur. Draw a sketch of the graph of the function on the interval.

11. $f(x) = 4 - 3x;\ (-1, 2]$

12. $f(x) = x^2 - 2x + 4;\ (-\infty, +\infty)$

13. $f(x) = \dfrac{1}{x};\ [-2, 3]$

14. $f(x) = \dfrac{1}{x};\ [2, 3)$

15. $f(x) = \sqrt{3 + x};\ [-3, +\infty)$

16. $f(x) = \dfrac{3x}{9 - x^2};\ (-3, 2)$

17. $f(x) = \dfrac{4}{(x - 3)^2};\ [2, 5]$

18. $f(x) = \sqrt{4 - x^2};\ (-2, 2)$

19. $f(x) = |x - 4| + 1;\ (0, 6)$

20. $f(x) = |4 - x^2|;\ (-\infty, +\infty)$

21. $f(x) = \begin{cases} \dfrac{2}{x - 5} & \text{if } x \neq 5 \\ 2 & \text{if } x = 5 \end{cases};\ [3, 5]$

22. $f(x) = \begin{cases} |x + 1| & \text{if } x \neq -1 \\ 3 & \text{if } x = -1 \end{cases};\ [-2, 1]$

23. $f(x) = x - [\![x]\!];\ (1, 3)$

24. $f(x) = U(x) - U(x - 1);\ (-1, 1)$

In Exercises 25 through 36, find the absolute maximum value and the absolute minimum value of the given function on the indicated interval by the method used in Examples 2 and 3 of this section. Draw a sketch of the graph of the function on the interval.

25. $f(x) = x^3 + 5x - 4;\ [-3, -1]$

26. $f(x) = x^3 + 3x^2 - 9x;\ [-4, 4]$

27. $f(x) = x^4 - 8x^2 + 16;\ [-4, 0]$

28. $f(x) = x^4 - 8x^2 + 16;\ [-1, 4]$

29. $f(x) = x^4 - 8x^2 + 16;\ [0, 3]$

30. $f(x) = x^4 - 8x^2 + 16;\ [-3, 2]$

31. $f(x) = \dfrac{x}{x + 2};\ [-1, 2]$

32. $f(x) = \dfrac{x + 5}{x - 3};\ [-5, 2]$

33. $f(x) = (x + 1)^{2/3};\ [-2, 1]$

34. $f(x) = 1 - (x - 3)^{2/3};\ [-5, 4]$

35. $f(x) = \begin{cases} 3x - 4 & \text{if } -3 \leq x < 1 \\ x^2 - 2 & \text{if } 1 \leq x \leq 3 \end{cases};\ [-3, 3]$

36. $f(x) = \begin{cases} 4 - (x + 5)^2 & \text{if } -6 \leq x \leq -4 \\ 12 - (x + 1)^2 & \text{if } -4 < x \leq 0 \end{cases};\ [-6, 0]$

37. Prove Theorem 4.5.3 for the case when f has a relative maximum value at c.

4.6 APPLICATIONS INVOLVING AN ABSOLUTE EXTREMUM ON A CLOSED INTERVAL   We consider some problems in which the solution is an absolute extremum of a function on a closed interval. Use is made of the extreme-value theorem, which assures us that both an absolute maximum value and an absolute minimum value of a function exist on a closed interval if the function is continuous on that closed interval. The procedure is illustrated by some examples.

EXAMPLE 1:   A cardboard box manufacturer wishes to make open boxes from pieces of cardboard 12 in. square by cutting equal squares from the four corners and turning up the sides. Find the length of the side of the square to be cut out in order to obtain a box of the largest possible volume.

Figure 4.6.1

Figure 4.6.2

SOLUTION: Let $x =$ the number of inches in the length of the side of the square to be cut out;

$V =$ the number of cubic inches in the volume of the box.

The number of inches in the dimensions of the box are then x, $(12 - 2x)$, and $(12 - 2x)$. Figure 4.6.1 represents a given piece of cardboard, and Fig. 4.6.2 represents the box.

The volume of the box is the product of the three dimensions, and so V is a function of x, and we write

$$V(x) = x(12 - 2x)(12 - 2x) \tag{1}$$

If $x = 0$, $V = 0$, and if $x = 6$, $V = 0$. The value of x that we wish to find is in the closed interval $[0, 6]$. Because V is continuous on the closed interval $[0, 6]$, it follows from the extreme-value theorem that V has an absolute maximum value on this interval. We also know that this absolute maximum value of V must occur either at a critical number or at an endpoint of the interval. To find the critical numbers of V, we find $V'(x)$, and then find the values of x for which either $V'(x) = 0$ or $V'(x)$ does not exist.

From Eq. (1), we obtain

$$V(x) = 144x - 48x^2 + 4x^3$$

Thus,

$$V'(x) = 144 - 96x + 12x^2$$

$V'(x)$ exists for all values of x. Setting $V'(x) = 0$, we have

$$12(x^2 - 8x + 12) = 0$$

from which we obtain

$$x = 6 \quad \text{and} \quad x = 2$$

The critical numbers of V are 2 and 6, both of which are in the closed interval $[0, 6]$. The absolute maximum value of V on $[0, 6]$ must occur at either a critical number or at an endpoint of the interval. Because $V(0) = 0$ and $V(6) = 0$, while $V(2) = 128$, we conclude that the absolute maximum value of V on $[0, 6]$ is 128, occurring at 2.

Therefore, the largest possible volume is 128 in.³, and this is obtained when the length of the side of the square cut out is 2 in.

We should emphasize that in Example 1 the existence of an absolute maximum value of V is guaranteed by the extreme-value theorem. In the following example, the existence of an absolute minimum value is guaranteed by the same theorem.

EXAMPLE 2:   An island is at point A, 6 miles offshore from

SOLUTION: Refer to Fig. 4.6.3. Let P be the point on the beach where the man lands. Therefore, the man rows from A to P and walks from P to C.

the nearest point B on a straight beach. A store is at point C, 7 miles down the beach from B. If a man can row at the rate of 4 mi/hr and walk at the rate of 5 mi/hr, where should he land in order to go from the island to the store in the least possible time?

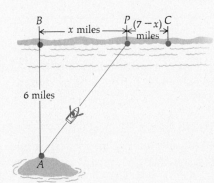

Figure 4.6.3

Let $x =$ the number of miles in the distance from B to P.

$T =$ the number of hours in the time it takes the man to make the trip from A to C.

Then $T =$ the number of hours in the time to go from A to P plus the number of hours in the time to go from P to C. Because time is obtained by dividing distance by rate, we have

$$T = \frac{|\overline{AP}|}{4} + \frac{|\overline{PC}|}{5} \tag{2}$$

From Fig. 4.6.3, we see that $|\overline{AP}|$ is the length of the hypotenuse of right triangle ABP. Therefore,

$$|\overline{AP}| = \sqrt{x^2 + 36}$$

We also see from the figure that $|\overline{PC}| = 7 - x$. So from Eq. (2) T can be expressed as a function of x, and we have

$$T(x) = \frac{\sqrt{x^2 + 36}}{4} + \frac{7 - x}{5}$$

Because the distance from B to C is 7 miles and because P can be any point on the line segment BC, we know that x is in the closed interval $[0, 7]$.

We wish to find the value of x for which T has an absolute minimum value on $[0, 7]$. Because T is a continuous function of x on $[0, 7]$, we know that such a value exists. The critical numbers of T are found by first computing $T'(x)$:

$$T'(x) = \frac{x}{4\sqrt{x^2 + 36}} - \frac{1}{5}$$

$T'(x)$ exists for all values of x. Setting $T'(x) = 0$ and solving for x, we have

$$\frac{x}{4\sqrt{x^2 + 36}} - \frac{1}{5} = 0 \tag{3}$$

$$5x = 4\sqrt{x^2 + 36}$$

$$25x^2 = 16(x^2 + 36)$$

$$9x^2 = 16 \cdot 36$$

$$x^2 = 64$$

$$x = \pm 8$$

The number -8 is an extraneous root of Eq. (3), and 8 is not in the interval $[0, 7]$. Therefore, there are no critical numbers of T in $[0, 7]$. The absolute minimum value of T on $[0, 7]$ must therefore occur at an endpoint of the interval. Computing $T(0)$ and $T(7)$, we get

$$T(0) = \tfrac{29}{10} \quad \text{and} \quad T(7) = \tfrac{1}{4}\sqrt{85}$$

Since $\frac{1}{4}\sqrt{85} < \frac{29}{10}$, the absolute minimum value of T on $[0, 7]$ is $\frac{1}{4}\sqrt{85}$, occurring when $x = 7$. Therefore, in order for the man to go from the island to the store in the least possible time, he should row directly there and do no walking.

EXAMPLE 3: A rectangular field is to be fenced off along the bank of a river and no fence is required along the river. If the material for the fence costs $4 per running foot for the two ends and $6 per running foot for the side parallel to the river, find the dimensions of the field of largest possible area that can be enclosed with $1800 worth of fence.

SOLUTION: Let $x =$ the number of feet in the length of an end of the field;
$y =$ the number of feet in the length of the side parallel to the river;
$A =$ the number of square feet in the area of the field.

Hence,

$$A = xy \tag{4}$$

Since the cost of the material for each end is $4 per running foot and the length of an end is x ft, the total cost for the fence for each end is $4x$ dollars. Similarly, the total cost of the fence for the third side is $6y$ dollars. We have, then,

$$4x + 4x + 6y = 1800 \tag{5}$$

To express A in terms of a single variable, we solve Eq. (5) for y in terms of x and substitute this value into Eq. (4), yielding A as a function of x, and

$$A(x) = x(300 - \tfrac{4}{3}x) \tag{6}$$

If $y = 0$, $x = 225$, and if $x = 0$, $y = 300$. Because both x and y must be nonnegative, the value of x that will make A an absolute maximum is in the closed interval $[0, 225]$. Because A is continuous on the closed interval $[0, 225]$, we conclude from the extreme-value theorem that A has an absolute maximum value on this interval. From Eq. (6), we have

$$A(x) = 300x - \tfrac{4}{3}x^2$$

Hence,

$$A'(x) = 300 - \tfrac{8}{3}x$$

Because $A'(x)$ exists for all x, the critical values of A will be found by setting $A'(x) = 0$, which gives

$$x = 112\tfrac{1}{2}$$

The only critical number of A is $112\tfrac{1}{2}$, which is in the closed interval $[0, 225]$. Thus, the absolute maximum value of A must occur at either 0, $112\tfrac{1}{2}$, or 225. Because $A(0) = 0$ and $A(225) = 0$, while $A(112\tfrac{1}{2}) = 16,875$, we conclude that the absolute maximum value of A on $[0, 225]$ is 16,875 occurring when $x = 112\tfrac{1}{2}$ and $y = 150$ (obtained from Eq. (5) by substituting $112\tfrac{1}{2}$ for x).

Therefore, the largest possible area that can be enclosed for $1800 is 16,875 square feet, and this is obtained when the side parallel to the river is 150 ft long and the ends are each $112\tfrac{1}{2}$ ft long.

EXAMPLE 4: In the planning of a coffee shop it is estimated that if there are places for 40 to 80 people, the weekly profit will be $8 per place. However, if the seating capacity is above 80 places, the weekly profit on each place will be decreased by 4 cents times the number of places above 80. What should be the seating capacity in order to yield the greatest weekly profit?

SOLUTION: Let $x =$ the number of places in the seating capacity;
$P =$ the number of dollars in the total weekly profit.

The value of P depends upon x, and it is obtained by multiplying x by the number of dollars in the profit per place. When $40 \leq x \leq 80$, $8 is the profit per place, and so $P = 8x$. However, when $x > 80$, the number of dollars in the profit per place is $[8 - 0.04(x - 80)]$, thus giving $P = x[8 - 0.04(x - 80)] = 11.20x - 0.04x^2$. So we have

$$P(x) = \begin{cases} 8x & \text{if } 40 \leq x \leq 80 \\ 11.20x - 0.04x^2 & \text{if } 80 \leq x \leq 280 \end{cases}$$

The upper bound of 280 for x is obtained by noting that $11.20x - 0.04x^2 = 0$ when $x = 280$; and when $x > 280$, $11.20x - 0.04x^2$ is negative.

Even though x, by definition, is an integer, to have a continuous function we let x take on all real values in the interval $[40, 280]$. Note that there is continuity at 80 because

$$\lim_{x \to 80^-} P(x) = \lim_{x \to 80^-} 8x = 640$$

and

$$\lim_{x \to 80^+} P(x) = \lim_{x \to 80^+} (11.20x - 0.04x^2) = 640$$

from which it follows that the two-sided limit $\lim_{x \to 80} P(x) = 640 = P(80)$. So P is continuous on the closed interval $[40, 280]$ and the extreme-value theorem guarantees an absolute maximum value of P on this interval.

When $40 < x < 80$, $P'(x) = 8$, and when $80 < x < 280$, $P'(x) = 11.20 - 0.08x$. $P'(80)$ does not exist since $P'_-(80) = 8$ and $P'_+(80) = 4.80$. Setting $P'(x) = 0$, we have

$$11.20 - 0.08x = 0$$

$$x = 140$$

The critical numbers of P are then 80 and 140. Evaluating $P(x)$ at the endpoints of the interval $[40, 280]$ and at the critical numbers, we have $P(40) = 320$, $P(80) = 640$, $P(140) = 784$, and $P(280) = 0$. The absolute maximum value of P, then, is 784 occurring when $x = 140$.

The seating capacity should be 140 places, which gives a total weekly profit of $784.

EXAMPLE 5: Find the dimensions of the right-circular cylinder of greatest volume which can be inscribed in a right-circular cone with a radius of 5 in. and a height of 12 in.

SOLUTION: Let $r =$ the number of inches in the radius of the cylinder;
$h =$ the number of inches in the height of the cylinder;
$V =$ the number of cubic inches in the volume of the cylinder.

Figure 4.6.4 illustrates the cylinder inscribed in the cone, and Fig. 4.6.5 illustrates a plane section through the axis of the cone.

Figure 4.6.4

Figure 4.6.5

If $r = 0$ and $h = 12$, we have a degenerate cylinder, which is the axis of the cone. If $r = 5$ and $h = 0$, we also have a degenerate cylinder, which is a diameter of the base of the cone. We conclude that r is in the closed interval $[0, 5]$ and h is in the closed interval $[0, 12]$.

The following formula expresses V in terms of r and h:

$$V = \pi r^2 h \tag{7}$$

To express V in terms of a single variable we need another equation involving r and h. From Fig. 4.6.5, and using similar triangles, we have

$$\frac{12 - h}{r} = \frac{12}{5}$$

Thus,

$$h = \frac{60 - 12r}{5} \tag{8}$$

Substituting from Eq. (8) into formula (7), we obtain V as a function of r and write

$$V(r) = \tfrac{12}{5}\pi(5r^2 - r^3) \qquad \text{with } r \text{ in } [0, 5] \tag{9}$$

Because V is continuous on the closed interval $[0, 5]$, it follows from the extreme-value theorem that V has an absolute maximum value on this interval. The values of r and h that give this absolute maximum value for V are the numbers we wish to find.

$$V'(r) = \tfrac{12}{5}\pi(10r - 3r^2)$$

To find the critical numbers of V, we set $V'(r) = 0$ and solve for r:

$$r(10 - 3r) = 0$$

from which we obtain

$$r = 0 \quad \text{and} \quad r = \tfrac{10}{3}$$

Because $V'(r)$ exists for all values of r, the only critical numbers of V are 0 and $\tfrac{10}{3}$, both of which are in the closed interval $[0, 5]$. The absolute maximum value of V on $[0, 5]$ must occur at either 0, $\tfrac{10}{3}$, or 5. From Eq. (9) we obtain $V(0) = 0$, $V(\tfrac{10}{3}) = \tfrac{400}{9}\pi$, and $V(5) = 0$. We therefore conclude that the absolute maximum value of V is $\tfrac{400}{9}\pi$, and this occurs when $r = \tfrac{10}{3}$. When $r = \tfrac{10}{3}$, we find from Eq. (8) that $h = 4$.

Thus, the greatest volume of an inscribed cylinder in the given cone is $\tfrac{400}{9}\pi$ in.^{3}, which occurs when the radius is $\tfrac{10}{3}$ in. and the height is 4 in.

Exercises 4.6

1. Find the area of the largest rectangle having a perimeter of 200 ft.

2. Find the area of the largest isosceles triangle having a perimeter of 18 in.

3. A manufacturer of tin boxes wishes to make use of pieces of tin with dimensions 8 in. by 15 in. by cutting equal squares from the four corners and turning up the sides. Find the length of the side of the square to be cut out if an open box having the largest possible volume is to be obtained from each piece of tin.

4. A rectangular plot of ground is to be enclosed by a fence and then divided down the middle by another fence. If the fence down the middle costs $1 per running foot and the other fence costs $2.50 per running foot, find the dimensions of the plot of largest possible area that can be enclosed with $480 worth of fence.

5. Points A and B are opposite each other on shores of a straight river that is 3 mi wide. Point C is on the same shore as B but 6 mi down the river from B. A telephone company wishes to lay a cable from A to C. If the cost per mile of the cable is 25% more under the water than it is on land, what line of cable would be least expensive for the company?

6. Solve Exercise 5 if point C is only 3 mi down the river from B.

7. Solve Example 2 of this section if the store is 9 mi down the beach from point B.

8. Example 2 and Exercises 5, 6, and 7 are special cases of the following more general problem. Let $f(x) = u \sqrt{a^2 + x^2} + v(b - x)$, where x is in $[0, b]$ and $u > v > 0$. Show that in order for the absolute minimum value of f to occur at a number in the open interval $(0, b)$ the following inequality must be satisfied: $av < b \sqrt{u^2 - v^2}$.

9. Find the dimensions of the right-circular cylinder of greatest lateral surface area that can be inscribed in a sphere with a radius of 6 in.

10. Find the dimensions of the right-circular cylinder of greatest volume that can be inscribed in a sphere with a radius of 6 in.

11. Given the circle having the equation $x^2 + y^2 = 9$, find (a) the shortest distance from the point (4, 5) to a point on the circle, and (b) the longest distance from the point (4, 5) to a point on the circle.

12. A manufacturer can make a profit of $20 on each item if not more than 800 items are produced each week. The profit decreases 2 cents per item over 800. How many items should the manufacturer produce each week in order to have the greatest profit?

13. A school-sponsored trip will cost each student $15 if not more than 150 students make the trip; however, the cost per student will be reduced 5 cents for each student in excess of 150. How many students should make the trip in order for the school to receive the largest gross income?

14. Solve Exercise 13 if the reduction per student in excess of 150 is 7 cents.

15. A private club charges annual membership dues of $100 per member less 50 cents for each member over 600 and plus 50 cents for each member less than 600. How many members would give the club the most revenue from annual dues?

16. Suppose a weight is to be held 10 ft below a horizontal line AB by a wire in the shape of a Y. If the points A and B are 8 ft apart, what is the shortest total length of wire that can be used?

17. A piece of wire 10 ft long is cut into two pieces. One piece is bent into the shape of a circle and the other into the shape of a square. How should the wire be cut so that (a) the combined area of the two figures is as small as possible and (b) the combined area of the two figures is as large as possible?

18. Solve Exercise 17 if one piece of wire is bent into the shape of an equilateral triangle and the other piece is bent into the shape of a square.

4.7 ROLLE'S THEOREM AND THE MEAN-VALUE THEOREM

Let f be a function which is continuous on the closed interval $[a, b]$, differentiable on the open interval (a, b), and such that $f(a) = 0$ and $f(b) = 0$. The French mathematician Michel Rolle (1652–1719) proved that if a

Figure 4.7.1

Figure 4.7.2

Figure 4.7.3

function f satisfies these conditions, there is at least one number c between a and b for which $f'(c) = 0$.

Let us see what this means geometrically. Figure 4.7.1 shows a sketch of the graph of a function f that satisfies the conditions in the preceding paragraph. We intuitively see that there is at least one point on the curve between the points $(a, 0)$ and $(b, 0)$ where the tangent line is parallel to the x axis; that is, the slope of the tangent line is zero. This situation is illustrated in Fig. 4.7.1 at the point P. So the abscissa of P would be the c such that $f'(c) = 0$.

The function, whose graph is sketched in Fig. 4.7.1, not only is differentiable on the open interval (a, b) but also is differentiable at the endpoints of the interval. However, the condition that f be differentiable at the endpoints is not necessary for the graph to have a horizontal tangent line at some point in the interval; Fig. 4.7.2 illustrates this. We see in Fig. 4.7.2 that the function is not differentiable at a and b; there is, however, a horizontal tangent line at the point where $x = c$, and c is between a and b.

It is necessary, however, that the function be continuous at the endpoints of the interval to guarantee a horizontal tangent line at an interior point. Figure 4.7.3 shows a sketch of the graph of a function that is continuous on the interval $[a, b)$ but discontinuous at b; the function is differentiable on the open interval (a, b), and the function values are zero at both a and b. However, there is no point at which the graph has a horizontal tangent line.

We now state and prove Rolle's theorem.

4.7.1 Theorem   Let f be a function such that
Rolle's Theorem

   (i) it is continuous on the closed interval $[a, b]$;
   (ii) it is differentiable on the open interval (a, b);
   (iii) $f(a) = f(b) = 0$.

Then there is a number c in the open interval (a, b) such that

$$f'(c) = 0$$

PROOF: We consider two cases.

Case 1: $f(x) = 0$ for all x in $[a, b]$.

Then $f'(x) = 0$ for all x in (a, b); therefore, any number between a and b can be taken for c.

Case 2: $f(x)$ is not zero for some value of x in the open interval (a, b).

Because f is continuous on the closed interval $[a, b]$, we know by Theorem 4.5.9 that f has an absolute maximum value on $[a, b]$ and an absolute minimum value on $[a, b]$. By hypothesis, $f(a) = f(b) = 0$. Furthermore, $f(x)$ is not zero for some x in (a, b). Hence, we can conclude that f will have either a positive absolute maximum value at some c_1 in (a, b) or a negative absolute minimum value at some c_2 in (a, b), or both. Thus, for $c = c_1$, or $c = c_2$ as the case may be, we have an absolute extremum at an interior point of the interval $[a, b]$. Therefore, the absolute extremum $f(c)$ is also a relative extremum, and because $f'(c)$ exists by hypothesis, it follows from Theorem 4.5.3 that $f'(c) = 0$. This proves the theorem. ∎

It should be noted that there may be more than one number in the open interval (a, b) for which the derivative of f is zero. This is illustrated geometrically in Fig. 4.7.4, where there is a horizontal tangent line at the point where $x = c_1$ and also at the point where $x = c_2$, so that both $f'(c_1) = 0$ and $f'(c_2) = 0$.

Figure 4.7.4

The converse of Rolle's theorem is not true. That is, we cannot conclude that if a function f is such that $f'(c) = 0$, with $a < c < b$, then the conditions (i), (ii), and (iii) must hold. (See Exercise 40.)

EXAMPLE 1: Given

$$f(x) = 4x^3 - 9x$$

verify that conditions (i), (ii), and (iii) of the hypothesis of Rolle's theorem are satisfied for each of the following intervals: $[-\frac{3}{2}, 0]$, $[0, \frac{3}{2}]$, and $[-\frac{3}{2}, \frac{3}{2}]$. Then find a suitable value for c in each of these intervals for which $f'(c) = 0$.

SOLUTION: $f'(x) = 12x^2 - 9$; $f'(x)$ exists for all values of x, and so f is differentiable on $(-\infty, +\infty)$ and therefore continuous on $(-\infty, +\infty)$. Conditions (i) and (ii) of Rolle's theorem thus hold on any interval. To determine on which intervals condition (iii) holds, we find the values of x for which $f(x) = 0$. Setting $f(x) = 0$, we have

$$4x(x^2 - \tfrac{9}{4}) = 0$$

which gives us

$$x = -\tfrac{3}{2} \qquad x = 0 \qquad x = \tfrac{3}{2}$$

Taking $a = -\frac{3}{2}$ and $b = 0$, we see that Rolle's theorem holds on $[-\frac{3}{2}, 0]$. Similarly, Rolle's theorem holds on $[0, \frac{3}{2}]$ and $[-\frac{3}{2}, \frac{3}{2}]$.

To find the suitable values for c, we set $f'(x) = 0$ and get

$$12x^2 - 9 = 0$$

which gives us

$$x = -\tfrac{1}{2}\sqrt{3} \quad \text{and} \quad x = \tfrac{1}{2}\sqrt{3}$$

Therefore, in the interval $[-\frac{3}{2}, 0]$ a suitable choice for c is $-\frac{1}{2}\sqrt{3}$. In the interval $[0, \frac{3}{2}]$, we take $c = \frac{1}{2}\sqrt{3}$. In the interval $[-\frac{3}{2}, \frac{3}{2}]$ there are two possibilities for c: either $-\frac{1}{2}\sqrt{3}$ or $\frac{1}{2}\sqrt{3}$.

We apply Rolle's theorem to prove one of the most important theorems in calculus—that known as the *mean-value theorem* (or law of the mean). The mean-value theorem is used to prove many theorems of both differential and integral calculus. You should become thoroughly familiar with the content of this theorem.

4.7.2 Theorem
Mean-Value Theorem

Let f be a function such that

(i) it is continuous on the closed interval $[a, b]$;
(ii) it is differentiable on the open interval (a, b).

Then there is a number c in the open interval (a, b) such that

$$f'(c) = \frac{f(b) - f(a)}{b - a}$$

Before proving this theorem, we interpret it geometrically. If we draw a sketch of the graph of the function f, then $[f(b) - f(a)]/(b - a)$ is the slope of the line segment joining the points $A(a, f(a))$ and $B(b, f(b))$. The mean-value theorem states that there is some point on the curve between A and B where the tangent line is parallel to the secant line through A and B; that is, there is some number c in (a, b) such that

$$f'(c) = \frac{f(b) - f(a)}{b - a}$$

Refer to Fig. 4.7.5.

By taking the x axis along the line segment AB, we observe that the mean-value theorem is a generalization of Rolle's theorem, which is used in its proof.

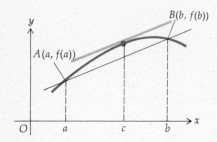

Figure 4.7.5

PROOF: An equation of the line through A and B in Fig. 4.7.5 is

$$y - f(a) = \frac{f(b) - f(a)}{b - a} (x - a)$$

or, equivalently,

$$y = \frac{f(b) - f(a)}{b - a} (x - a) + f(a)$$

Now if $F(x)$ measures the vertical distance between a point $(x, f(x))$ on the graph of the function f and the corresponding point on the secant line through A and B, then

$$F(x) = f(x) - \frac{f(b) - f(a)}{b - a} (x - a) - f(a) \qquad (1)$$

We show that this function F satisfies the three conditions of the hypothesis of Rolle's theorem.

The function F is continuous on the closed interval $[a, b]$ because it is the sum of f and a linear polynomial, both of which are continuous there. Therefore, condition (i) is satisfied by F. Condition (ii) is satisfied by F because f is differentiable on (a, b). From Eq. (1) we see that $F(a) = 0$ and $F(b) = 0$. Therefore, condition (iii) of Rolle's theorem is satisfied by F.

The conclusion of Rolle's theorem states that there is a c in the open interval (a, b) such that $F'(c) = 0$.

But

$$F'(x) = f'(x) - \frac{f(b) - f(a)}{b - a}$$

Thus

$$F'(c) = f'(c) - \frac{f(b) - f(a)}{b - a}$$

Therefore, there is a number c in (a, b) such that

$$0 = f'(c) - \frac{f(b) - f(a)}{b - a}$$

or, equivalently,

$$f'(c) = \frac{f(b) - f(a)}{b - a}$$

which was to be proved.   ∎

EXAMPLE 2: Given

$$f(x) = x^3 - 5x^2 - 3x$$

verify that the hypothesis of the mean-value theorem is satisfied for $a = 1$ and $b = 3$. Then find all numbers c in the open interval $(1, 3)$ such that

$$f'(c) = \frac{f(3) - f(1)}{3 - 1}$$

SOLUTION: Because f is a polynomial function, f is continuous and differentiable for all values of x. Therefore, the hypothesis of the mean-value theorem is satisfied for any a and b.

$$f'(x) = 3x^2 - 10x - 3$$

$$f(1) = -7 \quad \text{and} \quad f(3) = -27$$

Hence,

$$\frac{f(3) - f(1)}{3 - 1} = \frac{-27 - (-7)}{2} = -10$$

Setting $f'(c) = -10$, we obtain

$$3c^2 - 10c - 3 = -10$$

$$3c^2 - 10c + 7 = 0$$

$$(3c - 7)(c - 1) = 0$$

which gives us

$$c = \tfrac{7}{3} \quad \text{and} \quad c = 1$$

Because 1 is not in the open interval $(1, 3)$, the only possible value for c is $\tfrac{7}{3}$.

EXAMPLE 3: Given

$$f(x) = x^{2/3}$$

draw a sketch of the graph of f. Show that there is no number c in the open interval $(-2, 2)$ such that

SOLUTION: A sketch of the graph of f is shown in Fig. 4.7.6.

Figure 4.7.6

$$f'(c) = \frac{f(2) - f(-2)}{2 - (-2)}$$

Which condition of the hypothesis of the mean-value theorem fails to hold for f when $a = -2$ and $b = 2$?

$$f'(x) = \tfrac{2}{3}x^{-1/3}$$

So

$$f'(c) = \frac{2}{3c^{1/3}}$$

$$\frac{f(2) - f(-2)}{2 - (-2)} = \frac{4^{1/3} - 4^{1/3}}{4}$$

$$= 0$$

There is no number c for which $2/3c^{1/3} = 0$.

The function f is continuous on the closed interval $[-2, 2]$; however, f is not differentiable on the open interval $(-2, 2)$ because $f'(0)$ does not exist. Therefore, condition (ii) of the hypothesis of the mean-value theorem fails to hold for f when $a = -2$ and $b = 2$.

Exercises 4.7

In Exercises 1 through 4, verify that conditions (i), (ii), and (iii) of the hypothesis of Rolle's theorem are satisfied by the given function on the indicated interval. Then find a suitable value for c that satisfies the conclusion of Rolle's theorem.

1. $f(x) = x^2 - 4x + 3$; $[1, 3]$

2. $f(x) = x^3 - 2x^2 - x + 2$; $[1, 2]$

3. $f(x) = x^3 - 2x^2 - x + 2$; $[-1, 2]$

4. $f(x) = x^3 - 16x$; $[-4, 0]$

5. For the function f defined by $f(x) = 4x^3 + 12x^2 - x - 3$, determine three sets of values for a and b so that conditions (i), (ii), and (iii) of the hypothesis of Rolle's theorem are satisfied. Then find a suitable value for c in each of the three open intervals (a, b) for which $f'(c) = 0$.

In Exercises 6 through 13, verify that the hypothesis of the mean-value theorem is satisfied for the given function on the indicated interval. Then find a suitable value for c that satisfies the conclusion of the mean-value theorem.

6. $f(x) = x^3 + x^2 - x$; $[-2, 1]$

7. $f(x) = x^2 + 2x - 1$; $[0, 1]$

8. $f(x) = x - 1 + \dfrac{1}{x - 1}$; $[\tfrac{3}{2}, 3]$

9. $f(x) = x^{2/3}$; $[0, 1]$

10. $f(x) = \sqrt{100 - x^2}$; $[-6, 8]$

11. $f(x) = \sqrt{x + 2}$; $[4, 6]$

12. $f(x) = \dfrac{x^2 + 4x}{x - 7}$; $[2, 6]$

13. $f(x) = \dfrac{x^2 - 3x - 4}{x + 5}$; $[-1, 4]$

In Exercises 14 through 23, (a) draw a sketch of the graph of the given function on the indicated interval; (b) test the three conditions (i), (ii), and (iii) of the hypothesis of Rolle's theorem and determine which conditions are satisfied and which, if any, are not satisfied; and (c) if the three conditions in part (b) are satisfied, determine a point at which there is a horizontal tangent line.

14. $f(x) = x^{3/4} - 2x^{1/4}$; $[0, 4]$

15. $f(x) = x^{4/3} - 3x^{1/3}$; $[0, 3]$

16. $f(x) = \dfrac{2x^2 - 5x - 3}{x - 1}$; $[-\tfrac{1}{2}, 3]$

17. $f(x) = \begin{cases} x + 3 & \text{if } x \le 2 \\ 7 - x & \text{if } 2 < x \end{cases}$; $[-3, 7]$

18. $f(x) = \begin{cases} 3x + 6 & \text{if } x < 1 \\ x - 4 & \text{if } 1 \le x \end{cases}$; $[-2, 4]$

19. $f(x) = \dfrac{x^2 - x - 12}{x - 3}$; $[-3, 4]$

20. $f(x) = \begin{cases} \dfrac{x^2 - 5x + 4}{x - 1} & \text{if } x \neq 1 \\ 0 & \text{if } x = 1 \end{cases}$; $[1, 4]$

21. $f(x) = \begin{cases} x^2 - 4 & \text{if } x < 1 \\ 5x - 8 & \text{if } 1 \leq x \end{cases}$; $[-2, \frac{8}{5}]$

22. $f(x) = 1 - |x|$; $[-1, 1]$

23. $f(x) = |9 - 4x^2|$; $[-\frac{3}{2}, \frac{3}{2}]$

24. If $f(x) = (2x - 1)/(2x - 4)$ and if $a = 1$ and $b = 2$, show that there is no number c in the open interval (a, b) that satisfies the conclusion of the mean-value theorem. Which part of the hypothesis of the mean-value theorem fails to hold? Draw a sketch of the graph of f on $[1, 2]$.

The geometric interpretation of the mean-value theorem is that for a suitable c in the open interval (a, b), the tangent line to the curve $y = f(x)$ at the point $(c, f(c))$ is parallel to the secant line through the points $(a, f(a))$ and $(b, f(b))$. In Exercises 25 through 30, find a value of c satisfying the conclusion of the mean-value theorem, draw a sketch of the graph on the closed interval $[a, b]$, and show the tangent line and secant line.

25. $f(x) = x^2$; $a = 3$, $b = 5$

26. $f(x) = x^2$; $a = 2$, $b = 4$

27. $f(x) = \dfrac{2}{x - 3}$; $a = 3.1$, $b = 3.2$

28. $f(x) = x - 1$; $a = 10$, $b = 26$

29. $f(x) = x^3 - 9x + 1$; $a = -3$, $b = 4$

30. $f(x) = \dfrac{2}{x - 3}$; $a = 3.01$, $b = 3.02$

For each of the functions in Exercises 31 through 34, there is no number c in the open interval (a, b) that satisfies the conclusion of the mean-value theorem. In each exercise, determine which part of the hypothesis of the mean-value theorem fails to hold. Draw a sketch of the graph of $y = f(x)$ and the line through the points $(a, f(a))$ and $(b, f(b))$.

31. $f(x) = \dfrac{4}{(x - 3)^2}$; $a = 1$, $b = 6$

32. $f(x) = \dfrac{2x - 1}{3x - 4}$; $a = 1$, $b = 2$

33. $f(x) = 3(x - 4)^{2/3}$; $a = -4$, $b = 5$

34. $f(x) = \begin{cases} 2x + 3 & \text{if } x < 3 \\ 15 - 2x & \text{if } 3 \leq x \end{cases}$; $a = -1$, $b = 5$

35. If $f(x) = x^4 - 2x^3 + 2x^2 - x$, then $f'(x) = 4x^3 - 6x^2 + 4x - 1$. Prove by Rolle's theorem that the equation $4x^3 - 6x^2 + 4x - 1 = 0$ has at least one real root in the open interval $(0, 1)$.

36. Prove by Rolle's theorem that the equation $x^3 + 2x + c = 0$, where c is any constant, cannot have more than one real root.

37. Use Rolle's theorem to prove that the equation $4x^5 + 3x^3 + 3x - 2 = 0$ has exactly one root that lies in the interval $(0, 1)$. (HINT: First show that there is at least one number in $(0, 1)$ that is a root of the equation. Then assume that there is more than one root of the equation in $(0, 1)$ and show that this leads to a contradiction.)

38. Suppose $s = f(t)$ is an equation of motion of a particle moving in a straight line where f satisfies the hypothesis of the mean-value theorem. Show that the conclusion of the mean-value theorem assures us that there will be some instant during any time interval when the instantaneous velocity will equal the average velocity during that time interval.

39. Suppose that the function f is continuous on $[a, b]$ and $f'(x) = 1$ for all x in (a, b). Prove that $f(x) = x - a + f(a)$ for all x in $[a, b]$.

40. The converse of Rolle's theorem is not true. Make up an example of a function for which the conclusion of Rolle's theorem is true and for which (a) condition (i) is not satisfied but conditions (ii) and (iii) are satisfied; (b) condition (ii) is not satisfied but conditions (i) and (iii) are satisfied; (c) condition (iii) is not satisfied but conditions (i) and (ii) are satisfied. Draw a sketch of the graph showing the horizontal tangent line for each case.

41. Use Rolle's theorem to prove that if every polynomial of the fourth degree has at most four real roots, then every polynomial of the fifth degree has at most five real roots. (HINT: Assume a polynomial of the fifth degree has six real roots and show that this leads to a contradiction.)

42. Use the method of Exercise 41 and mathematical induction to prove that a polynomial of the nth degree has at most n real roots.

Review Exercises (Chapter 4)

In Exercises 1 through 4, evaluate the limit.

1. $\displaystyle\lim_{x\to+\infty} \frac{8x^3 - 5x^2 + 3}{2x^3 + 7x - 4}$

2. $\displaystyle\lim_{x\to-\infty} \frac{3x^2 - 4x - 1}{6x^3 + x^2 + 4}$

3. $\displaystyle\lim_{x\to-\infty} \frac{\sqrt{x^2 + 5}}{2x - 4}$

4. $\displaystyle\lim_{t\to+\infty} (\sqrt{t^2 + t} - \sqrt{t^2 + 4})$

In Exercises 5 and 6, find the horizontal and vertical asymptotes of the graph of the function defined by the given equation, and draw a sketch of the graph.

5. $f(x) = \dfrac{5x^2}{x^2 - 4}$

6. $g(x) = \dfrac{-2x}{\sqrt{x^2 - 5x + 6}}$

In Exercises 7 through 10, functions f and g are defined. In each exercise, define $f \circ g$, and determine all values of x for which $f \circ g$ is continuous.

7. $f(x) = \sqrt{x - 3}$; $g(x) = x + 2$

8. $f(x) = \dfrac{4}{3x - 5}$; $g(x) = \sqrt{x}$

9. $f(x) = \operatorname{sgn} x$; $g(x) = x^2 - 1$

10. $f(x) = \operatorname{sgn} x$; $g(x) = x^2 - x$

In Exercises 11 through 16, find the absolute extrema of the given function on the given interval, if there are any, and find the values of x at which the absolute extrema occur. Draw a sketch of the graph of the function on the interval.

11. $f(x) = \sqrt{5 + x}$; $[-5, +\infty)$

12. $f(x) = \sqrt{9 - x^2}$; $(-3, 3)$

13. $f(x) = |9 - x^2|$; $[-2, 3]$

14. $f(x) = x^4 - 12x^2 + 36$; $[-2, 6]$

15. $f(x) = x^4 - 12x^2 + 36$; $[0, 5]$

16. $f(x) = \begin{cases} 2x + 3 & \text{if } -2 \le x < 1 \\ x^2 + 4 & \text{if } 1 \le x \le 2 \end{cases}$; $[-2, 2]$

17. Find two numbers whose sum is 12 such that the sum of their squares is an absolute minimum.

18. A piece of wire 80 in. long is bent to form a rectangle. Find the dimensions of the rectangle so that its area is as large as possible.

19. In order for a package to be mailed by parcel post, the sum of the length and girth (the perimeter of a cross section) must not be greater than 100 in. If a package is to be in the shape of a rectangular box with a square cross section, find the dimensions of the package having the greatest possible volume that can be sent by parcel post.

20. If f is the function defined by $f(x) = |2x - 4| - 6$, then $f(-1) = f(5) = 0$. However, f' never has the value 0. Show why Rolle's theorem does not hold.

21. (a) If f is a polynomial function and $f(a) = f(b) = f'(a) = f'(b) = 0$, prove that there are at least two numbers in the open interval (a, b) that are roots of the equation $f''(x) = 0$. (b) Show that the function defined by the equation $f(x) = (x^2 - 4)^2$ satisfies part (a).

22. If f is a polynomial function, show that between any two consecutive roots of the equation $f'(x) = 0$ there is at most one root of the equation $f(x) = 0$.

23. Suppose that f and g are two functions that satisfy the hypothesis of the mean-value theorem on $[a, b]$. Furthermore, suppose that $f'(x) = g'(x)$ for all x in the open interval (a, b). Prove that $f(x) - g(x) = f(a) - g(a)$ for all x in the closed interval $[a, b]$.

24. Let f and g be two functions that are differentiable at every number in the closed interval $[a, b]$. Suppose further that

$f(a) = g(a)$ and $f(b) = g(b)$. Prove that there exists a number c in the open interval (a, b) such that $f'(c) = g'(c)$. (HINT: Consider the function $f - g$.)

25. If $f(x) = 2x/\sqrt{x^2 - 6x - 7}$, find the horizontal and vertical asymptotes of the graph of f, and draw a sketch of the graph.

26. Let

$$f(x) = \begin{cases} 3x + 6a & \text{if } x < -3 \\ 3ax - 7b & \text{if } -3 \leq x \leq 3 \\ x - 12b & \text{if } 3 < x \end{cases}$$

Find the values of the constants a and b that make the function f continuous on $(-\infty, +\infty)$, and draw a sketch of the graph of f.

27. Two towns A and B are to get their water supply from the same pumping station to be located on the bank of a straight river that is 15 mi from town A and 10 mi from town B. If the points on the river nearest to A and B are 20 mi apart and A and B are on the same side of the river, where should the pumping station be located so that the least amount of piping is required?

28. A manufacturer offers to deliver to a dealer 300 tables at $90 per table and to reduce the price per table on the entire order by 25 cents for each additional table over 300. Find the dollar total involved in the largest possible transaction between the manufacturer and the dealer under these circumstances.

29. Give an example of a function whose domain is the set of all real numbers and that (a) is continuous at every number except 0; (b) continuous at every number except 0 and 1; (c) continuous from the left at 1 but discontinuous from the right at 1.

5

Additional applications of the derivative

5.1 INCREASING AND DECREASING FUNCTIONS AND THE FIRST-DERIVATIVE TEST

Suppose that Fig. 5.1.1 represents a sketch of the graph of a function f for all x in the closed interval $[x_1, x_7]$. In drawing this sketch we have assumed that f is continuous on $[x_1, x_7]$.

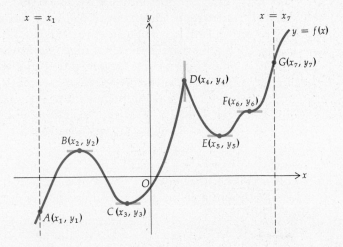

Figure 5.1.1

Figure 5.1.1 shows that as a point moves along the curve from A to B, the function values increase as the abscissa increases, and that as a point moves along the curve from B to C, the function values decrease as the abscissa increases. We say, then, that f is "increasing" on the closed interval $[x_1, x_2]$ and that f is "decreasing" on the closed interval $[x_2, x_3]$. Following are the precise definitions of a function increasing or decreasing on an interval.

5.1.1 Definition A function f defined on an interval is said to be *increasing* on that interval if and only if

$$f(x_1) < f(x_2) \qquad \text{whenever } x_1 < x_2$$

where x_1 and x_2 are any numbers in the interval.

The function of Fig. 5.1.1 is increasing on the following closed intervals: $[x_1, x_2]$; $[x_3, x_4]$; $[x_5, x_6]$; $[x_6, x_7]$; $[x_5, x_7]$.

5.1.2 Definition A function f defined on an interval is said to be *decreasing* on that interval if and only if

$$f(x_1) > f(x_2) \qquad \text{whenever } x_1 < x_2$$

where x_1 and x_2 are any numbers in the interval.

The function of Fig. 5.1.1 is decreasing on the following closed intervals: $[x_2, x_3]$; $[x_4, x_5]$.

If a function f is either increasing on an interval or decreasing on an interval, then f is said to be *monotonic* on the interval.

Before stating a theorem that gives a test for determining if a given function is monotonic on an interval, let us see what is happening geometrically. Referring to Fig. 5.1.1, we observe that when the slope of the tangent line is positive the function is increasing, and when the slope of the tangent line is negative the function is decreasing. Because $f'(x)$ is the slope of the tangent line to the curve $y = f(x)$, f is increasing when $f'(x) > 0$, and f is decreasing when $f'(x) < 0$. Also, because $f'(x)$ is the rate of change of the function values $f(x)$ with respect to x, when $f'(x) > 0$, the function values are increasing as x increases; and when $f'(x) < 0$, the function values are decreasing as x increases. We have the following theorem.

5.1.3 Theorem   Let the function f be continuous on the closed interval $[a, b]$ and differentiable on the open interval (a, b):

(i) if $f'(x) > 0$ for all x in (a, b), then f is increasing on $[a, b]$;
(ii) if $f'(x) < 0$ for all x in (a, b), then f is decreasing on $[a, b]$.

PROOF OF (i):   Let x_1 and x_2 be any two numbers in $[a, b]$ such that $x_1 < x_2$. Then f is continuous on $[x_1, x_2]$ and differentiable on (x_1, x_2). From the mean-value theorem it follows that there is some number c in (x_1, x_2) such that

$$f'(c) = \frac{f(x_2) - f(x_1)}{x_2 - x_1}$$

Because $x_1 < x_2$, then $x_2 - x_1 > 0$. Also, $f'(c) > 0$ by hypothesis. Therefore $f(x_2) - f(x_1) > 0$, and so $f(x_2) > f(x_1)$. We have shown, then, that $f(x_1) < f(x_2)$ whenever $x_1 < x_2$, where x_1 and x_2 are any numbers in the interval $[a, b]$. Therefore, by Definition 5.1.1, it follows that f is increasing on $[a, b]$.

The proof of part (ii) is similar and is left as an exercise (see Exercise 34).   ∎

An immediate application of Theorem 5.1.1, is in the proof of what is known as the *first-derivative test for relative extrema* of a function.

5.1.4 Theorem
First-Derivative Test for Relative Extrema

Let the function f be continuous at all points of the open interval (a, b) containing the number c, and suppose that f' exists at all points of (a, b) except possibly at c:

(i) if $f'(x) > 0$ for all values of x in some open interval having c as its right endpoint, and if $f'(x) < 0$ for all values of x in some open interval having c as its left endpoint, then f has a relative maximum value at c;

Figure 5.1.2

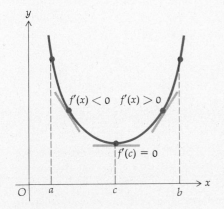

Figure 5.1.3

(ii) if $f'(x) < 0$ for all values of x in some open interval having c as its right endpoint, and if $f'(x) > 0$ for all values of x in some open interval having c as its left endpoint, then f has a relative minimum value at c.

PROOF OF (i):   Let (d, c) be the interval having c as its right endpoint for which $f'(x) > 0$ for all x in the interval. It follows from Theorem 5.1.3(i) that f is increasing on $[d, c]$. Let (c, e) be the interval having c as its left endpoint for which $f'(x) < 0$ for all x in the interval. By Theorem 5.1.3(ii) f is decreasing on $[c, e]$. Because f is increasing on $[d, c]$, it follows from Definition 5.1.1 that if x_1 is in $[d, c]$ and $x_1 \neq c$, then $f(x_1) < f(c)$. Also, because f is decreasing on $[c, e]$, it follows from Definition 5.1.2 that if x_2 is in $[c, e]$ and $x_2 \neq c$, then $f(c) > f(x_2)$. Therefore, from Definition 4.5.1, f has a relative maximum value at c.

The proof of part (ii) is similar to the proof of part (i), and it is left as an exercise (see Exercise 35).   ∎

The first-derivative test for relative extrema essentially states that if f is continuous at c and $f'(x)$ changes algebraic sign from positive to negative as x increases through the number c, then f has a relative maximum value at c; and if $f'(x)$ changes algebraic sign from negative to positive as x increases through c, then f has a relative minimum value at c.

Figures 5.1.2 and 5.1.3 illustrate parts (i) and (ii), respectively, of Theorem 5.1.4 when $f'(c)$ exists. Figure 5.1.4 shows a sketch of the graph of a function f that has a relative maximum value at a number c, but $f'(c)$ does not exist; however, $f'(x) > 0$ when $x < c$, and $f'(x) < 0$ when $x > c$. In Fig. 5.1.5, we show a sketch of the graph of a function f for which c is a critical number, and $f'(x) < 0$ when $x < c$, and $f'(x) < 0$ when $x > c$; f does not have a relative extremum at c.

Figure 5.1.4

Figure 5.1.5

Further illustrations of Theorem 5.1.4 occur in Fig. 5.1.1. At x_2 and x_4 the function has a relative maximum value, and at x_3 and x_5 the function has a relative minimum value; even though x_6 is a critical number for the function, there is no relative extremum at x_6.

In summary, to determine the relative extrema of a function f:

(1) Find $f'(x)$.
(2) Find the critical numbers of f, that is, the values of x for which $f'(x) = 0$ or for which $f'(x)$ does not exist.
(3) Apply the first-derivative test (Theorem 5.1.4).

The following examples illustrate this procedure.

EXAMPLE 1:   Given

$$f(x) = x^3 - 6x^2 + 9x + 1$$

find the relative extrema of f by applying the first-derivative test. Determine the values of x at which the relative extrema occur, as well as the intervals on which f is increasing and the intervals on which f is decreasing. Draw a sketch of the graph.

Figure 5.1.6

SOLUTION: $f'(x) = 3x^2 - 12x + 9$.

$f'(x)$ exists for all values of x. Setting $f'(x) = 0$, we have

$$3x^2 - 12x + 9 = 0$$

$$3(x - 3)(x - 1) = 0$$

which gives us

$$x = 3 \quad \text{and} \quad x = 1$$

Thus, the critical numbers of f are 1 and 3. To determine whether f has a relative extremum at either of these numbers, we apply the first-derivative test. The results are summarized in Table 5.1.1.

We see from the table that 5 is a relative maximum value of f occurring at 1, and 1 is a relative minimum value of f occurring at 3. A sketch of the graph is shown in Fig. 5.1.6.

Table 5.1.1

	$f(x)$	$f'(x)$	Conclusion
$x < 1$		+	f is increasing
$x = 1$	5	0	f has a relative maximum value
$1 < x < 3$		—	f is decreasing
$x = 3$	1	0	f has a relative minimum value
$3 < x$		+	f is increasing

EXAMPLE 2:   Given

$$f(x) = \begin{cases} x^2 - 4 & \text{if } x < 3 \\ 8 - x & \text{if } 3 \le x \end{cases}$$

find the relative extrema of f by applying the first-derivative test.

SOLUTION: If $x < 3$, $f'(x) = 2x$. If $x > 3$, $f'(x) = -1$. Because $f'_-(3) = 6$ and $f'_+(3) = -1$, we conclude that $f'(3)$ does not exist. Therefore, 3 is a critical number of f.

Because $f'(x) = 0$ when $x = 0$, it follows that 0 is a critical number of f. Applying the first-derivative test, we summarize the results in Table 5.1.2. A sketch of the graph is shown in Fig. 5.1.7.

Determine the values of x at which the relative extrema occur, as well as the intervals on which f is increasing and the intervals on which f is decreasing. Draw a sketch of the graph.

Figure 5.1.7

Table 5.1.2

	$f(x)$	$f'(x)$	Conclusion
$x < 0$		$-$	f is decreasing
$x = 0$	-4	0	f has a relative minimum value
$0 < x < 3$		$+$	f is increasing
$x = 3$	5	does not exist	f has a relative maximum value
$3 < x$		$-$	f is decreasing

EXAMPLE 3:   Given

$$f(x) = x^{4/3} + 4x^{1/3}$$

find the relative extrema of f, determine the values of x at which the relative extrema occur, and determine the intervals on which f is increasing and the intervals on which f is decreasing. Draw a sketch of the graph.

Figure 5.1.8

SOLUTION: $f'(x) = \frac{4}{3}x^{1/3} + \frac{4}{3}x^{-2/3} = \frac{4}{3}x^{-2/3}(x + 1)$.

Because $f'(x)$ does not exist when $x = 0$, and $f'(x) = 0$ when $x = -1$, the critical numbers of f are -1 and 0. We apply the first-derivative test and summarize the results in Table 5.1.3. A sketch of the graph is shown in Fig. 5.1.8.

Table 5.1.3

	$f(x)$	$f'(x)$	Conclusion
$x < -1$		$-$	f is decreasing
$x = -1$	-3	0	f has a relative minimum value
$-1 < x < 0$		$+$	f is increasing
$x = 0$	0	does not exist	f does not have a relative extremum at $x = 0$
$0 < x$		$+$	f is increasing

Exercises 5.1

In Exercises 1 through 30, do each of the following: (a) find the relative extrema of f by applying the first-derivative test; (b) determine the values of x at which the relative extrema occur; (c) determine the intervals on which f is increasing; (d) determine the intervals on which f is decreasing; (e) draw a sketch of the graph.

1. $f(x) = x^2 - 4x - 1$

2. $f(x) = x^3 - 9x^2 + 15x - 5$

3. $f(x) = 2x^3 - x^2 + 3x - 1$

4. $f(x) = x^4 + 4x$

5. $f(x) = x^5 - 5x^3 - 20x - 2$

6. $f(x) = 2x + \dfrac{1}{2x}$

7. $f(x) = \sqrt{x} - \dfrac{1}{\sqrt{x}}$

8. $f(x) = \dfrac{x-2}{x+2}$

9. $f(x) = 2x\sqrt{3-x}$

10. $f(x) = x\sqrt{5-x^2}$

11. $f(x) = (1-x)^2(1+x)^3$

12. $f(x) = (x+2)^2(x-1)^2$

13. $f(x) = 2 - 3(x-4)^{2/3}$

14. $f(x) = 2 - (x-1)^{1/3}$

15. $f(x) = \begin{cases} 2x+1 & \text{if } x \le 4 \\ 13-x & \text{if } 4 < x \end{cases}$

16. $f(x) = \begin{cases} 5-2x & \text{if } x < 3 \\ 3x-10 & \text{if } 3 \le x \end{cases}$

17. $f(x) = \begin{cases} 2x+9 & \text{if } x \le -2 \\ x^2+1 & \text{if } -2 < x \end{cases}$

18. $f(x) = \begin{cases} 4-(x+5)^2 & \text{if } x < -4 \\ 12-(x+1)^2 & \text{if } -4 \le x \end{cases}$

19. $f(x) = \begin{cases} (x-2)^2-3 & \text{if } x \le 5 \\ \frac{1}{2}(x+7) & \text{if } 5 < x \end{cases}$

20. $f(x) = \begin{cases} \sqrt{25-(x+7)^2} & \text{if } x \le -3 \\ 12-x^2 & \text{if } -3 < x \end{cases}$

21. $f(x) = \begin{cases} 3x+5 & \text{if } x < -1 \\ x^2+1 & \text{if } -1 \le x < 2 \\ 7-x & \text{if } 2 \le x \end{cases}$

22. $f(x) = \begin{cases} x-6 & \text{if } x \le 6 \\ -\sqrt{4-(x-8)^2} & \text{if } 6 < x \le 10 \\ 20-2x & \text{if } 10 < x \end{cases}$

23. $f(x) = \begin{cases} (x+9)^2-8 & \text{if } x < -7 \\ -\sqrt{25-(x+4)^2} & \text{if } -7 \le x \le 0 \\ (x-2)^2-7 & \text{if } 0 < x \end{cases}$

24. $f(x) = \begin{cases} 12-(x+5)^2 & \text{if } x \le -3 \\ 5-x & \text{if } -3 < x \le -1 \\ \sqrt{100-(x-7)^2} & \text{if } -1 < x \end{cases}$

25. $f(x) = x^{5/4} + 10x^{1/4}$

26. $f(x) = x^{5/3} - 10x^{2/3}$

27. $f(x) = (x+1)^{2/3}(x-2)^{1/3}$

28. $f(x) = (4x-a)^{1/3}(2x-a)^{2/3}$

29. $f(x) = x^{1/3}(x+4)^{-2/3}$

30. $f(x) = (x-a)^{2/5} + 1$

31. Find a and b so that the function defined by $f(x) = x^3 + ax^2 + b$ will have a relative extremum at $(2, 3)$.

32. Find a, b, and c so that the function defined by $f(x) = ax^2 + bx + c$ will have a relative maximum value of 7 at 1 and the graph of $y = f(x)$ will go through the point $(2, -2)$.

33. Find a, b, c, and d so that the function defined by $f(x) = ax^3 + bx^2 + cx + d$ will have relative extrema at $(1, 2)$ and $(2, 3)$.

34. Prove Theorem 5.1.3(ii).

35. Prove Theorem 5.1.4(ii).

36. Given that the function f is continuous for all values of x, $f(3) = 2$, $f'(x) < 0$ if $x < 3$, and $f'(x) > 0$ if $x > 3$, draw a sketch of a possible graph of f in each of the following cases, where the additional condition is satisfied: (a) f' is continuous at 3; (b) $f'(x) = -1$ if $x < 3$, and $f'(x) = 1$ if $x > 3$; (c) $\lim_{x \to 3} f'(x) = -1$, $\lim_{x \to 3} f'(x) = 1$, and $f'(a) \ne f'(b)$ if $a \ne b$.

37. Given $f(x) = x^p(1-x)^q$, where p and q are positive integers greater than 1, prove each of the following: (a) if p is even, f has a relative minimum value at 0; (b) if q is even, f has a relative minimum value at 1; (c) f has a relative maximum value at $p/(p+q)$ whether p and q are odd or even.

38. Prove that if f is increasing on $[a, b]$ and if g is increasing on $[f(a), f(b)]$, then if $g \circ f$ exists on $[a, b]$, $g \circ f$ is increasing on $[a, b]$.

39. The function f is increasing on the interval I. Prove: (a) if $g(x) = -f(x)$, then g is decreasing on I; (b) if $h(x) = 1/f(x)$ and $f(x) > 0$ on I, then h is decreasing on I.

40. The function f is differentiable at each number in the closed interval $[a, b]$. Prove that if $f'(a) \cdot f'(b) < 0$, there is a number c in the open interval (a, b) such that $f'(c) = 0$.

5.2 THE SECOND-DERIVATIVE TEST FOR RELATIVE EXTREMA

In Sec. 5.1 we learned how to determine whether a function f has a relative maximum value or a relative minimum value at a critical number c by checking the algebraic sign of f' at numbers in intervals to the left and right of c. Another test for relative extrema is one that involves only the critical number c, and often it is the easier test to apply. It is called the *second-derivative test for relative extrema*, and it is stated in the following theorem.

5.2.1 Theorem
Second-Derivative Test for Relative Extrema

Let c be a critical number of a function f at which $f'(c) = 0$, and let f' exist for all values of x in some open interval containing c. Then if $f''(c)$ exists and

(i) if $f''(c) < 0$, then f has a relative maximum value at c;
(ii) if $f''(c) > 0$, then f has a relative minimum value at c.

PROOF OF (i): By hypothesis, $f''(c)$ exists and is negative; so we have

$$f''(c) = \lim_{x \to c} \frac{f'(x) - f'(c)}{x - c} < 0$$

Therefore, by Theorem 4.3.2, there is an open interval I containing c such that

$$\frac{f'(x) - f'(c)}{x - c} < 0 \tag{1}$$

for every $x \neq c$ in the interval.

Let I' be the open interval containing all values of x in I for which $x < c$; therefore, c is the right endpoint of the open interval I'. Let I'' be the open interval containing all values of x in I for which $x > c$; so c is the left endpoint of the open interval I''.

Then if x is in I', $(x - c) < 0$, and it follows from inequality (1) that $[f'(x) - f'(c)] > 0$ or, equivalently, $f'(x) > f'(c)$. If x is in I'', $(x - c) > 0$, and it follows from (1) that $[f'(x) - f'(c)] < 0$ or, equivalently, $f'(x) < f'(c)$.

But because $f'(c) = 0$, we conclude that if x is in I', $f'(x) > 0$, and if x is in I'', $f'(x) < 0$. Therefore, $f'(x)$ changes algebraic sign from positive to negative as x increases through c, and so, by Theorem 5.1.4, f has a relative maximum value at c.

The proof of part (ii) is similar and is left as an exercise (see Exercise 18). ∎

EXAMPLE 1:   Given

$$f(x) = x^4 + \tfrac{4}{3}x^3 - 4x^2$$

find the relative maxima and the relative minima of f by applying the second-derivative test.

SOLUTION:

$$f'(x) = 4x^3 + 4x^2 - 8x$$
$$f''(x) = 12x^2 + 8x - 8$$

Setting $f'(x) = 0$, we have

$$4x(x+2)(x-1) = 0$$

which gives

$$x = 0 \qquad x = -2 \qquad x = 1$$

Thus, the critical numbers of f are -2, 0, and 1. We determine whether or not there is a relative extremum at any of these critical numbers by finding the sign of the second derivative there. The results are summarized in Table 5.2.1.

Table 5.2.1

	$f(x)$	$f'(x)$	$f''(x)$	Conclusion
$x = -2$	$-\tfrac{32}{3}$	0	$+$	f has a relative minimum value
$x = 0$	0	0	$-$	f has a relative maximum value
$x = 1$	$-\tfrac{5}{3}$	0	$+$	f has a relative minimum value

Figure 5.2.1   Figure 5.2.2

Figure 5.2.3

If $f''(c) = 0$, as well as $f'(c) = 0$, nothing can be concluded regarding a relative extremum of f at c. The following three illustrations justify this statement.

● ILLUSTRATION 1: If $f(x) = x^4$, then $f'(x) = 4x^3$ and $f''(x) = 12x^2$. Thus, $f(0)$, $f'(0)$, and $f''(0)$ all have the value zero. By applying the first-derivative test we see that f has a relative minimum value at 0. A sketch of the graph of f is shown in Fig. 5.2.1.   ●

● ILLUSTRATION 2: If $g(x) = -x^4$, then $g'(x) = -4x^3$ and $g''(x) = -12x^2$. Hence, $g(0) = g'(0) = g''(0) = 0$. In this case, g has a relative maximum value at 0, as can be seen by applying the first-derivative test. A sketch of the graph of g is shown in Fig. 5.2.2.   ●

● ILLUSTRATION 3: If $h(x) = x^3$, then $h'(x) = 3x^2$ and $h''(x) = 6x$; so $h(0) = h'(0) = h''(0) = 0$. The function h does not have a relative extremum at 0 because if $x < 0$, $h(x) < h(0)$; and if $x > 0$, $h(x) > h(0)$. A sketch of the graph of h is shown in Fig. 5.2.3.   ●

In Illustrations 1, 2, and 3 we have examples of three functions, each of which has zero for its second derivative at a number for which its first derivative is zero; yet one function has a relative minimum value at that number, another function has a relative maximum value at that number, and the third function has neither a relative maximum value nor a relative minimum value at that number.

Exercises 5.2

In Exercises 1 through 14, find the relative extrema of the given function by using the second-derivative test, if it can be applied. If the second-derivative test cannot be applied, use the first-derivative test.

1. $f(x) = 3x^2 - 2x + 1$

2. $g(x) = x^3 - 5x + 6$

3. $f(x) = -4x^3 + 3x^2 + 18x$

4. $h(x) = 2x^3 - 9x^2 + 27$

5. $f(x) = (x - 4)^2$

6. $G(x) = (x + 2)^3$

7. $G(x) = (x - 3)^4$

8. $f(x) = x(x - 1)^3$

9. $h(x) = x\sqrt{x + 3}$

10. $f(x) = x\sqrt{8 - x^2}$

11. $f(x) = 4x^{1/2} + 4x^{-1/2}$

12. $g(x) = \dfrac{9}{x} + \dfrac{x^2}{9}$

13. $F(x) = 6x^{1/3} - x^{2/3}$

14. $G(x) = x^{2/3}(x - 4)^2$

15. Given $f(x) = x^3 + 3rx + 5$, prove that (a) if $r > 0$, f has no relative extrema; (b) if $r < 0$, f has both a relative maximum value and a relative minimum value.

16. Given $f(x) = x^r - rx + k$, where $r > 0$ and $r \neq 1$, prove that (a) if $0 < r < 1$, f has a relative maximum value at 1; (b) if $r > 1$, f has a relative minimum value at 1.

17. Given $f(x) = x^2 + rx^{-1}$, prove that regardless of the value of r, f has a relative minimum value and no relative maximum value.

18. Prove Theorem 5.2.1(ii).

5.3 ADDITIONAL PROBLEMS INVOLVING ABSOLUTE EXTREMA

The extreme-value theorem (Theorem 4.5.9) guarantees an absolute maximum value and an absolute minimum value for a function which is continuous on a closed interval. We now consider some functions defined on intervals for which the extreme-value theorem does not apply and which may or may not have absolute extrema.

EXAMPLE 1:   Given

$$f(x) = \frac{x^2 - 27}{x - 6}$$

find the absolute extrema of f on the interval $[0, 6)$ if there are any.

SOLUTION: f is continuous on the interval $[0, 6)$ because the only discontinuity of f is at 6, which is not in the interval.

$$f'(x) = \frac{2x(x - 6) - (x^2 - 27)}{(x - 6)^2} = \frac{x^2 - 12x + 27}{(x - 6)^2} = \frac{(x - 3)(x - 9)}{(x - 6)^2}$$

$f'(x)$ exists for all values of x in $[0, 6)$, and $f'(x) = 0$ when $x = 3$ or 9; so the only critical number of f in the interval $[0, 6)$ is 3. The first-derivative test is applied to determine if f has a relative extremum at 3. The results are summarized in Table 5.3.1.

Because f has a relative maximum value at 3, and f is increasing on the interval $[0, 3)$ and decreasing on the interval $(3, 6)$, we conclude that on $[0, 6)$ f has an absolute maximum value at 3, and it is $f(3)$, which is 6. Noting that $\lim_{x \to 6^-} f(x) = -\infty$, we conclude that there is no absolute minimum value of f on $[0, 6)$.

Table 5.3.1

	$f(x)$	$f'(x)$	Conclusion
$0 \leq x < 3$		$+$	f is increasing
$x = 3$	6	0	f has a relative maximum value
$3 < x < 6$		$-$	f is decreasing

EXAMPLE 2: Given

$$f(x) = \frac{-x}{(x^2 + 6)^2}$$

find the absolute extrema of f on $(0, +\infty)$ if there are any.

SOLUTION: f is continuous for all values of x.

$$f'(x) = \frac{-1(x^2 + 6)^2 + 4x^2(x^2 + 6)}{(x^2 + 6)^4} = \frac{-(x^2 + 6) + 4x^2}{(x^2 + 6)^3} = \frac{3x^2 - 6}{(x^2 + 6)^3}$$

$f'(x)$ exists for all values of x. Setting $f'(x) = 0$, we obtain $x = \pm\sqrt{2}$; so $\sqrt{2}$ is the only critical number of f in $(0, +\infty)$. The first-derivative test is applied at $\sqrt{2}$, and the results are summarized in Table 5.3.2.

Because f has a relative minimum value at $\sqrt{2}$ and because f is decreasing on $(0, \sqrt{2})$ and increasing on $(\sqrt{2}, +\infty)$, we conclude that f has an absolute minimum value at $\sqrt{2}$ on $(0, +\infty)$. The absolute minimum value is $-\frac{1}{64}\sqrt{2}$. There is no absolute maximum value of f on $(0, +\infty)$.

Table 5.3.2

	$f(x)$	$f'(x)$	Conclusion
$0 < x < \sqrt{2}$		$-$	f is decreasing
$x = \sqrt{2}$	$-\frac{1}{64}\sqrt{2}$	0	f has a relative minimum value
$\sqrt{2} < x < +\infty$		$+$	f is increasing

EXAMPLE 3: Find the shortest distance from the point $A(2, \frac{1}{2})$ to a point on the parabola $y = x^2$, and find the point on the parabola that is closest to A.

SOLUTION: Let $z =$ the number of units in the distance from the point $A(2, \frac{1}{2})$ to a point $P(x, y)$ on the parabola. Refer to Fig. 5.3.1.

$$z = \sqrt{(x - 2)^2 + (y - \frac{1}{2})^2} \tag{1}$$

Because $P(x, y)$ is on the parabola, its coordinates satisfy the equation $y = x^2$. Substituting this value of y into Eq. (1), we obtain z as a function of x and write

$$z(x) = \sqrt{(x - 2)^2 + (x^2 - \frac{1}{2})^2}$$

$$z(x) = \sqrt{x^4 - 4x + \tfrac{17}{4}} \tag{2}$$

Because P can be any point on the parabola, x is any real number. We wish to find the absolute minimum value of z on $(-\infty, +\infty)$.

$$z'(x) = \tfrac{1}{2}(4x^3 - 4)(x^4 - 4x + \tfrac{17}{4})^{-1/2} = \frac{2(x-1)(x^2 + x + 1)}{\sqrt{x^4 - 4x + \tfrac{17}{4}}}$$

$z'(x)$ exists for all values of x because the denominator is $z(x)$, which is never zero. Consequently, the critical numbers are obtained by setting $z'(x) = 0$. The only real solution is 1; thus, 1 is the only critical number of z. We apply the first-derivative test and summarize the results in Table 5.3.3.

Table 5.3.3

	$z(x)$	$z'(x)$	Conclusion
$-\infty < x < 1$		$-$	z is decreasing
$x = 1$	$\tfrac{1}{2}\sqrt{5}$	0	z has a relative minimum value
$1 < x < +\infty$		$+$	z is increasing

Because z has a relative minimum value at 1, and because z is decreasing on $(-\infty, 1)$ and increasing on $(1, +\infty)$, we conclude that z has an absolute minimum value of $\tfrac{1}{2}\sqrt{5}$ at 1. So the point on the parabola closest to A is $(1, 1)$.

We can show that the point $A(2, \tfrac{1}{2})$ lies on the normal line at $(1, 1)$ of the graph of the parabola. Because the slope of the tangent line at any point (x, y) of the parabola is $2x$, the slope of the tangent line at $(1, 1)$ is 2. Therefore, the slope of the normal line at $(1, 1)$ is $-\tfrac{1}{2}$, which is the same as the slope of the line through $A(2, \tfrac{1}{2})$ and $(1, 1)$.

In the next two examples, where the second-derivative test is used to determine the relative extrema, we use the following theorem to determine the absolute extrema.

5.3.1 Theorem   Let the function f be continuous on the interval I containing the number c. If $f(c)$ is a relative extremum of f on I and c is the only number in I for which f has a relative extremum, then $f(c)$ is an absolute extremum of f on I. Furthermore,

(i) if $f(c)$ is a relative maximum value of f on I, then $f(c)$ is an absolute maximum value of f on I;

Figure 5.3.1

(ii) if $f(c)$ is a relative minimum value of f on I, then $f(c)$ is an absolute minimum value of f on I.

PROOF: We prove part (i). The proof of part (ii) is similar.

Because $f(c)$ is a relative maximum value of f on I, then by Definition 4.5.1 there is an open interval J, where $J \subset I$, and where J contains c, such that

$$f(c) \geq f(x) \qquad \text{for all } x \in J$$

Because c is the only number in I for which f has a relative maximum value, it follows that

$$f(c) > f(k) \qquad \text{if } k \in J \text{ and } k \neq c \tag{3}$$

In order to show that $f(c)$ is an absolute maximum value of f on I, we show that if d is any number other than c in I, then $f(c) > f(d)$. We assume that

$$f(c) \leq f(d) \tag{4}$$

and show that this assumption leads to a contradiction. Because $d \neq c$, then either $c < d$ or $d < c$. We consider the case that $c < d$ (the proof is similar if $d < c$).

Because f is continuous on I, then f is continuous on the closed interval $[c, d]$. Therefore, by Theorem 4.5.9, f has an absolute minimum value on $[c, d]$. Assume this absolute minimum value occurs at e where $c \leq e \leq d$. From inequality (3) it follows that $e \neq c$, and from inequalities (3) and (4) it follows that $e \neq d$. Consequently, $c < e < d$, and hence f has a relative minimum value at e. But this statement contradicts the hypothesis that c is the only number in I for which f has a relative extremum. Thus, our assumption that $f(c) \leq f(d)$ is false. Therefore, $f(c) > f(d)$ if $d \in I$ and $d \neq c$, and consequently $f(c)$ is an absolute maximum value of f on I. ∎

EXAMPLE 4: A closed box with a square base is to have a volume of 2000 cubic inches. The material for the top and bottom of the box is to cost $3 per square inch, and the material for the sides is to cost $1.50 per square inch. If the cost of the material is to be the least, find the dimensions of the box.

SOLUTION: Let $x =$ the number of inches in the length of a side of the square base;

$y =$ the number of inches in the depth of the box;

$C =$ the number of dollars in the cost of the material.

The total number of square inches in the combined area of the top and bottom is $2x^2$, and for the sides it is $4xy$; so we have

$$C = 3(2x^2) + \tfrac{3}{2}(4xy) \tag{5}$$

Because the volume of the box is the product of the area of the base and the depth, we have

$$x^2 y = 2000 \tag{6}$$

Solving Eq. (6) for y in terms of x and substituting into Eq. (5) we get

$$C = 6x^2 + \frac{12{,}000}{x} \tag{7}$$

x is in the interval $(0, +\infty)$, and C is a function of x, which is continuous on $(0, +\infty)$. From Eq. (7) we obtain

$$D_x C = 12x - \frac{12{,}000}{x^2} \tag{8}$$

$D_x C$ does not exist when $x = 0$, but 0 is not in $(0, +\infty)$. Hence, the only critical numbers will be those obtained by setting $D_x C = 0$. The only real solution is 10; thus, 10 is the only critical number. To determine if $x = 10$ makes C a relative minimum we apply the second-derivative test. From Eq. (8) it follows that

$$D_x{}^2 C = 12 + \frac{24{,}000}{x^3}$$

The results of the second-derivative test are summarized in Table 5.3.4.

Table 5.3.4

	$D_x C$	$D_x{}^2 C$	Conclusion
$x = 10$	0	+	C has a relative minimum value

From Eq. (7) we see that C is a continuous function of x on $(0, +\infty)$. Because the one and only relative extremum of C on $(0, +\infty)$ is at $x = 10$, it follows from Theorem 5.3.1(ii) that this relative minimum value of C is the absolute minimum value of C. Hence, we conclude that the total cost of the material will be the least when the side of the square base is 10 in. and the depth is 20 in.

In the preceding examples and in the exercises of Sec. 4.6, the variable for which we wished to find an absolute extremum was expressed as a function of only one variable. Sometimes this procedure is either too difficult or too laborious, or occasionally even impossible. Often the given information enables us to obtain two equations involving three variables. Instead of eliminating one of the variables, it may be more advantageous to differentiate implicitly. The following example illustrates this method.

EXAMPLE 5:   If a closed tin can of specific volume is to be in the form of a right-circular cylinder, find the ratio of the height to the base radius if the least amount of material is to be used in its manufacture.

SOLUTION: We wish to find a relationship between the height and the base radius of the right-circular cylinder in order for the total surface area to be an absolute minimum for a fixed volume. Therefore, we consider the volume of the cylinder a constant.

Let $V =$ the number of cubic units in the volume of a cylinder (a constant).

We now define the variables:

$r =$ the number of units in the base radius of the cylinder; $0 < r < +\infty$;

$h =$ the number of units in the height of the cylinder; $0 < h < +\infty$;

$S =$ the number of square units in the total surface area of the cylinder.

We have the following equations:

$$S = 2\pi r^2 + 2\pi rh \tag{9}$$

$$V = \pi r^2 h \tag{10}$$

Because V is a constant, we could solve Eq. (10) for either r or h in terms of the other and substitute into Eq. (9), which will give us S as a function of one variable. The alternative method is to consider S as a function of two variables r and h; however, r and h are not independent of each other. That is, if we choose r as the independent variable, then S depends on r; also, h depends on r.

Differentiating S and V with respect to r and bearing in mind that h is a function of r, we have

$$D_r S = 4\pi r + 2\pi h + 2\pi r\, D_r h \tag{11}$$

and

$$D_r V = 2\pi rh + \pi r^2\, D_r h \tag{12}$$

Because V is a constant, $D_r V = 0$; therefore, from Eq. (12) we have

$$2\pi rh + \pi r^2\, D_r h = 0$$

with $r \neq 0$, and we can divide by r and solve for $D_r h$, thus obtaining

$$D_r h = -\frac{2h}{r} \tag{13}$$

Substituting from Eq. (13) into Eq. (11), we obtain

$$D_r S = 2\pi \left[2r + h + r\left(-\frac{2h}{r} \right) \right]$$

$$D_r S = 2\pi(2r - h) \tag{14}$$

To find when S has a relative minimum value, we set $D_r S = 0$ and obtain $2r - h = 0$, which gives us

$$r = \tfrac{1}{2}h$$

To determine if this relationship between r and h makes S a relative minimum, we apply the second-derivative test. Then from Eq. (14) we find that

$$D_r^2 S = 2\pi(2 - D_r h) \tag{15}$$

Substituting from Eq. (13) into (15), we get

$$D_r^2 S = 2\pi \left[2 - \left(\frac{-2h}{r} \right) \right] = 2\pi \left(2 + \frac{2h}{r} \right)$$

The results of the second-derivative test are summarized in Table 5.3.5.

Table 5.3.5

	$D_r S$	$D_r^2 S$	Conclusion
$r = \frac{1}{2}h$	0	+	S has a relative minimum value

From Eqs. (9) and (10) we see that S is a continuous function of r on $(0, +\infty)$. Because the one and only relative extremum of S on $(0, +\infty)$ is at $r = \frac{1}{2}h$, we conclude from Theorem 5.3.1(ii) that S has an absolute minimum value at $r = \frac{1}{2}h$. Therefore, the total surface area of the tin can will be least for a specific volume when the ratio of the height to the base radius is 2.

Exercises 5.3

In Exercises 1 through 8, find the absolute extrema of the given function on the given interval if there are any.

1. $f(x) = x^2$; $(-3, 2]$

2. $g(x) = x^3 + 2x^2 - 4x + 1$; $(-3, 2)$

3. $F(x) = \frac{x+2}{x-2}$; $[-4, 4]$

4. $f(x) = \frac{x^2}{x+3}$; $[-4, -1]$

5. $g(x) = 4x^2 - 2x + 1$; $(-\infty, +\infty)$

6. $G(x) = (x-5)^{2/3}$; $(-\infty, +\infty)$

7. $f(x) = \frac{x}{(x^2+4)^{3/2}}$; $[0, +\infty)$

8. $f(x) = \frac{x^2 - 30}{x - 4}$; $(-\infty, 4)$

9. A rectangular field, having an area of 2700 yd², is to be enclosed by a fence, and an additional fence is to be used to divide the field down the middle. If the cost of the fence down the middle is $2 per running yard, and the fence along the sides costs $3 per running yard, find the dimensions of the field so that the cost of the fencing will be the least.

10. A rectangular open tank is to have a square base, and its volume is to be 125 yd³. The cost per square yard for the bottom is $8 and for the sides is $4. Find the dimensions of the tank in order for the cost of the material to be the least.

11. A box manufacturer is to produce a closed box of specific volume whose base is a rectangle having a length that is three times its width. Find the most economical dimensions.

12. Solve Exercise 11 if the box is to have an open top.

13. A funnel of specific volume is to be in the shape of a right-circular cone. Find the ratio of the height to the base radius if the least amount of material is to be used in its manufacture.

14. A Norman window consists of a rectangle surmounted by a semicircle. Find the shape of such a window that will admit the most light for a given perimeter.

15. Solve Exercise 14 if the window is such that the semicircle transmits only half as much light per square unit of area as the rectangle.

16. The strength of a rectangular beam is proportional to the breadth and the square of its depth. Find the dimensions of the strongest beam that can be cut from a log in the shape of a right-circular cylinder of radius a in.

17. The stiffness of a rectangular beam is proportional to the breadth and the cube of its depth. What is the shape of the stiffest beam that can be cut from a log in the shape of a right-circular cylinder?

18. A page of print is to contain 24 in.^{2} of printed area, a margin of $1\frac{1}{2}$ in. at the top and bottom, and a margin of 1 in. at the sides. What are the dimensions of the smallest page that would fill these requirements?

19. A one-story building having a rectangular floor space of 13,200 ft^2 is to be constructed where a 22-ft easement is required in the front and back and a 15-ft easement is required on each side. Find the dimensions of the lot having the least area on which this building can be located.

20. Find the point on the curve $y^2 - x^2 = 1$ that is closest to the point $(2, 0)$.

21. A direct current generator has an electromotive force of E volts and an internal resistance of r ohms. E and r are constants. If R ohms is the external resistance, the total resistance is $(r + R)$ ohms and if P watts is the power, then

$$P = \frac{E^2 R}{(r + R)^2}$$

What external resistance will consume the most power?

22. A right-circular cone is to be inscribed in a sphere of given radius. Find the ratio of the altitude to the base radius of the cone of largest possible volume.

23. A right-circular cone is to be circumscribed about a sphere of given radius. Find the ratio of the altitude to the base radius of the cone of least possible volume.

24. Prove by the method of this section that the shortest distance from the point $P_1(x_1, y_1)$ to the line l, having the equation $Ax + By + C = 0$, is $|Ax_1 + By_1 + C|/\sqrt{A^2 + B^2}$. (HINT: If s is the number of units from P_1 to a point $P(x, y)$ on l, then s will be an absolute minimum when s^2 is an absolute minimum.)

5.4 CONCAVITY AND POINTS OF INFLECTION

Figure 5.4.1 shows a sketch of the graph of a function f whose first and second derivatives exist on the closed interval $[x_1, x_7]$. Because both f and f' are differentiable there, f and f' are continuous on $[x_1, x_7]$.

If we consider a point P moving along the graph of Fig. 5.4.1 from A to G, then the position of P varies as we increase x from x_1 to x_7. As P

Figure 5.4.1

moves along the graph from A to B, the slope of the tangent line to the graph is positive and is decreasing; that is, the tangent line is turning clockwise, and the graph lies below the tangent line. When the point P is at B, the slope of the tangent line is zero and is still decreasing. As P moves along the graph from B to C, the slope of the tangent line is negative and is still decreasing; the tangent line is still turning clockwise, and the graph is below its tangent line. We say that the graph is "concave downward" from A to C. As P moves along the graph from C to D, the slope of the tangent line is negative and is increasing; that is, the tangent line is turning counterclockwise, and the graph is above its tangent line. At D, the slope of the tangent line is zero and is still increasing. From D to E, the slope of the tangent line is positive and increasing; the tangent line is still turning counterclockwise, and the graph is above its tangent line. We say that the graph is "concave upward" from C to E. At the point C, the graph changes from concave downward to concave upward. Point C is called a "point of inflection." We have the following definitions.

5.4.1 Definition The graph of a function f is said to be *concave upward* at the point $(c, f(c))$ if $f'(c)$ exists and if there is an open interval I containing c such that for all values of $x \neq c$ in I the point $(x, f(x))$ on the graph is above the tangent line to the graph at $(c, f(c))$.

5.4.2 Definition The graph of a function f is said to be *concave downward* at the point $(c, f(c))$ if $f'(c)$ exists and if there is an open interval I containing c such that for all values of $x \neq c$ in I the point $(x, f(x))$ on the graph is below the tangent line to the graph at $(c, f(c))$.

Figure 5.4.2

● ILLUSTRATION 1: Figure 5.4.2 shows a sketch of a portion of the graph of a function f that is concave upward at the point $(c, f(c))$, and Fig. 5.4.3 shows a sketch of a portion of the graph of a function f that is concave downward at the point $(c, f(c))$. ●

Figure 5.4.3

The graph of the function f of Fig. 5.4.1 is concave downward at all points $(x, f(x))$ for which x is in either of the following open intervals: (x_1, x_3) or (x_5, x_6). Similarly, the graph of the function f in Fig. 5.4.1 is concave upward at all points $(x, f(x))$ for which x is in either (x_3, x_5) or (x_6, x_7).

The following theorem gives a test for concavity.

5.4.3 Theorem Let f be a function which is differentiable on some open interval containing c. Then

(i) if $f''(c) > 0$, the graph of f is concave upward at $(c, f(c))$;
(ii) if $f''(c) < 0$, the graph of f is concave downward at $(c, f(c))$.

PROOF OF (i):

$$f''(c) = \lim_{x \to c} \frac{f'(x) - f'(c)}{x - c}$$

Because $f''(c) > 0$,

$$\lim_{x \to c} \frac{f'(x) - f'(c)}{x - c} > 0$$

Then, by Theorem 4.3.1, there is an open interval I containing c such that

$$\frac{f'(x) - f'(c)}{x - c} > 0 \tag{1}$$

for every $x \neq c$ in I.

Now consider the tangent line to the graph of f at the point $(c, f(c))$. An equation of this tangent line is

$$y = f(c) + f'(c)(x - c) \tag{2}$$

Let x be a number in the interval I such that $x \neq c$, and let Q be the point on the graph of f whose abscissa is x. Through Q draw a line parallel to the y axis, and let T be the point of intersection of this line with the tangent line (see Fig. 5.4.4).

To prove that the graph of f is concave upward at $(c, f(c))$, we must show that the point Q is above the point T or, equivalently, that the directed distance $\overline{TQ} > 0$ for all values of $x \neq c$ in I. $\overline{TQ}$ equals the ordinate of Q minus the ordinate of T. The ordinate of Q is $f(x)$, and the ordinate of T is obtained from Eq. (2); so we have

$$\overline{TQ} = f(x) - [f(c) + f'(c)(x - c)]$$
$$\overline{TQ} = [f(x) - f(c)] - f'(c)(x - c) \tag{3}$$

From the mean-value theorem there exists some number d between x and c such that

$$f'(d) = \frac{f(x) - f(c)}{x - c}$$

That is,

$$f(x) - f(c) = f'(d)(x - c) \qquad \text{for some } d \text{ between } x \text{ and } c \tag{4}$$

Substituting from Eq. (4) into (3), we have

$$\overline{TQ} = f'(d)(x - c) - f'(c)(x - c)$$
$$\overline{TQ} = (x - c)[f'(d) - f'(c)] \tag{5}$$

Because d is between x and c, d is in the interval I, and so by taking $x = d$

$(c, f(c))$

$Q(x, f(x))$

T

c x

Figure 5.4.4

Figure 5.4.5

Figure 5.4.6

in inequality (1), we obtain

$$\frac{f'(d) - f'(c)}{d - c} > 0 \tag{6}$$

To prove that $\overline{TQ} > 0$, we show that both of the factors on the right side of Eq. (5) have the same sign. If $(x - c) > 0$, then $x > c$. And because d is between x and c, then $d > c$; therefore, from inequality (6), $[f'(d) - f'(c)] > 0$. If $(x - c) < 0$, then $x < c$, and so $d < c$; therefore, from (6), $[f'(d) - f'(c)] < 0$. We conclude that $(x - c)$ and $[f'(d) - f'(c)]$ have the same sign; therefore, $\overline{TQ}$ is a positive number. Thus, the graph of f is concave upward at $(c, f(c))$, which is what we wished to prove.

The proof of part (ii) is similar and is left as an exercise (see Exercise 27). ∎

The converse of Theorem 5.4.3 is not true. For example, if f is the function defined by $f(x) = x^4$, the graph of f is concave upward at the point $(0, 0)$ but $f''(0) = 0$ (see Fig. 5.2.1). Accordingly, a sufficient condition for the graph of a function f to be concave upward at the point $(c, f(c))$ is that $f''(c) > 0$, but this is not a necessary condition. Similarly, a sufficient—but not a necessary—condition that the graph of a function f be concave downward at the point $(c, f(c))$ is that $f''(c) < 0$.

If there is a point on the graph of a function at which the sense of concavity changes, then the graph crosses its tangent line at this point, as shown in Figs. 5.4.5, 5.4.6, and 5.4.7. Such a point is called a "point of inflection."

5.4.4 Definition   The point $(c, f(c))$ is a *point of inflection* of the graph of the function f if the graph has a tangent line there, and if there exists an open interval I containing c such that if x is in I, then either

(i) $f''(x) < 0$ if $x < c$ and $f''(x) > 0$ if $x > c$; or
(ii) $f''(x) > 0$ if $x < c$ and $f''(x) < 0$ if $x > c$

Figure 5.4.7

• ILLUSTRATION 2: Figure 5.4.5 illustrates a point of inflection where condition (i) of Definition 5.4.4 holds; in this case, the graph is concave downward at points immediately to the left of the point of inflection, and the graph is concave upward at points immediately to the right of the point of inflection. Condition (ii) is illustrated in Fig. 5.4.6, where the sense of concavity changes from upward to downward at the point of inflection. Figure 5.4.7 is another illustration of condition (i), where the sense of concavity changes from downward to upward at the point of inflection. Note that in Fig. 5.4.7 there is a horizontal tangent line at the point of inflection. •

For the graph in Fig. 5.4.1 there are points of inflection at C, E, and F.

Definition 5.4.4 indicates nothing about the value of the second derivative of f at a point of inflection. The following theorem states that if the second derivative exists at a point of inflection, it must be zero there.

5.4.5 Theorem   If the function f is differentiable on some open interval containing c, and if $(c, f(c))$ is a point of inflection of the graph of f, then if $f''(c)$ exists, $f''(c) = 0$.

PROOF: Let g be the function such that $g(x) = f'(x)$; then $g'(x) = f''(x)$. Because $(c, f(c))$ is a point of inflection of the graph of f, then $f''(x)$ changes sign at c and so $g'(x)$ changes sign at c. Therefore, by the first-derivative test (Theorem 5.1.4), g has a relative extremum at c, and c is a critical number of g. Because $g'(c) = f''(c)$ and since by hypothesis $f''(c)$ exists, it follows that $g'(c)$ exists. Therefore, by Theorem 4.5.3 $g'(c) = 0$ and $f''(c) = 0$, which is what we wanted to prove. ∎

The converse of Theorem 5.4.5 is not true. That is, if the second derivative of a function is zero at a number c, it is not necessarily true that the graph of the function has a point of inflection at the point where $x = c$. This fact is shown in the following illustration.

● ILLUSTRATION 3: Consider the function f defined by $f(x) = x^4$. $f'(x) = 4x^3$ and $f''(x) = 12x^2$. Further, $f''(0) = 0$; but because $f''(x) > 0$ if $x < 0$ and $f''(x) > 0$ if $x > 0$, the graph is concave upward at points on the graph immediately to the left of $(0, 0)$ and at points immediately to the right of $(0, 0)$. Consequently, $(0, 0)$ is not a point of inflection. In Illustration 1 of Section 5.2 we showed that this function f has a relative minimum value at zero. Furthermore, the graph is concave upward at the point $(0, 0)$ (see Fig. 5.2.1).   ●

The graph of a function may have a point of inflection at a point, and the second derivative may fail to exist there, as shown in the next illustration.

● ILLUSTRATION 4:   If f is the function defined by $f(x) = x^{1/3}$, then

$$f'(x) = \tfrac{1}{3}x^{-2/3} \quad \text{and} \quad f''(x) = -\tfrac{2}{9}x^{-5/3}$$

$f''(0)$ does not exist; but if $x < 0$, $f''(x) > 0$, and if $x > 0$, $f''(x) < 0$. Hence, f has a point of inflection at $(0, 0)$. A sketch of the graph of this function is shown in Fig. 5.4.8. Note that for this function $f'(0)$ also fails to exist. The tangent line to the graph at $(0, 0)$ is the y axis.   ●

In drawing a sketch of a graph having points of inflection, it is helpful to draw a segment of the tangent line at a point of inflection. Such a tangent line is called an *inflectional tangent*.

Figure 5.4.8

EXAMPLE 1: For the function in Example 1 of Sec. 5.1, find the points of inflection of the graph of the function, and determine where the graph is concave upward and where it is concave downward.

Figure 5.4.9

SOLUTION:

$$f(x) = x^3 - 6x^2 + 9x + 1$$
$$f'(x) = 3x^2 - 12x + 9$$
$$f''(x) = 6x - 12$$

$f''(x)$ exists for all values of x; so the only possible point of inflection is where $f''(x) = 0$, which occurs at $x = 2$. To determine whether there is a point of inflection at $x = 2$, we must check to see if $f''(x)$ changes sign; at the same time, we determine the concavity of the graph for the respective intervals. The results are summarized in Table 5.4.1.

Table 5.4.1

	$f(x)$	$f'(x)$	$f''(x)$	Conclusion
$-\infty < x < 2$			$-$	graph is concave downward
$x = 2$	3	-3	0	graph has a point of inflection
$2 < x < +\infty$			$+$	graph is concave upward

In Example 1 of Sec. 5.1 we showed that f has a relative maximum value at 1 and a relative minimum value at 3. A sketch of the graph showing a segment of the inflectional tangent is shown in Fig. 5.4.9.

EXAMPLE 2: If $f(x) = (1 - 2x)^3$, find the points of inflection of the graph of f and determine where the graph is concave upward and where it is concave downward. Draw a sketch of the graph of f.

Figure 5.4.10

SOLUTION:

$$f'(x) = -6(1 - 2x)^2$$
$$f''(x) = 24(1 - 2x)$$

Because $f''(x)$ exists for all values of x, the only possible point of inflection is where $f''(x) = 0$, that is, at $x = \frac{1}{2}$. By using the results summarized in Table 5.4.2, we see that $f''(x)$ changes sign from "+" to "−" at $x = \frac{1}{2}$, and so the graph has a point of inflection there. Note also that because $f'(\frac{1}{2}) = 0$, the graph has a horizontal tangent line at the point of inflection. A sketch of the graph is shown in Fig. 5.4.10.

Table 5.4.2

	$f(x)$	$f'(x)$	$f''(x)$	Conclusion
$-\infty < x < \frac{1}{2}$			$+$	graph is concave upward
$x = \frac{1}{2}$	0	0	0	graph has a point of inflection
$\frac{1}{2} < x < +\infty$			$-$	graph is concave downward

Exercises 5.4

In Exercises 1 through 10, determine where the graph of the given function is concave upward, where it is concave downward, and find the points of inflection if there are any.

1. $f(x) = x^3 + 9x$

2. $g(x) = x^3 + 3x^2 - 3x - 3$

3. $F(x) = x^4 - 8x^3 + 24x^2$

4. $f(x) = 16x^4 + 32x^3 + 24x^2 - 5x - 20$

5. $g(x) = \dfrac{x}{x^2 - 1}$

6. $G(x) = \dfrac{2x}{(x^2 + 4)^{3/2}}$

7. $f(x) = (x - 2)^{1/5}$

8. $F(x) = (2x - 6)^{3/2} + 1$

9. $f(x) = \begin{cases} x^2 & \text{if } x < 0 \\ -x^2 & \text{if } x \geq 0 \end{cases}$

10. $f(x) = \begin{cases} x^2 & \text{if } x < 1 \\ x^3 - 4x^2 + 7x - 3 & \text{if } x \geq 1 \end{cases}$

11. If $f(x) = ax^3 + bx^2$, determine a and b so that the graph of f will have a point of inflection at $(1, 2)$.

12. If $f(x) = ax^3 + bx^2 + cx$, determine a, b, and c so that the graph of f will have a point of inflection at $(1, 2)$ and so that the slope of the inflectional tangent there will be -2.

13. If $f(x) = ax^3 + bx^2 + cx + d$, determine a, b, c, and d so that f will have a relative extremum at $(0, 3)$ and so that the graph of f will have a point of inflection at $(1, -1)$.

14. If $f(x) = ax^4 + bx^3 + cx^2 + dx + e$, determine the values of a, b, c, d, and e so the graph of f will have a point of inflection at $(1, -1)$, have the origin on it, and be symmetric with respect to the y axis.

In Exercises 15 through 24, draw a sketch of a portion of the graph of a function f through the point where $x = c$ if the given conditions are satisfied. If the conditions are incomplete or inconsistent, explain. It is assumed that f is continuous on some open interval containing c.

15. $f'(x) > 0$ if $x < c$; $f'(x) < 0$ if $x > c$; $f''(x) > 0$ if $x < c$; $f''(x) > 0$ if $x > c$.

16. $f'(x) > 0$ if $x < c$; $f'(x) > 0$ if $x > c$; $f''(x) > 0$ if $x < c$; $f''(x) < 0$ if $x > c$.

17. $f''(c) = 0$; $f'(c) = 0$; $f''(x) > 0$ if $x < c$; $f''(x) > 0$ if $x > c$.

18. $f'(c) = 0$; $f'(x) > 0$ if $x < c$; $f''(x) > 0$ if $x > c$.

19. $f'(c) = 0$; $f'(x) < 0$ if $x < c$; $f''(x) > 0$ if $x > c$.

20. $f''(c) = 0$; $f'(c) = \frac{1}{2}$; $f''(x) > 0$ if $x < c$; $f''(x) < 0$ if $x > c$.

21. $f'(c)$ does not exist; $f''(x) > 0$ if $x < c$; $f''(x) > 0$ if $x > c$.

22. $f'(c)$ does not exist; $f''(c)$ does not exist; $f''(x) < 0$ if $x < c$; $f''(x) > 0$ if $x > c$.

23. $\lim\limits_{x \to c^-} f'(x) = +\infty$; $\lim\limits_{x \to c^+} f'(x) = 0$; $f''(x) > 0$ if $x < c$; $f''(x) < 0$ if $x > c$.

24. $\lim\limits_{x \to c^-} f'(x) = +\infty$; $\lim\limits_{x \to c^+} f'(x) = -\infty$; $f''(x) > 0$ if $x < c$; $f''(x) > 0$ if $x > c$.

25. Draw a sketch of the graph of a function f for which $f(x)$, $f'(x)$, and $f''(x)$ exist and are positive for all x.

26. If $f(x) = 3x^2 + x|x|$, prove that $f''(0)$ does not exist but the graph of f is concave upward everywhere.

27. Prove Theorem 5.4.3(ii).

28. Suppose that f is a function for which $f''(x)$ exists for all values of x in some open interval I and that at a number c in I, $f''(c) = 0$ and $f'''(c)$ exists and is not zero. Prove that the point $(c, f(c))$ is a point of inflection of the graph of f. (HINT: The proof is similar to the proof of the second-derivative test (Theorem 5.2.1).)

5.5 APPLICATIONS TO DRAWING A SKETCH OF THE GRAPH OF A FUNCTION

We now apply the discussions in Secs. 5.1, 5.2, and 5.4 to drawing a sketch of the graph of a function. If we are given $f(x)$ and wish to draw a sketch of the graph of f, we proceed as follows. First, find $f'(x)$ and $f''(x)$. Then the critical numbers of f are the values of x in the domain of f for which either $f'(x)$ does not exist or $f'(x) = 0$. Next, apply the first-derivative test (Theorem 5.1.4) or the second-derivative test (Theorem 5.2.1) to determine whether we have at a critical number a relative maximum value, a relative minimum value, or neither. To determine the intervals on which f is increasing, we find the values of x for which $f'(x)$ is positive; to determine the intervals on which f is decreasing, we find the values of x for which $f'(x)$ is negative. In determining the intervals on which f is monotonic, we also check the critical numbers at which f does not have a relative extremum. The values of x for which $f''(x) = 0$ or $f''(x)$ does not exist give us the possible points of inflection, and we check to see if $f''(x)$ changes sign at each of these values of x to determine whether we actually have a point of inflection. The values of x for which $f''(x)$ is positive and those for which $f''(x)$ is negative will give us points at which the graph is concave upward and points at which the graph is concave downward. It is also helpful to find the slope of each inflectional tangent. It is suggested that all the information so obtained be incorporated into a table, as illustrated in the following examples.

EXAMPLE 1:   Given

$$f(x) = x^3 - 3x^2 + 3$$

find: the relative extrema of f; the points of inflection of the graph of f; the intervals on which f is increasing; the intervals on which f is decreasing; where the graph is concave upward; where the graph is concave downward; and the slope of any inflectional tangent. Draw a sketch of the graph.

SOLUTION: $f'(x) = 3x^2 - 6x$; $f''(x) = 6x - 6$. Setting $f'(x) = 0$, we obtain $x = 0$ and $x = 2$. Setting $f''(x) = 0$, we obtain $x = 1$. In making the table, we consider the points at which $x = 0$, $x = 1$, and $x = 2$, and the intervals excluding these values of x:

$$-\infty < x < 0 \qquad 0 < x < 1 \qquad 1 < x < 2 \qquad 2 < x < +\infty$$

Using the information in Table 5.5.1 and plotting a few points, we obtain the sketch of the graph shown in Fig. 5.5.1.

Figure 5.5.1

Table 5.5.1

	$f(x)$	$f'(x)$	$f''(x)$	Conclusion
$-\infty < x < 0$		$+$	$-$	f is increasing; graph is concave downward
$x = 0$	3	0	$-$	f has a relative maximum value; graph is concave downward
$0 < x < 1$		$-$	$-$	f is decreasing; graph is concave downward
$x = 1$	1	-3	0	f is decreasing; graph has a point of inflection
$1 < x < 2$		$-$	$+$	f is decreasing; graph is concave upward
$x = 2$	-1	0	$+$	f has a relative minimum value; graph is concave upward
$2 < x < +\infty$		$+$	$+$	f is increasing; graph is concave upward

EXAMPLE 2: Given

$$f(x) = 5x^{2/3} - x^{5/3}$$

find: the relative extrema of f; the points of inflection of the graph of f; the intervals on which f is increasing; the intervals on which f is decreasing; where the graph is concave upward; where the graph is concave downward; and the slope of any inflectional tangent. Draw a sketch of the graph.

SOLUTION:

$$f'(x) = \tfrac{10}{3}x^{-1/3} - \tfrac{5}{3}x^{2/3} \quad \text{and} \quad f''(x) = -\tfrac{10}{9}x^{-4/3} - \tfrac{10}{9}x^{-1/3}$$

$f'(x)$ does not exist when $x = 0$. Setting $f'(x) = 0$, we obtain $x = 2$. Therefore, the critical numbers of f are 0 and 2. $f''(x)$ does not exist when $x = 0$.

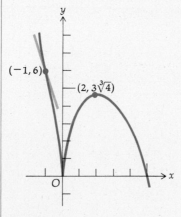

Figure 5.5.2

Setting $f''(x) = 0$, we obtain $x = -1$. In making the table, we consider the points at which $x = -1$, $x = 0$, and $x = 2$, and the following intervals:

$$-\infty < x < -1 \qquad -1 < x < 0 \qquad 0 < x < 2 \qquad 2 < x < +\infty$$

A sketch of the graph, drawn from the information in Table 5.5.2 and by plotting a few points, is shown in Fig. 5.5.2.

Table 5.5.2

	$f(x)$	$f'(x)$	$f''(x)$	Conclusion
$-\infty < x < -1$		$-$	$+$	f is decreasing; graph is concave upward
$x = -1$	6	-5	0	f is decreasing; graph has a point of inflection
$-1 < x < 0$		$-$	$-$	f is decreasing; graph is concave downward
$x = 0$	0	does not exist	does not exist	f has a relative minimum value
$0 < x < 2$		$+$	$-$	f is increasing; graph is concave downward
$x = 2$	$3\sqrt[3]{4} \approx 4.8$	0	$-$	f has a relative maximum value; graph is concave downward
$2 < x < +\infty$		$-$	$-$	f is decreasing; graph is concave downward

Exercises 5.5

For each of the following functions find: the relative extrema of f; the points of inflection of the graph of f; the intervals on which f is increasing; the intervals on which f is decreasing; where the graph is concave upward; where the graph is concave downward; the slope of any inflectional tangent. Draw a sketch of the graph.

1. $f(x) = 2x^3 - 6x + 1$

2. $f(x) = x^3 + x^2 - 5x$

3. $f(x) = x^4 - 2x^3$

4. $f(x) = 3x^4 + 2x^3$

5. $f(x) = x^3 + 5x^2 + 3x - 4$

6. $f(x) = 2x^3 - \frac{1}{2}x^2 - 12x + 1$

7. $f(x) = x^4 - 3x^3 + 3x^2 + 1$

8. $f(x) = x^4 - 4x^3 + 16x$

9. $f(x) = \frac{1}{4}x^4 - \frac{1}{3}x^3 - x^2 + 1$

10. $f(x) = 3x^4 + 4x^3 + 6x^2 - 4$

11. $f(x) = \begin{cases} x^2 & \text{if } x < 0 \\ 2x^2 & \text{if } x \geq 0 \end{cases}$

12. $f(x) = \begin{cases} -x^3 & \text{if } x < 0 \\ x^3 & \text{if } x \geq 0 \end{cases}$

13. $f(x) = \begin{cases} -x^4 & \text{if } x < 0 \\ x^4 & \text{if } x \geq 0 \end{cases}$

14. $f(x) = \begin{cases} 2(x-1)^3 & \text{if } x < 1 \\ (x-1)^4 & \text{if } x \geq 1 \end{cases}$

15. $f(x) = (x+1)^3(x-2)^2$

16. $f(x) = x^2(x+4)^3$

17. $f(x) = 3x^5 + 5x^4$

18. $f(x) = 3x^5 + 5x^3$

19. $f(x) = 3x^{2/3} - 2x$

20. $f(x) = 3x^{1/3} - x$

21. $f(x) = x^{1/3} + 2x^{4/3}$

22. $f(x) = 3x^{4/3} - 4x$

23. $f(x) = 2 + (x-3)^{1/3}$

24. $f(x) = 2 + (x-3)^{4/3}$

25. $f(x) = 2 + (x-3)^{5/3}$

26. $f(x) = 2 + (x-3)^{2/3}$

27. $f(x) = 3 + (x+1)^{6/5}$

28. $f(x) = 3 + (x+1)^{7/5}$

29. $f(x) = x^2\sqrt{4-x}$

30. $f(x) = x\sqrt{9-x^2}$

31. $f(x) = \dfrac{(x+1)^2}{x^2+1}$

32. $f(x) = \dfrac{9x}{x^2+9}$

33. $f(x) = (x+2)\sqrt{-x}$

34. $f(x) = \dfrac{x-1}{x^2-2x+2}$

5.6 AN APPLICATION OF THE DERIVATIVE IN ECONOMICS

In economics the variation of one quantity with respect to another can be described by either an *average* concept or a *marginal* concept. The average concept expresses the variation of one quantity over a specified range of values of a second quantity, whereas the marginal concept is the instantaneous change in the first quantity that results from a very small unit change in the second quantity. For example, in our discussion of rectilinear motion (Sec. 3.2) we considered both an average concept and a marginal concept. The average velocity in traveling a distance of s miles in t hours is s/t mi/hr, whereas the instantaneous velocity is a marginal concept as it gives the rate of change of s with respect to a small unit change in t at a particular instant of time. We begin our examples in economics with the definitions of average cost and marginal cost. It should be clear that to define a marginal concept precisely we must use the notion of a limit, and this will lead to the derivative.

Suppose that $C(x)$ dollars is the total cost of producing x units of a commodity. The function C is called a *total cost function*. In normal circumstances, x and $C(x)$ are nonnegative. If zero is in the domain of C, $C(0)$ is called the *overhead* cost of production. Note that since x represents the number of units of a commodity, x must be a nonnegative integer. However, to apply the calculus we assume that x is a nonnegative real number (and then round off any noninteger values of x to the nearest integer), thus giving us the continuity requirements for the function C.

The *average cost* of producing each unit of a commodity is obtained by dividing the total cost by the number of units produced. Letting $Q(x)$ be the number of dollars in the average cost, we have

$$Q(x) = \frac{C(x)}{x}$$

and Q is called an *average cost function*.

Now, let us suppose that the number of units in a particular output is x_1 and this is changed by Δx. Then the change in the total cost is given by $C(x_1 + \Delta x) - C(x_1)$, and the average change in the total cost with respect to the change in the number of units produced is given by

$$\frac{C(x_1 + \Delta x) - C(x_1)}{\Delta x} \tag{1}$$

Economists use the term *marginal cost* for the limit of the quotient in (1) as Δx approaches zero, provided the limit exists. Being the derivative of C at x_1, this limit gives us the following definition.

5.6.1 Definition   If $C(x)$ is the number of dollars in the total cost of producing x units of a commodity, then the *marginal cost,* when $x = x_1$, is given by $C'(x_1)$ if it exists. The function C' is called the *marginal cost function.*

In the above definition, $C'(x_1)$ can be interpreted as the rate of change of the total cost per unit change in the quantity produced, when x_1 units are produced.

• ILLUSTRATION 1: Suppose that $C(x)$ is the number of dollars in the total cost of producing x picture frames ($x \geq 10$) and

$$C(x) = 15 + 8x + \frac{200}{x}$$

(a) The marginal cost function is C' and

$$C'(x) = 8 - \frac{200}{x^2}$$

(b) The marginal cost when $x = 20$ is $C'(20)$ and

$$C'(20) = 8 - \frac{200}{20^2} = 8 - 0.50 = 7.50$$

(c) The number of dollars in the cost of producing the twenty-first frame is $C(21) - C(20)$ and

$$C(21) - C(20) = 192.52 - 185 = 7.52$$

Observe that the answers in parts (b) and (c) differ by 0.02. This discrepancy occurs because the marginal cost is the instantaneous rate of change of $C(x)$ with respect to a unit change in x. Hence, $C'(20)$ is the approximate number of dollars in the cost of producing the twenty-first frame. •

Reasoning similar to that preceding Definition 5.6.1 leads to the following definition.

5.6.2 Definition   If $Q(x)$ is the number of dollars in the average cost of producing one unit of x units of a commodity, then the *marginal average cost,* when $x = x_1$, is given by $Q'(x_1)$ if it exists, and Q' is called the *marginal average cost function.*

Figure 5.6.1

Figure 5.6.2

Figure 5.6.3

The graphs of the total cost function, the marginal cost function, and the average cost function are called the *total cost curve* (labeled TC), the *marginal cost curve* (labeled MC), and the *average cost curve* (labeled AC), respectively. $Q'(x_1)$ gives the slope of the tangent line to the average cost curve at the point where $x = x_1$.

● ILLUSTRATION 2: Consider a linear total cost function.

$$C(x) = mx + b$$

Note that b represents the overhead cost (the total cost when $x = 0$). The marginal cost is given by $C'(x) = m$. If Q is the average cost function, $Q(x) = m + b/x$, and the marginal average cost is given by $Q'(x) = -b/x^2$.

Refer to Fig. 5.6.1 for sketches of the total cost curve and the average cost curve. The total cost curve is a segment of a straight line in the first quadrant having slope m and y-intercept b. The average cost curve is a branch of an equilateral hyperbola in the first quadrant having as horizontal asymptote the line $y = m$. Because $Q'(x)$ is always negative, the average cost function is always decreasing, and as x increases, the value of $Q(x)$ gets closer and closer to m. ●

● ILLUSTRATION 3: Suppose that we have a quadratic total cost function

$$C(x) = ax^2 + bx + c$$

where a and c are positive. Here c is the number of dollars in the overhead cost. The total cost curve is a parabola opening upward. Because $C'(x) = 2ax + b$, a critical number of C is $-b/2a$. We distinguish two cases: $b \geq 0$ and $b < 0$.

Case 1: $b \geq 0$. $-b/2a$ is then either negative or zero, and the vertex of the parabola is either to the left of the y axis or on the y axis. Hence, the domain of C is the set of all nonnegative numbers. A sketch of TC for which $b > 0$ is shown in Fig. 5.6.2.

Case 2: $b < 0$. $-b/2a$ is positive; so the vertex of the parabola is to the right of the y axis, and the domain of C is restricted to numbers in the interval $[-b/2a, +\infty)$. A sketch of TC for which $b < 0$ is shown in Fig. 5.6.3. ●

EXAMPLE 1: Suppose that $C(x)$ dollars is the total cost of producing $100x$ units of a commodity and $C(x) = \frac{1}{2}x^2 - 2x + 5$. Find the function giving (a) the average cost; (b) the marginal cost; (c) the marginal average cost. (d) Find the absolute minimum average unit cost. (e) Draw sketches of the total cost curve, the average

SOLUTION:

(a) If Q is the average cost function,

$$Q(x) = \frac{C(x)}{x} = \frac{1}{2}x - 2 + \frac{5}{x}$$

(b) The marginal cost function is C', and

$$C'(x) = x - 2$$

cost curve, and the marginal cost curve on the same set of axes.

Figure 5.6.4

(c) Q' is the marginal average cost function, and

$$Q'(x) = \frac{1}{2} - \frac{5}{x^2}$$

(d) Setting $Q'(x) = 0$, we obtain $\sqrt{10}$ as a critical number of Q, and $Q(\sqrt{10}) = \sqrt{10} - 2 \approx 1.16$. Because $Q''(x) = 10/x^3$, $Q''(\sqrt{10}) > 0$, and so Q has a relative minimum value of approximately 1.16 at $x = \sqrt{10}$. From the equation defining $Q(x)$ we see that Q is continuous on $(0, +\infty)$. Because the only relative extremum of Q on $(0, +\infty)$ is at $x = \sqrt{10}$, it follows from Theorem 5.3.1(ii) that Q has an absolute minimum value there. When $x = \sqrt{10} \approx 3.16$, $100x = 316$, and so we conclude that the absolute minimum average unit cost is \$1.16 when 316 units are produced.

The sketches of the curves TC, AC, and MC are shown in Fig. 5.6.4.

In Fig. 5.6.4, note that the lowest point on curve AC occurs at the point of intersection of the curves AC and MC, and this is the point where the marginal average cost is zero. This is true in general and it follows from the fact that the value of x which causes the marginal average cost to be zero is a critical number of the function Q. That is, since $Q(x) = C(x)/x$,

$$Q'(x) = \frac{xC'(x) - C(x)}{x^2}$$

and so $Q'(x) = 0$ when $xC'(x) - C(x) = 0$ or, equivalently, when

$$C'(x) = \frac{C(x)}{x}$$

You should note the economic significance that when the marginal cost and the average cost are equal, the commodity is being produced at the very lowest average unit cost.

In normal circumstances, when the number of units of the commodity produced is large, the marginal cost will be eventually increasing or zero; hence, $C''(x) \geq 0$ for x greater than some positive number N. So unless $C''(x) = 0$, the graph of the total cost function is concave upward for $x > N$. However, the marginal cost may decrease for some values of x; hence, for these values of x, $C''(x) < 0$, and therefore the graph of the total cost function will be concave downward for these values of x. The following example involving a cubic cost function illustrates the case in which the concavity of the graph of the total cost function changes.

EXAMPLE 2:   Draw a sketch of the graph of the total cost function C for which

$$C(x) = x^3 - 6x^2 + 13x + 1$$

Determine where the graph is concave upward and where it is concave downward. Find any points of inflection and an equation of any inflectional tangent. Draw a segment of the inflectional tangent.

Figure 5.6.5

SOLUTION:
$$C'(x) = 3x^2 - 12x + 13$$
$$C''(x) = 6x - 12$$

$C'(x)$ can be written as $3(x-2)^2 + 1$. Hence, $C'(x)$ is never zero. $C''(x) = 0$ when $x = 2$. To determine the concavity of the graph for the intervals $(0, 2)$ and $(2, +\infty)$ and if the graph has a point of inflection at $x = 2$, we use the results summarized in Table 5.6.1.

Table 5.6.1

	$C(x)$	$C'(x)$	$C''(x)$	Conclusion
$0 < x < 2$			$-$	graph is concave downward
$x = 2$	11	1	0	graph has a point of inflection
$2 < x < +\infty$			$+$	graph is concave upward

An equation of the inflectional tangent is $x - y + 9 = 0$. A sketch of the graph of the total cost function together with a segment of the inflectional tangent is shown in Fig. 5.6.5.

Consider now an economic situation in which the variables are the price and quantity of the commodity demanded. Let p dollars be the price of one unit of the commodity and x be the number of units of the commodity. Upon reflection, it should seem reasonable that the amount of the commodity demanded in the marketplace by consumers depends on the price of the commodity. As the price falls, consumers generally demand more of the commodity. Should the price rise, the opposite occurs. Consumers demand less. Thus, if p_1 and p_2 are the number of dollars in the prices of x_1 and x_2 units, respectively, of a commodity, then

$$p_1 > p_2 \quad \text{if and only if} \quad x_1 < x_2 \qquad (2)$$

An equation giving the relationship between the amount, given by x, of a commodity demanded and the price, given by p, is called a *demand equation*. If the equation is solved for p, we have

$$p = P(x)$$

The function P is called the *price function* and $P(x)$ is the number of dollars in the unit price for which x units of the commodity are demanded at that price. Because of statement (2), P is a decreasing function. In a normal economic situation, x and $P(x)$ are nonnegative numbers. Even though x should be an integer (because x is the number of units of a commodity) we assume only that x is a real number in order that P may be a continuous function so that we can apply the calculus.

Another function important in economics is the *total revenue function*, which we denote by R, and

$$R(x) = xP(x)$$

where $P(x)$ dollars is the price of each unit and x is the number of units sold. When $x \neq 0$, from the above equation we obtain

$$\frac{R(x)}{x} = P(x)$$

which shows that the revenue per unit (the average revenue) and the price per unit are equal.

5.6.3 Definition   If $R(x)$ is the number of dollars in the total revenue obtained when x units of a commodity are demanded, then the *marginal revenue*, when $x = x_1$, is given by $R'(x_1)$, if it exists. The function R' is called the *marginal revenue function*.

$R'(x_1)$ can be positive, negative, or zero, and it can be interpreted as the rate of change of the total revenue per unit change in the demand when x_1 units are demanded. The graphs of the functions R and R' are called the *total revenue curve* (labeled TR) and the *marginal revenue curve* (labeled MR), respectively. The graph of the demand equation is called the *demand curve*.

EXAMPLE 3:   The demand equation for a particular commodity is $p^2 + x - 12 = 0$. Find the price function, the total revenue function, and the marginal revenue function. Draw sketches of the demand curve, the total revenue curve, and the marginal revenue curve on the same set of axes.

SOLUTION: If the demand equation is solved for p, we find $p = \pm\sqrt{12 - x}$. Since $P(x) \geq 0$, we have

$$P(x) = \sqrt{12 - x}$$

$$R(x) = x\sqrt{12 - x}$$

$$R'(x) = \frac{24 - 3x}{2\sqrt{12 - x}}$$

Setting $R'(x) = 0$, we obtain $x = 8$. Using the information in Table 5.6.2, we see that the required sketches are drawn as shown in Fig. 5.6.6.

Table 5.6.2

x	$P(x)$	$R(x)$	$R'(x)$
0	$\sqrt{12}$	0	$\sqrt{12}$
3	3	9	$\frac{5}{2}$
8	2	16	0
11	1	11	$-\frac{9}{2}$
12	0	0	does not exist

Figure 5.6.6

We have seen that for a given demand equation the amount demanded by the consumer depends only on the price of the commodity. Under a *monopoly* (which means that there is only one producer of a certain commodity), price and, hence, demand can be controlled by regulating the quantity of the commodity produced. The producer under a monopoly is called a *monopolist,* and he wishes to control the quantity produced and, hence, the price per unit so that the profit will be as large as possible.

The *profit* earned by a business is the difference between the total revenue and the total cost. That is, if $S(x)$ dollars is the profit obtained by producing x units of a commodity, then

$$S(x) = R(x) - C(x) \tag{3}$$

where $R(x)$ dollars is the total revenue and $C(x)$ dollars is the total cost. S is called the *profit function.* From Eq. (3), if we differentiate with respect to x, we obtain

$$S'(x) = R'(x) - C'(x) \tag{4}$$

and

$$S''(x) = R''(x) - C''(x) \tag{5}$$

It follows from Eq. (4) that $S'(x) > 0$ if and only if $R'(x) > C'(x)$; therefore, the profit is increasing if and only if the marginal revenue is greater than the marginal cost. Let us determine what level of production is necessary to obtain the greatest profit. S has a relative maximum function value at a number x for which $S'(x) = 0$ and $S''(x) < 0$. From Eqs. (4) and (5)

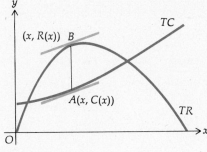

Figure 5.6.7

we observe that this will occur at a value of x for which the marginal revenue equals the marginal cost and $R''(x) < C''(x)$. The values of x will be restricted to a closed interval, in which the left endpoint is 0 (since $x \geq 0$) and the right endpoint (the largest permissible value of x) is determined from the demand equation. At each of the endpoints there will be no profit, and so the absolute maximum value of S occurs at a value of x where S has a relative maximum value.

To illustrate this geometrically, refer to Fig. 5.6.7, where both the total revenue curve and the total cost curve are drawn on the same set of axes. The vertical distance between the two curves for a particular value of x is $S(x)$, which gives the profit corresponding to that value of x. When this vertical distance is largest, $S(x)$ is an absolute maximum. This is the distance $\overline{AB}$ in the figure where A and B are the points on the two curves where the tangent lines are parallel, and hence $C'(x) = R'(x)$.

EXAMPLE 4: Suppose that the demand equation for a certain commodity is $p = 4 - 0.0002x$, where x is the number of units produced each week and p dollars is the price of each unit. The number of dollars in the total cost of producing x units is $600 + 3x$. If the weekly profit is to be as large as possible, find: (a) the number of units that should be produced each week; (b) the price of each unit; (c) the weekly profit.

SOLUTION: The price function is given by $P(x) = 4 - 0.0002x$, and x is in the closed interval [0, 20,000] because x and $P(x)$ must be nonnegative. $R(x) = xP(x)$, and so

$$R(x) = 4x - 0.0002x^2 \qquad x \text{ in } [0, 20{,}000] \tag{6}$$

The cost function is given by

$$C(x) = 600 + 3x \tag{7}$$

If $S(x)$ dollars is the profit, $S(x) = R(x) - C(x)$, and so

$$S(x) = x - 0.0002x^2 - 600 \qquad x \text{ in } [0, 20{,}000]$$

From Eqs. (6) and (7) we obtain

$$R'(x) = 4 - 0.0004x$$

and

$$C'(x) = 3$$

Also, $R''(x) = -0.0004$ and $C''(x) = 0$. Equating $R'(x)$ and $C'(x)$ we get

$$4 - 0.0004x = 3$$

$$x = 2500$$

Because $R''(x)$ is always less than $C''(x)$, $S''(x) = R''(x) - C''(x) < 0$, and so we conclude that $S(2500)$ is an absolute maximum value. (Note that $S(x)$ is negative for $x = 0$ and $x = 20{,}000$.) $P(2500) = 3.50$ and $S(2500) = 650$.

Therefore, to have the greatest weekly profit, 2500 units should be produced each week to be sold at $3.50 each for a total profit of $650.

EXAMPLE 5: Solve Example 4 if a tax of 20 cents is levied by the government on the monopolist for each unit produced.

SOLUTION: With the added tax, the total cost function is now given by

$$C(x) = (600 + 3x) + 0.20x$$

and so the marginal cost function is given by

$$C'(x) = 3.20$$

Equating $R'(x)$ and $C'(x)$, we get

$$4 - 0.0004x = 3.20$$

$$x = 2000$$

As in Example 4 it follows that when $x = 2000$, S has an absolute maximum value on $[0, 20,000]$. From $P(x) = 4 - 0.0002x$ and $S(x) = 0.8x - 0.0002x^2 - 600$, we have $P(2000) = 3.60$ and $S(2000) = 200$.

Therefore, if the tax of 20 cents per unit is levied, only 2000 units should be produced each week to be sold at \$3.60 in order to attain a maximum total weekly profit of \$200.

It is interesting to note that in comparing the results of Examples 4 and 5, the entire 20 cents rise should not be passed on to the consumer to achieve the greatest weekly profit. That is, it is most profitable to raise the unit price by only 10 cents. The economic significance of this result is that consumers are sensitive to price changes, which prohibits the monopolist from passing on the tax completely to the consumer.

A further note of interest in the two examples is how the fixed costs of a company do not affect the determination of the number of units to be produced or the unit price such that maximum profit is obtained. The *fixed cost* of a company is the cost that does not change as the company's output changes. Regardless of whether anything is produced, the fixed cost must be met. In Examples 4 and 5, because $C(x) = 600 + 3x$ and $600 + 3.2x$, respectively, the fixed cost is \$600. If the 600 in the expressions for $C(x)$ is replaced by any constant k, $C'(x)$ is not affected; hence, the value of x for which the marginal cost equals the marginal revenue is not affected by any such change. Of course, a change in fixed cost affects the unit cost and hence the actual profit; however, if a company is to have the greatest profit possible, a change in its fixed cost will not affect the number of units to be produced nor the price per unit.

Exercises 5.6

1. The number of dollars in the total cost of manufacturing x watches in a certain plant is given by $C(x) = 1500 + 30x + 20/x$. Find (a) the marginal cost function, (b) the marginal cost when $x = 40$, and (c) the cost of manufacturing the forty-first watch.

2. If $C(x)$ dollars is the total cost of manufacturing x toys and $C(x) = 110 + 4x + 0.02x^2$, find (a) the marginal cost function, (b) the marginal cost when $x = 10$, and (c) the cost of manufacturing the eleventh toy.

3. Suppose a liquid is produced by a certain chemical process and the total cost function C is given by $C(x) = 6 + 4\sqrt{x}$, where $C(x)$ dollars is the total cost of producing x gallons of the liquid. Find (a) the marginal cost when 16 gal are produced and (b) the number of gallons produced when the marginal cost is 40 cents per gal.

4. The number of dollars in the total cost of producing x units of a certain commodity is $C(x) = 40 + 3x + 9\sqrt{2x}$. Find (a) the marginal cost when 50 units are produced and (b) the number of units produced when the marginal cost is $4.50.

5. The number of dollars in the total cost of producing x units of a commodity is $C(x) = x^2 + 4x + 8$. Find the function giving (a) the average cost, (b) the marginal cost, and (c) the marginal average cost. (d) Find the absolute minimum average unit cost. (e) Draw sketches of the total cost, average cost, and marginal cost curves on the same set of axes. Verify that the average cost and marginal cost are equal when the average cost has its least value.

6. If $C(x)$ dollars is the total cost of producing x units of a commodity and $C(x) = 3x^2 - 6x + 4$, find (a) the average cost function, (b) the marginal cost function, and (c) the marginal average cost function. (d) What is the range of C? (e) Find the absolute minimum average unit cost. (f) Draw sketches of the total cost, average cost, and marginal cost curves on the same set of axes. Verify that the average cost and marginal cost are equal when the average cost has its least value.

7. The total cost function C is given by $C(x) = \frac{1}{3}x^3 - 2x^2 + 5x + 2$. (a) Determine the range of C. (b) Find the marginal cost function. (c) Find the interval on which the marginal cost function is decreasing and the interval on which it is increasing. (d) Draw a sketch of the graph of the total cost function; determine where the graph is concave upward and where it is concave downward, and find the points of inflection and an equation of any inflectional tangent.

8. If $C(x)$ dollars is the total cost of producing x units of a commodity and $C(x) = 2x^2 - 8x + 18$, find (a) the domain and range of C, (b) the average cost function, (c) the absolute minimum average unit cost, and (d) the marginal cost function. (e) Draw sketches of the total cost, average cost, and marginal cost curves on the same set of axes.

9. The fixed overhead expense of a manufacturer of children's toys is $400 per week, and other costs amount to $3 for each toy produced. Find (a) the total cost function, (b) the average cost function, and (c) the marginal cost function. (d) Show that there is no absolute minimum average unit cost. (e) What is the smallest number of toys that must be produced so that the average cost per toy is less than $3.42? (f) Draw sketches of the graphs of the functions in (a), (b), and (c) on the same set of axes.

10. The number of hundreds of dollars in the total cost of producing $100x$ radios per day in a certain factory is $C(x) = 4x + 5$. Find (a) the average cost function, (b) the marginal cost function, and (c) the marginal average cost function. (d) Show that there is no absolute minimum average unit cost. (e) What is the smallest number of radios that the factory must produce in a day so that the average cost per radio is less than $7? (f) Draw sketches of the total cost, average cost, and marginal cost curves on the same set of axes.

11. If the demand equation for a particular commodity is $3x + 4p = 12$, find (a) the price function, (b) the total revenue function, and (c) the marginal revenue function. Draw sketches of the demand, total revenue, and marginal revenue curves on the same set of axes. Verify that the marginal revenue curve intersects the x axis at the point whose abscissa is the value of x for which the total revenue is greatest and that the demand curve intersects the x axis at the point whose abscissa is twice that.

12. The demand equation for a particular commodity is $px^2 + 9p - 18 = 0$ where p dollars is the price per unit when $100x$ units are demanded. Find (a) the price function, (b) the total revenue function, and (c) the marginal revenue function. (d) Find the absolute maximum total revenue.

13. Follow the instructions of Exercise 12 if the demand equation is $x^2 + p^2 - 36 = 0$.

14. Let $R(x)$ dollars be the total revenue obtained when x units of a commodity are demanded and $R(x) = 2 + 3\sqrt{x - 1}$, where x is in the closed interval $[2, 17]$. Find (a) the demand equation, (b) the price function, and (c) the marginal revenue function. (d) Find the absolute maximum total revenue. (e) Draw sketches of the demand, total revenue, and marginal revenue curves on the same set of axes.

15. The demand equation for a certain commodity is $x + p = 14$, where x is the number of units produced daily and p is the number of hundreds of dollars in the price of each unit. The number of hundreds of dollars in the total cost of pro-

ducing x units is given by $C(x) = x^2 - 2x + 2$, and x is in the closed interval $[1, 14]$. (a) Find the profit function and draw a sketch of its graph. (b) On a set of axes different from that in (a), draw sketches of the total revenue and total cost curves and show the geometrical interpretation of the profit function. (c) Find the maximum daily profit. (d) Find the marginal revenue and marginal cost functions. (e) Draw sketches of the graphs of the marginal revenue and marginal cost functions on the same set of axes and show that they intersect at the point for which the value of x makes the profit a maximum.

16. Follow the instructions of Exercise 15 if the demand equation is $x^2 + p = 32$ and $C(x) = 5x$.

17. The demand equation for a certain commodity is $p = (x - 8)^2$, and the total cost function is given by $C(x) = 18x - x^2$, where $C(x)$ dollars is the total cost when x units are purchased. (a) Determine the permissible values of x. (b) Find the marginal revenue and marginal cost functions. (c) Find the value of x which yields the maximum profit. (d) Draw sketches of the marginal revenue and marginal cost functions on the same set of axes.

18. A monopolist determines that if $C(x)$ cents is the total cost of producing x units of a certain commodity, then $C(x) = 25x + 20,000$. The demand equation is $x + 50p = 5000$, where x units are demanded each week when the unit price is p cents. If the weekly profit is to be maximized, find (a) the number of units that should be produced each week, (b) the price of each unit, and (c) the weekly profit.

19. Solve Exercise 18 if the government levies a tax on the monopolist of 10 cents per unit produced.

20. Solve Exercise 18 if the government imposes a 10% tax based upon the consumer's price.

21. For the monopolist of Exercise 18, determine the amount of tax that should be levied by the government on each unit produced in order for the tax revenue received by the government to be maximized.

22. Find the maximum tax revenue that can be received by the government if an additive tax for each unit produced is levied on a monopolist for which the demand equation is $x + 3p = 75$, where x units are demanded when p dollars is the price of one unit, and $C(x) = 3x + 100$, where $C(x)$ dollars is the total cost of producing x units.

23. The demand equation for a certain commodity produced by a monopolist is $p = a - bx$, and the total cost, $C(x)$ dollars, of producing x units is determined by $C(x) = c + dx$, where $a, b, c,$ and d are positive constants. If the government levies a tax on the monopolist of t dollars per unit produced, show that in order for the monopolist to maximize his profits he should pass on to the consumer only one-half of the tax; that is, he should increase his unit price by $\frac{1}{2}t$ dollars.

Review Exercises (*Chapter 5*)

1. Find the shortest distance from the point $(\frac{9}{2}, 0)$ to the curve $y = \sqrt{x}$.

2. Prove that among all the rectangles having a given perimeter, the square has the greatest area.

3. Prove that among all the rectangles of a given area, the square has the least perimeter.

4. The demand in a certain market for a particular kind of breakfast cereal is given by the demand equation $px + 25p - 2000 = 0$, where p cents is the price of one box and x thousands of boxes is the quantity demanded per week. If the current price of the cereal is 40 cents per box and the price per box is increasing at the rate of 0.2 cent each week, find the rate of change in the demand.

5. Two particles start their motion at the same time. One particle is moving along a horizontal line and its equation of motion is $x = t^2 - 2t$, where x ft is the directed distance of the particle from the origin at t sec. The other particle is moving along a vertical line that intersects the horizontal line at the origin, and its equation of motion is $y = t^2 - 2$, where y ft is the directed distance of the particle from the origin at t sec. Find when the directed distance between the two particles is least, and their velocities at that time.

In Exercises 6 through 9, find: the relative extrema of f; the points of inflection of the graph of f; the intervals on which f is increasing; the intervals on which f is decreasing; where the graph is concave upward; where the graph is concave downward; the slope of any inflectional tangent. Draw a sketch of the graph.

6. $f(x) = (x + 2)^{4/3}$

7. $f(x) = (x - 4)^2(x + 2)^3$

8. $f(x) = x\sqrt{25 - x^2}$

9. $f(x) = (x - 3)^{5/3} + 1$

10. If

$$f(x) = \frac{x + 1}{x^2 + 1}$$

prove that the graph of f has three points of inflection that are collinear. Draw a sketch of the graph.

11. If $f(x) = x|x|$, show that the graph of f has a point of inflection at the origin.

12. Let $f(x) = x^n$ where n is a positive integer. Prove that the graph of f has a point of inflection at the origin if and only if n is an odd integer and $n > 1$. Furthermore show that if n is even, f has a relative minimum value at 0.

13. If $f(x) = (x^2 + a^2)^p$, where p is a rational number and $p \neq 0$, prove that if $p < \frac{1}{2}$ the graph of f has two points of inflection and if $p \geq \frac{1}{2}$ the graph of f has no points of inflection.

14. Suppose the graph of a function has a point of inflection at $x = c$. What can you conclude, if anything, about (a) the continuity of f at c; (b) the continuity of f' at c; (c) the continuity of f'' at c?

15. Suppose C is the number of millions of dollars in the capitalization of a certain corporation, P is the number of millions of dollars in the corporation's annual profit, and $P = 0.05C - 0.004C^2$. If its capitalization is increasing at the rate of \$400,000 per year, find the rate of change of the corporation's annual profit if its current capitalization is (a) \$3 million and (b) \$6 million.

16. A property development company rents each apartment at p dollars per month when x apartments are rented and $p = 20\sqrt{300 - 2x}$. How many apartments must be rented before the marginal revenue is zero?

17. Find the dimensions of the right-circular cone of least volume that can be circumscribed about a right-circular cylinder of radius r in. and altitude h in.

18. A tent is to be in the shape of a cone. Find the ratio of the measure of the radius to the measure of the altitude for a tent of given volume to require the least material.

19. The demand equation for a particular commodity is $(p + 4)(x + 3) = 48$, where p dollars is the price per unit when $100x$ units are demanded. Find (a) the price function, (b) the total revenue function, (c) the marginal revenue function. (d) Find the absolute maximum total revenue. (e) Draw sketches of the demand, total revenue, and marginal revenue curves on the same set of axes.

20. The demand equation for a certain commodity is $p + 2\sqrt{x - 1} = 6$ and the total cost function is given by $C(x) = 2x - 1$. (a) Determine the permissible values of x. (b) Find the marginal revenue and marginal cost functions. (c) Find the value of x which yields the maximum profit.

21. The demand equation for a certain commodity is

$$10^6 px = 10^9 - 2 \cdot 10^6 x + 18 \cdot 10^3 x^2 - 6x^3$$

where x is the number of units produced weekly and p dollars is the price of each unit, and $x \geq 100$. The number of dollars in the average cost of producing each unit is given by $Q(x) = \frac{1}{30}x - 24 + 11 \cdot 10^3 x^{-1}$. Find the number of units that should be produced each week and the price of each unit in order for the weekly profit to be maximized.

22. When $1000x$ boxes of a certain kind of material are produced, the number of dollars in the total cost of production is given by $C(x) = 135x^{1/3} + 450$. Find (a) the marginal cost when 8000 boxes are produced and (b) the number of boxes produced when the marginal cost (per thousand boxes) is $20.

23. A ladder is to reach over a fence h ft high to a wall w ft behind the fence. Find the length of the shortest ladder that may be used.

24. Draw a sketch of the graph of a function f on the interval I in each case: (a) I is the open interval $(0, 2)$ and f is continuous on I. At 1, f has a relative maximum value but $f'(1)$ does not exist. (b) I is the closed interval $[0, 2]$. The function f has a relative minimum value at 1, but the absolute minimum value of f is at 0. (c) I is the open interval $(0, 2)$, and f' has a relative maximum value at 1.

25. (a) If $f(x) = 3|x| + 4|x - 1|$, prove that f has an absolute minimum value of 3. (b) If $g(x) = 4|x| + 3|x - 1|$, prove that g has an absolute minimum value of 3. (c) If $h(x) = a|x| + b|x - 1|$, where $a > 0$ and $b > 0$, prove that h has an absolute minimum value that is the smaller of the two numbers a and b.

26. If $f(x) = |x|^a \cdot |x - 1|^b$, where a and b are positive rational numbers, prove that f has a relative maximum value of $a^a b^b / (a + b)^{a+b}$.

6

The differential
and antidifferentiation

6.1 THE DIFFERENTIAL Suppose that the function f is defined by

$$y = f(x)$$

Then, when $f'(x)$ exists,

$$f'(x) = \lim_{\Delta x \to 0} \frac{\Delta y}{\Delta x} \tag{1}$$

where $\Delta y = f(x + \Delta x) - f(x)$. From (1), it follows that for any $\epsilon > 0$ there exists a $\delta > 0$ such that

$$\left| \frac{\Delta y}{\Delta x} - f'(x) \right| < \epsilon \qquad \text{whenever } 0 < |\Delta x| < \delta$$

which is equivalent to

$$\frac{|\Delta y - f'(x)\, \Delta x|}{|\Delta x|} < \epsilon \qquad \text{whenever } 0 < |\Delta x| < \delta$$

This means that $|\Delta y - f'(x)\, \Delta x|$ is small compared to $|\Delta x|$. That is, for a sufficiently small $|\Delta x|$, $f'(x)\, \Delta x$ is a good approximation to the value of Δy. Using the symbol $\approx$, meaning "is approximately equal to," we say then that

$$\Delta y \approx f'(x)\, \Delta x$$

if $|\Delta x|$ is sufficiently small. The right side of the above expression is defined to be the "differential" of y.

6.1.1 Definition If the function f is defined by $y = f(x)$, then the *differential of y*, denoted by dy, is given by

$$dy = f'(x)\, \Delta x \tag{1}$$

where x is in the domain of f' and Δx is an arbitrary increment of x.

This concept of the differential involves a special type of function of two variables (a detailed study of such functions will be given in Chapter 19). The notation df may be used to represent this function, where the symbol df is regarded as a single entity. The variable x can be any number in the domain of f', and Δx can be any number whatsoever. To state that df is a function of the two independent variables x and Δx means that to each ordered pair $(x, \Delta x)$ in the domain of df there corresponds one and only one number in the range of df, and this number can be represented by $df(x, \Delta x)$, so that

$$df(x, \Delta x) = f'(x)\, \Delta x \tag{2}$$

Comparing Eqs. (1) and (2) we see that when $y = f(x)$, dy and $df(x, \Delta x)$

are two different notations for $f'(x)\ \Delta x$. We shall use the "dy" symbolism in subsequent discussions.

● ILLUSTRATION 1: If $y = 4x^2 - x$, then $f(x) = 4x^2 - x$, and so $f'(x) = 8x - 1$. Therefore, from Definition 6.1.1,

$$dy = (8x - 1)\ \Delta x$$

In particular, if $x = 2$, then $dy = 15\ \Delta x$.   ●

When $y = f(x)$, Definition 6.1.1 indicates what is meant by dy, the differential of the dependent variable. We also wish to define the differential of the independent variable, or dx. To arrive at a suitable definition for dx that is consistent with the definition of dy, we consider the identity function, which is the function f defined by $f(x) = x$. Then $f'(x) = 1$ and $y = x$; so $dy = 1 \cdot \Delta x = \Delta x$. Because $y = x$, we want dx to be equal to dy for this particular function; that is, for this function we want $dx = \Delta x$. It is this reasoning that leads us to the following definition.

6.1.2 Definition   If the function f is defined by $y = f(x)$, then the *differential of* x, denoted by dx, is given by

$$dx = \Delta x \tag{3}$$

where Δx is an arbitrary increment of x, and x is any number in the domain of f'.

From Eqs. (1) and (3) we obtain

$$dy = f'(x)\ dx \tag{4}$$

Dividing on both sides of the above by dx, we have

$$\frac{dy}{dx} = f'(x) \qquad \text{if } dx \neq 0 \tag{5}$$

Equation (5) expresses the derivative as the quotient of two differentials. The notation dy/dx often denotes the derivative of y with respect to x—a symbolism we have avoided until now.

EXAMPLE 1:   Given

$$y = 4x^2 - 3x + 1$$

find Δy, dy, and $\Delta y - dy$ for (a) any x and Δx; (b) $x = 2$, $\Delta x = 0.1$; (c) $x = 2$, $\Delta x = 0.01$; (d) $x = 2$, $\Delta x = 0.001$.

SOLUTION: (a) Because $y = 4x^2 - 3x + 1$, we have

$$y + \Delta y = 4(x + \Delta x)^2 - 3(x + \Delta x) + 1$$

$$(4x^2 - 3x + 1) + \Delta y = 4x^2 + 8x\ \Delta x + 4(\Delta x)^2 - 3x - 3\ \Delta x + 1$$

$$\Delta y = (8x - 3)\ \Delta x + 4(\Delta x)^2$$

Also,

$$dy = f'(x)\ dx$$

Thus,

$$dy = (8x - 3)\ dx$$
$$= (8x - 3)\ \Delta x$$
$$\Delta y - dy = 4(\Delta x)^2$$

The results for parts (b), (c), and (d) are given in Table 6.1.1, where $\Delta y = (8x - 3)\ \Delta x + 4(\Delta x)^2$ and $dy = (8x - 3)\ \Delta x$.

Table 6.1.1

x	Δx	Δy	dy	$\Delta y - dy$
2	0.1	1.34	1.3	0.04
2	0.01	0.1304	0.13	0.0004
2	0.001	0.013004	0.013	0.000004

Note from Table 6.1.1 that the closer Δx is to zero, the smaller is the difference between Δy and dy. Furthermore, observe that for each value of Δx, the corresponding value of $\Delta y - dy$ is smaller than the value of Δx. More generally, dy is an approximation of Δy when Δx is small, and the approximation is of better accuracy than the size of Δx.

For a fixed value of x, say x_0,

$$dy = f'(x_0)\ dx \tag{6}$$

That is, dy is a linear function of dx; consequently dy is usually easier to compute than Δy (this was seen in Example 1). Because $f(x_0 + \Delta x) - f(x_0) = \Delta y$, we have

$$f(x_0 + \Delta x) = f(x_0) + \Delta y$$

Thus,

$$f(x_0 + \Delta x) \approx f(x_0) + dy \tag{7}$$

We illustrate our results in Fig. 6.1.1. The equation of the curve in the figure is $y = f(x)$. The line PT is tangent to the curve at $P(x_0, f(x_0))$; Δx and dx are equal and are represented by the directed distance $\overline{PM}$, where M is the point $(x_0 + \Delta x, f(x_0))$. We let Q be the point $(x_0 + \Delta x, f(x_0 + \Delta x))$, and the directed distance $\overline{MQ}$ is Δy or, equivalently, $f(x_0 + \Delta x) - f(x_0)$. The slope of PT is $f'(x) = dy/dx$. Also, the slope of PT is $\overline{MR}/\overline{PM}$, and because $\overline{PM} = dx$, we have $dy = \overline{MR}$ and $\overline{RQ} = \Delta y - dy$. Note that the smaller the value of dx (i.e., the closer the point Q is to the point P), then the smaller will be the value of $\Delta y - dy$ (i.e., the smaller will be the length of the line segment RQ). An equation of the tangent line PT is

$$y = f(x_0) + f'(x_0)(x - x_0)$$

Figure 6.1.1

Thus, if $\bar{y}$ is the ordinate of R, then

$$\bar{y} = f(x_0) + dy \tag{8}$$

Comparing Eqs. (7) and (8), we see that when using $f(x_0) + dy$ to approximate the value of $f(x_0 + \Delta x)$ we are approximating the ordinate of the point $Q(x_0 + \Delta x, f(x_0 + \Delta x))$ on the curve by the ordinate of the point $R(x_0 + \Delta x, f(x_0) + dy)$ on the line that is tangent to the curve at $P(x_0, f(x_0))$.

Observe that in Fig. 6.1.1 the graph is concave upward. In Exercise 30 you are asked to draw a similar figure if the graph is concave downward.

EXAMPLE 2: Find an approximate value for $\sqrt[3]{28}$ without using tables.

SOLUTION: Consider the function f defined by $f(x) = \sqrt[3]{x}$ and let $y = f(x)$. Hence,

$$y = \sqrt[3]{x}$$

and

$$dy = f'(x)\ dx$$

$$= \frac{1}{3x^{2/3}}\ dx$$

The nearest perfect cube to 28 is 27. Thus, we compute dy with $x = 27$ and $dx = \Delta x = 1$.

$$dy = \frac{1}{3(27)^{2/3}}\ (1) = \frac{1}{27}$$

By applying formula (7) with $x_0 = 27$, $\Delta x = 1$, and $dy = \frac{1}{27}$, we have

$$f(27 + 1) \approx f(27) + \tfrac{1}{27}$$
$$\sqrt[3]{27 + 1} \approx \sqrt[3]{27} + \tfrac{1}{27}$$
$$\sqrt[3]{28} \approx 3 + \tfrac{1}{27}$$

Therefore, $\sqrt[3]{28} \approx 3.037$.

From Table 1 in the Appendix, we get $\sqrt[3]{28} = 3.037$. Thus, the approximation is accurate to three decimal places.

EXAMPLE 3: Find the approximate volume of a spherical shell whose inner radius is 4 in. and whose thickness is $\frac{1}{16}$ in.

SOLUTION: We consider the volume of the spherical shell as an increment of the volume of a sphere.

Let r = the number of inches in the radius of a sphere;
V = the number of cubic inches in the volume of a sphere;
ΔV = the number of cubic inches in the volume of a spherical shell.

$$V = \tfrac{4}{3}\pi r^3 \quad \text{so that} \quad dV = 4\pi r^2\ dr$$

Substituting $r = 4$ and $dr = \frac{1}{16}$ into the above, we obtain

$$dV = 4\pi(4)^2\ \tfrac{1}{16}$$

$$= 4\pi$$

Therefore, $\Delta V \approx 4\pi$, and we conclude that the volume of the spherical shell is approximately 4π in.[3]

Exercises 6.1

In Exercises 1 through 6, find (a) Δy; (b) dy; (c) $\Delta y - dy$.

1. $y = x^3$

2. $y = 4x^2 - 3x + 1$

3. $y = \sqrt{x}$

4. $y = \dfrac{1}{x^2 + 1}$

5. $y = 2x^3 + 3x^2$

6. $y = \dfrac{1}{\sqrt[3]{x}}$

In Exercises 7 through 12, find for the given values: (a) Δy; (b) dy; (c) $\Delta y - dy$.

7. $y = x^2 - 3x$; $x = 2$; $\Delta x = 0.03$

8. $y = x^2 - 3x$; $x = -1$; $\Delta x = 0.02$

9. $y = x^3 + 1$; $x = 1$; $\Delta x = -0.5$

10. $y = x^3 + 1$; $x = -1$; $\Delta x = 0.1$

11. $y = \dfrac{1}{x^2}$; $x = 2$; $\Delta x = 0.01$

12. $y = \dfrac{1}{x^2}$; $x = -3$; $\Delta x = -0.1$

In Exercises 13 through 20, use differentials to find an approximate value for the given quantity. Express each answer to three significant digits.

13. $\sqrt{37.5}$

14. $\sqrt[3]{7.5}$

15. $\sqrt[4]{82}$

16. $\sqrt{82}$

17. $\sqrt[3]{0.00098}$

18. $\sqrt{0.042}$

19. $\dfrac{1}{\sqrt[3]{120}}$

20. $\dfrac{1}{\sqrt[4]{15}}$

21. The measurement of an edge of a cube is found to be 15 in. with a possible error of 0.01 in. Using differentials find the approximate error in computing from this measurement (a) the volume; (b) the area of one of the faces.

22. The altitude of a right-circular cone is twice the radius of the base. The altitude is measured as 12 in., with a possible error of 0.005 in. Find the approximate error in the calculated volume of the cone.

23. An open cylindrical tank is to have an outside coating of thickness $\frac{1}{8}$ in. If the inner radius is 6 ft and the altitude is 10 ft, find by differentials the approximate amount of coating material to be used.

24. A metal box in the form of a cube is to have an interior volume of 64 in.[3] The six sides are to be made of metal $\frac{1}{4}$ in. thick. If the cost of the metal to be used is 8 cents per cubic inch, use differentials to find the approximate cost of the metal to be used in the manufacture of the box.

25. If the possible error in the measurement of the volume of a gas is 0.1 ft[3] and the allowable error in the pressure is $0.001C$ lb/ft[2], find the size of the smallest container for which Boyle's law (Exercise 10 in Exercises 3.9) holds.

26. A contractor agrees to paint on both sides of 1000 circular signs each of radius 3 ft. Upon receiving the signs, it is discovered that the radius is $\frac{1}{2}$ in. too large. Use differentials to find the approximate percent increase of paint that will be needed.

27. The measure of the electrical resistance of a wire is proportional to the measure of its length and inversely proportional to the square of the measure of its diameter. Suppose the resistance of a wire of given length is computed from a measurement of the diameter with a possible 2% error. Find the possible percent error in the computed value of the resistance.

28. If t sec is the time for one complete swing of a simple pendulum of length l ft, then $4\pi^2 l = gt^2$, where $g = 32.2$. A clock having a pendulum of length 1 ft gains 5 min each day. Find the approximate amount by which the pendulum should be lengthened in order to correct the inaccuracy.

29. For the adiabatic law for the expansion of air of Exercise 12 in Sec. 3.10, prove that $dP/P = -1.4\ dV/V$.

30. Draw a figure similar to Fig. 6.1.1, if the graph is concave downward. Indicate the line segments whose lengths represent the following quantities: Δx, Δy, dx, and dy.

6.2 DIFFERENTIAL FORMULAS

Suppose that y is a function of x and that x, in turn, is a function of a third variable t; that is,

$$y = f(x) \quad \text{and} \quad x = g(t) \tag{1}$$

The two equations in (1) together define y as a function of t. For example, suppose that $y = x^3$ and $x = 2t^2 - 1$. Combining these two equations, we get $y = (2t^2 - 1)^3$. In general, if the two equations in (1) are combined, we obtain

$$y = f(g(t)) \tag{2}$$

The derivative of y with respect to t can be found by the chain rule, which yields

$$D_t y = D_x y\ D_t x \tag{3}$$

Equation (3) expresses $D_t y$ as a function of x and t because $D_x y$ is a function of x and $D_t x$ is a function of t.

• ILLUSTRATION 1: If $y = x^3$ and $x = 2t^2 - 1$, then

$$\begin{aligned}
D_t y &= D_x y\ D_t x \\
&= 3x^2(4t) \\
&= 12x^2 t
\end{aligned}$$

•

Because Eq. (2) defines y as a function of the independent variable t, the differential of y is obtained from Definition 6.1.1:

$$dy = D_t y\ dt \tag{4}$$

Equation (4) expresses dy as a function of t and dt. Substituting from (3) into (4), we get

$$dy = D_x y\ D_t x\ dt \tag{5}$$

Now because x is a function of the independent variable t, Definition 6.1.1 can be applied to obtain the differential of x, and we have

$$dx = D_t x\ dt \tag{6}$$

Equation (6) expresses dx as a function of t and dt. From (5) and (6), we get

$$dy = D_x y\ dx \tag{7}$$

You should bear in mind that in Eq. (7) dy is a function of t and dt, and that dx is a function of t and dt. If $D_x y$ in Eq. (7) is replaced by $f'(x)$, we have

$$dy = f'(x)\ dx \tag{8}$$

Equation (8) resembles Eq. (4) of Sec. 6.1. However, in that equation x is the independent variable, and dy is expressed in terms of x and dx, whereas in Eq. (8) t is the independent variable, and both dy and dx are expressed in terms of t and dt. Thus, we have the following theorem.

6.2.1 Theorem If $y = f(x)$, then when $f'(x)$ exists,

$$dy = f'(x)\ dx$$

whether or not x is an independent variable.

If on both sides of Eq. (8) we divide by dx (provided $dx \neq 0$), we obtain

$$f'(x) = \frac{dy}{dx} \qquad dx \neq 0 \tag{9}$$

Equation (9) states that if $y = f(x)$, then $f'(x)$ is the quotient of the two differentials dy and dx, even though x may not be an independent variable.

We now proceed to write the chain rule for differentiation by expressing the derivatives as quotients of differentials. If $y = f(u)$ and $D_u y$ exists, and if $u = f(x)$ and $D_x u$ exists, then the chain rule gives

$$D_x y = D_u y\ D_x u \tag{10}$$

But $D_x y = dy/dx$ if $dx \neq 0$; $D_u y = dy/du$ if $du \neq 0$; and $D_x u = du/dx$ if $dx \neq 0$. From (10), therefore, we have

$$\frac{dy}{dx} = \left(\frac{dy}{du}\right) \cdot \left(\frac{du}{dx}\right) \qquad \text{if } du \neq 0 \text{ and } dx \neq 0$$

Observe the convenient form the chain rule takes with this notation.

The German mathematician Gottfried Wilhelm Leibniz (1646–1716) was the first to use the notation dy/dx for the derivative of y with respect to x. The concept of a derivative was introduced, in the seventeenth century, almost simultaneously by Leibniz and Sir Isaac Newton (1642–1727), who were working independently. Leibniz probably thought of dx and dy as small changes in the variables x and y and of the derivative of y with respect to x as the ratio of dy to dx as dy and dx become small. The concept of a limit as we know it today was not known to Leibniz.

Corresponding to the Leibniz notation dy/dx for the first derivative of y with respect to x, we have the symbol d^2y/dx^2 for the second derivative of y with respect to x. However, d^2y/dx^2 must not be thought of as a quotient because in this text the differential of a differential is not considered. Similarly, $d^n y/dx^n$ is a notation for the nth derivative of y with respect to x. The symbolism f', f'', f''', and so on, for the successive derivatives of a function f was introduced by the French mathematician Joseph Louis Lagrange (1736–1813) in the eighteenth century.

Earlier in this chapter, we derived formulas for finding derivatives. These formulas are now stated using the Leibniz notation. Along with the formula for the derivative, we shall give a corresponding formula for the differential. In these formulas, u and v are functions of x, and it is understood that the formulas hold if $D_x u$ and $D_x v$ exist. When c appears, it is a constant.

$$\text{I}\quad \frac{d(c)}{dx} = 0 \qquad\qquad \text{I}'\ \ d(c) = 0$$

$$\text{II}\quad \frac{d(x^n)}{dx} = nx^{n-1} \qquad\qquad \text{II}'\ \ d(x^n) = nx^{n-1}\,dx$$

$$\text{III}\quad \frac{d(cu)}{dx} = c\,\frac{du}{dx} \qquad\qquad \text{III}'\ \ d(cu) = c\,du$$

$$\text{IV}\quad \frac{d(u+v)}{dx} = \frac{du}{dx} + \frac{dv}{dx} \qquad\qquad \text{IV}'\ \ d(u+v) = du + dv$$

$$\text{V}\quad \frac{d(uv)}{dx} = u\,\frac{dv}{dx} + v\,\frac{du}{dx} \qquad\qquad \text{V}'\ \ d(uv) = u\,dv + v\,du$$

$$\text{VI}\quad \frac{d\left(\dfrac{u}{v}\right)}{dx} = \frac{v\,\dfrac{du}{dx} - u\,\dfrac{dv}{dx}}{v^2} \qquad\qquad \text{VI}'\ \ d\left(\frac{u}{v}\right) = \frac{v\,du - u\,dv}{v^2}$$

$$\text{VII}\quad \frac{d(u^n)}{dx} = nu^{n-1}\,\frac{du}{dx} \qquad\qquad \text{VII}'\ \ d(u^n) = nu^{n-1}\,du$$

The operation of differentiation is extended to include the process of finding the differential as well as finding the derivative. If $y = f(x)$, dy can be found either by applying formulas I'–VII' or by finding $f'(x)$ and multiplying it by dx.

EXAMPLE 1: Given

$$y = \frac{\sqrt{x^2 + 1}}{2x + 1}$$

find dy.

SOLUTION: Applying formula VI', we obtain

$$dy = \frac{(2x+1)\,d(\sqrt{x^2+1}\,) - \sqrt{x^2+1}\,\,d(2x+1)}{(2x+1)^2} \tag{11}$$

From formula VII',

$$d(\sqrt{x^2+1}\,) = \tfrac{1}{2}(x^2+1)^{-1/2}\,2x\,dx = x(x^2+1)^{-1/2}\,dx \tag{12}$$

and

$$d(2x+1) = 2\,dx \tag{13}$$

Substituting values from (12) and (13) into (11), we get

$$dy = \frac{x(2x+1)(x^2+1)^{-1/2}\,dx - 2(x^2+1)^{1/2}\,dx}{(2x+1)^2}$$

$$= \frac{(2x^2+x)\,dx - 2(x^2+1)\,dx}{(2x+1)^2(x^2+1)^{1/2}}$$

$$= \frac{x-2}{(2x+1)^2\sqrt{x^2+1}}\,dx$$

EXAMPLE 2: Given

$$2x^2y^2 - 3x^3 + 5y^3 + 6xy^2 = 5$$

where x and y are functions of a third variable t, find dy/dx by finding the differential term by term.

SOLUTION: This is a problem in implicit differentiation. Taking the differential term by term, we get

$$4xy^2\,dx + 4x^2y\,dy - 9x^2\,dx + 15y^2\,dy + 6y^2\,dx + 12xy\,dy = 0$$

Dividing by dx, if $dx \neq 0$, we have

$$(4x^2y + 15y^2 + 12xy)\,\frac{dy}{dx} = -4xy^2 + 9x^2 - 6y^2$$

$$\frac{dy}{dx} = \frac{9x^2 - 6y^2 - 4xy^2}{4x^2y + 15y^2 + 12xy}$$

Exercises 6.2

In Exercises 1 through 8, find dy.

1. $y = (3x^2 - 2x + 1)^3$

2. $y = \sqrt{4 - x^2}$

3. $y = x^2\sqrt[3]{2x+3}$

4. $y = \dfrac{3x}{x^2+2}$

5. $y = \sqrt{\dfrac{x-1}{x+1}}$

6. $y = (x+2)^{1/3}(x-2)^{2/3}$

7. $y = \dfrac{2x}{\sqrt{x^2+1}}$

8. $y = \sqrt{3x+4}\,\sqrt[3]{x^2-1}$

In Exercises 9 through 16, x and y are functions of a third variable t. Find dy/dx by finding the differential term by term (see Example 2).

9. $3x^3 + 4y^2 = 48$

10. $8x^2 - y^2 = 32$

11. $\sqrt{x} + \sqrt{y} = 4$

12. $2x^2y - 3xy^3 + 6y^2 = 1$

13. $x^4 - 3x^3y + 4xy^3 + y^4 = 2$

14. $x^{2/3} + y^{2/3} = a^{2/3}$

15. $3x^3 - x^2y + 2xy^2 - y^3 - 3x^2 + y^2 = 1$

16. $x^2 + y^2 = \sqrt[3]{x+y}$

In Exercises 17 through 24, find dy/dt.

17. $y = 3x^3 - 5x^2 + 1;\ x = t^2 - 1$

18. $y = \dfrac{5x-2}{x^2+1};\ x = (2t-1)^2$

19. $y = x^2 - 3x + 1;\ x = \sqrt{t^2 - t + 4}$

20. $y = \sqrt[3]{5x-1};\ x = \sqrt{2t+3}$

21. $y = x^2 - 5x + 1;\ x = s^3 - 2s + 1;\ s = \sqrt{t^2+1}$

22. $y = \dfrac{x^2-1}{x^2+1};\ x = \dfrac{2s+2}{\sqrt{s^2+2}};\ s = t^2 - 4t + 5$

23. $x^3 - 3x^2y + y^3 = 5;\ x = 4t^2 + 1$

24. $3x^2y - 4xy^2 + 7y^3 = 0;\ 2x^3 - 3xt^2 + t^3 = 1$

6.3 THE INVERSE OF DIFFERENTIATION

You are already familiar with *inverse operations*. Addition and subtraction are inverse operations; multiplication and division are also inverse operations, as well as raising to powers and extracting roots. The inverse operation of differentiation is called *antidifferentiation*.

6.3.1 Definition

A function F is called an *antiderivative* of a function f on an interval I if $F'(x) = f(x)$ for every value of x in I.

• ILLUSTRATION 1: If F is defined by $F(x) = 4x^3 + x^2 + 5$, then $F'(x) = 12x^2 + 2x$. Thus, if f is the function defined by $f(x) = 12x^2 + 2x$, we state that f is the derivative of F and that F is an antiderivative of f. If G is the function defined by $G(x) = 4x^3 + x^2 - 17$, then G is also an antiderivative of f because $G'(x) = 12x^2 + 2x$. Actually any function whose function value is given by $4x^3 + x^2 + C$, where C is any constant, is an antiderivative of f.   •

In general, if a function F is an antiderivative of a function f on an interval I and if G is defined by

$$G(x) = F(x) + C$$

where C is an arbitrary constant, then

$$G'(x) = F'(x) = f(x)$$

and G is also an antiderivative of f on the interval I.

We now proceed to prove that if F is any particular antiderivative of f on an interval I, then all possible antiderivatives of f on I are defined by $F(x) + C$, where C is an arbitrary constant. First, two preliminary theorems are needed.

6.3.2 Theorem

If f is a function such that $f'(x) = 0$ for all values of x in the interval I, then f is constant on I.

PROOF: Let us assume that f is not constant on the interval I. Then there exist two distinct numbers x_1 and x_2 in I where $x_1 < x_2$ such that $f(x_1) \neq f(x_2)$. Because, by hypothesis, $f'(x) = 0$ for all x in I, then $f'(x) = 0$ for all x in the closed interval $[x_1, x_2]$. Hence, f is differentiable at all x in $[x_1, x_2]$ and f is continuous on $[x_1, x_2]$. Therefore, the hypothesis of the mean-value theorem is satisfied, and we conclude that there is a number c, with $x_1 < c < x_2$, such that

$$f'(c) = \frac{f(x_1) - f(x_2)}{x_1 - x_2} \tag{1}$$

But because $f'(x) = 0$ for all x in the interval $[x_1, x_2]$, then $f'(c) = 0$, and from Eq. (1) it follows that $f(x_1) = f(x_2)$. Yet our assumption was that $f(x_1) \neq f(x_2)$. Hence, there is a contradiction, and so f is constant on I, which is what we wished to prove.   ∎

6.3.3 Theorem   If f and g are two functions such that $f'(x) = g'(x)$ for all values of x in the interval I, then there is a constant K such that

$$f(x) = g(x) + K \qquad \text{for all } x \text{ in } I$$

PROOF: Let h be the function defined on I by

$$h(x) = f(x) - g(x)$$

so that for all values of x in I we have

$$h'(x) = f'(x) - g'(x)$$

But, by hypothesis, $f'(x) = g'(x)$ for all values of x in I. Therefore,

$$h'(x) = 0 \qquad \text{for all values of } x \text{ in } I$$

Thus, Theorem 6.3.2 applies to the function h, and there is a constant K such that

$$h(x) = K \qquad \text{for all values of } x \text{ in } I$$

Replacing $h(x)$ by $f(x) - g(x)$, we have

$$f(x) = g(x) + K \qquad \text{for all values of } x \text{ in } I$$

and the theorem is proved.   ■

The next theorem follows immediately from Theorem 6.3.3.

6.3.4 Theorem   If F is any particular antiderivative of f on an interval I, then the most general antiderivative of f on I is given by

$$F(x) + C \tag{2}$$

where C is an arbitrary constant, and all antiderivatives of f on I can be obtained from (2) by assigning particular values to C.

PROOF: Let G be any antiderivative of f on I; then

$$G'(x) = f(x) \qquad \text{on } I \tag{3}$$

Because F is a particular antiderivative of f on I, we have

$$F'(x) = f(x) \qquad \text{on } I \tag{4}$$

From Eqs. (3) and (4), it follows that

$$G'(x) = F'(x) \qquad \text{on } I$$

Therefore, from Theorem 6.3.3, there is a constant K such that

$$G(x) = F(x) + K \qquad \text{for all } x \text{ in } I$$

Because G is any antiderivative of f on I, it follows that all antiderivatives of f can be obtained from $F(x) + C$, where C is an arbitrary constant. Hence, the theorem is proved.   ■

If F is an antiderivative of f, then $F'(x) = f(x)$, and so

$$d(F(x)) = f(x)\ dx$$

Antidifferentiation is the process of finding the most general antiderivative of a given function. The symbol

$$\int$$

denotes the operation of antidifferentiation, and we write

$$\int f(x)\ dx = F(x) + C \qquad (5)$$

where

$$F'(x) = f(x)$$

or, equivalently,

$$d(F(x)) = f(x)\ dx \qquad (6)$$

From Eqs. (5) and (6), we can write

$$\int d(F(x)) = F(x) + C \qquad (7)$$

Equation (7) states that when we antidifferentiate the differential of a function we obtain that function plus an arbitrary constant. So we can think of the $\int$ symbol for antidifferentiation as meaning that operation which is the inverse of the operation denoted by d for finding the differential.

Because antidifferentiation is the inverse operation of differentiation, we can obtain antidifferentiation formulas from differentiation formulas. We use the following formulas that can be proved from the corresponding formulas for differentiation.

6.3.5 Formula 1 $\int dx = x + C$

6.3.6 Formula 2 $\int af(x)\ dx = a\int f(x)\ dx$, where a is a constant

Formula 2 states that to find an antiderivative of a constant times a function, first find an antiderivative of the function, and then multiply it by the constant.

6.3.7 Formula 3 $\int [f_1(x) + f_2(x)]\ dx = \int f_1(x)\ dx + \int f_2(x)\ dx$

Formula 3 states that to find an antiderivative of the sum of two functions, find an antiderivative of each of the functions separately, and then add the results. It is understood that both functions must be defined on the same interval. Formula 3 can be extended to any finite number of functions. Combining Formula 3 with Formula 2, we have Formula 4.

6.3.8 Formula 4 $\int [c_1f_1(x) + c_2f_2(x) + \cdots + c_nf_n(x)]\ dx$

$$= c_1\int f_1(x)\ dx + c_2\int f_2(x)\ dx + \cdots + c_n\int f_n(x)\ dx$$

6.3.9 Formula 5 $\int x^n\ dx = \dfrac{x^{n+1}}{(n+1)} + C \qquad \text{if } n \neq -1$

As stated above, these formulas follow from the corresponding formulas for finding the differential. Following is the proof of Formula 5:

$$d\left(\frac{x^{n+1}}{n+1} + C\right) = \frac{(n+1)x^n}{n+1}\ dx$$

$$= x^n\ dx$$

Applications of the above formulas are illustrated in the following examples.

EXAMPLE 1: Evaluate

$$\int (3x+5)\ dx$$

SOLUTION:

$$\int (3x+5)\ dx = 3\int x\ dx + 5\int dx \quad \text{(by Formula 4)}$$

$$= 3\left(\frac{x^2}{2} + C_1\right) + 5(x + C_2) \quad \text{(by Formulas 5 and 1)}$$

$$= \tfrac{3}{2}x^2 + 5x + 3C_1 + 5C_2$$

Because $3C_1 + 5C_2$ is an arbitrary constant, it may be denoted by C, and so our answer is

$$\tfrac{3}{2}x^2 + 5x + C$$

This answer may be checked by finding the derivative. Doing this, we have

$$D_x(\tfrac{3}{2}x^2 + 5x + C) = 3x + 5$$

EXAMPLE 2: Evaluate

$$\int \sqrt[3]{x^2}\ dx$$

SOLUTION: $\displaystyle\int \sqrt[3]{x^2}\ dx = \int x^{2/3}\ dx$

$$= \frac{x^{2/3+1}}{\frac{2}{3}+1} + C \quad \text{(from Formula 5)}$$

$$= \tfrac{3}{5}x^{5/3} + C$$

EXAMPLE 3: Evaluate

$$\int \left(\frac{1}{x^4} + \frac{1}{\sqrt[4]{x}}\right) dx$$

SOLUTION: $\displaystyle\int \left(\frac{1}{x^4} + \frac{1}{\sqrt[4]{x}}\right) dx = \int (x^{-4} + x^{-1/4})\ dx$

$$= \frac{x^{-4+1}}{-4+1} + \frac{x^{-1/4+1}}{-\frac{1}{4}+1} + C$$

$$= \frac{x^{-3}}{-3} + \frac{x^{3/4}}{\frac{3}{4}} + C$$

$$= -\frac{1}{3x^3} + \frac{4}{3} x^{3/4} + C$$

Many antiderivatives cannot be found directly by applying formulas. However, sometimes it is possible to find an antiderivative by the formulas after changing the variable.

● ILLUSTRATION 2: Suppose that we wish to find

$$\int 2x \sqrt{1 + x^2} \; dx \qquad (8)$$

If we make the substitution $u = 1 + x^2$, then $du = 2x \; dx$, and (8) becomes

$$\int u^{1/2} \; du$$

which by Formula 5 gives

$$\tfrac{2}{3} u^{3/2} + C$$

Then, replacing u by $(1 + x^2)$, we have as our result

$$\tfrac{2}{3}(1 + x^2)^{3/2} + C \qquad\qquad ●$$

Justification of the procedure used in Illustration 2 is provided by the following theorem, which is analogous to the chain rule for differentiation, and hence may be called the *chain rule for antidifferentiation.*

6.3.10 Theorem
Chain Rule for Antidifferentiation

Let g be a differentiable function of x, and let the range of g be an interval I. Suppose that f is a function defined on I and that F is an antiderivative of f on I. Then if $u = g(x)$,

$$\int f(g(x))g'(x) \; dx = \int f(u) \; du = F(u) + C = F(g(x)) + C$$

PROOF: Because $u = g(x)$, then u is in I; and because F is an antiderivative of f on I, it follows that

$$\frac{dF(u)}{du} = f(u) \qquad (9)$$

and

$$\int f(u) \; du = F(u) + C \qquad (10)$$

Also,

$$\frac{dF(g(x))}{dx} = \frac{dF(u)}{dx} \qquad (11)$$

Applying the chain rule for differentiation to the right side of Eq. (11), we obtain

$$\frac{dF(g(x))}{dx} = \frac{dF(u)}{du} \cdot \frac{du}{dx} \tag{12}$$

Substituting from Eq. (9) into (12) gives

$$\frac{dF(g(x))}{dx} = f(u) \cdot \frac{du}{dx} \tag{13}$$

Because $u = g(x)$, from Eq. (13) we have

$$\frac{dF(g(x))}{dx} = f(g(x)) \cdot g'(x)$$

from which we conclude that

$$\int f(g(x)) \cdot g'(x) \, dx = F(g(x)) + C \tag{14}$$

Because $u = g(x)$, we have

$$F(g(x)) + C = F(u) + C \tag{15}$$

Therefore, from (10), (14), and (15), we have

$$\int f(g(x)) g'(x) \, dx = \int f(u) \, du = F(u) + C = F(g(x)) + C$$

which is what we wished to prove.   ∎

As a particular case of Theorem 6.3.10, from Formula 5 we have the generalized power formula for antiderivatives, which we state as Formula 6.

6.3.11 Formula 6   If g is a differentiable function, then if $u = g(x)$,

$$\int [g(x)]^n g'(x) \, dx = \int u^n \, du = \frac{u^{n+1}}{n+1} + C = \frac{[g(x)]^{n+1}}{n+1} + C$$

where $n \neq -1$.

Examples 4, 5, and 6 illustrate the application of Formula 6.

EXAMPLE 4:   Evaluate

$$\int \sqrt{3x + 4} \, dx$$

SOLUTION: To apply Formula 6, we make the substitution $u = 3x + 4$; then $du = 3 \, dx$, or $\frac{1}{3} du = dx$. Hence,

$$\int \sqrt{3x + 4} \, dx = \int u^{1/2} \cdot \frac{du}{3}$$

$$= \frac{1}{3} \int u^{1/2} \, du$$

$$= \frac{1}{3} \cdot \frac{u^{3/2}}{\frac{3}{2}} + C$$

$$= \tfrac{2}{9} u^{3/2} + C$$

$$= \tfrac{2}{9} (3x + 4)^{3/2} + C$$

The details of the solution of Example 4 can be shortened by not explicitly stating the substitution of u. The solution then takes the following form.

$$\int \sqrt{3x + 4} \ dx = \tfrac{1}{3} \int (3x + 4)^{1/2} 3 \ dx$$

$$= \frac{1}{3} \cdot \frac{(3x + 4)^{3/2}}{\frac{3}{2}} + C$$

$$= \tfrac{2}{9} (3x + 4)^{3/2} + C$$

EXAMPLE 5:   Evaluate

$$\int t(5 + 3t^2)^8 \, dt$$

SOLUTION: Since $d(5 + 3t^2) = 6t \, dt$, we write

$$\int t(5 + 3t^2)^8 \, dt = \tfrac{1}{6} \int (5 + 3t^2)^8 6t \, dt$$

$$= \frac{1}{6} \cdot \frac{(5 + 3t^2)^9}{9} + C$$

$$= \tfrac{1}{54} (5 + 3t^2)^9 + C$$

EXAMPLE 6:   Evaluate

$$\int x^2 \sqrt[5]{7 - 4x^3} \, dx$$

SOLUTION:

$$\int x^2 \sqrt[5]{7 - 4x^3} \, dx = -\tfrac{1}{12} \int (7 - 4x^3)^{1/5} (-12x^2) \, dx$$

$$= -\frac{1}{12} \cdot \frac{(7 - 4x^3)^{6/5}}{\frac{6}{5}} + C$$

$$= -\frac{5}{72} (7 - 4x^3)^{6/5} + C$$

EXAMPLE 7:   Evaluate

$$\int x^2 \sqrt{1 + x} \, dx$$

SOLUTION: Let $v = \sqrt{1 + x}$; then $v^2 = 1 + x$. Hence, $x = v^2 - 1$, and $dx = 2v \, dv$. Making these substitutions, we have

$$\int x^2 \sqrt{1 + x} \, dx = \int (v^2 - 1)^2 \cdot v \cdot (2v \, dv)$$

$$= 2 \int v^6 \, dv - 4 \int v^4 \, dv + 2 \int v^2 \, dv$$

$$= \tfrac{2}{7} v^7 - \tfrac{4}{5} v^5 + \tfrac{2}{3} v^3 + C$$

$$= \tfrac{2}{7} (1 + x)^{7/2} - \tfrac{4}{5} (1 + x)^{5/2} + \tfrac{2}{3} (1 + x)^{3/2} + C$$

The answers to each of the above examples can be checked by finding the derivative (or the differential) of the answer.

● ILLUSTRATION 3: In Example 5, we have

$$\int t(5 + 3t^2)^8 \, dt = \tfrac{1}{54}(5 + 3t^2)^9 + C$$

Checking by differentiation gives

$$D_t[\tfrac{1}{54}(5 + 3t^2)^9] = \tfrac{1}{54} \cdot 9(5 + 3t^2)^8 \cdot 6t$$
$$= t(5 + 3t^2)^8$$

● ILLUSTRATION 4: In Example 7, we have

$$\int x^2\sqrt{1 + x} \, dx = \tfrac{2}{7}(1 + x)^{7/2} - \tfrac{4}{5}(1 + x)^{5/2} + \tfrac{2}{3}(1 + x)^{3/2} + C$$

Checking by differentiation gives

$$D_x[\tfrac{2}{7}(1 + x)^{7/2} - \tfrac{4}{5}(1 + x)^{5/2} + \tfrac{2}{3}(1 + x)^{3/2}]$$
$$= (1 + x)^{5/2} - 2(1 + x)^{3/2} + (1 + x)^{1/2}$$
$$= (1 + x)^{1/2}[(1 + x)^2 - 2(1 + x) + 1]$$
$$= (1 + x)^{1/2}[1 + 2x + x^2 - 2 - 2x + 1]$$
$$= x^2\sqrt{1 + x}$$

Exercises 6.3

In Exercises 1 through 26, find the most general antiderivative. In Exercises 1 through 10, check by finding the derivative of your answer.

1. $\int 3x^4 \, dx$

2. $\int (4x^3 - 3x^2 + 6x - 1) \, dx$

3. $\int (3 - 2t + t^2) \, dt$

4. $\int (ax^2 + bx + c) \, dx$

5. $\int \left(\dfrac{2}{x^3} + \dfrac{3}{x^2} + 5\right) dx$

6. $\int \dfrac{y^4 + 2y^2 - 1}{\sqrt{y}} \, dy$

7. $\int \left(\sqrt{2x} - \dfrac{1}{\sqrt{2x}}\right) dx$

8. $\int \dfrac{27t^3 - 1}{\sqrt[3]{t}} \, dt$

9. $\int x^2\sqrt{x^3 - 1} \, dx$

10. $\int x\sqrt[3]{(4 - x^2)^2} \, dx$

11. $\int \dfrac{s \, ds}{\sqrt{3s^2 + 1}}$

12. $\int \sqrt{5r + 1} \, dr$

13. $\int \sqrt{1 + \dfrac{1}{3x}} \dfrac{dx}{x^2}$

14. $\int x^4\sqrt{3x^5 - 5} \, dx$

15. $\int x^2(4 - x^2)^3 \, dx$

16. $\int (x^2 - 4x + 4)^{4/3} \, dx$

17. $\int \dfrac{t \, dt}{\sqrt{t + 3}}$

18. $\int \dfrac{2r \, dr}{(1 - r)^{2/3}}$

19. $\int \sqrt{3 - x} \, x^2 \, dx$

20. $\int (x^3 + 3)^{1/4}x^5 \, dx$

21. $\int \dfrac{(x^2 + 2x) \, dx}{\sqrt{x^3 + 3x^2 + 1}}$

22. $\int \sqrt{3 + s}(s + 1)^2 \, ds$

23. $\int \dfrac{y + 3}{(3 - y)^{2/3}} \, dy$

24. $\int (2t^2 + 1)^{1/3}t^3 \, dt$

25. $\int \frac{(r^{1/3} + 2)^4}{\sqrt[3]{r^2}} \, dr$

26. $\int \left(t + \frac{1}{t}\right)^{3/2} \left(\frac{t^2 - 1}{t^2}\right) dt$

27. Evaluate $\int (2x + 1)^3 \, dx$ by two methods: (a) Expand $(2x + 1)^3$ by the binomial theorem, and apply Formulas 1, 4, and 5; (b) make the substitution $u = 2x + 1$. Explain the difference in appearance of the answers obtained in (a) and (b).

28. Evaluate $\int \sqrt{x - 1} \, x^2 \, dx$ by two methods: (a) Make the substitution $u = x - 1$; (b) make the substitution $v = \sqrt{x - 1}$.

29. Let $f(x) = 1$ for all x in $(-1, 1)$ and let

$$g(x) = \begin{cases} -1 & \text{if } -1 < x \le 0 \\ 1 & \text{if } 0 < x < 1 \end{cases}$$

Then $f'(x) = 0$ for all x in $(-1, 1)$ and $g'(x) = 0$ whenever g' exists in $(-1, 1)$. However, $f(x) \ne g(x) + K$ for x in $(-1, 1)$. Why doesn't Theorem 6.3.3 hold?

30. Let $f(x) = \text{sgn } x$ and $F(x) = |x|$. Show that $F'(x) = f(x)$ if $x \ne 0$. Is F an antiderivative of f on $(-\infty, +\infty)$? Explain.

31. Let $f(x) = |x|$ and let F be defined by

$$F(x) = \begin{cases} -\frac{1}{2}x^2 & \text{if } x < 0 \\ \frac{1}{2}x^2 & \text{if } x \ge 0 \end{cases}$$

Show that F is an antiderivative of f on $(-\infty, +\infty)$.

32. Show that the unit step function U (Exercise 21 in Exercises 1.8) does not have an antiderivative on $(-\infty, +\infty)$. (HINT: Assume that U has an antiderivative F on $(-\infty, +\infty)$, and a contradiction is obtained by showing that it follows from the mean-value theorem that there exists a number k such that $F(x) = x + k$ if $x > 0$, and $F(x) = k$ if $x < 0$.)

6.4 DIFFERENTIAL EQUATIONS WITH VARIABLES SEPARABLE

If F is a function defined by the equation

$$y = F(x) \tag{1}$$

and f is the derivative of F, then

$$\frac{dy}{dx} = f(x) \tag{2}$$

and F is an antiderivative of f.

Writing Eq. (2) using differentials, we have

$$dy = f(x) \, dx \tag{3}$$

Equations (2) and (3) are very simple types of *differential equations*. They are differential equations of the *first order* (because only derivatives of the first order are involved) for which the variables are separable. To solve Eq. (3) we must find all functions G for which $y = G(x)$ so that the equation is satisfied. So if F is an antiderivative of f, all functions G are defined by $G(x) = F(x) + C$, where C is an arbitrary constant. That is, if $d(G(x)) = d(F(x) + C) = f(x) \, dx$, then what is called the *complete solution* of Eq. (3) is given by

$$y = F(x) + C \tag{4}$$

Equation (4) represents a family of functions depending on an arbitrary constant C. This is called a *one-parameter family*. The graphs of these functions form a one-parameter family of curves in the plane, and through any particular point (x_1, y_1) there passes just one curve of the family.

• ILLUSTRATION 1: Suppose we wish to find the complete solution of the differential equation

$$dy = 2x \, dx \tag{5}$$

The most general antiderivative for the left side of Eq. (5) is $(y + C_1)$ and the most general antiderivative of $2x$ is $(x^2 + C_2)$. Thus, we have

$$y + C_1 = x^2 + C_2$$

Because $(C_2 - C_1)$ is an arbitrary constant if C_2 and C_1 are arbitrary, we can replace $(C_2 - C_1)$ by C, thereby obtaining

$$y = x^2 + C \tag{6}$$

which is the complete solution of the given differential equation.

Equation (6) represents a one-parameter family of functions. Figure 6.4.1 shows sketches of the graphs of the functions corresponding to $C = -4$, $C = -1$, $C = 0$, $C = 1$, and $C = 2$. •

Often in problems involving differential equations it is desired to find particular solutions which satisfy certain conditions called *boundary conditions* or *initial conditions*. For example, if differential equation (3) is given as well as the boundary condition that $y = y_1$ when $x = x_1$, then after the complete solution (4) is found, if x and y in (4) are replaced by x_1 and y_1, a particular value of C is determined. When this value of C is substituted back into Eq. (4), a particular solution is obtained.

• ILLUSTRATION 2: To find the particular solution of differential equation (5) satisfying the boundary condition that $y = 6$ when $x = 2$, we substitute these values in Eq. (6) and solve for C, giving $6 = 4 + C$, or $C = 2$. Substituting this value of C in (6), we obtain

$$y = x^2 + 2$$

which is the particular solution desired. •

Another type of differential equation is

$$\frac{d^2y}{dx^2} = f(x) \tag{7}$$

Equation (7) is a differential equation of the *second order*. Two successive antidifferentiations are necessary to solve Eq. (7), and two arbitrary constants occur in the complete solution. The complete solution of Eq. (7) therefore represents a *two-parameter family* of functions, and the graphs of these functions form a two-parameter family of curves in the plane.

$C = 2$
$C = 1$
$C = 0$
$C = -1$
$C = -4$

Figure 6.4.1

EXAMPLE 1: Find the complete solution of the differential equation

$$\frac{d^2y}{dx^2} = 4x + 3$$

SOLUTION: Because $d^2y/dx^2 = dy'/dx$, the given equation can be written as

$$\frac{dy'}{dx} = 4x + 3$$

Writing this in differential form, we have

$$dy' = (4x + 3)\ dx$$

Antidifferentiating, we have

$$\int dy' = \int (4x + 3)\ dx$$

from which we get

$$y' = 2x^2 + 3x + C_1$$

Because $y' = dy/dx$, we make this substitution in the above equation and get

$$\frac{dy}{dx} = 2x^2 + 3x + C_1$$

Using differentials, we have

$$dy = (2x^2 + 3x + C_1)\ dx$$

Antidifferentiating, we obtain

$$\int dy = \int (2x^2 + 3x + C_1)\ dx$$

from which we get

$$y = \tfrac{2}{3}x^3 + \tfrac{3}{2}x^2 + C_1 x + C_2$$

which is the complete solution.

EXAMPLE 2: Find the particular solution of the differential equation in Example 1 for which $y = 2$ and $y' = -3$ when $x = 1$.

SOLUTION: Because $y' = 2x^2 + 3x + C_1$, we substitute -3 for y' and 1 for x, giving $-3 = 2 + 3 + C_1$, or $C_1 = -8$. Substituting this value of C_1 into the complete solution gives

$$y = \tfrac{2}{3}x^3 + \tfrac{3}{2}x^2 - 8x + C_2$$

Because $y = 2$ when $x = 1$, we substitute these values in the above equation and get $2 = \tfrac{2}{3} + \tfrac{3}{2} - 8 + C_2$, from which we obtain $C_2 = \tfrac{47}{6}$. The particular solution desired, then, is

$$y = \tfrac{2}{3}x^3 + \tfrac{3}{2}x^2 - 8x + \tfrac{47}{6}$$

A more general type of differential equation of the first order is of the form

$$\frac{dy}{dx} = \frac{f(x)}{g(y)} \tag{8}$$

For such equations, the variables can be separated by multiplying on both sides of the equation by $g(y)\ dx$; thus, Eq. (8) can be written as

$$g(y)\ dy = f(x)\ dx$$

The following example gives us an equation of this type.

EXAMPLE 3:   The slope of the tangent line to a curve at any point (x, y) on the curve is equal to $3x^2y^2$. Find an equation of the curve if it contains the point $(2, 1)$.

SOLUTION: Because the slope of the tangent line to a curve at any point (x, y) is the value of the derivative at that point, we have

$$\frac{dy}{dx} = 3x^2y^2$$

This is a first-order differential equation, in which the variables can be separated, and we have

$$\frac{dy}{y^2} = 3x^2\ dx$$

Antidifferentiating, we have

$$\int y^{-2}\ dy = \int 3x^2\ dx$$

from which we obtain

$$-\frac{1}{y} = x^3 + C$$

This is an equation of a one-parameter family of curves. To find the particular curve of this family which contains the point $(2, 1)$, we substitute 2 for x and 1 for y, which gives us $-1 = 8 + C$, from which we obtain $C = -9$. Therefore, the required curve has the equation

$$-\frac{1}{y} = x^3 - 9$$

Exercises 6.4

In Exercises 1 through 8, find the complete solution of the given differential equation.

1. $\dfrac{dy}{dx} = 3x^2 + 2x - 7$ 2. $\dfrac{dy}{dx} = (3x + 1)^3$ 3. $\dfrac{dy}{dx} = 3xy^2$

4. $\dfrac{ds}{dt} = 5\sqrt{s}$

5. $\dfrac{dy}{dx} = \dfrac{3x\sqrt{1+y^2}}{y}$

6. $\dfrac{dy}{dx} = \dfrac{\sqrt{x}+x}{\sqrt{y}-y}$

7. $\dfrac{d^2y}{dx^2} = 5x^2 + 1$

8. $\dfrac{d^2y}{dx^2} = \sqrt{2x-3}$

In Exercises 9 through 14, for each of the differential equations find the particular solution determined by the given boundary conditions.

9. $\dfrac{dy}{dx} = x^2 - 2x - 4$; $y = -6$ when $x = 3$

10. $\dfrac{dy}{dx} = (x+1)(x+2)$; $y = -\frac{3}{2}$ when $x = -3$

11. $\dfrac{dx}{y} = \dfrac{4\,dy}{x}$; $y = -2$ when $x = 4$

12. $\dfrac{dy}{dx} = \dfrac{x}{4\sqrt{(1+x^2)^3}}$; $y = 0$ when $x = 1$

13. $\dfrac{d^2y}{dx^2} = 4(1+3x)^2$; $y = -1$ and $y' = -2$ when $x = -1$

14. $\dfrac{d^2y}{dx^2} = \sqrt[3]{3x-1}$; $y = 2$ and $y' = 5$ when $x = 3$

15. The point $(3, 2)$ is on a curve, and at any point (x, y) on the curve the tangent line has a slope equal to $2x - 3$. Find an equation of the curve.

16. The slope of the tangent line at any point (x, y) on a curve is $3\sqrt{x}$. If the point $(9, 4)$ is on the curve, find an equation of the curve.

17. The points $(-1, 3)$ and $(0, 2)$ are on a curve, and at any point (x, y) on the curve $D_x^2 y = 2 - 4x$. Find an equation of the curve.

18. An equation of the tangent line to a curve at the point $(1, 3)$ is $y = x + 2$. If at any point (x, y) on the curve, $D_x^2 y = 6x$, find an equation of the curve.

19. At any point (x, y) on a curve, $D_x^2 y = 1 - x^2$, and an equation of the tangent line to the curve at the point $(1, 1)$ is $y = 2 - x$. Find an equation of the curve.

20. At any point (x, y) on a curve, $D_x^3 y = 2$, and $(1, 3)$ is a point of inflection at which the slope of the inflectional tangent is -2. Find an equation of the curve.

21. The equation $x^2 = 4ay$ represents a one-parameter family of parabolas. Find an equation of another one-parameter family of curves such that at any point (x, y) there is a curve of each family through it and the tangent lines to the two curves at this point are perpendicular. (HINT: First show that the slope of the tangent line at any point (x, y), not on the y axis, of the parabola of the given family through that point is $2y/x$.)

22. Solve Exercise 21 if the given one-parameter family of curves has the equation $x^3 + y^3 = a^3$.

6.5 ANTIDIFFERENTIATION AND RECTILINEAR MOTION

We learned in Secs. 3.2 and 3.11 that in considering the motion of a particle along a straight line, when an equation of motion, $s = f(t)$, is given, then the instantaneous velocity and the instantaneous acceleration can be determined from the equations

$$v = D_t s = f'(t)$$

and

$$a = D_t^2 s = D_t v = f''(t)$$

Hence, if we are given v or a as a function of t, as well as some boundary conditions, it is possible to determine the equation of motion by antidifferentiation. This is illustrated in the following example.

EXAMPLE 1: A particle is moving on a straight line; s is the number of feet in the directed distance of the particle from the origin at t sec of time, v is the number of ft/sec in the velocity of the particle at t sec, and a is the number of ft/sec² in the acceleration of the particle at t sec. If $a = 2t - 1$ and $v = 3$, and $s = 4$ when $t = 1$, express v and s as functions of t.

SOLUTION: Because $a = D_t v$, we have

$$\frac{dv}{dt} = 2t - 1$$

which, expressed in differential form, gives

$$dv = (2t - 1)\ dt$$

Antidifferentiating, we have

$$\int dv = \int (2t - 1)\ dt$$

from which we get

$$v = t^2 - t + C_1 \tag{1}$$

Substituting $v = 3$ and $t = 1$, we have

$$3 = 1 - 1 + C_1$$

and hence $C_1 = 3$. Therefore, substituting this value of C_1 into Eq. (1), we obtain

$$v = t^2 - t + 3 \tag{2}$$

which expresses v as a function of t.

Now, letting $v = D_t s$ in Eq. (2), we have

$$\frac{ds}{dt} = t^2 - t + 3$$

and writing this in differential form gives

$$ds = (t^2 - t + 3)\ dt$$

Antidifferentiating, we have

$$\int ds = \int (t^2 - t + 3)\ dt$$

$$s = \tfrac{1}{3}t^3 - \tfrac{1}{2}t^2 + 3t + C_2 \tag{3}$$

Letting $s = 4$ and $t = 1$ in Eq. (3) and solving for C_2, we obtain $C_2 = \tfrac{7}{6}$. Therefore, by substituting $\tfrac{7}{6}$ for C_2 in Eq. (3) we have s expressed as a function of t, which is

$$s = \tfrac{1}{3}t^3 - \tfrac{1}{2}t^2 + 3t + \tfrac{7}{6}$$

If an object is moving freely in a vertical line and is being pulled toward the earth by a force of gravity, the acceleration of *gravity*, denoted by g ft/sec², varies with the distance of the object from the center of the earth. However, for small changes of distances the acceleration of gravity is almost constant, and an approximate value of g, if the object is near sea level, is 32.

EXAMPLE 2: A stone is thrown vertically upward from the ground with an initial velocity of 128 ft/sec. If the only force considered is that attributed to the acceleration of gravity, find how high the stone will rise and the speed with which it will strike the ground. Also, find how long it will take for the stone to strike the ground.

Figure 6.5.1

Table 6.5.1

t	0		$\bar{t}$
s	0	$\bar{s}$	0
v	128	0	$\bar{v}$

SOLUTION: The motion of the stone is illustrated in Fig. 6.5.1. The positive direction is taken as upward.

Let t = the number of seconds in the time that has elapsed since the stone was thrown;

s = the number of feet in the distance of the stone from the ground at t sec of time;

v = the number of feet per second in the velocity of the stone at t sec of time;

$|v|$ = the number of feet per second in the speed of the stone at t sec of time.

The stone will be at its highest point when the velocity is zero. Let $\bar{s}$ be the particular value of s when $v = 0$. When the stone strikes the ground, $s = 0$. Let $\bar{t}$ and $\bar{v}$ be the particular values of t and v when $s = 0$, and $t \neq 0$. Table 6.5.1 is a table of boundary conditions for this problem.

The positive direction of the stone from the starting point is taken as upward. Because the only acceleration is due to gravity, which is in the downward direction, the acceleration has a constant value of -32 ft/sec². Because the acceleration is given by the derivative of v with respect to t, we have

$$\frac{dv}{dt} = -32$$

Writing this in differential form, we have

$$dv = -32 \, dt$$

Antidifferentiating, we have

$$\int dv = \int -32 \, dt$$

from which we obtain

$$v = -32t + C_1$$

Because $v = 128$ when $t = 0$, we substitute these values in the above and get $C_1 = 128$. Therefore, we have

$$v = -32t + 128 \tag{4}$$

Because v is the derivative of s with respect to t, then $v = ds/dt$, and so

$$\frac{ds}{dt} = -32t + 128$$

which in differential form is

$$ds = (-32t + 128) \, dt$$

Antidifferentiating gives

$$\int ds = \int (-32t + 128) \, dt$$

from which we obtain

$$s = -16t^2 + 128t + C_2$$

Because $s = 0$ when $t = 0$, we get $C_2 = 0$, and substituting 0 for C_2 in the above equation gives

$$s = -16t^2 + 128t \tag{5}$$

Substituting $\bar{t}$ for t and 0 for s, we get

$$0 = -16\bar{t}(\bar{t} - 8)$$

from which we obtain $\bar{t} = 0$ and $\bar{t} = 8$. However, the value 0 occurs when the stone is thrown; so we conclude that it takes 8 sec for the stone to strike the ground.

To obtain $\bar{v}$, substitute 8 for t and $\bar{v}$ for v in Eq. (4), which gives $\bar{v} = (-32)(8) + 128$, from which we obtain $\bar{v} = -128$. So $|\bar{v}| = 128$. Therefore, the stone strikes the ground with a speed of 128 ft/sec.

To find $\bar{s}$, we first find the value of t for which v is 0. From Eq. (4), we obtain $t = 4$ when $v = 0$. In Eq. (5) we substitute 4 for t and $\bar{s}$ for s and obtain $\bar{s} = 256$. Thus, the stone will rise 256 ft.

Exercises 6.5

In Exercises 1 through 4, a particle is moving on a straight line, s ft is the directed distance of the particle from the origin at t sec of time, v ft/sec is the velocity of the particle at t sec, and a ft/sec^2 is the acceleration of the particle at t sec.

1. $a = 5 - 2t$; $v = 2$ and $s = 0$ when $t = 0$. Express v and s in terms of t.

2. $a = 3t - t^2$; $v = \frac{7}{6}$ and $s = 1$ when $t = 1$. Express v and s in terms of t.

3. $a = 800$; $v = 20$ when $s = 1$. Find an equation involving v and s. $\left(\text{HINT: } a = \dfrac{dv}{dt} = \dfrac{dv}{ds} \dfrac{ds}{dt} = v \dfrac{dv}{ds} \right)$

4. $a = 2s + 1$; $v = 2$ when $s = 1$. Find an equation involving v and s. (HINT: See Hint for Exercise 3.)

In Exercises 5 through 10, the only force considered is that due to the acceleration of gravity, which we take as 32 ft/sec^2 in the downward direction.

5. A stone is thrown vertically upward from the ground with an initial velocity of 20 ft/sec. How long will it take the stone to strike the ground, and with what speed will it strike? How long will the stone be going upward, and how high will it go?

6. A ball is dropped from the top of the Washington monument, which is 555 ft high. How long will it take the ball to reach the ground, and with what speed will it strike the ground?

7. A man in a balloon drops his binoculars when it is 150 ft above the ground and rising at the rate of 10 ft/sec. How long will it take the binoculars to strike the ground, and what is their speed on impact?

8. A stone is thrown vertically upward from the top of a house 60 ft above the ground with an initial velocity of 40 ft/sec. At what time will the stone reach its greatest height, and what is its greatest height? How long will it take the stone to pass the top of the house on its way down, and what is its velocity at that instant? How long will it take the stone to strike the ground, and with what velocity does it strike the ground?

9. A ball is thrown vertically upward with an initial velocity of 40 ft/sec from a point 20 ft above the ground. If v ft/sec is the velocity of the ball when it is s ft from the starting point, express v in terms of s. What is the velocity of the ball when it is 36 ft from the ground and rising? (HINT: See Hint for Exercise 3.)

10. If a ball is rolled across level ground with an initial velocity of 20 ft/sec and if the speed of the ball is decreasing at the rate of 6 ft/sec² due to friction, how far will the ball roll?

11. If the driver of an automobile wishes to increase his speed from 20 mi/hr to 50 mi/hr while traveling a distance of 528 ft, what constant acceleration should he maintain?

12. What constant acceleration (negative) will enable a driver to decrease his speed from 60 mi/hr to 20 mi/hr while traveling a distance of 300 ft?

13. If the brakes are applied on a car traveling 50 mi/hr and the brakes can give the car a constant negative acceleration of 20 ft/sec², how long will it take the car to come to a stop? How far will the car travel before stopping?

14. A ball started upward from the bottom of an inclined plane with an initial velocity of 6 ft/sec. If there is a downward acceleration of 4 ft/sec², how far up the plane will the ball go before rolling down?

15. If the brakes on a car can give the car a constant negative acceleration of 20 ft/sec², what is the greatest speed it may be going if it is necessary to be able to stop the car within 80 ft after the brake is applied?

6.6 APPLICATIONS OF ANTIDIFFERENTIATION IN ECONOMICS

In Sec. 5.6 we learned that the marginal cost function and the marginal revenue function are the first derivatives of the total cost function and the total revenue function, respectively. Hence, if the marginal cost function and the marginal revenue function are known, the total cost function and the total revenue function are obtained from them by antidifferentiation.

In finding the total cost function from the marginal cost function, the arbitrary constant can be evaluated if we know either the fixed cost (i.e., the cost when no units are produced) or the cost of production of a specific number of units of the commodity. Because it is generally true that the total revenue is zero when the number of units produced is zero, this fact may be used to evaluate the arbitrary constant when finding the total revenue function from the marginal revenue function.

EXAMPLE 1: If the marginal revenue is given by $27 - 12x + x^2$, find the total revenue function and the demand equation. Also determine the permissible values of x. Draw sketches of the demand curve, the total revenue curve, and the marginal revenue curve on the same set of axes.

SOLUTION: If R is the total revenue function, the marginal revenue function is R', and

$$R'(x) = 27 - 12x + x^2$$

Thus,

$$R(x) = \int (27 - 12x + x^2) \, dx$$

$$= 27x - 6x^2 + \tfrac{1}{3}x^3 + C$$

Figure 6.6.1

Because $R(0) = 0$, we get $C = 0$. Hence,

$$R(x) = 27x - 6x^2 + \tfrac{1}{3}x^3$$

If P is the price function, $R(x) = xP(x)$, and so

$$P(x) = 27 - 6x + \tfrac{1}{3}x^2$$

If we let p dollars be the price of one unit of the commodity when x units are demanded, and because $p = P(x)$, the demand equation is

$$3p = 81 - 18x + x^2$$

To determine the permissible values of x, we use the facts that $x \geq 0$, $p \geq 0$, and P is a decreasing function. Because

$$P'(x) = -6 + \tfrac{2}{3}x$$

P is decreasing when $x < 9$ (i.e., when $P'(x) < 0$). Also, when $x = 9$, $p = 0$, and so the permissible values of x are the numbers in the closed interval $[0, 9]$. The required sketches are shown in Fig. 6.6.1.

EXAMPLE 2:   The marginal cost function C' is given by $C'(x) = 4x - 8$. If the cost of producing 5 units is \$20, find the total cost function. Determine the permissible values of x and draw sketches of the total cost curve and the marginal cost curve on the same set of axes.

SOLUTION: The marginal cost must be nonnegative. Hence, $4x - 8 \geq 0$, and therefore the permissible values of x are $x \geq 2$.

$$C'(x) = 4x - 8$$

Therefore,

$$C(x) = \int (4x - 8)\ dx$$

$$= 2x^2 - 8x + k$$

Because $C(5) = 20$, we get $k = 10$. Hence,

$$C(x) = 2x^2 - 8x + 10 \qquad (x \geq 2)$$

The required sketches are shown in Fig. 6.6.2.

Figure 6.6.2

EXAMPLE 3:   After experimentation, a certain manufacturer determined that if x units of a particular commodity are produced per week, the marginal cost is given by $0.3x - 11$, where the production cost is in dollars. If the selling price of the commodity is fixed at $19 per unit, and the fixed cost is $100 per week, find the maximum weekly profit that can be obtained.

SOLUTION: Let $C(x) =$ the number of dollars in the total production cost of x units;

$R(x) =$ the number of dollars in the total revenue obtained by selling x units;

$S(x) =$ the number of dollars in the profit obtained by selling x units.

Because x units are sold at $19 per unit, we have

$$R(x) = 19x$$

The marginal revenue then is given by

$$R'(x) = 19$$

C' is the marginal cost function, and we are given that

$$C'(x) = 0.3x - 11$$

The profit will be a maximum when marginal revenue equals marginal cost (see Sec. 5.6). Equating $R'(x)$ and $C'(x)$, we get $x = 100$. So 100 units should be produced each week for maximum profit.

$$C(x) = \int (0.3x - 11) \, dx$$

$$= 0.15x^2 - 11x + k$$

Because the fixed cost is $100, $C(0) = 100$, and hence $k = 100$. Therefore,

$$C(x) = 0.15x^2 - 11x + 100$$

Setting $S(x) = R(x) - C(x)$, we have

$$S(x) = 19x - (0.15x^2 - 11x + 100)$$

$$= -0.15x^2 + 30x - 100$$

Hence, $S(100) = 1400$. Therefore, the maximum weekly profit is $1400, which is obtained if 100 units are produced weekly.

EXAMPLE 4:   A business firm has made an analysis of its production facilities and its personnel. With the present equipment and number of workers, the firm can produce 3000 units per day. It was estimated that without any change in investment, the rate of change of the number of units produced per day with respect to a

SOLUTION: Let $y =$ the number of units produced per day. Then

$$\frac{dy}{dx} = 80 - 6x^{1/2}$$

from which we get

$$dy = (80 - 6x^{1/2}) \, dx$$

Antidifferentiating gives us

$$y = 80x - 4x^{3/2} + C$$

change in the number of additional workers is $80 - 6x^{1/2}$, where x is the number of additional workers. Find the daily production if 25 workers are added to the labor force.

Because $y = 3000$ when $x = 0$, we get $C = 3000$. Hence,

$$y = 80x - 4x^{3/2} + 3000$$

Letting y_{25} be the value of y when $x = 25$, we have

$$y_{25} = 2000 - 500 + 3000$$

$$= 4500$$

Therefore, 4500 units are produced per day if the labor force is increased by 25 workers.

Exercises 6.6

1. Find an equation of the total revenue curve of a company if its slope at any point is given by $12 - 3x$ and $P(4) = 6$, where P is the price function. Draw sketches of the total revenue curve and the demand curve on the same set of axes.

2. The rate of change of the slope of the total cost curve of a particular company is the constant 2, and the total cost curve contains the points (2, 12) and (3, 18). Find the total cost function.

3. Find the demand equation for a commodity for which the marginal revenue function is given by $10/(x + 5)^2 - 4$.

4. The marginal cost function is given by $3/\sqrt{2x + 4}$. If the fixed cost is zero, find the total cost function.

5. The marginal revenue function is given by $16 - 3x^2$. Find the permissible values of x, the total revenue function, and the demand equation. Draw sketches of the demand curve, the total revenue curve, and the marginal revenue curve on the same set of axes.

6. Find the total revenue function, the demand equation, and the permissible values of x if the marginal revenue function is given by $\frac{3}{4}x^2 - 10x + 12$. Also draw sketches of the demand curve, the total revenue curve, and the marginal revenue curve on the same set of axes.

7. The marginal cost function is given by $3x^2 + 8x + 4$, and the fixed cost is \$6. If $C(x)$ dollars is the total cost of x units, find the total cost function, and draw sketches of the total cost curve and the marginal cost curve on the same set of axes.

8. The marginal cost function C' is defined by $C'(x) = 6x$, where $C(x)$ is the number of hundreds of dollars in the total cost of x hundred units of a certain commodity. If the cost of 200 units is \$2000, find the total cost function and the fixed cost. Draw sketches of the total cost curve and the marginal cost curve on the same set of axes.

9. The cost of a certain piece of machinery is \$700 and its value depreciates with time according to the formula $D_t V = -500(t + 1)^{-2}$ where V dollars is its value t years after its purchase. What is its value three years after its purchase?

10. Suppose that a particular company estimates its growth in income from sales by the formula $D_t S = 2(t - 1)^{2/3}$, where S millions of dollars is the gross income from sales t years hence. If the gross income from the current year's sales is \$8 million, what should be the expected gross income from sales two years from now?

Review Exercises (Chapter 6)

In Exercises 1 through 6, find the most general antiderivative.

1. $\int \dfrac{\sqrt[4]{x^3}}{3x^2} \, dx$

2. $\int \left(\sqrt[3]{t} - \dfrac{1}{\sqrt[3]{t}} \right) dt$

3. $\int 5x\sqrt{2 + 3x^2} \, dx$

4. $\int (x^3 + x)\sqrt{x^2 + 3} \, dx$

5. $\int \sqrt{4x + 3}(x^2 + 1) \, dx$

6. $\int \left(\dfrac{x^3 + 2}{x^3} \right) \sqrt{x - \dfrac{1}{x^2}} \, dx$

In Exercises 7 through 10, find the complete solution of the given differential equation.

7. $x^2y \dfrac{dy}{dx} = (y^2 - 1)^2$

8. $\dfrac{dy}{dx} = \dfrac{x+1}{\sqrt{x}}$

9. $y^2\, dx + y^2\, dy = dy$

10. $\dfrac{d^2y}{dx^2} = 12x^2 - 30x$

11. If $y = 80x - 16x^2$, find the difference $\Delta y - dy$ if (a) $x = 2$, $\Delta x = 0.1$; (b) $x = 4$, $\Delta x = -0.2$.

12. Use differentials to find an approximate value of $\sqrt[3]{126}$.

13. The slope of the tangent line at any point (x, y) on a curve is $10 - 4x$ and the point $(1, -1)$ is on the curve. Find an equation of the curve.

14. At any point (x, y) on a curve $D_x^2 y = 4 - x^2$ and an equation of the tangent line to the curve at the point $(1, -1)$ is $2x - 3y = 3$. Find an equation of the curve.

15. If $x^3 + y^3 - 3xy^2 + 1 = 0$, find dy at the point $(1, 1)$ if $dx = 0.1$.

16. Find dy/dt if $y = x^3 - 2x + 1$ and $x^3 + t^3 - 3t = 0$.

17. Find dy/dt if $8x^3 + 27y^3 - 4xy = 0$ and $t^3 + t^2x - x^3 = 4$.

18. Evaluate $\int (x^4)^6 4x^3\, dx$ as $\int u^6\, du$ and as $\int 4x^{27}\, dx$ and compare the results.

19. Evaluate $\int (x^3 + 1)^2 x^2\, dx$ by two methods: (a) Make the substitution $u = x^3 + 1$; (b) first expand $(x^3 + 1)^2$. Compare the results and explain the difference in the appearance of the answers obtained in (a) and (b).

20. Find the particular solution of the differential equation $x^2\, dy = y^3\, dx$ for which $y = 1$ when $x = 4$.

21. Find the particular solution of the differential equation $D_x^2 y = \sqrt{x + 4}$ for which $y = 3$ and $y' = 2$ when $x = 4$.

22. A ball is thrown vertically upward from the top of a house 64 ft above the ground, and the initial velocity is 48 ft/sec. How long will it take the ball to reach its greatest height, and what is its greatest height? How long will it take the ball to strike the ground and with what velocity does it strike the ground?

23. Suppose the ball in Exercise 22 is thrown downward with an initial velocity of 48 ft/sec. How long will it take the ball to strike the ground and with what velocity does it strike the ground?

24. Suppose the ball in Exercise 22 is dropped from the top of the house. Determine how long it takes for the ball to strike the ground and the velocity when it strikes the ground.

25. Neglecting air resistance, if an object is dropped from an airplane at a height of 30,000 ft above the ocean, how long would it take the object to strike the water?

26. Suppose a bullet is fired directly downward from the airplane in Exercise 25 with a muzzle velocity of 2500 ft/sec. If air resistance is neglected, how long would it take the bullet to reach the ocean?

27. A container in the form of a cube having a volume of 1000 in.^{3} is to be made by using 6 equal squares of material costing 2 cents per square inch. How accurately must the side of each square be made so that the total cost of the material shall be correct to within 50 cents?

28. The measure of the radius of a right-circular cone is $\frac{4}{3}$ times the measure of the altitude. How accurately must the altitude be measured if the error in the computed volume is not to exceed 3%?

29. If t sec is the time for one complete swing of a simple pendulum of length l ft, then $4\pi^2 l = gt^2$, where $g = 32.2$. What is the effect upon the time if an error of 0.01 ft is made in measuring the length of the pendulum?

30. An automobile traveling at a constant speed of 60 mi/hr along a straight highway fails to stop at a stop sign. If 3 sec later a highway patrol car starts from rest from the stop sign and maintains a constant acceleration of 8 ft/sec^2, how long will it take the patrol car to overtake the automobile, and how far from the stop sign will this occur? Also determine the speed of the patrol car when it overtakes the automobile.

31. If $f(x) = x + |x - 1|$, and

    $$F(x) = \begin{cases} x & \text{if } x < 1 \\ x^2 - x + 1 & \text{if } x \geq 1 \end{cases}$$

    show that F is an antiderivative of f on $(-\infty, +\infty)$.

32. Let f and g be two functions such that for all x in $(-\infty, +\infty)$, $f'(x) = g(x)$ and $g'(x) = -f(x)$. Furthermore, suppose that $f(0) = 0$ and $g(0) = 1$. Prove that $[f(x)]^2 + [g(x)]^2 = 1$. (HINT: Consider the functions F and G where $F(x) = [f(x)]^2$ and $G(x) = -[g(x)]^2$ and show that $F'(x) = G'(x)$ for all x.)

33. The marginal revenue function is given by $ab/(x + b)^2 - c$. Find the total revenue function and the demand equation.

34. A company has determined that the marginal cost function for the production of a particular commodity is given by

    $$C'(x) = 125 + 10x - \frac{x^2}{9}$$

    where $C(x)$ dollars is the cost of producing x units of the commodity. If the fixed cost is $250, what is the cost of producing 15 units?

7

The definite integral

7.1 THE SIGMA NOTATION

In this chapter we are concerned with the sums of many terms, and so a notation called the sigma notation is introduced to facilitate writing these sums. This notation involves the use of the symbol Σ, the capital sigma of the Greek alphabet, which corresponds to our letter S. Some examples of the sigma notation are given in the following illustration.

● ILLUSTRATION 1:

$$\sum_{i=1}^{5} i^2 = 1^2 + 2^2 + 3^2 + 4^2 + 5^2$$

$$\sum_{i=-2}^{2} (3i + 2) = [3(-2) + 2] + [3(-1) + 2] + [3 \cdot 0 + 2]$$
$$+ [3 \cdot 1 + 2] + [3 \cdot 2 + 2]$$

$$= (-4) + (-1) + 2 + 5 + 8$$

$$\sum_{j=1}^{n} j^3 = 1^3 + 2^3 + 3^3 + \cdots + n^3$$

$$\sum_{k=3}^{8} \frac{1}{k} = \frac{1}{3} + \frac{1}{4} + \frac{1}{5} + \frac{1}{6} + \frac{1}{7} + \frac{1}{8}$$

●

We have, in general,

$$\sum_{i=m}^{n} F(i) = F(m) + F(m + 1) + F(m + 2) + \cdots + F(n) \tag{1}$$

where m and n are integers, and $m \le n$.

The right side of formula (1) consists of the sum of $(n - m + 1)$ terms, the first of which is obtained by replacing i by m in $F(i)$, the second by replacing i by $(m + 1)$ in $F(i)$, and so on, until the last term is obtained by replacing i by n in $F(i)$.

The number m is called the *lower limit* of the sum, and n is called the *upper limit*. The symbol i is called the *index of summation*. It is a "dummy" symbol because any other letter can be used. For example,

$$\sum_{k=3}^{5} k^2 = 3^2 + 4^2 + 5^2$$

is equivalent to

$$\sum_{i=3}^{5} i^2 = 3^2 + 4^2 + 5^2$$

● ILLUSTRATION 2: By using the formula of Eq. (1), we have

$$\sum_{i=3}^{6} \frac{i^2}{i + 1} = \frac{3^2}{3 + 1} + \frac{4^2}{4 + 1} + \frac{5^2}{5 + 1} + \frac{6^2}{6 + 1}$$

●

Sometimes the terms of a sum involve subscripts, as shown in the next illustration.

● ILLUSTRATION 3:

$$\sum_{i=1}^{n} A_i = A_1 + A_2 + \cdots + A_n$$

$$\sum_{k=4}^{9} kb_k = 4b_4 + 5b_5 + 6b_6 + 7b_7 + 8b_8 + 9b_9$$

$$\sum_{i=1}^{5} f(x_i)\, \Delta x = f(x_1)\, \Delta x + f(x_2)\, \Delta x + f(x_3)\, \Delta x + f(x_4)\, \Delta x + f(x_5)\, \Delta x \quad ●$$

The following properties of the sigma notation are useful, and they are easily proved.

7.1.1 Property 1 $\displaystyle\sum_{i=1}^{n} c = cn$ where c is any constant

The proof is left as an exercise (see Exercise 9).

7.1.2 Property 2 $\displaystyle\sum_{i=1}^{n} c \cdot F(i) = c \sum_{i=1}^{n} F(i)$ where c is any constant

PROOF:

$$\sum_{i=1}^{n} c \cdot F(i) = c \cdot F(1) + c \cdot F(2) + c \cdot F(3) + \cdots + c \cdot F(n)$$

$$= c[F(1) + F(2) + F(3) + \cdots + F(n)]$$

$$= c \sum_{i=1}^{n} F(i) \qquad\qquad ■$$

7.1.3 Property 3 $\displaystyle\sum_{i=1}^{n} [F(i) + G(i)] = \sum_{i=1}^{n} F(i) + \sum_{i=1}^{n} G(i)$

The proof is left as an exercise (see Exercise 10). Property 3 can be extended to the sum of any number of functions.

7.1.4 Property 4 $\displaystyle\sum_{i=1}^{n} [F(i) - F(i-1)] = F(n) - F(0)$

PROOF:

$$\sum_{i=1}^{n} [F(i) - F(i-1)] = [F(1) - F(0)] + [F(2) - F(1)] + [F(3) - F(2)] + \cdots$$

$$+ [F(n-1) - F(n-2)] + [F(n) - F(n-1)]$$

$$= -F(0) + [F(1) - F(1)] + [F(2) - F(2)]$$
$$+ \cdots + [F(n-1) - F(n-1)] + F(n)$$
$$= -F(0) + 0 + 0 + \cdots + 0 + F(n)$$
$$= F(n) - F(0) \qquad \blacksquare$$

The following formulas, which are numbered for future reference, are also useful.

7.1.5 Formula 1
$$\sum_{i=1}^{n} i = \frac{n(n+1)}{2}$$

7.1.6 Formula 2
$$\sum_{i=1}^{n} i^2 = \frac{n(n+1)(2n+1)}{6}$$

7.1.7 Formula 3
$$\sum_{i=1}^{n} i^3 = \frac{n^2(n+1)^2}{4}$$

7.1.8 Formula 4
$$\sum_{i=1}^{n} i^4 = \frac{n(n+1)(6n^3 + 9n^2 + n - 1)}{30}$$

Formulas 1 through 4 can be proved with or without using mathematical induction. The next illustration shows how Formula 1 can be proved without using mathematical induction. The proof of Formula 1 by mathematical induction is left as an exercise (see Exercise 11).

● ILLUSTRATION 4: We prove Formula 1.

$$\sum_{i=1}^{n} i = 1 + 2 + 3 + \cdots + (n-1) + n$$

and

$$\sum_{i=1}^{n} i = n + (n-1) + (n-2) + \cdots + 2 + 1$$

If we add these two equations term by term, the left side is

$$2 \sum_{i=1}^{n} i$$

and on the right side are n terms, each having the value $(n+1)$. Hence,

$$2 \sum_{i=1}^{n} i = (n+1) + (n+1) + (n+1) + \cdots + (n+1) \qquad n \text{ terms}$$
$$= n(n+1)$$

Therefore,

$$\sum_{i=1}^{n} i = \frac{n(n+1)}{2}$$

●

EXAMPLE 1: Prove Formula 2 by mathematical induction.

SOLUTION: We wish to prove that

$$\sum_{i=1}^{n} i^2 = \frac{n(n+1)(2n+1)}{6}$$

First the formula is verified for $n = 1$. The left side is then $\sum_{i=1}^{1} i^2 = 1$. When $n = 1$, the right side is $[1(1+1)(2+1)]/6 = (1 \cdot 2 \cdot 3)/6 = 1$. Therefore, the formula is true when $n = 1$. Now we assume that the formula is true for $n = k$, where k is any positive integer; and with this assumption we wish to prove that the formula is also true for $n = k + 1$. If the formula is true for $n = k$, we have

$$\sum_{i=1}^{k} i^2 = \frac{k(k+1)(2k+1)}{6} \qquad (2)$$

When $n = k + 1$, we have

$$\sum_{i=1}^{k+1} i^2 = 1^2 + 2^2 + 3^2 + \cdots + k^2 + (k+1)^2$$

$$= \sum_{i=1}^{k} i^2 + (k+1)^2$$

$$= \frac{k(k+1)(2k+1)}{6} + (k+1)^2 \quad \text{(by applying Eq. (2))}$$

$$= \frac{k(k+1)(2k+1) + 6(k+1)^2}{6}$$

$$= \frac{(k+1)[k(2k+1) + 6(k+1)]}{6}$$

$$= \frac{(k+1)(2k^2 + 7k + 6)}{6}$$

$$= \frac{(k+1)(k+2)(2k+3)}{6}$$

$$= \frac{(k+1)[(k+1) + 1][2(k+1) + 1]}{6}$$

Therefore, the formula is true for $n = k + 1$. We have proved that the formula holds for $n = 1$, and we have also proved that when the formula holds for $n = k$, the formula also holds for $n = k + 1$. Therefore, it follows that the formula holds when n is any positive integer.

A proof of Formula 2, without using mathematical induction, is left as an exercise. The proofs of Formulas 3 and 4 are also left as exercises (see Exercises 12 to 16).

EXAMPLE 2: Evaluate

$$\sum_{i=1}^{n} (4^i - 4^{i-1})$$

SOLUTION: From Property 4, where $F(i) = 4^i$, it follows that

$$\sum_{i=1}^{n} (4^i - 4^{i-1}) = 4^n - 4^0$$

$$= 4^n - 1$$

EXAMPLE 3: Evaluate

$$\sum_{i=1}^{n} i(3i - 2)$$

by using Properties 1–4 and Formulas 1–4.

SOLUTION:

$$\sum_{i=1}^{n} i(3i - 2) = \sum_{i=1}^{n} (3i^2 - 2i)$$

$$= \sum_{i=1}^{n} (3i^2) + \sum_{i=1}^{n} (-2i) \quad \text{(by Property 3)}$$

$$= 3 \sum_{i=1}^{n} i^2 - 2 \sum_{i=1}^{n} i \quad \text{(by Property 2)}$$

$$= 3 \cdot \frac{n(n + 1)(2n + 1)}{6} - 2 \cdot \frac{n(n + 1)}{2}$$

$$\text{(by Formulas 2 and 1)}$$

$$= \frac{2n^3 + 3n^2 + n - 2n^2 - 2n}{2}$$

$$= \frac{2n^3 + n^2 - n}{2}$$

Exercises 7.1

In Exercises 1 through 8, find the given sum.

1. $\sum_{i=1}^{6} (3i - 2)$

2. $\sum_{i=1}^{7} (i + 1)^2$

3. $\sum_{i=2}^{5} \frac{i}{i - 1}$

4. $\sum_{j=3}^{6} \frac{2}{j(j - 2)}$

5. $\sum_{i=-2}^{3} 2^i$

6. $\sum_{i=0}^{3} \frac{1}{1 + i^2}$

7. $\sum_{k=1}^{4} \frac{(-1)^{k+1}}{k}$

8. $\sum_{k=-2}^{3} \frac{k}{k + 3}$

9. Prove Property 1 (7.1.1).

10. Prove Property 3 (7.1.3).

11. Prove Formula 1 (7.1.5) by mathematical induction.

12. Prove Formula 2 (7.1.6) without using mathematical induction. (HINT: $i^3 - (i - 1)^3 = 3i^2 - 3i + 1$, so that

$$\sum_{i=1}^{n} [i^3 - (i - 1)^3] = \sum_{i=1}^{n} (3i^2 - 3i + 1)$$

On the left side of the above equation, use Property 4; on the right side, use Properties 1, 2, and 3 and Formula 1.)

13. Prove Formula 3 (7.1.7) without using mathematical induction. (HINT: $i^4 - (i-1)^4 = 4i^3 - 6i^2 + 4i - 1$, and use a method similar to the one for Exercise 12.)

14. Prove Formula 4 (7.1.8) without using mathematical induction (see hints for Exercises 12 and 13 above).

15. Prove Formula 3 (7.1.7) by mathematical induction.

16. Prove Formula 4 (7.1.8) by mathematical induction.

In Exercises 17 through 25, evaluate the indicated sum by using Properties 1 through 4 and Formulas 1 through 4.

17. $\displaystyle\sum_{i=1}^{25} 2i(i-1)$

18. $\displaystyle\sum_{i=1}^{20} 3i(i^2+2)$

19. $\displaystyle\sum_{i=1}^{n} (10^{i+1} - 10^i)$

20. $\displaystyle\sum_{k=1}^{n} (2^{k-1} - 2^k)$

21. $\displaystyle\sum_{k=1}^{100} \left[\frac{1}{k} - \frac{1}{k+1} \right]$

22. $\displaystyle\sum_{i=1}^{40} [\sqrt{2i+1} - \sqrt{2i-1}]$

23. $\displaystyle\sum_{i=1}^{n} 4i^2(i-2)$

24. $\displaystyle\sum_{i=1}^{n} 2i(1+i^2)$

25. $\displaystyle\sum_{k=1}^{n} [(3^{-k} - 3^k)^2 - (3^{k-1} + 3^{-k-1})^2]$

26. Prove: $\displaystyle\sum_{i=-n}^{n} \left[1 - \left(\frac{i}{n}\right)^2 \right]^{1/2} = 2 \sum_{i=1}^{n} \left[1 - \left(\frac{i}{n}\right)^2 \right]^{1/2} + 1$

27. (a) Use Property 4 to show that

$$\sum_{i=1}^{n} [F(i+1) - F(i-1)] = F(n+1) + F(n) - F(1) - F(0)$$

(b) Prove that

$$\sum_{i=1}^{n} [(i+1)^3 - (i-1)^3] = (n+1)^3 + n^3 - 1$$

(c) Prove that

$$\sum_{i=1}^{n} [(i+1)^3 - (i-1)^3] = \sum_{i=1}^{n} (6i^2 + 2) = 2n + 6 \sum_{i=1}^{n} i^2$$

(d) Using the results of parts (b) and (c), prove Formula 2.

28. Use the method of Exercise 27 to prove Formula 3.

29. If $\bar{x} = \dfrac{\displaystyle\sum_{i=1}^{n} x_i}{n}$, prove that $\displaystyle\sum_{i=1}^{n} (x_i - \bar{x})^2 = \sum_{i=1}^{n} x_i^2 - \bar{x} \sum_{i=1}^{n} x_i$

7.2 AREA   We use the word *measure* extensively throughout the book. A measure refers to a number (no units are included). For example, if the area of a triangle is 10 in.², we say that the measure of the area of the triangle is 10. You probably have an intuitive idea of what is meant by the measure of the area of certain geometrical figures; it is a number that in some way

Figure 7.2.1

Figure 7.2.2

gives the size of the region enclosed by the figure. The area of a rectangle is the product of its length and width, and the area of a triangle is half the product of the lengths of the base and the altitude.

The area of a polygon can be defined as the sum of the areas of triangles into which it is decomposed, and it can be proved that the area thus obtained is independent of how the polygon is decomposed into triangles (see Fig. 7.2.1). However, how do we define the measure of the area of a region in a plane if the region is bounded by a curve? Are we even certain that such a region has an area?

Let us consider a region R in the plane as shown in Fig. 7.2.2. The region R is bounded by the x axis, the lines $x = a$ and $x = b$, and the curve having the equation $y = f(x)$, where f is a function continuous on the closed interval $[a, b]$. For simplicity, we take $f(x) \geq 0$ for all x in $[a, b]$. We wish to assign a number A to be the measure of the area of R. We use a limiting process similar to the one used in defining the area of a circle: The area of a circle is defined as the limit of the areas of inscribed regular polygons as the number of sides increases without bound. We realize intuitively that, whatever number is chosen to represent A, that number must be at least as great as the measure of the area of any polygonal region contained in R, and must be no greater than the measure of the area of any polygonal region containing R.

We first define a polygonal region contained in R. Divide the closed interval $[a, b]$ into n subintervals. For simplicity, we shall now take each of these subintervals as being of equal length, for instance, Δx. Therefore, $\Delta x = (b - a)/n$. Denote the endpoints of these subintervals by $x_0, x_1, x_2, \ldots, x_{n-1}, x_n$, where $x_0 = a$, $x_1 = a + \Delta x, \ldots, x_i = a + i \Delta x, \ldots,$ $x_{n-1} = a + (n-1) \Delta x, x_n = b$. Let the ith subinterval be denoted by $[x_{i-1}, x_i]$. Because f is continuous on the closed interval $[a, b]$, it is continuous on each closed subinterval. By the extreme-value theorem (4.5.9), there is a number in each subinterval for which f has an absolute minimum value. In the ith subinterval, let this number be c_i, so that $f(c_i)$ is the absolute minimum value of f on the subinterval $[x_{i-1}, x_i]$. Consider n rectangles, each having a width Δx units and an altitude $f(c_i)$ units (see Fig. 7.2.3). Let the sum of the areas of these n rectangles be given by S_n square units; then

$$S_n = f(c_1) \Delta x + f(c_2) \Delta x + \cdots + f(c_i) \Delta x + \cdots + f(c_n) \Delta x$$

or, with the sigma notation,

$$S_n = \sum_{i=1}^{n} f(c_i) \Delta x \tag{1}$$

The summation on the right side of Eq. (1) gives the sum of the measures of the areas of n inscribed rectangles. Thus, however we define A, it must be such that

$$A \geq S_n$$

Figure 7.2.3

Figure 7.2.4

In Fig. 7.2.3 the shaded region has an area of S_n square units. Now, let n increase. Specifically, multiply n by 2; then the number of rectangles is doubled, and the width of each rectangle is halved. This is illustrated in Fig. 7.2.4, showing twice as many rectangles as Fig. 7.2.3. By comparing the two figures, notice that the shaded region in Fig. 7.2.4 appears to approximate the region R more nearly than that of Fig. 7.2.3. So the sum of the measures of the areas of the rectangles in Fig. 7.2.4 is closer to the number we wish to represent the measure of the area of R.

As n increases, the values of S_n found from Eq. (1) increase, and successive values of S_n differ from each other by amounts that become arbitrarily small. This is proved in advanced calculus by a theorem which states that if f is continuous on $[a, b]$, then as n increases without bound, the value of S_n given by (1) approaches a limit. It is this limit that we take as the definition of the measure of the area of region R.

7.2.1 Definition Suppose that the function f is continuous on the closed interval $[a, b]$, with $f(x) \geq 0$ for all x in $[a, b]$, and that R is the region bounded by the curve $y = f(x)$, the x axis, and the lines $x = a$ and $x = b$. Divide the interval $[a, b]$ into n subintervals, each of length $\Delta x = (b - a)/n$, and denote the ith subinterval by $[x_{i-1}, x_i]$. Then if $f(c_i)$ is the absolute minimum function value on the ith subinterval, the measure of the area of region R is given by

$$A = \lim_{n \to +\infty} \sum_{i=1}^{n} f(c_i) \, \Delta x \qquad (2)$$

Equation (2) means that, for any $\epsilon > 0$, there is a number $N > 0$ such that

$$\left| \sum_{i=1}^{n} f(c_i) \, \Delta x - A \right| < \epsilon \qquad \text{whenever } n > N$$

and n is a positive integer.

We could take circumscribed rectangles instead of inscribed rectangles. In this case, we take as the measures of the altitudes of the rectangles the absolute maximum value of f on each subinterval. The existence of an absolute maximum value of f on each subinterval is guaranteed by the extreme-value theorem (4.5.9). The corresponding sums of the measures of the areas of the circumscribed rectangles are at least as great as the measure of the area of the region R, and it can be shown that the limit of these sums as n increases without bound is exactly the same as the limit of the sum of the measures of the areas of the inscribed rectangles. This is also proved in advanced calculus. Thus, we could define the measure of the area of the region R by

$$A = \lim_{n \to +\infty} \sum_{i=1}^{n} f(d_i) \, \Delta x \qquad (3)$$

where $f(d_i)$ is the absolute maximum value of f on $[x_{i-1}, x_i]$.

The measure of the altitude of the rectangle in the ith subinterval actually can be taken as the function value of any number in that subinterval, and the limit of the sum of the measures of the areas of the rectangles is the same no matter what numbers are selected. This is also proved in advanced calculus, and later in this chapter we extend the definition of the measure of the area of a region to be the limit of such a sum.

EXAMPLE 1:   Find the area of the region bounded by the curve $y = x^2$, the x axis, and the line $x = 3$ by taking inscribed rectangles.

Figure 7.2.5

SOLUTION: Figure 7.2.5 shows the region and the ith inscribed rectangle. We apply Definition 7.2.1. Divide the closed interval $[0, 3]$ into n subintervals, each of length Δx: $x_0 = 0$, $x_1 = \Delta x$, $x_2 = 2\,\Delta x$, . . . , $x_i = i\,\Delta x$, . . . , $x_{n-1} = (n-1)\,\Delta x$, $x_n = 3$.

$$\Delta x = \frac{3-0}{n} = \frac{3}{n}$$

The function value $f(x) = x^2$ and because f is increasing on $[0, 3]$, the absolute minimum value of f on the ith subinterval $[x_{i-1}, x_i]$ is $f(x_{i-1})$. Therefore, from Eq. (2)

$$A = \lim_{n \to +\infty} \sum_{i=1}^{n} f(x_{i-1})\,\Delta x \qquad (4)$$

Because $x_{i-1} = (i-1)\,\Delta x$ and $f(x) = x^2$, we have

$$f(x_{i-1}) = [(i-1)\,\Delta x]^2$$

Therefore,

$$\sum_{i=1}^{n} f(x_{i-1})\,\Delta x = \sum_{i=1}^{n} (i-1)^2 (\Delta x)^3$$

But $\Delta x = 3/n$, so that

$$\sum_{i=1}^{n} f(x_{i-1})\,\Delta x = \sum_{i=1}^{n} (i-1)^2 \frac{27}{n^3} = \frac{27}{n^3} \sum_{i=1}^{n} (i-1)^2$$

$$= \frac{27}{n^3} \left[\sum_{i=1}^{n} i^2 - 2\sum_{i=1}^{n} i + \sum_{i=1}^{n} 1 \right]$$

and using Formulas 2 and 1 and Property 1 from Sec. 7.1, we get

$$\sum_{i=1}^{n} f(x_{i-1})\,\Delta x = \frac{27}{n^3} \left[\frac{n(n+1)(2n+1)}{6} - 2 \cdot \frac{n(n+1)}{2} + n \right]$$

$$= \frac{27}{n^3} \cdot \frac{2n^3 + 3n^2 + n - 6n^2 - 6n + 6n}{6}$$

$$= \frac{9}{2} \cdot \frac{2n^2 - 3n + 1}{n^2}$$

Then, from Eq. (4), we have

$$A = \lim_{n \to +\infty} \left[\frac{9}{2} \cdot \frac{2n^2 - 3n + 1}{n^2} \right]$$

$$= \frac{9}{2} \cdot \lim_{n \to +\infty} \left(2 - \frac{3}{n} + \frac{1}{n^2} \right)$$

$$= \tfrac{9}{2}(2 - 0 + 0)$$

$$= 9$$

Therefore, the area of the region is 9 square units.

EXAMPLE 2:   Find the area of the region in Example 1 by taking circumscribed rectangles.

SOLUTION: We take as the measure of the altitude of the ith rectangle the absolute maximum value of f on the ith subinterval $[x_{i-1}, x_i]$ which is $f(x_i)$. From Eq. (3), we have

$$A = \lim_{n \to +\infty} \sum_{i=1}^{n} f(x_i)\, \Delta x \qquad (5)$$

Because $x_i = i\, \Delta x$, then $f(x_i) = (i\, \Delta x)^2$, and so

$$\sum_{i=1}^{n} f(x_i)\, \Delta x = \sum_{i=1}^{n} i^2 (\Delta x)^3 = \frac{27}{n^3} \sum_{i=1}^{n} i^2$$

$$= \frac{27}{n^3} \left[\frac{n(n+1)(2n+1)}{6} \right]$$

$$= \frac{9}{2} \cdot \frac{2n^2 + 3n + 1}{n^2}$$

Therefore, from Eq. (5), we obtain

$$A = \lim_{n \to +\infty} \frac{9}{2} \cdot \left(2 + \frac{3}{n} + \frac{1}{n^2} \right)$$

$$= 9 \quad \text{(as in Example 1)}$$

EXAMPLE 3:   Find the area of the trapezoid which is the region bounded by the line $2x + y = 8$, the x axis, and the lines $x = 1$ and $x = 3$. Take inscribed rectangles.

Figure 7.2.6

SOLUTION: The region and the ith inscribed rectangle are shown in Fig. 7.2.6. The closed interval $[1, 3]$ is divided into n subintervals, each of length Δx; $x_0 = 1$, $x_1 = 1 + \Delta x$, $x_2 = 1 + 2\, \Delta x$, . . . , $x_i = 1 + i\, \Delta x$, . . . , $x_{n-1} = 1 + (n-1)\, \Delta x$, $x_n = 3$.

$$\Delta x = \frac{3-1}{n} = \frac{2}{n}$$

Solving the equation of the line for y, we obtain $y = -2x + 8$. Therefore, $f(x) = -2x + 8$, and because f is decreasing on $[1, 3]$, the absolute minimum value of f on the ith subinterval $[x_{i-1}, x_i]$ is $f(x_i)$. Because $x_i = 1 + i\, \Delta x$ and $f(x) = -2x + 8$, then $f(x_i) = -2(1 + i\, \Delta x) + 8 = 6 - 2i\, \Delta x$. From Eq. (2), we have

$$A = \lim_{n \to +\infty} \sum_{i=1}^{n} f(x_i)\, \Delta x$$

$$= \lim_{n \to +\infty} \sum_{i=1}^{n} (6 - 2i\, \Delta x)\, \Delta x$$

$$= \lim_{n \to +\infty} \sum_{i=1}^{n} [6\, \Delta x - 2i(\Delta x)^2]$$

$$= \lim_{n \to +\infty} \sum_{i=1}^{n} \left[6 \left(\frac{2}{n} \right) - 2i \left(\frac{2}{n} \right)^2 \right]$$

$$= \lim_{n \to +\infty} \left[\frac{12}{n} \sum_{i=1}^{n} 1 - \frac{8}{n^2} \sum_{i=1}^{n} i \right]$$

Using Property 1 (7.1.1) and Formula 1 (7.1.5), we have

$$A = \lim_{n \to +\infty} \left[\frac{12}{n} \cdot n - \frac{8}{n^2} \cdot \frac{n(n+1)}{2} \right]$$

$$= \lim_{n \to +\infty} \left(8 - \frac{4}{n} \right)$$

$$= 8$$

Therefore, the area is 8 square units. Using the formula from plane geometry for the area of a trapezoid, $A = \frac{1}{2}h(b_1 + b_2)$, where h, b_1, and b_2 are, respectively, the number of units in the lengths of the altitude and the two bases, we get $A = \frac{1}{2}(2)(6 + 2) = 8$, which agrees with our result.

Exercises 7.2

In Exercises 1 through 14, use the method of this section to find the area of the given region; use inscribed or circumscribed rectangles as indicated. For each exercise, draw a figure showing the region and the ith rectangle.

1. The region bounded by $y = x^2$, the x axis, and the line $x = 2$; inscribed rectangles.

2. The region of Exercise 1; circumscribed rectangles.

3. The region bounded by $y = 2x$, the x axis, and the lines $x = 1$ and $x = 4$; circumscribed rectangles.

4. The region of Exercise 3; inscribed rectangles.

5. The region above the x axis and to the right of the line $x = 1$ bounded by the x axis, the line $x = 1$, and the curve $y = 4 - x^2$; inscribed rectangles.

6. The region of Exercise 5; circumscribed rectangles.

7. The region lying to the left of the line $x = 1$ bounded by the curve and lines of Exercise 5; circumscribed rectangles.

8. The region of Exercise 7; inscribed rectangles.

9. The region bounded by $y = 3x^4$, the x axis, and the line $x = 1$; inscribed rectangles.

10. The region of Exercise 9; circumscribed rectangles.

11. The region bounded by $y = x^3$, the x axis, and the lines $x = -1$ and $x = 2$; inscribed rectangles.

12. The region of Exercise 11; circumscribed rectangles.

13. The region bounded by $y = mx$, with $m > 0$, the x axis, and the lines $x = a$ and $x = b$, with $b > a > 0$; circumscribed rectangles.

14. The region of Exercise 13; inscribed rectangles.

15. Use the method of this section to find the area of an isosceles trapezoid whose bases have measures b_1 and b_2 and whose altitude has measure h.

16. The graph of $y = 4 - |x|$ and the x axis from $x = -4$ to $x = 4$ form a triangle.   Use the method of this section to find the area of this triangle.

In Exercises 17 through 22, find the area of the region by taking as the measure of the altitude of the ith rectangle $f(m_i)$, where m_i is the midpoint of the ith subinterval. (HINT: $m_i = \frac{1}{2}(x_i + x_{i-1})$.)

17. The region of Example 1.

18. The region of Exercise 1.

19. The region of Exercise 3.

20. The region of Exercise 5.

21. The region of Exercise 7.

22. The region of Exercise 9.

7.3 THE DEFINITE INTEGRAL   In the preceding section, the measure of the area of a region was defined as the following limit:

$$\lim_{n \to +\infty} \sum_{i=1}^{n} f(c_i) \, \Delta x \tag{1}$$

To lead up to this definition, we divided the closed interval $[a, b]$ into subintervals of equal length and then took c_i as the point in the ith subinterval for which f has an absolute minimum value. We also restricted the function values $f(x)$ to be nonnegative on $[a, b]$ and further required f to be continuous on $[a, b]$.

To define the definite integral, we need to consider a new kind of limiting process, of which the limit given in (1) is a special case. Let f be a function defined on the closed interval $[a, b]$. Divide this interval into n subintervals by choosing *any* $(n - 1)$ intermediate points between a and b. Let $x_0 = a$ and $x_n = b$, and $x_1, x_2, \ldots, x_{n-1}$ be the intermediate points so that

$$x_0 < x_1 < x_2 < \cdots < x_{n-1} < x_n$$

The points $x_0, x_1, x_2, \ldots, x_{n-1}, x_n$ are not necessarily equidistant. Let $\Delta_1 x$ be the length of the first subinterval so that $\Delta_1 x = x_1 - x_0$; let $\Delta_2 x$ be the length of the second subinterval so that $\Delta_2 x = x_2 - x_1$; and so forth, so that the length of the ith subinterval is $\Delta_i x$, and

$$\Delta_i x = x_i - x_{i-1}$$

A set of all such subintervals of the interval $[a, b]$ is called a *partition* of the interval $[a, b]$. Let Δ be such a partition. Figure 7.3.1 illustrates one such partition Δ of $[a, b]$.

Figure 7.3.1

The partition Δ contains n subintervals. One of these subintervals is longest; however, there may be more than one such subinterval. The length of the longest subinterval of the partition Δ, called the *norm* of the partition, is denoted by $\|\Delta\|$.

Choose a point in each subinterval of the partition Δ: Let ξ_1 be the point chosen in $[x_0, x_1]$ so that $x_0 \leq \xi_1 \leq x_1$. Let ξ_2 be the point chosen in

Figure 7.3.2

$[x_1, x_2]$ so that $x_1 \le \xi_2 \le x_2$, and so forth, so that ξ_i is the point chosen in $[x_{i-1}, x_i]$, and $x_{i-1} \le \xi_i \le x_i$. Form the sum

$$f(\xi_1)\,\Delta_1 x + f(\xi_2)\,\Delta_2 x + \cdots + f(\xi_i)\,\Delta_i x + \cdots + f(\xi_n)\,\Delta_n x$$

or

$$\sum_{i=1}^{n} f(\xi_i)\,\Delta_i x$$

Such a sum is called a *Riemann sum,* named for the mathematician Georg Friedrich Bernhard Riemann (1826–1866).

● ILLUSTRATION 1: Suppose $f(x) = 10 - x^2$, with $\frac{1}{4} \le x \le 3$. We will find the Riemann sum for the function f on $[\frac{1}{4}, 3]$ for the partition Δ: $x_0 = \frac{1}{4}$, $x_1 = 1$, $x_2 = 1\frac{1}{2}$, $x_3 = 1\frac{3}{4}$, $x_4 = 2\frac{1}{4}$, $x_5 = 3$, and $\xi_1 = \frac{1}{2}$, $\xi_2 = 1\frac{1}{4}$, $\xi_3 = 1\frac{3}{4}$, $\xi_4 = 2$, $\xi_5 = 2\frac{3}{4}$.

Figure 7.3.2 shows a sketch of the graph of f on $[\frac{1}{4}, 3]$ and the five rectangles, the measures of whose areas are the terms of the Riemann sum.

$$\sum_{i=1}^{5} f(\xi_i)\,\Delta_i x = f(\xi_1)\,\Delta_1 x + f(\xi_2)\,\Delta_2 x + f(\xi_3)\,\Delta_3 x + f(\xi_4)\,\Delta_4 x + f(\xi_5)\,\Delta_5 x$$

$$= f(\tfrac{1}{2})(1 - \tfrac{1}{4}) + f(\tfrac{5}{4})(1\tfrac{1}{2} - 1) + f(\tfrac{7}{4})(1\tfrac{3}{4} - 1\tfrac{1}{2})$$

$$\qquad\qquad + f(2)(2\tfrac{1}{4} - 1\tfrac{3}{4}) + f(\tfrac{11}{4})(3 - 2\tfrac{1}{4})$$

$$= (9\tfrac{3}{4})(\tfrac{3}{4}) + (8\tfrac{7}{16})(\tfrac{1}{2}) + (6\tfrac{15}{16})(\tfrac{1}{4}) + (6)(\tfrac{1}{2}) + (2\tfrac{7}{16})(\tfrac{3}{4})$$

$$= 18\tfrac{3}{32}$$

The norm of Δ is the length of the longest subinterval. Hence, $\|\Delta\| = \frac{3}{4}$.   ●

Because the function values $f(x)$ are not restricted to nonnegative values, some of the $f(\xi_i)$ could be negative. In such a case, the geometric interpretation of the Riemann sum would be the sum of the measures of the areas of the rectangles lying above the x axis plus the negatives of the measures of the areas of the rectangles lying below the x axis. This situation is illustrated in Fig. 7.3.3. Here

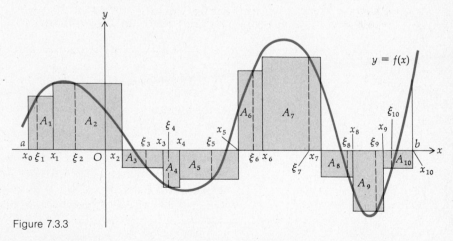

Figure 7.3.3

$$\sum_{i=1}^{10} f(\xi_i)\,\Delta_i x = A_1 + A_2 - A_3 - A_4 - A_5 + A_6 + A_7 - A_8 - A_9 - A_{10}$$

because $f(\xi_3)$, $f(\xi_4)$, $f(\xi_5)$, $f(\xi_8)$, $f(\xi_9)$, and $f(\xi_{10})$ are negative numbers.

We are now in a position to define what is meant by a function f being "integrable" on the closed interval $[a, b]$.

7.3.1 Definition   Let f be a function whose domain includes the closed interval $[a, b]$. Then f is said to be *integrable* on $[a, b]$ if there is a number L satisfying the condition that, for every $\epsilon > 0$, there exists a $\delta > 0$ such that

$$\left| \sum_{i=1}^{n} f(\xi_i)\,\Delta_i x - L \right| < \epsilon$$

for every partition Δ for which $\|\Delta\| < \delta$, and for any ξ_i in the closed interval $[x_{i-1}, x_i]$, $i = 1, 2, \ldots, n$.

In words, Definition 7.3.1 states that, for a given function f defined on the closed interval $[a, b]$, we can make the values of the Riemann sums as close to L as we please by taking the norms $\|\Delta\|$ of all partitions Δ of $[a, b]$ sufficiently small for all possible choices of the numbers ξ_i for which $x_{i-1} \leq \xi_i \leq x_i$. If Definition 7.3.1 holds, we write

$$\lim_{\|\Delta\| \to 0} \sum_{i=1}^{n} f(\xi_i)\,\Delta_i x = L \tag{2}$$

The above limiting process is different from that discussed in Chapter 2. From Definition 7.3.1, the number L in (2) exists if for every $\epsilon > 0$ there exists a $\delta > 0$ such that

$$\left| \sum_{i=1}^{n} f(\xi_i)\,\Delta_i x - L \right| < \epsilon$$

for every partition Δ for which $\|\Delta\| < \delta$, and for any ξ_i in the closed interval $[x_{i-1}, x_i]$, $i = 1, 2, \ldots, n$.

In Definition 2.1.1 we had the following:

$$\lim_{x \to a} f(x) = L \tag{3}$$

if for every $\epsilon > 0$ there exists a $\delta > 0$ such that

$$|f(x) - L| < \epsilon \qquad \text{whenever } 0 < |x - a| < \delta$$

In limiting process (2), for a particular $\delta > 0$ there are infinitely many partitions Δ having norm $\|\Delta\| < \delta$. This is analogous to the fact that in limiting process (3), for a given $\delta > 0$ there are infinitely many values of x for which $0 < |x - a| < \delta$. However, in limiting process (2), for each partition

Δ there are infinitely many choices of ξ_i. It is in this respect that the two limiting processes differ.

In Chapter 2 (Theorem 2.1.2) we showed that if the number L in limiting process (3) exists, it is unique. In a similar manner we can show that if there is a number L satisfying Definition 7.3.1, then it is unique. Now we can define the "definite integral."

7.3.2 Definition   If f is a function defined on the closed interval $[a, b]$, then the *definite integral* of f from a to b, denoted by $\int_a^b f(x) \, dx$, is given by

$$\int_a^b f(x) \, dx = \lim_{||\Delta|| \to 0} \sum_{i=1}^n f(\xi_i) \, \Delta_i x \qquad (4)$$

if the limit exists.

Note that the statement "the function f is integrable on the closed interval $[a, b]$" is synonymous with the statement "the definite integral of f from a to b exists."

In the notation for the definite integral $\int_a^b f(x) \, dx$, $f(x)$ is called the *integrand*, a is called the *lower limit*, and b is called the *upper limit*. The symbol

$$\int$$

is called an *integral sign*. The integral sign resembles a capital S, which is appropriate because the definite integral is the limit of a sum. It is the same symbol we used in Chapter 6 to indicate the operation of antidifferentiation. The reason for the common symbol is that a theorem (7.6.2), called the fundamental theorem of the calculus, enables us to evaluate a definite integral by finding an antiderivative (also called an *indefinite integral*).

A question that now arises is as follows: Under what conditions does a number L satisfying Definition 7.3.1 exist; that is, under what conditions is a function f integrable? An answer to this question is given by the following theorem.

7.3.3 Theorem   If a function f is continuous on the closed interval $[a, b]$, then f is integrable on $[a, b]$.

The proof of this theorem is beyond the scope of this book and is given in advanced calculus texts. The condition that f is continuous on $[a, b]$, while being sufficient to guarantee that f is integrable on $[a, b]$, is not a necessary condition for the existence of $\int_a^b f(x) \, dx$. That is, if f is continuous on $[a, b]$, then Theorem 7.3.3 assures us that $\int_a^b f(x) \, dx$ exists; however, it is possible for the integral to exist even if the function is discontinuous at some numbers in $[a, b]$. The following example gives a function which is discontinuous and yet integrable on a closed interval.

EXAMPLE 1:   Let f be the function defined by

$$f(x) = \begin{cases} 0 & \text{if } x \neq 0 \\ 1 & \text{if } x = 0 \end{cases}$$

Let $[a, b]$ be any interval such that $a < 0 < b$. Show that f is discontinuous on $[a, b]$ and yet integrable on $[a, b]$.

SOLUTION: Because $\lim\limits_{x \to 0} f(x) = 0 \neq f(0)$, f is discontinuous at 0 and hence discontinuous on $[a, b]$.

To prove that f is integrable on $[a, b]$ we show that Definition 7.3.1 is satisfied. Consider the Riemann sum

$$\sum_{i=1}^{n} f(\xi_i) \, \Delta_i x$$

If none of the numbers $\xi_1, \xi_2, \ldots, \xi_n$ is zero, then the Riemann sum is zero. Suppose that $\xi_j = 0$. Then

$$\sum_{i=1}^{n} f(\xi_i) \, \Delta_i x = 1 \cdot \Delta_j x$$

In either case

$$\left| \sum_{i=1}^{n} f(\xi_i) \, \Delta_i x \right| \leq \|\Delta\|$$

Hence,

$$\left| \sum_{i=1}^{n} f(\xi_i) \, \Delta_i x - 0 \right| < \epsilon \qquad \text{whenever } \|\Delta\| < \epsilon$$

Comparing the above with Definition 7.3.1 where $\delta = \epsilon$ and $L = 0$, we see that f is integrable on $[a, b]$.

In Definition 7.3.2, the closed interval $[a, b]$ is given, and so we assume that $a < b$. To consider the definite integral of a function f from a to b when $a > b$, or when $a = b$, we have the following definitions.

7.3.4 Definition   If $a > b$, then

$$\int_a^b f(x) \, dx = -\int_b^a f(x) \, dx$$

if $\int_b^a f(x) \, dx$ exists.

7.3.5 Definition $\int_a^a f(x) \, dx = 0$ if $f(a)$ exists.

At the beginning of this section, we stated that the limit used in Definition 7.2.1 to define the measure of the area of a region is a special case of the limit used in Definition 7.3.2 to define the definite integral. In the discussion of area, the interval $[a, b]$ was divided into n subintervals of equal length. Such a partition of the interval $[a, b]$ is called a *regular partition*. If Δx is the length of each subinterval in a regular partition, then each $\Delta_i x = \Delta x$, and the norm of the partition is Δx. Making these substitutions in Eq. (4), we have

$$\int_a^b f(x) \, dx = \lim_{\Delta x \to 0} \sum_{i=1}^n f(\xi_i) \, \Delta x \tag{5}$$

Furthermore,

$$\Delta x = \frac{b - a}{n} \tag{6}$$

and

$$n = \frac{b - a}{\Delta x} \tag{7}$$

So from Eq. (6)

$$\lim_{n \to +\infty} \Delta x = 0 \tag{8}$$

and from (7), because $b > a$ and Δx approaches zero through positive values (because $\Delta x > 0$),

$$\lim_{\Delta x \to 0} n = +\infty \tag{9}$$

From limits (8) and (9), we conclude that

$$\Delta x \to 0 \quad \text{is equivalent to} \quad n \to +\infty \tag{10}$$

Thus, we have from Eq. (5) and statement (10),

$$\int_a^b f(x) \, dx = \lim_{n \to +\infty} \sum_{i=1}^n f(\xi_i) \, \Delta x \tag{11}$$

It should be remembered that ξ_i can be any point in the ith subinterval $[x_{i-1}, x_i]$.

In applications of the definite integral, regular partitions are often used; therefore, formulas (5) and (11) are especially important.

Comparing the limit used in Definition 7.2.1, which gives the measure of the area of a region, with the limit on the right side of Eq. (11), we have in the first case,

$$\lim_{n \to +\infty} \sum_{i=1}^n f(c_i) \, \Delta x \tag{12}$$

where $f(c_i)$ is the absolute minimum function value on $[x_{i-1}, x_i]$. In the second case, we have

$$\lim_{n \to +\infty} \sum_{i=1}^{n} f(\xi_i) \, \Delta x \qquad (13)$$

where ξ_i is any number in $[x_{i-1}, x_i]$.

Because the function f is continuous on $[a, b]$, by Theorem 7.3.3, $\int_a^b f(x) \, dx$ exists; therefore, this definite integral is the limit of all Riemann sums of f on $[a, b]$ including those in (12) and (13). Because of this, we redefine the area of a region in a more general way.

Figure 7.3.4

7.3.6 Definition Let the function f be continuous on $[a, b]$ and $f(x) \geq 0$ for all x in $[a, b]$. Let R be the region bounded by the curve $y = f(x)$, the x axis, and the lines $x = a$ and $x = b$. Then the measure of the area of region R is given by

$$A = \lim_{||\Delta|| \to 0} \sum_{i=1}^{n} f(\xi_i) \, \Delta_i x = \int_a^b f(x) \, dx$$

The above definition states that if $f(x) \geq 0$ for all x in $[a, b]$, the definite integral $\int_a^b f(x) \, dx$ can be interpreted geometrically as the measure of the area of the region R shown in Fig. 7.3.4.

Equation (11) can be used to find the exact value of a definite integral as illustrated in the following example.

EXAMPLE 2: Find the exact value of the definite integral

$$\int_1^3 x^2 \, dx$$

Interpret the result geometrically.

SOLUTION: Consider a regular partition of the closed interval $[1, 3]$ into n subintervals. Then $\Delta x = 2/n$.

If we choose ξ_i as the right endpoint of each subinterval, we have

$$\xi_1 = 1 + \frac{2}{n}, \, \xi_2 = 1 + 2\left(\frac{2}{n}\right), \, \xi_3 = 1 + 3\left(\frac{2}{n}\right), \, \ldots, \, \xi_i = 1 + i\left(\frac{2}{n}\right),$$

$$\ldots, \, \xi_n = 1 + n\left(\frac{2}{n}\right)$$

Because $f(x) = x^2$,

$$f(\xi_i) = \left(1 + \frac{2i}{n}\right)^2 = \left(\frac{n + 2i}{n}\right)^2$$

Therefore, by using Eq. (11) and applying properties and formulas from Sec. 7.1, we get

$$\int_1^3 x^2 \, dx = \lim_{n \to +\infty} \sum_{i=1}^{n} \left(\frac{n + 2i}{n}\right)^2 \frac{2}{n}$$

$$= \lim_{n \to +\infty} \frac{2}{n^3} \sum_{i=1}^{n} (n^2 + 4ni + 4i^2)$$

$$= \lim_{n \to +\infty} \frac{2}{n^3} \left[n^2 \sum_{i=1}^{n} 1 + 4n \sum_{i=1}^{n} i + 4 \sum_{i=1}^{n} i^2 \right]$$

$$= \lim_{n \to +\infty} \frac{2}{n^3} \left[n^2 n + 4n \cdot \frac{n(n+1)}{2} + \frac{4n(n+1)(2n+1)}{6} \right]$$

$$= \lim_{n \to +\infty} \frac{2}{n^3} \left[n^3 + 2n^3 + 2n^2 + \frac{2n(2n^2 + 3n + 1)}{3} \right]$$

$$= \lim_{n \to +\infty} \left[6 + \frac{4}{n} + \frac{8n^2 + 12n + 4}{3n^2} \right]$$

$$= \lim_{n \to +\infty} \left[6 + \frac{4}{n} + \frac{8}{3} + \frac{4}{n} + \frac{4}{3n^2} \right]$$

$$= 6 + 0 + \tfrac{8}{3} + 0 + 0$$

$$= 8 \tfrac{2}{3}$$

We interpret the result geometrically. Because $x^2 \geq 0$ for all x in $[1, 3]$, the region bounded by the curve $y = x^2$, the x axis, and the lines $x = 1$ and $x = 3$ has an area of $8 \tfrac{2}{3}$ square units. The region is shown in Fig. 7.3.5.

Figure 7.3.5

Exercises 7.3

In Exercises 1 through 6, find the Riemann sum for the function on the interval, using the given partition Δ and the given values of ξ_i. Draw a sketch of the graph of the function on the given interval, and show the rectangles the measure of whose areas are the terms of the Riemann sum. (See Illustration 1 and Fig. 7.3.2.)

1. $f(x) = x^2$, $0 \leq x \leq 3$; for Δ: $x_0 = 0$, $x_1 = \tfrac{1}{2}$, $x_2 = 1\tfrac{1}{4}$, $x_3 = 2\tfrac{1}{4}$, $x_4 = 3$; $\xi_1 = \tfrac{1}{4}$, $\xi_2 = 1$, $\xi_3 = 1\tfrac{1}{2}$, $\xi_4 = 2\tfrac{1}{2}$

2. $f(x) = x^2$, $0 \leq x \leq 3$; for Δ: $x_0 = 0$, $x_1 = \tfrac{3}{4}$, $x_2 = 1\tfrac{1}{4}$, $x_3 = 2$, $x_4 = 2\tfrac{3}{4}$, $x_5 = 3$; $\xi_1 = \tfrac{1}{2}$, $\xi_2 = 1$, $\xi_3 = 1\tfrac{3}{4}$, $\xi_4 = 2\tfrac{1}{4}$, $\xi_5 = 2\tfrac{3}{4}$

3. $f(x) = 1/x$, $1 \leq x \leq 3$; for Δ: $x_0 = 1$, $x_1 = 1\tfrac{2}{3}$, $x_2 = 2\tfrac{1}{4}$, $x_3 = 2\tfrac{2}{3}$, $x_4 = 3$; $\xi_1 = 1\tfrac{1}{4}$, $\xi_2 = 2$, $\xi_3 = 2\tfrac{1}{2}$, $\xi_4 = 2\tfrac{3}{4}$

4. $f(x) = x^3$, $-1 \leq x \leq 2$; for Δ: $x_0 = -1$, $x_1 = -\tfrac{1}{3}$, $x_2 = \tfrac{1}{2}$, $x_3 = 1$, $x_4 = 1\tfrac{1}{4}$, $x_5 = 2$; $\xi_1 = -\tfrac{1}{2}$, $\xi_2 = 0$, $\xi_3 = \tfrac{2}{3}$, $\xi_4 = 1$, $\xi_5 = 1\tfrac{1}{2}$

5. $f(x) = x^2 - x + 1$, $0 \leq x \leq 1$; for Δ: $x_0 = 0$, $x_1 = 0.2$, $x_2 = 0.5$, $x_3 = 0.7$, $x_4 = 1$; $\xi_1 = 0.1$, $\xi_2 = 0.4$, $\xi_3 = 0.6$, $\xi_4 = 0.9$

6. $f(x) = 1/(x + 2)$, $-1 \leq x \leq 3$; for Δ: $x_0 = -1$, $x_1 = -\tfrac{1}{4}$, $x_2 = 0$, $x_3 = \tfrac{1}{2}$, $x_4 = 1\tfrac{1}{4}$, $x_5 = 2$, $x_6 = 2\tfrac{1}{4}$, $x_7 = 2\tfrac{3}{4}$, $x_8 = 3$; $\xi_1 = -\tfrac{3}{4}$, $\xi_2 = 0$, $\xi_3 = \tfrac{1}{4}$, $\xi_4 = 1$, $\xi_5 = 1\tfrac{1}{2}$, $\xi_6 = 2$, $\xi_7 = 2\tfrac{1}{2}$, $\xi_8 = 3$

In Exercises 7 through 14, find the exact value of the definite integral. Use the method of Example 2 of this section.

7. $\displaystyle\int_0^2 x^2 \, dx$

8. $\displaystyle\int_2^4 x^2 \, dx$

9. $\displaystyle\int_1^2 x^3 \, dx$

10. $\int_{-2}^{1} x^4 \, dx$

11. $\int_{1}^{4} (x^2 + 4x + 5) \, dx$

12. $\int_{0}^{4} (x^2 + x - 6) \, dx$

13. $\int_{-2}^{2} (x^3 + 1) \, dx$

14. $\int_{-1}^{2} (4x^3 - 3x^2) \, dx$

In Exercises 15 through 20, find the exact area of the region in the following way: (a) Express the measure of the area as the limit of a Riemann sum with regular partitions; (b) express this limit as a definite integral; (c) evaluate the definite integral by the method of this section and a suitable choice of ξ_i. Draw a figure showing the region.

15. Bounded by the line $y = 2x - 1$, the x axis, and the lines $x = 1$ and $x = 5$.

16. Bounded by the line $y = 2x - 6$, the x axis, and the lines $x = 4$ and $x = 7$.

17. Bounded by the curve $y = 4 - x^2$, the x axis, and the lines $x = 1$ and $x = 2$.

18. Bounded by the curve $y = (x + 3)^2$, the x axis, and the lines $x = -3$ and $x = 0$.

19. Bounded by the curve $y = 12 - x - x^2$, the x axis, and the lines $x = -3$ and $x = 2$.

20. Bounded by the curve $y = 6x + x^2 - x^3$, the x axis, and the lines $x = -1$ and $x = 3$.

21. Express as a definite integral: $\lim\limits_{n \to +\infty} \sum\limits_{i=1}^{n} (8i^2/n^3)$. (HINT: Consider the function f for which $f(x) = x^2$.)

22. Express as a definite integral: $\lim\limits_{n \to +\infty} \sum\limits_{i=1}^{n} 1/(n + i)$. (HINT: Consider the function f for which $f(x) = 1/x$ on $[1, 2]$.)

23. Express as a definite integral: $\lim\limits_{n \to +\infty} \sum\limits_{i=1}^{n} (n/i^2)$. (HINT: Consider the function f for which $f(x) = 1/x^2$.)

24. Let $[a, b]$ be any interval such that $a < 0 < b$. Prove that even though the unit step function (Exercise 21 in Exercises 1.8) is discontinuous on $[a, b]$, it is integrable on $[a, b]$ and $\int_a^b U(x) \, dx = b$.

25. Prove that the signum function is discontinuous on $[-1, 1]$ and yet integrable on $[-1, 1]$. Furthermore show that $\int_{-1}^{1} \operatorname{sgn} x \, dx = 0$.

26. Prove that the greatest integer function is discontinuous on $[0, \frac{3}{2}]$ and yet integrable on $[0, \frac{3}{2}]$. Furthermore, show that $\int_0^{3/2} [\![x]\!] \, dx = \frac{1}{2}$.

7.4 PROPERTIES OF THE DEFINITE INTEGRAL

Evaluating a definite integral from the definition, by actually finding the limit of a sum as we did in Sec. 7.3, is usually quite tedious and frequently almost impossible. To establish a much simpler method we first need to develop some properties of the definite integral. First the following two theorems about Riemann sums are needed.

7.4.1 Theorem   If Δ is any partition of the closed interval $[a, b]$, then

$$\lim_{\|\Delta\| \to 0} \sum_{i=1}^{n} \Delta_i x = b - a$$

PROOF:

$$\sum_{i=1}^{n} \Delta_i x - (b - a) = (b - a) - (b - a) = 0$$

Hence, for any $\epsilon > 0$ any choice of $\delta > 0$ guarantees the inequality

$$\left| \sum_{i=1}^{n} \Delta_i x - (b - a) \right| < \epsilon \qquad \text{whenever } \|\Delta\| < \delta$$

and so by Definition 7.3.1

$$\lim_{\|\Delta\| \to 0} \sum_{i=1}^{n} \Delta_i x = b - a \qquad \blacksquare$$

7.4.2 Theorem If f is defined on the closed interval $[a, b]$ and if

$$\lim_{\|\Delta\| \to 0} \sum_{i=1}^{n} f(\xi_i) \, \Delta_i x$$

exists, where Δ is any partition of $[a, b]$, then if k is any constant,

$$\lim_{\|\Delta\| \to 0} \sum_{i=1}^{n} k f(\xi_i) \, \Delta_i x = k \lim_{\|\Delta\| \to 0} \sum_{i=1}^{n} f(\xi_i) \, \Delta_i x$$

The proof of this theorem is left as an exercise (see Exercise 1).

We now state and prove some theorems that give important properties of the definite integral.

7.4.3 Theorem If the function f is integrable on the closed interval $[a, b]$ and if k is any constant, then

$$\int_a^b k f(x) \, dx = k \int_a^b f(x) \, dx$$

PROOF: Because f is integrable on $[a, b]$, $\displaystyle\lim_{\|\Delta\| \to 0} \sum_{i=1}^{n} f(\xi_i) \, \Delta_i x$ exists, and so by Theorem 7.4.2

$$\lim_{\|\Delta\| \to 0} \sum_{i=1}^{n} k f(\xi_i) \, \Delta_i x = k \lim_{\|\Delta\| \to 0} \sum_{i=1}^{n} f(\xi_i) \, \Delta_i x$$

Therefore,

$$\int_a^b k f(x) \, dx = k \int_a^b f(x) \, dx \qquad \blacksquare$$

7.4.4 Theorem If the functions f and g are integrable on $[a, b]$, then $f + g$ is integrable on $[a, b]$ and

$$\int_a^b [f(x) + g(x)] \, dx = \int_a^b f(x) \, dx + \int_a^b g(x) \, dx$$

PROOF: The functions f and g are integrable on $[a, b]$; thus, let

$$\int_a^b f(x)\ dx = M \quad \text{and} \quad \int_a^b g(x)\ dx = N$$

To prove that $f + g$ is integrable on $[a, b]$ and that $\int_a^b [f(x) + g(x)]\ dx = M + N$, we must show that for any $\epsilon > 0$ there exists a $\delta > 0$ such that

$$\left| \sum_{i=1}^n [f(\xi_i) + g(\xi_i)]\ \Delta_i x - (M + N) \right| < \epsilon$$

for all partitions Δ for which $\|\Delta\| < \delta$ and for any ξ_i in $[x_{i-1},\ x_i]$. Because

$$M = \lim_{\|\Delta\| \to 0} \sum_{i=1}^n f(\xi_i)\ \Delta_i x \quad \text{and} \quad N = \lim_{\|\Delta\| \to 0} \sum_{i=1}^n g(\xi_i)\ \Delta_i x$$

it follows that for any $\epsilon > 0$ there exist a $\delta_1 > 0$ and a $\delta_2 > 0$ such that

$$\left| \sum_{i=1}^n f(\xi_i)\ \Delta_i x - M \right| < \frac{\epsilon}{2} \quad \text{and} \quad \left| \sum_{i=1}^n g(\xi_i)\ \Delta_i x - N \right| < \frac{\epsilon}{2}$$

for all partitions Δ for which $\|\Delta\| < \delta_1$ and $\|\Delta\| < \delta_2$, and for any ξ_i in $[x_{i-1},\ x_i]$. Therefore, if $\delta = \min(\delta_1, \delta_2)$, then for any $\epsilon > 0$

$$\left| \sum_{i=1}^n f(\xi_i)\ \Delta_i x - M \right| + \left| \sum_{i=1}^n g(\xi_i)\ \Delta_i x - N \right| < \frac{\epsilon}{2} + \frac{\epsilon}{2} = \epsilon \tag{1}$$

for all partitions Δ for which $\|\Delta\| < \delta$ and for any ξ_i in $[x_{i-1},\ x_i]$.

By the triangle inequality, we have

$$\left| \left(\sum_{i=1}^n f(\xi_i)\ \Delta_i x - M \right) + \left(\sum_{i=1}^n g(\xi_i)\ \Delta_i x - N \right) \right|$$
$$\leq \left| \sum_{i=1}^n f(\xi_i)\ \Delta_i x - M \right| + \left| \sum_{i=1}^n g(\xi_i)\ \Delta_i x - N \right| \tag{2}$$

From inequalities (1) and (2), we have

$$\left| \left(\sum_{i=1}^n f(\xi_i)\ \Delta_i x + \sum_{i=1}^n g(\xi_i)\ \Delta_i x \right) - (M + N) \right| < \epsilon \tag{3}$$

From Property 3 (7.1.3) of the sigma notation, we have

$$\sum_{i=1}^n f(\xi_i)\ \Delta_i x + \sum_{i=1}^n g(\xi_i)\ \Delta_i x = \sum_{i=1}^n [f(\xi_i) + g(\xi_i)]\ \Delta_i x \tag{4}$$

So by substituting from (4) into (3) we are able to conclude that for any $\epsilon > 0$

$$\left| \sum_{i=1}^n [f(\xi_i) + g(\xi_i)]\ \Delta_i x - (M + N) \right| < \epsilon$$

for all partitions Δ for which $\|\Delta\| < \delta$, where $\delta = \min(\delta_1, \delta_2)$ and for any ξ_i

in $[x_{i-1}, x_i]$. This proves that $f + g$ is integrable on $[a, b]$ and that

$$\int_a^b [f(x) + g(x)] \, dx = \int_a^b f(x) \, dx + \int_a^b g(x) \, dx$$ ∎

Theorem 7.4.4 can be extended to any number of functions. That is, if the functions $f_1, f_2, \ldots, f_n$ are all integrable on $[a, b]$, then $(f_1 + f_2 + \cdots + f_n)$ is integrable on $[a, b]$ and

$$\int_a^b [f_1(x) + f_2(x) + \cdots + f_n(x)] \, dx$$

$$= \int_a^b f_1(x) \, dx + \int_a^b f_2(x) \, dx + \cdots + \int_a^b f_n(x) \, dx$$

The plus sign in the statement of Theorem 7.4.4 can be replaced by a minus sign as a result of applying Theorem 7.4.3, where $k = -1$.

7.4.5 Theorem   If the function f is integrable on the closed intervals $[a, b]$, $[a, c]$, and $[c, b]$,

$$\int_a^b f(x) \, dx = \int_a^c f(x) \, dx + \int_c^b f(x) \, dx$$

where $a < c < b$.

PROOF: Let Δ be a partition of $[a, b]$. Form the partition Δ' of $[a, b]$ in the following way. If c is one of the partitioning points of Δ (i.e., $c = x_i$ for some i), then Δ' is exactly the same as Δ. If c is not one of the partitioning points of Δ but is contained in the subinterval $[x_{i-1}, x_i]$, then the partition Δ' has as its partitioning points all the partitioning points of Δ and, in addition, the point c. Therefore, the subintervals of the partition Δ' are the same as the subintervals of Δ, with the exception that the subinterval $[x_{i-1}, x_i]$ of Δ is divided into the two subintervals $[x_{i-1}, c]$ and $[c, x_i]$.

If $\|\Delta'\|$ is the norm of Δ' and if $\|\Delta\|$ is the norm of Δ, then

$$\|\Delta'\| \leq \|\Delta\|$$

If in the partition Δ' the interval $[a, c]$ is divided into r subintervals and the interval $[c, b]$ is divided into $(n - r)$ subintervals, then the part of the partition Δ' from a to c gives a Riemann sum of the form

$$\sum_{i=1}^r f(\xi_i) \, \Delta_i x$$

and the other part of the partition Δ', from c to b, gives a Riemann sum of the form

$$\sum_{i=r+1}^n f(\xi_i) \, \Delta_i x$$

Using the definition of the definite integral and properties of the sigma notation, we have

$$\int_a^b f(x)\ dx = \lim_{||\Delta|| \to 0} \sum_{i=1}^n f(\xi_i)\ \Delta_i x$$

$$= \lim_{||\Delta|| \to 0} \left[\sum_{i=1}^r f(\xi_i)\ \Delta_i x + \sum_{i=r+1}^n f(\xi_i)\ \Delta_i x \right]$$

$$= \lim_{||\Delta|| \to 0} \sum_{i=1}^r f(\xi_i)\ \Delta_i x + \lim_{||\Delta|| \to 0} \sum_{i=r+1}^n f(\xi_i)\ \Delta_i x$$

Since $0 < ||\Delta'|| \le ||\Delta||$, we can replace $||\Delta|| \to 0$ by $||\Delta'|| \to 0$, giving us

$$\int_a^b f(x)\ dx = \lim_{||\Delta'|| \to 0} \sum_{i=1}^r f(\xi_i)\ \Delta_i x + \lim_{||\Delta'|| \to 0} \sum_{i=r+1}^n f(\xi_i)\ \Delta_i x$$

Applying the definition of the definite integral to the right side of the above equation, we have

$$\int_a^b f(x)\ dx = \int_a^c f(x)\ dx + \int_c^b f(x)\ dx \qquad \blacksquare$$

$y = f(x)$

Figure 7.4.1

• ILLUSTRATION 1: We interpret Theorem 7.4.5 geometrically. If $f(x) \ge 0$ for all x in $[a, b]$, then Theorem 7.4.5 states that the measure of the area of the region bounded by the curve $y = f(x)$ and the x axis from a to b is equal to the sum of the measures of the areas of the regions from a to c and from c to b. See Fig. 7.4.1.   •

The result of Theorem 7.4.5 is true for any ordering of the numbers a, b, and c. This is stated as another theorem.

7.4.6 Theorem   If f is integrable on a closed interval containing the three numbers a, b, and c, then

$$\int_a^b f(x)\ dx = \int_a^c f(x)\ dx + \int_c^b f(x)\ dx \qquad (5)$$

regardless of the order of a, b, and c.

PROOF: If a, b, and c are distinct, there are six possible orderings of these three numbers: $a < b < c, a < c < b, b < a < c, b < c < a, c < a < b$, and $c < b < a$. The second ordering, $a < c < b$, is Theorem 7.4.5. We make use of Theorem 7.4.5 in proving that Eq. (5) holds for the other orderings.

Suppose that $a < b < c$; then from Theorem 7.4.5 we have

$$\int_a^b f(x)\ dx + \int_b^c f(x)\ dx = \int_a^c f(x)\ dx \qquad (6)$$

From Definition 7.3.4

$$\int_b^c f(x)\ dx = -\int_c^b f(x)\ dx \tag{7}$$

Substituting from (7) into (6), we obtain

$$\int_a^b f(x)\ dx - \int_c^b f(x)\ dx = \int_a^c f(x)\ dx$$

Thus,

$$\int_a^b f(x)\ dx = \int_a^c f(x)\ dx + \int_c^b f(x)\ dx$$

which is the desired result.

The proofs for the other four orderings are similar and left as exercises (see Exercises 2 to 5).

There is also the possibility that two of the three numbers are equal; for example, $a = c < b$. Then

$$\int_a^c f(x)\ dx = \int_a^a f(x)\ dx = 0 \quad \text{(by Definition 7.3.5)}$$

Also, because $a = c$,

$$\int_c^b f(x)\ dx = \int_a^b f(x)\ dx$$

Therefore,

$$\int_a^c f(x)\ dx + \int_c^b f(x)\ dx = 0 + \int_a^b f(x)\ dx$$

which is the desired result.   ∎

7.4.7 Theorem   If k is any constant and if f is a function such that $f(x) = k$ for all x in $[a, b]$, then

$$\int_a^b f(x)\ dx = \int_a^b k\ dx = k(b - a)$$

PROOF: From Definition 7.3.2,

$$\int_a^b f(x)\ dx = \lim_{||\Delta|| \to 0} \sum_{i=1}^n f(\xi_i)\ \Delta_i x$$

$$= \lim_{||\Delta|| \to 0} \sum_{i=1}^n k\ \Delta_i x$$

$$= k \lim_{||\Delta|| \to 0} \sum_{i=1}^n \Delta_i x \quad \text{(by Theorem 7.4.2)}$$

$$= k(b - a) \quad \text{(by Theorem 7.4.1)}$$ ∎

● ILLUSTRATION 2: A geometric interpretation of Theorem 7.4.7 when $k > 0$ is given by Fig. 7.4.2. The definite integral $\int_a^b k\, dx$ gives the measure of the area of the shaded region, which is a rectangle whose dimensions are k units and $(b - a)$ units. ●

7.4.8 Theorem If the functions f and g are integrable on the closed interval $[a, b]$ and if $f(x) \geq g(x)$ for all x in $[a, b]$, then

$$\int_a^b f(x)\, dx \geq \int_a^b g(x)\, dx$$

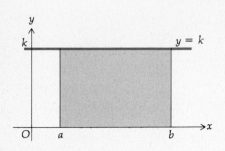

Figure 7.4.2

PROOF: Because f and g are integrable on $[a, b]$, $\int_a^b f(x)\, dx$ and $\int_a^b g(x)\, dx$ both exist. Therefore (by Theorem 7.4.3),

$$\int_a^b f(x)\, dx - \int_a^b g(x)\, dx = \int_a^b f(x)\, dx + \int_a^b [-g(x)]\, dx$$

$$= \int_a^b [f(x) - g(x)]\, dx \quad \text{(by Theorem 7.4.4)}$$

Let h be the function defined by

$$h(x) = f(x) - g(x)$$

Then $h(x) \geq 0$ for all x in $[a, b]$ because $f(x) \geq g(x)$ for all x in $[a, b]$. We wish to prove that $\int_a^b [f(x) - g(x)]\, dx \geq 0$.

$$\int_a^b [f(x) - g(x)]\, dx = \int_a^b h(x)\, dx = \lim_{\|\Delta\| \to 0} \sum_{i=1}^n h(\xi_i)\, \Delta_i x \qquad (8)$$

Assume that

$$\lim_{\|\Delta\| \to 0} \sum_{i=1}^n h(\xi_i)\, \Delta_i x = L < 0 \qquad (9)$$

Then by Definition 7.3.1, with $\epsilon = -L$, there exists a $\delta > 0$ such that

$$\left| \sum_{i=1}^n h(\xi_i)\, \Delta_i x - L \right| < -L \qquad \text{whenever } \|\Delta\| < \delta \qquad (10)$$

But because

$$\sum_{i=1}^n h(\xi_i)\, \Delta_i x - L \leq \left| \sum_{i=1}^n h(\xi_i)\, \Delta_i x - L \right|$$

from inequality (10) we have

$$\sum_{i=1}^n h(\xi_i)\, \Delta_i x - L < -L \qquad \text{whenever } \|\Delta\| < \delta$$

or

$$\sum_{i=1}^{n} h(\xi_i)\, \Delta_i x < 0 \qquad \text{whenever } \|\Delta\| < \delta \tag{11}$$

But statement (11) is impossible because every $h(\xi_i)$ is nonnegative and every $\Delta_i x > 0$; thus, we have a contradiction to our assumption (9). Therefore, (9) is false, and

$$\lim_{\|\Delta\|\to 0} \sum_{i=1}^{n} h(\xi_i)\, \Delta_i x \geq 0 \tag{12}$$

From (8) and (12), we have

$$\int_a^b [f(x) - g(x)]\, dx \geq 0$$

Hence,

$$\int_a^b f(x)\, dx - \int_a^b g(x)\, dx \geq 0$$

and so

$$\int_a^b f(x)\, dx \geq \int_a^b g(x)\, dx \qquad\blacksquare$$

Figure 7.4.3

● ILLUSTRATION 3: Figure 7.4.3 gives a geometric interpretation of Theorem 7.4.8 when $f(x) \geq g(x) \geq 0$ for all x in $[a, b]$. $\int_a^b f(x)\, dx$ gives the measure of the area of the region bounded by the curve $y = f(x)$, the x axis, and the lines $x = a$ and $x = b$. $\int_a^b g(x)\, dx$ gives the measure of the area of the region bounded by the curve $y = g(x)$, the x axis, and the lines $x = a$ and $x = b$. In the figure we see that the first area is greater than the second area. ●

7.4.9 Theorem   Suppose that the function f is continuous on the closed interval $[a, b]$. If m and M are, respectively, the absolute minimum and absolute maximum function values of f on $[a, b]$ so that

$$m \leq f(x) \leq M \qquad \text{for } a \leq x \leq b$$

then

$$m(b - a) \leq \int_a^b f(x)\, dx \leq M(b - a)$$

PROOF: Because f is continuous on $[a, b]$, the extreme-value theorem (4.5.9) guarantees the existence of m and M.

By Theorem 7.4.7

$$\int_a^b m \, dx = m(b - a) \tag{13}$$

and

$$\int_a^b M \, dx = M(b - a) \tag{14}$$

Because f is continuous on $[a, b]$, it follows from Theorem 7.3.3 that f is integrable on $[a, b]$. Then because $f(x) \geq m$ for all x in $[a, b]$, we have from Theorem 7.4.8

$$\int_a^b f(x) \, dx \geq \int_a^b m \, dx$$

which from (13) gives

$$\int_a^b f(x) \, dx \geq m(b - a) \tag{15}$$

Similarly, because $M \geq f(x)$ for all x in $[a, b]$, it follows from Theorem 7.4.8 that

$$\int_a^b M \, dx \geq \int_a^b f(x) \, dx$$

which from (14) gives

$$M(b - a) \geq \int_a^b f(x) \, dx \tag{16}$$

Combining inequalities (15) and (16) we have

$$m(b - a) \leq \int_a^b f(x) \, dx \leq M(b - a) \qquad \blacksquare$$

• ILLUSTRATION 4: A geometric interpretation of Theorem 7.4.9 is given in Fig. 7.4.4, where $f(x) \geq 0$ for all x in $[a, b]$. The integral $\int_a^b f(x) \, dx$ gives the measure of the area of the region bounded by the curve $y = f(x)$, the x axis, and the lines $x = a$ and $x = b$. This area is greater than that of the rectangle whose dimensions are m and $(b - a)$ and less than that of the rectangle whose dimensions are M and $(b - a)$. •

Figure 7.4.4

EXAMPLE 1: Apply Theorem 7.4.9 to find a smallest and a largest possible value of

$$\int_{1/2}^4 (x^3 - 6x^2 + 9x + 1) \, dx$$

SOLUTION: Referring to Example 1, Sec. 5.1, we see that f has a relative minimum value of 1 at $x = 3$ and a relative maximum value of 5 at $x = 1$. $f(\frac{1}{2}) = \frac{33}{8}$ and $f(4) = 5$. Hence, the absolute minimum value of f on $[\frac{1}{2}, 4]$ is 1, and the absolute maximum value is 5. Taking $m = 1$ and $M = 5$ in Theorem 7.4.9, we have

$$1(4 - \tfrac{1}{2}) \leq \int_{1/2}^4 (x^3 - 6x^2 + 9x + 1) \, dx \leq 5(4 - \tfrac{1}{2})$$

Use the results of Example 1,
Sec. 5.1.

and so

$$\tfrac{7}{2} \le \int_{1/2}^{4} (x^3 - 6x^2 + 9x + 1)\ dx \le \tfrac{35}{2}$$

In Example 1 , Sec. 7.6, the exact value of the definite integral is shown to be $10\tfrac{39}{64}$.

EXAMPLE 2: Apply Theorem 7.4.9 to find a smallest and a largest possible value of

$$\int_{-1}^{1} (x^{4/3} + 4x^{1/3})\ dx$$

Use the results of Example 3, Sec. 5.1.

SOLUTION: From Example 3, Sec. 5.1, we see that f has a relative minimum value of -3 at $x = -1$. Furthermore, $f(1) = 5$. Hence, on $[-1, 1]$ the absolute minimum value of f is -3 and the absolute maximum value is 5. So, taking $m = -3$ and $M = 5$ in Theorem 7.4.9, we have

$$(-3)[1 - (-1)] \le \int_{-1}^{1} (x^{4/3} + 4x^{1/3})\ dx \le 5[1 - (-1)]$$

Therefore,

$$-6 \le \int_{-1}^{1} (x^{4/3} + 4x^{1/3})\ dx \le 10$$

The exact value of the definite integral is $\tfrac{6}{7}$ as shown in Example 2, Sec. 7.6.

Exercises 7.4

1. Prove Theorem 7.4.2.

In Exercises 2 through 7, prove that Theorem 7.4.6 is valid; in each case use the result of Theorem 7.4.5.

2. $b < a < c$ 3. $b < c < a$ 4. $c < a < b$

5. $c < b < a$ 6. $a < c = b$ 7. $a = b < c$

In Exercises 8 through 17, apply Theorem 7.4.9 to find a smallest and a largest possible value of the given integral.

8. $\displaystyle\int_{2}^{5} 3x\ dx$ 9. $\displaystyle\int_{0}^{4} x^2\ dx$ 10. $\displaystyle\int_{-2}^{1} (x+1)^{2/3}\ dx$

11. $\displaystyle\int_{-3}^{6} \sqrt{3+x}\ dx$ 12. $\displaystyle\int_{-1}^{4} (x^4 - 8x^2 + 16)\ dx$ 13. $\displaystyle\int_{-4}^{0} (x^4 - 8x^2 + 16)\ dx$

14. $\displaystyle\int_{-5}^{2} \frac{x+5}{x-3}\ dx$ 15. $\displaystyle\int_{-1}^{2} \frac{x}{x+2}\ dx$ 16. $\displaystyle\int_{-1}^{2} \sqrt{x^2 + 5}\ dx$

17. $\displaystyle\int_{1}^{4} |x - 2|\ dx$

18. Show that if f is continuous on $[-1, 2]$, then

$$\int_{-1}^{2} f(x)\ dx + \int_{2}^{0} f(x)\ dx + \int_{0}^{1} f(x)\ dx + \int_{1}^{-1} f(x)\ dx = 0$$

19. Show that $\displaystyle\int_{0}^{1} x\ dx \ge \int_{0}^{1} x^2\ dx$ but $\displaystyle\int_{1}^{2} x\ dx \le \int_{1}^{2} x^2\ dx$. Do not evaluate the definite integrals.

20. If f is continuous on $[a, b]$, prove that

$$\left| \int_a^b f(x) \, dx \right| \leq \int_a^b |f(x)| \, dx$$

(HINT: $-|f(x)| \leq f(x) \leq |f(x)|$.)

7.5 THE MEAN-VALUE THEOREM FOR INTEGRALS

Before stating and proving the mean-value theorem for integrals, we discuss an important theorem about a function that is continuous on a closed interval. It is called the *intermediate-value theorem,* and we need to use it to prove the mean-value theorem for integrals.

7.5.1 Theorem
Intermediate-Value Theorem

If the function f is continuous on the closed interval $[a, b]$ and if $f(a) \neq f(b)$, then for any number k between $f(a)$ and $f(b)$ there exists a number c between a and b such that $f(c) = k$.

Figure 7.5.1

The proof of this theorem is beyond the scope of this book; it can be found in an advanced calculus text. However, we discuss the geometric interpretation of the theorem. In Fig. 7.5.1, $(0, k)$ is any point on the y axis between the points $(0, f(a))$ and $(0, f(b))$. Theorem 7.5.1 states that the line $y = k$ must intersect the curve whose equation is $y = f(x)$ at the point (c, k), where c lies between a and b. Figure 7.5.1 shows this intersection.

Note that for some values of k there may be more than one possible value for c. The theorem states that there is always at least one value of c, but that it is not necessarily unique. Figure 7.5.2 shows three possible values of c (c_1, c_2, and c_3) for a particular k. Theorem 7.5.1 states that if the function f is continuous on a closed interval $[a, b]$, then f assumes every value between $f(a)$ and $f(b)$ as x assumes all values between a and b. The importance of the continuity of f on $[a, b]$ is demonstrated in the following illustration.

Figure 7.5.2

● ILLUSTRATION 1: Consider the function f, defined by

$$f(x) = \begin{cases} x - 1 & \text{if } 0 \leq x \leq 2 \\ x^2 & \text{if } 2 < x \leq 3 \end{cases}$$

A sketch of the graph of this function is shown in Fig. 7.5.3.

The function f is discontinuous at 2, which is in the closed interval $[0, 3]$; $f(0) = -1$ and $f(3) = 9$. If k is any number between 1 and 4, there is no value of c such that $f(c) = k$ because there are no function values between 1 and 4. ●

Another function for which Theorem 7.5.1 does not hold is given in the next illustration.

● ILLUSTRATION 2: Let the function g be defined by

$$g(x) = \frac{2}{x - 4}$$

A sketch of the graph of this function is shown in Fig. 7.5.4.

The function g is discontinuous at 4, which is in the closed interval $[2, 5]$; $g(2) = -1$ and $g(5) = 2$. If k is any number between -1 and 2, there is no value of c between 2 and 5 such that $g(c) = k$. In particular, if $k = 1$, then $g(6) = 1$, but 6 is not in the interval $[2, 5]$.   ●

Figure 7.5.3   Figure 7.5.4

EXAMPLE 1: Given the function f defined by

$$f(x) = 4 + 3x - x^2 \quad 2 \leq x \leq 5$$

verify the intermediate-value theorem if $k = 1$.

SOLUTION: $f(2) = 6$; $f(5) = -6$.

To find c, set $f(c) = k = 1$; that is,

$$4 + 3c - c^2 = 1$$

$$c^2 - 3c - 3 = 0$$

This gives

$$c = \frac{3 \pm \sqrt{21}}{2}$$

We reject $\frac{1}{2}(3 - \sqrt{21})$ because this number is outside the interval $[2, 5]$. The number $\frac{1}{2}(3 + \sqrt{21})$ is in the interval $[2, 5]$, and

$$f\left(\frac{3 + \sqrt{21}}{2}\right) = 1$$

7.5.2 Theorem
Mean-Value Theorem
for Integrals

We are now ready to state and prove the mean-value theorem for integrals.

If the function f is continuous on the closed interval $[a, b]$, then there exists a number X such that $a \leq X \leq b$, and

$$\int_a^b f(x) \, dx = f(X)(b - a)$$

PROOF: Because f is continuous on $[a, b]$, from the extreme-value theorem (4.5.9) f has an absolute maximum value and an absolute minimum value on $[a, b]$.

Let m be the absolute minimum value occurring at $x = x_m$. Thus,

$$f(x_m) = m \qquad a \leq x_m \leq b \tag{1}$$

Let M be the absolute maximum value, occurring at $x = x_M$. Thus,

$$f(x_M) = M \qquad a \leq x_M \leq b \tag{2}$$

We have, then,

$$m \leq f(x) \leq M \qquad \text{for all } x \text{ in } [a, b]$$

From Theorem 7.4.9 it follows that

$$m(b - a) \leq \int_a^b f(x) \, dx \leq M(b - a)$$

Dividing by $(b - a)$ and noting that $(b - a)$ is positive because $b > a$, we get

$$m \leq \frac{\displaystyle\int_a^b f(x) \, dx}{b - a} \leq M$$

But from Eqs. (1) and (2), $m = f(x_m)$ and $M = f(x_M)$, and so we have

$$f(x_m) \leq \frac{\displaystyle\int_a^b f(x) \, dx}{b - a} \leq f(x_M) \tag{3}$$

From inequalities (3) and the intermediate-value theorem (7.5.1), there is some number X in a closed interval containing x_m and x_M such that

$$f(X) = \frac{\displaystyle\int_a^b f(x) \, dx}{b - a}$$

or

$$\int_a^b f(x) \, dx = f(X)(b - a) \qquad a \leq X \leq b \qquad \blacksquare$$

• ILLUSTRATION 3: To interpret Theorem 7.5.2 geometrically, we consider $f(x) \geq 0$ for all values of x in $[a, b]$. Then $\int_a^b f(x) \, dx$ is the measure of the area of the region bounded by the curve whose equation is $y = f(x)$, the x axis, and the lines $x = a$ and $x = b$ (see Fig. 7.5.5). Theorem 7.5.2 states that there is a number X in $[a, b]$ such that the area of the rectangle $AEFB$ of height $f(X)$ units and width $(b - a)$ units is equal to the area of the region $ADCB$. •

The value of X is not necessarily unique. The theorem does not provide a method for finding X, but it states that a value of X exists, and

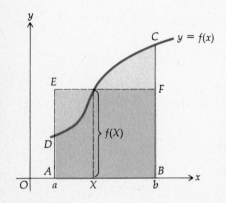

Figure 7.5.5

this is used to prove other theorems. In some particular cases we can find the value of X, as is illustrated in the following example.

EXAMPLE 2:   Find the value of X such that

$$\int_1^3 f(x)\ dx = f(X)(3-1)$$

if $f(x) = x^2$. Use the result of Example 2 in Sec. 7.3.

SOLUTION: In Example 2 of Sec. 7.3, we obtained

$$\int_1^3 x^2\ dx = 8\tfrac{2}{3}$$

Therefore, we wish to find X such that

$$f(X)\cdot(2) = \tfrac{26}{3}$$

that is,

$$X^2 = \tfrac{13}{3}$$

Therefore,

$$X = \pm\tfrac{1}{3}\sqrt{39}$$

We reject $-\tfrac{1}{3}\sqrt{39}$ since it is not in the interval [1, 3], and we have

$$\int_1^3 f(x)\ dx = f(\tfrac{1}{3}\sqrt{39})(3-1)$$

The value $f(X)$ given by Theorem 7.5.2 is called the *mean value* (or *average value*) of f on the interval $[a, b]$. It is a generalization of the arithmetic mean of a finite set of numbers. That is, if $\{f(x_1), f(x_2), \ldots, f(x_n)\}$ is a set of n numbers, then the arithmetic mean is given by

$$\frac{\sum_{i=1}^n f(x_i)}{n}$$

To generalize this definition, consider a regular partition of the closed interval $[a, b]$, which is divided into n subintervals of equal length $\Delta x = (b-a)/n$. Let ξ_i be any point in the ith subinterval. Form the sum:

$$\frac{\sum_{i=1}^n f(\xi_i)}{n} \tag{4}$$

The quotient (4) corresponds to the arithmetic mean of n numbers. Because $\Delta x = (b-a)/n$, we have

$$n = \frac{b-a}{\Delta x} \tag{5}$$

Substituting from (5) into (4), we obtain

$$\frac{\sum_{i=1}^n f(\xi_i)}{\dfrac{(b-a)}{\Delta x}}$$

or, equivalently,

$$\frac{\sum\limits_{i=1}^{n} f(\xi_i)\ \Delta x}{b - a}$$

Taking the limit as $n \to +\infty$ (or $\Delta x \to 0$), we have, if the limit exists,

$$\lim_{n \to +\infty} \frac{\sum\limits_{i=1}^{n} f(\xi_i)\ \Delta x}{b - a} = \frac{\displaystyle\int_a^b f(x)\ dx}{b - a}$$

This leads to the following definition.

7.5.3 Definition   If the function f is integrable on the closed interval $[a, b]$, the *average value* of f on $[a, b]$ is

$$\frac{\displaystyle\int_a^b f(x)\ dx}{b - a}$$

EXAMPLE 3:   Find the average value of the function f defined by $f(x) = x^2$ on the interval $[1, 3]$.

SOLUTION: In Example 2, Sec. 7.3, we obtained

$$\int_1^3 x^2\ dx = \tfrac{26}{3}$$

So if A.V. is the average value of f on $[1, 3]$, we have

$$\text{A.V.} = \frac{\tfrac{26}{3}}{3 - 1} = \frac{13}{3}$$

An important application of the average value of a function occurs in physics and engineering in connection with the concept of center of mass. This is discussed in the next chapter.

In economics, Definition 7.5.3 can be used to find an average total cost or an average total revenue.

● ILLUSTRATION 4: If the total cost function C is given by $C(x) = x^2$, where $C(x)$ thousands of dollars is the total cost of producing $100x$ units of a certain commodity, then the number of thousands of dollars in the average total cost, when the number of units produced takes on all values from 100 to 300, is given by the average value of C on $[1, 3]$. From Example 3, this is $\tfrac{13}{3} = 4.33$. Hence, the average total cost is \$4333.   ●

Exercises 7.5

In Exercises 1 through 8, a function f and a closed interval $[a, b]$ are given. Determine if the intermediate-value theorem holds for the given value of k. If the theorem holds, find a number c such that $f(c) = k$. If the theorem does not hold, give the reason. Draw a sketch of the curve and the line $y = k$.

1. $f(x) = 2 + x - x^2$; $[a, b] = [0, 3]$; $k = 1$

2. $f(x) = x^2 + 5x - 6$; $[a, b] = [-1, 2]$; $k = 4$

3. $f(x) = \sqrt{25 - x^2}$; $[a, b] = [-4.5, 3]$; $k = 3$

4. $f(x) = -\sqrt{100 - x^2}$; $[a, b] = [0, 8]$; $k = -8$

5. $f(x) = \dfrac{4}{x + 2}$; $[a, b] = [-3, 1]$; $k = \frac{1}{2}$

6. $f(x) = \begin{cases} 1 + x & \text{if } -4 \le x \le -2 \\ 2 - x & \text{if } -2 < x \le 1 \end{cases}$; $[a, b] = [-4, 1]$; $k = \frac{1}{2}$

7. $f(x) = \begin{cases} x^2 - 4 & \text{if } -2 \le x < 1 \\ x^2 - 1 & \text{if } 1 \le x \le 3 \end{cases}$; $[a, b] = [-2, 3]$; $k = -1$

8. $f(x) = \dfrac{5}{2x - 1}$; $[a, b] = [0, 1]$; $k = 2$

In Exercises 9 through 13, find the value of X satisfying the mean-value theorem for integrals. For the value of the definite integral, use the results of the corresponding Exercises 9 through 13 in Exercises 7.3 Draw a figure illustrating the application of the theorem.

9. $\displaystyle\int_1^2 x^3 \, dx$

10. $\displaystyle\int_{-2}^1 x^4 \, dx$

11. $\displaystyle\int_1^4 (x^2 + 4x + 5) \, dx$

12. $\displaystyle\int_0^4 (x^2 + x - 6) \, dx$

13. $\displaystyle\int_{-2}^2 (x^3 + 1) \, dx$

14. Find the average value of the function f defined by $f(x) = x^2$ on the interval $[2, 4]$, and find the value of x at which it occurs. Make a sketch. Use the result of Exercise 8 of Exercises 7.3 for the value of the definite integral.

15. Suppose a ball is dropped from rest and after t sec its velocity is v ft/sec. Neglecting air resistance, express v in terms of t as $v = f(t)$ and find the average value of f on $[0, 2]$.

16. Suppose $C(x)$ hundreds of dollars is the total cost of producing $10x$ units of a certain commodity, and $C(x) = x^2$. Find the average total cost when the number of units produced takes on all values from 0 to 20. Use the result of Exercise 7 in Exercises 7.3 for the value of the definite integral.

17. Find the average value of the function f defined by $f(x) = \sqrt{16 - x^2}$ on the interval $[-4, 4]$. Draw a figure. (HINT: Find the value of the definite integral by interpreting it as the measure of the area of a region enclosed by a semicircle.)

18. Find the average value of the function f defined by $f(x) = \sqrt{49 - x^2}$ on the interval $[0, 7]$. Draw a figure. (HINT: Find the value of the definite integral by interpreting it as the measure of the area of a region enclosed by a quarter-circle.)

19. Show that the intermediate-value theorem guarantees that the equation $x^3 - 4x^2 + x + 3 = 0$ has a root between 1 and 2.

20. Suppose f is a function for which $0 \le f(x) \le 1$ if $0 \le x \le 1$. Prove that if f is continuous on $[0, 1]$ there is at least one number c in $[0, 1]$ such that $f(c) = c$. (HINT: If neither 0 nor 1 qualifies as c, then $f(0) > 0$ and $f(1) < 1$. Consider the function g for which $g(x) = f(x) - x$ and apply the intermediate-value theorem to g on $[0, 1]$.)

21. If f is continuous on $[a, b]$ and $\int_a^b f(x) \, dx = 0$, prove that there is at least one number c in $[a, b]$ such that $f(c) = 0$.

7.6 THE FUNDAMENTAL THEOREM OF THE CALCULUS   Historically the basic concepts of the definite integral were used by the ancient Greeks, principally Archimedes (287–212 B.C.), more than 2000 years ago, which was many years before the differential calculus was discovered.

In the seventeenth century, almost simultaneously but working independently, Newton and Leibniz showed how the calculus could be used to
find the area of a region bounded by a curve or a set of curves, by
evaluating a definite integral by antidifferentiation. The procedure involves what is known as the *fundamental theorem of the calculus*. Before we
state and prove this important theorem, we discuss definite integrals
having a variable upper limit, and a preliminary theorem.

Let f be a function continuous on the closed interval $[a, b]$. Then the
value of the definite integral $\int_a^b f(x)\ dx$ depends only on the function f and
the numbers a and b, and not on the symbol x, which is used here as the
independent variable. In Example 2, Sec. 7.3, we found the value of $\int_1^3 x^2\ dx$
to be $8\frac{2}{3}$. Any other symbol instead of x could have been used; for example,

$$\int_1^3 t^2\ dt = \int_1^3 u^2\ du = \int_1^3 r^2\ dr = 8\tfrac{2}{3}$$

If f is continuous on the closed interval $[a, b]$, then by Theorem 7.3.3 and
the definition of the definite integral, $\int_a^b f(t)\ dt$ exists. We previously
stated that if the definite integral exists, it is a unique number. If x is a
number in $[a, b]$, then f is continuous on $[a, x]$ because it is continuous on
$[a, b]$. Consequently, $\int_a^x f(t)\ dt$ exists and is a unique number whose value
depends on x. Therefore, $\int_a^x f(t)\ dt$ defines a function F having as its
domain all numbers in the closed interval $[a, b]$ and whose function value
at any number x in $[a, b]$ is given by

$$F(x) = \int_a^x f(t)\ dt \tag{1}$$

As a notational observation, if the limits of the definite integral are
variables, different symbols are used for these limits and for the independent variable in the integrand. Hence, in Eq. (1), because x is the upper
limit, we use the letter t as the independent variable in the integrand.

If, in Eq. (1), $f(t) \geq 0$ for all values of t in $[a, b]$, then the function value
$F(x)$ can be interpreted geometrically as the measure of the area of the
region bounded by the curve whose equation is $y = f(t)$, the t axis, and
the lines $t = a$ and $t = x$. (See Fig. 7.6.1.) Note that $F(a) = \int_a^a f(t)\ dt$, which
by Definition 7.3.5 equals 0.

We now state and prove an important theorem giving the derivative
of a function F defined as a definite integral having a variable upper limit.

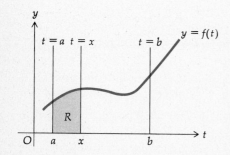

Figure 7.6.1

7.6.1 Theorem   Let the function f be continuous on the closed interval $[a, b]$ and let x be
any number in $[a, b]$. If F is the function defined by

$$F(x) = \int_a^x f(t)\ dt$$

then

$$F'(x) = f(x) \tag{2}$$

(If $x = a$, the derivative in (2) may be a derivative from the right, and if $x = b$, the derivative in (2) may be a derivative from the left.)

PROOF: Consider two numbers x_1 and $(x_1 + \Delta x)$ in $[a, b]$. Then

$$F(x_1) = \int_a^{x_1} f(t) \ dt$$

and

$$F(x_1 + \Delta x) = \int_a^{x_1 + \Delta x} f(t) \ dt$$

so that

$$F(x_1 + \Delta x) - F(x_1) = \int_a^{x_1 + \Delta x} f(t) \ dt - \int_a^{x_1} f(t) \ dt \tag{3}$$

By Theorem 7.4.6,

$$\int_a^{x_1} f(t) \ dt + \int_{x_1}^{x_1 + \Delta x} f(t) \ dt = \int_a^{x_1 + \Delta x} f(t) \ dt$$

or, equivalently,

$$\int_a^{x_1 + \Delta x} f(t) \ dt - \int_a^{x_1} f(t) \ dt = \int_{x_1}^{x_1 + \Delta x} f(t) \ dt \tag{4}$$

Substituting from Eq. (4) into (3), we get

$$F(x_1 + \Delta x) - F(x_1) = \int_{x_1}^{x_1 + \Delta x} f(t) \ dt \tag{5}$$

By the mean-value theorem for integrals (7.5.2), there is some number X in the closed interval bounded by x_1 and $(x_1 + \Delta x)$ such that

$$\int_{x_1}^{x_1 + \Delta x} f(t) \ dt = f(X) \ \Delta x \tag{6}$$

From Eqs. (5) and (6), we obtain

$$F(x_1 + \Delta x) - F(x_1) = f(X) \ \Delta x$$

or, if we divide by Δx,

$$\frac{F(x_1 + \Delta x) - F(x_1)}{\Delta x} = f(X)$$

Taking the limit as Δx approaches zero, we have

$$\lim_{\Delta x \to 0} \frac{F(x_1 + \Delta x) - F(x_1)}{\Delta x} = \lim_{\Delta x \to 0} f(X) \tag{7}$$

The left side of Eq. (7) is $F'(x_1)$. To determine $\lim_{\Delta x \to 0} f(X)$, recall that X is in the closed interval bounded by x_1 and $x_1 + \Delta x$, and because

$$\lim_{\Delta x \to 0} x_1 = x_1 \quad \text{and} \quad \lim_{\Delta x \to 0} (x_1 + \Delta x) = x_1$$

it follows from the squeeze theorem (4.3.3) that $\lim_{\Delta x \to 0} X = x_1$. Because f is continuous at x_1, we have $\lim_{\Delta x \to 0} f(X) = \lim_{X \to x_1} f(X) = f(x_1)$; thus, from Eq. (7) we get

$$F'(x_1) = f(x_1) \tag{8}$$

If the function f is not defined for values of x less than a but is continuous from the right at a, then in the above argument, if $x_1 = a$ in Eq. (7), Δx must approach 0 from the right. Hence, the left side of Eq. (8) will be $F'_+(x_1)$. Similarly, if f is not defined for values of x greater than b but is continuous from the left at b, then if $x_1 = b$ in Eq. (7), Δx must approach 0 from the left. Hence, we have $F'_-(x_1)$ on the left side of Eq. (8).

Because x_1 is any number in $[a, b]$, Eq. (8) states what we wished to prove. ∎

Theorem 7.6.1 states that the definite integral $\int_a^x f(t)\, dt$, with variable upper limit x, is an antiderivative of f.

7.6.2 Theorem
Fundamental Theorem of the Calculus

Let the function f be continuous on the closed interval $[a, b]$ and let g be a function such that

$$g'(x) = f(x) \tag{9}$$

for all x in $[a, b]$. Then

$$\int_a^b f(t)\, dt = g(b) - g(a)$$

(If $x = a$, the derivative in (9) may be a derivative from the right, and if $x = b$, the derivative in (9) may be a derivative from the left.)

PROOF: If f is continuous at all numbers in $[a, b]$, we know from Theorem 7.6.1 that the definite integral $\int_a^x f(t)\, dt$, with variable upper limit x, defines a function F whose derivative on $[a, b]$ is f. Because by hypothesis $g'(x) = f(x)$, it follows from Theorem 6.3.3 that

$$g(x) = \int_a^x f(t)\, dt + k \tag{10}$$

where k is some constant.

Letting $x = b$ and $x = a$, successively, in Eq. (10), we get

$$g(b) = \int_a^b f(t)\, dt + k \tag{11}$$

and

$$g(a) = \int_a^a f(t) \, dt + k \tag{12}$$

From Eqs. (11) and (12), we obtain

$$g(b) - g(a) = \int_a^b f(t) \, dt - \int_a^a f(t) \, dt$$

But, by Definition 7.3.5, $\int_a^a f(t) \, dt = 0$, and so we have

$$g(b) - g(a) = \int_a^b f(t) \, dt$$

which is what we wished we prove.

If f is not defined for values of x greater than b but is continuous from the left at b, the derivative in (9) is a derivative from the left, and we have $g'_-(b) = F'_-(b)$, from which (11) follows. Similarly, if f is not defined for values of x less than a but is continuous from the right at a, then the derivative in (9) is a derivative from the right, and we have $g'_+(a) = F'_+(a)$, from which (12) follows.   ∎

We are now in a position to find the exact value of a definite integral by applying Theorem 7.6.2. In applying the theorem, we denote

$$[g(b) - g(a)] \quad \text{by} \quad g(x) \Big]_a^b$$

● ILLUSTRATION 1: We apply the fundamental theorem of the calculus to evaluate

$$\int_1^3 x^2 \, dx$$

Here, $f(x) = x^2$. An antiderivative of x^2 is $\frac{1}{3}x^3$. From this we choose

$$g(x) = \frac{x^3}{3}$$

Therefore, from Theorem 7.6.2, we get

$$\int_1^3 x^2 \, dx = \frac{x^3}{3} \Big]_1^3 = 9 - \frac{1}{3}$$

$$= 8\tfrac{2}{3}$$

Compare this result with that of Example 2, Sec. 7.3.   ●

Because of the connection between definite integrals and antiderivatives, we used the integral sign $\int$ for the notation $\int f(x) \, dx$ for an antiderivative. We now dispense with the terminology of antiderivatives and antidifferentiation and begin to call $\int f(x) \, dx$ the *indefinite integral* of "*f* of *x, dx*." The process of evaluating an indefinite integral or a definite integral is called *integration*.

The difference between an indefinite integral and a definite integral should be emphasized. The indefinite integral $\int f(x) \, dx$ is defined as a function *g* such that its derivative $D_x[g(x)] = f(x)$. However, the definite integral $\int_a^b f(x) \, dx$ is a number whose value depends on the function *f* and the numbers *a* and *b*, and it is defined as the limit of a Riemann sum. The definition of the definite integral makes no reference to differentiation.

The general indefinite integral involves an arbitrary constant; for instance,

$$\int x^2 \, dx = \frac{x^3}{3} + C$$

This arbitrary constant *C* is called a *constant of integration*. In applying the fundamental theorem to evaluate a definite integral, we do not need to include the arbitrary constant *C* in the expression for $g(x)$ because the fundamental theorem permits us to select *any* antiderivative, including the one for which $C = 0$.

EXAMPLE 1: **Evaluate**

$$\int_{1/2}^4 (x^3 - 6x^2 + 9x + 1) \, dx$$

SOLUTION:

$$\int_{1/2}^4 (x^3 - 6x^2 + 9x + 1) \, dx = \int_{1/2}^4 x^3 \, dx - 6 \int_{1/2}^4 x^2 \, dx$$
$$+ 9 \int_{1/2}^4 x \, dx + \int_{1/2}^4 dx$$
$$= \frac{x^4}{4} - 6 \cdot \frac{x^3}{3} + 9 \cdot \frac{x^2}{2} + x \Big]_{1/2}^4$$
$$= (64 - 128 + 72 + 4) - (\tfrac{1}{64} - \tfrac{1}{4} + \tfrac{9}{8} + \tfrac{1}{2})$$
$$= \tfrac{679}{64}$$

EXAMPLE 2: Evaluate

$$\int_{-1}^1 (x^{4/3} + 4x^{1/3}) \, dx$$

SOLUTION: $\int_{-1}^1 (x^{4/3} + 4x^{1/3}) \, dx = \tfrac{3}{7} x^{7/3} + 4 \cdot \tfrac{3}{4} x^{4/3} \Big]_{-1}^1$
$$= \tfrac{3}{7} + 3 - (-\tfrac{3}{7} + 3)$$
$$= \tfrac{6}{7}$$

EXAMPLE 3: Evaluate

$$\int_0^2 2x^2 \sqrt{x^3 + 1} \, dx$$

SOLUTION: $\int_0^2 2x^2 \sqrt{x^3 + 1} \, dx = \tfrac{2}{3} \int_0^2 \sqrt{x^3 + 1} \, (3x^2) \, dx$
$$= \frac{2}{3} \frac{(x^3 + 1)^{3/2}}{\frac{3}{2}} \Big]_0^2$$

$$= \tfrac{4}{9}(8+1)^{3/2} - \tfrac{4}{9}(0+1)^{3/2}$$

$$= \tfrac{4}{9}(27-1)$$

$$= \tfrac{104}{9}$$

EXAMPLE 4:   Evaluate

$$\int_0^3 x\sqrt{1+x}\ dx$$

SOLUTION: To evaluate the indefinite integral $\int x\sqrt{1+x}\ dx$ we let

$$u = \sqrt{1+x} \qquad u^2 = 1+x \qquad x = u^2 - 1 \qquad dx = 2u\ du$$

Substituting, we have

$$\int x\sqrt{1+x}\ dx = \int (u^2 - 1)u(2u\ du)$$

$$= 2\int (u^4 - u^2)\ du$$

$$= \tfrac{2}{5}u^5 - \tfrac{2}{3}u^3 + C$$

$$= \tfrac{2}{5}(1+x)^{5/2} - \tfrac{2}{3}(1+x)^{3/2} + C$$

Therefore, the definite integral

$$\int_0^3 x\sqrt{1+x}\ dx = \tfrac{2}{5}(1+x)^{5/2} - \tfrac{2}{3}(1+x)^{3/2}\ \Big]_0^3$$

$$= \tfrac{2}{5}(4)^{5/2} - \tfrac{2}{3}(4)^{3/2} - \tfrac{2}{5}(1)^{5/2} + \tfrac{2}{3}(1)^{3/2}$$

$$= \tfrac{64}{5} - \tfrac{16}{3} - \tfrac{2}{5} + \tfrac{2}{3}$$

$$= \tfrac{116}{15}$$

Another method for evaluating the definite integral in Example 4 involves changing the limits of the definite integral to values of u. The procedure is shown in the following illustration. Often this second method is shorter and its justification follows immediately from Theorems 6.3.10 and 7.6.2.

• ILLUSTRATION 2: Because $u = \sqrt{1+x}$, we see that when $x = 0$, $u = 1$; and when $x = 3$, $u = 2$. Thus, we have

$$\int_0^3 x\sqrt{1+x}\ dx = 2\int_1^2 (u^4 - u^2)\ du$$

$$= \tfrac{2}{5}u^5 - \tfrac{2}{3}u^3\ \Big]_1^2$$

$$= \tfrac{64}{5} - \tfrac{16}{3} - \tfrac{2}{5} + \tfrac{2}{3}$$

$$= \tfrac{116}{15}$$ •

EXAMPLE 5· Evaluate

$$\int_{-3}^{4} |x + 2| \, dx$$

SOLUTION: If we let $f(x) = |x + 2|$, instead of finding an antiderivative of f directly, we write $f(x)$ as

$$f(x) = \begin{cases} x + 2 & \text{if } x \geq -2 \\ -x - 2 & \text{if } x \leq -2 \end{cases}$$

Applying Theorem 7.4.6, we have

$$\int_{-3}^{4} |x + 2| \, dx = \int_{-3}^{-2} (-x - 2) \, dx + \int_{-2}^{4} (x + 2) \, dx$$

$$= \left[-\frac{x^2}{2} - 2x \right]_{-3}^{-2} + \left[\frac{x^2}{2} + 2x \right]_{-2}^{4}$$

$$= \tfrac{1}{2} + 18$$

$$= \tfrac{37}{2}$$

EXAMPLE 6: Find the area of the region in the first quadrant bounded by the curve whose equation is $y = x\sqrt{x^2 + 5}$, the x axis, and the line $x = 2$. Make a sketch.

SOLUTION: See Fig. 7.6.2: The region is shown together with one of the rectangular elements of area.

We take a regular partition of the interval $[0, 2]$. The width of each rectangle is Δx units, and the altitude of the ith rectangle is $\xi_i \sqrt{\xi_i^2 + 5}$ units, where ξ_i is any number in the ith subinterval. Therefore, the measure of the area of the rectangular element is $\xi_i \sqrt{\xi_i^2 + 5} \, \Delta x$. The sum of the measures of the areas of n such rectangles is

$$\sum_{i=1}^{n} \xi_i \sqrt{\xi_i^2 + 5} \, \Delta x$$

which is a Riemann sum. The limit of this sum as Δx approaches zero (or $n \to +\infty$) gives the measure of the desired area. The limit of the Riemann sum is a definite integral which we evaluate by the fundamental theorem of the calculus.

Let $A =$ the number of square units in the area of the region. Then,

$$A = \lim_{\Delta x \to 0} \sum_{i=1}^{n} \xi_i \sqrt{\xi_i^2 + 5} \, \Delta x$$

$$= \int_{0}^{2} x\sqrt{x^2 + 5} \, dx$$

$$= \tfrac{1}{2} \int_{0}^{2} \sqrt{x^2 + 5} \, (2x \, dx)$$

$$= \tfrac{1}{2} \cdot \tfrac{2}{3} (x^2 + 5)^{3/2} \Big]_{0}^{2}$$

$$= \tfrac{1}{3} [(9)^{3/2} - (5)^{3/2}]$$

$$= \tfrac{1}{3} (27 - 5\sqrt{5})$$

Hence, the area is $\tfrac{1}{3}(27 - 5\sqrt{5})$ square units.

$y = x\sqrt{x^2 + 5}$

Figure 7.6.2

EXAMPLE 7:   Given

$$f(x) = x\sqrt{x-4}$$

find the average value of f on the interval $[5, 8]$.

SOLUTION: Let A.V. = the average value of f on $[5, 8]$. We have, from Definition 7.5.3,

$$\text{A.V.} = \frac{1}{8-5} \int_5^8 x\sqrt{x-4}\ dx$$

Let $u = \sqrt{x-4}$; then $u^2 = x - 4$; $x = u^2 + 4$; $dx = 2u\ du$. When $x = 5, u = 1$; when $x = 8, u = 2$. Therefore,

$$\text{A.V.} = \tfrac{1}{3} \int_1^2 (u^2 + 4)u(2u\ du)$$

$$= \tfrac{2}{3} \int_1^2 (u^4 + 4u^2)\ du$$

$$= \tfrac{2}{3} \left[\tfrac{1}{5}u^5 + \tfrac{4}{3}u^3 \right]_1^2$$

$$= \tfrac{2}{3} \left[\tfrac{32}{5} + \tfrac{32}{3} - \tfrac{1}{5} - \tfrac{4}{3} \right]$$

$$= \tfrac{466}{45}$$

Exercises 7.6

In Exercises 1 through 18, evaluate the definite integral by using the fundamental theorem of the calculus.

1. $\displaystyle\int_2^7 (x^2 - 2x)\ dx$

2. $\displaystyle\int_{-1}^3 (3x^2 + 5x - 1)\ dx$

3. $\displaystyle\int_0^4 (y^3 - y^2 + 1)\ dy$

4. $\displaystyle\int_{-1}^3 \frac{dy}{(y+2)^3}$

5. $\displaystyle\int_{-2}^0 3w\sqrt{4 - w^2}\ dw$

6. $\displaystyle\int_1^3 \frac{x\ dx}{(3x^2 - 1)^3}$

7. $\displaystyle\int_0^1 \frac{(y^2 + 2y)\ dy}{\sqrt[3]{y^3 + 3y^2 + 4}}$

8. $\displaystyle\int_4^5 x^2\sqrt{x-4}\ dx$

9. $\displaystyle\int_0^{15} \frac{w\ dw}{(1+w)^{3/4}}$

10. $\displaystyle\int_{-2}^1 (x+1)\sqrt{x+3}\ dx$

11. $\displaystyle\int_{-2}^5 |x-3|\ dx$

12. $\displaystyle\int_{-3}^3 \sqrt{3 + |x|}\ dx$

13. $\displaystyle\int_{-1}^1 \sqrt{|x| - x}\ dx$

14. $\displaystyle\int_1^4 \frac{x^5 - x}{3x^3}\ dx$

15. $\displaystyle\int_1^2 \frac{x^3 + 2x^2 + x + 2}{(x+1)^2}\ dx$

16. $\displaystyle\int_{-3}^2 \frac{3x^3 - 24x^2 + 48x + 5}{x^2 - 8x + 16}\ dx$

(HINT: Divide the numerator by the denominator.)

17. $\displaystyle\int_1^{64} \left(\sqrt{t} - \frac{1}{\sqrt{t}} + \sqrt[3]{t} \right) dt$

18. $\displaystyle\int_0^1 \sqrt{x}\sqrt{1 + x\sqrt{x}}\ dx$

In Exercises 19 through 22, use Theorem 7.6.1 to find the indicated derivative.

19. $D_x \int_0^x \sqrt{4 + t^6} \, dt$

20. $D_x \int_x^5 \sqrt{1 + t^4} \, dt$

21. $D_x \int_{-x}^x \dfrac{dt}{3 + t^2}$

22. $D_x \int_1^{x^2} \sqrt{1 + t^4} \, dt$

In Exercises 23 through 28, find the area of the region bounded by the given curve and lines. Draw a figure showing the region and a rectangular element of area. Express the measure of the area as the limit of a Riemann sum and then as a definite integral. Evaluate the definite integral by the fundamental theorem of the calculus.

23. $y = 4x - x^2$; x axis; $x = 1$, $x = 3$

24. $y = x^2 - 2x + 3$; x axis; $x = -2$, $x = 1$

25. $y = \sqrt{x + 1}$; x axis, y axis; $x = 8$

26. $y = x\sqrt{x^2 + 9}$; x axis, y axis; $x = 4$

27. $y = x\sqrt{x + 5}$; x axis; $x = -1$, $x = 4$

28. $y = \dfrac{1}{x^2} - x$; x axis; $x = 2$, $x = 3$

In Exercises 29 through 32, find the average value of the function f on the given interval $[a, b]$. In Exercises 29 and 30, find the value of x at which the average value of f occurs and make a sketch.

29. $f(x) = 8x - x^2$; $[a, b] = [0, 4]$

30. $f(x) = 9 - x^2$; $[a, b] = [0, 3]$

31. $f(x) = x^2 \sqrt{x - 3}$; $[a, b] = [7, 12]$

32. $f(x) = 3x\sqrt{x^2 - 16}$; $[a, b] = [4, 5]$

33. A ball is dropped from rest and after t sec its velocity is v ft/sec. Neglecting air resistance, show that the average velocity during the first $\frac{1}{2}T$ sec is one-third of the average velocity during the next $\frac{1}{2}T$ sec.

34. A stone is thrown downward with an initial velocity of v_0 ft/sec. Neglect air resistance. (a) Show that if v ft/sec is the velocity of the stone after falling s ft, then $v = \sqrt{v_0^2 + 2gs}$. (b) Find the average velocity during the first 100 ft of fall if the initial velocity is 60 ft/sec. (Take $g = 32$ and downward as the positive direction.)

35. The demand equation for a certain commodity is $x^2 + p^2 = 100$, where p dollars is the price of one unit when $100x$ units of the commodity are demanded. Find the average total revenue when the number of units demanded takes on all values from 600 to 800.

36. Let f be a function whose derivative f' is continuous on $[a, b]$. Find the average value of the slope of the tangent line of the graph of f on $[a, b]$ and give a geometric interpretation of the result.

Review Exercises (Chapter 7)

In Exercises 1 and 2, find the exact value of the definite integral by using the definition of the definite integral; do not use the fundamental theorem of the calculus.

1. $\displaystyle\int_{-2}^1 (x^3 + 2x) \, dx$

2. $\displaystyle\int_{-1}^3 (x^2 - 1)^2 \, dx$

In Exercises 3 and 4, find the sum.

3. $\displaystyle\sum_{i=1}^{100} 2i(i^3 - 1)$

4. $\displaystyle\sum_{i=1}^{41} (\sqrt[3]{3i - 1} - \sqrt[3]{3i + 2})$

5. Prove that $\displaystyle\sum_{i=1}^n i^3 = \left(\sum_{i=1}^n i\right)^2$ and verify the formula for $n = 1, 2$, and 3.

6. Express as a definite integral and evaluate the definite integral: $\displaystyle\lim_{n \to +\infty} \sum_{i=1}^n (8\sqrt{i} / n^{3/2})$ (HINT: Consider the function f for which $f(x) = \sqrt{x}$.)

In Exercises 7 through 16, evaluate the definite integral by using the fundamental theorem of the calculus.

7. $\int_{-3}^{3} (t^6 - 3t) \, dt$

8. $\int_{2}^{4} \frac{4 \, dx}{5x^4}$

9. $\int_{1}^{5} \frac{dx}{\sqrt{3x - 1}}$

10. $\int_{-5}^{5} 2x \sqrt[3]{x^2 + 2} \, dx$

11. $\int_{0}^{2} x\sqrt{3x + 4} \, dx$

12. $\int_{1}^{2} \frac{x \, dx}{\sqrt{5 - x}}$

13. $\int_{-1}^{7} \frac{x^2 \, dx}{\sqrt{x + 2}}$

14. $\int_{0}^{1} (x^2 + 4x) \sqrt{x^3 + 6x^2 + 1} \, dx$

15. $\int_{-3}^{3} |x - 2|^3 \, dx$

16. $\int_{-2}^{2} x|x - 3| \, dx$

17. Show that each of the following inequalities holds:

(a) $\int_{-2}^{-1} \frac{dx}{x - 3} \geq \int_{-2}^{-1} \frac{dx}{x}$; (b) $\int_{1}^{2} \frac{dx}{x} \geq \int_{1}^{2} \frac{dx}{x - 3}$; (c) $\int_{4}^{5} \frac{dx}{x - 3} \geq \int_{4}^{5} \frac{dx}{x}$

18. If

$$f(x) = \begin{cases} 0 & \text{if } a \leq x < c \\ k & \text{if } x = c \\ 1 & \text{if } c < x \leq b \end{cases}$$

prove that f is integrable on $[a, b]$ and $\int_{a}^{b} f(x) \, dx = b - c$ regardless of the value of k.

In Exercises 19 and 20, find a smallest and a largest possible value of the given integral.

19. $\int_{1}^{4} \sqrt{5 + 4x - x^2} \, dx$

20. $\int_{-2}^{1} \sqrt[3]{2x^3 - 3x^2 + 1} \, dx$

In Exercises 21 through 24, find the area of the region bounded by the given curve and lines. Draw a figure showing the region and a rectangular element of area. Express the measure of the area as the limit of a Riemann sum and then as a definite integral. Evaluate the definite integral by the fundamental theorem of the calculus.

21. $y = 9 - x^2$; x axis; y axis; $x = 3$

22. $y = 16 - x^2$; x axis; $x = -4$, $x = 4$

23. $y = 2\sqrt{x - 1}$; x axis; $x = 5$, $x = 17$

24. $y = \dfrac{4}{x^2} - x$; x axis; $x = -2$, $x = -1$

25. If $f(x) = x^2 \sqrt{x - 3}$, find the average value of f on $[7, 12]$.

26. Interpret the mean-value theorem for integrals (7.5.2) in terms of an average function value.

27. A body falls from rest and travels a distance of s ft before striking the ground. If the only force acting is that of gravity, which gives the body an acceleration of g ft/sec² toward the ground, show that the average value of the velocity, expressed as a function of distance, while traveling this distance is $\frac{2}{3}\sqrt{2gs}$ ft/sec, and that this average velocity is two-thirds of the final velocity.

28. Suppose a ball is dropped from rest and after t sec its directed distance from the starting point is s ft and its velocity is v ft/sec. Neglect air resistance. When $t = t_1$, $s = s_1$, and $v = v_1$. (a) Express v as a function of t as $v = f(t)$ and find the average value of f on $[0, t_1]$. (b) Express v as a function of s as $v = g(s)$ and find the average velocity of g on $[0, s_1]$. (c) Write the results of parts (a) and (b) in terms of t_1, and determine which average velocity is larger.

29. The demand equation of a certain commodity is $p^2 + x - 10 = 0$, where p dollars is the price of one unit when $100x$ units of the commodity are demanded. Find the average total revenue when the number of units demanded takes on all values from 600 to 800.

30. (a) Find the average value of the function f defined by $f(x) = 1/x^2$ on the interval $[1, r]$. (b) If A is the average value found in part (a), find $\lim_{r \to +\infty} A$.

31. Given $F(x) = \int_x^{2x} \frac{1}{t} \, dt$ and $x > 0$. Prove that F is a constant function by showing that $F'(x) = 0$. (HINT: Use Theorem 7.6.1 after writing the given integral as the difference of two integrals.)

32. Make up an example of a discontinuous function for which the mean-value theorem for integrals (a) does not hold, and (b) does hold.

33. Let f be continuous on $[a, b]$ and $\int_a^b f(t) \, dt \neq 0$. Show that for any number k in $(0, 1)$ there is a number c in (a, b) such that

$$\int_a^c f(t) \, dt = k \int_a^b f(t) \, dt$$

(HINT: Consider the function F for which $F(x) = \int_a^x f(t) \, dt \Big/ \int_a^b f(t) \, dt$ and apply the intermediate-value theorem.)

8

Applications of
the definite integral

8.1 AREA OF A REGION IN A PLANE

From Definition 7.3.6, if f is a function continuous on the closed interval $[a, b]$ and if $f(x) \geq 0$ for all x in $[a, b]$, then the number of square units in the area of the region bounded by the curve $y = f(x)$, the x axis, and the lines $x = a$ and $x = b$ is

$$\lim_{||\Delta|| \to 0} \sum_{i=1}^{n} f(\xi_i) \, \Delta x$$

which is equal to the definite integral $\int_a^b f(x) \, dx$.

Suppose that $f(x) < 0$ for all x in $[a, b]$. Then each $f(\xi_i)$ is a negative number, and so we define the number of square units in the area of the region bounded by $y = f(x)$, the x axis, and the lines $x = a$ and $x = b$ to be

$$\lim_{||\Delta|| \to 0} \sum_{i=1}^{n} [-f(\xi_i)] \, \Delta x$$

which equals

$$-\int_a^b f(x) \, dx$$

EXAMPLE 1: Find the area of the region bounded by the curve $y = x^2 - 4x$, the x axis, and the lines $x = 1$ and $x = 3$.

$y = x^2 - 4x$

$(\xi_i, \xi_i^2 - 4\xi_i)$

Figure 8.1.1

SOLUTION: The region, together with a rectangular element of area, is shown in Fig. 8.1.1.

If one takes a regular partition of the interval $[1, 3]$, the width of each rectangle is Δx. Because $x^2 - 4x < 0$ on $[1, 3]$, the altitude of the ith rectangle is $-(\xi_i^2 - 4\xi_i) = 4\xi_i - \xi_i^2$. Hence, the sum of the measures of the areas of n rectangles is given by

$$\sum_{i=1}^{n} (4\xi_i - \xi_i^2) \, \Delta x$$

The measure of the desired area is given by the limit of this sum as Δx approaches 0; so if A square units is the area of the region, we have

$$A = \lim_{\Delta x \to 0} \sum_{i=1}^{n} (4\xi_i - \xi_i^2) \, \Delta x$$

$$= \int_1^3 (4x - x^2) \, dx$$

$$= 2x^2 - \tfrac{1}{3}x^3 \Big]_1^3$$

$$= \tfrac{22}{3}$$

Thus, the area of the region is $\tfrac{22}{3}$ square units.

EXAMPLE 2: Find the area of the region bounded by the curve $y = x^3 - 2x^2 - 5x + 6$, the x axis, and the lines $x = -1$ and $x = 2$.

SOLUTION: The region is shown in Fig. 8.1.2. Let $f(x) = x^3 - 2x^2 - 5x + 6$. Because $f(x) \geq 0$ when x is in the closed interval $[-1, 1]$ and $f(x) \leq 0$ when x is in the closed interval $[1, 2]$, we separate the region into two parts. Let A_1 be the number of square units in the area of the region when

Figure 8.1.2

x is in $[-1, 1]$, and let A_2 be the number of square units in the area of the region when x is in $[1, 2]$. Then

$$A_1 = \lim_{\Delta x \to 0} \sum_{i=1}^{n} f(\xi_i) \, \Delta x$$

$$= \int_{-1}^{1} f(x) \, dx$$

$$= \int_{-1}^{1} (x^3 - 2x^2 - 5x + 6) \, dx$$

and

$$A_2 = \lim_{\Delta x \to 0} \sum_{i=1}^{n} [-f(\xi_i)] \, \Delta x = \int_{1}^{2} -(x^3 - 2x^2 - 5x + 6) \, dx$$

If A square units is the area of the entire region, then

$$A = A_1 + A_2$$

$$= \int_{-1}^{1} (x^3 - 2x^2 - 5x + 6) \, dx - \int_{1}^{2} (x^3 - 2x^2 - 5x + 6) \, dx$$

$$= \left[\tfrac{1}{4}x^4 - \tfrac{2}{3}x^3 - \tfrac{5}{2}x^2 + 6x \right]_{-1}^{1} - \left[\tfrac{1}{4}x^4 - \tfrac{2}{3}x^3 - \tfrac{5}{2}x^2 + 6x \right]_{1}^{2}$$

$$= [(\tfrac{1}{4} - \tfrac{2}{3} - \tfrac{5}{2} + 6) - (\tfrac{1}{4} + \tfrac{2}{3} - \tfrac{5}{2} - 6)]$$

$$\qquad - [(4 - \tfrac{16}{3} - 10 + 12) - (\tfrac{1}{4} - \tfrac{2}{3} - \tfrac{5}{2} + 6)]$$

$$= \tfrac{32}{3} - (-\tfrac{29}{12})$$

$$= \tfrac{157}{12}$$

The area of the region is therefore $\tfrac{157}{12}$ square units.

Now consider two functions f and g continuous on the closed interval $[a, b]$ and such that $f(x) \geq g(x)$ for all x in $[a, b]$. We wish to find the area of the region bounded by the two curves $y = f(x)$ and $y = g(x)$ and the two lines $x = a$ and $x = b$. Such a situation is shown in Fig. 8.1.3.

Take a regular partition of the interval $[a, b]$, with each subinterval having a length of Δx. In each subinterval choose a point ξ_i. Consider the rectangle having altitude $[f(\xi_i) - g(\xi_i)]$ units and width Δx units. Such a rectangle is shown in Fig. 8.1.3. There are n such rectangles, one associated with each subinterval. The sum of the measures of the areas of these n rectangles is given by the following Riemann sum:

$$\sum_{i=1}^{n} [f(\xi_i) - g(\xi_i)] \, \Delta x$$

This Riemann sum is an approximation to what we intuitively think of as

Figure 8.1.3

the number representing the "measure of the area" of the region. The larger the value of n—or, equivalently, the smaller the value of Δx—the better is this approximation. If A square units is the area of the region, we define

$$A = \lim_{\Delta x \to 0} \sum_{i=1}^{n} [f(\xi_i) - g(\xi_i)] \, \Delta x \tag{1}$$

Because f and g are continuous on $[a, b]$, so also is $(f - g)$; therefore, the limit in Eq. (1) exists and is equal to the definite integral

$$\int_{a}^{b} [f(x) - g(x)] \, dx$$

EXAMPLE 3: Find the area of the region bounded by the curves $y = x^2$ and $y = -x^2 + 4x$.

Figure 8.1.4

SOLUTION: To find the points of intersection of the two curves, we solve the equations simultaneously and obtain the points $(0, 0)$ and $(2, 4)$. The region is shown in Fig. 8.1.4.

Let $f(x) = -x^2 + 4x$, and $g(x) = x^2$. Therefore, in the interval $[0, 2]$ the curve $y = f(x)$ is above the curve $y = g(x)$. We draw a vertical rectangular element of area, having altitude $[f(\xi_i) - g(\xi_i)]$ units and width Δx units. The measure of the area of this rectangle then is given by $[f(\xi_i) - g(\xi_i)] \, \Delta x$. The sum of the measures of the areas of n such rectangles is given by the Riemann sum

$$\sum_{i=1}^{n} [f(\xi_i) - g(\xi_i)] \, \Delta x$$

If A square units is the area of the region, then

$$A = \lim_{\Delta x \to 0} \sum_{i=1}^{n} [f(\xi_i) - g(\xi_i)] \, \Delta x$$

and the limit of the Riemann sum is a definite integral. Hence,

$$A = \int_{0}^{2} [f(x) - g(x)] \, dx$$

$$= \int_{0}^{2} [(-x^2 + 4x) - x^2] \, dx$$

$$= \int_{0}^{2} (-2x^2 + 4x) \, dx$$

$$= \left[-\tfrac{2}{3}x^3 + 2x^2 \right]_{0}^{2}$$

$$= -\tfrac{16}{3} + 8 - 0$$

$$= \tfrac{8}{3}$$

The area of the region is $\tfrac{8}{3}$ square units.

EXAMPLE 4: Find the area of the region bounded by the parabola $y^2 = 2x - 2$ and the line $y = x - 5$.

Figure 8.1.5

Figure 8.1.6

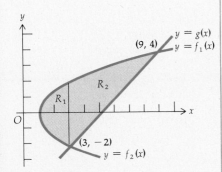

Figure 8.1.7

SOLUTION: The two curves intersect at the points $(3, -2)$ and $(9, 4)$. The region is shown in Fig. 8.1.5.

The equation $y^2 = 2x - 2$ is equivalent to the two equations

$$y = \sqrt{2x - 2} \quad \text{and} \quad y = -\sqrt{2x - 2}$$

with the first equation giving the upper half of the parabola and the second equation giving the bottom half. If we let $f_1(x) = \sqrt{2x - 2}$ and $f_2(x) = -\sqrt{2x - 2}$, the equation of the top half of the parabola is $y = f_1(x)$, and the equation of the bottom half of the parabola is $y = f_2(x)$. If we let $g(x) = x - 5$, the equation of the line is $y = g(x)$.

In Fig. 8.1.6 we see two vertical rectangular elements of area. Each rectangle has the upper base on the curve $y = f_1(x)$. Because the base of the first rectangle is on the curve $y = f_2(x)$, the altitude is $[f_1(\xi_i) - f_2(\xi_i)]$ units. Because the base of the second rectangle is on the curve $y = g(x)$, its altitude is $[f_1(\xi_i) - g(\xi_i)]$ units. If we wish to solve this problem by using vertical rectangular elements of area, we must divide the region into two separate regions, for instance R_1 and R_2, where R_1 is the region bounded by the curves $y = f_1(x)$ and $y = f_2(x)$ and the line $x = 3$, and where R_2 is the region bounded by the curves $y = f_1(x)$ and $y = g(x)$ and the line $x = 3$ (see Fig. 8.1.7).

If A_1 is the number of square units in the area of region R_1, we have

$$A_1 = \lim_{\Delta x \to 0} \sum_{i=1}^{n} [f_1(\xi_i) - f_2(\xi_i)] \Delta x$$

$$= \int_1^3 [f_1(x) - f_2(x)] \, dx$$

$$= \int_1^3 [\sqrt{2x - 2} + \sqrt{2x - 2}] \, dx$$

$$= 2 \int_1^3 \sqrt{2x - 2} \, dx$$

$$= \tfrac{2}{3}(2x - 2)^{3/2} \Big]_1^3$$

$$= \tfrac{16}{3}$$

If A_2 is the number of square units in the area of region R_2, we have

$$A_2 = \lim_{\Delta x \to 0} \sum_{i=1}^{n} [f_1(\xi_i) - g(\xi_i)] \Delta x$$

$$= \int_3^9 [f_1(x) - g(x)] \, dx$$

$$= \int_3^9 [\sqrt{2x - 2} - (x - 5)] \, dx$$

$$= \left[\tfrac{1}{3}(2x-2)^{3/2} - \tfrac{1}{2}x^2 + 5x \right]_3^9$$

$$= \left[\tfrac{64}{3} - \tfrac{81}{2} + 45 \right] - \left[\tfrac{8}{3} - \tfrac{9}{2} + 15 \right]$$

$$= \tfrac{38}{3}$$

Hence $A_1 + A_2 = \tfrac{16}{3} + \tfrac{38}{3} = 18$. Therefore, the area of the entire region is 18 square units.

EXAMPLE 5: Find the area of the region in Example 4 by taking horizontal rectangular elements of area.

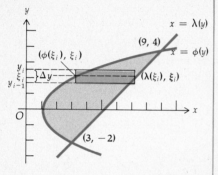

Figure 8.1.8

SOLUTION: Figure 8.1.8 illustrates the region with a horizontal rectangular element of area.

If in the equations of the parabola and the line we solve for x, we have

$$x = \tfrac{1}{2}(y^2 + 2) \quad \text{and} \quad x = y + 5$$

Letting $\phi(y) = \tfrac{1}{2}(y^2 + 2)$ and $\lambda(y) = y + 5$, the equation of the parabola may be written as $x = \phi(y)$ and the equation of the line as $x = \lambda(y)$. If we consider the closed interval $[-2, 4]$ on the y axis and take a regular partition of this interval, each subinterval will have a length of Δy. In the ith subinterval $[y_{i-1}, y_i]$, choose a point ξ_i. Then the length of the ith rectangular element is $[\lambda(\xi_i) - \phi(\xi_i)]$ units and the width is Δy units. The measure of the area of the region can be approximated by the Riemann sum:

$$\sum_{i=1}^{n} [\lambda(\xi_i) - \phi(\xi_i)] \, \Delta y$$

If A square units is the area of the region, then

$$A = \lim_{\Delta y \to 0} \sum_{i=1}^{n} [\lambda(\xi_i) - \phi(\xi_i)] \, \Delta y$$

Because λ and ϕ are continuous on $[-2, 4]$, so also is $(\lambda - \phi)$, and the limit of the Riemann sum is a definite integral:

$$A = \int_{-2}^{4} [\lambda(y) - \phi(y)] \, dy$$

$$= \int_{-2}^{4} \left[(y + 5) - \tfrac{1}{2}(y^2 + 2) \right] dy$$

$$= \tfrac{1}{2} \int_{-2}^{4} (-y^2 + 2y + 8) \, dy$$

$$= \tfrac{1}{2} \left[-\tfrac{1}{3}y^3 + y^2 + 8y \right]_{-2}^{4}$$

$$= \tfrac{1}{2} \left[-\tfrac{64}{3} + 16 + 32 \right) - \left(\tfrac{8}{3} + 4 - 16 \right)]$$

$$= 18$$

Comparing the solutions in Examples 4 and 5, we see that in the first case we have two definite integrals to evaluate, whereas in the second case we have only one. In general, if possible, the rectangular elements of area should be constructed so that a single definite integral is obtained. The following example illustrates a situation where two definite integrals are necessary.

EXAMPLE 6: Find the area of the region bounded by the two curves $y = x^3 - 6x^2 + 8x$ and $y = x^2 - 4x$.

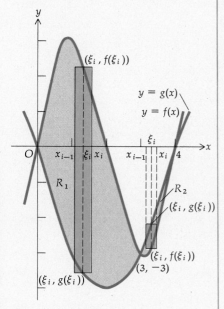

Figure 8.1.9

SOLUTION: The points of intersection of the two curves are $(0, 0)$, $(3, -3)$, and $(4, 0)$. The region is shown in Fig. 8.1.9.

Let $f(x) = x^3 - 6x^2 + 8x$ and $g(x) = x^2 - 4x$. In the interval $[0, 3]$ the curve $y = f(x)$ is above the curve $y = g(x)$, and in the interval $[3, 4]$ the curve $y = g(x)$ is above the curve $y = f(x)$. So the region must be divided into two separate regions R_1 and R_2, where R_1 is the region bounded by the two curves in the interval $[0, 3]$ and R_2 is the region bounded by the two curves in the interval $[3, 4]$. Letting A_1 square units be the area of R_1 and A_2 square units be the area of R_2, we have

$$A_1 = \lim_{\Delta x \to 0} \sum_{i=1}^{n} [f(\xi_i) - g(\xi_i)] \, \Delta x$$

and

$$A_2 = \lim_{\Delta x \to 0} \sum_{i=1}^{n} [g(\xi_i) - f(\xi_i)] \, \Delta x$$

so that

$$A_1 + A_2 = \int_0^3 [(x^3 - 6x^2 + 8x) - (x^2 - 4x)] \, dx$$
$$+ \int_3^4 [(x^2 - 4x) - (x^3 - 6x^2 + 8x)] \, dx$$

$$= \int_0^3 (x^3 - 7x^2 + 12x) \, dx + \int_3^4 (-x^3 + 7x^2 - 12x) \, dx$$

$$= \left[\tfrac{1}{4}x^4 - \tfrac{7}{3}x^3 + 6x^2 \right]_0^3 + \left[-\tfrac{1}{4}x^4 + \tfrac{7}{3}x^3 - 6x^2 \right]_3^4$$

$$= \tfrac{45}{4} + \tfrac{7}{12}$$

$$= \tfrac{71}{6}$$

Therefore, the required area is $\tfrac{71}{6}$ square units.

Exercises 8.1

In Exercises 1 through 20, find the area of the region bounded by the given curves. In each problem do the following: (a) Draw a figure showing the region and a rectangular element of area; (b) express the area of the region as the limit of a Riemann sum; (c) find the limit in part (b) by evaluating a definite integral by the fundamental theorem of the calculus.

1. $x^2 = -y$; $y = -4$

2. $y^2 = -x$; $x = -2$; $x = -4$

3. $x^2 + y + 4 = 0$; $y = -8$. Take the elements of area perpendicular to the y axis.

4. The same region as in Exercise 3. Take the elements of area parallel to the y axis.

5. $x^3 = 2y^2$; $x = 0$, $y = -2$

6. $y^3 = 4x$; $x = 0$; $y = -2$

7. $y = 2 - x^2$; $y = -x$

8. $y = x^2$; $y = x^4$

9. $y^2 = x - 1$; $x = 3$

10. $y = x^2$; $x^2 = 18 - y$

11. $y = \sqrt{x}$; $y = x^3$

12. $x = 4 - y^2$; $x = 4 - 4y$

13. $y^3 = x^2$; $x - 3y + 4 = 0$

14. $xy^2 = y^2 - 1$; $x = 1$; $y = 1$; $y = 4$

15. $x = y^2 - 2$; $x = 6 - y^2$

16. $x = y^2 - y$; $x = y - y^2$

17. $y = 2x^3 - 3x^2 - 9x$; $y = x^3 - 2x^2 - 3x$

18. $3y = x^3 - 2x^2 - 15x$; $y = x^3 - 4x^2 - 11x + 30$

19. $y = |x|$, $y = x^2 - 1$, $x = -1$, $x = 1$

20. $y = |x + 1| + |x|$, $y = 0$, $x = -2$, $x = 3$

21. Find by integration the area of the triangle having vertices at $(5, 1)$, $(1, 3)$, and $(-1, -2)$.

22. Find by integration the area of the triangle having vertices at $(3, 4)$, $(2, 0)$, and $(0, 1)$.

23. Find the area of the region bounded by the curve $x^3 - x^2 + 2xy - y^2 = 0$ and the line $x = 4$. (HINT: Solve the cubic equation for y in terms of x, and express y as two functions of x.)

24. Find the area of the region bounded by the three curves $y = x^2$, $x = y^3$, and $x + y = 2$.

25. Find the area of the region bounded by the three curves $y = x^2$, $y = 8 - x^2$, and $4x - y + 12 = 0$.

26. Find the area of the region above the parabola $x^2 = 4py$ and inside the triangle formed by the x axis and the lines $y = x + 8p$ and $y = -x + 8p$.

27. (a) Find the area of the region bounded by the curves $y^2 = 4px$ and $x^2 = 4py$. (b) Find the rate of change of the measure of the area in part (a) with respect to p when $p = 3$.

28. Find the rate of change of the measure of the area of Exercise 26 with respect to p when $p = \frac{3}{8}$.

29. If A square units is the area of the region bounded by the parabola $y^2 = 4x$ and the line $y = mx$ $(m > 0)$, find the rate of change of A with respect to m.

30. Determine m so that the region above the line $y = mx$ and below the parabola $y = 2x - x^2$ has an area of 36 square units.

8.2 VOLUME OF A SOLID OF REVOLUTION: CIRCULAR-DISK AND CIRCULAR-RING METHODS

We have developed a method for finding the area of a plane region. Now this process is extended to find the volume of a *solid of revolution*, which is a solid obtained by revolving a region in a plane about a line in the plane, called the *axis of revolution*, which either touches the boundary of the region or does not intersect the region at all. For example, if the region bounded by a semicircle and its diameter is revolved about the diameter, a sphere is generated (see Fig. 8.2.1). A right-circular cone is generated if the region bounded by a right triangle is revolved about one of its legs (see Fig. 8.2.2).

We must first define what is meant by the "volume" of a solid of revolution; that is, we wish to assign a number, for example V, to what we intuitively think of as the measure of the volume of such a solid. We define the measure of the volume of a right-circular cylinder by $\pi r^2 h$, where r and h are, respectively, the number of units in the base radius and altitude.

Consider first the case where the axis of revolution is a boundary of

Figure 8.2.1

Figure 8.2.2

Figure 8.2.3

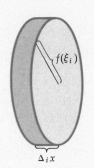

Figure 8.2.4

the region that is revolved. Let the function f be continuous on the closed interval $[a, b]$ and assume that $f(x) \geq 0$ for all x in $[a, b]$. Let R be the region bounded by the curve $y = f(x)$, the x axis, and the lines $x = a$ and $x = b$. Let S be the solid of revolution obtained by revolving the region R about the x axis. We proceed to find a suitable definition for the number V which gives the measure of the volume of S.

Let Δ be a partition of the closed interval $[a, b]$ given by

$$a = x_0 < x_1 < x_2 < \cdots < x_{n-1} < x_n = b$$

Then we have n subintervals of the form $[x_{i-1}, x_i]$, where $i = 1, 2, \ldots, n$, with the length of the ith subinterval being $\Delta_i x = x_i - x_{i-1}$. Choose any point ξ_i, with $x_{i-1} \leq \xi_i \leq x_i$, in each subinterval and draw the rectangles having widths $\Delta_i x$ units and altitudes $f(\xi_i)$ units. Figure 8.2.3 shows the region R together with the ith rectangle.

When the ith rectangle is revolved about the x axis, we obtain a circular disk in the form of a right-circular cylinder whose base radius is given by $f(\xi_i)$ units and whose altitude is given by $\Delta_i x$ units, as shown in Fig. 8.2.4. The measure of the volume of this circular disk, which we denote by $\Delta_i V$, is given by

$$\Delta_i V = \pi [f(\xi_i)]^2 \, \Delta_i x \tag{1}$$

Because there are n rectangles, n circular disks are obtained in this way, and the sum of the measures of the volumes of these n circular disks is given by

$$\sum_{i=1}^{n} \Delta_i V = \sum_{i=1}^{n} \pi [f(\xi_i)]^2 \, \Delta_i x \tag{2}$$

which is a Riemann sum.

The Riemann sum given in Eq. (2) is an approximation to what we intuitively think of as the number of cubic units in the volume of the solid of revolution. The smaller we take the norm $\|\Delta\|$ of the partition, the larger will be n, and the closer this approximation will be to the number V we wish to assign to the measure of the volume. We therefore define V to be the limit of the Riemann sum in Eq. (2) as $\|\Delta\|$ approaches zero. This limit exists because f^2 is continuous on $[a, b]$, which is true because f is continuous there. We have, then, the following definition.

8.2.1 Definition   Let the function f be continuous on the closed interval $[a, b]$, and assume that $f(x) \geq 0$ for all x in $[a, b]$. If S is the solid of revolution obtained by revolving about the x axis the region bounded by the curve $y = f(x)$, the x axis, and the lines $x = a$ and $x = b$, and if V is the number of cubic units in the volume of S, then

$$V = \lim_{\|\Delta\| \to 0} \sum_{i=1}^{n} \pi [f(\xi_i)]^2 \, \Delta_i x = \pi \int_a^b [f(x)]^2 \, dx \tag{3}$$

Figure 8.2.5

Figure 8.2.6

A similar definition applies when both the axis of revolution and a boundary of the revolved region is the y axis or any line parallel to either the x axis or the y axis.

● ILLUSTRATION 1: We find the volume of the solid of revolution generated when the region bounded by the curve $y = x^2$, the x axis, and the lines $x = 1$ and $x = 2$ is revolved about the x axis. Refer to Fig. 8.2.5, showing the region and a rectangular element of area. Figure 8.2.6 shows an element of volume and the solid of revolution. The measure of the volume of the circular disk is given by

$$\Delta_i V = \pi(\xi_i^2)^2 \, \Delta_i x = \pi \xi_i^4 \, \Delta_i x$$

Then

$$V = \lim_{\|\Delta\| \to 0} \sum_{i=1}^{n} \pi \xi_i^4 \, \Delta_i x$$

$$= \pi \int_1^2 x^4 \, dx$$

$$= \pi (\tfrac{1}{5} x^5) \Big]_1^2$$

$$= \tfrac{31}{5} \pi$$

Therefore, the volume of the solid of revolution is $\tfrac{31}{5}\pi$ cubic units. ●

Now suppose that the axis of revolution is not a boundary of the region being revolved. Let f and g be two continuous functions on the closed interval $[a, b]$, and assume that $f(x) \geq g(x) \geq 0$ for all x in $[a, b]$. Let R be the region bounded by the curves $y = f(x)$ and $y = g(x)$ and the lines $x = a$ and $x = b$. Let S be the solid of revolution generated by revolving the region R about the x axis. If V cubic units is the volume of S, we wish to find a value for V.

Let Δ be a partition of the interval $[a, b]$, given by

$$a = x_0 < x_1 < x_2 < \cdots < x_{n-1} < x_n = b$$

and the ith subinterval $[x_{i-1}, x_i]$ has length $\Delta_i x = x_i - x_{i-1}$. In the ith subinterval, choose any ξ_i, with $x_{i-1} \leq \xi_i \leq x_i$. Consider the n rectangular elements of area for the region R. See Fig. 8.2.7 illustrating the region and the ith rectangle, and Fig. 8.2.8 showing the solid of revolution.

When the ith rectangle is revolved about the x axis, a circular ring (or "washer"), as shown in Fig. 8.2.9, is obtained. The number giving the difference of the measures of the areas of the two circular regions is $(\pi[f(\xi_i)]^2 - \pi[g(\xi_i)]^2)$ and the thickness is $\Delta_i x$ units. Therefore, the measure of the volume of the circular ring is given by

$$\Delta_i V = \pi([f(\xi_i)]^2 - [g(\xi_i)]^2) \, \Delta_i x$$

The sum of the measures of the volumes of the n circular rings formed by

Figure 8.2.7

Figure 8.2.8   Figure 8.2.9

revolving the n rectangular elements of area about the x axis is

$$\sum_{i=1}^{n} \Delta_i V = \sum_{i=1}^{n} \pi([f(\xi_i)]^2 - [g(\xi_i)]^2)\,\Delta_i x \tag{4}$$

The number of cubic units in the volume, then, is defined to be the limit of the Riemann sum in Eq. (4) as $\|\Delta\|$ approaches zero. The limit exists since f^2 and g^2 are continuous on $[a, b]$ because f and g are continuous there.

8.2.2 Definition   Let the functions f and g be continuous on the closed interval $[a, b]$, and assume that $f(x) \geq g(x) \geq 0$ for all x in $[a, b]$. Then if V cubic units is the volume of the solid of revolution generated by revolving about the x axis the region bounded by the curves $y = f(x)$ and $y = g(x)$ and the lines $x = a$ and $x = b$,

$$V = \lim_{\|\Delta\| \to 0} \sum_{i=1}^{n} \pi([f(\xi_i)]^2 - [g(\xi_i)]^2)\,\Delta_i x = \pi \int_{a}^{b} ([f(x)]^2 - [g(x)]^2)\,dx \tag{5}$$

As before, a similar definition applies when the axis of revolution is the y axis or any line parallel to either the x axis or the y axis.

EXAMPLE 1:   Find the volume of the solid generated by revolving about the x axis the region bounded by the parabola $y = x^2 + 1$ and the line $y = x + 3$.

SOLUTION: The points of intersection are $(-1, 2)$ and $(2, 5)$. Figure 8.2.10 shows the region and a rectangular element of area. An element of volume and the solid of revolution are shown in Fig. 8.2.11.

Taking $f(x) = x + 3$ and $g(x) = x^2 + 1$, we find that the measure of the volume of the circular ring is

$$\Delta_i V = \pi([f(\xi_i)]^2 - [g(\xi_i)]^2)\,\Delta_i x$$

Figure 8.2.10

Figure 8.2.11

If V cubic units is the volume of the solid, then

$$V = \lim_{||\Delta|| \to 0} \sum_{i=1}^{n} \pi([f(\xi_i)]^2 - [g(\xi_i)]^2)\,\Delta_i x$$

$$= \pi \int_{-1}^{2} ([f(x)]^2 - [g(x)]^2)\,dx$$

$$= \pi \int_{-1}^{2} [(x+3)^2 - (x^2+1)^2]\,dx$$

$$= \pi \int_{-1}^{2} [-x^4 - x^2 + 6x + 8]\,dx$$

$$= \pi \left[-\tfrac{1}{5}x^5 - \tfrac{1}{3}x^3 + 3x^2 + 8x \right]_{-1}^{2}$$

$$= \pi[(-\tfrac{32}{5} - \tfrac{8}{3} + 12 + 16) - (\tfrac{1}{5} + \tfrac{1}{3} + 3 - 8)]$$

$$= \tfrac{117}{5}\pi$$

Therefore, the volume of the solid of revolution is $\tfrac{117}{5}\pi$ cubic units.

EXAMPLE 2:   Find the volume of the solid generated by revolving about the line $x = -4$ the region bounded by the two parabolas $x = y - y^2$ and $x = y^2 - 3$.

Figure 8.2.12

SOLUTION: The curves intersect at the points $(-2, -1)$ and $(-\frac{3}{4}, \frac{3}{2})$. The region and a rectangular element of area are shown in Fig. 8.2.12. Figure 8.2.13 shows the solid of revolution as well as an element of volume, which is a circular ring.

Figure 8.2.13

Let $F(y) = y - y^2$ and $G(y) = y^2 - 3$. The number of cubic units in the volume of the circular ring is

$$\Delta_i V = \pi([4 + F(\xi_i)]^2 - [4 + G(\xi_i)]^2)\, \Delta_i y$$

Thus,

$$V = \lim_{\|\Delta\| \to 0} \sum_{i=1}^{n} \pi([4 + F(\xi_i)]^2 - [4 + G(\xi_i)]^2)\, \Delta_i y$$

$$= \pi \int_{-1}^{3/2} [(4 + y - y^2)^2 - (4 + y^2 - 3)^2]\, dy$$

$$= \pi \int_{-1}^{3/2} (-2y^3 - 9y^2 + 8y + 15)\, dy$$

$$= \pi \left[-\tfrac{1}{2}y^4 - 3y^3 + 4y^2 + 15y \right]_{-1}^{3/2}$$

$$= \tfrac{875}{32}\pi$$

The volume of the solid of revolution is then $\frac{875}{32}\pi$ cubic units.

Exercises 8.2

In Exercises 1 through 8, find the volume of the solid of revolution when the given region of Fig. 8.2.14 is revolved about the indicated line. An equation of the curve in the figure is $y^2 = x^3$.

1. *OAC* about the *x* axis

2. *OAC* about the line *AC*

3. *OAC* about the line *BC*

4. *OAC* about the *y* axis

5. *OBC* about the *y* axis

6. *OBC* about the line *BC*

7. *OBC* about the line *AC*

8. *OBC* about the *x* axis

Figure 8.2.14

9. Find the volume of the sphere generated by revolving the circle whose equation is $x^2 + y^2 = r^2$ about a diameter.

10. Find by integration the volume of a right-circular cone of altitude h units and base radius a units.

11. Find the volume of the solid generated by revolving about the x axis the region bounded by the curve $y = x^3$ and the lines $y = 0$ and $x = 2$.

12. Find the volume of the solid generated by revolving the region in Exercise 11 about the y axis.

13. Find the volume of the solid generated by revolving about the line $x = -4$ the region bounded by that line and the parabola $x = 4 + 6y - 2y^2$.

14. Find the volume of the solid generated by revolving the region bounded by the curves $y^2 = 4x$ and $y = x$ about the x axis.

15. Find the volume of the solid generated by revolving the region of Exercise 14 about the line $x = 4$.

16. An oil tank in the shape of a sphere has a diameter of 60 ft. How much oil does the tank contain if the depth of the oil is 25 ft?

17. A paraboloid of revolution is obtained by revolving the parabola $y^2 = 4px$ about the x axis. Find the volume bounded by a paraboloid of revolution and a plane perpendicular to its axis if the plane is 10 in. from the vertex, and if the plane section of intersection is a circle having a radius of 6 in.

18. Find the volume of the solid generated by revolving about the x axis the region bounded by the loop of the curve whose equation is $2y^2 = x(x^2 - 4)$.

19. Find the volume of the solid generated when the region bounded by one loop of the curve whose equation is $x^2y^2 = (x^2 - 9)(1 - x^2)$ is revolved about the x axis.

20. The region bounded by a pentagon having vertices at $(-4, 4)$, $(-2, 0)$, $(0, 8)$, $(2, 0)$, and $(4, 4)$ is revolved about the x axis. Find the volume of the solid generated.

8.3 VOLUME OF A SOLID OF REVOLUTION: CYLINDRICAL-SHELL METHOD

In the preceding section we found the volume of a solid of revolution by taking the rectangular elements of area perpendicular to the axis of revolution, and the element of volume was either a circular disk or a circular ring. If a rectangular element of area is parallel to the axis of revolution, then when this element of area is revolved about the axis of revolution, a *cylindrical shell* is obtained. A cylindrical shell is a solid contained between two cylinders having the same center and axis. Such a cylindrical shell is shown in Fig. 8.3.1.

If the cylindrical shell has an inner radius r_1 units, outer radius r_2 units, and altitude h units, then its volume V cubic units is given by

$$V = \pi r_2^2 h - \pi r_1^2 h \tag{1}$$

Let R be the region bounded by the curve $y = f(x)$, the x axis, and the lines $x = a$ and $x = b$, where f is continuous on the closed interval $[a, b]$ and $f(x) \geq 0$ for all x in $[a, b]$; furthermore, assume that $a \geq 0$. Such a region is shown in Fig. 8.3.2. If R is revolved about the y axis, a solid of revolution S is generated. Such a solid is shown in Fig. 8.3.3. To find the volume of S when the rectangular elements of area are taken parallel to the y axis, we proceed in the following manner.

Let Δ be a partition of the closed interval $[a, b]$ given by

$$a = x_0 < x_1 < x_2 < \cdots < x_{n-1} < x_n = b$$

Figure 8.3.1

Figure 8.3.2

Figure 8.3.3

Let m_i be the midpoint of the ith subinterval $[x_{i-1}, x_i]$. Then $m_i = \frac{1}{2}(x_{i-1} + x_i)$. Consider the rectangle having altitude $f(m_i)$ units and width $\Delta_i x$ units. If this rectangle is revolved about the y axis, a cylindrical shell is obtained. Figure 8.3.3 shows the cylindrical shell generated by the rectangular element of area.

If $\Delta_i V$ gives the measure of the volume of this cylindrical shell, we have, from formula (1), where $r_1 = x_{i-1}$, $r_2 = x_i$, and $h = f(m_i)$,

$$\Delta_i V = \pi x_i^2 f(m_i) - \pi x_{i-1}^2 f(m_i)$$

$$= \pi(x_i^2 - x_{i-1}^2) f(m_i)$$

$$\Delta_i V = \pi(x_i - x_{i-1})(x_i + x_{i-1}) f(m_i) \tag{2}$$

Because $x_i - x_{i-1} = \Delta_i x$ and because $x_i + x_{i-1} = 2m_i$, we have from Eq. (2)

$$\Delta_i V = 2\pi m_i f(m_i) \, \Delta_i x \tag{3}$$

If n rectangular elements of area are revolved about the y axis, n cylindrical shells are obtained. The sum of the measures of their volumes is given by

$$\sum_{i=1}^{n} \Delta_i V = \sum_{i=1}^{n} 2\pi m_i f(m_i) \, \Delta_i x \tag{4}$$

which is a Riemann sum.

Then we define the measure of the volume of the solid of revolution to be the limit of the Riemann sum in Eq. (4) as $\|\Delta\|$ approaches zero. The limit exists because if f is continuous on $[a, b]$, so is the function having function values $2\pi x f(x)$.

8.3.1 Definition   Let the function f be continuous on the closed interval $[a, b]$ where $a \geq 0$. Assume that $f(x) \geq 0$ for all x in $[a, b]$. If R is the region bounded by the curve $y = f(x)$, the x axis, and the lines $x = a$ and $x = b$, if S is the solid of revolution obtained by revolving R about the y axis, and if V cubic units is the volume of S, then

$$V = \lim_{\|\Delta\| \to 0} \sum_{i=1}^{n} 2\pi m_i f(m_i) \, \Delta_i x = 2\pi \int_a^b x f(x) \, dx \tag{5}$$

Definition 8.3.1 is consistent with Definitions 8.2.1 and 8.2.2 for the measure of the volume of a solid of revolution for which the definitions apply.

The formula for the measure of the volume of the shell is easily remembered by noticing that $2\pi m_i$, $f(m_i)$, and $\Delta_i x$ are, respectively, the numbers giving the circumference of the circle having as radius the mean of the inner and outer radii of the shell, the altitude of the shell, and the thickness.

EXAMPLE 1: The region bounded by the curve $y = x^2$, the x axis, and the line $x = 2$ is revolved about the y axis. Find the volume of the solid generated. Take the elements of area parallel to the axis of revolution.

SOLUTION: Figure 8.3.4 shows the region and a rectangular element of area. Figure 8.3.5 shows the solid of revolution and the cylindrical shell obtained by revolving the rectangular element of area about the y axis.

Figure 8.3.4   Figure 8.3.5

The element of volume is a cylindrical shell the measure of whose volume is given by

$$\Delta_i V = 2\pi m_i(m_i^2)\Delta_i x = 2\pi m_i^3 \, \Delta_i x$$

Thus,

$$V = \lim_{\|\Delta\| \to 0} \sum_{i=1}^{n} 2\pi m_i^3 \, \Delta_i x$$

$$= 2\pi \int_0^2 x^3 \, dx$$

$$= 2\pi(\tfrac{1}{4}x^4) \Big]_0^2$$

$$= 8\pi$$

Therefore, the volume of the solid of revolution is 8π cubic units.

EXAMPLE 2: The region bounded by the curve $y = x^2$ and the lines $y = 1$ and $x = 2$ is revolved about the line $y = -3$. Find the volume of the solid generated by taking the rectangular elements of area parallel to the axis of revolution.

SOLUTION: The region and a rectangular element of area are shown in Fig. 8.3.6.

The equation of the curve is $y = x^2$. Solving for x, we obtain $x = \pm\sqrt{y}$. Because $x > 0$ for the given region, we have $x = \sqrt{y}$.

The solid of revolution as well as a cylindrical shell element of volume is shown in Fig. 8.3.7. The outer radius of the cylindrical shell is $(y_i + 3)$ units and the inner radius is $(y_{i-1} + 3)$ units. Hence, the mean of the inner

Figure 8.3.6

Figure 8.3.7

and outer radii is $(m_i + 3)$ units. Because the altitude and thickness of the cylindrical shell are, respectively, $(2 - \sqrt{m_i})$ units and $\Delta_i y$ units,

$$\Delta_i V = 2\pi(m_i + 3)(2 - \sqrt{m_i})\,\Delta_i y$$

Hence, if V cubic units is the volume of the solid of revolution,

$$V = \lim_{\|\Delta\| \to 0} \sum_{i=1}^{n} 2\pi(m_i + 3)(2 - \sqrt{m_i})\,\Delta_i y$$

$$= \int_1^4 2\pi(y + 3)(2 - \sqrt{y})\,dy$$

$$= 2\pi \int_1^4 (-y^{3/2} + 2y - 3y^{1/2} + 6)\,dy$$

$$= 2\pi \left[-\tfrac{2}{5}y^{5/2} + y^2 - 2y^{3/2} + 6y \right]_1^4$$

$$= \tfrac{66}{5}\pi$$

Therefore, the volume is $\frac{66}{5}\pi$ cubic units.

Exercises 8.3

1–8. Solve Exercises 1 through 8 in Sec. 8.2 by taking the rectangular elements parallel to the axis of revolution.

In Fig. 8.3.8 the region bounded by the x axis, the line $x = 1$, and the curve $y = x^2$ is denoted by R_1; the region bounded by the two curves $y = x^2$ and $y^2 = x$ is denoted by R_2; the region bounded by the y axis, the line $y = 1$, and the curve $y^2 = x$ is denoted by R_3. In Exercises 9 through 16, find the volume of the solid generated when the indicated region is revolved about the given line.

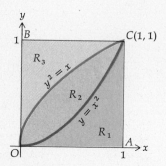

Figure 8.3.8

9. R_1 is revolved about the y axis; the rectangular elements are parallel to the axis of revolution.

10. Same as Exercise 9; but the rectangular elements are perpendicular to the axis of revolution.

11. R_2 is revolved about the x axis; the rectangular elements are parallel to the axis of revolution.

12. Same as Exercise 11; but the rectangular elements are perpendicular to the axis of revolution.

13. R_3 is revolved about the line $y = 2$; the rectangular elements are parallel to the axis of revolution.

14. Same as Exercise 13; but the rectangular elements are perpendicular to the axis of revolution.

15. R_2 is revolved about the line $x = -2$; the rectangular elements are parallel to the axis of revolution.

16. Same as Exercise 15; but the rectangular elements are perpendicular to the axis of revolution.

17. Find the volume of the solid generated if the region bounded by the parabola $y^2 = 4ax$ $(a > 0)$ and the line $x = a$ is revolved about $x = a$.

18. Find the volume of the solid generated by revolving the region bounded by the curve $x^{2/3} + y^{2/3} = a^{2/3}$ about the y axis.

19. Find the volume of the solid generated by revolving about the y axis the region outside the curve $y = x^2$ and between the lines $y = 2x - 1$ and $y = x + 2$.

20. Through a spherical shaped solid of radius 6 in., a hole of radius 2 in. is bored, and the axis of the hole is a diameter of the sphere. Find the volume of the part of the solid that remains.

21. A hole of radius $2\sqrt{3}$ in. is bored through the center of a spherical shaped solid of radius 4 in. Find the volume of the portion of the solid cut out.

22. Find the volume of the solid generated if the region bounded by the parabola $y^2 = 4px$ and the line $x = p$ is revolved about the y axis.

8.4 VOLUME OF A SOLID HAVING KNOWN PARALLEL PLANE SECTIONS

Let S be a solid. By a *plane section* of S is meant a plane region formed by the intersection of a plane with S. In Sec. 8.2 we learned how to find the volume of a solid of revolution for which all plane sections perpendicular to the axis of revolution are circular. We now generalize this method to find the volume of a solid for which it is possible to express the area of any plane section perpendicular to a fixed line in terms of the perpendicular distance of the plane section from a fixed point. We first define what we mean when we say that a solid is a "cylinder."

8.4.1 Definition

A solid is a *right cylinder* if it is bounded by two congruent plane regions R_1 and R_2 lying in parallel planes and by a lateral surface generated by a line segment, having its endpoints on the boundaries of R_1 and R_2, which moves so that it is always perpendicular to the planes of R_1 and R_2.

Figure 8.4.1   Figure 8.4.2   Figure 8.4.3

Figure 8.4.1 illustrates a right cylinder. The *height* of the cylinder is the perpendicular distance between the planes of R_1 and R_2, and the base is either R_1 or R_2. If the base of the right cylinder is a region enclosed by a circle, we have a *right-circular cylinder* (see Fig. 8.4.2); if the base is a region enclosed by a rectangle, we have a *rectangular parallelepiped* (see Fig. 8.4.3).

If the area of the base of a right cylinder is A square units and the height is h units, then by definition we let the volume of the right cylinder be measured by the product of A and h. As stated above, we are considering solids for which the area of any plane section that is perpendicular to a fixed line is a function of the perpendicular distance of the plane section from a fixed point. The solid S of Fig. 8.4.4 is such a solid, and it lies between the planes perpendicular to the x axis at a and b. We represent the number of square units in the area of the plane section of S in the plane perpendicular to the x axis at x by $A(x)$, where A is continuous on $[a, b]$.

Let Δ be a partition of the closed interval $[a, b]$ given by

$$a = x_0 < x_1 < x_2 < \cdots < x_n = b$$

We have, then, n subintervals of the form $[x_{i-1}, x_i]$, where $i = 1, 2, \ldots, n$, with the length of the ith subinterval being $\Delta_i x = x_i - x_{i-1}$. Choose any

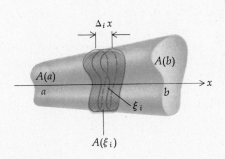

Figure 8.4.4

number ξ_i, with $x_{i-1} \le \xi_i \le x_i$, in each subinterval and construct the right cylinders of heights $\Delta_i x$ units and plane section areas $A(\xi_i)$ square units. The volume of the ith cylinder is $A(\xi_i) \Delta_i x$ cubic units. We obtain n right cylinders, and the sum of the measures of the volumes of these n cylinders is given by the Riemann sum

$$\sum_{i=1}^{n} A(\xi_i) \Delta_i x \tag{1}$$

This Riemann sum is an approximation of what we intuitively think of as the measure of the volume of S, and the smaller we take the norm $\|\Delta\|$ of the partition Δ, the larger will be n, and the closer this approximation will be to the number we wish to assign to the measure of the volume. We have, then, the following definition.

8.4.2 Definition   Let S be a solid such that S lies between planes drawn perpendicular to the x axis at a and b. If the measure of the area of the plane section of S drawn perpendicular to the x axis at x is given by $A(x)$, where A is continuous on $[a, b]$, then the measure of the volume of S is given by

$$V = \lim_{\|\Delta\| \to 0} \sum_{i=1}^{n} A(\xi_i) \Delta_i x = \int_a^b A(x) \, dx \tag{2}$$

Note that Definitions 8.2.1 and 8.2.2 are special cases of Definition 8.4.2. If in Eq. (2) we take $A(x) = \pi [f(x)]^2$, we have Eq. (3) of Sec. 8.2. If we take $A(x) = \pi([f(x)]^2 - [g(x)]^2)$, we have Eq. (5) of Sec. 8.2.

EXAMPLE 1:   If the base of a solid is a circle with a radius of r units and if all plane sections perpendicular to a fixed diameter of the base are squares, find the volume of the solid.

SOLUTION: Take the circle in the xy plane, the center at the origin, and the fixed diameter along the x axis. Therefore, an equation of the circle is $x^2 + y^2 = r^2$. Figure 8.4.5 shows the solid and an element of volume, which is a right cylinder of altitude $\Delta_i x$ units and with an area of the base given by $[2f(\xi_i)]^2$ square units, where $f(x)$ is obtained by solving the equation of the circle for y and setting $y = f(x)$. This computation gives $f(x) = \sqrt{r^2 - x^2}$. Therefore, if V cubic units is the volume of the solid, we have

$$V = \lim_{\|\Delta\| \to 0} \sum_{i=1}^{n} [2f(\xi_i)]^2 \Delta_i x$$

$$= 4 \int_{-r}^{r} (r^2 - x^2) \, dx$$

$$= 4 \left[r^2 x - \tfrac{1}{3} x^3 \right]_{-r}^{r}$$

$$= \tfrac{16}{3} r^3$$

Figure 8.4.5

EXAMPLE 2:   A wedge is cut from a right-circular cylinder with a radius of r in. by two planes, one perpendicular to the axis of the cylinder and the other intersecting the first at an angle of measurement 60° along a diameter of the circular plane section. Find the volume of the wedge.

SOLUTION: The wedge is shown in Fig. 8.4.6. The xy plane is taken as the plane perpendicular to the axis of the cylinder, and the origin is at the point of perpendicularity. An equation of the circular plane section is then $x^2 + y^2 = r^2$. Every plane section of the wedge perpendicular to the x axis is a right triangle. An element of volume is a right cylinder having altitude $\Delta_i x$ in., and area of the base given by $\frac{1}{2}\sqrt{3}\,[f(\xi_i)]^2$ in.^{2}, where $f(x)$ is obtained by solving the equation of the circle for y and setting $y = f(x)$, thereby giving $f(x) = \sqrt{r^2 - x^2}$. Therefore, if V in.^{3} is the volume of the wedge,

$$V = \lim_{||\Delta|| \to 0} \sum_{i=1}^{n} \tfrac{1}{2}\sqrt{3}\,(r^2 - \xi_i^2)\,\Delta_i x$$

$$= \tfrac{1}{2}\sqrt{3}\int_{-r}^{r} (r^2 - x^2)\,dx$$

$$= \tfrac{1}{2}\sqrt{3}\left[r^2 x - \tfrac{1}{3}x^3 \right]_{-r}^{r}$$

$$= \tfrac{2}{3}\sqrt{3}\,r^3$$

Hence, the volume of the wedge is $\tfrac{2}{3}\sqrt{3}\,r^3$ in.^{3}

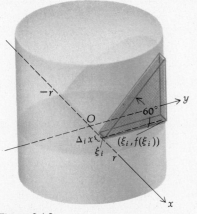

Figure 8.4.6

Exercises 8.4

1. The base of a solid is a circle having a radius of r units. Find the volume of the solid if all plane sections perpendicular to a fixed diameter of the base are equilateral triangles.

2. The base of a solid is a circle with a radius of r units, and all plane sections perpendicular to a fixed diameter of the base are isosceles right triangles having the hypotenuse in the plane of the base. Find the volume of the solid.

3. Solve Exercise 2 if the isosceles right triangles have one leg in the plane of the base.

4. Find the volume of a right pyramid having a height of h units and a square base of side a units.

5. Find the volume of the tetrahedron having 3 mutually perpendicular faces and three mutually perpendicular edges whose lengths have measures a, b, and c.

6. The base of a solid is a circle with a radius of 4 in., and each plane section perpendicular to a fixed diameter of the base is an isosceles triangle having an altitude of 10 in. and a chord of the circle as a base. Find the volume of the solid.

7. The base of a solid is a circle with a radius of 9 in., and each plane section perpendicular to a fixed diameter of the base is a square having a chord of the circle as a diagonal. Find the volume of the solid.

8. Two right-circular cylinders, each having a radius of r units, have axes that intersect at right angles. Find the volume of the solid common to the two cylinders.

9. A wedge is cut from a solid in the shape of a right-circular cylinder with a radius of r in. by a plane through a diameter of the base and inclined to the plane of the base at an angle of measurement 45°. Find the volume of the wedge.

10. A wedge is cut from a solid in the shape of a right-circular cone having a base radius of 5 ft and an altitude of 20 ft by two half planes through the axis of the cone. The angle between the two planes has a measurement of 30°. Find the volume of the wedge cut out.

8.5 WORK   The "work" done by a force acting on an object is defined in physics as "force times displacement." For example, suppose that an object is moving to the right along the x axis from a point a to a point b, and a constant force of F lb is acting on the object in the direction of motion. Then if the displacement is measured in feet, $(b - a)$ is the number of feet in the displacement. And if W is the number of foot-pounds of work done by the force, W is defined by

$$W = F(b - a) \qquad (1)$$

● ILLUSTRATION 1: If W is the number of foot-pounds in the work necessary to lift a 70-lb weight to a height of 3 ft, then

$$W = 70 \cdot 3 = 210$$ ●

In this section we consider the work done by a variable force, which is a function of the position of the object on which the force is acting. We wish to define what is meant by the term "work" in such a case.

Suppose that $f(x)$, where f is continuous on $[a, b]$, is the number of units in the force acting in the direction of motion on an object as it moves to the right along the x axis from point a to point b. Let Δ be a partition of the closed interval $[a, b]$:

$$a = x_0 < x_1 < x_2 < \cdots < x_{n-1} < x_n = b$$

The ith subinterval is $[x_{i-1}, x_i]$; and if x_{i-1} is close to x_i, the force is almost constant in this subinterval. If we assume that the force is constant in the ith subinterval and if ξ_i is any point such that $x_{i-1} \leq \xi_i \leq x_i$, then if $\Delta_i W$ is the number of units of work done on the object as it moves from the point x_{i-1} to the point x_i, from formula (1) we have

$$\Delta_i W = f(\xi_i)(x_i - x_{i-1})$$

Replacing $x_i - x_{i-1}$ by $\Delta_i x$, we have

$$\Delta_i W = f(\xi_i) \Delta_i x$$

and

$$\sum_{i=1}^{n} \Delta_i W = \sum_{i=1}^{n} f(\xi_i) \Delta_i x \tag{2}$$

The smaller we take the norm of the partition Δ, the larger n will be and the closer the Riemann sum in Eq. (2) will be to what we intuitively think of as the measure of the total work done. We therefore define the measure of the total work as the limit of the Riemann sum in Eq. (2).

8.5.1 Definition   Let the function f be continuous on the closed interval $[a, b]$ and $f(x)$ be the number of units in the force acting on an object at the point x on the x axis. Then if W units is the *work* done by the force as the object moves from a to b, W is given by

$$W = \lim_{\|\Delta\| \to 0} \sum_{i=1}^{n} f(\xi_i) \Delta_i x = \int_a^b f(x)\, dx \tag{3}$$

In the following example we use *Hooke's law*, which states that if a spring is stretched x in. beyond its natural length, it is pulled back with a force equal to kx lb, where k is a constant depending on the wire used.

EXAMPLE 1:   A spring has a natural length of 14 in. If a force of 5 lb is required to keep the spring stretched 2 in., how much work is done in stretching the spring from its natural length to a length of 18 in.?

SOLUTION: Place the spring along the x axis with the origin at the point where the stretching starts (see Fig. 8.5.1).

Figure 8.5.1

Let $x =$ the number of inches the spring is stretched;
$f(x) =$ the number of pounds in the force acting on the spring x in. beyond its natural length.

Then, by Hooke's law, $f(x) = kx$. Because $f(2) = 5$, we have

$$5 = k \cdot 2$$

$$k = \tfrac{5}{2}$$

Therefore,

$$f(x) = \tfrac{5}{2}x$$

If $W =$ the number of inch-pounds of work done in stretching the spring from its natural length of 14 in. to a length of 18 in., we have

$$W = \lim_{||\Delta|| \to 0} \sum_{i=1}^{n} f(\xi_i) \, \Delta_i x$$

$$= \int_0^4 f(x) \, dx$$

$$= \int_0^4 \tfrac{5}{2}x \, dx$$

$$= \tfrac{5}{4}x^2 \Big]_0^4$$

$$= 20$$

Therefore, the work done in stretching the spring is 20 in.-lb.

EXAMPLE 2: A water tank in the form of an inverted right-circular cone is 20 ft across the top and 15 ft deep. If the surface of the water is 5 ft below the top of the tank, find the work done in pumping the water to the top of the tank.

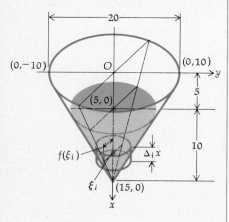

Figure 8.5.2

SOLUTION: Refer to Fig. 8.5.2. The positive x axis is chosen in the downward direction because the motion is vertical. Take the origin at the top of the tank. We consider a partition of the closed interval $[5, 15]$ on the x axis and let ξ_i be any point in the ith subinterval $[x_{i-1}, x_i]$. An element of volume is a circular disk having thickness $\Delta_i x$ ft and radius $f(\xi_i)$ ft, where the function f is determined by an equation of the line through the points $(0, 10)$ and $(15, 0)$ in the form $y = f(x)$. The number of cubic feet in the volume of this element is given by $\Delta_i V = \pi[f(\xi_i)]^2 \, \Delta_i x$. If w is the number of pounds in the weight of 1 ft³ of water, then the number of pounds in the weight of this element is $w\pi[f(\xi_i)]^2 \, \Delta_i x$, which is the force required to pump the element to the top of the tank. If x_{i-1} is close to x_i, then the distance through which this element moves is approximately ξ_i ft. Thus, if $\Delta_i W$ ft-lb is the work done in pumping the element to the top of the tank, $\Delta_i W$ is approximately $(w\pi[f(\xi_i)]^2 \, \Delta_i x) \cdot \xi_i$; so if W is the number of foot-pounds of work done,

$$W = \lim_{||\Delta|| \to 0} \sum_{i=1}^{n} w\pi[f(\xi_i)]^2 \cdot \xi_i \, \Delta_i x$$

$$= w\pi \int_5^{15} [f(x)]^2 x \, dx$$

To determine $f(x)$, we find an equation of the line through the points

$(15, 0)$ and $(0, 10)$ by using the intercept form:

$$\frac{x}{15} + \frac{y}{10} = 1 \quad \text{or} \quad y = -\tfrac{2}{3}x + 10$$

Therefore, $f(x) = -\tfrac{2}{3}x + 10$, and

$$W = w\pi \int_5^{15} (-\tfrac{2}{3}x + 10)^2 x \, dx$$

$$= w\pi \int_5^{15} (\tfrac{4}{9}x^3 - \tfrac{40}{3}x^2 + 100x) \, dx$$

$$= w\pi \left[\tfrac{1}{9}x^4 - \tfrac{40}{9}x^3 + 50x^2 \right]_5^{15}$$

$$= \tfrac{1}{9}(10{,}000\pi w)$$

Therefore, the work done is $10{,}000\pi w/9$ ft-lb.

Exercises 8.5

1. A spring has a natural length of 8 in. If a force of 20 lb stretches the spring $\tfrac{1}{2}$ in., find the work done in stretching the spring from 8 in. to 11 in.

2. A spring has a natural length of 10 in., and a 30-lb force stretches it to $11\tfrac{1}{2}$ in. Find the work done in stretching the spring from 10 in. to 12 in. Then find the work done in stretching the spring from 12 in. to 14 in.

3. A spring has a natural length of 6 in. A 12,000-lb force compresses the spring to $5\tfrac{1}{2}$ in. Find the work done in compressing it from 6 in. to 5 in. Hooke's law holds for compression as well as for extension.

4. A spring has a natural length of 6 in. A 1200-lb force compresses it to $5\tfrac{1}{2}$ in. Find the work done in compressing it from 6 in. to $4\tfrac{1}{2}$ in.

5. A swimming pool full of water is in the form of a rectangular parallelepiped 5 ft deep, 15 ft wide, and 25 ft long. Find the work required to pump the water in the pool up to a level 1 ft above the surface of the pool.

6. A trough full of water is 10 ft long, and its cross section is in the shape of an isosceles triangle 2 ft wide across the top and 2 ft high. How much work is done in pumping all the water out of the trough over the top?

7. A hemispherical tank with a radius of 6 ft is filled with water to a depth of 4 ft. Find the work done in pumping the water to the top of the tank.

8. A right-circular cylindrical tank with a depth of 12 ft and a radius of 4 ft is half full of oil weighing 60 lb/ft³. Find the work done in pumping the oil to a height 6 ft above the tank.

9. A cable 200 ft long and weighing 4 lb/ft is hanging vertically down a well. If a weight of 100 lb is suspended from the lower end of the cable, find the work done in pulling the cable and weight to the top of the well.

10. A bucket weighing 20 lb containing 60 lb of sand is attached to the lower end of a 100 ft long chain that weighs 10 lb and is hanging in a deep well. Find the work done in raising the bucket to the top of the well.

11. Solve Exercise 10 if the sand is leaking out of the bucket at a constant rate and has all leaked out just as soon as the bucket is at the top of the well.

12. As a water tank is being raised, water spills out at a constant rate of 2 ft³ per foot of rise. If the tank originally contained 1000 ft³ of water, find the work done in raising the tank 20 ft.

13. A tank in the form of a rectangular parallelepiped 6 ft deep, 4 ft wide, and 12 ft long is full of oil weighing 50 lb/ft³. When one-third of the work necessary to pump the oil to the top of the tank has been done, find by how much the surface of the oil is lowered.

14. A cylindrical tank 10 ft high and 5 ft in radius is standing on a platform 50 ft high. Find the depth of the water when one-half of the work required to fill the tank from the ground level through a pipe in the bottom has been done.

15. A one horsepower motor can do 550 ft-lb of work per second. If a 0.1 hp motor is used to pump water from a full tank in the shape of a rectangular parallelepiped 2 ft deep, 2 ft wide, and 6 ft long to a point 5 ft above the top of the tank, how long will it take?

16. A meteorite is a miles from the center of the earth and falls to the surface of the earth. The force of gravity is inversely proportional to the square of the distance of a body from the center of the earth. Find the work done by gravity if the weight of the meteorite is w lb at the surface of the earth. Let R miles be the radius of the earth.

8.6 LIQUID PRESSURE

Another application of the definite integral in physics is to find the force caused by liquid pressure on a plate submerged in the liquid or on a side of a container holding the liquid. First of all, suppose that a flat plate is inserted horizontally into a liquid in a container. The weight of the liquid exerts a force on the plate. The force per square unit of area exerted by the liquid on the plate is called the *pressure* of the liquid.

Let w be the number of pounds in the weight of one cubic foot of the liquid and h be the number of feet in the depth of a point below the surface of the liquid. If p is the number of pounds per square foot of pressure exerted by the liquid at the point, then

$$p = wh \tag{1}$$

If A is the number of square feet in the area of a flat plate that is submerged horizontally in the liquid, and F is the number of pounds in the force caused by liquid pressure acting on the upper face of the plate, then

$$F = pA \tag{2}$$

Substituting from formula (1) into (2) gives us

$$F = whA \tag{3}$$

Note that formula (1) states that the size of the container is immaterial so far as liquid pressure is concerned. For example, at a depth of 5 ft in a swimming pool filled with salt water the pressure is the same as at a depth of 5 ft in the Pacific Ocean, assuming the density of the water is the same.

Now suppose that the plate is submerged vertically in the liquid. Then at points on the plate at different depths the pressure, computed from formula (1), will be different and will be greater at the bottom of the plate than at the top. We now proceed to define the force caused by liquid pressure when the plate is submerged vertically in the liquid. We use

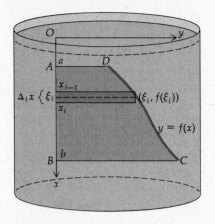

Figure 8.6.1

Pascal's principle: At any point in a liquid, the pressure is the same in all directions.

In Fig. 8.6.1 let $ABCD$ be the region bounded by the x axis, the lines $x = a$ and $x = b$, and the curve $y = f(x)$, where the function f is continuous and $f(x) \geq 0$ on the closed interval $[a, b]$. Choose the coordinate axes so the y axis lies along the line of the surface of the liquid. Take the x axis vertical with the positive direction downward. The length of the plate at a depth x ft is given by $f(x)$ ft.

Let Δ be a partition of the closed interval $[a, b]$ which divides the interval into n subintervals. Choose a point ξ_i in the ith subinterval, with $x_{i-1} \leq \xi_i \leq x_i$. Draw n horizontal rectangles. The ith rectangle has a length of $f(\xi_i)$ ft and a width of $\Delta_i x$ ft (see Fig. 8.6.1).

If we rotate each rectangular element through an angle of 90°, each element becomes a plate submerged in the liquid at a depth of ξ_i ft below the surface of the liquid and perpendicular to the region $ABCD$. Then the force on the ith rectangular element is given by $w\xi_i f(\xi_i) \, \Delta_i x$ lb. An approximation to F, the number of pounds in the total force on the vertical plate, is given by

$$\sum_{i=1}^{n} w\xi_i f(\xi_i) \, \Delta_i x \tag{4}$$

which is a Riemann sum.

The smaller we take $\|\Delta\|$, the larger n will be and the closer the approximation given by (4) will be to what we wish to be the measure of the total force. We have, then, the following definition.

8.6.1 Definition   Suppose that a flat plate is submerged vertically in a liquid of weight w pounds per cubic unit. The length of the plate at a depth of x units below the surface of the liquid is $f(x)$ units, where f is continuous on the closed interval $[a, b]$ and $f(x) \geq 0$ on $[a, b]$. Then F, the number of pounds of *force caused by liquid pressure* on the plate, is given by

$$F = \lim_{\|\Delta\| \to 0} \sum_{i=1}^{n} w\xi_i f(\xi_i) \, \Delta_i x = \int_a^b wxf(x) \, dx \tag{5}$$

EXAMPLE 1:   A trough having a trapezoidal cross section is full of water. If the trapezoid is 3 ft wide at the top, 2 ft wide at the bottom, and 2 ft deep, find the total force owing to liquid pressure on one end of the trough.

SOLUTION: Figure 8.6.2 illustrates one end of the trough together with a rectangular element of area. An equation of line AB is $y = \frac{3}{2} - \frac{1}{4}x$. Let $f(x) = \frac{3}{2} - \frac{1}{4}x$. If we rotate the rectangular element through 90°, the force on the element is given by $2w\xi_i f(\xi_i) \, \Delta_i x$ lb. If F is the number of pounds in the total force on the side of the trough,

$$F = \lim_{\|\Delta\| \to 0} \sum_{i=1}^{n} 2w\xi_i f(\xi_i) \, \Delta_i x$$

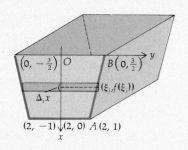

Figure 8.6.2

$$= 2w \int_0^2 xf(x) \, dx$$

$$= 2w \int_0^2 x(\tfrac{3}{2} - \tfrac{1}{4}x) \, dx$$

$$= 2w \left[\tfrac{3}{4}x^2 - \tfrac{1}{12}x^3 \right]_0^2$$

$$= \tfrac{14}{3}w$$

Taking $w = 62.5$, we find that the total force is 291.2 lb.

EXAMPLE 2:   The ends of a trough are semicircular regions, each with a radius of 2 ft. Find the force caused by liquid pressure on one end if the trough is full of water.

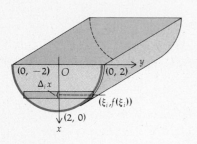

Figure 8.6.3

SOLUTION: Figure 8.6.3 shows one end of the trough together with a rectangular element of area. An equation of the semicircle is $x^2 + y^2 = 4$. Solving for y gives $y = \sqrt{4 - x^2}$, and so let $f(x) = \sqrt{4 - x^2}$. The force on the rectangular element is given by $2w\xi_i f(\xi_i) \, \Delta_i x$. So if F pounds is the total force on the side of the trough,

$$F = \lim_{\|\Delta\| \to 0} \sum_{i=1}^n 2w\xi_i f(\xi_i) \, \Delta_i x$$

$$= 2w \int_0^2 xf(x) \, dx$$

$$= 2w \int_0^2 x\sqrt{4 - x^2} \, dx$$

$$= -\tfrac{2}{3}w(4 - x^2)^{3/2} \Big]_0^2$$

$$= \tfrac{16}{3}w$$

Therefore, the total force is $\tfrac{16}{3}w$ lb.

Exercises 8.6

1. A plate in the shape of a rectangle is submerged vertically in a tank of water, with the upper edge lying in the surface. If the width of the plate is 10 ft and the depth is 8 ft, find the force due to liquid pressure on one side of the plate.

2. A square plate of side 4 ft is submerged vertically in a tank of water and its center is 2 ft below the surface. Find the force due to liquid pressure on one side of the plate.

3. Solve Exercise 2 if the center of the plate is 4 ft below the surface.

4. A plate in the shape of an isosceles right triangle is submerged vertically in a tank of water, with one leg lying in the surface. The legs are each 6 ft long. Find the force due to liquid pressure on one side of the plate.

5. A rectangular tank full of water is 2 ft wide and 18 in. deep. Find the force due to liquid pressure on one end of the tank.

6. The ends of a trough are equilateral triangles having sides with lengths of 2 ft. If the water in the trough is 1 ft deep, find the force due to liquid pressure on one end.

7. The face of a dam adjacent to the water is vertical, and its shape is in the form of an isosceles triangle 250 ft wide across the top and 100 ft high in the center. If the water is 10 ft deep in the center, find the total force on the dam due to liquid pressure.

8. An oil tank is in the shape of a right-circular cylinder 4 ft in diameter, and its axis is horizontal. If the tank is half full of oil weighing 50 lb/ft³, find the total force on one end due to liquid pressure.

9. The face of the gate of a dam is in the shape of an isosceles triangle 4 ft wide at the top and 3 ft high. If the upper edge of the face of the gate is 15 ft below the surface of the water, find the total force due to liquid pressure on the gate.

10. The face of a gate of a dam is vertical and in the shape of an isosceles trapezoid 3 ft wide at the top, 4 ft wide at the bottom, and 3 ft high. If the upper base is 20 ft below the surface of the water, find the total force due to liquid pressure on the gate.

11. The face of a dam adjacent to the water is inclined at an angle of 30° from the vertical. The shape of the face is a rectangle of width 50 ft and slant height 30 ft. If the dam is full of water, find the total force due to liquid pressure on the face.

12. Solve Exercise 11 if the face of the dam is an isosceles trapezoid 120 ft wide at the top, 80 ft wide at the bottom, and with a slant height of 40 ft.

13. The bottom of a swimming pool is an inclined plane. The pool is 2 ft deep at one end and 8 ft deep at the other. If the width of the pool is 25 ft and the length is 40 ft, find the total force due to liquid pressure on the bottom.

14. If the end of a water tank is in the shape of a rectangle and the tank is full, show that the measure of the force due to liquid pressure on the end is the product of the measure of the area of the end and the measure of the force at the geometrical center.

8.7 CENTER OF MASS OF A ROD

In Sec. 7.5 we learned that if the function f is continuous on the closed interval $[a, b]$, the average value of f on $[a, b]$ is given by

$$\frac{\int_a^b f(x)\ dx}{b - a}$$

An important application of the average value of a function occurs in physics in connection with the concept of *center of mass*.

To arrive at a definition of "mass," consider a particle that is set into motion along an axis by a force of F lb exerted on the particle. So long as the force is acting on the particle, the velocity of the particle is increasing; that is, the particle has an acceleration. The ratio of the force to the acceleration is constant regardless of the magnitude of the force, and this constant ratio is called the *mass* of the particle.

● ILLUSTRATION 1: If the acceleration of a certain particle is 10 ft/sec² when the force is 30 lb, the mass of the particle is

$$\frac{30\ \text{lb}}{10\ \text{ft/sec}^2} = \frac{3\ \text{lb}}{1\ \text{ft/sec}^2}$$

Thus, for every 1 ft/sec² of acceleration, a force of 3 lb must be exerted on the particle.   ●

When the unit of force is 1 lb and the unit of acceleration is 1 ft/sec², the unit of mass is called *one slug*. That is, 1 slug is the mass of a particle whose acceleration is 1 ft/sec² when the magnitude of the force on the particle is 1 lb. Hence, the particle of Illustration 1 that has an acceleration of 10 ft/sec² when the force is 30 lb has a mass of 3 slugs.

From physics, if W lb is the weight of an object having a mass of m slugs, and g ft/sec² is the constant of acceleration due to gravity, then

$$W = mg$$

Consider now a horizontal rod, of negligible weight and thickness, placed on the x axis. On the rod is a system of n particles located at points $x_1, x_2, \ldots, x_n$. The ith particle $(i = 1, 2, \ldots, n)$ is at a directed distance x_i ft from the origin and its mass is m_i slugs. See Fig. 8.7.1. The number of slugs in the total mass of the system is $\sum_{i=1}^{n} m_i$. We define the

Figure 8.7.1

moment of mass of the ith particle with respect to the origin as $m_i x_i$ slug-ft. The moment of mass for the system is defined as the sum of the moments of mass of all the particles. Hence, if M_o slug-ft is the moment of mass of the system with respect to the origin, then

$$M_o = \sum_{i=1}^{n} m_i x_i$$

Now we wish to find a point $\bar{x}$ such that if the total mass of the system were concentrated there, its moment of mass with respect to the origin would be equal to the moment of mass of the system with respect to the origin. Then $\bar{x}$ must satisfy the equation

$$\bar{x} \sum_{i=1}^{n} m_i = \sum_{i=1}^{n} m_i x_i$$

and so

$$\bar{x} = \frac{\sum_{i=1}^{n} m_i x_i}{\sum_{i=1}^{n} m_i} \tag{1}$$

The point $\bar{x}$ is called the *center of mass* of the system, and it is the point where the system will balance. The position of the center of mass is independent of the position of the origin; that is, the location of the center of mass relative to the positions of the particles does not change when the origin is changed.

EXAMPLE 1: Given four particles of masses 2, 3, 1, and 5 slugs located on the x axis at the points having coordinates 5, 2, -3, and -4, respectively, where distance measurement is in feet, find the center of mass of this system.	SOLUTION: If $\bar{x}$ is the coordinate of the center of mass, we have from formula (1) $$\bar{x} = \frac{2(5) + 3(2) + (1)(-3) + 5(-4)}{2 + 3 + 1 + 5} = -\frac{7}{11}$$ Thus, the center of mass is $\frac{7}{11}$ ft to the left of the origin.

The preceding discussion is now extended to a rigid horizontal rod having a continuously distributed mass. The rod is said to be *homogeneous* if its mass is directly proportional to its length. In other words, if the segment of the rod whose length is $\Delta_i x$ ft has a mass of $\Delta_i m$ slugs, and $\Delta_i m = k \, \Delta_i x$, then the rod is homogeneous. The number k is a constant and k slugs/ft is called the *linear density* of the rod.

Figure 8.7.2

Suppose that we have a nonhomogeneous rod, in which case the linear density varies along the rod. Let L ft be the length of the rod, and place the rod on the x axis so the left endpoint of the rod is at the origin and the right endpoint is at L. See Fig. 8.7.2. The linear density at any point x on the rod is $\rho(x)$ slugs/ft, where ρ is continuous on $[0, L]$. To find the total mass of the rod we consider a partition Δ of the closed interval $[0, L]$ into n subintervals. The ith subinterval is $[x_{i-1}, x_i]$, and its length is $\Delta_i x$ ft. If ξ_i is any point in $[x_{i-1}, x_i]$, an approximation to the mass of the part of the rod contained in the ith subinterval is $\Delta_i m$ slugs, where

$$\Delta_i m = \rho(\xi_i) \, \Delta_i x$$

The number of slugs in the total mass of the rod is approximated by

$$\sum_{i=1}^{n} \Delta_i m = \sum_{i=1}^{n} \rho(\xi_i) \, \Delta_i x \tag{2}$$

The smaller we take the norm of the partition Δ, the closer the Riemann sum in Eq. (2) will be to what we intuitively think of as the measure of the mass of the rod, and so we define the measure of the mass as the limit of the Riemann sum in Eq. (2).

8.7.1 Definition A rod of length L ft has its left endpoint at the origin. If the number of slugs per foot in the linear density at a point x ft from the origin is $\rho(x)$, where ρ is continuous on $[0, L]$, then the total *mass* of the rod is M slugs,

where

$$M = \lim_{||\Delta|| \to 0} \sum_{i=1}^{n} \rho(\xi_i)\ \Delta_i x = \int_0^L \rho(x)\ dx \tag{3}$$

EXAMPLE 2: The density at any point of a rod 4 ft long varies directly as the distance from the point to an external point in the line of the rod and 2 ft from an end, where the density is 5 slugs/ft. Find the total mass of the rod.

SOLUTION: Figure 8.7.3 shows the rod placed on the x axis. If $\rho(x)$ is the number of slugs per foot in the density of the rod at the point x ft from the end having the greater density, then

$$\rho(x) = c(6 - x)$$

where c is the constant of proportionality. Because $\rho(4) = 5$, we have $5 = 2c$ or $c = \frac{5}{2}$. Hence, $\rho(x) = \frac{5}{2}(6 - x)$. Therefore, if M slugs is the total mass of the rod, we have from Definition 8.7.1.

$$M = \lim_{||\Delta|| \to 0} \sum_{i=1}^{n} \tfrac{5}{2}(6 - \xi_i)\ \Delta_i x$$

$$= \int_0^4 \tfrac{5}{2}(6 - x)\ dx$$

$$= \tfrac{5}{2}\left[6x - \tfrac{1}{2}x^2\right]_0^4$$

$$= 40$$

The total mass of the rod is therefore 40 slugs.

Figure 8.7.3

We now proceed to define the center of mass of the rod of Definition 8.7.1. However, first we must define the moment of mass of the rod with respect to the origin.

Figure 8.7.4

As before, place the rod on the x axis with the left endpoint at the origin and the right endpoint at L. See Fig. 8.7.4. Let Δ be a partition of $[0, L]$ into n subintervals, with the ith subinterval $[x_{i-1}, x_i]$ having length $\Delta_i x$ ft. If ξ_i is any point in $[x_{i-1}, x_i]$, an approximation to the moment of mass with respect to the origin of the part of the rod contained in the ith subinterval is $\xi_i \, \Delta_i m$ slug-ft, where $\Delta_i m = \rho(\xi_i) \, \Delta_i x$. The number of slug-feet in the moment of mass of the entire rod is approximated by

$$\sum_{i=1}^{n} \xi_i \, \Delta_i m = \sum_{i=1}^{n} \xi_i \, \rho(\xi_i) \, \Delta_i x \tag{4}$$

The smaller we take the norm of the partition Δ, the closer the Riemann sum in Eq. (4) will be to what we intuitively think of as the measure of the moment of mass of the rod with respect to the origin. We have, then, the following definition.

8.7.2 Definition   A rod of length L ft has its left endpoint at the origin and the number of slugs per foot in the linear density at a point x ft from the origin is $\rho(x)$, where ρ is continuous on $[0, L]$. The *moment of mass* of the rod with respect to the origin is M_o slug-ft, where

$$M_o = \lim_{||\Delta|| \to 0} \sum_{i=1}^{n} \xi_i \rho(\xi_i) \, \Delta_i x = \int_0^L x\rho(x) \, dx \tag{5}$$

The center of mass of the rod is at the point $\bar{x}$ such that if M slugs is the total mass of the rod, $\bar{x}M = M_o$. Thus, from Eqs. (3) and (5) we get

$$\bar{x} = \frac{\displaystyle\int_0^L x\rho(x) \, dx}{\displaystyle\int_0^L \rho(x) \, dx} \tag{6}$$

EXAMPLE 3:   Find the center of mass for the rod in Example 2.

SOLUTION: In Example 2, we found $M = 40$. Using Eq. (6) with $\rho(x) = \frac{5}{2}(6 - x)$, we have

$$\bar{x} = \frac{\displaystyle\int_0^4 \frac{5}{2} x(6 - x) \, dx}{40} = \frac{1}{16} \left[3x^2 - \frac{1}{3} x^3 \right]_0^4 = \frac{5}{3}$$

Therefore, the center of mass is at $\frac{5}{3}$ ft from the end having the greater density.

● ILLUSTRATION 2: If a rod is of uniform density k slugs/ft, where k is a constant, then from formula (6) we have

$$\bar{x} = \frac{\displaystyle\int_0^L xk \, dx}{\displaystyle\int_0^L k \, dx} = \frac{\dfrac{kx^2}{2} \Big]_0^L}{kx \Big]_0^L} = \frac{\dfrac{kL^2}{2}}{kL} = \frac{L}{2}$$

Thus, the center of mass is at the center of the rod, as is to be expected.●

Exercises 8.7

In Exercises 1 through 4, a system of particles is located on the x axis. The number of slugs in the mass of each particle and the coordinate of its position are given. Distance is measured in feet. Find the center of mass of each system.

1. $m_1 = 5$ at 2; $m_2 = 6$ at 3; $m_3 = 4$ at 5; $m_4 = 3$ at 8.

2. $m_1 = 2$ at -4; $m_2 = 8$ at -1; $m_3 = 4$ at 2; $m_4 = 2$ at 3.

3. $m_1 = 2$ at -3; $m_2 = 4$ at -2; $m_3 = 20$ at 4; $m_4 = 10$ at 6; $m_5 = 30$ at 9.

4. $m_1 = 5$ at -7; $m_2 = 3$ at -2; $m_3 = 5$ at 0; $m_4 = 1$ at 2; $m_5 = 8$ at 10.

In Exercises 5 through 9, find the total mass of the given rod and the center of mass.

5. The length of a rod is 9 in. and the linear density of the rod at a point x in. from one end is $(4x + 1)$ slugs/in.

6. The length of a rod is 3 ft, and the linear density of the rod at a point x ft from one end is $(5 + 2x)$ slugs/ft.

7. The length of a rod is 10 ft and the measure of the linear density at a point is a linear function of the measure of the distance of the point from the left end of the rod. The linear density at the left end is 2 slugs/ft and at the right end is 3 slugs/ft.

8. A rod is 10 ft long, and the measure of the linear density at a point is a linear function of the measure of the distance from the center of the rod. The linear density at each end of the rod is 5 slugs/ft and at the center the linear density is $3\frac{1}{2}$ slugs/ft.

9. The measure of the linear density at a point of a rod varies directly as the third power of the measure of the distance of the point from one end. The length of the rod is 4 ft and the linear density is 2 slugs/ft at the center.

10. A rod is 6 ft long and its mass is 24 slugs. If the measure of the linear density at any point of the rod varies directly as the square of the distance of the point from one end, find the largest value of the linear density.

11. The length of a rod is L ft and the center of mass of the rod is at the point $\frac{3}{4}L$ ft from the left end. If the measure of the linear density at a point is proportional to a power of the measure of the distance of the point from the left end and the linear density at the right end is 20 slugs/ft, find the linear density at a point x ft from the left end. Assume the mass is measured in slugs.

12. The total mass of a rod of length L ft is M slugs and the measure of the linear density at a point x ft from the left end is proportional to the measure of the distance of the point from the right end. Show that the linear density at a point on the rod x ft from the left end is $2M(L - x)/L^2$ slugs/ft.

8.8 CENTER OF MASS OF A PLANE REGION

Let the masses of n particles located at the points (x_1, y_1), (x_2, y_2), . . . , (x_n, y_n) in the xy plane be measured in slugs by $m_1, m_2, \ldots , m_n$, and consider the problem of finding the center of mass of this system. We may imagine the particles being supported by a sheet of negligible weight and negligible thickness and may assume that each particle has its position at exactly one point. The center of mass is the point where the sheet will balance. To determine the center of mass, we must find two averages: $\bar{x}$, which is the average value for the abscissas of the n points, and $\bar{y}$, the average value for the ordinates of the n points. We first define the moment of mass of a system of particles with respect to an axis.

If a particle at a distance d ft from an axis has a mass of m slugs, then if

M_1 slug-ft is the moment of mass of the particle with respect to the axis,

$$M_1 = md \tag{1}$$

If the ith particle, having mass m_i slugs, is located at the point (x_i, y_i), its distance from the y axis is x_i ft; thus, from formula (1), the moment of mass of this particle with respect to the y axis is $m_i x_i$ slug-ft. Similarly, the moment of mass of the particle with respect to the x axis is $m_i y_i$ slug-ft. The moment of the system of n particles with respect to the y axis is M_y slug-ft, where

$$M_y = \sum_{i=1}^{n} m_i x_i \tag{2}$$

and the moment of the system with respect to the x axis is M_x slug-ft, where

$$M_x = \sum_{i=1}^{n} m_i y_i \tag{3}$$

The total mass of the system is M slugs, where

$$M = \sum_{i=1}^{n} m_i \tag{4}$$

The center of mass of the system is at the point $(\bar{x}, \bar{y})$, where

$$\bar{x} = \frac{M_y}{M} \tag{5}$$

and

$$\bar{y} = \frac{M_x}{M} \tag{6}$$

The point $(\bar{x}, \bar{y})$ can be interpreted as the point such that, if the total mass M slugs of the system were concentrated there, its moment of mass with respect to the y axis, M_y slug-ft, would be determined by $M_y = M\bar{x}$, and its moment of mass with respect to the x axis, M_x slug-ft, would be determined by $M_x = M\bar{y}$.

EXAMPLE 1: Find the center of mass of the four particles having masses 2, 6, 4, and 1 slugs located at the points $(5, -2)$, $(-2, 1)$, $(0, 3)$, and $(4, -1)$, respectively.

SOLUTION:

$$M_y = \sum_{i=1}^{4} m_i x_i = 2(5) + 6(-2) + 4(0) + 1(4) = 2$$

$$M_x = \sum_{i=1}^{4} m_i y_i = 2(-2) + 6(1) + 4(3) + 1(-1) = 13$$

$$M = \sum_{i=1}^{4} m_i = 2 + 6 + 4 + 1 = 13$$

Therefore,

$$\bar{x} = \frac{M_y}{M} = \frac{2}{13} \quad \text{and} \quad \bar{y} = \frac{M_x}{M} = \frac{13}{13} = 1$$

The center of mass is at $(\frac{2}{13}, 1)$.

Figure 8.8.1

Consider now a thin sheet of continuously distributed mass, for example, a piece of paper or a flat strip of tin. We regard such sheets as being two dimensional and call such a plane region a *lamina*. In this section we confine our discussion to homogeneous laminae, that is, laminae having constant area density. Laminae of variable area density are considered in Chapter 21 in connection with applications of multiple integrals.

Let a homogeneous lamina of area A ft^2 have a mass of M slugs. Then if the constant area density is k slugs/ft^2, $M = kA$. If the homogeneous lamina is a rectangle, its center of mass is defined to be at the center of the rectangle. We use this definition to define the center of mass of a more general homogeneous lamina.

Let L be the homogeneous lamina whose constant area density is k slugs/ft^2, and which is bounded by the curve $y = f(x)$, the x axis, and the lines $x = a$ and $x = b$. The function f is continuous on the closed interval $[a, b]$, and $f(x) \geq 0$ for all x in $[a, b]$. See Fig. 8.8.1. Let Δ be a partition of the interval $[a, b]$ into n subintervals. The ith subinterval is $[x_{i-1}, x_i]$ and $\Delta_i x = x_i - x_{i-1}$. The midpoint of $[x_{i-1}, x_i]$ is γ_i. Associated with each subinterval is a rectangular lamina whose width, altitude, and area density are given by $\Delta_i x$ ft, $f(\gamma_i)$ ft, and k slugs/ft^2, respectively, and whose center of mass is at the point $(\gamma_i, \frac{1}{2}f(\gamma_i))$. The area of the rectangular lamina is $f(\gamma_i) \Delta_i x$ ft^2; hence, $kf(\gamma_i) \Delta_i x$ slugs is its mass. Consequently, if $\Delta_i M_y$ slug-ft is the moment of mass of this rectangular element with respect to the y axis,

$$\Delta_i M_y = \gamma_i k f(\gamma_i) \Delta_i x$$

The sum of the measures of the moments of mass of n such rectangular laminae with respect to the y axis is given by the Riemann sum

$$\sum_{i=1}^{n} k \gamma_i f(\gamma_i) \Delta_i x$$

If M_y slug-ft is the moment of mass of the lamina L with respect to the y axis, we define

$$M_y = \lim_{\|\Delta\| \to 0} \sum_{i=1}^{n} k \gamma_i f(\gamma_i) \Delta_i x = k \int_a^b x f(x) \, dx \tag{7}$$

Similarly, if $\Delta_i M_x$ slug-ft is the moment of mass of the ith rectangular lamina with respect to the x axis,

$$\Delta_i M_x = \tfrac{1}{2} f(\gamma_i) k f(\gamma_i) \ \Delta_i x$$

and the sum of the measures of the moments of mass of n such rectangular laminae with respect to the x axis is given by the Riemann sum

$$\sum_{i=1}^{n} \tfrac{1}{2} k [f(\gamma_i)]^2 \ \Delta_i x \tag{8}$$

Thus, if M_x slug-ft is the moment of mass of the lamina L with respect to the x axis, we define

$$M_x = \lim_{||\Delta|| \to 0} \sum_{i=1}^{n} \tfrac{1}{2} k [f(\gamma_i)]^2 \ \Delta_i x = \tfrac{1}{2} k \int_a^b [f(x)]^2 \ dx \tag{9}$$

The mass of the ith rectangular lamina is $k f(\gamma_i) \ \Delta_i x$ slugs, and so the sum of the measures of the masses of n rectangular laminae is given by

$$\sum_{i=1}^{n} k f(\gamma_i) \ \Delta_i x$$

So, if M slugs is the total mass of the lamina L, we define

$$M = \lim_{||\Delta|| \to 0} \sum_{i=1}^{n} k f(\gamma_i) \ \Delta_i x = k \int_a^b f(x) \ dx \tag{10}$$

Denoting the center of mass of the lamina L by the point $(\bar{x}, \bar{y})$, we define

$$\bar{x} = \frac{M_y}{M} \quad \text{and} \quad \bar{y} = \frac{M_x}{M}$$

which by using formulas (7), (9), and (10) gives

$$\bar{x} = \frac{k \int_a^b x f(x) \ dx}{k \int_a^b f(x) \ dx} \quad \text{and} \quad \bar{y} = \frac{\tfrac{1}{2} k \int_a^b [f(x)]^2 \ dx}{k \int_a^b f(x) \ dx}$$

Dividing both the numerator and denominator by k, we get

$$\bar{x} = \frac{\int_a^b x f(x) \ dx}{\int_a^b f(x) \ dx} \tag{11}$$

and

$$\bar{y} = \frac{\tfrac{1}{2} \int_a^b [f(x)]^2 \ dx}{\int_a^b f(x) \ dx} \tag{12}$$

In formulas (11) and (12) the denominator is the number of square units in the area of the region, and so we have expressed a physical problem in terms of a geometric one. That is, $\bar{x}$ and $\bar{y}$ can be considered as the average abscissa and the average ordinate, respectively, of a geometric region. In such a case, $\bar{x}$ and $\bar{y}$ depend only on the region, not on the mass of the lamina. So we refer to the center of mass of a plane region instead of to the center of mass of a homogeneous lamina. In such a case, we call the center of mass the *centroid* of the region. Instead of moments of mass, we consider moments of the region. We define the moments of the plane region in the above discussion with respect to the x axis and the y axis by the following:

$$M_x = \lim_{||\Delta|| \to 0} \sum_{i=1}^{n} \tfrac{1}{2}[f(\gamma_i)]^2 \, \Delta_i x = \tfrac{1}{2} \int_a^b [f(x)]^2 \, dx$$

$$M_y = \lim_{||\Delta|| \to 0} \sum_{i=1}^{n} \gamma_i f(\gamma_i) \, \Delta_i x = \int_a^b x f(x) \, dx$$

If $(\bar{x}, \bar{y})$ is the centroid of the plane region and if M_x and M_y are defined as above,

$$\bar{x} = \frac{M_y}{A} \quad \text{and} \quad \bar{y} = \frac{M_x}{A}$$

EXAMPLE 2: Find the centroid of the first quadrant region bounded by the curve $y^2 = 4x$, the x axis, and the lines $x = 1$ and $x = 4$.

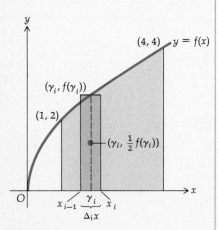

Figure 8.8.2

SOLUTION: Let $f(x) = 2x^{1/2}$. The equation of the curve is then $y = f(x)$. In Fig. 8.8.2, the region is shown together with the ith rectangular element. The centroid of the rectangle is at $(\gamma_i, \tfrac{1}{2}f(\gamma_i))$. The area A square units of the region is given by

$$A = \lim_{||\Delta|| \to 0} \sum_{i=1}^{n} f(\gamma_i) \, \Delta_i x$$

$$= \int_1^4 f(x) \, dx$$

$$= \int_1^4 2x^{1/2} \, dx$$

$$= \tfrac{4}{3} x^{3/2} \Big]_1^4$$

$$= \tfrac{28}{3}$$

We now compute M_y and M_x.

$$M_y = \lim_{||\Delta|| \to 0} \sum_{i=1}^{n} \gamma_i f(\gamma_i) \, \Delta_i x$$

$$= \int_1^4 x f(x) \, dx$$

$$= \int_1^4 x(2x^{1/2})\ dx$$

$$= 2 \int_1^4 x^{3/2}\ dx$$

$$= \tfrac{4}{5}x^{5/2} \Big]_1^4$$

$$= \tfrac{124}{5}$$

$$M_x = \lim_{||\Delta|| \to 0} \sum_{i=1}^n \tfrac{1}{2}f(\gamma_i) \cdot f(\gamma_i)\ \Delta_i x$$

$$= \tfrac{1}{2} \int_1^4 [f(x)]^2\ dx$$

$$= \tfrac{1}{2} \int_1^4 4x\ dx$$

$$= x^2 \Big]_1^4$$

$$= 15$$

Hence,

$$\bar{x} = \frac{M_y}{A} = \frac{\frac{124}{5}}{\frac{28}{3}} = \frac{93}{35}$$

and

$$\bar{y} = \frac{M_x}{A} = \frac{15}{\frac{28}{3}} = \frac{45}{28}$$

Therefore, the centroid is at the point $(\tfrac{93}{35}, \tfrac{45}{28})$.

EXAMPLE 3:   Find the centroid of the region bounded by the curves $y = x^2$ and $y = 2x + 3$.

SOLUTION: The points of intersection of the two curves are $(-1, 1)$ and $(3, 9)$. The region is shown in Fig. 8.8.3, together with the ith rectangular element.

Let $f(x) = x^2$ and $g(x) = 2x + 3$. The centroid of the ith rectangular element is at the point $(\gamma_i, \tfrac{1}{2}[f(\gamma_i) + g(\gamma_i)])$ where γ_i is the midpoint of the ith subinterval $[x_{i-1}, x_i]$. The measure of the area of the region is given by

$$A = \lim_{||\Delta|| \to 0} \sum_{i=1}^n [g(\gamma_i) - f(\gamma_i)]\ \Delta_i x$$

$$= \int_{-1}^3 [g(x) - f(x)]\ dx$$

$$= \int_{-1}^3 [2x + 3 - x^2]\ dx$$

$$= \tfrac{32}{3}$$

Figure 8.8.3

We now compute M_y and M_x.

$$M_y = \lim_{||\Delta|| \to 0} \sum_{i=1}^{n} \gamma_i [g(\gamma_i) - f(\gamma_i)] \, \Delta_i x$$

$$= \int_{-1}^{3} x[g(x) - f(x)] \, dx$$

$$= \int_{-1}^{3} x[2x + 3 - x^2] \, dx$$

$$= \tfrac{32}{3}$$

$$M_x = \lim_{||\Delta|| \to 0} \sum_{i=1}^{n} \tfrac{1}{2}[g(\gamma_i) + f(\gamma_i)][g(\gamma_i) - f(\gamma_i)] \, \Delta_i x$$

$$= \tfrac{1}{2} \int_{-1}^{3} [g(x) + f(x)][g(x) - f(x)] \, dx$$

$$= \tfrac{1}{2} \int_{-1}^{3} [2x + 3 + x^2][2x + 3 - x^2] \, dx$$

$$= \tfrac{1}{2} \int_{-1}^{3} [4x^2 + 12x + 9 - x^4] \, dx$$

$$= \tfrac{544}{15}$$

Therefore,

$$\bar{x} = \frac{M_y}{A} = \frac{\frac{32}{3}}{\frac{32}{3}} = 1 \quad \text{and} \quad \bar{y} = \frac{M_x}{A} = \frac{\frac{544}{15}}{\frac{32}{3}} = \frac{17}{5}$$

Hence, the centroid is at the point $(1, \frac{17}{5})$.

If a plane region has an axis of symmetry, the centroid of the region lies on the axis of symmetry. This is now stated and proved as a theorem.

8.8.1 Theorem   If the plane region R has the line L as an axis of symmetry, the centroid of R lies on L.

PROOF: Choose the coordinate axes so that L is on the y axis and the origin is in the region R. Figure 8.8.4 illustrates an example of this situation. In the figure, R is the region CDE, C is the point $(-a, 0)$, E is the point $(a, 0)$, and an equation of the curve CDE is $y = f(x)$.

Consider a partition of the interval $[0, a]$. Let γ_i be the midpoint of the ith subinterval $[x_{i-1}, x_i]$. The moment with respect to the y axis of the rectangular element having an altitude $f(\gamma_i)$ and a width $\Delta_i x$ is $\gamma_i[f(\gamma_i) \Delta_i x]$. Because of symmetry, for a similar partition of the interval $[-a, 0]$ there is a corresponding element having as its moment with respect to the y axis $-\gamma_i f(\gamma_i) \Delta_i x$. The sum of these two moments is 0; therefore, $M_y = 0$. Because $\bar{x} = M_y/A$, we conclude that $\bar{x} = 0$. Thus, the centroid of the region R lies on the y axis, which is what was to be proved.   ∎

Figure 8.8.4

By applying the preceding theorem, we can simplify the problem of finding the centroid of a plane region that can be divided into regions having axes of symmetry.

EXAMPLE 4:   Find the centroid of the region bounded by the semicircle $y = \sqrt{4 - x^2}$ and the x axis.

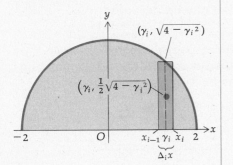

Figure 8.8.5

SOLUTION: The region is shown in Fig. 8.8.5.

Because the y axis is an axis of symmetry, we conclude that the centroid lies on the y axis; so $\bar{x} = 0$.

The moment of the region with respect to the x axis is given by

$$M_x = \lim_{||\Delta|| \to 0} \sum_{i=1}^{n} \tfrac{1}{2} [\sqrt{4 - \gamma_i^2}]^2 \Delta_i x$$

$$= 2 \cdot \tfrac{1}{2} \int_0^2 (4 - x^2) \, dx$$

$$= 4x - \tfrac{1}{3}x^3 \Big]_0^2$$

$$= \tfrac{16}{3}$$

The area of the region is 2π square units; so

$$\bar{y} = \frac{\frac{16}{3}}{2\pi} = \frac{8}{3\pi}$$

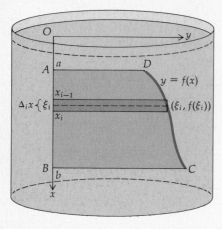

Figure 8.8.6

There is a useful relation between the force caused by liquid pressure on a plane region and the location of the centroid of the region. As in Sec. 8.6, let $ABCD$ be the region bounded by the x axis, the lines $x = a$ and $x = b$, and the curve $y = f(x)$, where f is continuous and $f(x) \geq 0$ on the closed interval $[a, b]$. The region $ABCD$ can be considered as a vertical plate immersed in a liquid having weight w pounds per cubic unit of the liquid (see Fig. 8.8.6). If F lb is the force owing to liquid pressure on the vertical plate,

$$F = \lim_{||\Delta|| \to 0} \sum_{i=1}^{n} w\xi_i f(\xi_i) \, \Delta_i x$$

or, equivalently,

$$F = w \int_a^b xf(x) \, dx \tag{13}$$

If $\bar{x}$ is the abscissa of the centroid of the region $ABCD$, then $\bar{x} = M_y / A$. Because $M_y = \int_a^b xf(x) \, dx$, we have

$$\bar{x} = \frac{\int_a^b xf(x) \, dx}{A}$$

and so

$$\int_a^b xf(x) \, dx = \bar{x}A \tag{14}$$

Substituting from Eq. (14) into (13), we obtain

$$F = w\bar{x}A \tag{15}$$

Formula (15) states that the total force owing to liquid pressure against a vertical plane region is the same as it would be if the region were horizontal at a depth $\bar{x}$ units below the surface of a liquid.

• ILLUSTRATION 1: Consider a trough full of water having as ends semicircular regions each with a radius of 2 ft. Using the result of Example 4, we find that the centroid of the region is at a depth of $8/3\pi$ ft. Therefore, using formula (15), we see that if F lb is the force on one end of the trough,

$$F = w \cdot \frac{8}{3\pi} \cdot 2\pi = \frac{16}{3} w$$

This agrees with the result found in Example 2 of Sec. 8.6. •

For various simple plane regions, the centroid may be found in a table. When both the area of the region and the centroid of the region may be obtained directly, formula (15) is easy to apply and is used in such cases by engineers to find the force caused by liquid pressure.

Exercises 8.8

1. Find the center of mass of the three particles having masses of 1, 2, and 3 slugs and located at the points $(-1, 3)$, $(2, 1)$, and $(3, -1)$, respectively.

2. Find the center of mass of the four particles having masses of 2, 3, 3, and 4 slugs and located at the points $(-1, -2)$, $(1, 3)$, $(0, 5)$, and $(2, 1)$, respectively.

3. Prove that the centroid of three particles, having equal masses, in a plane lies at the point of intersection of the medians of the triangle having as vertices the points at which the particles are located.

In Exercises 4 through 11, find the centroid of the region with the indicated boundaries.

4. The parabola $x = 2y - y^2$ and the y axis.

5. The parabola $y = 4 - x^2$ and the x axis.

6. The parabola $y^2 = 4x$, the y axis, and the line $y = 4$.

7. The parabola $y = x^2$ and the line $y = 4$.

8. The lines $y = 2x + 1$, $x + y = 7$, and $x = 8$.

9. The curves $y = x^3$ and $y = 4x$ in the first quadrant.

10. The curves $y = x^2$ and $y = x^3$.

11. The curves $y = x^2 - 4$ and $y = 2x - x^2$.

12. Prove that the distance from the centroid of a triangle to any side of the triangle is equal to one-third the length of the altitude to that side.

13. If the centroid of the region bounded by the parabola $y^2 = 4px$ and the line $x = a$ is to be at the point $(p, 0)$, find the value of a.

14. Solve Exercise 4 of Sec. 8.6 by using formula (15) of this section.

15. Solve Exercise 5 of Sec. 8.6 by using formula (15) of this section.

16. The face of a dam adjacent to the water is vertical and is in the shape of an isosceles trapezoid 90 ft wide at the top, 60 ft wide at the bottom, and 20 ft high. Use formula (15) of this section to find the total force due to liquid pressure on the face of the dam.

17. Find the moment about the lower base of the trapezoid of the force in Exercise 16.

18. Solve Exercise 6 of Sec. 8.6 by using formula (15) of this section.

19. Find the center of mass of the lamina bounded by the parabola $2y^2 = 18 - 3x$ and the y axis if the area density at any point (x, y) is $\sqrt{6 - x}$ slugs/ft².

20. Solve Exercise 19 if the area density at any point (x, y) is x slugs/ft².

21. Let R be the region bounded by the curves $y = f_1(x)$ and $y = f_2(x)$ (see Fig. 8.8.7). If A is the measure of the area of R and if $\bar{y}$ is the ordinate of the centroid of R, prove that the measure of the volume, V, of the solid of revolution obtained by revolving R about the x axis is given by

$$V = 2\pi \bar{y} A$$

Stating this formula in words we have:

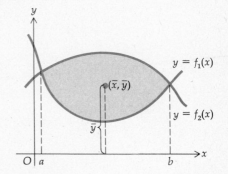

Figure 8.8.7

If a plane region is revolved about a line in its plane that does not cut the region, then the measure of the volume of the solid of revolution generated is equal to the product of the measure of the area of the region and the measure of the distance traveled by the centroid of the region.

The above statement is known as the *theorem of Pappus* for volumes of solids of revolution.

22. Use the theorem of Pappus to find the volume of the torus (doughnut-shaped) generated by revolving a circle with a radius of r units about a line in its plane at a distance of b units from its center, where $b > r$.

23. Use the theorem of Pappus to find the centroid of the region bounded by a semicircle and its diameter.

24. Use the theorem of Pappus to find the volume of a sphere with a radius of r units.

25. Let R be the region bounded by the semicircle $y = \sqrt{r^2 - x^2}$ and the x axis. Use the theorem of Pappus to find the moment of R with respect to the line $y = -4$.

26. If R is the region of Exercise 25, use the theorem of Pappus to find the volume of the solid of revolution generated by revolving R about the line $x - y = r$. (HINT: Use the result of Exercise 24 in Sec. 5.3.)

8.9 CENTER OF MASS OF A SOLID OF REVOLUTION

To find the center of mass of a solid, in general we must make use of multiple integration. This procedure is taken up in Chapter 21 as an application of multiple integrals. However, if the shape of the solid is that of a solid of revolution, and its volume density is constant, we find the center of mass by a method similar to the one used to obtain the center of mass of a homogeneous lamina. Following is the procedure for finding the center of mass of a homogeneous solid of revolution, with the assumption that the center of mass is on the axis of revolution.

We first set up a three-dimensional coordinate system. The x and y axes are taken as in two dimensions, and the third axis, the z axis, is taken perpendicular to them at the origin. A point in three dimensions is then given by (x, y, z). The plane containing the x and y axes is called the xy plane, and the xz plane and the yz plane are defined similarly.

Suppose that the x axis is the axis of revolution. Then under the assumption that the center of mass lies on the axis of revolution, the y and z coordinates of the center of mass are each zero, and so it is only necessary to find the x coordinate, which we call $\bar{x}$. To find $\bar{x}$ we make use of the moment of the solid of revolution with respect to the yz plane.

Let f be a function that is continuous on the closed interval $[a, b]$, and assume that $f(x) \geq 0$ for all x in $[a, b]$. R is the region bounded by the curve $y = f(x)$, the x axis, and the lines $x = a$ and $x = b$; S is the homogeneous solid of revolution whose volume density is k slugs/ft^3, where k is a constant, and which is generated by revolving the region R about the x axis. Take a partition Δ of the closed interval $[a, b]$, and denote the ith subinterval by $[x_{i-1}, x_i]$ (with $i = 1, 2, \ldots, n$). Let γ_i be the midpoint of $[x_{i-1}, x_i]$. Form n rectangles having altitudes of $f(\gamma_i)$ ft and bases whose width is $\Delta_i x$ ft. Refer to Fig. 8.9.1, showing the region R and the ith rectangle. If each of the n rectangles is revolved about the x axis, n circular disks are generated. The ith rectangle generates a circular disk having a radius of $f(\gamma_i)$ ft and a thickness of $\Delta_i x$ ft; its volume is $\pi[f(\gamma_i)]^2 \Delta_i x$ ft^3,

Figure 8.9.1

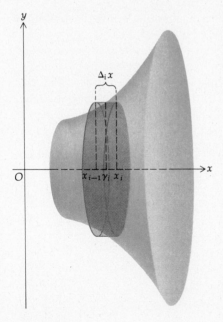

Figure 8.9.2

and its mass is $k\pi[f(\gamma_i)]^2 \Delta_i x$ slugs. Figure 8.9.2 shows the solid of revolution S and the ith circular disk.

The center of mass of the circular disk lies on the axis of revolution at the center of the disk: $(\gamma_i, 0, 0)$. The moment of mass of the disk with respect to the yz plane is then $\Delta_i M_{yz}$ slug-ft where

$$\Delta_i M_{yz} = \gamma_i(k\pi[f(\gamma_i)]^2 \Delta_i x)$$

The sum of the measures of the moments of mass of the n circular disks with respect to the yz plane is given by the Riemann sum

$$\sum_{i=1}^{n} \gamma_i k\pi[f(\gamma_i)]^2 \Delta_i x \tag{1}$$

The number of slugs-feet in the moment of mass of S with respect to the yz plane, denoted by M_{yz}, is then defined to be the limit of the Riemann sum in (1) as $\|\Delta\|$ approaches zero; so we have

$$M_{yz} = \lim_{\|\Delta\| \to 0} \sum_{i=1}^{n} \gamma_i k\pi[f(\gamma_i)]^2 \Delta_i x = k\pi \int_a^b x[f(x)]^2 \, dx \tag{2}$$

The volume, V ft³, of S was defined in Sec. 8.2 by

$$V = \lim_{\|\Delta\| \to 0} \sum_{i=1}^{n} \pi[f(\gamma_i)]^2 \Delta_i x = \pi \int_a^b [f(x)]^2 \, dx \tag{3}$$

The mass, M slugs, of solid S is defined by

$$M = \lim_{\|\Delta\| \to 0} \sum_{i=1}^{n} k\pi[f(\gamma_i)]^2 \Delta_i x = k\pi \int_a^b [f(x)]^2 \, dx \tag{4}$$

We define the center of mass of S as the point $(\bar{x}, 0, 0)$ such that

$$\bar{x} = \frac{M_{yz}}{M} \tag{5}$$

Substituting from Eqs. (2) and (4) into (5), we get

$$\bar{x} = \frac{k\pi \int_a^b x[f(x)]^2 \, dx}{k\pi \int_a^b [f(x)]^2 \, dx}$$

or, equivalently,

$$\bar{x} = \frac{\int_a^b x[f(x)]^2 \, dx}{\int_a^b [f(x)]^2 \, dx} \tag{6}$$

From Eq. (6), we see that the center of mass of a homogeneous solid of revolution depends only on the shape of the solid, not on its substance. Therefore, as for a homogeneous lamina, we refer to the center of mass as the centroid of the solid of revolution. When we have a homogeneous solid of revolution, instead of the moment of mass we consider the moment of the solid. The moment, M_{yz}, of the solid S with respect to the yz plane is given by

$$M_{yz} = \lim_{||\Delta|| \to 0} \sum_{i=1}^{n} \gamma_i \pi [f(\gamma_i)]^2 \, \Delta_i x = \pi \int_a^b x[f(x)]^2 \, dx \qquad (7)$$

Thus, if $(\bar{x}, 0, 0)$ is the centroid of S, from Eqs. (3), (6), and (7) we have

$$\bar{x} = \frac{M_{yz}}{V}$$

EXAMPLE 1: Find the centroid of the solid of revolution generated by revolving about the x axis the region bounded by the curve $y = x^2$, the x axis, and the line $x = 3$.

Figure 8.9.3

SOLUTION: The region and a rectangular element are shown in Fig. 8.9.3. The solid of revolution and an element of volume are shown in Fig. 8.9.4.

$$f(x) = x^2$$

$$M_{yz} = \lim_{||\Delta|| \to 0} \sum_{i=1}^{n} \gamma_i \pi [f(\gamma_i)]^2 \, \Delta_i x$$

$$= \pi \int_0^3 x[f(x)]^2 \, dx$$

$$= \pi \int_0^3 x^5 \, dx$$

$$= \frac{243}{2} \pi$$

$$V = \lim_{||\Delta|| \to 0} \sum_{i=1}^{n} \pi [f(\gamma_i)]^2 \, \Delta_i x$$

$$= \pi \int_0^3 [f(x)]^2 \, dx$$

$$= \pi \int_0^3 x^4 \, dx$$

$$= \frac{243}{5} \pi$$

Therefore,

$$\bar{x} = \frac{M_{yz}}{V} = \frac{\frac{243}{2}\pi}{\frac{243}{5}\pi} = \frac{5}{2}$$

Therefore, the centroid is at the point $(\frac{5}{2}, 0, 0)$.

Figure 8.9.4

The portion of the curve from the point $A(a, f(a))$ to the point $B(b, f(b))$ is called an arc. We wish to assign a number to what we intuitively think of as the length of such an arc. If the arc is a line segment from the point (x_1, y_1) to the point (x_2, y_2), we know from the formula for the distance between two points that its length is given by $\sqrt{(x_1 - x_2)^2 + (y_1 - y_2)^2}$. We use this formula for defining the length of an arc in general. Recall from geometry that the circumference of a circle is defined as the limit of the perimeters of regular polygons inscribed in the circle. For other curves we proceed in a similar way.

Let Δ be a partition of the closed interval $[a, b]$ formed by dividing the interval into n subintervals by choosing any $(n - 1)$ intermediate numbers between a and b. Let $x_0 = a$, and $x_n = b$, and let $x_1, x_2, x_3, \ldots,$ x_{n-1} be the intermediate numbers so that $x_0 < x_1 < x_2 < \cdots < x_{n-1} < x_n$. Then the ith subinterval is $[x_{i-1}, x_i]$; and its length, denoted by $\Delta_i x$, is $x_i - x_{i-1}$, where $i = 1, 2, 3, \ldots, n$. Then if $\|\Delta\|$ is the norm of the partition Δ, each $\Delta_i x \leq \|\Delta\|$.

Figure 8.10.2

Associated with each point $(x_i, 0)$ on the x axis is a point $P_i(x_i, f(x_i))$ on the curve. Draw a line segment from each point P_{i-1} to the next point P_i as shown in Fig. 8.10.2 The length of the line segment from P_{i-1} to P_i is denoted by $|\overline{P_{i-1}P_i}|$ and is given by the distance formula

$$|\overline{P_{i-1}P_i}| = \sqrt{(x_i - x_{i-1})^2 + (y_i - y_{i-1})^2} \tag{1}$$

The sum of the lengths of the line segments is

$$|\overline{P_0P_1}| + |\overline{P_1P_2}| + |\overline{P_2P_3}| + \cdots + |\overline{P_{i-1}P_i}| + \cdots + |\overline{P_{n-1}P_n}|$$

which can be written in sigma notation as

$$\sum_{i=1}^{n} |\overline{P_{i-1}P_i}| \tag{2}$$

It seems plausible that if n is sufficiently large, the sum in (2) will be "close to" what we would intuitively think of as the length of the arc AB. So we define the length of the arc as the limit of the sum in (2) as the norm of Δ approaches zero, in which case n increases without bound. We have, then, the following definition.

8.10.1 Definition If the function f is continuous on the closed interval $[a, b]$ and if there exists a number L having the following property: for any $\epsilon > 0$ there is a $\delta > 0$ such that

$$\left| \sum_{i=1}^{n} |\overline{P_{i-1}P_i}| - L \right| < \epsilon$$

for every partition Δ of the interval $[a, b]$ for which $\|\Delta\| < \delta$, then we write

$$L = \lim_{\|\Delta\| \to 0} \sum_{i=1}^{n} |\overline{P_{i-1}P_i}| \tag{3}$$

and L is called the *length of the arc* of the curve $y = f(x)$ from the point $A(a, f(a))$ to the point $B(b, f(b))$.

If the limit in Eq. (3) exists, the arc is said to be *rectifiable*.

We derive a formula for finding the length L of an arc that is rectifiable. The derivation requires that the derivative of f be continuous on $[a, b]$; such a function is said to be "smooth" on $[a, b]$.

8.10.2 Definition A function f is said to be *smooth* on an interval I if f' is continuous on I.

Figure 8.10.3

Refer now to Figure 8.10.3. If P_{i-1} has coordinates (x_{i-1}, y_{i-1}) and P_i has coordinates (x_i, y_i), then the length of the chord $P_{i-1}P_i$ is given by formula (1).

Letting $x_i - x_{i-1} = \Delta_i x$ and $y_i - y_{i-1} = \Delta_i y$, we have

$$|\overline{P_{i-1}P_i}| = \sqrt{(\Delta_i x)^2 + (\Delta_i y)^2} \tag{4}$$

or, equivalently, because $\Delta_i x \neq 0$,

$$|\overline{P_{i-1}P_i}| = \sqrt{1 + \left(\frac{\Delta_i y}{\Delta_i x}\right)^2} \; (\Delta_i x) \tag{5}$$

Because we required that f' be continuous on $[a, b]$, the hypothesis of the mean-value theorem (4.7.2) is satisfied by f, and so there is a number z_i in the open interval (x_{i-1}, x_i) such that

$$f(x_i) - f(x_{i-1}) = f'(z_i)(x_i - x_{i-1}) \tag{6}$$

Because $\Delta_i y = f(x_i) - f(x_{i-1})$ and $\Delta_i x = x_i - x_{i-1}$, from Eq. (6) we have

$$\frac{\Delta_i y}{\Delta_i x} = f'(z_i) \tag{7}$$

Substituting from Eq. (7) into (5), we get

$$|\overline{P_{i-1}P_i}| = \sqrt{1 + [f'(z_i)]^2} \; \Delta_i x \tag{8}$$

where $x_{i-1} < z_i < x_i$.

For each i from 1 to n there is an equation of the form (8).

$$\sum_{i=1}^{n} |\overline{P_{i-1}P_i}| = \sum_{i=1}^{n} \sqrt{1 + [f'(z_i)]^2} \; \Delta_i x \tag{9}$$

Taking the limit on both sides of Eq. (9) as $\|\Delta\|$ approaches zero, we obtain

$$\lim_{\|\Delta\| \to 0} \sum_{i=1}^{n} |\overline{P_{i-1}P_i}| = \lim_{\|\Delta\| \to 0} \sum_{i=1}^{n} \sqrt{1 + [f'(z_i)]^2} \; \Delta_i x \tag{10}$$

if this limit exists.

To show that the limit on the right side of Eq. (10) exists, let g be the function defined by

$$g(x) = \sqrt{1 + [f'(x)]^2}$$

Because f' is continuous on $[a, b]$, g is continuous on $[a, b]$. Therefore, because $x_{i-1} < z_i < x_i$, for $i = 1, 2, \ldots, n$,

$$\lim_{\|\Delta\| \to 0} \sum_{i=1}^{n} \sqrt{1 + [f'(z_i)]^2} \; \Delta_i x = \lim_{\|\Delta\| \to 0} \sum_{i=1}^{n} g(z_i) \; \Delta_i x$$

or, equivalently,

$$\lim_{\|\Delta\| \to 0} \sum_{i=1}^{n} \sqrt{1 + [f'(z_i)]^2} \; \Delta_i x = \int_a^b g(x) \; dx \tag{11}$$

Because $g(x) = \sqrt{1 + [f'(x)]^2}$, from Eq. (11) we have

$$\lim_{\|\Delta\| \to 0} \sum_{i=1}^{n} \sqrt{1 + [f'(z_i)]^2} \; \Delta_i x = \int_a^b \sqrt{1 + [f'(x)]^2} \; dx \tag{12}$$

Substituting from Eq. (12) into (10), we get

$$\lim_{\|\Delta\| \to 0} \sum_{i=1}^{n} |\overline{P_{i-1}P_i}| = \int_a^b \sqrt{1 + [f'(x)]^2} \; dx \tag{13}$$

Then from Eqs. (3) and (13) we obtain

$$L = \int_a^b \sqrt{1 + [f'(x)]^2} \, dx \tag{14}$$

In this way, we have proved the following theorem.

8.10.3 Theorem If the function f and its derivative f' are continuous on the closed interval $[a, b]$, then the length of arc of the curve $y = f(x)$ from the point $(a, f(a))$ to the point $(b, f(b))$ is given by

$$L = \int_a^b \sqrt{1 + [f'(x)]^2} \, dx$$

We also have the following theorem, which gives the length of the arc of a curve when x is expressed as a function of y.

8.10.4 Theorem If the function F and its derivative F' are continuous on the closed interval $[c, d]$, then the length of arc of the curve $x = F(y)$ from the point $(F(c), c)$ to the point $(F(d), d)$ is given by

$$L = \int_c^d \sqrt{1 + [F'(y)]^2} \, dy$$

The proof of Theorem 8.10.4 is identical with that of Theorem 8.10.3; here we interchange x and y as well as the functions f and F.

The definite integral obtained when applying Theorem 8.10.3 or Theorem 8.10.4 is often difficult to evaluate. Because our techniques of integration have so far been limited to integration of powers, we are further restricted in finding equations of curves for which we can evaluate the resulting definite integrals to find the length of an arc.

EXAMPLE 1: Find the length of the arc of the curve $y = x^{2/3}$ from the point $(1, 1)$ to $(8, 4)$ by using Theorem 8.10.3.

Figure 8.10.4

SOLUTION: See Fig. 8.10.4. Because $f(x) = x^{2/3}$, $f'(x) = \frac{2}{3}x^{-1/3}$. From Theorem 8.10.3 we have

$$L = \int_1^8 \sqrt{1 + \frac{4}{9x^{2/3}}} \, dx$$

$$= \frac{1}{3} \int_1^8 \frac{\sqrt{9x^{2/3} + 4}}{x^{1/3}} \, dx$$

To evaluate this definite integral, let $u = 9x^{2/3} + 4$; then $du = 6x^{-1/3} \, dx$. When $x = 1$, $u = 13$; when $x = 8$, $u = 40$. Therefore,

$$L = \frac{1}{18} \int_{13}^{40} u^{1/2} \, du$$

$$= \tfrac{1}{18} \left[\tfrac{2}{3} u^{3/2} \right]_{13}^{40}$$

$$= \tfrac{1}{27} (40^{3/2} - 13^{3/2})$$

$$\approx 7.6$$

EXAMPLE 2: Find the length of the arc in Example 1 by using Theorem 8.10.4.

SOLUTION: Because $y = x^{2/3}$ and $x > 0$, we solve for x and obtain $x = y^{3/2}$. Letting $F(y) = y^{3/2}$, we have

$$F'(y) = \tfrac{3}{2} y^{1/2}$$

Then, from Theorem 8.10.4, we have

$$L = \int_1^4 \sqrt{1 + \tfrac{9}{4}y}\ dy$$

$$= \tfrac{1}{2} \int_1^4 \sqrt{4 + 9y}\ dy$$

$$= \tfrac{1}{18} \left[\tfrac{2}{3} (4 + 9y)^{3/2} \right]_1^4$$

$$= \tfrac{1}{27} (40^{3/2} - 13^{3/2})$$

$$\approx 7.6$$

If f' is continuous on $[a, b]$, then the definite integral $\int_a^x \sqrt{1 + [f'(t)]^2}\ dt$ is a function of x; and it gives the length of the arc of the curve $y = f(x)$ from the point $(a, f(a))$ to the point $(x, f(x))$, where x is any number in the closed interval $[a, b]$. Let s denote the length of this arc; thus, s is a function of x, and we have

$$s(x) = \int_a^x \sqrt{1 + [f'(t)]^2}\ dt$$

From Theorem 7.6.1, we have

$$s'(x) = \sqrt{1 + [f'(x)]^2}$$

or, because $s'(x) = ds/dx$ and $f'(x) = dy/dx$,

$$\frac{ds}{dx} = \sqrt{1 + \left(\frac{dy}{dx}\right)^2}$$

Multiplying by dx, we obtain

$$ds = \sqrt{1 + \left(\frac{dy}{dx}\right)^2}\ dx \tag{15}$$

Similarly, if we are talking about the length of arc of the curve $x = g(y)$

from $(g(c), c)$ to $(g(y), y)$, we have

$$ds = \sqrt{\left(\frac{dx}{dy}\right)^2 + 1}\ dy \qquad (16)$$

Squaring on both sides of Eq. (15) gives

$$(ds)^2 = (dx)^2 + (dy)^2 \qquad (17)$$

From Eq. (17) we get the geometric interpretation of ds, which is shown in Fig. 8.10.5.

Figure 8.10.5

In Fig. 8.10.5, line T is tangent to the curve $y = f(x)$ at the point P. $|\overline{PM}| = \Delta x = dx$; $|\overline{MQ}| = \Delta y$; $|\overline{MR}| = dy$; $|\overline{PR}| = ds$; the length of arc $PQ = \Delta s$.

Exercises 8.10

1. Find the length of the arc of the curve $9y^2 = 4x^3$ from the origin to the point $(3, 2\sqrt{3})$.

2. Find the length of the arc of the curve $x^2 = (2y + 3)^3$ from $(1, -1)$ to $(7\sqrt{7}, 2)$.

3. Find the length of the arc of the curve $8y = x^4 + 2x^{-2}$ from the point where $x = 1$ to the point where $x = 2$.

4. Use Theorem 8.10.3 to find the length of the arc of the curve $y^3 = 8x^2$ from the point $(1, 2)$ to the point $(27, 18)$.

5. Solve Exercise 4 by using Theorem 8.10.4.

6. Find the entire length of the curve $x^{2/3} + y^{2/3} = 1$.

7. Find the length of the arc of the curve $y = \frac{1}{3}(x^2 + 2)^{3/2}$ from the point where $x = 0$ to the point where $x = 3$.

8. Find the length of the curve $6xy = y^4 + 3$ from the point where $y = 1$ to the point where $y = 2$.

9. Find the length of the curve $(x/a)^{2/3} + (y/b)^{2/3} = 1$ in the first quadrant from $x = \frac{1}{8}a$ to $x = a$.

10. Find the length of the curve $9y^2 = 4(1 + x^2)^3$ in the first quadrant from $x = 0$ to $x = 2\sqrt{2}$.

11. Find the length of the loop of the curve $9y^2 = x(x - 3)^2$.

12. Find the length of the loop of the curve $9y^2 = x^2(2x + 3)$.

Review Exercises (Chapter 8)

1. Find the area of the region bounded by the loop of the curve $y^2 = x^2(4 - x)$.

2. The region in the first quadrant bounded by the curves $x = y^2$ and $x = y^4$ is revolved about the y axis. Find the volume of the solid generated.

3. The base of a solid is the region bounded by the parabola $y^2 = 8x$ and the line $x = 8$. Find the volume of the solid if every plane section perpendicular to the axis of the base is a square.

4. A container has the same shape and dimensions as a solid of revolution formed by revolving about the y axis the region in the first quadrant bounded by the parabola $x^2 = 4py$, the y axis, and the line $y = p$. If the container is full of water, find the work done in pumping all the water up to a point $3p$ ft above the top of the container.

5. The surface of a tank is the same as that of a paraboloid of revolution which is obtained by revolving the parabola $y = x^2$ about the x axis. The vertex of the parabola is at the bottom of the tank and the tank is 36 ft high. If the tank is filled with water to a depth of 20 ft, find the work done in pumping all of the water out over the top.

6. A plate in the shape of a region bounded by the parabola $x^2 = 6y$ and the line $2y = 3$ is placed in a water tank with its vertex downward and the line in the surface of the water. Find the force due to liquid pressure on one side of the plate.

7. Find the area of the region bounded by the curves $y = |x - 1|$, $y = x^2 - 2x$, the y axis, and the line $x = 2$.

8. Find the area of the region bounded by the curves $y = |x| + |x - 1|$ and $y = x + 1$.

9. Find the volume of the solid generated by revolving the region bounded by the curve $y = |x - 2|$, the x axis, and the lines $x = 1$ and $x = 4$ about the x axis.

10. Find the length of arc of the curve $ay^2 = x^3$ from the origin to $(4a, 8a)$.

11. Find the length of the curve $6y^2 = x(x - 2)^2$ from $(2, 0)$ to $(8, 4\sqrt{3})$.

12. Find the center of mass of the four particles having equal masses located at the points $(3, 0)$, $(2, 2)$, $(2, 4)$, and $(-1, 2)$.

13. Three particles having masses 5, 2, and 8 slugs are located, respectively, at the points $(-1, 3)$, $(2, -1)$, and $(5, 2)$. Find the center of mass.

14. The length of a rod is 8 in. and the linear density of the rod at a point x in. from the left end is $2\sqrt{x + 1}$ slugs/in. Find the total mass of the rod and the center of mass.

15. Find the centroid of the region bounded by the parabola $y^2 = x$ and the line $y = x - 2$.

16. Find the centroid of the region bounded by the loop of the curve $y^2 = x^2 - x^3$.

17. The length of a rod is 4 ft and the linear density of the rod at a point x ft from the left end is $(3x + 1)$ slugs/ft. Find the total mass of the rod and the center of mass.

18. Give an example to show that the centroid of a plane region is not necessarily a point within the region.

19. Find the volume of the solid generated by revolving about the line $y = -1$ the region bounded by the line $2y = x + 3$ and outside the curves $y^2 + x = 0$ and $y^2 - 4x = 0$.

20. Use integration to find the volume of a segment of a sphere if the sphere has a radius of r units and the altitude of the segment is h units.

21. A church steeple is 30 ft high and every horizontal plane section is a square having sides of length one-tenth of the distance of the plane section from the top of the steeple. Find the volume of the steeple.

22. A trough full of water is 6 ft long, and its cross section is in the shape of a semicircle with a diameter of 2 ft at the top. How much work is required to pump the water out over the top?

23. A water tank is in the shape of a hemisphere surmounted by a right-circular cylinder. The radius of both the hemisphere and the cylinder is 4 ft and the altitude of the cylinder is 8 ft. If the tank is full of water, find the work necessary to empty the tank by pumping it through an outlet at the top of the tank.

24. A force of 500 lb is required to compress a spring whose natural length is 10 in. to a length of 9 in. Find the work done to compress the spring to a length of 8 in.

25. A cable is 20 ft long and weighs 2 lb/ft, and is hanging vertically from the top of a pole. Find the work done in raising the entire cable to the top of the pole.

26. The work necessary to stretch a spring from 9 in. to 10 in. is $\frac{3}{2}$ times the work necessary to stretch it from 8 in. to 9 in. What is the natural length of the spring?

27. Find the length of the curve $9x^{2/3} + 4y^{2/3} = 36$ in the second quadrant from $x = -1$ to $x = -\frac{1}{8}$.

28. A semicircular plate with a radius of 3 ft is submerged vertically in a tank of water, with its diameter lying in the surface. Use formula (15) of Sec. 8.8 to find the force due to liquid pressure on one side of the plate.

29. A cylindrical tank is half full of gasoline weighing 42 lb/ft³. If the axis is horizontal and the diameter is 6 ft, find the force on an end due to liquid pressure.

30. Find the centroid of the region bounded above by the parabola $4x^2 = 36 - 9y$ and below by the x axis.

31. Use the theorem of Pappus to find the volume of a right-circular cone with a base radius of r units and an altitude of h units.

32. The region bounded by the parabola $x^2 = 4y$, the x axis, and the line $x = 4$ is revolved about the y axis. Find the centroid of the solid of revolution formed.

33. Find the center of mass of the region of Exercise 30 if the measure of the area density at any point (x, y) is $\sqrt{4 - y}$.

34. Find the center of mass of the solid of revolution of Exercise 32 if the measure of the volume density of the solid at any point is equal to the measure of the distance of the point from the xz plane.

9

Logarithmic and exponential functions

9.1 THE NATURAL LOGARITHMIC FUNCTION

The definition of the logarithmic function that you encountered in algebra is based on exponents. The laws of logarithms are then proved from corresponding laws of exponents. One such law of exponents is

$$a^x \cdot a^y = a^{x+y} \tag{1}$$

If the exponents, x and y, are positive integers and a is any real number, (1) follows from the definition of a positive integer exponent and mathematical induction. If the exponents are allowed to be any integers, either positive, negative, or zero, and $a \neq 0$, then (1) will hold if a zero exponent and a negative integer exponent are defined by

$$a^0 = 1$$

and

$$a^{-n} = \frac{1}{a^n} \qquad n > 0$$

If the exponents are rational numbers and $a \geq 0$, then Eq. (1) holds when $a^{m/n}$ is defined by

$$a^{m/n} = (\sqrt[n]{a})^m$$

It is not quite so simple to define a^x when x is an irrational number. For example, what is meant by $4^{\sqrt{3}}$? The definition of the logarithmic function, as given in elementary algebra, is based on the assumption that a^x exists if a is any positive number and x is any real number.

This definition states that the equation

$$a^x = N$$

where a is any positive number except 1 and N is any positive number, can be solved for x, and x is uniquely determined by

$$x = \log_a N$$

In elementary algebra, logarithms are used mainly as an aid to computation, and for such purposes the number a (called the *base*) is taken as 10. The following laws of logarithms are proved from the laws of exponents:

Law 1 $\log_a MN = \log_a M + \log_a N$
Law 2 $\log_a \dfrac{M}{N} = \log_a M - \log_a N$
Law 3 $\log_a 1 = 0$
Law 4 $\log_a M^n = n \log_a M$
Law 5 $\log_a a = 1$

In this chapter we define the logarithmic function by using calculus and prove the laws of logarithms by means of this definition. Then the exponential function is defined in terms of the logarithmic function. This definition enables us to define a^x when x is any real number and $a \neq 0$.

Figure 9.1.1

The laws of exponents will then be proved if the exponent is any real number.

Let us recall the formula

$$\int t^n \, dt = \frac{t^{n+1}}{n+1} + C \qquad n \neq -1$$

This formula does not hold when $n = -1$. Consider the function defined by the equation $y = t^{-1}$, where t is positive. A sketch of the graph of this equation is shown in Fig. 9.1.1.

Let R be the region bounded above by the curve $y = 1/t$, below by the t axis, on the left by the line $t = 1$, and on the right by the line $t = x$, where x is greater than 1. This region R is shown in Fig. 9.1.1. The measure of the area of R is a function of x; call it $A(x)$ and define it as a definite integral by

$$A(x) = \int_1^x \frac{1}{t} \, dt \tag{2}$$

Now consider the integral in (2) if $0 < x < 1$. From Definition 7.3.4, we have

$$\int_1^x \frac{1}{t} \, dt = -\int_x^1 \frac{1}{t} \, dt$$

Then the integral $\int_x^1 (1/t) \, dt$ represents the measure of the area of the region bounded above by the curve $y = 1/t$, below by the t axis, on the left by the line $t = x$, and on the right by the line $t = 1$. So the integral $\int_1^x (1/t) \, dt$ is then the negative of the measure of the area of the region shown in Fig. 9.1.2.

If $x = 1$, the integral $\int_1^x (1/t) \, dt$ becomes $\int_1^1 (1/t) \, dt$, which equals 0 by Definition 7.3.5. In this case the left and right boundaries of the region are the same and the measure of the area is 0.

Thus, we see that the integral $\int_1^x (1/t) \, dt$ for $x > 0$ can be interpreted in terms of the measure of the area of a region. Its value depends on x and is therefore a function of x. This integral is used to define the "natural logarithmic function."

Figure 9.1.2

9.1.1 Definition　The *natural logarithmic function* is the function defined by

$$\ln x = \int_1^x \frac{1}{t} \, dt \qquad x > 0$$

The domain of the natural logarithmic function is the set of all positive numbers. We read $\ln x$ as "the natural logarithm of x."

The natural logarithmic function is differentiable because by applying Theorem 7.6.1 we have

$$D_x(\ln x) = D_x \left(\int_1^x \frac{1}{t} \, dt \right) = \frac{1}{x}$$

Therefore,

$$D_x(\ln x) = \frac{1}{x} \tag{3}$$

From formula (3) and the chain rule, if u is a differentiable function of x, and $u(x) > 0$, then

$$D_x(\ln u) = \frac{1}{u} \cdot D_x u \tag{4}$$

EXAMPLE 1:   Given

$$y = \ln(3x^2 - 6x + 8)$$

find dy/dx.

SOLUTION: Applying formula (4), we get

$$\frac{dy}{dx} = \frac{1}{3x^2 - 6x + 8} \cdot (6x - 6) = \frac{6x - 6}{3x^2 - 6x + 8}$$

EXAMPLE 2:   Given

$$y = \ln[(4x^2 + 3)(2x - 1)]$$

find $D_x y$.

SOLUTION: Applying formula (4), we get

$$D_x y = \frac{1}{(4x^2 + 3)(2x - 1)} \cdot [8x(2x - 1) + 2(4x^2 + 3)]$$

$$= \frac{24x^2 - 8x + 6}{(4x^2 + 3)(2x - 1)} \tag{5}$$

EXAMPLE 3:   Given

$$y = \ln\left(\frac{x}{x + 1}\right)$$

find dy/dx.

SOLUTION: From formula (4), we have

$$\frac{dy}{dx} = \frac{1}{\frac{x}{x + 1}} \cdot \frac{(x + 1) - x}{(x + 1)^2}$$

$$= \frac{x + 1}{x} \cdot \frac{1}{(x + 1)^2}$$

$$= \frac{1}{x(x + 1)}$$

It should be emphasized that when using formula (4), $u(x)$ must be positive; that is, a number in the domain of the derivative must be in the domain of the given natural logarithmic function.

● ILLUSTRATION 1: In Example 1, the domain of the given natural logarithmic function is the set of all real numbers because $3x^2 - 6x + 8 > 0$ for all x. This can be seen from the fact that the parabola having equation $y = 3x^2 - 6x + 8$ has its vertex at $(1, 5)$ and opens upward. Hence, $(6x - 6)/(3x^2 - 6x + 8)$ is the derivative for all values of x.

In Example 2, because $(4x^2 + 3)(2x - 1) > 0$ only when $x > \frac{1}{2}$, the domain of the given natural logarithmic function is the interval $(\frac{1}{2}, +\infty)$.

Therefore, it is understood that fraction (5) is the derivative only if $x > \frac{1}{2}$.

Because $x/(x + 1) > 0$ when either $x < -1$ or $x > 0$, the domain of the natural logarithmic function in Example 3 is $(-\infty, -1) \cup (0, +\infty)$, and so $1/x(x + 1)$ is the derivative if either $x < -1$ or $x > 0$.   •

We show that the natural logarithmic function obeys the laws of logarithms as stated earlier. However, first we need a preliminary theorem, which we state and prove.

9.1.2 Theorem   If a and b are any positive numbers, then

$$\int_a^{ab} \frac{1}{t}\, dt = \int_1^b \frac{1}{t}\, dt$$

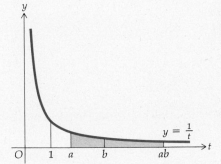

Figure 9.1.3

PROOF: In the integral $\int_a^{ab} (1/t)\, dt$, make the substitution $t = au$; then $dt = a\, du$. When $t = a$, $u = 1$, and when $t = ab$, $u = b$. Therefore, we have

$$\int_a^{ab} \frac{1}{t}\, dt = \int_1^b \frac{1}{au}\, (a\, du)$$

$$= \int_1^b \frac{1}{u}\, du$$

$$= \int_1^b \frac{1}{t}\, dt \qquad \blacksquare$$

• ILLUSTRATION 2: In terms of geometry, Theorem 9.1.2 states that the measure of the area of the region shown in Fig. 9.1.3 is the same as the measure of the area of the region shown in Fig. 9.1.4.   •

If we take $x = 1$ in Definition 9.1.1, we have

$$\ln 1 = \int_1^1 \frac{1}{t}\, dt$$

The right side of the above is zero by Definition 7.3.5. So we have

$$\ln 1 = 0 \tag{6}$$

Figure 9.1.4

Equation (6) corresponds to Law 3 of logarithms, given earlier.

The following three theorems give some properties of the natural logarithmic function.

9.1.3 Theorem   If a and b are any positive numbers, then

$$\ln (ab) = \ln a + \ln b$$

PROOF: From Definition 9.1.1,

$$\ln(ab) = \int_1^{ab} \frac{1}{t} \, dt$$

which, from Theorem 7.4.6, gives

$$\ln(ab) = \int_1^a \frac{1}{t} \, dt + \int_a^{ab} \frac{1}{t} \, dt$$

Applying Theorem 9.1.2 to the second integral on the right side of the above, we obtain

$$\ln(ab) = \int_1^a \frac{1}{t} \, dt + \int_1^b \frac{1}{t} \, dt$$

and so from Definition 9.1.1 we have

$$\ln(ab) = \ln a + \ln b \qquad \blacksquare$$

9.1.4 Theorem   If a and b are any positive numbers, then

$$\ln \frac{a}{b} = \ln a - \ln b$$

PROOF: Because $a = (a/b) \cdot b$, we have

$$\ln a = \ln \left(\frac{a}{b} \cdot b \right)$$

Applying Theorem 9.1.3 to the right side of the above equation, we get

$$\ln a = \ln \frac{a}{b} + \ln b$$

Subtracting $\ln b$ on both sides of the above equation, we obtain

$$\ln \frac{a}{b} = \ln a - \ln b \qquad \blacksquare$$

9.1.5 Theorem   If a is any positive number and r is any rational number, then

$$\ln a^r = r \ln a$$

PROOF: From formula (4), if r is any rational number and $x > 0$, we have

$$D_x(\ln x^r) = \frac{1}{x^r} \cdot rx^{r-1} = \frac{r}{x}$$

and

$$D_x(r \ln x) = \frac{r}{x}$$

Therefore,

$$D_x(\ln x^r) = D_x(r \ln x)$$

From the above equation the derivatives of $\ln x^r$ and $r \ln x$ are equal, and so it follows from Theorem 6.3.3 that there is a constant K such that

$$\ln x^r = r \ln x + K \qquad \text{for all } x > 0 \tag{7}$$

To determine K, substitute 1 for x in Eq. (7) and we have

$$\ln 1^r = r \ln 1 + K$$

But, by Eq. (6), $\ln 1 = 0$; hence, $K = 0$. Replacing K by 0 in Eq. (7), we get

$$\ln x^r = r \ln x \qquad \text{for all } x > 0$$

from which it follows that if $x = a$, where a is any positive number, then

$$\ln a^r = r \ln a \qquad\qquad\blacksquare$$

Note that Theorems 9.1.3, 9.1.4, and 9.1.5 are the same properties as the laws of logarithms 1, 2, and 4, respectively, given earlier.

• ILLUSTRATION 3: In Example 2, if Theorem 9.1.3 is applied before finding the derivative, we have

$$y = \ln(4x^2 + 3) + \ln(2x - 1) \tag{8}$$

Now the domain of the function defined by the above equation is the interval $(\frac{1}{2}, +\infty)$, which is the same as the domain of the given function. From Eq. (8) we get

$$D_x y = \frac{8x}{4x^2 + 3} + \frac{2}{2x - 1}$$

and combining the fractions gives

$$D_x y = \frac{8x(2x - 1) + 2(4x^2 + 3)}{(4x^2 + 3)(2x - 1)}$$

which is the same as the first line of the solution of Example 2.   •

• ILLUSTRATION 4: If we apply Theorem 9.1.4 before finding the derivative in Example 3, we have

$$\ln y = \ln x - \ln(x + 1) \tag{9}$$

$\ln x$ is defined only when $x > 0$, and $\ln(x + 1)$ is defined only when $x > -1$. Therefore, the domain of the function defined by Eq. (9) is the interval $(0, +\infty)$. But the domain of the function given in Example 3 consists of the two intervals $(-\infty, -1)$ and $(0, +\infty)$. Finding $D_x y$ from Eq. (9), we have

$$D_x y = \frac{1}{x} - \frac{1}{x + 1} = \frac{1}{x(x + 1)}$$

but remember here that x must be greater than 0, whereas in the solution of Example 3 values of x less than -1 are also included.   ●

Illustration 4 shows the care that must be taken when applying Theorems 9.1.3, 9.1.4, and 9.1.5 to natural logarithmic functions.

EXAMPLE 4:   Given

$$y = \ln(2x - 1)^3$$

find $D_x y$.

SOLUTION: From Theorem 9.1.5 we have

$$y = \ln(2x - 1)^3 = 3 \ln(2x - 1)$$

Note that $\ln(2x - 1)^3$ and $3 \ln(2x - 1)$ both have the same domain, $x > \frac{1}{2}$. Applying formula (4) gives

$$D_x y = 3 \cdot \frac{1}{2x - 1} \cdot 2 = \frac{6}{2x - 1}$$

In the discussion that follows we need to make use of $D_x(\ln |x|)$. To find this by using formula (4), $\sqrt{x^2}$ is substituted for $|x|$, and so we have

$$D_x(\ln |x|) = D_x(\ln \sqrt{x^2})$$

$$= \frac{1}{\sqrt{x^2}} \cdot D_x(\sqrt{x^2})$$

$$= \frac{1}{\sqrt{x^2}} \cdot \frac{x}{\sqrt{x^2}}$$

$$= \frac{x}{x^2}$$

Hence,

$$D_x(\ln |x|) = \frac{1}{x} \tag{10}$$

From formula (10) and the chain rule, if u is a differentiable function of x, we get

$$D_x(\ln |u|) = \frac{1}{u} \cdot D_x u \tag{11}$$

The following example illustrates how the properties of the natural logarithmic function, given in Theorems 9.1.3, 9.1.4, and 9.1.5, can simplify the work involved in differentiating complicated expressions involving products, quotients, and powers.

EXAMPLE 5:   Given

$$y = \frac{\sqrt[3]{x + 1}}{(x + 2)\sqrt{x + 3}}$$

find $D_x y$.

SOLUTION: From the given equation

$$|y| = \left| \frac{\sqrt[3]{x + 1}}{(x + 2)\sqrt{x + 3}} \right| = \frac{|\sqrt[3]{x + 1}|}{|x + 2||\sqrt{x + 3}|}$$

Taking the natural logarithm and applying the properties of logarithms, we obtain

$$\ln |y| = \tfrac{1}{3} \ln |x + 1| - \ln |x + 2| - \tfrac{1}{2} \ln |x + 3|$$

Differentiating on both sides implicitly with respect to x and applying formula (11), we get

$$\frac{1}{y} D_x y = \frac{1}{3(x + 1)} - \frac{1}{x + 2} - \frac{1}{2(x + 3)}$$

Multiplying on both sides by y, we obtain

$$D_x y = y \cdot \frac{2(x + 2)(x + 3) - 6(x + 1)(x + 3) - 3(x + 1)(x + 2)}{6(x + 1)(x + 2)(x + 3)}$$

Replacing y by its given value, we obtain $D_x y$ equal to

$$\frac{(x + 1)^{1/3}}{(x + 2)(x + 3)^{1/2}} \cdot \frac{2x^2 + 10x + 12 - 6x^2 - 24x - 18 - 3x^2 - 9x - 6}{6(x + 1)(x + 2)(x + 3)}$$

and so

$$D_x y = \frac{-7x^2 - 23x - 12}{6(x + 1)^{2/3}(x + 2)^2(x + 3)^{3/2}}$$

The process illustrated in Example 5 is called *logarithmic differentiation*, which was developed in 1697 by Johann Bernoulli (1667–1748).

From formula (11) we obtain the following formula for indefinite integration:

$$\int \frac{1}{u} \, du = \ln |u| + C \tag{12}$$

Combining (12) with Formula 6.3.9 we have, for n any real number,

$$\int u^n \, du = \begin{cases} \dfrac{u^{n+1}}{n + 1} + C & \text{if } n \neq -1 \\ \ln |u| + C & \text{if } n = -1 \end{cases} \tag{13}$$

EXAMPLE 6: Evaluate

$$\int \frac{x^2 \, dx}{x^3 + 1}$$

SOLUTION:

$$\int \frac{x^2 \, dx}{x^3 + 1} = \frac{1}{3} \int \frac{3x^2 \, dx}{x^3 + 1} = \frac{1}{3} \ln |x^3 + 1| + C$$

EXAMPLE 7: Evaluate

$$\int_0^2 \frac{x^2 + 2}{x + 1} \, dx$$

SOLUTION: Because $(x^2 + 2)/(x + 1)$ is an improper fraction, we divide the numerator by the denominator and obtain

$$\frac{x^2 + 2}{x + 1} = x - 1 + \frac{3}{x + 1}$$

Therefore,

$$\int_0^2 \frac{x^2 + 2}{x + 1} \, dx = \int_0^2 \left(x - 1 + \frac{3}{x + 1} \right) dx$$

$$= \tfrac{1}{2}x^2 - x + 3 \ln |x + 1| \; \Big]_0^2$$

$$= 2 - 2 + 3 \ln 3 - 3 \ln 1$$

$$= 3 \ln 3 - 3 \cdot 0$$

$$= 3 \ln 3$$

The answer in the above example also can be written as ln 27 because, by Theorem 9.1.5, $3 \ln 3 = \ln 3^3$.

EXAMPLE 8: Evaluate

$$\int \frac{\ln x}{x} \, dx$$

SOLUTION: Let $u = \ln x$; then $du = dx/x$; so we have

$$\int \frac{\ln x}{x} \, dx = \int u \, du = \frac{1}{2} u^2 + C = \frac{1}{2} (\ln x)^2 + C$$

Exercises 9.1

In Exercises 1 through 10, differentiate the given function and simplify the result.

1. $f(x) = \ln(1 + 4x^2)$

2. $f(x) = \ln \sqrt{1 + 4x^2}$

3. $f(x) = \ln \sqrt{4 - x^2}$

4. $g(x) = \ln(\ln x)$

5. $h(x) = \ln(x^2 \ln x)$

6. $f(x) = \ln \sqrt[4]{\dfrac{x^2 - 1}{x^2 + 1}}$

7. $f(x) = \ln |x^3 + 1|$

8. $f(x) = \sqrt[3]{\ln x^3}$

9. $F(x) = \sqrt{x + 1} - \ln(1 + \sqrt{x + 1})$

10. $G(x) = x \ln(x + \sqrt{1 + x^2}) - \sqrt{1 + x^2}$

In Exercises 11 through 16, find $D_x y$ by logarithmic differentiation.

11. $y = \dfrac{x^3 + 2x}{\sqrt[5]{x^7 + 1}}$

12. $y = \dfrac{x \sqrt{x + 1}}{\sqrt[3]{x - 1}}$

13. $y = \dfrac{3x}{\sqrt{(x + 1)(x + 2)}}$

14. $y = \dfrac{\sqrt{1 - x^2}}{(x + 1)^{2/3}}$

15. $y = \sqrt{x^2 + 1} \, \ln(x^2 - 1)$

16. $y = (5x - 4)(x^2 + 3)(3x^3 - 5)$

In Exercises 17 and 18, find $D_x y$ by implicit differentiation.

17. $\ln xy + x + y = 2$

18. $\ln \dfrac{y}{x} + xy = 1$

In Exercises 19 through 26, evaluate the indefinite integral.

19. $\displaystyle\int \frac{dx}{3 - 2x}$

20. $\displaystyle\int \frac{3x\ dx}{5x^2 - 1}$

21. $\displaystyle\int \frac{dx}{x \ln x}$

22. $\displaystyle\int \frac{dx}{\sqrt{x}\ (1 + \sqrt{x})}$

23. $\displaystyle\int \frac{\ln^2 3x}{x}\ dx$

24. $\displaystyle\int \frac{5 - 4x^2}{3 + 2x}\ dx$

25. $\displaystyle\int \frac{2x^3\ dx}{x^2 - 4}$

26. $\displaystyle\int \frac{(2 + \ln^2 x)\ dx}{x(1 - \ln x)}$

In Exercises 27 through 30, evaluate the definite integral.

27. $\displaystyle\int_3^5 \frac{2x\ dx}{x^2 - 5}$

28. $\displaystyle\int_1^3 \frac{2x + 3}{x + 1}\ dx$

29. $\displaystyle\int_4^5 \frac{x\ dx}{4 - x^2}$

30. $\displaystyle\int_1^5 \frac{4x^3 - 1}{2x - 1}\ dx$

31. Prove that $\ln x^n = n \cdot \ln x$ by first showing that $\ln x^n$ and $n \cdot \ln x$ differ by a constant and then find the constant by taking $x = 1$.

32. Prove that $x - 1 - \ln x > 0$ and $1 - \ln x - 1/x < 0$ for all $x > 0$ and $x \neq 1$, thus establishing the inequality

$$1 - \frac{1}{x} < \ln x < x - 1$$

for all $x > 0$ and $x \neq 1$. (HINT: Let $f(x) = x - 1 - \ln x$ and $g(x) = 1 - \ln x - 1/x$ and determine the signs of $f'(x)$ and $g'(x)$ on the intervals $(0, 1)$ and $(1, +\infty)$.)

33. Use the result of Exercise 32 to prove

$$\lim_{x \to 0} \frac{\ln(1 + x)}{x} = 1$$

34. Establish the limit of Exercise 33 by using the definition of the derivative to find $F'(0)$ for the function F for which $F(x) = \ln(1 + x)$.

35. Prove $\lim_{x \to +\infty} (\ln x)/x = 0$. (HINT: First prove that $\displaystyle\int_1^x (1/\sqrt{t})\ dt \geq \int_1^x (1/t)\ dt$ by using Theorem 7.4.8.)

9.2 THE GRAPH OF THE NATURAL LOGARITHMIC FUNCTION

To draw a sketch of the graph of the natural logarithmic function, we must first consider some properties of this function.

Let f be the function defined by

$$f(x) = \ln x = \int_1^x \frac{1}{t}\ dt \qquad x > 0$$

The domain of f is the set of all positive numbers. The function f is differentiable for all x in its domain, and

$$f'(x) = \frac{1}{x} \tag{1}$$

Because f is differentiable for all $x > 0$, f is continuous for all $x > 0$. From (1) we conclude that $f'(x) > 0$ for all $x > 0$, and therefore f is an increasing function.

$$f''(x) = -\frac{1}{x^2} \tag{2}$$

From (2) it follows that $f''(x) < 0$ when $x > 0$. Therefore, the graph of $y = f(x)$ is concave downward at every point. Because $f(1) = \ln 1 = 0$, the x intercept of the graph is 1.

$$f(2) = \ln 2 = \int_1^2 \frac{1}{t}\, dt$$

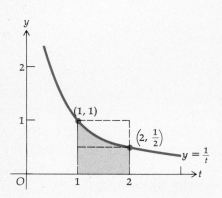

Figure 9.2.1

To determine an approximate numerical value for $\ln 2$, the definite integral $\int_1^2 (1/t)\, dt$ is interpreted as the number of square units in the area of the region shown in Fig. 9.2.1.

From Fig. 9.2.1 we see that $\ln 2$ is between the measures of the areas of the rectangles, each having a base of length 1 unit and altitudes of lengths $\frac{1}{2}$ unit and 1 unit; that is,

$$0.5 < \ln 2 < 1 \tag{3}$$

An inequality can be obtained analytically, using Theorem 7.4.8, by proceeding as follows. Let $f(t) = 1/t$ and $g(t) = \frac{1}{2}$. Then $f(t) \geq g(t)$ for all t in $[1, 2]$. Because f and g are continuous on $[1, 2]$, they are integrable on $[1, 2]$, and we have from Theorem 7.4.8

$$\int_1^2 \frac{1}{t}\, dt \geq \int_1^2 \frac{1}{2}\, dt$$

or, equivalently,

$$\ln 2 \geq \tfrac{1}{2} \tag{4}$$

Similarly, if $f(t) = 1/t$ and $h(t) = 1$, then $h(t) \geq f(t)$ for all t in $[1, 2]$. Because h and f are continuous on $[1, 2]$, they are integrable there; and again using Theorem 7.4.8, we obtain

$$\int_1^2 1\, dt \geq \int_1^2 \frac{1}{t}\, dt$$

or, equivalently,

$$1 \geq \ln 2 \tag{5}$$

Combining (4) and (5), we get

$$0.5 \leq \ln 2 \leq 1 \tag{6}$$

The number 0.5 is a lower bound of $\ln 2$ and 1 is an upper bound of $\ln 2$. In a similar manner we obtain a lower and upper bound for the natural logarithm of any positive real number. Later we learn, by applying infinite series, how to compute the natural logarithm of any positive real number to any desired number of decimal places.

The value of $\ln 2$ to five decimal places is given by

$$\ln 2 \approx 0.69315$$

Using this value of $\ln 2$ and applying Theorem 9.1.5, we can find an approximate value for the natural logarithm of any power of 2. In particular, we have

$$\ln 4 = \ln 2^2 \;=\; 2 \ln 2 \approx \;\; 1.38630$$

$$\ln 8 = \ln 2^3 \;=\; 3 \ln 2 \approx \;\; 2.07945$$

$$\ln \tfrac{1}{2} = \ln 2^{-1} = -1 \ln 2 \approx -0.69315$$

$$\ln \tfrac{1}{4} = \ln 2^{-2} = -2 \ln 2 \approx -1.38630$$

In the appendix there is a table of natural logarithms, giving the values to four decimal places.

We now determine the behavior of the natural logarithmic function for large values of x by considering $\lim\limits_{x \to +\infty} \ln x$.

Because the natural logarithmic function is an increasing function, if we take p as any positive number,

$$\ln x > \ln 2^p \qquad \text{whenever} \qquad x > 2^p \tag{7}$$

From Theorem 9.1.5 we have

$$\ln 2^p = p \ln 2 \tag{8}$$

Substituting from (8) into (7), we get

$$\ln x > p \ln 2 \qquad \text{whenever} \qquad x > 2^p$$

Because from (6), $\ln 2 \geq \tfrac{1}{2}$, we have from the above

$$\ln x > \tfrac{1}{2}p \qquad \text{whenever} \qquad x > 2^p$$

Letting $p = 2n$, where $n > 0$, we have

$$\ln x > n \qquad \text{whenever} \qquad x > 2^{2n} \tag{9}$$

It follows from (9), by taking $N = 2^{2n}$, that for any $n > 0$,

$$\ln x > n \qquad \text{whenever} \qquad x > N$$

So we may conclude that

$$\lim_{x \to +\infty} \ln x = +\infty \tag{10}$$

To determine the behavior of the natural logarithmic function for positive values of x near zero, we investigate $\lim\limits_{x \to 0^+} \ln x$.

Because $\ln x = \ln(x^{-1})^{-1}$, we have

$$\ln x = -\ln \frac{1}{x} \tag{11}$$

The expression "$x \to 0^+$" is equivalent to "$1/x \to +\infty$," and so from

(11) we write

$$\lim_{x \to 0^+} \ln x = - \lim_{1/x \to +\infty} \ln \frac{1}{x} \qquad (12)$$

From (10) we have

$$\lim_{1/x \to +\infty} \ln \frac{1}{x} = +\infty \qquad (13)$$

Therefore, from (12) and (13) we get

$$\lim_{x \to 0^+} \ln x = -\infty \qquad (14)$$

From (14) and (10) and the intermediate-value theorem (7.5.1) we conclude that the range of the natural logarithmic function is the set of all real numbers. From (14) we conclude that the graph of the natural logarithmic function is asymptotic to the negative side of the y axis through the fourth quadrant. The properties of the natural logarithmic function are summarized as follows:

(i) The domain is the set of all positive numbers.
(ii) The range is the set of all real numbers.
(iii) The function is increasing on its entire domain.
(iv) The function is continuous at all numbers in its domain.
(v) The graph of the function is concave downward at all points.
(vi) The graph of the function is asymptotic to the negative side of the y axis through the fourth quadrant.

By using these properties and plotting a few points with a piece of the tangent line at the points, we can draw a sketch of the graph of the natural logarithmic function. In Fig. 9.2.2 we have plotted the points having abscissas of $\frac{1}{4}, \frac{1}{2}, 1, 2, 4,$ and 8. The slope of the tangent line is found from $D_x(\ln x) = 1/x$.

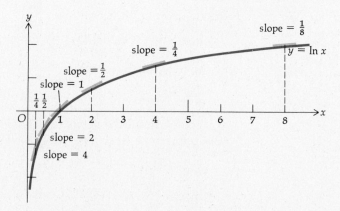

Figure 9.2.2

Exercises 9.2

1. Draw a sketch of the graph of $y = \ln x$ by plotting the points having the abscissas $\frac{1}{9}$, $\frac{1}{3}$, 1, 3, and 9, and use $\ln 3 \approx 1.09861$. At each of the five points, find the slope of the tangent line and draw a piece of the tangent line.

In Exercises 2 through 9, draw a sketch of the graph of the curve having the given equation.

2. $x = \ln y$

3. $y = \ln(-x)$

4. $y = \ln |x|$

5. $y = \ln(x + 1)$

6. $y = \ln(x - 1)$

7. $y = x - \ln x$

8. $y = x \ln x$

9. $y = \ln \dfrac{1}{x}$

10. Show the geometric interpretation of the inequality in Exercise 32 of Exercises 9.1 by drawing on the same pair of axes sketches of the graphs of the functions f, g, and h defined by the equations $f(x) = 1 - 1/x$, $g(x) = \ln x$, and $h(x) = x - 1$.

11. Find an equation of the tangent line to the curve $y = \ln x$ at the point whose abscissa is 2.

12. Find an equation of the normal line to the curve $y = \ln x$ that is parallel to the line $x + 2y - 1 = 0$.

In Exercises 13 through 20, find the exact value of the number to be found and then give an approximation of this number to three decimal places by using the table of natural logarithms in the appendix.

13. Find the area of the region bounded by the curve $y = 2/(x - 3)$, the x axis, and the lines $x = 4$ and $x = 5$.

14. If $f(x) = 1/x$, find the average value of f on the interval $[1, 5]$.

15. Using Boyle's law for the expansion of a gas (see Exercise 10 in Exercises 3.9), find the average pressure with respect to the volume as the volume increases from 4 ft³ to 8 ft³ and the pressure is 2000 lb/ft² when the volume is 4 ft³.

16. Find the volume of the solid of revolution generated when the region bounded by the curve $y = 1 - 3/x$, the x axis, and the line $x = 1$ is revolved about the x axis.

17. In a telegraph cable, the measure of the speed of the signal is proportional to $x^2 \ln(1/x)$, where x is the ratio of the measure of the radius of the core of the cable to the measure of the thickness of the cable's winding. Find the value of x for which the speed of the signal is greatest.

18. A particle is moving on a straight line according to the equation of motion $s = (t + 1)^2 \ln(t + 1)$ where s ft is the directed distance of the particle from the starting point at t sec. Find the velocity and acceleration when $t = 3$.

19. The linear density of a rod at a point x ft from one end is $2/(1 + x)$ slugs/ft. If the rod is 3 ft long, find the mass and center of mass of the rod.

20. A manufacturer of electric generators began operations on Jan. 1, 1966. During the first year there were no sales because the company concentrated on product development and research. After the first year, the sales have increased steadily according to the equation $y = x \ln x$, where x is the number of years during which the company has been operating and y is the number of millions of dollars in the sales volume. (a) Draw a sketch of the graph of the equation. Determine the rate at which the sales were increasing (b) on Jan. 1, 1970, and (c) on Jan. 1, 1976.

9.3 THE INVERSE OF A FUNCTION

Let us consider the equation

$$x^2 - y^2 = 4 \tag{1}$$

If this equation is solved for y in terms of x, we obtain

$$y = \pm\sqrt{x^2 - 4}$$

Figure 9.3.1

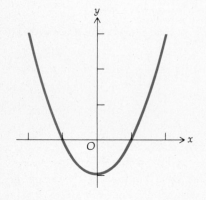

Figure 9.3.2

Therefore, Eq. (1) does not define y as a function of x because for each value of x greater than 2 or less than -2 there are two values of y, and to have a functional relationship, there must be a unique value of the dependent variable for a value of the independent variable. If Eq. (1) is solved for x in terms of y, we obtain

$$x = \pm \sqrt{y^2 + 4}$$

and so x is not a function of y. Therefore, Eq. (1) neither defines y as a function of x nor x as a function of y. The equation

$$y = x^2 - 1 \tag{2}$$

expresses y as a function of x because for each value of x a unique value of y is determined. As stated in Sec. 1.7, no vertical line can intersect the graph of a function in more than one point. In Fig. 9.3.1 we have a sketch of the graph of Eq. (1). We see that if $a > 2$ or $a < -2$, the straight line $x = a$ intersects the graph in two points. In Fig. 9.3.2 we have a sketch of the graph of Eq. (2). Here we see that any vertical line intersects the graph in only one point. Equation (2) does not define x as a function of y because for each value of y greater than -1, two values of x are determined.

In some cases, an equation involving x and y will define both y as a function of x and x as a function of y, as shown in the following illustration.

• ILLUSTRATION 1: Consider the equation

$$y = x^3 + 1 \tag{3}$$

If we let f be the function defined by

$$f(x) = x^3 + 1 \tag{4}$$

then Eq. (3) can be written as $y = f(x)$, and y is a function of x. If we solve Eq. (3) for x, we obtain

$$x = \sqrt[3]{y - 1} \tag{5}$$

and if we let g be the function defined by

$$g(y) = \sqrt[3]{y - 1} \tag{6}$$

then Eq. (5) may be written as $x = g(y)$, and x is a function of y. •

The functions f and g defined by Eqs. (4) and (6) are called *inverse functions*. We also say that the function g is the *inverse* of the function f and that f is the *inverse* of g. The notation f^{-1} denotes the inverse of function f. Note that in using -1 to denote the inverse of a function, it should not be confused with the exponent -1. We have the following formal definition of the inverse of a function.

9.3.1 Definition   If the function f is the set of ordered pairs (x, y), and if there is a function f^{-1} such that

$$x = f^{-1}(y) \quad \text{if and only if} \quad y = f(x) \qquad (7)$$

then f^{-1}, which is the set of ordered pairs (y, x), is called the *inverse of the function f*, and f and f^{-1} are called *inverse functions*. The domain of f^{-1} is the range of f, and the range of f^{-1} is the domain of f.

Eliminating y between the equations in (7), we obtain

$$x = f^{-1}(f(x)), \qquad (8)$$

and eliminating x between the same pair of equations, we get

$$y = f(f^{-1}(y)) \qquad (9)$$

So from Eqs. (8) and (9) we see that if the inverse of the function f is the function f^{-1}, then the inverse of the function f^{-1} is the function f.

Because the functions f and g defined by Eqs. (4) and (6) are inverse functions, f^{-1} can be written in place of g. We have from (4) and (6)

$$f(x) = x^3 + 1 \quad \text{and} \quad f^{-1}(x) = \sqrt[3]{x - 1} \qquad (10)$$

Figure 9.3.3

Sketches of the graphs of functions f and f^{-1} defined in (10) are shown in Figs. 9.3.3 and 9.3.4, respectively.

We observe that in Fig. 9.3.3 the function f is continuous and increasing on its entire domain. The definition of an increasing function (Definition 5.1.1) is satisfied by f for all values of x in its domain. We also observe in Fig. 9.3.3 that a horizontal line intersects the graph of f in only one point. We intuitively suspect that if a function is continuous and increasing, then a horizontal line will intersect the graph of the function in only one point, and so the function will have an inverse. The following theorem verifies this fact.

Figure 9.3.4

9.3.2 Theorem   Suppose that the function f is continuous and increasing on the closed interval $[a, b]$. Then

(i) f has an inverse f^{-1}, which is defined on $[f(a), f(b)]$;
(ii) f^{-1} is increasing on $[f(a), f(b)]$;
(iii) f^{-1} is continuous on $[f(a), f(b)]$.

PROOF OF (i):   Since f is continuous on $[a, b]$, then if k is any number such that $f(a) < k < f(b)$, by the intermediate-value theorem (7.5.1), there exists a number c in (a, b) such that $f(c) = k$. So if y is any number in the closed interval $[f(a), f(b)]$, there is at least one number x in $[a, b]$ such that $y = f(x)$. We wish to show that for each number y there corresponds only one number x. Suppose to a number y_1 in $[f(a), f(b)]$ there correspond two numbers x_1 and x_2 $(x_1 \neq x_2)$ in $[a, b]$ such that $y_1 = f(x_1)$ and $y_1 = f(x_2)$. Then, we must have

$$f(x_1) = f(x_2) \tag{11}$$

Because we have assumed $x_1 \neq x_2$, either $x_1 < x_2$ or $x_2 < x_1$. If $x_1 < x_2$, because f is increasing on $[a, b]$, it follows that $f(x_1) < f(x_2)$; this contradicts (11). If $x_2 < x_1$, then $f(x_2) < f(x_1)$, and this also contradicts (11). Therefore, our assumption that $x_1 \neq x_2$ is false, and so to each value of y in $[f(a), f(b)]$ there corresponds exactly one number x in $[a, b]$ such that $y = f(x)$. Therefore, f has an inverse f^{-1}, which is defined for all numbers in $[f(a), f(b)]$.

PROOF OF (ii): To prove that f^{-1} is increasing on $[f(a), f(b)]$, we must show that if y_1 and y_2 are two numbers in $[f(a), f(b)]$ such that $y_1 < y_2$, then $f^{-1}(y_1) < f^{-1}(y_2)$. Because f^{-1} is defined on $[f(a), f(b)]$, there exist numbers x_1 and x_2 in $[a, b]$ such that $y_1 = f(x_1)$ and $y_2 = f(x_2)$. Therefore,

$$f^{-1}(y_1) = f^{-1}(f(x_1)) = x_1 \tag{12}$$

and

$$f^{-1}(y_2) = f^{-1}(f(x_2)) = x_2 \tag{13}$$

If $x_2 < x_1$, then because f is increasing on $[a,b]$, $f(x_2) < f(x_1)$ or, equivalently, $y_2 < y_1$. But $y_1 < y_2$; therefore, x_2 cannot be less than x_1.

If $x_2 = x_1$, then because f is a function, $f(x_1) = f(x_2)$ or, equivalently, $y_1 = y_2$, but this also contradicts the fact that $y_1 < y_2$. Therefore, $x_2 \neq x_1$.

So if x_2 is not less than x_1 and $x_2 \neq x_1$, it follows that $x_1 < x_2$; hence, from (12) and (13), $f^{-1}(y_1) < f^{-1}(y_2)$. Thus, we have proved that f^{-1} is increasing on $[f(a), f(b)]$.

PROOF OF (iii): To prove that f^{-1} is continuous on the closed interval $[f(a), f(b)]$, we must show that if r is any number in the open interval $(f(a), f(b))$, then f^{-1} is continuous at r, and f^{-1} is continuous from the right at $f(a)$, and f^{-1} is continuous from the left at $f(b)$.

We prove that f^{-1} is continuous at any r in the open interval $(f(a), f(b))$ by showing that Definition 2.6.4 holds at r. We wish to show that, for any $\epsilon > 0$ small enough so that $f^{-1}(r) - \epsilon$ and $f^{-1}(r) + \epsilon$ are both in $[a, b]$, there exists a $\delta > 0$ such that

$$|f^{-1}(y) - f^{-1}(r)| < \epsilon \qquad \text{whenever} \qquad |y - r| < \delta$$

Let $f^{-1}(r) = s$. Then $f(s) = r$. Because from (ii), f^{-1} is increasing on $[f(a), f(b)]$, we conclude that $a < s < b$. Therefore,

$$a \leq s - \epsilon < s < s + \epsilon \leq b$$

Because f is increasing on $[a, b]$,

$$f(a) \leq f(s - \epsilon) < r < f(s + \epsilon) \leq f(b) \tag{14}$$

Let δ be the smaller of the two numbers $r - f(s - \epsilon)$ and $f(s + \epsilon) - r$; so $\delta \leq r - f(s - \epsilon)$ and $\delta \leq f(s + \epsilon) - r$ or, equivalently,

$$f(s - \epsilon) \leq r - \delta \qquad (15)$$

and

$$r + \delta \leq f(s + \epsilon) \qquad (16)$$

Whenever $|y - r| < \delta$, we have $-\delta < y - r < \delta$ or, equivalently,

$$r - \delta < y < r + \delta \qquad (17)$$

From (14), (15), (16), and (17), we have, whenever $|y - r| < \delta$,

$$f(a) \leq f(s - \epsilon) < y < f(s + \epsilon) \leq f(b)$$

Because f^{-1} is increasing on $[f(a), f(b)]$, it follows from the above that

$$f^{-1}(f(s - \epsilon)) < f^{-1}(y) < f^{-1}(f(s + \epsilon)) \qquad \text{whenever} \qquad |y - r| < \delta$$

or, equivalently,

$$s - \epsilon < f^{-1}(y) < s + \epsilon \qquad \text{whenever} \qquad |y - r| < \delta$$

or, equivalently,

$$-\epsilon < f^{-1}(y) - s < \epsilon \qquad \text{whenever} \qquad |y - r| < \delta$$

or, equivalently,

$$|f^{-1}(y) - f^{-1}(r)| < \epsilon \qquad \text{whenever} \qquad |y - r| < \delta$$

So f^{-1} is continuous on the open interval $(f(a), f(b))$.

The proofs that f^{-1} is continuous from the right at $f(a)$ and continuous from the left at $f(b)$ are left as an exercise (see Exercise 24). ∎

A theorem analogous to the above theorem is obtained if the function f is continuous and *decreasing* (instead of increasing) on the closed interval $[a, b]$.

9.3.3 Theorem Suppose that the function f is continuous and decreasing on the closed interval $[a, b]$. Then

(i) f has an inverse f^{-1}, which is defined on $[f(b), f(a)]$;
(ii) f^{-1} is decreasing on $[f(b), f(a)]$;
(iii) f^{-1} is continuous on $[f(b), f(a)]$.

The proof is similar to the proof of Theorem 9.3.2 and is left as an exercise (see Exercises 25 to 27).

● ILLUSTRATION 2: We reconsider Eq. (2): $y = x^2 - 1$. As stated earlier in this section, this equation does not define x as a function of y because if we solve for x we obtain

$$x = \sqrt{y + 1} \quad \text{and} \quad x = -\sqrt{y + 1} \qquad (18)$$

So actually Eq. (2) defines x as two distinct functions of y. If in Eq. (2) we restrict x to the closed interval $[0, c]$ and let $y = f_1(x)$ if x is in $[0, c]$, we have

$$f_1(x) = x^2 - 1 \qquad \text{and } x \text{ in } [0, c] \tag{19}$$

If in Eq. (2) we restrict x to the closed interval $[-c, 0]$ and let $y = f_2(x)$ if x is in $[-c, 0]$, we have

$$f_2(x) = x^2 - 1 \qquad \text{and } x \text{ in } [-c, 0] \tag{20}$$

The functions f_1 and f_2 defined by (19) and (20) are distinct functions because their domains are different. If we find the derivatives of f_1 and f_2, we obtain

$$f_1'(x) = 2x \qquad \text{and } x \text{ in } [0, c]$$

and

$$f_2'(x) = 2x \qquad \text{and } x \text{ in} [-c, 0]$$

Because f_1 is continuous on $[0, c]$ and $f_1'(x) > 0$ for all x in $(0, c)$, by Theorem 5.1.3 (i), f is increasing on $[0, c]$; and so by Theorem 9.3.2, f_1 has an inverse on $[-1, c^2 - 1]$. The inverse function is given by

$$f_1^{-1}(y) = \sqrt{y + 1} \tag{21}$$

Similarly, because f_2 is continuous on $[-c, 0]$ and because $f_2'(x) < 0$ for all x in $(-c, 0)$, by Theorem 5.1.3 (ii), f_2 is decreasing on $[-c, 0]$. Hence, by Theorem 9.3.3, f_2 has an inverse on $[-1, c^2 - 1]$, and the inverse function is given by

$$f_2^{-1}(y) = -\sqrt{y + 1} \tag{22}$$

Because the letter used to represent the independent variable is irrelevant as far as the function is concerned, x could be used instead of y in (21) and (22), and we write

$$f_1^{-1}(x) = \sqrt{x + 1} \qquad \text{and } x \text{ in } [-1, c^2 - 1] \tag{23}$$

and

$$f_2^{-1}(x) = -\sqrt{x + 1} \qquad \text{and } x \text{ in } [-1, c^2 - 1] \tag{24} \quad \bullet$$

In Fig. 9.3.5 there are sketches of the graphs of f_1 and its inverse f_1^{-1}, as defined in (19) and (23), plotted on the same set of axes. In Fig. 9.3.6 there are sketches of the graphs of f_2 and its inverse f_2^{-1}, as defined in (20) and (24), plotted on the same set of axes. It appears intuitively true from Fig. 9.3.5 that if the point $Q(u, v)$ is on the graph of f_1, then the point $R(v, u)$ is on the graph of f_1^{-1}. From Fig. 9.3.6 it appears to be true that if the point $Q(u, v)$ is on the graph of f_2, then the point $R(v, u)$ is on the graph of f_2^{-1}.

In general, if Q is the point (u, v) and R is the point (v, u), the line

Figure 9.3.5

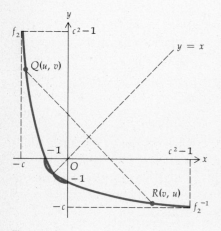

Figure 9.3.6

segment QR is perpendicular to the line $y = x$ and is bisected by it. We state that the point Q is a *reflection* of the point R with respect to the line $y = x$, and the point R is a *reflection* of the point Q with respect to the line $y = x$. If x and y are interchanged in the equation $y = f(x)$, we obtain the equation $x = f(y)$, and the graph of the equation $x = f(y)$ is said to be a *reflection of the graph* of the equation $y = f(x)$ with respect to the line $y = x$. Because the equation $x = f(y)$ is equivalent to the equation $y = f^{-1}(x)$, we conclude that the graph of the equation $y = f^{-1}(x)$ is a reflection of the graph of the equation $y = f(x)$ with respect to the line $y = x$. Therefore, if a function f has an inverse f^{-1}, their graphs are reflections of each other with respect to the line $y = x$.

EXAMPLE 1: Given the function f is defined by

$$f(x) = \frac{2x + 3}{x - 1}$$

find the inverse f^{-1} if it exists. Draw a sketch of the graph of f, and if f^{-1} exists, draw a sketch of the graph of f^{-1} on the same set of axes as the graph of f.

Figure 9.3.7

SOLUTION: $f'(x) = -5/(x - 1)^2$. Because f is continuous for all values of x except 1, and $f'(x) < 0$ if $x \neq 1$, it follows from Theorem 9.3.3 that f has an inverse if x is any real number except 1. To find f^{-1}, let $y = f(x)$, and solve for x, thus giving $x = f^{-1}(y)$. So we have

$$y = \frac{2x + 3}{x - 1}$$

$$xy - y = 2x + 3$$

$$x(y - 2) = y + 3$$

$$x = \frac{y + 3}{y - 2}$$

Thus,

$$f^{-1}(y) = \frac{y + 3}{y - 2}$$

or, equivalently,

$$f^{-1}(x) = \frac{x + 3}{x - 2}$$

The domain of f^{-1} is the set of all real numbers except 2. Sketches of the graphs of f and f^{-1} are shown in Fig. 9.3.7.

The following theorem expresses a relationship between the derivative of a function and the derivative of the inverse of the function if the function has an inverse.

9.3.4 Theorem   Suppose that the function f is continuous and monotonic on the closed interval $[a, b]$, and let $y = f(x)$. If f is differentiable on $[a, b]$ and $f'(x) \neq 0$ for any x in $[a, b]$, then the derivative of the inverse function f^{-1}, defined by $x = f^{-1}(y)$, is given by

$$D_y x = \frac{1}{D_x y}$$

PROOF: Because f is continuous and monotonic on $[a, b]$, then by Theorems 9.3.2 and 9.3.3, f has an inverse which is continuous and monotonic on $[f(a), f(b)]$ (or $[f(b), f(a)]$ if $f(b) < f(a)$).

If x is a number in $[a, b]$, let Δx be an increment of x, $\Delta x \neq 0$, such that $x + \Delta x$ is also in $[a, b]$. Then the corresponding increment of y is given by

$$\Delta y = f(x + \Delta x) - f(x) \tag{25}$$

$\Delta y \neq 0$ since $\Delta x \neq 0$ and f is monotonic on $[a, b]$; that is, either

$$f(x + \Delta x) < f(x) \quad \text{or} \quad f(x + \Delta x) > f(x) \qquad \text{on } [a, b]$$

If x is in $[a, b]$ and $y = f(x)$, then y is in $[f(a), f(b)]$ (or $[f(b), f(a)]$). Also, if $x + \Delta x$ is in $[a, b]$, then $y + \Delta y$ is in $[f(a), f(b)]$ (or $[f(b), f(a)]$) because $y + \Delta y = f(x + \Delta x)$ by (25). So

$$x = f^{-1}(y) \tag{26}$$

and

$$x + \Delta x = f^{-1}(y + \Delta y) \tag{27}$$

It follows from (26) and (27) that

$$\Delta x = f^{-1}(y + \Delta y) - f^{-1}(y) \tag{28}$$

From the definition of a derivative,

$$D_y x = \lim_{\Delta y \to 0} \frac{f^{-1}(y + \Delta y) - f^{-1}(y)}{\Delta y}$$

Substituting from (25) and (28) into the above equation, we get

$$D_y x = \lim_{\Delta y \to 0} \frac{\Delta x}{f(x + \Delta x) - f(x)}$$

and because $\Delta x \neq 0$,

$$D_y x = \lim_{\Delta y \to 0} \frac{1}{\dfrac{f(x + \Delta x) - f(x)}{\Delta x}} \tag{29}$$

Before we find the limit in (29) we show that under the hypothesis of this theorem "$\Delta x \to 0$" is equivalent to "$\Delta y \to 0$." First we show that $\lim\limits_{\Delta y \to 0} \Delta x = 0$. From (28) we have

$$\lim_{\Delta y \to 0} \Delta x = \lim_{\Delta y \to 0} [f^{-1}(y + \Delta y) - f^{-1}(y)]$$

Because f^{-1} is continuous on $[f(a), f(b)]$ (or $[f(b), f(a)]$), the limit on the right side of the above equation is zero. So

$$\lim_{\Delta y \to 0} \Delta x = 0 \tag{30}$$

Now we demonstrate that $\lim_{\Delta x \to 0} \Delta y = 0$. From (25) we have

$$\lim_{\Delta x \to 0} \Delta y = \lim_{\Delta x \to 0} [f(x + \Delta x) - f(x)]$$

Because f is continuous on $[a, b]$, the limit on the right side of the above equation is zero, and therefore we have

$$\lim_{\Delta x \to 0} \Delta y = 0 \tag{31}$$

From (30) and (31) it follows that

$$\Delta x \to 0 \quad \text{if and only if} \quad \Delta y \to 0 \tag{32}$$

Thus, applying the limit theorem (regarding the limit of a quotient) to (29) and using (32), we have

$$D_y x = \cfrac{1}{\lim_{\Delta x \to 0} \cfrac{f(x + \Delta x) - f(x)}{\Delta x}}$$

Because f is differentiable on $[a, b]$, the limit in the denominator of the above is $f'(x)$ or, equivalently, $D_x y$, and so we have

$$D_y x = \frac{1}{D_x y} \qquad \blacksquare$$

EXAMPLE 2: Show that Theorem 9.3.4 holds for the function of Example 1.

SOLUTION: If $y = f(x) = (2x + 3)/(x - 1)$, then

$$D_x y = f'(x) = -\frac{5}{(x - 1)^2}$$

Because $f'(x)$ exists if $x \neq 1$, f is differentiable and hence continuous at all $x \neq 1$. Furthermore, $f'(x) < 0$ if $x \neq 1$, and so f is decreasing for all $x \neq 1$. Therefore, the hypothesis of Theorem 9.3.4 holds for any interval $[a, b]$ which does not contain the number 1.

In the solution of Example 1 we showed that

$$x = f^{-1}(y) = \frac{y + 3}{y - 2}$$

Computing $D_y x$ from this equation, we get

$$D_y x = (f^{-1})'(y) = -\frac{5}{(y - 2)^2}$$

If in the above equation we let $y = (2x + 3)/(x - 1)$, we obtain

$$D_y x = -\frac{5}{\left(\dfrac{2x + 3}{x - 1} - 2\right)^2}$$

$$= -\frac{5(x-1)^2}{(2x+3-2x+2)^2}$$

$$= -\tfrac{5}{25}(x-1)^2$$

$$= -\tfrac{1}{5}(x-1)^2$$

$$= \frac{1}{D_x y}$$

EXAMPLE 3:   Given f is the function defined by $f(x) = x^3 + x$, determine if f has an inverse. If it does, find the derivative of the inverse function.

SOLUTION: Because $f(x) = x^3 + x$, $f'(x) = 3x^2 + 1$. Therefore, $f'(x) > 0$ for all real numbers, and so f is increasing on its entire domain. Because f is also continuous on its entire domain, it follows from Theorem 9.3.2 that f has an inverse f^{-1}.

Let $y = f(x)$ and then $x = f^{-1}(y)$. So by Theorem 9.3.4,

$$D_y x = \frac{1}{D_x y} = \frac{1}{3x^2 + 1}$$

Exercises 9.3

In Exercises 1 through 8, find the inverse of the given function, if it exists, and determine its domain. Draw a sketch of the graph of the given function, and if the given function does not have an inverse, show that a horizontal line intersects the graph in more than one point. If the given function has an inverse, draw a sketch of the graph of the inverse function on the same set of axes as the graph of the given function.

1. $f(x) = x^3$

2. $f(x) = x^2 + 5$

3. $f(x) = \dfrac{1}{x^2}$

4. $f(x) = (x+2)^3$

5. $f(x) = \dfrac{2x-1}{x}$

6. $f(x) = \dfrac{8}{x^3+1}$

7. $f(x) = 2|x| + x$

8. $f(x) = \dfrac{3}{1+|x|}$

In Exercises 9 through 14, perform each of the following steps: (a) Solve the equation for y in terms of x and express y as one or more functions of x; (b) for each of the functions obtained in (a) determine if the function has an inverse, and if it does, determine the domain of the inverse function; (c) use implicit differentiation to find $D_x y$ and $D_y x$ and determine the values of x and y for which $D_x y$ and $D_y x$ are reciprocals.

9. $x^2 + y^2 = 9$

10. $x^2 - 4y^2 = 16$

11. $xy = 4$

12. $9y^2 - 8x^3 = 0$

13. $2x^2 - 3xy + 1 = 0$

14. $2x^2 + 2y + 1 = 0$

In Exercises 15 through 20, determine if the given function has an inverse, and if it does, determine the domain and range of the inverse function.

15. $f(x) = \sqrt{x-4}$

16. $f(x) = (x+3)^3$

17. $f(x) = x^2 - \dfrac{1}{x}$, $x > 0$

18. $f(x) = \dfrac{1}{x^2+4}$, $x \le 0$

19. $f(x) = x^5 + x^3$

20. $f(x) = x^3 + x$

21. Let the function f be defined by $f(x) = \int_0^x \sqrt{1 - t^4}\ dt$. Determine if f has an inverse, and if it does, find the derivative of the inverse function.

22. Determine the value of the constant k so that the function defined by $f(x) = (x + 5)/(x + k)$ will be its own inverse.

23. Given $f(x) = \begin{cases} x & \text{if } x < 1 \\ x^2 & \text{if } 1 \le x \le 9 \\ 27\sqrt{x} & \text{if } x > 9 \end{cases}$

    Prove that f has an inverse function and find $f^{-1}(x)$.

24. Given that the function f is continuous and increasing on the closed interval $[a, b]$. Assuming Theorem 9.3.1(i) and (ii), prove f^{-1} is continuous from the right at $f(a)$ and continuous from the left at $f(b)$.

25. Prove Theorem 9.3.3(i).   26. Prove Theorem 9.3.3(ii).   27. Prove Theorem 9.3.3(iii).

28. Show that the formula of Theorem 9.3.4 can be written as

$$(f^{-1})'(x) = \frac{1}{f'(f^{-1}(x))}$$

29. Use the formula of Exercise 28 to show that

$$(f^{-1})''(x) = -\frac{f''(f^{-1}(x))}{[f'(f^{-1}(x))]^3}$$

9.4 THE EXPONENTIAL FUNCTION

Because the natural logarithmic function is increasing on its entire domain, then by Theorem 9.3.2 it has an inverse which is also an increasing function. The inverse of the natural logarithmic function is called the "exponential function," which we now define.

9.4.1 Definition   The *exponential function* is the inverse of the natural logarithmic function, and it is defined by

$$\exp(x) = y \quad \text{if and only if} \quad x = \ln y \tag{1}$$

The exponential function "$\exp(x)$" is read as "the value of the exponential function at x."

Because the range of the natural logarithmic function is the set of all real numbers, the domain of the exponential function is the set of all real numbers. The range of the exponential function is the set of positive numbers because this is the domain of the natural logarithmic function.

Because the natural logarithmic function and the exponential function are inverses of each other, it follows from Eqs. (8) and (9) of Sec. 9.3 that

$$\ln(\exp(x)) = x \tag{2}$$

and

$$\exp(\ln x) = x \tag{3}$$

Because $0 = \ln 1$, we have

$$\exp 0 = \exp(\ln 1)$$

which from (3) gives us

$$\exp 0 = 1 \tag{4}$$

We now state some properties of the exponential function as theorems.

9.4.2 Theorem If a and b are any real numbers, then

$$\exp(a + b) = \exp(a) \cdot \exp(b)$$

PROOF: Let $A = \exp(a)$, and so from Definition 9.4.1 we have

$$a = \ln A \tag{5}$$

Let $B = \exp(b)$, and from Definition 9.4.1 it follows that

$$b = \ln B \tag{6}$$

From Theorem 9.1.3 we have

$$\ln A + \ln B = \ln AB \tag{7}$$

Substituting from (5) and (6) into (7), we obtain

$$a + b = \ln AB$$

So

$$\exp(a + b) = \exp(\ln AB) \tag{8}$$

From Eq. (3) it follows that the right side of Eq. (8) is AB, and so we have

$$\exp(a + b) = AB$$

Replacing A and B by their values, we get

$$\exp(a + b) = \exp(a) \cdot \exp(b) \qquad \blacksquare$$

9.4.3 Theorem If a and b are any real numbers,

$$\exp(a - b) = \exp(a) \div \exp(b)$$

The proof is analogous to the proof of Theorem 9.4.2, where Theorem 9.1.3 is replaced by Theorem 9.1.4. It is left as an exercise (see Exercise 1).

9.4.4 Theorem If a is any real number and r is any rational number, then

$$\exp(ra) = [\exp(a)]^r$$

PROOF: If in Eq. (3) $x = [\exp(a)]^r$, we have

$$[\exp(a)]^r = \exp\{\ln[\exp(a)]^r\}$$

Applying Theorem 9.1.5 to the right side of the above equation, we obtain

$$[\exp(a)]^r = \exp\{r \ln[\exp(a)]\}$$

But from Eq. (2), $\ln[\exp(a)] = a$, and therefore

$$[\exp(a)]^r = \exp(ra) \qquad \blacksquare$$

We now wish to define what is meant by a^x, where a is a positive number and x is an irrational number. To arrive at a reasonable definition, consider the case a^r, where $a > 0$ and r is a rational number. We have from Eq. (3)

$$a^r = \exp[\ln (a^r)] \qquad (9)$$

But by Theorem 9.1.5, $\ln a^r = r \ln a$; so from Eq. (9)

$$a^r = \exp(r \ln a) \qquad (10)$$

Because the right side of Eq. (10) has a meaning if r is any real number, we use it for our definition.

9.4.5 Definition   If a is any positive number and x is any real number, we define

$$a^x = \exp(x \ln a)$$

9.4.6 Theorem   If a is any positive number and x is any real number,

$$\ln a^x = x \ln a$$

PROOF: From Definition 9.4.5,

$$a^x = \exp(x \ln a)$$

Hence, from Definition 9.4.1, we have

$$\ln a^x = x \ln a \qquad \blacksquare$$

Following is the definition of one of the most important numbers in mathematics.

9.4.7 Definition   The number e is defined by the formula

$$e = \exp 1$$

The letter "e" was chosen because of the Swiss mathematician and physicist Leonhard Euler (1707–1783).

The number e is a *transcendental* number; that is, it cannot be expressed as the root of any polynomial with integer coefficients. The number π is another example of a transcendental number. The proof that e is transcendental was first given in 1873, by Charles Hermite, and its value can be expressed to any required degree of accuracy. In Chapter 16 we learn a method for doing this. The value of e to seven decimal places is 2.7182818.

9.4.8 Theorem $\ln e = 1$.

PROOF: By Definition 9.4.7,

$$e = \exp 1$$

Hence,

$$\ln e = \ln(\exp 1) \tag{11}$$

Because the natural logarithmic function and the exponential function are inverse functions, it follows that

$$\ln(\exp 1) = 1 \tag{12}$$

Substituting from (12) into (11), we have

$$\ln e = 1$$ ■

9.4.9 Theorem $\exp(x) = e^x$, for all values of x.

PROOF: By Definition 9.4.5,

$$e^x = \exp(x \ln e) \tag{13}$$

But by Theorem 9.4.8, $\ln e = 1$. Substituting this in (13), we obtain

$$e^x = \exp(x)$$ ■

From now on, we write e^x in place of $\exp(x)$, and so from Definition 9.4.1 we have

$$e^x = y \quad \text{if and only if} \quad x = \ln y \tag{14}$$

We now derive the formula for the derivative of the exponential function. Let

$$y = e^x$$

Then from (14) we have

$$x = \ln y \tag{15}$$

Differentiating on both sides of (15) implicitly with respect to x, we get

$$1 = \frac{1}{y} \cdot D_x y$$

So,

$$D_x y = y$$

Replacing y by e^x, we obtain

$$D_x(e^x) = e^x \tag{16}$$

If u is a differentiable function of x, it follows from (16) and the chain rule that

$$D_x(e^u) = e^u \, D_x u \tag{17}$$

It follows that the derivative of the function defined by $f(x) = ke^x$, where k is a constant, is itself. The only other function we have previously encountered that has this property is the constant function zero; actually, this is the special case of $f(x) = ke^x$ when $k = 0$. It can be proved that the most general function which is its own derivative is given by $f(x) = ke^x$ (see Exercise 36).

EXAMPLE 1: Given $y = e^{1/x^2}$, find dy/dx.

SOLUTION: From (17)

$$\frac{dy}{dx} = e^{1/x^2}\left(-\frac{2}{x^3}\right) = -\frac{2e^{1/x^2}}{x^3}$$

From (17) we obtain the following indefinite integration formula:

$$\int e^u \, du = e^u + C \tag{18}$$

EXAMPLE 2: Find

$$\int \frac{e^{\sqrt{x}}}{\sqrt{x}} \, dx$$

SOLUTION: Let $u = \sqrt{x}$; then $du = \frac{1}{2}x^{-1/2} \, dx$; so

$$\int \frac{e^{\sqrt{x}}}{\sqrt{x}} \, dx = 2 \int e^u \, du$$

$$= 2e^u + C$$

$$= 2e^{\sqrt{x}} + C$$

Because from (14), $e^x = y$ if and only if $x = \ln y$, the graph of $y = e^x$ is identical with the graph of $x = \ln y$. So we can obtain the graph of $y = e^x$ by interchanging the x and y axes in Fig. 9.2.2 (see Fig. 9.4.1).

The graph of $y = e^x$ can be obtained without referring to the graph of the natural logarithmic function. Because the range of the exponential function is the set of all positive numbers, it follows that $e^x > 0$ for all values of x. So the graph lies entirely above the x axis. $D_x y = e^x > 0$ for all x; so the function is increasing for all x. $D_x^2 y = e^x > 0$ for all x; so the graph is concave upward at all points.

Figure 9.4.1

We have the following two limits:

$$\lim_{x \to +\infty} e^x = +\infty \tag{19}$$

and

$$\lim_{x \to -\infty} e^x = 0 \tag{20}$$

The proofs of (19) and (20) are left as exercises (see Exercises 44 and 45). To plot some specific points use the table in the Appendix giving powers of e.

EXAMPLE 3: Find the area of the region bounded by the curve $y = e^x$, the coordinate axes, and the line $x = 2$.

Figure 9.4.2

SOLUTION: The region is shown in Fig. 9.4.2.

$$A = \lim_{||\Delta|| \to 0} \sum_{i=1}^{n} e^{\xi_i} \Delta_i x$$

$$= \int_0^2 e^x \, dx$$

$$= e^x \Big]_0^2$$

$$= e^2 - e^0$$

$$= e^2 - 1$$

From a table of powers of e, we see that the value of e^2 to two decimal places is 7.39. Therefore, the area of the region is approximately 6.39 square units.

The conclusions of Theorems 9.4.2, 9.4.3, and 9.4.4 are now restated by using e^x in place of $\exp(x)$. If a and b are any real numbers, then

$$e^{a+b} = e^a \cdot e^b$$

$$e^{a-b} = e^a \div e^b$$

$$e^{ra} = (e^a)^r \qquad \text{where } r \text{ is any rational number.}$$

Writing Eqs. (2), (3), and (4) by substituting e^x in place of $\exp(x)$, we have

$$\ln(e^x) = x$$

$$e^{\ln x} = x$$

and

$$e^0 = 1$$

EXAMPLE 4:   Given

$$y = e^{2x + \ln x}$$

find $D_x y$.

SOLUTION: $e^{2x + \ln x} = e^{2x} e^{\ln x} = e^{2x}(x)$. So

$$y = xe^{2x}$$

Therefore,

$$D_x y = e^{2x} + 2xe^{2x}$$

In Definition 9.4.7, the number e was defined as the value of the exponential function at 1; that is, $e = \exp 1$. To arrive at another way of defining e, we consider the natural logarithmic function

$$f(x) = \ln x$$

We know that the derivative of f is given by $f'(x) = 1/x$; hence, $f'(1) = 1$. However, let us apply the definition of the derivative to find $f'(1)$. We have

$$f'(1) = \lim_{\Delta x \to 0} \frac{f(1 + \Delta x) - f(1)}{\Delta x}$$

$$= \lim_{\Delta x \to 0} \frac{\ln(1 + \Delta x) - \ln 1}{\Delta x}$$

$$= \lim_{\Delta x \to 0} \frac{1}{\Delta x} \ln(1 + \Delta x)$$

Therefore,

$$\lim_{\Delta x \to 0} \frac{1}{\Delta x} \ln(1 + \Delta x) = 1$$

Replacing Δx by h, we have from the above equation and Theorem 9.4.6

$$\lim_{h \to 0} \ln(1 + h)^{1/h} = 1 \tag{21}$$

Now, because the exponential function and the natural logarithmic function are inverse functions, we have

$$\lim_{h \to 0} (1 + h)^{1/h} = \lim_{h \to 0} \exp[\ln(1 + h)^{1/h}] \tag{22}$$

Because the exponential function is continuous and $\lim\limits_{h \to 0} \ln(1 + h)^{1/h}$ exists and equals 1 as shown in Eq. (21), we can apply Theorem 2.6.5 to the right side of Eq. (22) and get

$$\lim_{h \to 0} (1 + h)^{1/h} = \exp \left[\lim_{h \to 0} \ln(1 + h)^{1/h} \right] = \exp 1$$

Hence,

$$\lim_{h \to 0} (1 + h)^{1/h} = e \tag{23}$$

Equation (23) is sometimes used to define e; however, to use this as a definition it is necessary to prove that the limit exists.

Let us consider the function F defined by

$$F(h) = (1 + h)^{1/h} \tag{24}$$

and determine the function values for some values of h close to zero. These values are given in Table 9.4.1.

Table 9.4.1

h	1	0.5	0.05	0.01	0.001	−0.001	−0.01	−0.05	−0.5
$F(h) = (1 + h)^{1/h}$	2	2.25	2.65	2.70	2.7169	2.7196	2.73	2.79	4

Table 9.4.1 leads us to suspect that $\lim\limits_{h \to 0} (1 + h)^{1/h}$ is probably a number that lies between 2.7169 and 2.7196. As previously mentioned, in Chapter 16 we learn a method for finding the value of e to any desired number of decimal places.

Exercises 9.4

1. Prove Theorem 9.4.3.

2. Draw a sketch of the graph of $y = e^{-x}$.

3. Draw a sketch of the graph of $y = e^{|x|}$.

In Exercises 4 through 14, find dy/dx.

4. $y = e^{5x}$

5. $y = e^{-3x^2}$

6. $y = \dfrac{e^x}{x}$

7. $y = \dfrac{e^{2x}}{x^2}$

8. $y = e^{e^x}$

9. $y = \dfrac{e^x - e^{-x}}{e^x + e^{-x}}$

10. $y = \ln \dfrac{e^{4x} - 1}{e^{4x} + 1}$

11. $y = x^5 e^{-3 \ln x}$

12. $y = \ln(e^x + e^{-x})$

13. $y = e^{x \ln x}$

14. $y = e^{x/\sqrt{4 + x^2}}$

In Exercises 15 through 18, find $D_x y$ by implicit differentiation.

15. $e^x + e^y = e^{x+y}$

16. $ye^{2x} + xe^{2y} = 1$

17. $y^2 e^{2x} + xy^3 = 1$

18. $e^y = \ln(x^3 + 3y)$

In Exercises 19 through 26, evaluate the indefinite integral.

19. $\displaystyle\int e^{2-5x}\, dx$

20. $\displaystyle\int e^{2x+1}\, dx$

21. $\displaystyle\int \frac{1 + e^{2x}}{e^x}\, dx$

22. $\displaystyle\int e^{3x} e^{2x}\, dx$

23. $\displaystyle\int \frac{e^{3x}}{(1 - 2e^{3x})^2}\, dx$

24. $\displaystyle\int x^2 e^{2x^3}\, dx$

25. $\displaystyle\int \frac{e^{2x}}{e^x + 3}\, dx$

26. $\displaystyle\int \frac{dx}{1 + e^x}$

In Exercises 27 through 30, evaluate the definite integral.

27. $\displaystyle\int_0^1 e^2\, dx$

28. $\displaystyle\int_1^2 \frac{e^x}{e^x + e}\, dx$

29. $\displaystyle\int_0^2 xe^{4-x^2}\, dx$

30. $\displaystyle\int_0^3 \frac{e^x + e^{-x}}{2}\, dx$

In Exercises 31 and 32, find the relative extrema of f, the points of inflection of the graph of f, the intervals on which f is increasing, the intervals on which f is decreasing, where the graph is concave upward, where the graph is concave downward, and the slope of any inflectional tangent. Draw a sketch of the graph of f.

31. $f(x) = xe^{-x}$

32. $f(x) = e^{-x^2}$

33. Find an equation of the tangent line to the curve $y = e^{-x}$ that is perpendicular to the line $2x - y = 5$.

34. Find the area of the region bounded by the curve $y = e^x$ and the line through the points $(0, 1)$ and $(1, e)$.

35. A solid has as its base the region bounded by the curves $y = e^x$ and $y = e^{-x}$ and the line $x = 1$. If every plane section perpendicular to the x axis is a square find the volume of the solid.

36. Prove that the most general function that is equal to its derivative is given by $f(x) = ke^x$. (HINT: Let $y = f(x)$ and solve the differential equation $dy/dx = y$.)

37. If p lb/ft^2 is the atmospheric pressure at a height of h ft above sea level, then $p = 2116e^{-0.0000318h}$. Find the time rate of change of the atmospheric pressure outside of an airplane that is 5000 ft high and rising at the rate of 160 ft/sec.

38. At a certain height the gauge on an airplane indicates that the atmospheric pressure is 1500 lb/ft^2. Applying the formula of Exercise 37, approximate by differentials how much higher the airplane must rise so that the pressure will be 1480 lb/ft^2.

39. If l ft is the length of an iron rod when t degrees is its temperature, then $l = 60e^{0.00001t}$. Use differentials to find the approximate increase in l when t increases from 0 to 10.

40. A simple electric circuit containing no condensers, a resistance of R ohms, and an inductance of L henrys has the electromotive force cut off when the current is I_0 amperes. The current dies down so that at t sec the current is i amperes and

$$i = I_0 e^{-(R/L)t}$$

Show that the rate of change of the current is proportional to the current.

41. A body is moving along a straight line and at t sec the velocity is v ft/sec where $v = e^3 - e^{2t}$. Find the distance traveled by the particle while $v > 0$ after $t = 0$.

42. An advertising agency determined statistically that if a breakfast food manufacturer increases its budget for television commercials by x thousand dollars there will be an increase in the total profit of $25x^2e^{-0.2x}$ hundred dollars. What should be the advertising budget increase in order for the manufacturer to have the greatest profit? What will be the corresponding increase in the company's profit?

43. A tank is in the shape of the solid of revolution formed by rotating about the x axis the region bounded by the curve $y^2x = e^{-2x}$ and the lines $x = 1$ and $x = 4$. If the tank is full of water, find the work done in pumping all the water to a point 1 ft above the top of the tank. Distance is measured in feet.

44. Prove: $\lim\limits_{x \to +\infty} e^x = +\infty$, by showing that for any $N > 0$ there exists an $M > 0$ such that $e^x > N$ whenever $x > M$.

45. Prove: $\lim\limits_{x \to -\infty} e^x = 0$, by showing that for any $\epsilon > 0$ there exists an $N < 0$ such that $e^x < \epsilon$ whenever $x < N$.

46. Draw a sketch of the graph of F if $F(h) = (1 + h)^{1/h}$.

9.5 OTHER EXPONENTIAL AND LOGARITHMIC FUNCTIONS

From Definition 9.4.5, we have

$$a^x = e^{x \ln a} \tag{1}$$

The expression on the left side of Eq. (1) is called the "exponential function to the base a."

9.5.1 Definition   If a is any positive number and x is any real number; then the function f defined by

$$f(x) = a^x$$

is called the *exponential function to the base a.*

The exponential function to the base a satisfies the same properties as the exponential function to the base e.

● ILLUSTRATION 1: If x and y are any real numbers and a is positive, then from Eq. (1) we have

$$a^x a^y = e^{x \ln a} e^{y \ln a}$$

$$= e^{x \ln a + y \ln a}$$

$$= e^{(x+y) \ln a}$$

$$= a^{x+y}$$

●

From Illustration 1 we have the property

$$a^x a^y = a^{x+y} \tag{2}$$

We also have the following properties:

$$a^x \div a^y = a^{x-y} \tag{3}$$

$$(a^x)^y = a^{xy} \tag{4}$$

$$(ab)^x = a^x b^x \tag{5}$$

$$a^0 = 1 \tag{6}$$

The proofs of (3) through (6) are left as exercises (see Exercises 1 to 4).

To find the derivative of the exponential function to the base a, we set $a^x = e^{x \ln a}$ and apply the chain rule. We have

$$a^x = e^{x \ln a}$$

$$D_x(a^x) = e^{x \ln a} D_x(x \ln a)$$

$$= e^{x \ln a}(\ln a)$$

$$= a^x \ln a$$

Hence, if u is a differentiable function of x,

$$D_x(a^u) = a^u \ln a \, D_x u \tag{7}$$

● ILLUSTRATION 2: If $y = 3^{x^2}$, then from formula (7) we have

$$D_x y = 3^{x^2} \ln 3(2x) = 2(\ln 3)x3^{x^2} \qquad\qquad ●$$

From (7) we obtain the following indefinite integration formula:

$$\int a^u \, du = \frac{a^u}{\ln a} + C \tag{8}$$

EXAMPLE 1:   Find

$$\int \sqrt{10^{3x}} \, dx$$

SOLUTION: $\displaystyle\int \sqrt{10^{3x}} \, dx = \int 10^{3x/2} \, dx$. Let $u = \frac{3}{2}x$; then $du = \frac{3}{2} \, dx$; thus $\frac{2}{3} \, du = dx$. We have then

$$\int 10^{3x/2} \, dx = \int 10^u \tfrac{2}{3} \, du$$

$$= \frac{2}{3} \cdot \frac{10^u}{\ln 10} + C$$

$$= \frac{2 \cdot 10^{3x/2}}{3 \ln 10} + C$$

EXAMPLE 2:   Draw sketches of the graphs of $y = 2^x$ and $y = 2^{-x}$ on the same set of axes. Find the area of the region bounded by these two graphs and the line $x = 2$.

SOLUTION: The required sketches are shown in Fig. 9.5.1. The region is shaded in the figure. If A square units is the desired area, we have

$$A = \lim_{\|\Delta\| \to 0} \sum_{i=1}^{n} [2^{\xi_i} - 2^{-\xi_i}] \, \Delta_i x$$

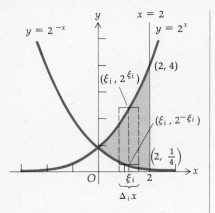

Figure 9.5.1

$$= \int_0^2 (2^x - 2^{-x})\, dx$$

$$= \frac{2^x}{\ln 2} + \frac{2^{-x}}{\ln 2} \Big]_0^2$$

$$= \frac{4}{\ln 2} + \frac{\frac{1}{4}}{\ln 2} - \frac{1}{\ln 2} - \frac{1}{\ln 2}$$

$$= \frac{9}{4 \ln 2}$$

$$\approx 3.25$$

We can now define the "logarithmic function to the base a" if a is any positive number other than 1.

9.5.2 Definition If a is any positive number except 1, the *logarithmic function to the base a* is the inverse of the exponential function to the base a; and we write

$$y = \log_a x \quad \text{if and only if} \quad a^y = x \tag{9}$$

The above is the definition of the logarithmic function to the base a usually given in elementary algebra; however, (9) has meaning for y any real number because a^y has been precisely defined. It should be noted that if $a = e$, we have the logarithmic function to the base e, which is the natural logarithmic function.

$\log_a x$ is read as "the logarithm of x to the base a."

The logarithmic function to the base a obeys the same laws as the natural logarithmic function. We list them.

$$\log_a(xy) = \log_a x + \log_a y \tag{10}$$

$$\log_a(x \div y) = \log_a x - \log_a y \tag{11}$$

$$\log_a 1 = 0 \tag{12}$$

$$\log_a x^y = y \log_a x \tag{13}$$

The proofs of (10) through (13) are left as exercises (see Exercises 5 to 8).

A relationship between logarithms to the base a and natural logarithms follows easily. Let

$$y = \log_a x$$

Then

$$a^y = x$$

$$\ln a^y = \ln x$$

$$y \ln a = \ln x$$

$$y = \frac{\ln x}{\ln a}$$

Replacing y by $\log_a x$, we obtain

$$\log_a x = \frac{\ln x}{\ln a} \tag{14}$$

Equation (14) sometimes is used as the definition of the logarithmic function to the base a. Because the natural logarithmic function is continuous at all $x > 0$, it follows from (14) that the logarithmic function to the base a is continuous at all $x > 0$.

If in (14) we take $x = e$, we have

$$\log_a e = \frac{\ln e}{\ln a}$$

or, equivalently,

$$\log_a e = \frac{1}{\ln a} \tag{15}$$

We now find the derivative of the logarithmic function to the base a. We differentiate on both sides of Eq. (14) with respect to x, and we obtain

$$D_x(\log_a x) = \frac{1}{\ln a} D_x(\ln x)$$

$$D_x(\log_a x) = \frac{1}{\ln a} \cdot \frac{1}{x} \tag{16}$$

Substituting from (15) into (16), we get

$$D_x(\log_a x) = \frac{\log_a e}{x} \tag{17}$$

If u is a differentiable function of x, we have

$$D_x(\log_a u) = \frac{\log_a e}{u} D_x u \tag{18}$$

Note that if in (18) we take $a = e$, we get

$$D_x(\log_e u) = \frac{\log_e e}{u} D_x u$$

or, equivalently,

$$D_x(\ln u) = \frac{1}{u} D_x u$$

which is the formula we had previously for the derivative of the natural logarithmic function.

EXAMPLE 3:   Given

$$y = \log_{10} \frac{x+1}{x^2+1}$$

find dy/dx.

SOLUTION: Using (11), we write

$$y = \log_{10}(x+1) - \log_{10}(x^2+1)$$

From (18) we have

$$\frac{dy}{dx} = \frac{\log_{10} e}{x+1} - \frac{\log_{10} e}{x^2+1} \cdot 2x$$

$$= \log_{10} e \left(\frac{1}{x+1} - \frac{2x}{x^2+1} \right)$$

$$= \frac{\log_{10} e(1 - 2x - x^2)}{(x+1)(x^2+1)}$$

Because x^n has been defined for any real number n, we can now prove the formula for finding the derivative of the power function if the exponent is any real number.

9.5.3 Theorem   If n is any real number and the function f is defined by

$$f(x) = x^n \qquad \text{where } x > 0$$

then

$$f'(x) = nx^{n-1}$$

PROOF: Let $y = x^n$. Then from (1)

$$y = e^{n \ln x}$$

Thus,

$$D_x y = e^{n \ln x} D_x(n \ln x)$$

$$= e^{n \ln x} \left(\frac{n}{x} \right)$$

$$= x^n \cdot \frac{n}{x}$$

$$= nx^{n-1} \qquad \blacksquare$$

Theorem 9.5.3 enables us to find the derivative of a variable to a constant power. Previously in this section we learned how to differentiate a constant to a variable power. We now consider the derivative of a function whose function value is a variable to a variable power. The method of *logarithmic differentiation* is used and is illustrated in the following example.

EXAMPLE 4:   Given $y = x^x$, find dy/dx.

SOLUTION: Because $y = x^x$, then $|y| = |x^x|$. We take the natural logarithm on both sides of the equation, and we have

$$\ln |y| = \ln |x^x|$$

or, equivalently,

$$\ln |y| = x \ln |x|$$

Differentiating on both sides of the above equation with respect to x, we obtain

$$\frac{1}{y} \frac{dy}{dx} = \ln |x| + x \frac{1}{x}$$

So

$$\frac{dy}{dx} = y(\ln |x| + 1)$$

$$= x^x(\ln |x| + 1)$$

Exercises 9.5

In Exercises 1 through 4, prove the given property if a is any positive number and x and y are any real numbers.

1. $a^x \div a^y = a^{x-y}$

2. $(a^x)^y = a^{xy}$

3. $(ab)^x = a^x b^x$

4. $a^0 = 1$

In Exercises 5 through 8, prove the given property if a is any positive number and x and y are any positive numbers.

5. $\log_a(xy) = \log_a x + \log_a y$

6. $\log_a(x \div y) = \log_a x - \log_a y$

7. $\log_a x^y = y \log_a x$

8. $\log_a 1 = 0$

In Exercises 9 through 24, find $f'(x)$.

9. $f(x) = 3^{5x}$

10. $f(x) = 6^{-3x}$

11. $f(x) = 2^{5x} 3^{4x^2}$

12. $f(x) = (x^3 + 3)2^{-7x}$

13. $f(x) = \dfrac{\log_{10} x}{x}$

14. $f(x) = \log_{10} \dfrac{x}{x+1}$

15. $f(x) = \sqrt{\log_a x}$

16. $f(x) = \log_a[\log_a(\log_a x)]$

17. $f(x) = \log_{10}[\log_{10}(x + 1)]$

18. $f(x) = x^{\ln x}$

19. $f(x) = x^{\sqrt{x}}$

20. $f(x) = x^{x^2}$

21. $f(x) = x^{e^x}$

22. $f(x) = (x)^{x^x}$

23. $f(x) = (4e^x)^{3x}$

24. $f(x) = (\ln x)^{\ln x}$

In Exercises 25 through 32, evaluate the indefinite integral.

25. $\displaystyle\int 3^{2x}\,dx$

26. $\displaystyle\int a^{nx}\,dx$

27. $\displaystyle\int a^x e^x\,dx$

28. $\displaystyle\int 5^{x^4+2x}(2x^3+1)\,dx$

29. $\displaystyle\int x^2 10^{x^3}\,dx$

30. $\displaystyle\int a^{x\ln x}(\ln x+1)\,dx$

31. $\displaystyle\int e^x 2^{e^x} 3^{e^x}\,dx$

32. $\displaystyle\int \frac{4^{\ln(1/x)}}{x}\,dx$

33. Find an equation of the tangent line to the curve $y^2 4^y = x2^x$ at $(4, 2)$.

34. A particle is moving along a straight line according to the equation of motion $s = A2^{kt} + B2^{-kt}$, where s ft is the directed distance of the particle from the starting point at t sec. Prove that if a ft/sec² is the acceleration at t sec, then a is proportional to s.

35. A company has learned that when it initiates a new sales campaign the number of sales per day increases. However, the number of extra daily sales per day decreases as the impact of the campaign wears off. For a specific campaign the company has determined that if S is the number of extra daily sales as a result of the campaign and x is the number of days that have elapsed since the campaign ended, then

$$S = 1000 \cdot 3^{-x/2}$$

Find the rate at which the extra daily sales is decreasing when (a) $x = 4$ and (b) $x = 10$.

In Exercises 36 and 37, use differentials to find an approximate value of the given logarithm and express the answer to three decimal places.

36. $\log_{10} 1.015$

37. $\log_{10} 997$

38. Draw sketches of the graphs of $y = \log_{10} x$ and $y = \ln x$ on the same set of axes.

39. Given: $f(x) = \frac{1}{2}(a^x + a^{-x})$. Prove that $f(b + c) + f(b - c) = 2f(b)f(c)$.

40. A particle moves along a straight line according to the equation of motion $s = t^{1/t}$ where s ft is the directed distance of the particle from the starting point at t sec. Find the velocity and acceleration at 2 sec.

9.6 LAWS OF GROWTH AND DECAY

The laws of growth and decay provide applications of the exponential function in chemistry, physics, biology, and business. Such a situation would arise when the rate of change of the amount of a substance with respect to time is proportional to the amount of the substance present at a given instant. This would occur in biology, where under certain circumstances the rate of growth of a culture of bacteria is proportional to the amount of bacteria present at any given instant. In a chemical reaction, it is often the case that the rate of the reaction is proportional to the quantity of the substance present; for instance, it is known from experiments that the rate of decay of radium is proportional to the amount of radium present at a given instant. An application in business occurs when interest is compounded continuously.

In such cases, if the time is represented by t units, and A units represents the amount of the substance present at any time, then

$$\frac{dA}{dt} = kA$$

where k is a constant. If A increases as t increases, then $k > 0$, and we have the *law of natural growth*. If A decreases as t increases, then $k < 0$, and we have the *law of natural decay*. In problems involving the law of natural decay, the *half life* of a substance is the time required for half of it to decay.

EXAMPLE 1:   The rate of decay of radium is proportional to the amount present at any time. If 60 mg of radium are present now, and its half life is 1690 years, how much radium will be present 100 years from now?

Table 9.6.1

t	0	1690	100
A	60	30	A_{100}

SOLUTION: Let $t =$ the number of years in the time from now;
$A =$ the number of milligrams of radium present at t years.

We have the initial conditions given in Table 9.6.1. The differential equation is

$$\frac{dA}{dt} = kA$$

Separating the variables, we obtain

$$\frac{dA}{A} = k \, dt$$

Integrating, we have

$$\int \frac{dA}{A} = k \int dt$$

$$\ln |A| = kt + \bar{c}$$

$$|A| = e^{kt+\bar{c}} = e^{\bar{c}} \cdot e^{kt}$$

Letting $e^{\bar{c}} = C$, we have $|A| = Ce^{kt}$, and because A is nonnegative we can omit the absolute-value bars around A, thereby giving us

$$A = Ce^{kt}$$

Because $A = 60$ when $t = 0$, we obtain $60 = C$. So

$$A = 60e^{kt} \tag{1}$$

Because $A = 30$ when $t = 1690$, we get $30 = 60e^{1690k}$ or

$$0.5 = e^{1690k}$$

So

$$\ln 0.5 = 1690k$$

and

$$k = \frac{\ln 0.5}{1690} = \frac{-0.6931}{1690} = -0.000411$$

Substituting this value of k into Eq. (1), we obtain

$$A = 60e^{-0.000411t}$$

When $t = 100$, $A = A_{100}$, and we have

$$A_{100} = 60e^{-0.0411} = 58$$

Therefore, there will be 58 mg of radium present 100 years from now.

EXAMPLE 2: In a certain culture, the rate of growth of bacteria is proportional to the amount present. If there are 1000 bacteria present initially, and the amount doubles in 12 min, how long will it take before there will be 1,000,000 bacteria present?

Table 9.6.2

t	0	12	T
A	1,000	2,000	1,000,000

SOLUTION: Let t = the number of minutes in the time from now;
A = the number of bacteria present at t min.

Even though by definition A is a nonnegative integer, we assume that A can be any nonnegative number for A to be a continuous function of t. Table 9.6.2 gives the initial conditions. The differential equation is

$$\frac{dA}{dt} = kA$$

The differential equation is the same as we had in Example 1; hence, as above, the general solution is

$$A = Ce^{kt}$$

When $t = 0$, $A = 1000$; hence, $C = 1000$, which gives

$$A = 1000e^{kt}$$

From the condition that $A = 2000$ when $t = 12$, we obtain

$$e^{12k} = 2$$

and so

$$k = \tfrac{1}{12} \ln 2 = 0.05776$$

Hence, we have

$$A = 1000e^{0.05776t}$$

Replacing t by T and A by 1,000,000, we get

$$1,000,000 = 1000e^{0.05776T}$$

$$e^{0.05776T} = 1000$$

$$0.05776T = \ln 1000$$

$$T = \frac{\ln 1000}{0.05776} = 119.6$$

Therefore, there will be 1,000,000 bacteria present in 1 hr, 59 min, 36 sec.

EXAMPLE 3: Newton's law of cooling states that the rate at which a body changes temperature is proportional to the difference between its temperature and that of the surrounding medium. If a body is in air of temperature 35° and the body cools

SOLUTION: Let t = the number of minutes in the time that has elapsed since the body started to cool;
x = the number of degrees in the temperature of the body at t minutes.

Table 9.6.3 gives the initial conditions. From Newton's law of cooling, we have

$$\frac{dx}{dt} = k(x - 35)$$

from 120° to 60° in 40 min, find the temperature of the body after 100 min.

Table 9.6.3

t	0	40	100
x	120	60	x_{100}

Separating the variables, we obtain

$$\frac{dx}{x-35} = k\ dt$$

So

$$\int \frac{dx}{x-35} = k \int dt$$

$$\ln |x - 35| = kt + \bar{c}$$

$$x - 35 = Ce^{kt}$$

$$x = Ce^{kt} + 35$$

When $t = 0$, $x = 120$; so $C = 85$. Therefore,

$$x = 85e^{kt} + 35$$

When $t = 40$, $x = 60$; and we obtain

$$60 = 85e^{40k} + 35$$

$$40k = \ln \tfrac{5}{17}$$

$$k = \tfrac{1}{40}(\ln 5 - \ln 17)$$

$$= \tfrac{1}{40}(1.6094 - 2.8332)$$

$$= -0.0306$$

So

$$x = 85e^{-0.0306t} + 35$$

Then

$$x_{100} = 85e^{-3.06} + 35 = 39$$

Therefore, the temperature of the body is 39° after 100 min.

EXAMPLE 4:   There are 100 gal of brine in a tank and the brine contains 70 lb of dissolved salt. Fresh water runs into the tank at the rate of 3 gal/min, and the mixture, kept uniform by stirring, runs out at the same rate. How many pounds of salt are there in the tank at the end of 1 hr?

SOLUTION: Let $t = $ the number of minutes that have elapsed since the water started flowing into the tank;
$x = $ the number of pounds of salt in the tank at t min.
Because 100 gal of brine are in the tank at all times, at t minutes the number of pounds of salt per gallon is $x/100$. Three gallons of the mixture run out of the tank each minute, and so the tank loses $3(x/100)$ pounds of salt per minute. Because $D_t x$ is the rate of change of x with respect to t, and x is decreasing as t increases, we have the differential equation

$$\frac{dx}{dt} = -\frac{3x}{100}$$

We also have the initial conditions given in Table 9.6.4. Separating the variables and integrating, we have

Table 9.6.4

t	0	60
x	70	x_{60}

$$\int \frac{dx}{x} = -0.03 \int dt$$

$$\ln |x| = -0.03t + \bar{c}$$

$$x = Ce^{-0.03t}$$

When $t = 0$, $x = 70$, and so $C = 70$. Letting $t = 60$ and $x = x_{60}$, we have

$$x_{60} = 70e^{-1.8}$$

$$= 70(0.1653)$$

$$= 11.57$$

So there are 11.57 lb of salt in the tank after 1 hr.

The calculus is often very useful to the economist for evaluating certain business decisions. However, to use the calculus we must be concerned with continuous functions. Consider, for example, the following formula which gives A, the number of dollars in the amount after t years, if P dollars is invested at a rate of $100i$ percent, compounded m times per year:

$$A = P \left(1 + \frac{i}{m}\right)^{mt} \tag{2}$$

Let us conceive of a situation in which the interest is continuously compounding; that is, consider formula (2), where we let the number of interest periods per year increase without bound. Then going to the limit in formula (2), we have

$$A = P \lim_{m \to +\infty} \left(1 + \frac{i}{m}\right)^{mt}$$

which can be written as

$$A = P \lim_{m \to +\infty} \left[\left(1 + \frac{i}{m}\right)^{m/i}\right]^{it} \tag{3}$$

Now consider

$$\lim_{m \to +\infty} \left(1 + \frac{i}{m}\right)^{m/i}$$

Letting $h = i/m$, we have $m/i = 1/h$; and because "$m \to +\infty$" is equivalent to "$h \to 0^+$," we have

$$\lim_{m \to +\infty} \left(1 + \frac{i}{m}\right)^{m/i} = \lim_{h \to 0^+} (1 + h)^{1/h} = e$$

Hence, using Theorem 2.6.5, we have

$$\lim_{m \to +\infty} \left[\left(1 + \frac{i}{m}\right)^{m/i}\right]^{it} = \left[\lim_{m \to +\infty} \left(1 + \frac{i}{m}\right)^{m/i}\right]^{it} = e^{it}$$

and so Eq. (3) becomes

$$A = Pe^{it} \tag{4}$$

By letting t vary through the set of nonnegative real numbers, we see that Eq. (4) expresses A as a continuous function of t.

Another way of looking at the same situation is to consider an investment of P dollars, which increases at a rate proportional to its size. This is the law of natural growth. Then if A dollars is the amount at t years, we have

$$\frac{dA}{dt} = kA$$

$$\int \frac{dA}{A} = k \int dt$$

$$\ln |A| = kt + \bar{c}$$

$$A = Ce^{kt}$$

When $t = 0$, $A = P$, and so $C = P$. Therefore, we have

$$A = Pe^{kt} \tag{5}$$

Comparing Eq. (5) with Eq. (4), we see that they are the same if $k = i$. So if an investment increases at a rate proportional to its size, we say that the interest is *compounded continuously*, and the interest rate is the constant of proportionality.

● ILLUSTRATION 1: If P dollars is invested at a rate of 8% per year compounded continuously, and A dollars is the amount of the investment at t years,

$$\frac{dA}{dt} = 0.08A$$

and

$$A = Pe^{0.08t}$$ ●

If in Eq. (4) we take $P = 1$, $i = 1$, and $t = 1$, we get $A = e$, which gives a justification for the economist's interpretation of the number "e" as the yield on an investment of one dollar for a year at an interest rate of 100% compounded continuously.

EXAMPLE 5: If $5000 is borrowed at an interest rate of 12% per year, compounded continuously, and the loan is to be repaid in one payment at the end of a year, how much must the borrower repay? Also, find the effective rate of interest which is the rate that gives the same amount of interest compounded once a year.

SOLUTION: Letting A dollars be the amount to be repaid, and because $P = 5000$, $i = 0.12$, and $t = 1$, we have from Eq. (4)

$$A = 5000e^{0.12}$$

$$= 5000(1.1275)$$

$$= 5637.50$$

Hence, the borrower must repay $5637.50. Letting j be the effective rate of interest, we have

$$5000(1 + j) = 5000e^{0.12}$$

$$1 + j = e^{0.12}$$

$$j = 1.1275 - 1$$

$$= 0.1275$$

$$= 12.75\%$$

Exercises 9.6

1. Bacteria grown in a certain culture increase at a rate proportional to the amount present. If there are 1000 bacteria present initially and the amount doubles in 1 hr, how many bacteria will there be in $3\frac{1}{2}$ hr?

2. In a certain culture where the rate of growth of bacteria is proportional to the amount present, the number triples in 3 hr, and at the end of 12 hr there were 10 million bacteria. How many bacteria were present initially?

3. In a certain chemical reaction the rate of conversion of a substance is proportional to the amount of the substance still untransformed at that time. After 10 min one-third of the original amount of the substance has been converted, and 20 g has been converted after 15 min. What was the original amount of the substance?

4. Sugar decomposes in water at a rate proportional to the amount still unchanged. If there were 50 lb of sugar present initially and at the end of 5 hr this is reduced to 20 lb, how long will it take until 90% of the sugar is decomposed?

5. The rate of natural increase of the population of a certain city is proportional to the population. If the population increases from 40,000 to 60,000 in 40 years, when will the population be 80,000?

6. Using Newton's law of cooling (see Example 3), if a body in air at a temperature of 0° cools from 200° to 100° in 40 min, how many more minutes will it take for the body to cool to 50°?

7. Under the conditions of Example 3, after how many minutes will the temperature of the body be 45°?

8. When a simple electric circuit, containing no condensers but having inductance and resistance, has the electromotive force removed, the rate of decrease of the current is proportional to the current. The current is i amperes t sec after the cutoff, and $i = 40$ when $t = 0$. If the current dies down to 15 amperes in 0.01 sec, find i in terms of t.

9. If a thermometer is taken from a room in which the temperature is 75° into the open, where the temperature is 35°, and the reading of the thermometer is 65° after 30 sec, (a) how long after the removal will the reading be 50°? (b) What is the thermometer reading 3 min after the removal? Use Newton's law of cooling (see Example 3).

10. Thirty percent of a radioactive substance disappears in 15 years. Find the half life of the substance.

11. If the half life of radium is 1690 years, what percent of the amount present now will be remaining after (a) 100 years and (b) 1000 years?

12. A tank contains 200 gal of brine in which there are 3 lb of salt per gallon. It is desired to dilute this solution by adding brine containing 1 lb of salt per gallon, which flows into the tank at the rate of 4 gal/min and runs out at the same rate. When will the tank contain $1\frac{1}{2}$ lb of salt per gallon?

13. A tank contains 100 gal of fresh water and brine containing 2 lb of salt per gallon flows into the tank at the rate of 3 gal/min. If the mixture, kept uniform by stirring, flows out at the same rate, how many pounds of salt are there in the tank at the end of 30 min?

14. A loan of $100 is repaid in one payment at the end of a year. If the interest rate is 8% compounded continuously, determine (a) the total amount repaid and (b) the effective rate of interest.

15. If an amount of money invested doubles itself in 10 years at interest compounded continuously, how long will it take for the original amount to triple itself?

16. If the purchasing power of a dollar is decreasing at the rate of 8% annually, compounded continuously, how long will it take for the purchasing power to be 50 cents?

17. Professor Willard Libby of University of California at Los Angeles was awarded the Nobel prize in chemistry for discovering a method of determining the date of death of a once-living object. Professor Libby made use of the fact that the tissue of a living organism is composed of two kinds of carbons, a radioactive carbon A and a stable carbon B, in which the ratio of the amount of A to the amount of B is approximately constant. When the organism dies, the law of natural decay applies to A. If it is determined that the amount of A in a piece of charcoal is only 15% of its original amount and the half life of A is 5500 years, when did the tree from which the charcoal came die?

Review Exercises (Chapter 9)

In Exercises 1 through 8, differentiate the given function.

1. $f(x) = (\ln x^2)^2$

2. $f(x) = \dfrac{e^x}{(e^x + e^{-x})^2}$

3. $f(x) = \sqrt{\log_{10} \dfrac{1+x}{1-x}}$

4. $f(x) = 10^{-5x^2}$

5. $f(x) = x^{3/\ln x}$

6. $f(x) = e^{x/(4+x^2)}$

7. $f(x) = (x)^{x e^x}$

8. $f(x) = 3^{x^{x^n}}$

In Exercises 9 through 14, evaluate the indefinite integral.

9. $\displaystyle\int \frac{3e^{2x}}{1 + e^{2x}}\, dx$

10. $\displaystyle\int e^{2x^2 - 4x}(x - 1)\, dx$

11. $\displaystyle\int (e^{3x} + a^{3x})\, dx$

12. $\displaystyle\int \frac{10^{\ln x^2}}{x}\, dx$

13. $\displaystyle\int \frac{2^x\, dx}{\sqrt{3 \cdot 2^x + 4}}$

14. $\displaystyle\int \frac{10^x + 1}{10^x - 1}\, dx$

In Exercises 15 through 18, evaluate the definite integral.

15. $\displaystyle\int_0^2 x^2 e^{x^3}\, dx$

16. $\displaystyle\int_0^1 (e^{2x} + 1)^2\, dx$

17. $\displaystyle\int_1^8 \frac{x^{1/3}}{x^{4/3} + 4}\, dx$

18. $\displaystyle\int_{1/3}^{1/2} \frac{4x^{-3} + 2}{x^{-2} - x}\, dx$

19. Find $D_x y$ if $ye^x + xe^y + x + y = 0$.

20. If $f(x) = \log_{(e^x)}(x + 1)$, find $f'(x)$.

21. The linear density of a rod at a point x ft from one end is $1/(x + 1)$ slugs/ft. If the rod is 4 ft long, find the mass and center of mass of the rod.

22. Find an equation of the tangent line to the curve $y = x^{x-1}$ at $(2, 2)$.

23. A particle is moving on a straight line where s ft is the directed distance of the particle from the origin, v ft/sec is the velocity of the particle, and a ft/sec² is the acceleration of the particle at t sec. If $a = e^t + e^{-t}$ and $v = 1$ and $s = 2$ when $t = 0$, find v and s in terms of t.

24. The area of the region, bounded by the curve $y = e^{-x}$, the coordinate axes, and the line $x = b(b > 0)$, is a function of b. If f is this function, find $f(b)$. Also find $\lim\limits_{b \to +\infty} f(b)$.

25. The volume of the solid of revolution obtained by revolving the region in Exercise 24 about the x axis is a function of b. If g is this function, find $g(b)$. Also find $\lim\limits_{b \to +\infty} g(b)$.

26. The rate of natural increase of the population of a certain city is proportional to the population. If the population doubles in 60 years and if the population in 1950 was 60,000, estimate the population in the year 2000.

27. The rate of decay of a radioactive substance is proportional to the amount present. If half of a given deposit of the substance disappears in 1900 years, how long will it take for 95% of the deposit to disappear?

28. Prove that if a rectangle is to have its base on the x axis and two of its vertices on the curve $y = e^{-x^2}$, then the rectangle will have the largest possible area if the two vertices are at the points of inflection of the graph.

29. Given $f(x) = \ln |x|$ and $x < 0$. Show that f has an inverse function. If g is the inverse function, find $g(x)$ and the domain of g.

In Exercises 30 and 31, find the inverse of the given function if there is one, and determine its domain. Draw a sketch of the given function, and if the given function has an inverse, draw a sketch of the graph of the inverse function on the same set of axes.

30. $f(x) = \dfrac{x + 4}{2x - 3}$

31. $f(x) = \dfrac{2}{8x^3 - 1}$

32. Prove that if $x < 1$, $\ln x < x$. (HINT: Let $f(x) = x - \ln x$ and show that f is decreasing on $(0, 1)$ and find $f(1)$.)

33. When a gas undergoes an adiabatic (no gain or loss of heat) expansion or compression, then the rate of change of the pressure with respect to the volume varies directly as the pressure and inversely as the volume. If the pressure is p lb/in.² when the volume is v in.³, and the initial pressure and volume are p_0 lb/in.² and v_0 in.³, show that $pv^k = p_0 v_0^k$.

34. If W in.-lb is the work done by a gas expanding against a piston in a cylinder and P lb/in.² is the pressure of the gas when the volume of the gas is V in.³, show that if V_1 in.³ and V_2 in.³ are the initial and final volumes, respectively, then

$$W = \int_{V_1}^{V_2} P \, dV$$

35. Suppose a piston compresses a gas in a cylinder from an initial volume of 60 in.³ to a volume of 40 in.³. If Boyle's law (Exercise 10 in Exercises 3.9) holds, and the initial pressure is 50 lb/in.², find the work done by the piston. (Use the result of Exercise 34.)

36. The charge of electricity on a spherical surface leaks off at a rate proportional to the charge. Initially, the charge of electricity was 8 coulombs and one-fourth leaks off in 15 min. When will there be only 2 coulombs remaining?

37. How long will it take for an investment to double itself if interest is paid at the rate of 8% compounded continuously?

38. A tank contains 60 gal of salt water with 120 lb of dissolved salt. Salt water with 3 lb of salt per gallon flows into the tank at the rate of 2 gal/min and the mixture, kept uniform by stirring, flows out at the same rate. How long will it be before there are 200 lb of salt in the tank?

39. Find $\int_0^t e^{-|x|} \, dx$ if t is any real number.

40. Prove that if $x > 0$, and $\int_1^x t^{h-1} \, dt = 1$, then $\lim\limits_{h \to 0} x = \lim\limits_{h \to 0} (1 + h)^{1/h}$.

41. Prove that

$$\lim_{x \to 0} \frac{\log_a(1 + x)}{x} = \log_a e$$

   (NOTE: Compare with Exercise 33 in Exercises 9.1.)

42. Prove that

$$\lim_{x \to 0} \frac{a^x - 1}{x} = \ln a$$

   (HINT: Let $y = a^x - 1$ and express $(a^x - 1)/x$ as a function of y, say $g(y)$. Then show that $y \to 0$ as $x \to 0$, and find $\lim\limits_{y \to 0} g(y)$.)

43. Use the results of Exercises 41 and 42 to prove that

$$\lim_{x \to 1} \frac{x^b - 1}{x - 1} = b$$

   (HINT: Write

$$\frac{x^b - 1}{x - 1} = \frac{e^{b \ln x} - 1}{b \ln x} \cdot \frac{b \ln x}{x - 1}$$

   Then let $s = b \ln x$ and $t = x - 1$.)

44. Prove that

$$\lim_{x \to 0} \frac{e^{ax} - 1}{x} = a$$

   (HINT: Let $f(x) = e^{ax}$ and find $f'(0)$ by two methods.)

45. If the domain of f is the set of all real numbers and $f'(x) = cf(x)$ for all x where c is a constant, prove that there is a constant k for which $f(x) = ke^{cx}$ for all x. (HINT: Consider the function g for which $g(x) = f(x)e^{-cx}$ and find $g'(x)$.)

46. Prove that

$$D_x{}^n(\ln x) = (-1)^{n-1} \frac{(n - 1)!}{x^n}$$

   (HINT: Use mathematical induction.)

47. Do Exercise 17 in the Review Exercises of Chapter 7 by evaluating each integral.

10

Trigonometric functions

10.1 THE SINE AND COSINE FUNCTIONS

In geometry an *angle* is defined as the union of two rays called the *sides*, having a common endpoint called the *vertex*. Any angle is congruent to some angle having its vertex at the origin and one side, called the *initial side*, lying on the positive side of the x axis. Such an angle is said to be in *standard position*. Figure 10.1.1 shows an angle AOB in standard position with AO as the initial side. The other side, OB, is called the *terminal side*. The angle AOB can be formed by rotating the side OA to the side OB, and under such a rotation the point A moves along the circumference of a circle, having its center at O and radius $|\overline{OA}|$ to the point B.

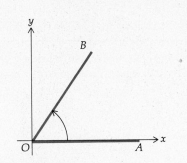

Figure 10.1.1

In the study of trigonometry dealing with problems involving angles of triangles, the measurement of an angle is usually given in degrees. However, in the calculus we are concerned with trigonometric functions of real numbers, and we use *radian measure* to define these functions.

To define the radian measure of an angle we use the length of an arc of a circle. If such an arc is smaller than a semicircle, it can be considered the graph of a function having a continuous derivative; and so by Theorem 8.10.2 it has length. If the arc is a semicircle or larger, it has a length that is the sum of the lengths of arcs which are smaller than semicircles.

10.1.1 Definition

Let AOB be an angle in standard position and $|\overline{OA}| = 1$. If s units is the length of the arc of the circle traveled by point A as the initial side OA is rotated to the terminal side OB, the *radian measure, t,* of angle AOB is given by

$$t = s \qquad \text{if the rotation is counterclockwise}$$

and

$$t = -s \qquad \text{if the rotation is clockwise}$$

● ILLUSTRATION 1: By using the fact that the measure of the length of the unit circle's circumference is 2π, we determine the radian measures of the angles in Fig. 10.1.2a, b, c, d, e, and f. They are $\frac{1}{2}\pi$, $\frac{1}{4}\pi$, $-\frac{1}{2}\pi$, $\frac{3}{2}\pi$, $-\frac{3}{4}\pi$, and $\frac{7}{4}\pi$, respectively.   ●

Figure 10.1.2

In Definition 10.1.1 it is possible that there may be more than one complete revolution in the rotation of OA.

(a)

(b)

Figure 10.1.3

● ILLUSTRATION 2: Figure 10.1.3a shows such an angle whose radian measure is $\frac{5}{2}\pi$, and Fig. 10.1.3b shows one whose radian measure is $-\frac{13}{4}\pi$. ●

An angle formed by one complete revolution so that OA is coincident with OB has degree measure of 360 and radian measure of 2π. Hence, there is the following correspondence between degree measure and radian measure (where the symbol $\sim$ indicates that the given measurements are for the same or congruent angles):

$$360° \sim 2\pi \text{ rad}$$

or, equivalently,

$$180° \sim \pi \text{ rad}$$

From this it follows that

$$1° \sim \tfrac{1}{180}\pi \text{ rad}$$

and

$$1 \text{ rad} \sim \frac{180°}{\pi} \approx 57°18'$$

From this correspondence the measurement of an angle can be converted from one system of units to the other.

● ILLUSTRATION 3:

$$162° \sim 162 \cdot \tfrac{1}{180}\pi \text{ rad} = \tfrac{9}{10}\pi \text{ rad}$$

and

$$\frac{5}{12}\pi \text{ rad} \sim \frac{5}{12}\pi \cdot \frac{180°}{\pi} = 75°$$ ●

Table 10.1.1 gives the corresponding degree and radian measures of certain angles.

Table 10.1.1

degree measure	30	45	60	90	120	135	150	180	270	360
radian measure	$\frac{1}{6}\pi$	$\frac{1}{4}\pi$	$\frac{1}{3}\pi$	$\frac{1}{2}\pi$	$\frac{2}{3}\pi$	$\frac{3}{4}\pi$	$\frac{5}{6}\pi$	π	$\frac{3}{2}\pi$	2π

We now define the sine and cosine functions of any real number.

10.1.2 Definition Suppose that t is a real number. Place an angle, having radian measure t, in standard position and let point P be at the intersection of the terminal side of the angle with the unit circle having its center at the origin. If P is the point (x, y), then the *cosine function* is defined by

$$\cos t = x$$

Figure 10.1.4

Figure 10.1.5

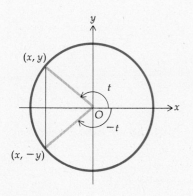

Figure 10.1.6

and the *sine function* is defined by

$$\sin t = y$$

From the above definition it is seen that $\sin t$ and $\cos t$ are defined for any value of t. Hence, the domain of the sine and cosine functions is the set of all real numbers. The largest value either function may have is 1, and the smallest value is -1. It will be shown later that the sine and cosine functions are continuous everywhere, and from this it follows that the range of the two functions is $[-1, 1]$.

For certain values of t, the cosine and sine are easily obtained from a figure. From Fig. 10.1.4 we see that $\cos 0 = 1$ and $\sin 0 = 0$, $\cos \frac{1}{4}\pi = \frac{1}{2}\sqrt{2}$ and $\sin \frac{1}{4}\pi = \frac{1}{2}\sqrt{2}$, $\cos \frac{1}{2}\pi = 0$ and $\sin \frac{1}{2}\pi = 1$, $\cos \pi = -1$ and $\sin \pi = 0$, $\cos \frac{3}{2}\pi = 0$ and $\sin \frac{3}{2}\pi = -1$. Table 10.1.2 gives these values and some others that are frequently used.

Table 10.1.2

x	0	$\frac{1}{6}\pi$	$\frac{1}{4}\pi$	$\frac{1}{3}\pi$	$\frac{1}{2}\pi$	$\frac{2}{3}\pi$	$\frac{3}{4}\pi$	$\frac{5}{6}\pi$	π	$\frac{3}{2}\pi$	2π
$\sin x$	0	$\frac{1}{2}$	$\frac{1}{2}\sqrt{2}$	$\frac{1}{2}\sqrt{3}$	1	$\frac{1}{2}\sqrt{3}$	$\frac{1}{2}\sqrt{2}$	$\frac{1}{2}$	0	-1	0
$\cos x$	1	$\frac{1}{2}\sqrt{3}$	$\frac{1}{2}\sqrt{2}$	$\frac{1}{2}$	0	$-\frac{1}{2}$	$-\frac{1}{2}\sqrt{2}$	$-\frac{1}{2}\sqrt{3}$	-1	0	1

An equation of the unit circle having its center at the origin is $x^2 + y^2 = 1$. Because $x = \cos t$ and $y = \sin t$, it follows that

$$\cos^2 t + \sin^2 t = 1 \tag{1}$$

Note that $\cos^2 t$ and $\sin^2 t$ stand for $(\cos t)^2$ and $(\sin t)^2$. Equation (1) is called an *identity* because it is valid for any real number t.

Figures 10.1.5 and 10.1.6 show angles having a negative radian measure of $-t$ and corresponding angles having a positive radian measure of t. From these figures we see that

$$\cos(-t) = \cos t \quad \text{and} \quad \sin(-t) = -\sin t \tag{2}$$

These equations hold for any real number t because the points where the terminal sides of the angles (having radian measures t and $-t$) intersect the unit circle have equal abscissas and ordinates that differ only in sign. Hence, Eqs. (2) are identities. From these equations it follows that the cosine function is even and the sine function is odd.

From Definition 10.1.2 the following identities are obtained.

$$\cos(t + 2\pi) = \cos t \quad \text{and} \quad \sin(t + 2\pi) = \sin t \tag{3}$$

The property of cosine and sine stated by Eqs. (3) is called *periodicity*, which is now defined.

10.1.3 Definition A function f is said to be *periodic* with *period* $p \neq 0$ if whenever x is in the domain of f, then $x + p$ is also in the domain of f and

$$f(x + p) = f(x)$$

From the above definition and Eqs. (3) it is seen that the sine and cosine functions are periodic with period 2π; that is, whenever the value of the independent variable t is increased by 2π, the value of each of the functions is repeated. It is because of the periodicity of the sine and cosine that these functions have important applications in physics and engineering in connection with periodically repetitive phenomena such as wave motion and vibrations.

We now proceed to derive a useful formula because other important identities can be obtained from it. The formula we derive is as follows:

$$\cos(a + b) = \cos a \cos b - \sin a \sin b \tag{4}$$

where a and b are any real numbers.

Refer to Fig. 10.1.7 showing a unit circle with the points $Q(1, 0)$, $P_1(\cos a, \sin a)$, $P_2(\cos b, \sin b)$, $P_3(\cos(a + b), \sin(a + b))$, and $P_4(\cos a, -\sin a)$. Using the notation $\overset{\frown}{RS}$ to denote the measure of the length of arc from R to S, we have $\overset{\frown}{QP_1} = a$, $\overset{\frown}{QP_2} = b$, $\overset{\frown}{P_2P_3} = a$, and $\overset{\frown}{P_4Q} = |-a| = a$. Because $\overset{\frown}{QP_3} = \overset{\frown}{QP_2} + \overset{\frown}{P_2P_3}$, we have

$$\overset{\frown}{QP_3} = b + a \tag{5}$$

and because $\overset{\frown}{P_4P_2} = \overset{\frown}{P_4Q} + \overset{\frown}{QP_2}$, it follows that

$$\overset{\frown}{P_4P_2} = a + b \tag{6}$$

From Eqs. (5) and (6) we see that $\overset{\frown}{QP_3} = \overset{\frown}{P_4P_2}$; therefore, the length of the chord joining the points Q and P_3 is the same as the length of the chord joining the points P_4 and P_2. Squaring the measures of these lengths, we have

$$|\overline{QP_3}|^2 = |\overline{P_4P_2}|^2 \tag{7}$$

Using the distance formula, we get

$$|\overline{QP_3}|^2 = [\cos(a + b) - 1]^2 + [\sin(a + b) - 0]^2$$
$$= \cos^2(a + b) - 2\cos(a + b) + 1 + \sin^2(a + b)$$

and because $\cos^2(a + b) + \sin^2(a + b) = 1$, the above may be written as

$$|\overline{QP_3}|^2 = 2 - 2\cos(a + b) \tag{8}$$

Again applying the distance formula, we have

$$|\overline{P_4P_2}|^2 = (\cos b - \cos a)^2 + (\sin b + \sin a)^2$$

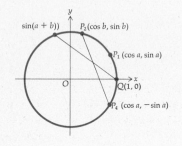

Figure 10.1.7

$$= \cos^2 b - 2 \cos a \cos b + \cos^2 a$$
$$+ \sin^2 b + 2 \sin a \sin b + \sin^2 a$$

and because $\cos^2 b + \sin^2 b = 1$ and $\cos^2 a + \sin^2 a = 1$, the above becomes

$$|\overline{P_4 P_2}|^2 = 2 - 2 \cos a \cos b + 2 \sin a \sin b \qquad (9)$$

Substituting from Eqs. (8) and (9) into (7), we obtain

$$2 - 2 \cos(a + b) = 2 - 2 \cos a \cos b + 2 \sin a \sin b$$

from which follows

$$\cos(a + b) = \cos a \cos b - \sin a \sin b$$

which is formula (4).

A formula for $\cos(a - b)$ can be obtained from formula (4) by substituting $-b$ for b. Doing this, we have

$$\cos(a + (-b)) = \cos a \cos(-b) - \sin a \sin(-b)$$

Because $\cos(-b) = \cos b$ and $\sin(-b) = -\sin b$, we get

$$\cos(a - b) = \cos a \cos b + \sin a \sin b \qquad (10)$$

for all real numbers a and b.

Letting $a = \frac{1}{2}\pi$ in formula (10), we have the equation $\cos(\frac{1}{2}\pi - b) = \cos \frac{1}{2}\pi \cos b + \sin \frac{1}{2}\pi \sin b$; and because $\cos \frac{1}{2}\pi = 0$ and $\sin \frac{1}{2}\pi = 1$, it becomes $\cos(\frac{1}{2}\pi - b) = \sin b$. Now if in this equation we let $\frac{1}{2}\pi - b = c$, then $b = \frac{1}{2}\pi - c$ and we obtain $\cos c = \sin(\frac{1}{2}\pi - c)$. We have therefore proved the following two identities.

$$\cos(\tfrac{1}{2}\pi - t) = \sin t \quad \text{and} \quad \sin(\tfrac{1}{2}\pi - t) = \cos t \qquad (11)$$

Formulas similar to (4) and (10) for the sine of the sum and difference of two numbers follow easily from those we have. A formula for the sine of the sum of two numbers follows from (10) and (11). We have from (11)

$$\sin(a + b) = \cos(\tfrac{1}{2}\pi - (a + b)) = \cos((\tfrac{1}{2}\pi - a) - b)$$

With (10) it follows that

$$\sin(a + b) = \cos(\tfrac{1}{2}\pi - a) \cos b + \sin(\tfrac{1}{2}\pi - a) \sin b$$

and from (11) we get

$$\sin(a + b) = \sin a \cos b + \cos a \sin b \qquad (12)$$

for all real numbers a and b.

To obtain a formula for the sine of the difference of two numbers we write $a - b$ as $a + (-b)$ and apply formula (12). Doing this, we have

$$\sin(a + (-b)) = \sin a \cos(-b) + \cos a \sin(-b)$$

and because $\cos(-b) = \cos b$ and $\sin(-b) = -\sin b$, we obtain

$$\sin(a - b) = \sin a \cos b - \cos a \sin b \tag{13}$$

which is valid for all real numbers a and b.

By letting $a = b = t$ in formulas (12) and (4), respectively, we get the formulas

$$\sin 2t = 2 \sin t \cos t \tag{14}$$

and

$$\cos 2t = \cos^2 t - \sin^2 t \tag{15}$$

Using the identity $\sin^2 t + \cos^2 t = 1$ we may rewrite formula (15) as

$$\cos 2t = 2 \cos^2 t - 1 \tag{16}$$

or as

$$\cos 2t = 1 - 2 \sin^2 t \tag{17}$$

Replacing t by $\frac{1}{2}t$ in formulas (16) and (17) and performing some algebraic manipulations, we get, respectively,

$$\cos^2 \frac{1}{2} t = \frac{1 + \cos t}{2} \tag{18}$$

and

$$\sin^2 \frac{1}{2} t = \frac{1 - \cos t}{2} \tag{19}$$

Formulas (14) through (19) are identities because they hold for all real numbers t.

By subtracting the terms of formula (4) from the corresponding terms of formula (10) the following is obtained:

$$\sin a \sin b = \tfrac{1}{2} [-\cos(a + b) + \cos(a - b)] \tag{20}$$

By adding corresponding terms of formulas (4) and (10) we get

$$\cos a \cos b = \tfrac{1}{2} [\cos(a + b) + \cos(a - b)] \tag{21}$$

and by adding corresponding terms of formulas (12) and (13) we have

$$\sin a \cos b = \tfrac{1}{2} [\sin(a + b) + \sin(a - b)] \tag{22}$$

By letting $c = a + b$ and $d = a - b$ in formulas (22), (21), and (20), we obtain, respectively,

$$\sin c + \sin d = 2 \sin \frac{c + d}{2} \cos \frac{c - d}{2} \tag{23}$$

$$\cos c + \cos d = 2 \cos \frac{c + d}{2} \cos \frac{c - d}{2} \tag{24}$$

and

$$\cos c - \cos d = -2 \sin \frac{c + d}{2} \sin \frac{c - d}{2} \tag{25}$$

Figure 10.1.8

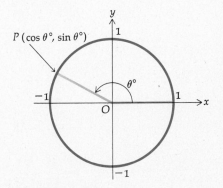

Figure 10.1.9

If the terms of formula (13) are subtracted from the corresponding terms of formula (12) and $a + b$ and $a - b$ are replaced by c and d, respectively, we have

$$\sin c - \sin d = 2 \cos \frac{c+d}{2} \sin \frac{c-d}{2} \tag{26}$$

You are asked to perform the indicated operations in the derivation of some of the above formulas in Exercises 1 to 6.

When referring to the trigonometric functions with a domain of angle measurements we use the notation $\theta°$ to denote the measurement of an angle if its degree measure is θ. For example, 45° is the measurement of an angle whose degree measure is 45 or, equivalently, radian measure is $\frac{1}{4}\pi$.

Consider an angle of $\theta°$ in standard position on a rectangular cartesian-coordinate system. Choose any point P, excluding the vertex, on the terminal side of the angle and let its abscissa be x, its ordinate be y, and $|\overline{OP}| = r$. Refer to Fig. 10.1.8. The ratios x/y and y/r are independent of the choice of P because if the point P_1 is chosen instead of P, we see by Fig. 10.1.8 that $x/r = x_1/r_1$ and $y/r = y_1/r_1$. Because the position of the terminal side depends on the angle, these two ratios are functions of the measurement of the angle, and we define

$$\cos \theta° = \frac{x}{r} \quad \text{and} \quad \sin \theta° = \frac{y}{r} \tag{27}$$

Because any point P (other than the origin) may be chosen on the terminal side, we could choose the point for which $r = 1$, and this is the point where the terminal side intersects the unit circle $x^2 + y^2 = 1$ (see Fig. 10.1.9). Then $\cos \theta°$ is the abscissa of the point and $\sin \theta°$ is the ordinate of the point. This gives the analogy between the sine and cosine of real numbers and those of angle measurements. We have the next definition.

10.1.4 Definition   If α degrees and x radians are measurements for the same angle, then

$$\sin \alpha° = \sin x \quad \text{and} \quad \cos \alpha° = \cos x$$

Exercises 10.1

1. Derive formula (20) by subtracting the terms of formula (4) from the corresponding terms of formula (10).

2. Derive formula (21) by a method similar to that suggested in Exercise 1.

3. Derive formula (22) by a method similar to that suggested in Exercise 1.

4. Derive formula (23) by using formula (22).

5. Derive formula (24) by using formula (21).

6. Derive formula (25) by using formula (20).

7. Derive a formula for $\sin 3t$ in terms of $\sin t$ by using formulas (12), (14), (15), and (1).

8. Derive a formula for $\cos 3t$ in terms of $\cos t$. Use a method similar to that suggested in Exercise 7.

9. Without using tables, find the value of (a) $\sin \frac{1}{12}\pi$ and (b) $\cos \frac{1}{12}\pi$.

10. Without using tables, find the value of (a) $\sin \frac{1}{8}\pi$ and (b) $\cos \frac{1}{8}\pi$.

11. Without using tables, find the value of (a) $\sin \frac{5}{12}\pi$ and (b) $\cos \frac{5}{12}\pi$.

12. Express each of the following in terms of $\sin t$ or $\sin(\frac{1}{2}\pi - t)$: (a) $\sin(\frac{3}{2}\pi - t)$; (b) $\cos(\frac{3}{2}\pi - t)$; (c) $\sin(\frac{3}{2}\pi + t)$; (d) $\cos(\frac{3}{2}\pi + t)$.

13. Express the function values of Exercise 12 in terms of $\cos t$ or $\cos(\frac{1}{2}\pi - t)$.

14. Express each of the following in terms of $\sin t$ or $\sin(\frac{1}{2}\pi - t)$: (a) $\sin(\pi - t)$; (b) $\cos(\pi - t)$; (c) $\sin(\pi + t)$; (d) $\cos(\pi + t)$.

15. Express the function values of Exercise 14 in terms of $\cos t$ or $\cos(\frac{1}{2}\pi - t)$.

16. Find all values of t for which (a) $\sin t = 0$, and (b) $\cos t = 0$.

17. Find all values of t for which (a) $\sin t = 1$, and (b) $\cos t = 1$.

18. Find all values of t for which (a) $\sin t = -1$, and (b) $\cos t = -1$.

19. Find all values of t for which (a) $\sin t = \frac{1}{2}$, and (b) $\cos t = \frac{1}{2}$.

20. Find all values of t for which (a) $\sin t = -\frac{1}{2}\sqrt{2}$, and (b) $\cos t = -\frac{1}{2}\sqrt{2}$.

21. Suppose f is a function which is periodic with period 2π, and whose domain is the set of all real numbers. Prove that f is also periodic with period -2π.

22. Prove that the function of Exercise 21 is periodic with period $2\pi n$ for every integer n. (HINT: Use mathematical induction.)

23. Prove that if f is defined by $f(x) = x - [\![x]\!]$, then f is periodic. What is the smallest positive period of f?

10.2 DERIVATIVES OF THE SINE AND COSINE FUNCTIONS

Before the formula for the derivative of the sine function can be derived we need to know the value of

$$\lim_{t \to 0} \frac{\sin t}{t}$$

Letting $f(t) = (\sin t)/t$, we see that $f(0)$ is not defined. However, we prove that $\lim_{t \to 0} f(t)$ exists and is equal to 1.

10.2.1 Theorem

$$\lim_{t \to 0} \frac{\sin t}{t} = 1$$

PROOF: We first assume that $0 < t < \frac{1}{2}\pi$.

Refer to Fig. 10.2.1, which shows the unit circle $x^2 + y^2 = 1$ and the shaded sector BOP, where B is the point $(1, 0)$ and P is the point $(\cos t, \sin t)$. The area of a circular sector of radius r and central angle of radian measure t is determined by $\frac{1}{2}r^2 t$; and so if S square units is the area of sector BOP,

$$S = \frac{1}{2}t \tag{1}$$

Figure 10.2.1

Consider now the triangle BOP, and let K_1 square units be the area of this triangle. Hence,

$$K_1 = \tfrac{1}{2}|\overline{AP}| \cdot |\overline{OB}| = \tfrac{1}{2}(\sin t) \cdot (1) = \tfrac{1}{2}\sin t \qquad (2)$$

The line through the points $O(0,0)$ and $P(\cos t, \sin t)$ has slope $\sin t/\cos t$; therefore, its equation is

$$y = \frac{\sin t}{\cos t}\, x$$

This line intersects the line $x = 1$ at the point $(1, \sin t/\cos t)$, which is the point T in the figure.

Letting K_2 square units be the area of right triangle BOT, we have

$$K_2 = \frac{1}{2}|\overline{BT}| \cdot |\overline{OB}| = \frac{1}{2} \cdot \frac{\sin t}{\cos t} \cdot 1 = \frac{1}{2} \cdot \frac{\sin t}{\cos t} \qquad (3)$$

From Fig. 10.2.1 we see that

$$K_1 < S < K_2 \qquad (4)$$

Substituting from Eqs. (1), (2), and (3) in inequality (4), we get

$$\frac{1}{2}\sin t < \frac{1}{2}t < \frac{1}{2} \cdot \frac{\sin t}{\cos t}$$

Multiplying each member of the above inequality by $2/\sin t$, which is positive because $0 < t < \tfrac{1}{2}\pi$, we obtain

$$1 < \frac{t}{\sin t} < \frac{1}{\cos t}$$

Taking the reciprocal of each member of the above inequality and reversing the direction of the inequality signs, we get

$$\cos t < \frac{\sin t}{t} < 1 \qquad (5)$$

From the right-hand inequality in the above we have

$$\sin t < t \qquad (6)$$

and from formula (19) in Sec. 10.1 we have

$$\frac{1 - \cos t}{2} = \sin^2 \frac{1}{2}t \qquad (7)$$

Replacing t by $\tfrac{1}{2}t$ in inequality (6) and squaring, we obtain

$$\sin^2 \tfrac{1}{2}t < \tfrac{1}{4}t^2 \qquad (8)$$

Thus, from (7) and (8) it follows that

$$\frac{1 - \cos t}{2} < \frac{t^2}{4}$$

which is equivalent to

$$1 - \tfrac{1}{2}t^2 < \cos t \tag{9}$$

From (5) and (9) and because $0 < t < \tfrac{1}{2}\pi$, we have

$$1 - \frac{1}{2}t^2 < \frac{\sin t}{t} < 1 \qquad \text{if } 0 < t < \frac{1}{2}\pi \tag{10}$$

If $-\tfrac{1}{2}\pi < t < 0$, then $0 < -t < \tfrac{1}{2}\pi$; and so from (10) we have

$$1 - \frac{1}{2}(-t)^2 < \frac{\sin(-t)}{-t} < 1 \qquad \text{if } -\frac{1}{2}\pi < t < 0$$

But $\sin(-t) = -\sin t$; thus, the above can be written as

$$1 - \frac{1}{2}t^2 < \frac{\sin t}{t} < 1 \qquad \text{if } -\frac{1}{2}\pi < t < 0 \tag{11}$$

From (10) and (11) we conclude that

$$1 - \frac{1}{2}t^2 < \frac{\sin t}{t} < 1 \qquad \text{if } -\frac{1}{2}\pi < t < \frac{1}{2}\pi \text{ and } t \neq 0 \tag{12}$$

Because $\lim_{t \to 0} (1 - \tfrac{1}{2}t^2) = 1$ and $\lim_{t \to 0} 1 = 1$, it follows from (12) and the squeeze theorem (4.3.5) that

$$\lim_{t \to 0} \frac{\sin t}{t} = 1$$

∎

EXAMPLE 1: Find

$$\lim_{x \to 0} \frac{\sin 3x}{\sin 5x}$$

if it exists.

SOLUTION: We wish to write the quotient $\sin 3x / \sin 5x$ in such a way that we can apply Theorem 10.2.1. We have, if $x \neq 0$,

$$\frac{\sin 3x}{\sin 5x} = \frac{3\left(\dfrac{\sin 3x}{3x}\right)}{5\left(\dfrac{\sin 5x}{5x}\right)}$$

As x approaches zero, so do $3x$ and $5x$. Hence, we have

$$\lim_{x \to 0} \frac{\sin 3x}{3x} = \lim_{3x \to 0} \frac{\sin 3x}{3x} = 1$$

and

$$\lim_{x \to 0} \frac{\sin 5x}{5x} = \lim_{5x \to 0} \frac{\sin 5x}{5x} = 1$$

Therefore,

$$\lim_{x \to 0} \frac{\sin 3x}{\sin 5x} = \frac{3 \lim\limits_{x \to 0} \left(\dfrac{\sin 3x}{3x}\right)}{5 \lim\limits_{x \to 0} \left(\dfrac{\sin 5x}{5x}\right)} = \frac{3 \cdot 1}{5 \cdot 1} = \frac{3}{5}$$

From Theorem 10.2.1 we can prove that the sine function and the cosine function are continuous at 0.

10.2.2 Theorem   The sine function is continuous at 0.

PROOF: We show that the three conditions necessary for continuity at a number are satisfied.

(i) $\sin 0 = 0$.

(ii) $\lim\limits_{t \to 0} \sin t = \lim\limits_{t \to 0} \dfrac{\sin t}{t} \cdot t = \lim\limits_{t \to 0} \dfrac{\sin t}{t} \cdot \lim\limits_{t \to 0} t = 1 \cdot 0 = 0$.

(iii) $\lim\limits_{t \to 0} \sin t = \sin 0$.

Therefore, the sine function is continuous at 0.   ■

10.2.3 Theorem   The cosine function is continuous at 0.

PROOF:

(i) $\cos 0 = 1$.

(ii) $\lim\limits_{t \to 0} \cos t = \lim\limits_{t \to 0} \sqrt{1 - \sin^2 t}$

$$= \sqrt{\lim\limits_{t \to 0} (1 - \sin^2 t)} = \sqrt{1 - 0} = 1.$$

NOTE: We can replace $\cos t$ by $\sqrt{1 - \sin^2 t}$ since $\cos t > 0$ when $0 < t < \tfrac{1}{2}\pi$ and when $-\tfrac{1}{2}\pi < t < 0$.

(iii) $\lim\limits_{t \to 0} \cos t = \cos 0$.

Therefore, the cosine function is continuous at 0.   ■

The limit in the following theorem is also important. It follows from the previous three theorems and limit theorems.

10.2.4 Theorem $\lim\limits_{t \to 0} \dfrac{1 - \cos t}{t} = 0$

PROOF:

$$\lim\limits_{t \to 0} \dfrac{1 - \cos t}{t} = \lim\limits_{t \to 0} \dfrac{(1 - \cos t)(1 + \cos t)}{t(1 + \cos t)}$$

$$= \lim\limits_{t \to 0} \dfrac{(1 - \cos^2 t)}{t(1 + \cos t)}$$

$$= \lim\limits_{t \to 0} \dfrac{\sin^2 t}{t(1 + \cos t)}$$

$$= \lim_{t \to 0} \frac{\sin t}{t} \cdot \lim_{t \to 0} \frac{\sin t}{1 + \cos t}$$

By Theorem 10.2.1, $\lim_{t \to 0} (\sin t / t) = 1$, and because the sine and cosine functions are continuous at 0, it follows that $\lim_{t \to 0} [\sin t / (1 + \cos t)] = 0/(1 + 1) = 0$. Therefore,

$$\lim_{t \to 0} \frac{1 - \cos t}{t} = 0$$
∎

We now show that the sine function has a derivative. Let f be the function defined by

$$f(x) = \sin x$$

From the definition of a derivative, we have

$$f'(x) = \lim_{\Delta x \to 0} \frac{f(x + \Delta x) - f(x)}{\Delta x}$$

$$= \lim_{\Delta x \to 0} \frac{\sin(x + \Delta x) - \sin x}{\Delta x}$$

$$= \lim_{\Delta x \to 0} \frac{\sin x \cos(\Delta x) + \cos x \sin(\Delta x) - \sin x}{\Delta x}$$

$$= \lim_{\Delta x \to 0} \frac{\sin x [\cos(\Delta x) - 1]}{\Delta x} + \lim_{\Delta x \to 0} \frac{\cos x \sin(\Delta x)}{\Delta x}$$

$$= - \lim_{\Delta x \to 0} \frac{1 - \cos(\Delta x)}{\Delta x} \left(\lim_{\Delta x \to 0} \sin x \right) + \left(\lim_{\Delta x \to 0} \cos x \right) \lim_{\Delta x \to 0} \frac{\sin(\Delta x)}{\Delta x}$$

$$= -0 \cdot \sin x + \cos x \cdot 1 \quad \text{(by Theorems 10.2.4 and 10.2.1)}$$

$$= \cos x$$

Therefore, we have the formula

$$D_x(\sin x) = \cos x \tag{13}$$

If u is a differentiable function of x, we have from (13) and the chain rule

$$D_x(\sin u) = \cos u \, D_x u \tag{14}$$

The derivative of the cosine function is obtained by making use of (13) and the following identities:

$$\cos x = \sin(\tfrac{1}{2}\pi - x) \quad \text{and} \quad \sin x = \cos(\tfrac{1}{2}\pi - x)$$

$$D_x(\cos x) = D_x[\sin(\tfrac{1}{2}\pi - x)]$$

$$= \cos(\tfrac{1}{2}\pi - x) \cdot D_x(\tfrac{1}{2}\pi - x) = \sin x(-1)$$

Therefore,

$$D_x(\cos x) = -\sin x \tag{15}$$

So if u is a differentiable function of x, it follows from (15) and the chain rule that

$$D_x(\cos u) = -\sin u \, D_x u \tag{16}$$

EXAMPLE 2: Given

$$f(x) = \frac{\sin x}{1 - 2 \cos x}$$

find $f'(x)$.

SOLUTION:

$$f'(x) = \frac{(1 - 2 \cos x) \, D_x(\sin x) - \sin x \cdot D_x(1 - 2 \cos x)}{(1 - 2 \cos x)^2}$$

$$= \frac{(1 - 2 \cos x)(\cos x) - \sin x(2 \sin x)}{(1 - 2 \cos x)^2}$$

$$= \frac{\cos x - 2(\cos^2 x + \sin^2 x)}{(1 - 2 \cos x)^2}$$

$$= \frac{\cos x - 2}{(1 - 2 \cos x)^2}$$

EXAMPLE 3: Given

$$y = (1 + \cos 3x^2)^4$$

find dy/dx.

SOLUTION:

$$\frac{dy}{dx} = 4(1 + \cos 3x^2)^3(-\sin 3x^2)(6x)$$

$$= -24x \sin 3x^2(1 + \cos 3x^2)^3$$

EXAMPLE 4: Given

$$x \cos y + y \cos x = 1$$

find $D_x y$.

SOLUTION: Differentiating implicitly with respect to x, we get

$$1 \cdot \cos y + x(-\sin y) \, D_x y + D_x y(\cos x) + y(-\sin x) = 0$$

$$D_x y(\cos x - x \sin y) = y \sin x - \cos y$$

$$D_x y = \frac{y \sin x - \cos y}{\cos x - x \sin y}$$

Geometric problems involving absolute extrema occasionally are more easily solved by using trigonometric functions. The following example illustrates this fact.

EXAMPLE 5:   A right-circular cylinder is to be inscribed in a sphere of given radius. Find the ratio of the altitude to the base radius of the cylinder having the largest lateral surface area.

Figure 10.2.2

SOLUTION: Refer to Fig. 10.2.2. The measure of the constant radius of the sphere is taken as a.

Let $\theta =$ the number of radians in the angle at the center of the sphere subtended by the radius of the cylinder;

$r =$ the number of inches in the radius of the cylinder;

$h =$ the number of inches in the altitude of the cylinder;

$S =$ the number of square inches in the lateral surface area of the cylinder.

From Fig. 10.2.2, we see that

$$r = a \sin \theta \quad \text{and} \quad h = 2a \cos \theta$$

Because $S = 2\pi rh$, we have

$$S = 2\pi(a \sin \theta)(2a \cos \theta) = 2\pi a^2(2 \sin \theta \cos \theta) = 2\pi a^2 \sin 2\theta$$

So

$$D_\theta S = 4\pi a^2 \cos 2\theta \quad \text{and} \quad D_\theta^2 S = -8\pi a^2 \sin 2\theta$$

Setting $D_\theta S = 0$, we get

$$\cos 2\theta = 0$$

Because $0 < \theta < \frac{1}{2}\pi$,

$$\theta = \frac{1}{4}\pi$$

We apply the second derivative test for relative extrema and summarize the results in Table 10.2.1.

Table 10.2.1

	$D_\theta S$	$D_\theta^2 S$	Conclusion
$\theta = \frac{1}{4}\pi$	0	$-$	S has a relative maximum value

Because the domain of θ is the open interval $(0, \frac{1}{2}\pi)$, the relative maximum value of S is the absolute maximum value of S.

When $\theta = \frac{1}{4}\pi$, $r = \frac{1}{2}\sqrt{2}\,a$, and $h = \sqrt{2}\,a$. So for the cylinder having the largest lateral surface area, $h/r = 2$.

Because $D_x(\sin x) = \cos x$ and $\cos x$ exists for all values of x, the sine function is differentiable everywhere and therefore continuous everywhere. Similarly, the cosine function is differentiable and continuous everywhere.

We now discuss the graph of the sine function. Let

$$f(x) = \sin x$$

Then $f'(x) = \cos x$ and $f''(x) = -\sin x$. To determine the relative extrema, we set $f'(x) = 0$ and get $x = \frac{1}{2}\pi + n\pi$, where $n = 0, \pm 1, \pm 2, \ldots$. If n is an even integer, then $f''(\frac{1}{2}\pi + n\pi) = -\sin(\frac{1}{2}\pi + n\pi) = -\sin \frac{1}{2}\pi = -1$; and if n is an odd integer, $f''(\frac{1}{2}\pi + n\pi) = -\sin(\frac{1}{2}\pi + n\pi) = -\sin \frac{3}{2}\pi = 1$. Therefore, f has relative extrema when $x = \frac{1}{2}\pi + n\pi$; and if n is an even integer, f has a relative maximum value; and if n is an odd integer, f has a relative minimum value.

To determine the points of inflection of the graph, we set $f''(x) = 0$ and obtain $x = n\pi$, where $n = 0, \pm 1, \pm 2, \ldots$. Because $f''(x)$ changes sign at each of these values of x, the graph has a point of inflection at each point having these abscissas. At each point of inflection $f'(x) = \cos n\pi = \pm 1$. Therefore, the slopes of the inflectional tangents are either $+1$ or -1. Furthermore, because $\sin(x + 2\pi) = \sin x$, the sine function is periodic and has the period 2π. The absolute maximum value of the sine function is 1, and the absolute minimum value is -1. The graph intersects the x axis at those points where $\sin x = 0$, that is, at the points where $x = n\pi$ (n is any integer).

From the information obtained above, we draw a sketch of the graph of the sine function; it is shown in Fig. 10.2.3.

$y = \sin x$

Figure 10.2.3

To obtain the graph of the cosine function, we use the identity

$$\cos x = \sin(\tfrac{1}{2}\pi + x)$$

which follows from formula (12) of Sec. 10.1. Hence, the graph of the cosine function is obtained from the graph of the sine function by translating the y axis $\frac{1}{2}\pi$ units to the right (see Fig. 10.2.4).

$y = \cos x$

Figure 10.2.4

Exercises 10.2

In Exercises 1 through 8, evaluate the limit, if it exists.

1. $\lim\limits_{x \to 0} \dfrac{\sin 4x}{x}$

2. $\lim\limits_{x \to 0} \dfrac{x}{\cos x}$

3. $\lim\limits_{x \to 0} \dfrac{\sin 9x}{\sin 7x}$

4. $\lim\limits_{x \to \pi/2} \dfrac{\frac{1}{2}\pi - x}{\cos x}$

5. $\lim\limits_{x \to 0} \dfrac{1 - \cos x}{x^2}$

6. $\lim\limits_{x \to 0} \dfrac{1 - \cos x}{\sin x}$

7. $\lim\limits_{x \to 0} \dfrac{3x^2}{1 - \cos^2 \frac{1}{2}x}$

8. $\lim\limits_{x \to 0} \dfrac{1 - \cos^2 x}{2x^2}$

In Exercises 9 through 24, find the derivative of the given function.

9. $f(x) = 3 \sin 2x$

10. $f(x) = \cos(3x^2 + 1)$

11. $g(x) = \sin 3x \cos 3x$

12. $f(t) = \cos t^2$

13. $h(t) = 2 \cos \sqrt{t}$

14. $g(x) = \sqrt{\sin x}$

15. $f(x) = \ln \sin 5x$

16. $F(x) = \sin(\ln x)$

17. $h(x) = \dfrac{\sin x}{2 + \cos x}$

18. $g(t) = \sin(\cos t)$

19. $g(x) = 2 \cos x \sin 2x - \sin x \cos 2x$

20. $h(y) = y^3 - y^2 \cos y + 2y \sin y + 2 \cos y$

21. $f(x) = (\sin x^2)^{4x}$

22. $g(x) = x^{\sin x}$

23. $h(x) = (\cos x)^{\sin x}$

24. $f(x) = (\ln \sin x)^{e^x}$

In Exercises 25 and 26, use logarithmic differentiation to find dy/dx.

25. $y = \dfrac{\sin x \sqrt{1 + \cos^2 x}}{\cos^3 x}$

26. $y = \dfrac{\sin^3 x}{\sqrt{1 - 3 \cos x}}$

In Exercises 27 and 28, find $D_x y$ by implicit differentiation.

27. $y = \cos(x - y)$

28. $\cos(x + y) = y \sin x$

In Exercises 29 through 34, draw a sketch of the graph of the function defined by the given equations.

29. $f(x) = \sin 2x$

30. $f(x) = 2 \sin 3x$

31. $f(x) = |\cos 3x|$

32. $f(x) = \frac{1}{2}(1 - \cos x)$

33. $f(x) = \begin{cases} \sin x & \text{if } 0 \le x < \frac{1}{2}\pi \\ \sin(x - \frac{1}{2}\pi) & \text{if } \frac{1}{2}\pi \le x \le \pi \end{cases}$

34. $f(x) = \begin{cases} \cos x & \text{if } -\pi \le x \le 0 \\ \cos(\pi - x) & \text{if } 0 < x \le \pi \end{cases}$

35. If a ladder of length 30 ft which is leaning against a wall has its upper end sliding down the wall at the rate of $\frac{1}{2}$ ft/sec, what is the rate of change of the measure of the acute angle made by the ladder with the ground when the upper end is 18 ft above the ground?

36. The cross section of a trough has the shape of an inverted isosceles triangle. If the lengths of the equal sides are 15 in., find the size of the vertex angle that will give maximum capacity for the trough.

37. If a body of weight W lb is dragged along a horizontal floor by means of a force of magnitude F lb and directed at an angle of θ radians with the plane of the floor, then F is given by the equation

$$F = \frac{kW}{k \sin \theta + \cos \theta}$$

where k is a constant and is called the coefficient of friction. Find $\cos \theta$ when F is least.

38. Find the altitude of the right-circular cone of largest possible volume that can be inscribed in a sphere of radius a units. Let 2θ be the radian measure of the vertical angle of the cone.

39. A particle moving in a straight line is said to have *simple harmonic motion* if the measure of its acceleration is always proportional to the measure of its displacement from a fixed point on the line and its acceleration and displacement are oppositely directed. Show that the straight-line motion of a particle described by $s = A \sin 2\pi kt + B \cos 2\pi kt$, where s ft is the directed distance of the particle from the origin at t sec, and A, B, and k are constants, is a simple harmonic motion.

40. Show that if a particle is moving along a straight line according to the equation of motion $s = a \cos(kt + \theta)$ (where a, k, and θ are constants) and s ft is the directed distance of the particle from the origin at t sec, then the motion is simple harmonic. (See Exercise 39.)

41. Given $f(x) = x \sin(\pi/x)$, prove that f has an infinite number of relative extrema.

42. If the domain of the function of Exercise 41 is the interval $(0, 1]$, how should $f(0)$ be defined so that f is continuous on the closed interval $[0, 1]$?

10.3 INTEGRALS INVOLVING POWERS OF SINE AND COSINE

The formulas for the indefinite integral of the sine and cosine functions follow immediately from the corresponding formulas for differentiation.

$$\int \sin u \, du = -\cos u + C \tag{1}$$

PROOF: $D_u(-\cos u) = \sin u.$

$$\int \cos u \, du = \sin u + C \tag{2}$$

PROOF: $D_u(\sin u) = \cos u.$

EXAMPLE 1: Find

$$\int \frac{\cos(\ln x)}{x} \, dx$$

SOLUTION: Let $u = \ln x$. Then $du = dx/x$; so we have

$$\int \frac{\cos(\ln x)}{x} \, dx = \int \cos u \, du$$

$$= \sin u + C$$

$$= \sin(\ln x) + C$$

EXAMPLE 2: Find

$$\int \frac{\sin x}{1 - \cos x} \, dx$$

SOLUTION: Let $u = 1 - \cos x$. Then $du = \sin x \, dx$; so

$$\int \frac{\sin x \, dx}{1 - \cos x} = \int \frac{du}{u}$$

$$= \ln |u| + C$$

$$= \ln |1 - \cos x| + C$$

EXAMPLE 3:   Find

$$\int_0^\pi (1 + \sin x)\, dx$$

SOLUTION:

$$
\begin{aligned}
\int_0^\pi (1 + \sin x)\, dx &= x - \cos x \Big]_0^\pi \\
&= \pi - \cos \pi - (0 - \cos 0) \\
&= \pi + 1 - (0 - 1) \\
&= \pi + 2
\end{aligned}
$$

We now consider four cases of integrals involving powers of sine and cosine. The method used in each case is shown by an illustration.

Case 1: $\int \sin^n u\, du$ or $\int \cos^n u\, du$, where n is an odd integer.

● ILLUSTRATION 1:

$$
\begin{aligned}
\int \cos^3 x\, dx &= \int \cos^2 x\, (\cos x\, dx) \\
&= \int (1 - \sin^2 x)(\cos x\, dx)
\end{aligned}
$$

So

$$\int \cos^3 x\, dx = \int \cos x\, dx - \int \sin^2 x \cos x\, dx \tag{3}$$

To evaluate the second integral on the right side of (3), we let $u = \sin x$; then $du = \cos x\, dx$. This gives

$$
\begin{aligned}
\int \sin^2 x\, (\cos x\, dx) &= \int u^2\, du \\
&= \tfrac{1}{3} u^3 + C_1 \\
&= \tfrac{1}{3} \sin^3 x + C_1
\end{aligned}
$$

Because the first integral on the right side of (3) is $\sin x + C_2$, we have

$$\int \cos^3 x\, dx = \sin x - \tfrac{1}{3} \sin^3 x + C \qquad ●$$

EXAMPLE 4:   Find

$$\int \sin^5 x\, dx$$

SOLUTION:

$$
\begin{aligned}
\int \sin^5 x\, dx &= \int (\sin^2 x)^2 \sin x\, dx \\
&= \int (1 - \cos^2 x)^2 \sin x\, dx \\
&= \int (1 - 2\cos^2 x + \cos^4 x) \sin x\, dx
\end{aligned}
$$

Therefore,

$$\int \sin^5 x\, dx = \int \sin x\, dx - 2 \int \cos^2 x \sin x\, dx + \int \cos^4 x(\sin x\, dx) \quad (4)$$

To evaluate the second and third integrals in (4), we let $u = \cos x$ and $du = -\sin x\, dx$; and we obtain

$$\int \sin^5 x\, dx = -\cos x + 2 \int u^2\, du - \int u^4\, du$$

$$= -\cos x + \tfrac{2}{3}u^3 - \tfrac{1}{5}u^5 + C$$

$$= -\cos x + \tfrac{2}{3}\cos^3 x - \tfrac{1}{5}\cos^5 x + C$$

Case 2: $\int \sin^n u\, du$ and $\int \cos^n u\, du$, where n is an even integer.

The method used in Case 1 does not work in this case. We use the following formulas which are obtained from formulas (19) and (18) of Sec. 10.1 by substituting $2x$ for t.

$$\sin^2 x = \frac{1 - \cos 2x}{2}$$

$$\cos^2 x = \frac{1 + \cos 2x}{2}$$

• ILLUSTRATION 2:

$$\int \sin^2 x\, dx = \int \frac{1 - \cos 2x}{2}\, dx$$

$$= \tfrac{1}{2}x - \tfrac{1}{4}\sin 2x + C \qquad\qquad •$$

EXAMPLE 5: Find

$$\int \cos^4 x\, dx$$

SOLUTION:

$$\int \cos^4 x\, dx = \int (\cos^2 x)^2\, dx = \int \left(\frac{1 + \cos 2x}{2}\right)^2 dx$$

$$= \frac{1}{4}\int dx + \frac{1}{2}\int \cos 2x\, dx + \frac{1}{4}\int \cos^2 2x\, dx$$

$$= \frac{1}{4}x + \frac{1}{4}\sin 2x + \frac{1}{4}\int \frac{1 + \cos 4x}{2}\, dx$$

$$= \tfrac{1}{4}x + \tfrac{1}{4}\sin 2x + \tfrac{1}{8}x + \tfrac{1}{32}\sin 4x + C$$

$$= \tfrac{3}{8}x + \tfrac{1}{4}\sin 2x + \tfrac{1}{32}\sin 4x + C$$

Case 3: $\int \sin^n x \cos^m x\, dx$, where at least one of the exponents is odd.

The solution of this case is similar to the method used for Case 1.

• ILLUSTRATION 3:

$$\int \sin^3 x \cos^4 x\, dx = \int \sin^2 x \cos^4 x(\sin x\, dx)$$

$$= \int (1 - \cos^2 x) \cos^4 x (\sin x \, dx)$$

$$= \int \cos^4 x \sin x \, dx - \int \cos^6 x \sin x \, dx$$

$$= -\tfrac{1}{5} \cos^5 x + \tfrac{1}{7} \cos^7 x + C$$ •

Case 4: $\int \sin^n x \cos^m x \, dx$, where both m and n are even. The solution of this case is similar to the method used in Case 2.

• ILLUSTRATION 4:

$$\int \sin^2 x \cos^4 x \, dx = \int \left(\frac{1 - \cos 2x}{2}\right) \left(\frac{1 + \cos 2x}{2}\right)^2 dx$$

$$= \frac{1}{8} \int dx + \frac{1}{8} \int \cos 2x \, dx$$

$$- \frac{1}{8} \int \cos^2 2x \, dx - \frac{1}{8} \int \cos^3 2x \, dx$$

$$= \frac{1}{8} x + \frac{1}{16} \sin 2x - \frac{1}{8}\int \frac{1 + \cos 4x}{2} dx$$

$$- \frac{1}{8} \int (1 - \sin^2 2x) \cos 2x \, dx$$

$$= \frac{x}{8} + \frac{\sin 2x}{16} - \frac{x}{16} - \frac{\sin 4x}{64}$$

$$- \frac{1}{8} \int \cos 2x \, dx + \frac{1}{8} \int \sin^2 2x \cos 2x \, dx$$

$$= \frac{x}{16} + \frac{\sin 2x}{16} - \frac{\sin 4x}{64} - \frac{\sin 2x}{16} + \frac{\sin^3 2x}{48} + C$$

$$= \frac{x}{16} + \frac{\sin^3 2x}{48} - \frac{\sin 4x}{64} + C$$ •

EXAMPLE 6:   Find

$$\int \sin^4 x \cos^4 x \, dx$$

SOLUTION: If we make use of the formula $\sin x \cos x = \tfrac{1}{2} \sin 2x$, we have,

$$\int \sin^4 x \cos^4 x \, dx = \frac{1}{16} \int \sin^4 2x \, dx$$

$$= \frac{1}{16} \int \left(\frac{1 - \cos 4x}{2}\right)^2 dx$$

$$= \frac{1}{64} \int dx - \frac{1}{32} \int \cos 4x \, dx + \frac{1}{64} \int \cos^2 4x \, dx$$

$$= \frac{x}{64} - \frac{\sin 4x}{128} + \frac{1}{64} \int \frac{1 + \cos 8x}{2} dx$$

$$= \frac{x}{64} - \frac{\sin 4x}{128} + \frac{x}{128} + \frac{\sin 8x}{1024} + C$$

$$= \frac{3x}{128} - \frac{\sin 4x}{128} + \frac{\sin 8x}{1024} + C$$

The following example illustrates another type of integral involving a product of a sine and a cosine.

EXAMPLE 7:   Find

$$\int \sin 3x \cos 2x \, dx$$

SOLUTION: We use formula (22) of Sec. 10.1, which is

$$\sin a \cos b = \tfrac{1}{2} \sin(a - b) + \tfrac{1}{2} \sin(a + b)$$

So

$$\int \sin 3x \cos 2x \, dx = \int \left[\tfrac{1}{2} \sin x + \tfrac{1}{2} \sin 5x \right] dx$$

$$= \frac{1}{2} \int \sin x \, dx + \frac{1}{2} \int \sin 5x \, dx$$

$$= -\tfrac{1}{2} \cos x - \tfrac{1}{10} \cos 5x + C$$

Exercises 10.3

In Exercises 1 through 22, evaluate the indefinite integral.

1. $\int (3 \sin x + 2 \cos x) \, dx$

2. $\int (\sin 3x + \cos 2x) \, dx$

3. $\int \sin x \, e^{\cos x} \, dx$

4. $\int \frac{\cos x}{2 + \sin x} \, dx$

5. $\int \sin x \cdot \sin(\cos x) \, dx$

6. $\int \frac{\cos 3\sqrt{x}}{\sqrt{x}} \, dx$

7. $\int \sin^3 x \, dx$

8. $\int \cos^5 x \, dx$

9. $\int \sin^4 x \, dx$

10. $\int \cos^6 x \, dx$

11. $\int \cos^2 \tfrac{1}{2}x \, dx$

12. $\int \sin^3 x \cos^3 x \, dx$

13. $\int \sin^5 x \cos^2 x \, dx$

14. $\int \sin^2 2t \cos^4 2t \, dt$

15. $\int \sin^2 3t \cos^2 3t \, dt$

16. $\int \sqrt{\cos z} \, \sin^3 z \, dz$

17. $\int \frac{\cos^3 3x}{\sqrt{\sin 3x}} \, dx$

18. $\int \sin 2x \cos 4x \, dx$

19. $\int \cos 4x \cos 3x \, dx$

21. $\int (\sin 3x - \sin 2x)^2 \, dx$

22. $\int \sin x \sin 3x \sin 5x \, dx$

In Exercises 23 through 28, evaluate the definite integral.

23. $\int_0^{\pi/2} \sin 2x \, dx$

24. $\int_{\ln \pi}^2 e^x \sin e^x \, dx$

25. $\int_0^{\pi/2} \cos^3 x \, dx$

26. $\displaystyle\int_0^1 \sin^4 \tfrac{1}{2}\pi x\, dx$
   27. $\displaystyle\int_0^1 \sin^2 \pi x \cos^2 \pi x\, dx$
   28. $\displaystyle\int_0^{\pi/6} \sin 2x \cos 4x\, dx$

29. If n is any positive integer, prove that $\displaystyle\int_0^\pi \sin^2 nx\, dx = \tfrac{1}{2}\pi$.

30. If n is a positive odd integer, prove that $\displaystyle\int_0^\pi \cos^n x\, dx = 0$.

In Exercises 31 through 33, m and n are any integers except zero; show that the given formula is true.

31. $\displaystyle\int_{-1}^1 \cos n\pi x \cos m\pi x\, dx = \begin{cases} 0 & \text{if } m \ne n \\ 1 & \text{if } m = n \end{cases}$
   32. $\displaystyle\int_{-1}^1 \cos n\pi x \sin m\pi x\, dx = 0$

33. $\displaystyle\int_{-1}^1 \sin n\pi x \sin m\pi x\, dx = \begin{cases} 0 & \text{if } m \ne n \\ 1 & \text{if } m = n \end{cases}$

34. If q coulombs is the charge of electricity received by a condenser from an electric circuit of i amperes at t sec, then $i = D_t q$. Suppose $i = 5 \sin 60t$ and $q = 0$ when $t = \tfrac{1}{2}\pi$, find the greatest positive charge on the condenser.

35. In an electric circuit suppose that E volts is the electromotive force at t sec and $E = 2 \sin 3t$. Find the average value of E from $t = 0$ to $t = \tfrac{1}{3}\pi$.

36. For the electric circuit of Exercise 35, find the square root of the average value of E^2 from $t = 0$ to $t = \tfrac{1}{3}\pi$.

37. Find the area of the region bounded by one arch of the sine curve.

38. Find the volume of the solid of revolution generated if the region of Exercise 37 is revolved about the x axis.

39. Find the volume of the solid generated if the region bounded by the curve $y = \sin^2 x$ and the x axis from $x = 0$ to $x = \pi$ is revolved about the line $y = 1$.

40. Find the area of the region bounded by the two curves $y = \sin x$ and $y = \cos x$ between two consecutive points of intersection.

10.4 THE TANGENT, COTANGENT, SECANT, AND COSECANT FUNCTIONS

The other trigonometric functions, tangent, cotangent, secant, and cosecant, are defined in terms of the sine and cosine.

10.4.1 Definition   The *tangent* and *secant* functions are defined by

$$\tan x = \frac{\sin x}{\cos x} \qquad \sec x = \frac{1}{\cos x}$$

for all real numbers x for which $\cos x \ne 0$.

The *cotangent* and *cosecant* functions are defined by

$$\cot x = \frac{\cos x}{\sin x} \qquad \csc x = \frac{1}{\sin x}$$

for all real numbers x for which $\sin x \ne 0$.

The tangent and secant functions are not defined when $\cos x = 0$, which occurs when x is $\tfrac{1}{2}\pi, \tfrac{3}{2}\pi$, or $\tfrac{1}{2}\pi + n\pi$, where n is any positive or negative integer, or zero. Therefore, the domain of the tangent and secant functions is the set of all real numbers except numbers of the form $\frac{1}{2}\pi + n\pi$, where n is any integer. Similarly, because $\cot x$ and $\csc x$ are not defined when $\sin x = 0$, the domain of the cotangent and cosecant functions is the set of all real numbers except numbers of the form $n\pi$, where n is any integer.

By Theorem 2.6.1(iv), if the functions f and g are continuous at the number a, then f/g is continuous at a, provided that $g(a) \neq 0$. Because the sine and cosine functions are continuous at all real numbers, it follows that the tangent, cotangent, secant, and cosecant functions are continuous at all numbers in their domain.

By using the identity

$$\cos^2 x + \sin^2 x = 1 \tag{1}$$

and Definition 10.4.1, we obtain two other important identities. If on both sides of (1) we divide by $\cos^2 x$, when $\cos x \neq 0$, we get

$$\frac{\cos^2 x}{\cos^2 x} + \frac{\sin^2 x}{\cos^2 x} = \frac{1}{\cos^2 x}$$

and because $\sin x/\cos x = \tan x$ and $1/\cos x = \sec x$, we have the identity

$$1 + \tan^2 x = \sec^2 x \tag{2}$$

By dividing on both sides of (1) by $\sin^2 x$ when $\sin x \neq 0$, we obtain in a similar way the identity

$$\cot^2 x + 1 = \csc^2 x \tag{3}$$

Three other important formulas follow immediately from Definition 10.4.1. They are

$$\sin x \csc x = 1 \tag{4}$$

$$\cos x \sec x = 1 \tag{5}$$

and

$$\tan x \cot x = 1 \tag{6}$$

Formulas (4), (5), and (6) are valid for all values of x for which the functions are defined, and therefore they are identities.

Another formula that we need is one that expresses the tangent of the difference of two numbers in terms of the tangents of the two numbers. By using formulas (13) and (10) from Sec. 10.1, we have

$$\tan(a - b) = \frac{\sin(a - b)}{\cos(a - b)} = \frac{\sin a \cos b - \cos a \sin b}{\cos a \cos b + \sin a \sin b}$$

Dividing both the numerator and denominator by $\cos a \cos b$, we get

$$\tan(a - b) = \frac{\dfrac{\sin a \cos b}{\cos a \cos b} - \dfrac{\cos a \sin b}{\cos a \cos b}}{\dfrac{\cos a \cos b}{\cos a \cos b} + \dfrac{\sin a \sin b}{\cos a \cos b}} = \frac{\dfrac{\sin a}{\cos a} - \dfrac{\sin b}{\cos b}}{1 + \dfrac{\sin a}{\cos a}\dfrac{\sin b}{\cos b}}$$

Therefore, we have the identity

$$\tan(a - b) = \frac{\tan a - \tan b}{1 + \tan a \tan b} \tag{7}$$

Taking $a = 0$ in formula (7) gives

$$\tan(0 - b) = \frac{\tan 0 - \tan b}{1 + \tan 0 \tan b}$$

Because $\tan 0 = 0$, we have from the above equation

$$\tan(-b) = -\tan b \tag{8}$$

Therefore, the tangent is an odd function.

Taking $b = -b$ in formula (7) gives

$$\tan(a - (-b)) = \frac{\tan a - \tan(-b)}{1 + \tan a \tan(-b)}$$

and replacing $\tan(-b)$ by $-\tan b$, we get the identity

$$\tan(a + b) = \frac{\tan a + \tan b}{1 - \tan a \tan b} \tag{9}$$

The derivatives of the tangent, cotangent, secant, and cosecant functions are obtained from those of the sine and cosine functions and differentiation formulas.

$$D_x(\tan x) = D_x\left(\frac{\sin x}{\cos x}\right) = \frac{\cos x \cdot D_x(\sin x) - \sin x \cdot D_x(\cos x)}{\cos^2 x}$$

$$= \frac{(\cos x)(\cos x) - (\sin x)(-\sin x)}{\cos^2 x}$$

$$= \frac{\cos^2 x + \sin^2 x}{\cos^2 x}$$

$$= \frac{1}{\cos^2 x}$$

$$= \sec^2 x$$

So we have

$$D_x(\tan x) = \sec^2 x \tag{10}$$

If u is a differentiable function of x, then from (10) and the chain rule we obtain

$$D_x(\tan u) = \sec^2 u\, D_x u \tag{11}$$

EXAMPLE 1: Find $f'(x)$ if

$$f(x) = 2 \tan \tfrac{1}{2}x - x$$

SOLUTION: $f'(x) = 2 \sec^2 \tfrac{1}{2}x(\tfrac{1}{2}) - 1 = \sec^2 \tfrac{1}{2}x - 1$.
If we use identity (2), this simplifies to

$$f'(x) = \tan^2 \tfrac{1}{2}x$$

The formula for the derivative of the cotangent function is obtained in a manner analogous to that for the tangent function. The result is

$$D_x(\cot x) = -\csc^2 x \tag{12}$$

The derivation of (12) is left as an exercise (see Exercise 1).

From (12) and the chain rule, if u is a differentiable function of x, we have

$$D_x(\cot u) = -\csc^2 u\, D_x u \tag{13}$$

$$D_x(\sec x) = D_x[(\cos x)^{-1}]$$

$$= -1(\cos x)^{-2}(-\sin x)$$

$$= \frac{1}{\cos^2 x} \cdot \sin x$$

$$= \frac{1}{\cos x} \cdot \frac{\sin x}{\cos x}$$

$$= \sec x \tan x$$

We have, then, the following formula:

$$D_x(\sec x) = \sec x \tan x \tag{14}$$

If u is a differentiable function of x, then from (14) and the chain rule we get

$$D_x(\sec u) = \sec u \tan u\, D_x u \tag{15}$$

EXAMPLE 2: Find $f'(x)$ if

$$f(x) = \sec^4 3x$$

SOLUTION:

$$f'(x) = 4 \sec^3 3x \cdot D_x(\sec 3x)$$

$$= 4 \sec^3 3x(\sec 3x \tan 3x)(3)$$

$$= 12 \sec^4 3x \tan 3x$$

In a manner similar to that for the secant, the formula for the derivative of the cosecant function may be derived, and we obtain

$$D_x(\csc x) = -\csc x \cot x \tag{16}$$

So by applying (16) and the chain rule, if u is a differentiable function of x, we have

$$D_x(\csc u) = -\csc u \cot u \, D_x u \tag{17}$$

The derivation of (16) is left as an exercise (see Exercise 2).

EXAMPLE 3: Find $f'(x)$ if

$$f(x) = \cot x \csc x$$

SOLUTION:

$$f'(x) = \cot x \cdot D_x(\csc x) + \csc x \cdot D_x(\cot x)$$
$$= \cot x(-\csc x \cot x) + \csc x(-\csc^2 x)$$
$$= -\csc x \cot^2 x - \csc^3 x$$

In Definition 10.1.4 we gave the analogy between the sine and cosine of real numbers and those of angle measurements. The following definition gives a similar analogy for the other four trigonometric functions.

10.4.2 Definition

If α degrees and x radians are measurements for the same angle, then

$$\tan \alpha° = \tan x \qquad \cot \alpha° = \cot x \qquad \sec \alpha° = \sec x \qquad \csc \alpha° = \csc x$$

EXAMPLE 4: An airplane is flying west at 500 ft/sec at an altitude of 4000 ft. The airplane is in a vertical plane with a searchlight on the ground. If the light is to be kept on the plane, how fast is the searchlight revolving when the airplane is due east of the searchlight at an airline distance of 2000 ft?

SOLUTION: Refer to Fig. 10.4.1. The searchlight is at point L, and at a particular instant of time the airplane is at point P.

Let $t =$ the number of seconds in the time;
   $x =$ the number of feet due east in the airline distance of the airplane from the searchlight at time t sec;
   $\theta =$ the number of radians in the angle of elevation of the airplane at the searchlight at time t sec.

We are given $D_t x = -500$. We wish to find $D_t \theta$ when $x = 2000$.

$$\tan \theta = \frac{4000}{x} \tag{18}$$

Differentiating on both sides of Eq. (18) with respect to t, we obtain

$$\sec^2 \theta \, D_t \theta = -\frac{4000}{x^2} D_t x$$

Substituting $D_t x = -500$ in the above and dividing by $\sec^2 \theta$ gives

$$D_t \theta = \frac{2{,}000{,}000}{x^2 \sec^2 \theta} \tag{19}$$

P

4000 ft

θ

L

x ft

Figure 10.4.1

When $x = 2000$, $\tan \theta = 2$. Therefore, $\sec^2 \theta = 1 + \tan^2 \theta = 5$. Substituting these values into Eq. (19), we have, when $x = 2000$,

$$D_t \theta = \frac{2{,}000{,}000}{4{,}000{,}000\,(5)} = \frac{1}{10}$$

We conclude that at the given instant the measurement of the angle is increasing at the rate of $\frac{1}{10}$ rad/sec, and this is how fast the searchlight is revolving.

We now consider the graph of the tangent function. Because from Eq. (8) $\tan(-x) = -\tan x$, the graph is symmetric with respect to the origin. Furthermore,

$$\tan(x + \pi) = \frac{\sin(x + \pi)}{\cos(x + \pi)}$$

$$= \frac{\sin x \cos \pi + \cos x \sin \pi}{\cos x \cos \pi - \sin x \sin \pi}$$

$$= \frac{\sin x(-1) + \cos x(0)}{\cos x(-1) - \sin x(0)}$$

$$= \frac{-\sin x}{-\cos x}$$

$$= \tan x$$

and so by Definition 10.1.3, the tangent function is periodic with period π.

The tangent function is continuous at all numbers in its domain which is the set of all real numbers except those of the form $\frac{1}{2}\pi + n\pi$, where n is any integer. However, $\lim\limits_{x \to (\pi/2 + n\pi)} \tan x = \pm\infty$, and so the lines having equations $x = \frac{1}{2}\pi + n\pi$ are vertical asymptotes of the graph.

If n is any integer, $\sin n\pi = 0$ and $\cos n\pi$ is either $+1$ or -1, and so $\tan n\pi = 0$. Therefore, the graph intersects the x axis at the points $(n\pi, 0)$.

To find the relative extrema of the tangent function and the points of inflection of its graph, we consider the first and second derivatives. So if $f(x) = \tan x$, then $f'(x) = \sec^2 x$ and $f''(x) = 2 \sec^2 x \tan x$.

Setting $f'(x) = 0$ gives $\sec^2 x = 0$. Because $\sec^2 x \geq 1$ for all x, we conclude that there are no relative extrema. Setting $f''(x) = 0$, we obtain

$2 \sec^2 x \tan x = 0$, from which we get $\tan x = 0$ because $\sec^2 x \neq 0$. Therefore, $f''(x) = 0$ if $x = n\pi$, where n is any integer. At these values of x, $f''(x)$ changes sign, and so the points of inflection are the points $(n\pi, 0)$, which are the points where the graph intersects the x axis. Because $f'(n\pi) = \sec^2 n\pi = 1$, the slopes of the inflectional tangents are 1.

Consider now the open interval $(-\tfrac{1}{2}\pi, \tfrac{1}{2}\pi)$ on which the tangent function is defined everywhere. Because $f'(x) = \sec^2 x > 0$ for all values of x, it follows that the tangent is an increasing function on this interval. When $-\tfrac{1}{2}\pi < x < 0$, $f''(x) = 2 \sec^2 x \tan x < 0$; hence, the graph is concave downward on the open interval $(-\tfrac{1}{2}\pi, 0)$. When $0 < x < \tfrac{1}{2}\pi$, $f''(x) > 0$, from which it follows that the graph is concave upward on the open interval $(0, \tfrac{1}{2}\pi)$.

Table 10.4.1

x	0	$\tfrac{1}{6}\pi$	$\tfrac{1}{4}\pi$	$\tfrac{1}{3}\pi$
$\tan x$	0	$\tfrac{1}{3}\sqrt{3} \approx 0.58$	1	$\sqrt{3} \approx 1.73$

In Table 10.4.1 there are some corresponding values of x and y satisfying the equation $y = \tan x$. By plotting the points having as coordinates the number pairs (x, y) and using the above information, a sketch of the graph of the tangent function may be drawn, and it is shown in Fig. 10.4.2.

$y = \tan x$

Figure 10.4.2

The graph of the cotangent function can be obtained from the graph of the tangent function by using an identity which will now be proved.

$$\tan(\tfrac{1}{2}\pi + x) = \frac{\sin(\tfrac{1}{2}\pi + x)}{\cos(\tfrac{1}{2}\pi + x)}$$

$$= \frac{\sin\frac{1}{2}\pi \, \cos x + \cos\frac{1}{2}\pi \, \sin x}{\cos\frac{1}{2}\pi \, \cos x - \sin\frac{1}{2}\pi \, \sin x}$$

$$= \frac{(1) \, \cos x + (0) \, \sin x}{(0) \, \cos x - (1) \, \sin x}$$

$$= \frac{\cos x}{-\sin x}$$

$$= -\cot x$$

Therefore,

$$\cot x = -\tan(\tfrac{1}{2}\pi + x)$$

From the above identity it follows that the graph of the cotangent function is obtained from the graph of the tangent function by translating the y axis $\frac{1}{2}\pi$ units to the right and then taking a reflection of the graph with respect to the x axis. A sketch of the graph of the cotangent function is in Fig. 10.4.3.

Figure 10.4.3

The secant function is periodic with period 2π because

$$\sec(x + 2\pi) = \frac{1}{\cos(x + 2\pi)} = \frac{1}{\cos x} = \sec x$$

The domain of the secant function is the set of all real numbers except those of the form $\frac{1}{2}\pi + n\pi$, and the function is continuous on its domain. Because $\lim\limits_{x \to \pi/2 + n\pi} \sec x = \pm\infty$, the graph of the secant function has the lines $x = \frac{1}{2}\pi + n\pi$ as vertical asymptotes. There is no intersection of the graph with the x axis because $\sec x$ is never zero. The secant function is even because

$$\sec(-x) = \frac{1}{\cos(-x)} = \frac{1}{\cos x} = \sec x$$

and so the graph of the secant function is symmetric with respect to the y axis.

If $f(x) = \sec x$, it follows that $f'(x) = \sec x \tan x$ and $f''(x) = \sec x (2 \tan^2 x + 1)$. Setting $f'(x) = 0$ gives $\sec x \tan x = 0$. Because $\sec x \neq 0, f'(x) = 0$ when $\tan x = 0$, which is when $x = n\pi$, where n is any integer. Also, $f''(n\pi) = \sec n\pi [2 \tan^2 n\pi + 1]$. If n is an even integer, $f''(n\pi) = 1 \cdot (0 + 1) = 1$; and if n is an odd integer, $f''(n\pi) = (-1)(0 + 1) = -1$. Therefore, when $x = n\pi$ and n is an even integer, f has a relative minimum value; and when $x = n\pi$ and n is an odd integer, f has a relative maximum value. There are no points of inflection because for all x, $f''(x) \neq 0$.

Using the above information and plotting a few points, we get a sketch of the graph of the secant function shown in Fig. 10.4.4.

Because

$$\sec(x + \tfrac{1}{2}\pi) = \frac{1}{\cos(x + \tfrac{1}{2}\pi)} = \frac{1}{-\sin x} = -\csc x$$

then

$$\csc x = -\sec(x + \tfrac{1}{2}\pi)$$

and so the graph of the cosecant function is obtained from that of the secant function by translating the y axis $\tfrac{1}{2}\pi$ units to the right and taking a reflection of the graph with respect to the x axis. A sketch of the graph of the cosecant function is in Fig. 10.4.5.

$y = \sec x$

Figure 10.4.4

$y = \csc x$

Figure 10.4.5

Exercises 10.4

1. Derive: $D_x(\cot x) = -\csc^2 x$.

2. Derive: $D_x(\csc x) = -\csc x \cot x$.

In Exercises 3 through 20, find the derivative of the given function.

3. $f(x) = \sec x^2$

4. $g(x) = \ln \csc^2 x$

5. $F(x) = \ln |\sec 2x|$

6. $h(x) = \ln |\cot \frac{1}{2}x|$

7. $G(r) = \sqrt{\cot 3r}$

8. $h(t) = \sec^2 2t - \tan^2 2t$

9. $g(x) = \sec x \tan x$

10. $f(x) = \sin x \tan x$

11. $f(t) = \csc(t^3 + 1)$

12. $g(t) = 2 \sec \sqrt{t}$

13. $H(t) = \cot^4 t - \csc^4 t$

14. $F(x) = \dfrac{\cot^2 2x}{1 + x^2}$

15. $f(x) = \ln |\sec 5x + \tan 5x|$

16. $f(x) = \frac{1}{3} \sec^3 2x - \sec 2x$

17. $g(x) = 3^x \sec x$

18. $G(x) = \log_{10} |\csc x - \cot x|$

19. $F(x) = (\sin x)^{\tan x}$

20. $G(x) = (\tan x)^x$

In Exercises 21 and 22, use logarithmic differentiation to find $D_x y$.

21. $y = \dfrac{\sec x \sqrt{1 - \cot^2 x}}{\csc^3 x}$

22. $y = \dfrac{\tan^2 x}{\sqrt{1 + \sec^2 x}}$

In Exercises 23 through 26, find $D_x y$ by implicit differentiation.

23. $y = \tan(x + y)$

24. $\cot xy + xy = 0$

25. $\sec^2 x + \csc^2 y = 4$

26. $\csc(x - y) + \sec(x + y) = x$

In Exercises 27 through 30, draw a sketch of the graph of the given function.

27. $f(x) = \tan 2x$

28. $f(x) = \frac{1}{2} \sec 2x$

29. $f(x) = \frac{1}{2} |\cot x|$

30. $f(x) = |\csc \frac{1}{2}x|$

31. Find an equation of the tangent line to the curve $y = \sec x$ at the point $(\frac{1}{4}\pi, \sqrt{2})$.

32. A radar antenna is located on a ship that is 4 miles from a straight shore and it is rotating at 32 rpm. How fast is the radar beam moving along the shoreline when the beam makes an angle of 45° with the shore?

33. A steel girder 27 ft long is moved horizontally along a passageway 8 ft wide and into a corridor at right angles to the passageway. How wide must the corridor be in order for the girder to go around the corner? Neglect the horizontal width of the girder.

34. If two corridors at right angles to each other are 10 ft and 15 ft wide, respectively, what is the length of the longest steel girder that can be moved horizontally around the corner? Neglect the horizontal width of the girder.

10.5 AN APPLICATION OF THE TANGENT FUNCTION TO THE SLOPE OF A LINE

The tangent function can be used in connection with the slope of a straight line. We first define the "angle of inclination" of a line.

10.5.1 Definition

The *angle of inclination* of a line not parallel to the x axis is the smallest angle measured counterclockwise from the positive direction of the x axis to the line. The inclination of a line parallel to the x axis is defined to have measure zero.

If α is the degree measure of the angle of inclination of a line, α may be any number in the interval $0 \le \alpha < 180$. Figure 10.5.1 shows a line L for which $0 < \alpha < 90$, and Fig. 10.5.2 shows one for which $90 < \alpha < 180$.

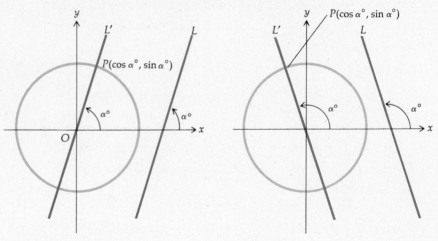

Figure 10.5.1   Figure 10.5.2

10.5.2 Theorem   If α is the degree measure of the angle of inclination of line L, not parallel to the y axis, then the slope m of L is given by

$$m = \tan \alpha°$$

PROOF: Refer to Figs. 10.5.1 and 10.5.2, which show the given line L whose angle of inclination has degree measure α and whose slope is m. The line L' that passes through the origin and is parallel to L also has slope m and an angle of inclination whose degree measure is α. The point $P(\cos \alpha°, \sin \alpha°)$, at the intersection of L and the unit circle $x^2 + y^2 = 1$, lies on L'. And because the point $(0, 0)$ also lies on L', it follows from Definition 1.5.1 that

$$m = \frac{\sin \alpha° - 0}{\cos \alpha° - 0} = \frac{\sin \alpha°}{\cos \alpha°} = \tan \alpha° \qquad \blacksquare$$

If the line L is parallel to the y axis, the degree measure of the angle of inclination of L is 90 and $\tan 90°$ does not exist. This is consistent with the fact that a vertical line has no slope.

Theorem 10.5.2 is used to obtain a formula for finding the angle between two nonvertical intersecting lines. If two lines intersect, two supplementary angles are formed at their point of intersection. To distinguish these two angles, let L_2 be the line with the greater angle of inclination of degree measure α_2 and let L_1 be the other line for which the degree measure of its angle of inclination is α_1. If θ is the degree measure of the angle between the two lines, then we define

$$\theta = \alpha_2 - \alpha_1 \qquad (1)$$

If L_1 and L_2 are parallel, then $\alpha_1 = \alpha_2$ and the angle between the two lines has degree measure 0. Thus, if L_1 and L_2 are two distinct lines, $0 \leq \theta < 180$. Refer to Figs. 10.5.3 and 10.5.4.

Figure 10.5.3

Figure 10.5.4

The following theorem enables us to find θ when the slopes of L_1 and L_2 are known.

10.5.3 Theorem Let L_1 and L_2 be two nonvertical lines, which intersect and are not perpendicular, and let L_2 be the line having the greater angle of inclination. Then if m_1 is the slope of L_1, m_2 is the slope of L_2, and θ is the degree measure of the angle between L_1 and L_2,

$$\tan \theta° = \frac{m_2 - m_1}{1 + m_1 m_2} \tag{2}$$

PROOF: If α_1 and α_2 are degree measures of the angles of inclination of L_1 and L_2, respectively, from Eq. (1) we have

$$\theta = \alpha_2 - \alpha_1$$

and so

$$\tan \theta° = \tan(\alpha_2° - \alpha_1°)$$

Applying formula (7) of Sec. 10.4 to the right side of the above, we get

$$\tan \theta° = \frac{\tan \alpha_2° - \tan \alpha_1°}{1 + \tan \alpha_2° \tan \alpha_1°}$$

$$= \frac{m_2 - m_1}{1 + m_1 m_2}$$

■

EXAMPLE 1: Find to the nearest degree the measurements of the interior angles of the triangle having vertices $B(-2, 1), C(2, 2), D(-3, 4)$.

Figure 10.5.5

SOLUTION: Let β, γ, and δ be the degree measures of the interior angles of the triangle at the vertices B, C, and D, respectively. Let u denote the line through B and C, let v denote the line through C and D, let w denote the line through B and D, and let m_u, m_v, and m_w be their respective slopes. Refer to Fig. 10.5.5.

Using the formula for the slope of a line through two given points, we get

$$m_u = \tfrac{1}{4} \qquad m_v = -\tfrac{2}{5} \qquad m_w = -3$$

To determine β, we observe that line w has a greater angle of inclination than line u; so in formula (2), $m_2 = m_w = -3$ and $m_1 = m_u = \tfrac{1}{4}$. The degree measure of the angle between lines u and v is β. Thus, from formula (2) we have

$$\tan \beta° = \frac{-3 - \tfrac{1}{4}}{1 + \tfrac{1}{4}(-3)} = -13$$

Therefore,

$$\beta = 94$$

To determine γ, because line v has a greater angle of inclination than line u, $m_2 = m_v = -\tfrac{2}{5}$ and $m_1 = m_u = \tfrac{1}{4}$. The degree measure of the angle between lines u and v is, by definition, $180 - \gamma$. Applying formula (2), then, we get

$$\tan(180° - \gamma°) = \frac{-\tfrac{2}{5} - \tfrac{1}{4}}{1 + \tfrac{1}{4}\left(-\tfrac{2}{5}\right)} = -\tfrac{13}{18}$$

Hence,

$$180 - \gamma = 144$$

so that

$$\gamma = 36$$

To determine δ, because line v has a greater angle of inclination than line w, $m_2 = m_v = -\tfrac{2}{5}$ and $m_1 = m_w = -3$. The degree measure of the angle between lines v and w is then δ. Applying formula (2), we obtain

$$\tan \delta° = \frac{-\tfrac{2}{5} - (-3)}{1 + \left(-\tfrac{2}{5}\right)(-3)} = \tfrac{13}{11}$$

Therefore,

$$\delta = 50$$

The sum of the degree measures of the angles of a triangle must be 180. We use this to check the results, and we have

$$\beta + \gamma + \delta = 94 + 36 + 50 = 180$$

10.5.4 Definition   The *angle between two curves* at a point of intersection is the angle between the tangent lines to the curves at the point.

EXAMPLE 2:   Find to the nearest degree the measurement of the angle between the curves $y = x^2 - 2$ and $y = -2x^2 + 10$ at their points of intersection.

Figure 10.5.6

SOLUTION: Solving the two equations simultaneously, we obtain $(2, 2)$ and $(-2, 2)$ as the points of intersection. In Fig. 10.5.6 sketches of the two curves are shown together with the tangent lines at one point of intersection. Because of the symmetry of the two curves with respect to the y axis, the angle between the curves at $(2, 2)$ has the same measure as the angle between them at $(-2, 2)$. Let P be the point $(2, 2)$, T_1 be the tangent line to $y = x^2 - 2$ at P, and T_2 be the tangent line to $y = -2x^2 + 10$ at P. The line T_2 has a greater angle of inclination than T_1. So if θ is the degree measure of the angle between T_1 and T_2,

$$\tan \theta° = \frac{m_2 - m_1}{1 + m_1 m_2}$$

where m_2 is the slope of T_2 and m_1 is the slope of T_1. From the equation $y = x^2 - 2$, we get $D_x y = 2x$, and so $m_1 = 4$. From the equation $y = -2x^2 + 10$, we get $D_x y = -4x$; thus, $m_2 = -8$. Hence,

$$\tan \theta° = \frac{-8 - 4}{1 + (4)(-8)} = \frac{12}{31} \approx 0.387$$

Therefore, to the nearest degree, $\theta° = 21°$.

Exercises 10.5

1. Find $\tan \theta°$ if $\theta°$ is the measurement of the angle between the lines whose slopes are (a) 1 and $\frac{1}{3}$; (b) 5 and $-\frac{5}{3}$; (c) $-\frac{2}{3}$ and $\frac{1}{2}$; (d) $-\frac{1}{3}$ and $-\frac{1}{10}$; (e) $-\frac{4}{3}$ and $-\frac{5}{2}$.

2. Find, to the nearest degree, the measurement of the angle between the lines whose slopes are (a) 5 and $-\frac{7}{9}$; (b) -3 and 2; (c) $\frac{3}{2}$ and $\frac{1}{4}$; (d) $-\frac{3}{2}$ and $-\frac{1}{4}$.

3. Find, to the nearest degree, the measurements of the interior angles of the triangle formed by the lines that have equations $2x + y - 6 = 0$, $3x - y - 4 = 0$, and $3x + 4y + 8 = 0$.

4. Find, to the nearest degree, the measurements of the interior angles of the triangle having vertices at $(1, 0)$, $(-3, 2)$, and $(2, 3)$.

5. Find an equation of a line through the point $(-1, 4)$ making an angle of radian measure $\frac{1}{4}\pi$ with the line having equation $2x + y - 5 = 0$ (two solutions).

6. Find an equation of a line through the point $(-3, -2)$ making an angle of radian measure $\frac{1}{3}\pi$ with the line having equation $3x - 2y - 7 = 0$.

7. Using Theorem 10.5.3, prove that the triangle having vertices at (2, 3), (6, 2), and (3, −1) is isosceles.

8. Using Theorem 10.5.3, prove that the triangle having vertices at (−3, 0), (−1, 0), and (−2, $\sqrt{3}$) is equilateral.

9. Find the slope of the bisector of the angle at A in the triangle having the vertices $A(4, 1)$; $B(6, 5)$; and $C(−1, 8)$.

10. Find the slope of the bisector of the angle at A in the triangle having the vertices $A(−3, 5)$; $B(2, −4)$; and $C(−1, 7)$.

11. Let A, B, and C be the vertices of an oblique triangle (no right angle), and let α, β, and γ be the radian measures of the interior angles at vertices A, B, and C, respectively. Prove that $\tan \alpha + \tan \beta + \tan \gamma = \tan \alpha \tan \beta \tan \gamma$. (HINT: First show that $\tan(\alpha + \beta) = −\tan \gamma$.)

12. Find the tangents of the measurements of the interior angles of the triangle having vertices at (−3, −2), (−6, 3), and (5, 1) and check by applying the result of Exercise 11.

13. Find the points of intersection of the graphs of the sine and cosine functions and find the measurement of the angle between their tangent lines at their points of intersection.

14. Find, to the nearest 10 minutes, the measurement of the angle between the curves $y = 2x^2 − 11$ and $y = x^2 − 2$ at their points of intersection.

10.6 INTEGRALS INVOLVING THE TANGENT, COTANGENT, SECANT, AND COSECANT

A formula for the indefinite integral of the tangent function is derived as follows. Because

$$\int \tan u \; du = \int \frac{\sin u}{\cos u} \; du$$

we let $v = \cos u$, $dv = −\sin u \; du$, and obtain

$$\int \tan u \; du = −\int \frac{dv}{v} = −\ln |v| + C$$

Hence,

$$\int \tan u \; du = −\ln |\cos u| + C \tag{1}$$

Because $−\ln |\cos u| = \ln |(\cos u)^{-1}| = \ln |\sec u|$, we can also write

$$\int \tan u \; du = \ln |\sec u| + C \tag{2}$$

● ILLUSTRATION 1:

$$\int \tan 3x \; dx = \frac{1}{3} \int \tan 3x \; (3 \; dx)$$

$$= \tfrac{1}{3} \ln |\sec 3x| + C \qquad ●$$

The following formula is derived in a way similar to the derivation of (2). (See Exercise 29.)

$$\int \cot u \; du = \ln |\sin u| + C \tag{3}$$

To integrate $\int \sec u \, du$, we multiply the numerator and denominator of the integrand by $(\sec u + \tan u)$, and we have

$$\int \sec u \, du = \int \frac{\sec u (\sec u + \tan u)}{\sec u + \tan u} \, du = \int \frac{(\sec^2 u + \sec u \tan u)}{\sec u + \tan u} \, du$$

Let $v = \sec u + \tan u$. Then $dv = (\sec u \tan u + \sec^2 u) \, du$; and so we have

$$\int \sec u \, du = \int \frac{dv}{v} = \ln |v| + C$$

Therefore,

$$\int \sec u \, du = \ln |\sec u + \tan u| + C \qquad (4)$$

The formula for $\int \csc u \, du$ is derived by multiplying the numerator and denominator of the integrand by $(\csc u - \cot u)$ and proceeding as above. This derivation is left as an exercise (see Exercise 30). The formula is

$$\int \csc u \, du = \ln |\csc u - \cot u| + C \qquad (5)$$

● ILLUSTRATION 2:

$$\int \frac{dx}{\sin 2x} = \int \csc 2x \, dx = \frac{1}{2} \int \csc 2x \, (2dx)$$

$$= \tfrac{1}{2} \ln |\csc 2x - \cot 2x| + C \qquad ●$$

The following two indefinite integral formulas follow immediately from the corresponding differentiation formulas.

$$\int \sec^2 u \, du = \tan u + C \qquad (6)$$

$$\int \sec u \tan u \, du = \sec u + C \qquad (7)$$

Many integrals involving powers of tangent and secant can be evaluated by applying these two formulas and the identity given by formula (2) in Sec. 10.4, which is

$$1 + \tan^2 u = \sec^2 u \qquad (8)$$

There are similar formulas involving the cotangent and cosecant.

$$\int \csc^2 u \, du = -\cot u + C \qquad (9)$$

PROOF: $D_u(-\cot u) = -(-\csc^2 u) = \csc^2 u.$

$$\int \csc u \cot u \, du = -\csc u + C \qquad (10)$$

PROOF: $D_u(-\csc u) = -(-\csc u \cot u) = \csc u \cot u.$

● ILLUSTRATION 3:

$$\int \frac{2 + 3 \cos u}{\sin^2 u} \, du = 2 \int \frac{1}{\sin^2 u} \, du + 3 \int \frac{1}{\sin u} \cdot \frac{\cos u}{\sin u} \, du$$

$$= 2 \int \csc^2 u \, du + 3 \int \csc u \cot u \, du$$

$$= -2 \cot u - 3 \csc u + C \qquad \bullet$$

From formula (3) in Sec. 10.4 we have the identity

$$1 + \cot^2 u = \csc^2 u \qquad (11)$$

Formulas (6), (7), and (8) are used to evaluate integrals of the form

$$\int \tan^m u \, \sec^n u \, du$$

and formulas (9), (10), and (11) are used to evaluate integrals of the form

$$\int \cot^m u \, \csc^n u \, du$$

where m and n are positive integers.
We distinguish various cases.

Case 1: $\int \tan^n u \, du$ or $\int \cot^n u \, du$, where n is a positive integer.
We write

$$\tan^n u = \tan^{n-2} u \, \tan^2 u$$

$$= \tan^{n-2} u (\sec^2 u - 1)$$

and

$$\cot^n u = \cot^{n-2} u \, \cot^2 u$$

$$= \cot^{n-2} u (\csc^2 u - 1)$$

EXAMPLE 1:   Find

$$\int \tan^3 x \, dx$$

SOLUTION:

$$\int \tan^3 x \, dx = \int \tan x (\sec^2 x - 1) \, dx = \int \tan x \sec^2 x \, dx - \int \tan x \, dx$$

$$= \tfrac{1}{2} \tan^2 x + \ln |\cos x| + C$$

EXAMPLE 2: Find

$$\int \cot^4 3x \, dx$$

SOLUTION:

$$\int \cot^4 3x \, dx = \int \cot^2 3x (\csc^2 3x - 1) \, dx$$

$$= \int \cot^2 3x \, \csc^2 3x \, dx - \int \cot^2 3x \, dx$$

$$= \tfrac{1}{9} (-\cot^3 3x) - \int (\csc^2 3x - 1) \, dx$$

$$= -\tfrac{1}{9} \cot^3 3x + \tfrac{1}{3} \cot 3x + x + C$$

Case 2: $\int \sec^n u \, du$ or $\int \csc^n u \, du$, where n is a positive even integer. We write

$$\sec^n u = \sec^{n-2} u \, \sec^2 u = (\tan^2 u + 1)^{(n-2)/2} \sec^2 u$$

and

$$\csc^n u = \csc^{n-2} u \, \csc^2 u = (\cot^2 u + 1)^{(n-2)/2} \csc^2 u$$

EXAMPLE 3: Find

$$\int \csc^6 x \, dx$$

SOLUTION:

$$\int \csc^6 x \, dx = \int (\cot^2 x + 1)^2 \csc^2 x \, dx$$

$$= \int \cot^4 x \, \csc^2 x \, dx + 2 \int \cot^2 x \, \csc^2 x \, dx + \int \csc^2 x \, dx$$

$$= -\tfrac{1}{5} \cot^5 x - \tfrac{2}{3} \cot^3 x - \cot x + C$$

To integrate $\int \sec^n u \, du$ or $\int \csc^n u \, du$ when n is a positive odd integer, we must use integration by parts, which is discussed in Sec. 11.2.

Case 3: $\int \tan^m u \, \sec^n u \, du$ or $\int \cot^m u \, \csc^n u \, du$, where n is a positive even integer.

This case is illustrated by the following example.

EXAMPLE 4: Find

$$\int \tan^5 x \, \sec^4 x \, dx$$

SOLUTION:

$$\int \tan^5 x \, \sec^4 x \, dx = \int \tan^5 x \, (\tan^2 x + 1) \, \sec^2 x \, dx$$

$$= \int \tan^7 x \, \sec^2 x \, dx + \int \tan^5 x \, \sec^2 x \, dx$$

$$= \tfrac{1}{8} \tan^8 x + \tfrac{1}{6} \tan^6 x + C$$

Case 4: $\int \tan^m u \, \sec^n u \, du$ or $\int \cot^m u \, \csc^n u \, du$, where m is a positive odd integer.

The following example illustrates this case.

EXAMPLE 5:   Find

$$\int \tan^5 x \sec^7 x \, dx$$

SOLUTION:

$$\int \tan^5 x \sec^7 x \, dx = \int \tan^4 x \sec^6 x \sec x \tan x \, dx$$

$$= \int (\sec^2 x - 1)^2 \sec^6 x \, (\sec x \tan x \, dx)$$

$$= \int \sec^{10} x \, (\sec x \tan x \, dx)$$

$$- 2 \int \sec^8 x \, (\sec x \tan x \, dx) + \int \sec^6 x \, (\sec x \tan x \, dx)$$

$$= \tfrac{1}{11} \sec^{11} x - \tfrac{2}{9} \sec^9 x + \tfrac{1}{7} \sec^7 x + C$$

Integration by parts (Sec. 11.2) is used to integrate $\int \tan^m u \sec^n u \, du$ and $\int \cot^m u \csc^n u \, du$ when m is a positive even integer and n is a positive odd integer.

Exercises 10.6

In Exercises 1 through 22, evaluate the indefinite integral.

1. $\displaystyle\int \tan 2x \, dx$

2. $\displaystyle\int \cot(3x + 1) \, dx$

3. $\displaystyle\int x \csc 5x^2 \, dx$

4. $\displaystyle\int \sec x \tan x \tan(\sec x) \, dx$

5. $\displaystyle\int \cot^3 x \, dx$

6. $\displaystyle\int \csc^4 x \, dx$

7. $\displaystyle\int \csc^2 6x \, dx$

8. $\displaystyle\int x^2 \sec^2 x^3 \, dx$

9. $\displaystyle\int \tan^6 x \sec^4 x \, dx$

10. $\displaystyle\int \tan^5 x \sec^3 x \, dx$

11. $\displaystyle\int \cot^2 3x \csc^4 3x \, dx$

12. $\displaystyle\int (\sec 5x + \csc 5x)^2 \, dx$

13. $\displaystyle\int (\tan 3x + \cot 3x)^2 \, dx$

14. $\displaystyle\int \frac{dx}{1 + \cos x}$

15. $\displaystyle\int \tan^4 \tfrac{1}{2}x \, dx$

16. $\displaystyle\int \tan^5 3x \, dx$

17. $\displaystyle\int \cot^6 2t \, dt$

18. $\displaystyle\int \frac{\tan^4 y}{\sec^5 y} \, dy$

19. $\displaystyle\int \frac{du}{1 + \sec \tfrac{1}{2}u}$

20. $\displaystyle\int \frac{\csc^4 x}{\cot^2 x} \, dx$

21. $\displaystyle\int \frac{\sec^3 x}{\tan^4 x} \, dx$

22. $\displaystyle\int \frac{\sin^2 \pi x}{\cos^6 \pi x} \, dx$

In Exercises 23 through 28, evaluate the definite integral.

23. $\displaystyle\int_{\pi/16}^{\pi/12} \tan 4x \, dx$

24. $\displaystyle\int_{\pi/8}^{\pi/4} 3 \csc 2x \, dx$

25. $\displaystyle\int_{-\pi/4}^{\pi/4} \sec^6 x \, dx$

26. $\displaystyle\int_{\pi/6}^{\pi/4} \cot^3 w \, dw$

27. $\displaystyle\int_{\pi/4}^{\pi/2} \frac{\cos^4 t}{\sin^6 t} \, dt$

28. $\displaystyle\int_0^{\pi/3} \frac{\tan^3 x}{\sec x} \, dx$

29. Derive the formula $\int \cot u \, du = \ln |\sin u| + C$.

30. Derive the formula $\int \csc u \, du = \ln |\csc u - \cot u| + C$.

31. Find the length of the arc of the curve $y = \ln \csc x$ from $x = \tfrac{1}{6}\pi$ to $x = \tfrac{1}{2}\pi$.

32. Find the area of the region bounded by the curve $y = \tan^2 x$, the x axis, and the line $x = \tfrac{1}{4}\pi$.

33. Find the volume of the solid of revolution generated if the region bounded by the curve $y = \sec^2 x$, the axes, and the line $x = \tfrac{1}{4}\pi$ is revolved about the x axis.

34. Prove: $\displaystyle\int \cot x \csc^n x \, dx = -\frac{\csc^n x}{n} + C$, if $n \neq 0$.

35. Prove: $\displaystyle\int \tan^n x \, dx = \frac{\tan^{n-1} x}{n-1} - \int \tan^{n-2} x \, dx$ if n is a positive integer greater than 1.

36. Derive a formula similar to that in Exercise 34 for $\int \tan x \sec^n x \, dx$ if $n \neq 0$.

37. Derive a formula similar to that in Exercise 35 for $\int \cot^n x \, dx$, if n is a positive integer greater than 1.

38. We can integrate $\int \sec^2 x \tan x \, dx$ in two ways as follows: $\int \sec^2 x \tan x \, dx = \int \tan x (\sec^2 x \, dx) = \tfrac{1}{2} \tan^2 x + C$ and $\int \sec^2 x \tan x \, dx = \int \sec x (\sec x \tan x \, dx) = \tfrac{1}{2} \sec^2 x + C$. Explain the difference in the appearance of the two answers.

39. Prove that $\int \csc u \, du = -\ln|\csc u + \cot u| + C$.

10.7 INVERSE TRIGONOMETRIC FUNCTIONS

Consider the equation $x = \sin y$. A sketch of the graph of this equation is in Fig. 10.7.1. In the figure, the vertical line $x = \tfrac{1}{2}$ is shown; this line intersects the graph at the points for which $y = \tfrac{1}{6}\pi, \tfrac{5}{6}\pi, -\tfrac{7}{6}\pi, -\tfrac{11}{6}\pi$, and so on. We see, then, that the equation $x = \sin y$ does not define y as a function of x because every vertical line must intersect the graph of a function in at most one point. Hence, we conclude that the sine function does not have an inverse function.

Refer now to the graph of the sine function (Fig. 10.2.3). We see from the figure that the sine is an increasing function on the interval $[-\tfrac{1}{2}\pi, \tfrac{1}{2}\pi]$. This follows from Theorem 5.1.3 because if $f(x) = \sin x$, then $f'(x) = \cos x > 0$ for all x in $(-\tfrac{1}{2}\pi, \tfrac{1}{2}\pi)$. Thus, even though the sine function does not have an inverse function, it follows from Theorem 9.3.2 that the function F for which

$$F(x) = \sin x \quad \text{and} \quad -\tfrac{1}{2}\pi \leq x \leq \tfrac{1}{2}\pi \tag{1}$$

does have an inverse function. The domain of F is $[-\tfrac{1}{2}\pi, \tfrac{1}{2}\pi]$ and its range is $[-1, 1]$. A sketch of the graph of F is shown in Fig. 10.7.2. The inverse of the function defined by (1) is called the "inverse sine function" and is denoted by the symbol $\sin^{-1}$. Following is the formal definition.

Figure 10.7.1

Figure 10.7.2

10.7.1 Definition   The *inverse sine function,* denoted by $\sin^{-1}$, is defined as follows:

$$y = \sin^{-1} x \quad \text{if and only if} \quad x = \sin y \text{ and } -\tfrac{1}{2}\pi \leq y \leq \tfrac{1}{2}\pi$$

Figure 10.7.3

The domain of $\sin^{-1}$ is the closed interval $[-1, 1]$, and the range is the closed interval $[-\tfrac{1}{2}\pi, \tfrac{1}{2}\pi]$. A sketch of the graph is shown in Fig. 10.7.3.

It follows from Definition 10.7.1 that

$$\sin(\sin^{-1} x) = x \qquad \text{for } x \text{ in } [-1, 1] \tag{2}$$

and

$$\sin^{-1}(\sin y) = y \qquad \text{for } y \text{ in } [-\tfrac{1}{2}\pi, \tfrac{1}{2}\pi] \tag{3}$$

In (1) the domain of F was restricted to the closed interval $[-\tfrac{1}{2}\pi, \tfrac{1}{2}\pi]$ so the function would be monotonic on its domain and therefore have an inverse function. However, the sine function has period 2π and is increasing on other intervals, for instance, $[-\tfrac{5}{2}\pi, -\tfrac{3}{2}\pi]$ and $[\tfrac{3}{2}\pi, \tfrac{5}{2}\pi]$. Also, the function is decreasing on certain closed intervals, in particular the intervals $[-\tfrac{3}{2}\pi, -\tfrac{1}{2}\pi]$ and $[\tfrac{1}{2}\pi, \tfrac{3}{2}\pi]$. Any one of these intervals could just as well have been chosen for the domain of the inverse sine function. The choice of the interval $[-\tfrac{1}{2}\pi, \tfrac{1}{2}\pi]$, however, is customary because it is the largest interval containing the number 0 on which the function is monotonic.

The cosine function does not have an inverse function for the same reason that the sine function doesn't. To define the inverse cosine function, we restrict the cosine to an interval on which the function is monotonic. We choose the interval $[0, \pi]$ on which the cosine is decreasing. So consider the function G defined by

$$G(x) = \cos x \quad \text{and} \quad 0 \leq x \leq \pi \tag{4}$$

The range of this function G is the closed interval $[-1, 1]$, and its domain is the closed interval $[0, \pi]$. A sketch of the graph of G is shown in Fig. 10.7.4. Because this function is continuous and decreasing on its domain, it has an inverse function which is called the "inverse cosine function" and is denoted by $\cos^{-1}$.

10.7.2 Definition   The *inverse cosine function,* denoted by $\cos^{-1}$, is defined as follows:

$$y = \cos^{-1} x \quad \text{if and only if} \quad x = \cos y \quad \text{and} \quad 0 \leq y \leq \pi$$

The domain of $\cos^{-1}$ is the closed interval $[-1, 1]$, and the range is the closed interval $[0, \pi]$. A sketch of its graph is shown in Fig. 10.7.5.

From Definition 10.7.2 it follows that

$$\cos(\cos^{-1} x) = x \qquad \text{for } x \text{ in } [-1, 1] \tag{5}$$

and

$$\cos^{-1}(\cos y) = y \qquad \text{for } y \text{ in } [0, \pi] \tag{6}$$

There is an interesting equation relating $\sin^{-1}$ and $\cos^{-1}$ that is given in the following example.

Figure 10.7.4

$y = \cos^{-1} x$

Figure 10.7.5

EXAMPLE 1: Prove

$$\cos^{-1} x = \tfrac{1}{2}\pi - \sin^{-1} x$$

for $|x| \leq 1$.

SOLUTION: Let x be in $[-1, 1]$ and $w = \tfrac{1}{2}\pi - \sin^{-1} x$. Then

$$\sin^{-1} x = \tfrac{1}{2}\pi - w$$

and so

$$\sin(\sin^{-1} x) = \sin(\tfrac{1}{2}\pi - w)$$

and using (2), we get

$$x = \sin(\tfrac{1}{2}\pi - w)$$

Applying (11) in Sec. 10.1 to the right side of the above equation, we get

$$x = \cos w \tag{7}$$

Because $-\tfrac{1}{2}\pi \leq \sin^{-1} x \leq \tfrac{1}{2}\pi$, by adding $-\tfrac{1}{2}\pi$ to each member we have

$$-\pi \leq -\tfrac{1}{2}\pi + \sin^{-1} x \leq 0$$

Multiplying each member of the above inequality by -1 and reversing the direction of the inequality signs, we have

$$0 \leq \tfrac{1}{2}\pi - \sin^{-1} x \leq \pi$$

Replacing $\tfrac{1}{2}\pi - \sin^{-1} x$ by w, we obtain

$$0 \leq w \leq \pi \tag{8}$$

From (7), (8), and Definition 10.7.2 it follows that

$$w = \cos^{-1} x \qquad \text{for } |x| \leq 1$$

and replacing w by $\tfrac{1}{2}\pi - \sin^{-1} x$, we get

$$\tfrac{1}{2}\pi - \sin^{-1} x = \cos^{-1} x \qquad \text{for } |x| \leq 1 \tag{9}$$

which is what we wished to prove.

Note in the above solution that the relation given by (9) depends on choosing the range of the inverse cosine function to be $[0, \pi]$.

To obtain the inverse tangent function we first restrict the tangent function to the open interval $(-\frac{1}{2}\pi, \frac{1}{2}\pi)$ on which the function is continuous and increasing. We let H be the function defined by

$$H(x) = \tan x \quad \text{and} \quad -\tfrac{1}{2}\pi < x < \tfrac{1}{2}\pi \tag{10}$$

The domain of H is the open interval $(-\frac{1}{2}\pi, \frac{1}{2}\pi)$, and the range is the set of all real numbers. A sketch of its graph is shown in Fig. 10.7.6. Because the function H is continuous and increasing on its domain, it has an inverse function, which is called the "inverse tangent function" and is denoted by $\tan^{-1}$.

Figure 10.7.6

$y = \tan^{-1} x$

Figure 10.7.7

10.7.3 Definition   The *inverse tangent function*, denoted by $\tan^{-1}$, is defined as follows:

$$y = \tan^{-1} x \quad \text{if and only if} \quad x = \tan y \quad \text{and} \quad -\tfrac{1}{2}\pi < y < \tfrac{1}{2}\pi$$

The domain of $\tan^{-1}$ is the set of all real numbers, and the range is the open interval $(-\frac{1}{2}\pi, \frac{1}{2}\pi)$. A sketch of its graph is shown in Fig. 10.7.7.

Before defining the inverse cotangent function, we refer back to Example 1, in which we proved the relationship between $\cos^{-1}$ and $\sin^{-1}$ given by Eq. (9). This equation can be used to define the inverse cosine function, and then it can be proved that the range of $\cos^{-1}$ is $[0, \pi]$. We use this kind of procedure in discussing the inverse cotangent function.

10.7.4 Definition   The *inverse cotangent function*, denoted by $\cot^{-1}$, is defined by

$$\cot^{-1} x = \tfrac{1}{2}\pi - \tan^{-1} x \quad \text{where } x \text{ is any real number} \tag{11}$$

It follows from the definition that the domain of $\cot^{-1}$ is the set of all real numbers. To obtain the range we write Eq. (11) as

$$\tan^{-1} x = \tfrac{1}{2}\pi - \cot^{-1} x \tag{12}$$

Because

$$-\tfrac{1}{2}\pi < \tan^{-1} x < \tfrac{1}{2}\pi$$

by substituting from Eq. (12) into this inequality, we get

$$-\tfrac{1}{2}\pi < \tfrac{1}{2}\pi - \cot^{-1} x < \tfrac{1}{2}\pi$$

Subtracting $\tfrac{1}{2}\pi$ from each member, we get

$$-\pi < -\cot^{-1} x < 0$$

and now multiplying each member by -1 and reversing the direction of the inequality signs, we obtain

$$0 < \cot^{-1} x < \pi$$

Therefore, the range of the inverse cotangent function is the open interval $(0, \pi)$. A sketch of its graph is in Fig. 10.7.8.

The inverse secant and the inverse cosecant functions are defined in terms of $\cos^{-1}$ and $\sin^{-1}$, respectively.

$y = \cot^{-1}x$

Figure 10.7.8

10.7.5 Definition The *inverse secant function,* denoted by $\sec^{-1}$, is defined by

$$\sec^{-1} x = \cos^{-1}\left(\frac{1}{x}\right) \qquad \text{for } |x| \geq 1$$

10.7.6 Definition The *inverse cosecant function,* denoted by $\csc^{-1}$, is defined by

$$\csc^{-1} x = \sin^{-1}\left(\frac{1}{x}\right) \qquad \text{for } |x| \geq 1$$

From Definition 10.7.5 it follows that the domain of $\sec^{-1}$ is $(-\infty, -1] \cup [1, +\infty)$, and the range is $[0, \tfrac{1}{2}\pi) \cup (\tfrac{1}{2}\pi, \pi]$. Note that the number $\tfrac{1}{2}\pi$ is not in the range because $\sec \tfrac{1}{2}\pi$ is not defined. A sketch of the graph of $\sec^{-1}$ is shown in Fig. 10.7.9.

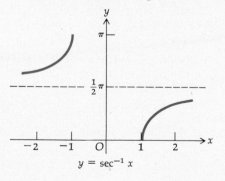

$y = \sec^{-1} x$

Figure 10.7.9

It follows from Definition 10.7.6 that the domain of $\csc^{-1}$ is $(-\infty, -1] \cup [1, +\infty)$, and the range is $[-\frac{1}{2}\pi, 0) \cup (0, \frac{1}{2}\pi]$. The number 0 is not in the range because $\csc 0$ is not defined. A sketch of the graph of $\csc^{-1}$ is shown in Fig. 10.7.10.

$y = \csc^{-1} x$

Figure 10.7.10

EXAMPLE 2: Find the exact value of $\sec[\sin^{-1}(-\frac{3}{4})]$.

Figure 10.7.11

SOLUTION: Let $t = \sin^{-1}(-\frac{3}{4})$. Then $\sin t = -\frac{3}{4}$. Because the range of $\sin^{-1}$ is $[-\frac{1}{2}\pi, \frac{1}{2}\pi]$, and because $\sin t$ is negative, it follows that $-\frac{1}{2}\pi < t < 0$. Figure 10.7.11 shows an angle having radian measure t that satisfies these requirements. From the figure we see that $\sec t = \frac{4}{7}\sqrt{7}$, and so we conclude that $\sec[\sin^{-1}(-\frac{3}{4})] = \frac{4}{7}\sqrt{7}$.

EXAMPLE 3: Find the exact value of $\sin[2 \cos^{-1}(-\frac{3}{5})]$.

SOLUTION: Let $t = \cos^{-1}(-\frac{3}{5})$. So we wish to find the exact value of $\sin 2t$. From formula (14) of Sec. 10.1, we have

$$\sin 2t = 2 \sin t \cos t \qquad (13)$$

Because $t = \cos^{-1}(-\frac{3}{5})$, it follows that $\cos t = -\frac{3}{5}$ and $\frac{1}{2}\pi < t < \pi$. From the identity, $\sin^2 t + \cos^2 t = 1$, and because $\sin t > 0$, since t is in $(\frac{1}{2}\pi, \pi)$, we obtain

$$\sin t = \sqrt{1 - \cos^2 t} = \sqrt{1 - (-\frac{3}{5})^2} = \frac{4}{5}$$

Therefore, from formula (13) we get

$$\sin 2t = 2(\tfrac{4}{5})(-\tfrac{3}{5}) = -\tfrac{24}{25}$$

from which we conclude that

$$\sin[2 \cos^{-1}(-\tfrac{3}{5})] = -\tfrac{24}{25}$$

Exercises 10.7

1. Find the value of each of the following: (a) $\sin^{-1}(-1)$; (b) $\cos^{-1}(-1)$; (c) $\tan^{-1}(-1)$; (d) $\cot^{-1}(-1)$; (e) $\sec^{-1}(-1)$; (f) $\csc^{-1}(-1)$.

2. Find the value of each of the following: (a) $\sin^{-1}(\frac{1}{2})$; (b) $\sin^{-1}(-\frac{1}{2})$; (c) $\cos^{-1}(\frac{1}{2})$; (d) $\cos^{-1}(-\frac{1}{2})$; (e) $\sec^{-1}(2)$; (f) $\csc^{-1}(-2)$.

3. Given: $y = \sin^{-1}\frac{1}{3}$. Find the exact value of each of the following: (a) $\cos y$; (b) $\tan y$; (c) $\cot y$; (d) $\sec y$; (e) $\csc y$.

4. Given: $y = \cos^{-1}(-\frac{2}{3})$. Find the exact value of each of the following: (a) $\sin y$; (b) $\tan y$; (c) $\cot y$; (d) $\sec y$; (e) $\csc y$.

5. Given: $y = \tan^{-1}(-2)$. Find the exact value of each of the following: (a) $\sin y$; (b) $\cos y$; (c) $\cot y$; (d) $\sec y$; (e) $\csc y$.

6. Given: $y = \cot^{-1}(-\frac{1}{2})$. Find the exact value of each of the following: (a) $\sin y$; (b) $\cos y$; (c) $\tan y$; (d) $\sec y$; (e) $\csc y$.

7. Find the exact value of each of the following: (a) $\tan[\sin^{-1}(\frac{1}{2}\sqrt{3})]$; (b) $\sin[\tan^{-1}(\frac{1}{2}\sqrt{3})]$.

8. Find the exact value of each of the following: (a) $\cos[\tan^{-1}(-3)]$; (b) $\tan[\sec^{-1}(-3)]$.

9. Find the exact value of each of the following: (a) $\sin^{-1}[\tan\frac{1}{4}\pi]$; (b) $\tan^{-1}[\sin(-\frac{1}{2}\pi)]$; (c) $\sec^{-1}[\tan(-\frac{1}{4}\pi)]$; (d) $\cot^{-1}[\csc(-\frac{1}{2}\pi)]$.

10. Find the exact value of each of the following: (a) $\cos^{-1}[\sin(-\frac{1}{6}\pi)]$; (b) $\sin^{-1}[\cos(-\frac{1}{6}\pi)]$; (c) $\cos^{-1}[\sin\frac{2}{3}\pi]$; (d) $\sin^{-1}[\cos\frac{2}{3}\pi]$.

In Exercises 11 through 18, find the exact value of the given quantity.

11. $\cos[2\sin^{-1}(-\frac{5}{13})]$

12. $\tan[2\sec^{-1}(-\frac{5}{4})]$

13. $\sin[\sin^{-1}\frac{2}{3} + \cos^{-1}\frac{1}{3}]$

14. $\cos[\sin^{-1}(-\frac{1}{2}) + \sin^{-1}\frac{1}{4}]$

15. $\tan(\tan^{-1}\frac{3}{4} - \sin^{-1}\frac{1}{2})$

16. $\tan[\sec^{-1}\frac{5}{3} + \csc^{-1}(-\frac{13}{12})]$

17. $\cos(\sin^{-1}\frac{1}{3} - \tan^{-1}\frac{1}{2})$

18. $\sin[\cos^{-1}(-\frac{2}{3}) + 2\sin^{-1}(-\frac{1}{3})]$

19. Prove: $\cos^{-1}(3/\sqrt{10}) + \cos^{-1}(2/\sqrt{5}) = \frac{1}{4}\pi$.

20. Prove: $2\tan^{-1}\frac{1}{3} - \tan^{-1}(-\frac{1}{7}) = \frac{1}{4}\pi$.

In Exercises 21 through 28, draw a sketch of the graph of the given equation.

21. $y = \frac{1}{2}\sin^{-1}x$

22. $y = \sin^{-1}\frac{1}{2}x$

23. $y = \tan^{-1}2x$

24. $y = 2\tan^{-1}x$

25. $y = \cos^{-1}3x$

26. $y = \frac{1}{2}\sec^{-1}2x$

27. $y = 2\cot^{-1}\frac{1}{2}x$

28. $y = \frac{1}{2}\csc^{-1}\frac{1}{2}x$

10.8 DERIVATIVES OF THE INVERSE TRIGONOMETRIC FUNCTIONS

Because the inverse trigonometric functions are continuous and monotonic on their domains, it follows from Theorem 9.3.4 that they have derivatives. To derive the formula for the derivative of the inverse sine function, let

$$y = \sin^{-1}x$$

which is equivalent to

$$x = \sin y \quad \text{and} \quad y \text{ in } [-\tfrac{1}{2}\pi, \tfrac{1}{2}\pi] \tag{1}$$

Differentiating on both sides of (1) with respect to y, we obtain

$$D_y x = \cos y \quad \text{and} \quad y \text{ in } [-\tfrac{1}{2}\pi, \tfrac{1}{2}\pi] \tag{2}$$

From the identity $\sin^2 y + \cos^2 y = 1$, and replacing $\sin y$ by x, we obtain

$$\cos^2 y = 1 - x^2 \tag{3}$$

If y is in $[-\tfrac{1}{2}\pi, \tfrac{1}{2}\pi]$, $\cos y$ is nonnegative, and so from (3) it follows that

$$\cos y = \sqrt{1 - x^2} \quad \text{if } y \text{ is in } [-\tfrac{1}{2}\pi, \tfrac{1}{2}\pi] \tag{4}$$

Substituting from (4) into (2), we get

$$D_y x = \sqrt{1 - x^2}$$

From Theorem 9.3.4, $D_x y = 1/D_y x$; hence,

$$D_x(\sin^{-1} x) = \frac{1}{\sqrt{1 - x^2}} \tag{5}$$

The domain of the derivative of the inverse sine function is the open interval $(-1, 1)$.

If u is a differentiable function of x, we obtain from (5) and the chain rule

$$D_x(\sin^{-1} u) = \frac{1}{\sqrt{1 - u^2}} D_x u \tag{6}$$

• ILLUSTRATION 1: If $y = \sin^{-1} x^2$, then

$$\frac{dy}{dx} = \frac{1}{\sqrt{1 - (x^2)^2}} (2x) = \frac{2x}{\sqrt{1 - x^4}} \qquad •$$

To derive the formula for the derivative of the inverse cosine function, we use Eq. (9) of Sec. 10.7, which is

$$\cos^{-1} x = \tfrac{1}{2}\pi - \sin^{-1} x$$

Differentiating with respect to x, we have

$$D_x(\cos^{-1} x) = D_x(\tfrac{1}{2}\pi - \sin^{-1} x)$$

and so

$$D_x(\cos^{-1} x) = -\frac{1}{\sqrt{1 - x^2}} \tag{7}$$

where x is in $(-1, 1)$.

If u is a differentiable function of x, we obtain from (7) and the chain rule

$$D_x(\cos^{-1} u) = -\frac{1}{\sqrt{1 - u^2}} D_x u \tag{8}$$

We now derive the formula for the derivative of the inverse tangent function. If

$$y = \tan^{-1} x$$

then

$$x = \tan y \quad \text{and} \quad y \text{ is in } (-\tfrac{1}{2}\pi, \tfrac{1}{2}\pi)$$

Differentiating on both sides of the above equation with respect to y, we obtain

$$D_y x = \sec^2 y \quad \text{and} \quad y \text{ is in } (-\tfrac{1}{2}\pi, \tfrac{1}{2}\pi) \tag{9}$$

From the identity $\sec^2 y = 1 + \tan^2 y$, and replacing $\tan y$ by x, we have

$$\sec^2 y = 1 + x^2 \tag{10}$$

Substituting from (10) into (9), we get

$$D_y x = 1 + x^2$$

So from Theorem 9.3.4 we obtain

$$D_x(\tan^{-1} x) = \frac{1}{1 + x^2} \tag{11}$$

The domain of the derivative of the inverse tangent function is the set of all real numbers.

If u is a differentiable function of x, we obtain from (11) and the chain rule

$$D_x(\tan^{-1} u) = \frac{1}{1 + u^2} D_x u \tag{12}$$

● ILLUSTRATION 2: If $f(x) = \tan^{-1} \dfrac{1}{x + 1}$, then

$$f'(x) = \frac{1}{1 + \dfrac{1}{(x + 1)^2}} \cdot \frac{-1}{(x + 1)^2}$$

$$= \frac{-1}{(x + 1)^2 + 1}$$

$$= \frac{-1}{x^2 + 2x + 2}$$

●

From Definition 10.7.4 we have

$$\cot^{-1} x = \tfrac{1}{2}\pi - \tan^{-1} x$$

Differentiating with respect to x, we obtain the formula

$$D_x(\cot^{-1} x) = -\frac{1}{1 + x^2}$$

From this formula and the chain rule, it follows that if u is a differentiable function of x, then

$$D_x(\cot^{-1} u) = -\frac{1}{1 + u^2} D_x u \tag{13}$$

EXAMPLE 1: Given

$$y = x^3 \cot^{-1} \tfrac{1}{3}x$$

find dy/dx.

SOLUTION:

$$\frac{dy}{dx} = 3x^2 \cot^{-1} \frac{1}{3} x + x^3 \cdot \frac{-1}{1 + \frac{1}{9}x^2} \cdot \frac{1}{3}$$

$$= 3x^2 \cot^{-1} \frac{1}{3} x - \frac{3x^3}{9 + x^2}$$

EXAMPLE 2: Given

$$\ln(x + y) = \tan^{-1}\left(\frac{x}{y}\right)$$

find $D_x y$.

SOLUTION: Differentiating implicitly on both sides of the given equation with respect to x, we get

$$\frac{1}{x + y}(1 + D_x y) = \frac{1}{1 + \dfrac{x^2}{y^2}} \cdot \frac{y - x D_x y}{y^2}$$

$$\frac{1 + D_x y}{x + y} = \frac{y - x D_x y}{y^2 + x^2}$$

$$y^2 + x^2 + (y^2 + x^2) D_x y = xy + y^2 - (x^2 + xy) D_x y$$

$$D_x y = \frac{xy - x^2}{2x^2 + xy + y^2}$$

Definition 10.7.5 and formula (8) of this section are used to derive the formula for the derivative of the inverse secant function. From Definition 10.7.5 we have

$$\sec^{-1} x = \cos^{-1}\left(\frac{1}{x}\right) \qquad \text{for } |x| \geq 1$$

So

$$D_x(\sec^{-1} x) = -\frac{1}{\sqrt{1 - \left(\dfrac{1}{x}\right)^2}}\left(-\frac{1}{x^2}\right)$$

$$= \frac{1}{\dfrac{x^2 \sqrt{x^2 - 1}}{\sqrt{x^2}}}$$

$$= \frac{|x|}{x^2 \sqrt{x^2 - 1}}$$

Therefore, we have

$$D_x(\sec^{-1} x) = \frac{1}{|x| \sqrt{x^2 - 1}} \tag{14}$$

where $|x| > 1$.

If u is a differentiable function of x, it follows from (14) and the chain rule that

$$D_x(\sec^{-1} u) = \frac{1}{|u|\sqrt{u^2 - 1}} D_x u \tag{15}$$

● ILLUSTRATION 3: If $f(x) = \sec^{-1} 3x$, then

$$f'(x) = \frac{1}{|3x|\sqrt{(3x)^2 - 1}} \cdot 3 = \frac{1}{|x|\sqrt{9x^2 - 1}}$$

●

From (9) of Sec. 10.7 we have

$$\sin^{-1} x = \tfrac{1}{2}\pi - \cos^{-1} x \qquad \text{for } |x| \leq 1$$

Replacing x by $1/x$ in the above equation, we obtain

$$\sin^{-1}\left(\frac{1}{x}\right) = \frac{1}{2}\pi - \cos^{-1}\left(\frac{1}{x}\right) \qquad \text{for } |x| \geq 1$$

From the above equation and Definitions 10.7.5 and 10.7.6 it follows that

$$\csc^{-1} x = \tfrac{1}{2}\pi - \sec^{-1} x \qquad \text{for } |x| \geq 1$$

Equations (16) and (14) are used to find the derivative of the inverse cosecant function. Differentiating on both sides of (16) with respect to x, we get

$$D_x(\csc^{-1} x) = -\frac{1}{|x|\sqrt{x^2 - 1}} \tag{17}$$

where $|x| > 1$.

From (17) and the chain rule, if u is a differentiable function of x, we have

$$D_x(\csc^{-1} u) = -\frac{1}{|u|\sqrt{u^2 - 1}} D_x u \tag{18}$$

EXAMPLE 3: A picture 7 ft high is placed on a wall with its base 9 ft above the level of the eye of an observer. How far from the wall should the observer stand in order for the angle subtended at his eye by the picture to be the greatest?

SOLUTION: Let x ft be the distance of the observer from the wall, θ be the radian measure of the angle subtended at the observer's eye by the picture, α be the radian measure of the angle subtended at the observer's eye by the portion of the wall above his eye level and below the picture, and $\beta = \alpha + \theta$. Refer to Fig. 10.8.1.

We wish to find the value of x that will make θ an absolute maximum. Because x is in the interval $(0, +\infty)$, the absolute maximum value of θ will be a relative maximum value. We see from the figure that

$$\cot \beta = \frac{x}{16} \quad \text{and} \quad \cot \alpha = \frac{x}{9}$$

Because $0 < \beta < \frac{1}{2}\pi$ and $0 < \alpha < \frac{1}{2}\pi$, we have

$$\beta = \cot^{-1} \frac{x}{16} \quad \text{and} \quad \alpha = \cot^{-1} \frac{x}{9}$$

Substituting these values of β and α in the equation $\theta = \beta - \alpha$, we get

$$\theta = \cot^{-1} \frac{x}{16} - \cot^{-1} \frac{x}{9}$$

Differentiating with respect to x gives

$$D_x\theta = -\frac{\frac{1}{16}}{1 + \left(\frac{x}{16}\right)^2} + \frac{\frac{1}{9}}{1 + \left(\frac{x}{9}\right)^2}$$

$$= -\frac{16}{16^2 + x^2} + \frac{9}{9^2 + x^2}$$

Setting $D_x\theta = 0$, we obtain

$$9(16^2 + x^2) - 16(9^2 + x^2) = 0$$

$$-7x^2 + 9 \cdot 16(16 - 9) = 0$$

$$x^2 = 9 \cdot 16$$

$$x = 12$$

The -12 is rejected because it is not in the interval $(0, +\infty)$. The results of the first-derivative test are shown in Table 10.8.1. Because the relative maximum value of θ is an absolute maximum value, we conclude that the observer should stand 12 ft from the wall.

Table 10.8.1

	$D_x\theta$	Conclusion
$0 < x < 12$	$+$	
$x = 12$	0	θ has a relative maximum value
$12 < x < +\infty$	$-$	

Figure 10.8.1

Exercises 10.8

1. Derive the formula $D_x(\cot^{-1} x) = \dfrac{-1}{(1 + x^2)}$.

2. Derive the formula $D_x(\csc^{-1} x) = \dfrac{-1}{|x| \sqrt{x^2 - 1}}$.

In Exercises 3 through 22, find the derivative of the given function.

3. $f(x) = \sin^{-1} \frac{1}{2}x$

4. $g(x) = \tan^{-1} 2x$

5. $g(t) = \sec^{-1} 5t$

6. $F(x) = \cos^{-1} \sqrt{x}$

7. $F(x) = \cot^{-1} \frac{2}{x} + \tan^{-1} \frac{x}{2}$

8. $f(x) = \csc^{-1} 2x$

9. $h(y) = y \sin^{-1} 2y$

10. $f(t) = t^2 \cos^{-1} t$

11. $g(x) = x \csc^{-1} \frac{1}{x}$

12. $h(x) = \tan^{-1} \frac{2x}{1 - x^2}$

13. $f(x) = 4 \sin^{-1} \frac{1}{2}x + x\sqrt{4 - x^2}$

14. $g(s) = \cos^{-1} s + \frac{s}{1 - s^2}$

15. $f(t) = a \sin^{-1} \frac{t}{a} + \sqrt{a^2 - t^2}$

16. $F(x) = \ln(\tan^{-1} 3x)$

17. $g(x) = \cos^{-1}(\sin x)$

18. $f(x) = \sin^{-1} x + \cos^{-1} x$

19. $h(x) = \sec^{-1} x + \csc^{-1} x$

20. $F(x) = \sec^{-1} \sqrt{x^2 + 4}$

21. $G(x) = x \cot^{-1} x + \ln \sqrt{1 + x^2}$

22. $f(t) = \sin^{-1} \frac{t - 1}{t + 1}$

In Exercises 23 through 26, find $D_x y$ by implicit differentiation.

23. $e^x + y = \cos^{-1} x$

24. $\ln(\sin^2 3x) = e^x + \cot^{-1} y$

25. $x \sin y + x^3 = \tan^{-1} y$

26. $\sin^{-1}(xy) = \cos^{-1}(x + y)$

27. A light is 3 mi from a straight beach. If the light revolves and makes 2 rpm, find the speed of the spot of light along the beach when the spot is 2 mi from the point on the beach nearest the light.

28. A ladder 25 ft long is leaning against a vertical wall. If the bottom of the ladder is pulled horizontally away from the wall so that the top is sliding down at 3 ft/sec, how fast is the measure of the angle between the ladder and the ground changing when the bottom of the ladder is 15 ft from the wall?

29. A picture 4 ft high is placed on a wall with its base 3 ft above the level of the eye of an observer. If the observer is approaching the wall at the rate of 4 ft/sec, how fast is the measure of the angle subtended at his eye by the picture changing when the observer is 10 ft from the wall?

30. A man on a dock is pulling in at the rate of 2 ft/sec a rowboat by means of a rope. The man's hands are 20 ft above the level of the point where the rope is attached to the boat. How fast is the measure of the angle of depression of the rope changing when there are 52 ft of rope out?

31. A man is walking at the rate of 5 ft/sec along the diameter of a circular courtyard. A light at one end of a diameter perpendicular to his path casts a shadow on the circular wall. How fast is the shadow moving along the wall when the distance from the man to the center of the courtyard is $\frac{1}{2}r$, where r ft is the radius of the courtyard?

32. In Exercise 31, how far is the man from the center of the courtyard when the speed of his shadow along the wall is 9 ft/sec?

33. A rope is attached to a weight and it passes over a hook that is 8 ft above the ground. The rope is pulled over the hook at the rate of $\frac{3}{4}$ ft/sec and drags the weight along level ground. If the length of the rope between the weight and the hook is x ft when the radian measure of the angle between the rope and the floor is θ, find the time rate of change of θ in terms of x.

34. Given: $f(x) = \tan^{-1}(1/x) - \cot^{-1} x$. (a) Show that $f'(x) = 0$ for all x in the domain of f. (b) Prove that there is no constant C for which $f(x) = C$ for all x in its domain. (c) Why doesn't the statement in part (b) contradict Theorem 6.3.2?

10.9 INTEGRALS YIELDING INVERSE TRIGONOMETRIC FUNCTIONS

From the formulas for the derivatives of the inverse trigonometric functions, we obtain the following indefinite integral formulas:

$$\int \frac{du}{\sqrt{1-u^2}} = \sin^{-1} u + C \tag{1}$$

$$\int \frac{du}{1+u^2} = \tan^{-1} u + C \tag{2}$$

$$\int \frac{du}{u\sqrt{u^2-1}} = \sec^{-1} |u| + C \tag{3}$$

Formulas (1) and (2) follow directly from the formulas for the derivatives of $\sin^{-1} u$ and $\tan^{-1} u$. Formula (3) needs an explanation.

If $u > 0$, then $u = |u|$, and we have

$$\int \frac{du}{u\sqrt{u^2-1}} = \int \frac{du}{|u|\sqrt{u^2-1}} = \sec^{-1} u + C = \sec^{-1} |u| + C$$

If $u < 0$, then $u = -|u|$, and we have

$$\int \frac{du}{u\sqrt{u^2-1}} = \int \frac{du}{-|u|\sqrt{u^2-1}}$$

$$= \int \frac{-du}{|u|\sqrt{u^2-1}}$$

$$= \int \frac{d(-u)}{|-u|\sqrt{(-u)^2-1}}$$

$$= \sec^{-1}(-u) + C$$

$$= \sec^{-1} |u| + C$$

Therefore, if $u > 0$ or $u < 0$, we obtain (3). We also have the following formulas.

$$\int \frac{du}{\sqrt{a^2-u^2}} = \sin^{-1} \frac{u}{a} + C \qquad \text{where } a > 0 \tag{4}$$

$$\int \frac{du}{a^2+u^2} = \frac{1}{a} \tan^{-1} \frac{u}{a} + C \tag{5}$$

$$\int \frac{du}{u\sqrt{u^2-a^2}} = \frac{1}{a} \sec^{-1} \left|\frac{u}{a}\right| + C \qquad \text{where } a > 0 \tag{6}$$

These formulas can be proved by finding the derivative of the right side and obtaining the integrand. This is illustrated by proving (4).

$$D_u \left(\sin^{-1} \frac{u}{a}\right) = \frac{1}{\sqrt{1-\left(\frac{u}{a}\right)^2}} D_u \left(\frac{u}{a}\right)$$

$$= \frac{\sqrt{a^2}}{\sqrt{a^2 - u^2}} \cdot \frac{1}{a}$$

$$= \frac{a}{\sqrt{a^2 - u^2}} \cdot \frac{1}{a} \quad \text{if } a > 0$$

$$= \frac{1}{\sqrt{a^2 - u^2}} \quad \text{if } a > 0$$

The proofs of (5) and (6) are left as exercises (see Exercises 1 and 2).

EXAMPLE 1: **Evaluate**

$$\int \frac{dx}{\sqrt{4 - 9x^2}}$$

SOLUTION:

$$\int \frac{dx}{\sqrt{4 - 9x^2}} = \frac{1}{3} \int \frac{d(3x)}{\sqrt{4 - (3x)^2}}$$

$$= \frac{1}{3} \sin^{-1} \frac{3x}{2} + C$$

EXAMPLE 2: **Evaluate**

$$\int \frac{dx}{3x^2 - 2x + 5}$$

SOLUTION:

$$\int \frac{dx}{3x^2 - 2x + 5} = \int \frac{dx}{3(x^2 - \frac{2}{3}x) + 5}$$

To complete the square of $x^2 - \frac{2}{3}x$ we add $\frac{1}{9}$, and because $\frac{1}{9}$ is multiplied by 3, we actually add $\frac{1}{3}$ to the denominator, and so we also subtract $\frac{1}{3}$ from the denominator. Therefore, we have

$$\int \frac{dx}{3x^2 - 2x + 5} = \int \frac{dx}{3(x^2 - \frac{2}{3}x + \frac{1}{9}) + 5 - \frac{1}{3}}$$

$$= \int \frac{dx}{3(x - \frac{1}{3})^2 + \frac{14}{3}} = \frac{1}{3} \int \frac{dx}{(x - \frac{1}{3})^2 + \frac{14}{9}}$$

$$= \frac{1}{3} \cdot \frac{3}{\sqrt{14}} \tan^{-1} \left(\frac{x - \frac{1}{3}}{\frac{1}{3}\sqrt{14}} \right) + C$$

$$= \frac{1}{\sqrt{14}} \tan^{-1} \left(\frac{3x - 1}{\sqrt{14}} \right) + C$$

EXAMPLE 3: **Evaluate**

$$\int \frac{(2x + 7)\, dx}{x^2 + 2x + 5}$$

SOLUTION: Because $d(x^2 + 2x + 5) = (2x + 2)\, dx$, we write the numerator as $(2x + 2)\, dx + 5\, dx$, and express the original integral as the sum of two integrals.

$$\int \frac{(2x + 7)\, dx}{x^2 + 2x + 5} = \int \frac{(2x + 2)\, dx}{x^2 + 2x + 5} + 5 \int \frac{dx}{x^2 + 2x + 5}$$

$$= \ln |x^2 + 2x + 5| + 5 \int \frac{dx}{(x+1)^2 + 4}$$

$$= \ln(x^2 + 2x + 5) + \frac{5}{2} \tan^{-1} \frac{x+1}{2} + C$$

NOTE: Because $x^2 + 2x + 5 > 0$, for all x, $|x^2 + 2x + 5| = x^2 + 2x + 5$.

EXAMPLE 4: Evaluate

$$\int \frac{3\, dx}{(x+2)\sqrt{x^2 + 4x + 3}}$$

SOLUTION:

$$\int \frac{3\, dx}{(x+2)\sqrt{x^2 + 4x + 3}} = \int \frac{3\, dx}{(x+2)\sqrt{(x^2 + 4x + 4) - 1}}$$

$$= 3 \int \frac{d(x+2)}{(x+2)\sqrt{(x+2)^2 - 1}}$$

$$= 3 \sec^{-1} |x+2| + C$$

EXAMPLE 5: Find the area of the region in the first quadrant bounded by the curve

$$y = \frac{1}{1 + x^2}$$

the x axis, the y axis, and the line $x = 1$.

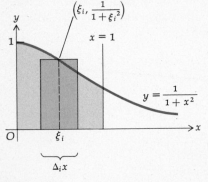

Figure 10.9.1

SOLUTION: Figure 10.9.1 shows the region and a rectangular element of area. If A square units is the area of the region, we have

$$A = \lim_{\|\Delta\| \to 0} \sum_{i=1}^{n} \frac{1}{1 + \xi_i^2} \Delta_i x$$

$$= \int_0^1 \frac{dx}{1 + x^2}$$

$$= \tan^{-1} x \Big]_0^1$$

$$= \tan^{-1} 1 - \tan^{-1} 0$$

$$= \tfrac{1}{4}\pi - 0$$

$$= \tfrac{1}{4}\pi$$

The result of Example 5 states that the number π is four times the number of square units in the area of the region shown in Fig. 10.9.1.

Exercises 10.9

In Exercises 1 through 5, prove the given formula by showing that the derivative of the right side is equal to the integrand.

1. $\displaystyle \int \frac{du}{a^2 + u^2} = \frac{1}{a} \tan^{-1} \frac{u}{a} + C$

2. $\int \dfrac{du}{u\sqrt{u^2 - a^2}} = \dfrac{1}{a} \sec^{-1} \left|\dfrac{u}{a}\right| + C$ if $a > 0$

Take two cases: $u > 0$ and $u < 0$.

3. $\int \dfrac{du}{\sqrt{1 - u^2}} = -\cos^{-1} u + C$

Is this formula equivalent to formula (1)? Why?

4. $\int \dfrac{du}{1 + u^2} = -\cot^{-1} u + C$

Is this formula equivalent to formula (2)? Why?

5. $\int \dfrac{du}{u\sqrt{u^2 - 1}} = -\csc^{-1} |u| + C$

Take two cases: $u > 0$ and $u < 0$. Is this formula equivalent to formula (3)? Why?

In Exercises 6 through 25, evaluate the indefinite integral.

6. $\int \dfrac{dx}{\sqrt{1 - 4x^2}}$

7. $\int \dfrac{dx}{x^2 + 25}$

8. $\int \dfrac{x\,dx}{x^4 + 16}$

9. $\int \dfrac{dx}{\sqrt{2 - 5x^2}}$

10. $\int \dfrac{3\,dx}{x\sqrt{x^2 - 9}}$

11. $\int \dfrac{r\,dr}{\sqrt{16 - 9r^4}}$

12. $\int \dfrac{du}{u\sqrt{16u^2 - 9}}$

13. $\int \dfrac{e^x\,dx}{7 + e^{2x}}$

14. $\int \dfrac{\sin x\,dx}{\sqrt{2 - \cos^2 x}}$

15. $\int \dfrac{dx}{(1 + x)\sqrt{x}}$

16. $\int \dfrac{ds}{\sqrt{2s - s^2}}$

17. $\int \dfrac{dx}{x^2 - x + 2}$

18. $\int \dfrac{dx}{\sqrt{3x - x^2 - 2}}$

19. $\int \dfrac{dx}{\sqrt{15 + 2x - x^2}}$

20. $\int \dfrac{dx}{2x^2 + 2x + 3}$

21. $\int \dfrac{x\,dx}{\sqrt{3 - 2x - x^2}}$

22. $\int \dfrac{x\,dx}{x^2 + x + 1}$

23. $\int \dfrac{(2 + x)\,dx}{\sqrt{4 - 2x - x^2}}$

24. $\int \dfrac{3\,dx}{(x + 2)\sqrt{x^2 + 4x + 3}}$

25. $\int \dfrac{2x^3\,dx}{2x^2 - 4x + 3}$

In Exercises 26 through 33, evaluate the definite integral.

26. $\displaystyle\int_0^{1/2} \dfrac{dx}{\sqrt{1 - x^2}}$

27. $\displaystyle\int_0^1 \dfrac{1 + x}{1 + x^2}\,dx$

28. $\displaystyle\int_0^{\sqrt{3}} \dfrac{x\,dx}{\sqrt{1 + x^2}}$

29. $\displaystyle\int_{-4}^{-2} \dfrac{dt}{\sqrt{-t^2 - 6t - 5}}$

30. $\displaystyle\int_2^5 \dfrac{dx}{x^2 - 4x + 13}$

31. $\displaystyle\int_0^1 \dfrac{dx}{e^x + e^{-x}}$

32. $\displaystyle\int_{1/\sqrt{2}}^1 \dfrac{dx}{x\sqrt{4x^2 - 1}}$

33. $\displaystyle\int_1^e \dfrac{dx}{x[1 + (\ln x)^2]}$

34. Find the area of the region bounded by the curve $y = 8/(x^2 + 4)$, the x axis, the y axis, and the line $x = 2$.

35. Find the abscissa of the centroid of the region of Exercise 34.

36. Find the area of the region bounded by the curves $x^2 = 4ay$ and $y = 8a^3/(x^2 + 4a^2)$.

37. Find the circumference of the circle $x^2 + y^2 = r^2$ by integration.

38. A particle moving in a straight line is said to have *simple harmonic motion* if the measure of its acceleration is always proportional to the measure of its displacement from a fixed point on the line and its acceleration and displacement are oppositely directed. So if at t sec, s ft is the directed distance of the particle from the origin and v ft/sec is the velocity of the particle, then a differential equation for simple harmonic motion is

$$\frac{dv}{dt} = -k^2 s \tag{7}$$

where k^2 is the constant of proportionality and the minus sign indicates that the acceleration is opposite in direction from the displacement. Because $dv/dt = (dv/ds)(ds/dt) = v(dv/ds)$, Eq. (7) may be written as

$$v \frac{dv}{ds} = -k^2 s \tag{8}$$

(a) Solve Eq. (8) for v to get $v = \pm k \sqrt{a^2 - s^2}$. Note: Take $a^2 k^2$ as the arbitrary constant of integration and justify this choice. (b) Letting $v = ds/dt$ in the solution of part (a), we obtain the differential equation

$$\frac{ds}{dt} = \pm k \sqrt{a^2 - s^2} \tag{9}$$

Taking $t = 0$ at the instant when $v = 0$ (and hence $s = a$), solve Eq. (9) to obtain

$$s = a \cos kt \tag{10}$$

(c) Show that the largest value for $|s|$ is a. The number a is called the *amplitude* of the motion. (d) The particle will oscillate between the points where $s = a$ and $s = -a$. If T sec is the time for the particle to go from a to $-a$ and return, show that $T = 2\pi/k$. The number T is called the *period* of the motion.

39. A particle is moving in a straight line according to the equation of motion $s = 5 - 10 \sin^2 2t$, where s ft is the directed distance of the particle from the origin at t sec. Use the result of part (b) of Exercise 38 to show that the motion is simple harmonic. Find the amplitude and period of this motion.

40. Show that the motion of Exercise 39 is simple harmonic by showing that differential equation (7) is satisfied.

Review Exercises (Chapter 10)

In Exercises 1 through 4, evaluate the given limit, if it exists.

1. $\displaystyle\lim_{x \to 0} \frac{\sin^2 x}{3x^2}$

2. $\displaystyle\lim_{x \to 0} \frac{\tan x}{2x}$

3. $\displaystyle\lim_{x \to 0} \frac{\tan^4 2x}{4x^4}$

4. $\displaystyle\lim_{x \to \pi/2} \frac{\cos 5x}{\cos 7x}$

5. Show that $\dfrac{d(\ln \sin x)}{d(\ln x)} = x \cot x$

6. Prove that $\displaystyle\lim_{x \to 0} \frac{\sin x^2}{x} = 0$.

In Exercises 7 through 14, find the derivative of the function defined by the given equation.

7. $f(x) = \sqrt[4]{\sin 4x}$

8. $f(x) = \sqrt{\csc 3x}$

9. $g(x) = x \cos \dfrac{1}{x}$

10. $f(t) = \dfrac{\ln t}{\sec t}$

11. $F(x) = \tan^{-1} 2^x$

12. $g(x) = \cot 3x \sqrt{\sin 2x}$

13. $f(x) = (\tan x)^{1/x^2}$

14. $h(x) = (\cos x)^{e^x}$

In Exercises 15 and 16, find $D_x y$ by implicit differentiation.

15. $\cot^{-1} \dfrac{x^2}{3y} + xy^2 = 0$

16. $\sin(x + y) + \sin(x - y) = 1$

In Exercises 17 through 24, find the indefinite integral.

17. $\displaystyle\int \sin^4 \tfrac{1}{2}x \cos^2 \tfrac{1}{2}x \, dx$

18. $\displaystyle\int \sqrt{1 - \cos x} \, dx$

19. $\displaystyle\int \dfrac{dx}{2x^2 + 3x + 5}$

20. $\displaystyle\int (\csc 2x - \cot 2x) \, dx$

21. $\displaystyle\int \dfrac{dt}{1 + \sec 3t}$

22. $\displaystyle\int \dfrac{dx}{\sqrt{7 + 5x - 2x^2}}$

23. $\displaystyle\int \sin 3x \cos 5x \, dx$

24. $\displaystyle\int \sin^3 2x \cos^5 2x \, dx$

In Exercises 25 through 28, evaluate the definite integral.

25. $\displaystyle\int_0^{\pi/3} \sec^3 x \tan^5 x \, dx$

26. $\displaystyle\int_0^{\pi/6} \tan^4 2x \, dx$

27. $\displaystyle\int_1^2 \dfrac{(x + 2) \, dx}{\sqrt{4x - x^2}}$

28. $\displaystyle\int_{\pi/4}^{\pi/2} (\sin^4 2x - 2 \sin 4x) \, dx$

29. Find the length of the arc of the curve $y = \ln \cos x$ from the origin to the point $(\tfrac{1}{3}\pi, -\ln 2)$.

30. Find the average value of the cosine function on the closed interval $[a, a + 2\pi]$.

31. Find to the nearest degree the measurements of the four interior angles of the quadrilateral having vertices at $(5, 6)$, $(-2, 4)$, $(-2, 1)$ and $(3, 1)$ and verify that the sum is 360°.

32. Find the volume of the solid generated if the region bounded by the curve $y = \sin^2 x$ and the x axis from $x = 0$ to $x = \pi$ is revolved about the x axis.

33. Two points A and B are diametrically opposite each other on the shores of a circular lake 1 mi in diameter. A man desires to go from point A to point B. He can row at the rate of $1\tfrac{1}{2}$ mi/hr and walk at the rate of 5 mi/hr. Find the least amount of time it can take for him to get from point A to point B.

34. Solve Exercise 33 if the rates of rowing and walking are, respectively, 2 mi/hr and 4 mi/hr.

35. A particle is moving along a straight line and

$$s = \sin(4t + \tfrac{1}{3}\pi) + \sin(4t + \tfrac{1}{6}\pi)$$

where s ft is the directed distance of the particle from the origin at t sec. Show that the motion is simple harmonic and find the amplitude of the motion. (See Exercise 38 in Exercises 10.9.)

36. If an equation of motion is $s = \cos 2t + \cos t$, prove that the motion is not simple harmonic.

37. Evaluate: $\displaystyle\int_0^\pi |\cos x + \tfrac{1}{2}| \, dx$.

38. Evaluate: $\displaystyle\int_0^{\pi/2} |\cos x - \sin x| \, dx$.

39. Find the area of the region in the first quadrant bounded by the y axis and the curves $y = \sec^2 x$ and $y = 2 \tan^2 x$.

40. Find an equation of the normal line to the curve $y = \cos x$ at the point $(\tfrac{2}{3}\pi, -\tfrac{1}{2})$.

41. A particle is moving along a straight line according to the equation of motion $s = 5 - 2 \cos^2 t$ where s ft is the directed

distance of the particle from the origin at t sec. If v ft/sec and a ft/sec² are, respectively, the velocity and acceleration of the particle at t sec, find v and a in terms of s.

42. If y ft is the range of a projectile, then

$$y = \frac{v_0^2 \sin 2\theta}{g}$$

where v_0 ft/sec is the initial velocity, g ft/sec² is the acceleration due to gravity, and θ is the radian measure of the angle that the gun makes with the horizontal. Find the value of θ that makes the range a maximum.

43. A searchlight is $\frac{1}{2}$ mi from a straight road and it keeps a light trained on an automobile that is traveling at the constant speed of 60 mi/hr. Find the rate at which the light beam is changing direction (a) when the car is at the point on the road nearest the searchlight and (b) when the car is $\frac{1}{2}$ mi down the road from this point.

44. A helicopter leaves the ground at a point 800 ft from an observer and rises vertically at 25 ft/sec. Find the time rate of change of the measure of the observer's angle of elevation of the helicopter when the helicopter is 600 ft above the ground.

45. In an electric circuit let $E = f(t)$ and $i = g(t)$ where E volts and i amperes are, respectively, the electromotive force and current at t sec. If P watts is the average power in the interval $[0, T]$, where T sec is the common period of f and g, then

$$P = \frac{1}{T} \int_0^T f(t)g(t)\, dt$$

If $E = 100 \sin t$ and $i = 4(\sin t - \frac{1}{3}\pi)$, first determine T and then find P.

46. Find the area of the region bounded by the curve $y = 9/\sqrt{9 - x^2}$, the two coordinate axes, and the line $x = 2\sqrt{2}$.

47. Find the absolute maximum value attained by the function f if $f(x) = A \sin kx + B \cos kx$, where $A, B,$ and k are positive constants.

48. Suppose the function f is defined on the open interval $(0, 1)$ and

$$f(x) = \frac{\sin \pi x}{x(x - 1)}$$

Define f at 0 and 1 so that f is continuous on the closed interval $\lfloor 0, 1 \rfloor$.

49. Prove: $D_x{}^n(\sin x) = \sin(x + \frac{1}{2}n\pi)$. (HINT: Use mathematical induction and the formulas $\sin(x + \frac{1}{2}\pi) = \cos x$ or $\cos(x + \frac{1}{2}\pi) = -\sin x$ after each differentiation.)

11

Techniques of integration

11.1 INTRODUCTION   In Chapter   the definite integral of a function f from a to b was defined as the limit of a Riemann sum as follows:

$$\int_a^b f(x)\ dx = \lim_{||\Delta|| \to 0} \sum_{i=1}^{n} f(\xi_i)\ \Delta_i x \tag{1}$$

if the limit exists. We stated a theorem, proved in advanced calculus, that the limit on the right side of (1) exists if f is continuous on the closed interval $[a, b]$.

The exact value of a definite integral may be calculated by the fundamental theorem of the calculus, provided that we can find an antiderivative of the integrand. The process of finding the most general antiderivative of a given integrand is called *indefinite integration.* We use the term *indefinite integral* to mean the most general antiderivative of a given integrand. In practice, it is not always possible to find the indefinite integral. That is, we may have a definite integral that exists, but the integrand has no antiderivative that can be expressed in terms of elementary functions. An example of this is $\int_0^{1/2} e^{-t^2}\ dt$ (a method for computing the value of this definite integral to any required degree of accuracy by using infinite series is given in Sec. 16.9). However, many of the definite integrals that occur in practice can be evaluated by finding an antiderivative of the integrand. Some methods for doing this were given previously, and additional ones are presented in this chapter. Often you may find it desirable to resort to a *table of integrals* instead of performing a complicated integration. (A short table of integrals can be found on the front and back endpapers.) However, it may be necessary to employ some of the techniques of integration in order to express the integrand in a form that is found in a table. Therefore, you should acquire proficiency in recognizing which technique to apply to a given integral. Furthermore, development of computational skills is important in all branches of mathematics, and the exercises in this chapter provide a good training ground. For these reasons you are advised to use a table of integrals only after you have mastered integration.

The standard indefinite integration formulas, which we learned in previous chapters and which are used frequently, are listed below.

$$\int du = u + C \qquad\qquad\qquad \int a^u\ du = \frac{a^u}{\ln a} + C$$

$$\int a\ du = au + C \quad \text{where } a \text{ is any constant} \qquad \int e^u\ du = e^u + C$$

$$\int [f(u) + g(u)]\ du = \int f(u)\ du + \int g(u)\ du \qquad \int \sin u\ du = -\cos u + C$$

$$\int u^n\ du = \frac{u^{n+1}}{n+1} + C \quad n \neq -1 \qquad\qquad \int \cos u\ du = \sin u + C$$

$$\int \frac{du}{u} = \ln |u| + C \qquad\qquad\qquad \int \sec^2 u\ du = \tan u + C$$

$$\int \csc^2 u \ du = -\cot u + C$$

$$\int \sec u \tan u \ du = \sec u + C$$

$$\int \csc u \cot u \ du = -\csc u + C$$

$$\int \tan u \ du = \ln |\sec u| + C$$

$$\int \cot u \ du = \ln |\sin u| + C$$

$$\int \sec u \ du = \ln |\sec u + \tan u| + C$$

$$\int \csc u \ du = \ln |\csc u - \cot u| + C$$

$$\int \frac{du}{\sqrt{a^2 - u^2}} = \sin^{-1} \frac{u}{a} + C \qquad \text{where } a > 0$$

$$\int \frac{du}{a^2 + u^2} = \frac{1}{a} \tan^{-1} \frac{u}{a} + C$$

$$\int \frac{du}{u \sqrt{u^2 - a^2}} = \frac{1}{a} \sec^{-1} \left| \frac{u}{a} \right| + C \qquad \text{where } a > 0$$

11.2 INTEGRATION BY PARTS A method of integration that is quite useful is *integration by parts*. It depends on the formula for the differential of a product:

$$d(uv) = u \ dv + v \ du$$

or, equivalently,

$$u \ dv = d(uv) - v \ du \tag{1}$$

Integrating on both sides of (1), we have

$$\int u \ dv = uv - \int v \ du \tag{2}$$

Formula (2) is called the *formula for integration by parts*. This formula expresses the integral $\int u \ dv$ in terms of another integral, $\int v \ du$. By a suitable choice of u and dv, it may be easier to integrate the second integral than the first. When choosing the substitutions for u and dv, we usually want dv to be the most complicated factor of the integrand that can be integrated directly and u to be a function whose derivative is a simpler function. The method is shown by the following illustrations and examples.

● ILLUSTRATION 1: We wish to evaluate

$$\int \tan^{-1} x \ dx$$

Let $u = \tan^{-1} x$ and $dv = dx$. Then

$$du = \frac{dx}{1 + x^2}$$

and

$$v = x + C_1$$

So from (2) we have

$$\int \tan^{-1} x \, dx = (\tan^{-1} x)(x + C_1) - \int (x + C_1) \frac{dx}{1 + x^2}$$

$$= x \tan^{-1} x + C_1 \tan^{-1} x - \int \frac{x \, dx}{1 + x^2} - C_1 \int \frac{dx}{1 + x^2}$$

$$= x \tan^{-1} x + C_1 \tan^{-1} x - \tfrac{1}{2} \ln |1 + x^2| - C_1 \tan^{-1} x + C_2$$

$$= x \tan^{-1} x - \tfrac{1}{2} \ln (1 + x^2) + C_2 \qquad \bullet$$

In Illustration 1 observe that the first constant of integration C_1 does not appear in the final result. This is true in general, and we prove it as follows: By writing $v + C_1$ in place of v in formula 2, we have

$$\int u \, dv = u(v + C_1) - \int (v + C_1) \, du$$

$$= uv + C_1 u - \int v \, du - C_1 \int du$$

$$= uv + C_1 u - \int v \, du - C_1 u$$

$$= uv - \int v \, du$$

Therefore, it is not necessary to write C_1 when finding v from dv.

EXAMPLE 1:   Find

$$\int x \ln x \, dx$$

SOLUTION: Let $u = \ln x$ and $dv = x \, dx$. Then

$$du = \frac{dx}{x} \qquad v = \frac{x^2}{2}$$

So

$$\int x \ln x \, dx = \frac{x^2}{2} \ln x - \int \frac{x^2}{2} \cdot \frac{dx}{x}$$

$$= \frac{x^2}{2} \ln x - \frac{1}{2} \int x \, dx$$

$$= \tfrac{1}{2} x^2 \ln x - \tfrac{1}{4} x^2 + C$$

EXAMPLE 2:   Find

$$\int x \sin x \, dx$$

SOLUTION: Let $u = x$ and $dv = \sin x \, dx$. Then

$$du = dx \quad \text{and} \quad v = -\cos x$$

Therefore, we have

$$\int x \sin x \, dx = -x \cos x + \int \cos x \, dx$$

$$= -x \cos x + \sin x + C$$

● ILLUSTRATION 2: In Example 2, if instead of our choices of u and dv as above, we let

$$u = \sin x \quad \text{and} \quad dv = x \, dx$$

we get

$$du = \cos x \, dx \quad \text{and} \quad v = \tfrac{1}{2}x^2$$

So we have

$$\int x \sin x \, dx = \frac{x^2}{2} \sin x - \frac{1}{2} \int x^2 \cos x \, dx$$

The integral on the right is more complicated than the integral with which we started, thereby indicating that these are not desirable choices for u and dv. ●

It may happen that a particular integral may require repeated applications of integration by parts. This is illustrated in the following example.

EXAMPLE 3: Find

$$\int x^2 e^x \, dx$$

SOLUTION: Let $u = x^2$ and $dv = e^x \, dx$. Then

$$du = 2x \, dx \quad \text{and} \quad v = e^x$$

We have, then,

$$\int x^2 e^x \, dx = x^2 e^x - 2 \int x e^x \, dx$$

We now apply integration by parts to the integral on the right. Let

$$\bar{u} = x \quad \text{and} \quad d\bar{v} = e^x \, dx$$

Then

$$d\bar{u} = dx \quad \text{and} \quad \bar{v} = e^x$$

So we obtain

$$\int x e^x \, dx = x e^x - \int e^x \, dx$$

$$= x e^x - e^x + \bar{C}$$

Therefore,

$$\int x^2 e^x \, dx = x^2 e^x - 2[x e^x - e^x + \bar{C}]$$

$$= x^2 e^x - 2x e^x + 2 e^x + C$$

Another situation that sometimes occurs when using integration by parts is shown in Example 4.

EXAMPLE 4: Find

$$\int e^x \sin x \, dx$$

SOLUTION: Let $u = e^x$ and $dv = \sin x \, dx$. Then

$$du = e^x \, dx \quad \text{and} \quad v = -\cos x$$

Therefore,

$$\int e^x \sin x \, dx = -e^x \cos x + \int e^x \cos x \, dx$$

The integral on the right is similar to the first integral, except it has $\cos x$ in place of $\sin x$. We apply integration by parts again by letting

$$\bar{u} = e^x \quad \text{and} \quad d\bar{v} = \cos x \, dx$$

So

$$d\bar{u} = e^x \, dx \quad \text{and} \quad \bar{v} = \sin x$$

Thus, we have

$$\int e^x \sin x \, dx = -e^x \cos x + \left[e^x \sin x - \int e^x \sin x \, dx \right]$$

Now we have on the right the same integral that we have on the left. So we add $\int e^x \sin x \, dx$ to both sides of the equation, thus giving us

$$2 \int e^x \sin x \, dx = -e^x \cos x + e^x \sin x + \bar{C}$$

Dividing on both sides by 2, we obtain

$$\int e^x \sin x \, dx = \tfrac{1}{2} e^x (\sin x - \cos x) + C$$

In applying integration by parts to a specific integral, one pair of choices for u and dv may work while another pair may not. We saw this in Illustration 2, and another case occurs in Illustration 3.

● ILLUSTRATION 3: In Example 4, in the step where we have

$$\int e^x \sin x \, dx = -e^x \cos x + \int e^x \cos x \, dx$$

if we evaluate the integral on the right by letting

$$\bar{u} = \cos x \quad \text{and} \quad d\bar{v} = e^x \, dx$$

$$d\bar{u} = -\sin x \, dx \quad \text{and} \quad \bar{v} = e^x$$

we get

$$\int e^x \sin x \, dx = -e^x \cos x + \left(e^x \cos x + \int e^x \sin x \, dx \right)$$

$$\int e^x \sin x \, dx = \int e^x \sin x \, dx$$

●

In Sec. 10.8 we noted that in order to integrate odd powers of the secant and cosecant we use integration by parts. This process is illustrated in Example 5.

EXAMPLE 5:   Find

$$\int \sec^3 x \, dx$$

SOLUTION: Let $u = \sec x$ and $dv = \sec^2 x \, dx$. Then

$$du = \sec x \tan x \, dx \quad \text{and} \quad v = \tan x$$

Therefore,

$$\int \sec^3 x \, dx = \sec x \tan x - \int \sec x \tan^2 x \, dx$$

$$\int \sec^3 x \, dx = \sec x \tan x - \int \sec x (\sec^2 x - 1) \, dx$$

$$\int \sec^3 x \, dx = \sec x \tan x - \int \sec^3 x \, dx + \int \sec x \, dx$$

Adding $\int \sec^3 x \, dx$ to both sides, we get

$$2 \int \sec^3 x \, dx = \sec x \tan x + \ln |\sec x + \tan x| + 2C$$

So

$$\int \sec^3 x \, dx = \tfrac{1}{2} \sec x \tan x + \tfrac{1}{2} \ln |\sec x + \tan x| + C$$

Integration by parts often is used when the integrand involves logarithms, inverse trigonometric functions, and products.

Exercises 11.2

In Exercises 1 through 16, evaluate the indefinite integral.

1. $\displaystyle\int \ln x \, dx$

2. $\displaystyle\int x \cos 2x \, dx$

3. $\displaystyle\int x \sec^2 x \, dx$

4. $\displaystyle\int x \, 3^x \, dx$

5. $\displaystyle\int \sin^{-1} x \, dx$

6. $\displaystyle\int x^2 \ln x \, dx$

7. $\displaystyle\int x \tan^{-1} x \, dx$

8. $\displaystyle\int x^2 \sin 3x \, dx$

9. $\displaystyle\int e^x \cos x \, dx$

10. $\displaystyle\int \sin(\ln x) \, dx$

11. $\displaystyle\int \frac{x^3 \, dx}{\sqrt{1 - x^2}}$

12. $\displaystyle\int x^3 e^{x^2} \, dx$

13. $\displaystyle\int x^2 \sin x \, dx$

14. $\displaystyle\int \csc^3 x \, dx$

15. $\displaystyle\int \sec^5 x \, dx$

16. $\displaystyle\int \frac{\cot^{-1} \sqrt{x}}{\sqrt{x}} \, dx$

In Exercises 17 through 24, evaluate the definite integral.

17. $\displaystyle\int_0^{\pi/3} \sin 3x \cos x \, dx$

18. $\displaystyle\int_{-\pi}^{\pi} x^2 \cos 2x \, dx$

19. $\displaystyle\int_0^2 xe^{2x} \, dx$

20. $\displaystyle\int_0^{\pi^2/2} \cos \sqrt{2x} \, dx$

21. $\displaystyle\int_0^{\pi/4} e^{3x} \sin 4x \, dx$

22. $\displaystyle\int_{\pi/4}^{3\pi/4} x \cot x \csc x \, dx$

23. $\displaystyle\int_1^4 \sec^{-1} \sqrt{x} \, dx$

24. $\displaystyle\int_0^1 x \sin^{-1} x \, dx$

25. Find the area of the region bounded by the curve $y = \ln x$, the x axis, and the line $x = e^2$.

26. Find the volume of the solid generated by revolving the region in Exercise 25 about the x axis.

27. Find the volume of the solid generated by revolving the region in Exercise 25 about the y axis.

28. Find the centroid of the region bounded by the curve $y = e^x$, the coordinate axes, and the line $x = 3$.

29. The linear density of a rod at a point x ft from one end is $2e^{-x}$ slugs/ft. If the rod is 6 ft long, find the mass and center of mass of the rod.

30. Find the centroid of the solid of revolution obtained by revolving about the x axis the region bounded by the curve $y = \sin x$, the x axis, and the line $x = \frac{1}{2}\pi$.

31. A board is in the shape of a region bounded by a straight line and one arch of the sine curve. If the board is submerged vertically in water so that the straight line is the lower boundary 2 ft below the surface of the water, find the force on the board due to liquid pressure.

32. A particle is moving along a straight line and s ft is the directed distance of the particle from the origin at t sec. If v ft/sec is the velocity at t sec, $s = 0$ when $t = 0$, and $v \cdot s = t \sin t$, find s in terms of t and also s when $t = \frac{1}{2}\pi$.

33. A water tank full of water is in the shape of the solid of revolution formed by rotating about the x axis the region bounded by the curve $y = e^{-x}$, the coordinate axes, and the line $x = 4$. Find the work done in pumping all the water to the top of the tank. Distance is measured in feet. Take the positive x axis vertically downward.

34. The face of a dam is in the shape of one arch of the curve $y = 100 \cos \frac{1}{200}\pi x$ and the surface of the water is at the top of the dam. Find the force due to liquid pressure on the face of the dam. Distance is measured in feet.

35. A manufacturer has discovered that if x hundreds of units of a particular commodity are produced per week, the marginal cost is determined by $x2^{x/2}$ and the marginal revenue is determined by $8 \cdot 2^{-x/2}$, where both the production cost and the revenue are in thousands of dollars. If the weekly fixed costs amount to $2000, find the maximum weekly profit that can be obtained.

11.3 INTEGRATION BY TRIGONOMETRIC SUBSTITUTION

If the integrand contains an expression of the form $\sqrt{a^2 - u^2}$, $\sqrt{a^2 + u^2}$, or $\sqrt{u^2 - a^2}$, where $a > 0$, it is often possible to perform the integration by making a trigonometric substitution which results in an integral involving trigonometric functions. We consider each form as a separate case.

Case 1: The integrand contains an expression of the form $\sqrt{a^2 - u^2}$, $a > 0$. We introduce a new variable θ by letting $u = a \sin \theta$, where $0 \leq \theta \leq \frac{1}{2}\pi$ if $u \geq 0$ and $-\frac{1}{2}\pi \leq \theta < 0$ if $u < 0$. Then $du = a \cos \theta \, d\theta$, and

$$\sqrt{a^2 - u^2} = \sqrt{a^2 - a^2 \sin^2 \theta} = \sqrt{a^2(1 - \sin^2 \theta)} = a\sqrt{\cos^2 \theta}$$

Because $-\frac{1}{2}\pi \leq \theta \leq \frac{1}{2}\pi$, $\cos \theta \geq 0$; hence, $\sqrt{\cos^2 \theta} = \cos \theta$, and we have $\sqrt{a^2 - u^2} = a \cos \theta$. Because $\sin \theta = u/a$ and $-\frac{1}{2}\pi \leq \theta \leq \frac{1}{2}\pi$, it follows that $\theta = \sin^{-1}(u/a)$.

EXAMPLE 1: Evaluate

$$\int \frac{\sqrt{9 - x^2}}{x^2}\, dx$$

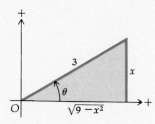

Figure 11.3.1 $x \geq 0$

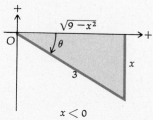

Figure 11.3.2 $x < 0$

SOLUTION: Let $x = 3 \sin \theta$, where $0 \leq \theta \leq \frac{1}{2}\pi$ if $x \geq 0$ and $-\frac{1}{2}\pi \leq \theta < 0$ if $x < 0$. Then $dx = 3 \cos \theta\, d\theta$ and

$$\sqrt{9 - x^2} = \sqrt{9 - 9 \sin^2 \theta} = 3 \sqrt{\cos^2 \theta} = 3 \cos \theta$$

Therefore,

$$\int \frac{\sqrt{9 - x^2}}{x^2}\, dx = \int \frac{3 \cos \theta}{9 \sin^2 \theta} (3 \cos \theta\, d\theta)$$

$$= \int \cot^2 \theta\, d\theta$$

$$= \int (\csc^2 \theta - 1)\, d\theta$$

$$= -\cot \theta - \theta + C$$

Because $\sin \theta = \frac{1}{3}x$ and $-\frac{1}{2}\pi \leq \theta \leq \frac{1}{2}\pi$, $\theta = \sin^{-1}(\frac{1}{3}x)$. To find $\cot \theta$ refer to Figs. 11.3.1   (for $x \geq 0$) and 11.3.2   (for $x < 0$). We see that $\cot \theta = \sqrt{9 - x^2}/x$. Therefore,

$$\int \frac{\sqrt{9 - x^2}}{x^2}\, dx = -\frac{\sqrt{9 - x^2}}{x} - \sin^{-1} \frac{x}{3} + C$$

Case 2:   The integrand contains an expression of the form $\sqrt{a^2 + u^2}$, $a > 0$. We introduce a new variable θ by letting $u = a \tan \theta$, where $0 \leq \theta < \frac{1}{2}\pi$ if $u \geq 0$ and $-\frac{1}{2}\pi < \theta < 0$ if $u < 0$. Then $du = a \sec^2 \theta\, d\theta$, and

$$\sqrt{a^2 + u^2} = \sqrt{a^2 + a^2 \tan^2 \theta} = a \sqrt{1 + \tan^2 \theta} = a \sqrt{\sec^2 \theta}$$

Because $-\frac{1}{2}\pi < \theta < \frac{1}{2}\pi$, $\sec \theta \geq 1$; thus $\sqrt{\sec^2 \theta} = \sec \theta$, and we have $\sqrt{a^2 + u^2} = \sec \theta$. Because $\tan \theta = u/a$ and $-\frac{1}{2}\pi < \theta < \frac{1}{2}\pi$, it follows that $\theta = \tan^{-1}(u/a)$.

EXAMPLE 2: Evaluate

$$\int \sqrt{x^2 + 5}\, dx$$

SOLUTION: Let $x = \sqrt{5} \tan \theta$, where $0 \leq \theta < \frac{1}{2}\pi$ if $x \geq 0$ and $-\frac{1}{2}\pi < \theta < 0$ if $x < 0$. Then $dx = \sqrt{5} \sec^2 \theta\, d\theta$ and

$$\sqrt{x^2 + 5} = \sqrt{5 \tan^2 \theta + 5} = \sqrt{5} \sqrt{\sec^2 \theta} = \sqrt{5} \sec \theta$$

Therefore,

$$\int \sqrt{x^2 + 5}\, dx = \int \sqrt{5} \sec \theta(\sqrt{5} \sec^2 \theta\, d\theta) = 5 \int \sec^3 \theta\, d\theta$$

Using the result of Example 5 of Sec. 11.2, we have

$$\int \sqrt{x^2 + 5}\, dx = \frac{5}{2} \sec \theta \tan \theta + \frac{5}{2} \ln |\sec \theta + \tan \theta| + C$$

Figure 11.3.3   Figure 11.3.4

We find sec θ from Figs. 11.3.3 (for $x \geq 0$) and 11.3.4 (for $x < 0$), where $\tan \theta = x/\sqrt{5}$. We see that sec $\theta = \sqrt{x^2 + 5}/\sqrt{5}$. Hence,

$$\int \sqrt{x^2 + 5}\ dx = \frac{5}{2} \cdot \frac{\sqrt{x^2 + 5}}{\sqrt{5}} \cdot \frac{x}{\sqrt{5}} + \frac{5}{2} \ln \left| \frac{\sqrt{x^2 + 5}}{\sqrt{5}} + \frac{x}{\sqrt{5}} \right| + C$$

$$= \tfrac{1}{2}x \sqrt{x^2 + 5} + \tfrac{5}{2} \ln |\sqrt{x^2 + 5} + x| - \tfrac{5}{2} \ln \sqrt{5} + C$$

$$= \tfrac{1}{2}x \sqrt{x^2 + 5} + \tfrac{5}{2} \ln (\sqrt{x^2 + 5} + x) + C_1$$

NOTE: Because $\sqrt{x^2 + 5} + x > 0$, we drop the absolute-value bars.

Case 3: The integrand contains an expression of the form $\sqrt{u^2 - a^2}$, $a > 0$. We introduce a new variable θ by letting $u = a \sec \theta$, where $0 \leq \theta < \tfrac{1}{2}\pi$ if $u \geq a$ and $\pi \leq \theta < \tfrac{3}{2}\pi$ if $u \leq -a$. Then $du = a \sec \theta \tan \theta\ d\theta$ and

$$\sqrt{u^2 - a^2} = \sqrt{a^2 \sec^2 \theta - a^2} = \sqrt{a^2(\sec^2 \theta - 1)} = a\sqrt{\tan^2 \theta}$$

Because either $0 \leq \theta < \tfrac{1}{2}\pi$ or $\pi \leq \theta < \tfrac{3}{2}\pi$, $\tan \theta \geq 0$; thus, $\sqrt{\tan^2 \theta} = \tan \theta$, and we have $\sqrt{u^2 - a^2} = a \tan \theta$. Note in Fig. 11.3.5 that $u \geq a$, sec $\theta = u/a \geq 1$, and $0 \leq \theta < \tfrac{1}{2}\pi$. Hence, $\theta = \sec^{-1}(u/a)$ if $u \geq a$. In Fig. 11.3.6, $u \leq -a$, sec $\theta = u/a \leq -1$, and $\pi \leq \theta < \tfrac{3}{2}\pi$. Because when $u \leq -a, \tfrac{1}{2}\pi < \sec^{-1}(u/a) \leq \pi$, it follows that $\theta = 2\pi - \sec^{-1}(u/a)$.

Figure 11.3.5   Figure 11.3.6

EXAMPLE 3:   Evaluate

$$\int \frac{dx}{x^3 \sqrt{x^2 - 9}}$$

Figure 11.3.7

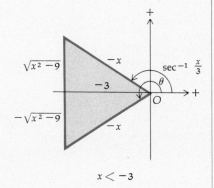

Figure 11.3.8

SOLUTION: Let $x = 3 \sec \theta$, where $0 < \theta < \frac{1}{2}\pi$ if $x > 3$ and $\pi < \theta < \frac{3}{2}\pi$ if $x < -3$. Then $dx = 3 \sec \theta \tan \theta \, d\theta$ and

$$\sqrt{x^2 - 9} = \sqrt{9 \sec^2 \theta - 9} = 3\sqrt{\tan^2 \theta} = 3 \tan \theta$$

Hence,

$$\int \frac{dx}{x^3 \sqrt{x^2 - 9}} = \int \frac{3 \sec \theta \tan \theta \, d\theta}{27 \sec^3 \theta \cdot 3 \tan \theta} = \frac{1}{27} \int \cos^2 \theta \, d\theta$$

$$= \frac{1}{54} \int (1 + \cos 2\theta) \, d\theta = \tfrac{1}{54}(\theta + \tfrac{1}{2} \sin 2\theta) + C$$

$$= \tfrac{1}{54}(\theta + \sin \theta \cos \theta) + C$$

When $x > 3$, $0 < \theta < \frac{1}{2}\pi$, and we obtain $\sin \theta$ and $\cos \theta$ from Fig. 11.3.7. When $x < -3$, $\pi < \theta < \frac{3}{2}\pi$, and we obtain $\sin \theta$ and $\cos \theta$ from Fig. 11.3.8. In either case, $\sin \theta = \sqrt{x^2 - 9}/x$ and $\cos \theta = 3/x$. To express θ in terms of x we must distinguish between the two cases: $x > 3$ and $x < -3$. When $x > 3$, $\theta = \sec^{-1} \frac{1}{3}x$. However, when $x < -3$, $\theta = 2\pi - \sec^{-1} \frac{1}{3}x$ (refer to Fig. 11.3.8). We have, then,

$$\int \frac{dx}{x^3 \sqrt{x^2 - 9}} = \begin{cases} \dfrac{1}{54}\left(\sec^{-1} \dfrac{x}{3} + \dfrac{\sqrt{x^2 - 9}}{x} \cdot \dfrac{3}{x}\right) + C & \text{if } x > 3 \\[3mm] \dfrac{1}{54}\left(2\pi - \sec^{-1} \dfrac{x}{3} + \dfrac{\sqrt{x^2 - 9}}{x} \cdot \dfrac{3}{x}\right) + C_1 & \text{if } x < -3 \end{cases}$$

and letting $C = C_1 + \frac{1}{27}\pi$, we get

$$\int \frac{dx}{x^3 \sqrt{x^2 - 9}} = \begin{cases} \dfrac{1}{54} \sec^{-1} \dfrac{x}{3} + \dfrac{\sqrt{x^2 - 9}}{18x^2} + C & \text{if } x > 3 \\[3mm] -\dfrac{1}{54} \sec^{-1} \dfrac{x}{3} + \dfrac{\sqrt{x^2 - 9}}{18x^2} + C & \text{if } x < -3 \end{cases}$$

EXAMPLE 4:   Evaluate

$$\int \frac{dx}{\sqrt{x^2 - 25}}$$

SOLUTION: Let $x = 5 \sec \theta$, where $0 < \theta < \frac{1}{2}\pi$ if $x > 5$ and $\pi < \theta < \frac{3}{2}\pi$ if $x < -5$. Then $dx = 5 \sec \theta \tan \theta \, d\theta$ and

$$\sqrt{x^2 - 25} = \sqrt{25 \sec^2 \theta - 25} = 5\sqrt{\tan^2 \theta} = 5 \tan \theta$$

Therefore,

$$\int \frac{dx}{\sqrt{x^2 - 25}} = \int \frac{5 \sec \theta \tan \theta \, d\theta}{5 \tan \theta} = \int \sec \theta \, d\theta$$

$$= \ln |\sec \theta + \tan \theta| + C$$

To find $\sec \theta$ and $\tan \theta$ refer to Fig. 11.3.9 (for $x > 5$) and Fig. 11.3.10 (for

$x < -5$). In either case, $\sec \theta = \frac{1}{5}x$ and $\tan \theta = \frac{1}{5}\sqrt{x^2 - 25}$. We have, then,

$$\int \frac{dx}{\sqrt{x^2 - 25}} = \ln \left| \frac{x}{5} + \frac{\sqrt{x^2 - 25}}{5} \right| + C$$

$$= \ln |x + \sqrt{x^2 - 25}| - \ln 5 + C$$

$$= \ln |x + \sqrt{x^2 - 25}| + C_1$$

x > 5

Figure 11.3.9

x < -5

Figure 11.3.10

EXAMPLE 5:   Evaluate

$$\int_1^2 \frac{dx}{(6 - x^2)^{3/2}}$$

SOLUTION: To evaluate the indefinite integral $\int dx/(6 - x^2)^{3/2}$, we make the substitution $x = \sqrt{6}\,\sin \theta$. In this case we can restrict θ to the interval $0 < \theta < \frac{1}{2}\pi$ because we are evaluating a definite integral for which $x > 0$ because x is in [1, 2]. So we have $x = \sqrt{6}\,\sin \theta$, $0 < \theta < \frac{1}{2}\pi$, and $dx = \sqrt{6}\,\cos \theta\,d\theta$. Furthermore,

$$(6 - x^2)^{3/2} = (6 - 6 \sin^2 \theta)^{3/2}$$

$$= 6\sqrt{6}\,(1 - \sin^2 \theta)^{3/2}$$

$$= 6\sqrt{6}\,(\cos^2 \theta)^{3/2}$$

$$= 6\sqrt{6}\,\cos^3 \theta$$

Hence,

$$\int \frac{dx}{(6 - x^2)^{3/2}} = \int \frac{\sqrt{6}\,\cos \theta\,d\theta}{6\sqrt{6}\,\cos^3 \theta}$$

$$= \frac{1}{6} \int \frac{d\theta}{\cos^2 \theta}$$

$$= \frac{1}{6} \int \sec^2 \theta\,d\theta$$

$$= \tfrac{1}{6} \tan \theta + C$$

We find $\tan \theta$ from Fig. 11.3.11, in which $\sin \theta = x/\sqrt{6}$ and $0 < \theta < \frac{1}{2}\pi$. We

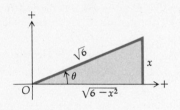

Figure 11.3.11

see that $\tan \theta = x/\sqrt{6 - x^2}$, and so we have

$$\int \frac{dx}{(6 - x^2)^{3/2}} = \frac{x}{6\sqrt{6 - x^2}} + C$$

Therefore,

$$\int_1^2 \frac{dx}{(6 - x^2)^{3/2}} = \frac{x}{6\sqrt{6 - x^2}} \Big]_1^2$$

$$= \frac{1}{3\sqrt{2}} - \frac{1}{6\sqrt{5}}$$

$$= \frac{2\sqrt{5} - \sqrt{2}}{6\sqrt{10}}$$

Exercises 11.3

In Exercises 1 through 18, evaluate the indefinite integral.

1. $\displaystyle\int \frac{dx}{x^2\sqrt{4 - x^2}}$

2. $\displaystyle\int \frac{dx}{x\sqrt{x^2 + 4}}$

3. $\displaystyle\int \frac{\sqrt{9 - x^2}}{x^2}\,dx$

4. $\displaystyle\int \frac{x^2\,dx}{\sqrt{x^2 + 6}}$

5. $\displaystyle\int \frac{dx}{x\sqrt{25 - x^2}}$

6. $\displaystyle\int \frac{dx}{\sqrt{x^2 - a^2}}$

7. $\displaystyle\int \sqrt{1 - u^2}\,du$

8. $\displaystyle\int \frac{dw}{w^2\sqrt{w^2 - 7}}$

9. $\displaystyle\int x^2\sqrt{16 - x^2}\,dx$

10. $\displaystyle\int \frac{dx}{(4 + x^2)^{3/2}}$

11. $\displaystyle\int \frac{dx}{(4x^2 - 9)^{3/2}}$

12. $\displaystyle\int \frac{dx}{x^4\sqrt{16 + x^2}}$

13. $\displaystyle\int \frac{dx}{\sqrt{4x + x^2}}$

14. $\displaystyle\int \frac{dx}{\sqrt{4x - x^2}}$

15. $\displaystyle\int \frac{dx}{(5 - 4x - x^2)^{3/2}}$

16. $\displaystyle\int \frac{dx}{x\sqrt{x^4 - 4}}$

17. $\displaystyle\int \frac{\sec^2 x\,dx}{(4 - \tan^2 x)^{3/2}}$

18. $\displaystyle\int \frac{e^{-x}\,dx}{(9e^{-2x} + 1)^{3/2}}$

In Exercises 19 through 26, evaluate the definite integral.

19. $\displaystyle\int_0^2 \frac{x^3\,dx}{\sqrt{16 - x^2}}$

20. $\displaystyle\int_0^4 \frac{dx}{(16 + x^2)^{3/2}}$

21. $\displaystyle\int_{\sqrt{3}}^{3\sqrt{3}} \frac{dx}{x^2\sqrt{x^2 + 9}}$

22. $\displaystyle\int_0^1 \frac{x^2\,dx}{\sqrt{4 - x^2}}$

23. $\displaystyle\int_4^6 \frac{dx}{x\sqrt{x^2 - 4}}$

24. $\displaystyle\int_4^8 \frac{dw}{(w^2 - 4)^{3/2}}$

25. $\displaystyle\int_0^5 x^2\sqrt{25 - x^2}\,dx$

26. $\displaystyle\int_1^3 \frac{dx}{x^4\sqrt{x^2 + 3}}$

27. Find the area of the region bounded by the curve $y = \sqrt{x^2 - 9}/x^2$, the x axis, and the line $x = 5$.

28. Find the centroid of the region of Exercise 27.

29. Find the length of the arc of the curve $y = \ln x$ from $x = 1$ to $x = 3$.

30. Find the volume of the solid generated by revolving the region of Exercise 27 about the y axis.

31. Find the centroid of the solid of revolution of Exercise 30.

32. The linear density of a rod at a point x ft from one end is $\sqrt{9 + x^2}$ slugs/ft. If the rod is 3 ft long, find the mass and center of mass of the rod.

33. If an object is moving vertically due to the forces produced by a spring and gravity, then under certain conditions $v^2 = c^2 - k^2s^2$, where at t sec, s ft is the directed distance of the object from the starting point and v ft/sec is the velocity of the object. Find s in terms of t where v is positive.

34. A gate in an irrigation ditch is in the shape of a segment of a circle of radius 4 ft. The top of the gate is horizontal and 3 ft above the lowest point on the gate. If the water level is 2 ft above the top of the gate, find the force on the gate due to the water pressure.

35. A cylindrical pipe is 4 ft in diameter and is closed at one end by a circular gate which just fits over the pipe. If the pipe contains water to a depth of 3 ft, find the force on the gate due to the water pressure.

36. An automobile's gasoline tank is in the shape of a right-circular cylinder of radius 8 in. with a horizontal axis. Find the total force on one end when the gasoline is 12 in. deep and w oz. is the weight of 1 in.[3] of gasoline.

11.4 INTEGRATION OF RATIONAL FUNCTIONS BY PARTIAL FRACTIONS. CASES 1 AND 2: THE DENOMINATOR HAS ONLY LINEAR FACTORS

In Sec. 1.8 a rational function was defined as one which can be expressed as the quotient of two polynomial functions. That is, the function H is a rational function if $H(x) = P(x)/Q(x)$, where $P(x)$ and $Q(x)$ are polynomials. We saw previously that if the degree of the numerator is not less than the degree of the denominator, we have an improper fraction, and in that case we divide the numerator by the denominator until we obtain a proper fraction, one in which the degree of the numerator is less than the degree of the denominator. For example,

$$\frac{x^4 - 10x^2 + 3x + 1}{x^2 - 4} = x^2 - 6 + \frac{3x - 23}{x^2 - 4}$$

So if we wish to integrate

$$\int \frac{x^4 - 10x^2 + 3x + 1}{x^2 - 4} \, dx$$

the problem is reduced to integrating

$$\int (x^2 - 6) \, dx + \int \frac{3x - 23}{x^2 - 4} \, dx$$

In general, then, we are concerned with the integration of expressions of the form

$$\int \frac{P(x)}{Q(x)} \, dx$$

where the degree of $P(x)$ is less than the degree of $Q(x)$.

To do this it is often necessary to write $P(x)/Q(x)$ as the sum of *partial fractions*. The denominators of the partial fractions are obtained by factoring $Q(x)$ into a product of linear and quadratic factors. Sometimes it may be difficult to find these factors of $Q(x)$; however, a theorem from advanced algebra states that theoretically this can always be done. We state this theorem without proof.

11.4.1 Theorem   Any polynomial with real coefficients can be expressed as a product of linear and quadratic factors in such a way that each of the factors has real coefficients.

After $Q(x)$ has been factored into products of linear and quadratic factors, the method of determining the partial fractions depends on the nature of these factors. We consider various cases separately. The results of advanced algebra, which we do not prove here, provide us with the form of the partial fractions in each case.

We may assume, without loss of generality, that if $Q(x)$ is a polynomial of the nth degree, then the coefficient of x^n is 1 because if

$$Q(x) = C_0 x^n + C_1 x^{n-1} + \cdots + C_{n-1}x + C_n$$

then if $C_0 \neq 1$, we divide the numerator and the denominator of the fraction $P(x)/Q(x)$ by C_0.

Case 1:   The factors of $Q(x)$ are all linear and none is repeated. That is,

$$Q(x) = (x - a_1)(x - a_2) \cdots (x - a_n)$$

where no two of the a_i are identical.

In this case we write

$$\frac{P(x)}{Q(x)} \equiv \frac{A_1}{x - a_1} + \frac{A_2}{x - a_2} + \cdots + \frac{A_n}{x - a_n} \tag{1}$$

where $A_1, A_2, \ldots, A_n$ are constants to be determined.

Note that we used "$\equiv$" (read as "identically equal") instead of "$=$" in (1). This is because (1) is an identity for the value of each A_i.

The following illustration shows how the values of A_i are found.

● ILLUSTRATION 1: We wish to evaluate

$$\int \frac{(x - 1)\,dx}{x^3 - x^2 - 2x}$$

We factor the denominator, and we have

$$\frac{x - 1}{x^3 - x^2 - 2x} \equiv \frac{x - 1}{x(x - 2)(x + 1)}$$

So we write

$$\frac{x - 1}{x(x - 2)(x + 1)} \equiv \frac{A}{x} + \frac{B}{x - 2} + \frac{C}{x + 1} \tag{2}$$

Equation (2) is an identity for all x (except $x = 0, 2, -1$). From (2) we get

$$x - 1 \equiv A(x - 2)(x + 1) + Bx(x + 1) + Cx(x - 2) \tag{3}$$

Equation (3) is an identity which is true for all values of x including 0, 2, and -1. We wish to find the constants A, B, and C. Substituting 0 for x in (3), we obtain

$$-1 = -2A \quad \text{or} \quad A = \tfrac{1}{2}$$

Substituting 2 for x in (3), we get

$$1 = 6B \quad \text{or} \quad B = \tfrac{1}{6}$$

Substituting -1 for x in (3), we obtain

$$-2 = 3C \quad \text{or} \quad C = -\tfrac{2}{3}$$

There is another method for finding the values of A, B, and C. If on the right side of (3) we combine terms, we have

$$x - 1 \equiv (A + B + C)x^2 + (-A + B - 2C)x - 2A \tag{4}$$

For (4) to be an identity, the coefficients on the left must equal the corresponding coefficients on the right. Hence,

$$A + B + C = 0$$

$$-A + B - 2C = 1$$

$$- 2A = -1$$

Solving these equations simultaneously, we get $A = \tfrac{1}{2}$, $B = \tfrac{1}{6}$, and $C = -\tfrac{2}{3}$. Substituting these values in (2), we get

$$\frac{x - 1}{x(x - 2)(x + 1)} \equiv \frac{\tfrac{1}{2}}{x} + \frac{\tfrac{1}{6}}{x - 2} + \frac{-\tfrac{2}{3}}{x + 1}$$

So our given integral can be expressed as follows:

$$\int \frac{x - 1}{x^3 - x^2 - 2x}\, dx = \frac{1}{2} \int \frac{dx}{x} + \frac{1}{6} \int \frac{dx}{x - 2} - \frac{2}{3} \int \frac{dx}{x + 1}$$

$$= \tfrac{1}{2} \ln |x| + \tfrac{1}{6} \ln |x - 2| - \tfrac{2}{3} \ln |x + 1| + \tfrac{1}{6} \ln C$$

$$= \tfrac{1}{6}(3 \ln |x| + \ln |x - 2| - 4 \ln |x + 1| + \ln C)$$

$$= \frac{1}{6} \ln \left| \frac{Cx^3(x - 2)}{(x + 1)^4} \right|$$
●

Case 2: The factors of $Q(x)$ are all linear, and some are repeated.

Suppose that $(x - a_i)$ is a p-fold factor. Then, corresponding to this factor, there will be the sum of p partial fractions

$$\frac{A_1}{(x - a_i)^p} + \frac{A_2}{(x - a_i)^{p-1}} + \cdots + \frac{A_{p-1}}{(x - a_i)^2} + \frac{A_p}{x - a_i}$$

where A_1, A_2, . . . , A_p are constants to be determined.

Example 1 following illustrates this case and the method of determining each A_i.

EXAMPLE 1: **Find**

$$\int \frac{(x^3-1)\, dx}{x^2(x-2)^3}$$

SOLUTION: The fraction in the integrand is written as a sum of partial fractions as follows:

$$\frac{x^3-1}{x^2(x-2)^3} \equiv \frac{A}{x^2} + \frac{B}{x} + \frac{C}{(x-2)^3} + \frac{D}{(x-2)^2} + \frac{E}{x-2} \tag{5}$$

The above is an identity for all x (except $x = 0, 2$). Multiplying on both sides of (5) by the lowest common denominator, we get

$$x^3 - 1 \equiv A(x-2)^3 + Bx(x-2)^3 + Cx^2 + Dx^2(x-2) + Ex^2(x-2)^2$$

$$x^3 - 1 \equiv A(x^3 - 6x^2 + 12x - 8) + Bx(x^3 - 6x^2 + 12x - 8)$$
$$+ Cx^2 + Dx^3 - 2Dx^2 + Ex^2(x^2 - 4x + 4)$$

$$x^3 - 1 \equiv (B + E)x^4 + (A - 6B + D - 4E)x^3$$
$$+ (-6A + 12B + C - 2D + 4E)x^2 + (12A - 8B)x - 8A$$

Equating the coefficients of like powers of x, we obtain

$$B + E = 0$$
$$A - 6B + D - 4E = 1$$
$$-6A + 12B + C - 2D + 4E = 0$$
$$12A - 8B = 0$$
$$-8A = -1$$

Solving, we get

$$A = \tfrac{1}{8} \qquad B = \tfrac{3}{16} \qquad C = \tfrac{7}{4} \qquad D = \tfrac{5}{4} \qquad E = -\tfrac{3}{16}$$

Therefore, from (5) we have

$$\frac{x^3-1}{x^2(x-2)^3} \equiv \frac{\tfrac{1}{8}}{x^2} + \frac{\tfrac{3}{16}}{x} + \frac{\tfrac{7}{4}}{(x-2)^3} + \frac{\tfrac{5}{4}}{(x-2)^2} + \frac{-\tfrac{3}{16}}{x-2}$$

Thus,

$$\int \frac{x^3-1}{x^2(x-2)^3}\, dx$$

$$= \frac{1}{8}\int \frac{dx}{x^2} + \frac{3}{16}\int \frac{dx}{x} + \frac{7}{4}\int \frac{dx}{(x-2)^3} + \frac{5}{4}\int \frac{dx}{(x-2)^2} - \frac{3}{16}\int \frac{dx}{x-2}$$

$$= -\frac{1}{8x} + \frac{3}{16}\ln|x| - \frac{7}{8(x-2)^2} - \frac{5}{4(x-2)} - \frac{3}{16}\ln|x-2| + C$$

$$= \frac{-11x^2 + 17x - 4}{8x(x-2)^2} + \frac{3}{16}\ln\left|\frac{x}{x-2}\right| + C$$

EXAMPLE 2: **Find**

$$\int \frac{du}{u^2 - a^2}$$

SOLUTION:

$$\frac{1}{u^2 - a^2} \equiv \frac{A}{u - a} + \frac{B}{u + a}$$

Multiplying by $(u - a)(u + a)$, we get

$$1 \equiv A(u + a) + B(u - a)$$

$$1 \equiv (A + B)u + Aa - Ba$$

Equating coefficients, we have

$$A + B = 0$$

$$Aa - Ba = 1$$

Solving simultaneously, we get

$$A = \frac{1}{2a} \quad \text{and} \quad B = -\frac{1}{2a}$$

Therefore,

$$\int \frac{du}{u^2 - a^2} = \frac{1}{2a} \int \frac{du}{u - a} - \frac{1}{2a} \int \frac{du}{u + a}$$

$$= \frac{1}{2a} \ln |u - a| - \frac{1}{2a} \ln |u + a| + C$$

or, equivalently,

$$\int \frac{du}{u^2 - a^2} = \frac{1}{2a} \ln \left| \frac{u - a}{u + a} \right| + C$$

The type of integral of the above example occurs frequently enough for it to be listed as a formula. It is not necessary to memorize it because an integration by partial fractions is fairly simple.

$$\int \frac{du}{u^2 - a^2} = \frac{1}{2a} \ln \left| \frac{u - a}{u + a} \right| + C \tag{6}$$

If we have $\int du/(a^2 - u^2)$, we write

$$\int \frac{du}{a^2 - u^2} = -\int \frac{du}{u^2 - a^2}$$

$$= -\frac{1}{2a} \ln \left| \frac{u - a}{u + a} \right| + C$$

$$= \frac{1}{2a} \ln \left| \frac{u + a}{u - a} \right| + C$$

This is also listed as a formula.

$$\int \frac{du}{a^2 - u^2} = \frac{1}{2a} \ln \left| \frac{u + a}{u - a} \right| + C \tag{7}$$

In chemistry, the *law of mass action* affords us an application of integration that leads to the use of partial fractions. Under certain conditions it is found that a substance A reacts with a substance B to form a third substance C in such a way that the rate of change of the amount of C is proportional to the product of the amounts of A and B remaining at any given time.

Suppose that initially there are α grams of A and β grams of B and that r grams of A combine with s grams of B to form $(r + s)$ grams of C. If we let x be the number of grams of substance C present at t units of time, then C contains $rx/(r + s)$ grams of A and $sx/(r + s)$ grams of B. The number of grams of substance A remaining is then $\alpha - rx/(r + s)$, and the number of grams of substance B remaining is $\beta - sx/(r + s)$. Therefore, the law of mass action gives us

$$\frac{dx}{dt} = K\left(\alpha - \frac{rx}{r + s}\right)\left(\beta - \frac{sx}{r + s}\right)$$

where K is the constant of proportionality. This equation can be written as

$$\frac{dx}{dt} = \frac{Krs}{(r + s)^2}\left(\frac{r + s}{r}\alpha - x\right)\left(\frac{r + s}{s}\beta - x\right) \tag{8}$$

Letting

$$k = \frac{Krs}{(r + s)^2} \qquad a = \frac{r + s}{r}\alpha \qquad b = \frac{r + s}{s}\beta$$

Eq. (8) becomes

$$\frac{dx}{dt} = k(a - x)(b - x) \tag{9}$$

We can separate the variables in Eq. (9) and get

$$\frac{dx}{(a - x)(b - x)} = k \, dt$$

If $a = b$, then the left side of the above equation can be integrated by the power formula. If $a \neq b$, partial fractions can be used for the integration.

EXAMPLE 3: A chemical reaction causes a substance A to combine with a substance B to form a substance C so that the law of mass action is obeyed. If in Eq. (9) $a = 8$ and $b = 6$, and 2 g of substance C are formed in 10 min, how many grams of C are formed in 15 min?

SOLUTION: Letting x grams be the amount of substance C present at t minutes, we have the initial conditions shown in Table 11.4.1. Equation (9) becomes

$$\frac{dx}{dt} = k(8 - x)(6 - x)$$

Separating the variables we have

$$\int \frac{dx}{(8 - x)(6 - x)} = k \int dt \tag{10}$$

Table 11.4.1

t	0	10	15
x	0	2	x_{15}

Writing the integrand as the sum of partial fractions gives

$$\frac{1}{(8-x)(6-x)} \equiv \frac{A}{8-x} + \frac{B}{6-x}$$

from which we obtain

$$1 \equiv A(6-x) + B(8-x)$$

Substituting 6 for x gives $B = \frac{1}{2}$, and substituting 8 for x gives $A = -\frac{1}{2}$. Hence, Eq. (10) is written as

$$-\frac{1}{2}\int \frac{dx}{8-x} + \frac{1}{2}\int \frac{dx}{6-x} = k\int dt$$

Integrating, we have

$$\tfrac{1}{2}\ln|8-x| - \tfrac{1}{2}\ln|6-x| + \tfrac{1}{2}\ln|C| = kt$$

$$\ln\left|\frac{6-x}{C(8-x)}\right| = -2kt$$

$$\frac{6-x}{8-x} = Ce^{-2kt} \tag{11}$$

Substituting $x = 0$, $t = 0$ in Eq. (11) we get $C = \frac{3}{4}$. Hence,

$$\frac{6-x}{8-x} = \frac{3}{4}e^{-2kt} \tag{12}$$

Substituting $x = 2$, $t = 10$ in Eq. (12), we have

$$\tfrac{4}{6} = \tfrac{3}{4}e^{-20k}$$

$$e^{-20k} = \tfrac{8}{9}$$

Substituting $x = x_{15}$, $t = 15$ into Eq. (12), we get

$$\frac{6-x_{15}}{8-x_{15}} = \frac{3}{4}e^{-30k}$$

$$4(6-x_{15}) = 3(e^{-20k})^{3/2}(8-x_{15})$$

$$24 - 4x_{15} = 3(\tfrac{8}{9})^{3/2}(8-x_{15})$$

$$24 - 4x_{15} = \frac{16\sqrt{2}}{9}(8-x_{15})$$

$$x_{15} = \frac{54 - 32\sqrt{2}}{9 - 4\sqrt{2}}$$

$$\approx 2.6$$

Therefore, there will be 2.6 g of substance C formed in 15 min.

Exercises 11.4

In Exercises 1 through 16, evaluate the indefinite integral.

1. $\displaystyle\int \frac{dx}{x^2 - 4}$

2. $\displaystyle\int \frac{x^2\,dx}{x^2 + x - 6}$

3. $\displaystyle\int \frac{5x - 2}{x^2 - 4}\,dx$

4. $\displaystyle\int \frac{(4x - 2)\,dx}{x^3 - x^2 - 2x}$

5. $\displaystyle\int \frac{6x^2 - 2x - 1}{4x^3 - x}\,dx$

6. $\displaystyle\int \frac{x^2 + x + 2}{x^2 - 1}\,dx$

7. $\displaystyle\int \frac{dx}{x^3 + 3x^2}$

8. $\displaystyle\int \frac{3x^2 - x + 1}{x^3 - x^2}\,dx$

9. $\displaystyle\int \frac{dx}{(x + 2)^3}$

10. $\displaystyle\int \frac{dt}{(t + 2)^2(t + 1)}$

11. $\displaystyle\int \frac{x^2 - 3x - 7}{(2x + 3)(x + 1)^2}\,dx$

12. $\displaystyle\int \frac{(5x^2 - 11x + 5)\,dx}{x^3 - 4x^2 + 5x - 2}$

13. $\displaystyle\int \frac{x^4 + 3x^3 - 5x^2 - 4x + 17}{x^3 + x^2 - 5x + 3}\,dx$

14. $\displaystyle\int \frac{2x^4 - 2x + 1}{2x^5 - x^4}\,dx$

15. $\displaystyle\int \frac{-24x^3 + 30x^2 + 52x + 17}{9x^4 - 6x^3 - 11x^2 + 4x + 4}\,dx$

16. $\displaystyle\int \frac{dx}{16x^4 - 8x^2 + 1}$

In Exercises 17 through 24, evaluate the definite integral.

17. $\displaystyle\int_1^2 \frac{x - 3}{x^3 + x^2}\,dx$

18. $\displaystyle\int_0^4 \frac{(x - 2)\,dx}{2x^2 + 7x + 3}$

19. $\displaystyle\int_1^3 \frac{x^2 - 4x + 3}{x(x + 1)^2}\,dx$

20. $\displaystyle\int_1^4 \frac{(2x^2 + 13x + 18)\,dx}{x^3 + 6x^2 + 9x}$

21. $\displaystyle\int_1^2 \frac{5x^2 - 3x + 18}{9x - x^3}\,dx$

22. $\displaystyle\int_0^1 \frac{(3x^2 + 7x)\,dx}{x^3 + 6x^2 + 11x + 6}$

23. $\displaystyle\int_0^5 \frac{(x^2 - 3)\,dx}{x^3 + 4x^2 + 5x + 2}$

24. $\displaystyle\int_0^4 \frac{x^2\,dx}{2x^3 + 9x^2 + 12x + 4}$

25. Find the area of the region bounded by the curve $y = (x - 1)/(x^2 - 5x + 6)$, the x axis, and the lines $x = 4$ and $x = 6$.

26. Find the centroid of the region in Exercise 25.

27. Find the volume of the solid of revolution generated by revolving the region in Exercise 25 about the y axis.

28. Find the area of the region in the first quadrant bounded by the curve $(x + 2)^2 y = 4 - x$.

29. Find the centroid of the region of Exercise 28.

30. Find the volume of the solid of revolution generated if the region in Exercise 28 is revolved about the x axis.

31. Suppose in Example 3 that $a = 5$ and $b = 4$ and 1 g of substance C is formed in 5 min. How many grams of C are formed in 10 min?

32. Suppose in Example 3 that $a = 6$ and $b = 3$ and 1 g of substance C is formed in 4 min. How long will it take 2 g of substance C to be formed?

33. At any instant the rate at which a substance dissolves is proportional to the product of the amount of the substance present at that instant and the difference between the concentration of the substance in solution at that instant and the concentration of the substance in a saturated solution. A quantity of insoluble material is mixed with 10 lb of salt initially, and the salt is dissolving in a tank containing 20 gal of water. If 5 lb of salt dissolves in 10 min and the concentration of salt in a saturated solution is 3 lb/gal, how much salt will dissolve in 20 min?

34. A particle is moving along a straight line so that if v ft/sec is the velocity of the particle at t sec, then

$$v = \frac{t + 3}{t^2 + 3t + 2}$$

Find the distance traveled by the particle from the time when $t = 0$ to the time when $t = 2$.

11.5 INTEGRATION OF RATIONAL FUNCTIONS BY PARTIAL FRACTIONS. CASES 3 AND 4: THE DENOMINATOR CONTAINS QUADRATIC FACTORS

Case 3:   The factors of $Q(x)$ are linear and quadratic, and none of the quadratic factors is repeated.

Corresponding to the quadratic factor $x^2 + px + q$ in the denominator is the partial fraction of the form

$$\frac{Ax + B}{x^2 + px + q}$$

EXAMPLE 1:   Find

$$\int \frac{(x^2 - 2x - 3)\ dx}{(x - 1)(x^2 + 2x + 2)}$$

SOLUTION: The fraction in the integrand is written as a sum of partial fractions as follows:

$$\frac{x^2 - 2x - 3}{(x - 1)(x^2 + 2x + 2)} \equiv \frac{Ax + B}{x^2 + 2x + 2} + \frac{C}{x - 1} \tag{1}$$

Multiplying on both sides of (1) by the lowest common denominator, we have

$$x^2 - 2x - 3 \equiv (Ax + B)(x - 1) + C(x^2 + 2x + 2)$$
$$x^2 - 2x - 3 \equiv (A + C)x^2 + (B - A + 2C)x + (2C - B)$$

Equating coefficients of like powers of x gives

$$A + C = 1$$
$$B - A + 2C = -2$$
$$2C - B = -3$$

Solving for A, B, and C, we obtain

$$A = \tfrac{9}{5} \qquad B = \tfrac{7}{5} \qquad C = -\tfrac{4}{5}$$

Substituting these values into (1), we get

$$\frac{x^2 - 2x - 3}{(x - 1)(x^2 + 2x + 2)} \equiv \frac{\tfrac{9}{5}x + \tfrac{7}{5}}{x^2 + 2x + 2} + \frac{-\tfrac{4}{5}}{x - 1}$$

So

$$\int \frac{x^2 - 2x - 3}{(x - 1)(x^2 + 2x + 2)}\ dx$$

$$= \frac{9}{5} \int \frac{x\ dx}{x^2 + 2x + 2} + \frac{7}{5} \int \frac{dx}{x^2 + 2x + 2} - \frac{4}{5} \int \frac{dx}{x - 1} \tag{2}$$

To integrate $\int (x\ dx)/(x^2 + 2x + 2)$, we see that the differential of the denominator is $2(x + 1)\ dx$; so we add and subtract 1 in the numerator, thereby giving us

$$\frac{9}{5} \int \frac{x\ dx}{x^2 + 2x + 2} = \frac{9}{5} \int \frac{(x + 1)\ dx}{x^2 + 2x + 2} - \frac{9}{5} \int \frac{dx}{x^2 + 2x + 2} \tag{3}$$

Substituting from (3) into (2) and combining terms, we get

$$\int \frac{x^2 - 2x - 3}{(x-1)(x^2 + 2x + 2)} \, dx$$

$$= \frac{9}{5} \cdot \frac{1}{2} \int \frac{2(x+1) \, dx}{x^2 + 2x + 2} - \frac{2}{5} \int \frac{dx}{x^2 + 2x + 2} - \frac{4}{5} \int \frac{dx}{x-1} \tag{4}$$

$$= \frac{9}{10} \ln |x^2 + 2x + 2| - \frac{2}{5} \int \frac{dx}{(x+1)^2 + 1} - \frac{4}{5} \ln |x - 1|$$

$$= \tfrac{9}{10} \ln |x^2 + 2x + 2| - \tfrac{2}{5} \tan^{-1}(x+1) - \tfrac{8}{10} \ln |x-1| + \tfrac{1}{10} \ln C$$

$$= \frac{1}{10} \ln \left| \frac{C(x^2 + 2x + 2)^9}{(x-1)^8} \right| - \frac{2}{5} \tan^{-1}(x+1)$$

• ILLUSTRATION 1: In Example 1 we would have saved some steps if instead of (1) we had expressed the original fraction as

$$\frac{x^2 - 2x - 3}{(x-1)(x^2 + 2x + 2)} \equiv \frac{D(2x+2) + E}{x^2 + 2x + 2} + \frac{F}{x-1}$$

NOTE: We write $D(2x+2) + E$ instead of $Ax + B$ because

$$2x + 2 = D_x(x^2 + 2x + 2)$$

Then, solving for D, E, and F, we obtain

$$D = \tfrac{9}{10} \qquad E = -\tfrac{2}{5} \qquad F = -\tfrac{4}{5}$$

giving us (4) directly.   •

Case 4:   The factors of $Q(x)$ are linear and quadratic, and some of the quadratic factors are repeated.

   If $x^2 + px + q$ is an n-fold quadratic factor of $Q(x)$, then, corresponding to this factor $(x^2 + px + q)^n$, we have the sum of the following n partial fractions:

$$\frac{A_1 x + B_1}{(x^2 + px + q)^n} + \frac{A_2 x + B_2}{(x^2 + px + q)^{n-1}} + \cdots + \frac{A_n x + B_n}{x^2 + px + q}$$

• ILLUSTRATION 2: If the denominator contains the factor $(x^2 - 5x + 2)^3$, we have, corresponding to this factor,

$$\frac{Ax + B}{(x^2 - 5x + 2)^3} + \frac{Cx + D}{(x^2 - 5x + 2)^2} + \frac{Ex + F}{x^2 - 5x + 2}$$

or, more conveniently,

$$\frac{A(2x-5) + B}{(x^2 - 5x + 2)^3} + \frac{C(2x-5) + D}{(x^2 - 5x + 2)^2} + \frac{E(2x-5) + F}{x^2 - 5x + 2}$$ •

EXAMPLE 2: Find	SOLUTION:

$$\int \frac{(x-2) \, dx}{x(x^2 - 4x + 5)^2}$$

$$\frac{x-2}{x(x^2 - 4x + 5)^2} \equiv \frac{A}{x} + \frac{B(2x-4) + C}{(x^2 - 4x + 5)^2} + \frac{D(2x-4) + E}{x^2 - 4x + 5} \tag{5}$$

Multiplying on both sides of (5) by the lowest common denominator, we have

$$x - 2 \equiv A(x^2 - 4x + 5)^2 + x(2Bx - 4B + C)$$
$$+ x(x^2 - 4x + 5)(2Dx - 4D + E)$$
$$x - 2 \equiv Ax^4 + 16Ax^2 + 25A - 8Ax^3 + 10Ax^2 - 40Ax + 2Bx^2 - 4Bx + Cx$$
$$+ 2Dx^4 - 12Dx^3 + Ex^3 + 26Dx^2 - 4Ex^2 - 20Dx + 5Ex$$
$$x - 2 \equiv (A + 2D)x^4 + (-8A - 12D + E)x^3 + (26A + 2B + 26D - 4E)x^2$$
$$+ (-40A - 4B + C - 20D + 5E)x + 25A$$

Equating coefficients and solving simultaneously, we obtain

$$A = -\tfrac{2}{25} \qquad B = \tfrac{1}{5} \qquad C = \tfrac{1}{5} \qquad D = \tfrac{1}{25} \qquad E = -\tfrac{4}{25}$$

Therefore,

$$\int \frac{(x - 2)\, dx}{x(x^2 - 4x + 5)^2}$$

$$= -\frac{2}{25} \int \frac{dx}{x} + \frac{1}{5} \int \frac{(2x - 4)\, dx}{(x^2 - 4x + 5)^2} + \frac{1}{5} \int \frac{dx}{(x^2 - 4x + 5)^2} + \frac{1}{25} \int \frac{(2x - 4)\, dx}{x^2 - 4x + 5}$$

$$- \frac{4}{25} \int \frac{dx}{x^2 - 4x + 5}$$

$$= -\frac{2}{25} \ln |x| - \frac{1}{5(x^2 - 4x + 5)} + \frac{1}{5} \int \frac{dx}{[(x^2 - 4x + 4) + 1]^2} + \frac{1}{25} \ln |x^2 - 4x + 5|$$
$$\tag{6}$$
$$- \frac{4}{25} \int \frac{dx}{(x^2 - 4x + 4) + 1}$$

We evaluate separately the integrals in the third and fifth terms on the right side of (6).

$$\int \frac{dx}{[(x^2 - 4x + 4) + 1]^2} = \int \frac{dx}{[(x - 2)^2 + 1]^2}$$

Let $x - 2 = \tan \theta$, where $0 \le \theta < \tfrac{1}{2}\pi$, if $x \ge 2$ and $-\tfrac{1}{2}\pi < \theta < 0$ if $x < 2$. Then $dx = \sec^2 \theta\, d\theta$ and $(x - 2)^2 + 1 = \tan^2 \theta + 1 = \sec^2 \theta$. Hence,

$$\int \frac{dx}{[(x - 2)^2 + 1]^2} = \int \frac{\sec^2 \theta\, d\theta}{(\tan^2 \theta + 1)^2}$$

$$= \int \frac{\sec^2 \theta\, d\theta}{\sec^4 \theta}$$

$$= \int \frac{d\theta}{\sec^2 \theta}$$

$$= \int \cos^2 \theta\, d\theta$$

Figure 11.5.1

Figure 11.5.2

$$= \int \frac{1 + \cos 2\theta}{2} \, d\theta$$

$$= \frac{\theta}{2} + \frac{1}{4} \sin 2\theta + C_1$$

$$= \frac{\theta}{2} + \frac{1}{2} \sin \theta \cos \theta + C_1$$

Because $\tan \theta = x - 2$ and $-\frac{1}{2}\pi < \theta < \frac{1}{2}\pi$, $\theta = \tan^{-1}(x - 2)$. We find $\sin \theta$ and $\cos \theta$ from Figs. 11.5.1 (if $x \geq 2$) and 11.5.2 (if $x < 2$). In either case

$$\sin \theta = \frac{x - 2}{\sqrt{x^2 - 4x + 5}} \quad \text{and} \quad \cos \theta = \frac{1}{\sqrt{x^2 - 4x + 5}}$$

So we have

$$\int \frac{dx}{[(x-2)^2 + 1]^2} = \frac{1}{2} \tan^{-1}(x - 2) + \frac{1}{2} \frac{x - 2}{\sqrt{x^2 - 4x + 5}} \cdot \frac{1}{\sqrt{x^2 - 4x + 5}} + C_1$$

Thus,

$$\int \frac{dx}{[(x-2)^2 + 1]^2} = \frac{1}{2} \tan^{-1}(x - 2) + \frac{x - 2}{2(x^2 - 4x + 5)} + C_1 \qquad (7)$$

Now, considering the other integral on the right side of (6), we have

$$\int \frac{dx}{(x^2 - 4x + 4) + 1} = \int \frac{dx}{(x - 2)^2 + 1} = \tan^{-1}(x - 2) + C_2 \qquad (8)$$

Substituting from (7) and (8) into (6), we get

$$\int \frac{(x - 2) \, dx}{x(x^2 - 4x + 5)^2}$$

$$= -\frac{2}{25} \ln |x| - \frac{1}{5(x^2 - 4x + 5)} + \frac{1}{10} \tan^{-1}(x - 2) + \frac{x - 2}{10(x^2 - 4x + 5)}$$

$$+ \frac{1}{25} \ln |x^2 - 4x + 5| - \frac{4}{25} \tan^{-1}(x - 2) + C$$

$$= \frac{1}{25} \ln \left| \frac{x^2 - 4x + 5}{x^2} \right| - \frac{3}{50} \tan^{-1}(x - 2) + \frac{x - 4}{10(x^2 - 4x + 5)} + C$$

Exercises 11.5

In Exercises 1 through 16, evaluate the indefinite integral.

1. $\int \dfrac{dx}{2x^3 + x}$

2. $\int \dfrac{(x + 4) \, dx}{x(x^2 + 4)}$

3. $\int \dfrac{dx}{16x^4 - 1}$

4. $\int \dfrac{(x^2 - 4x - 4) \, dx}{x^3 - 2x^2 + 4x - 8}$

5. $\int \dfrac{(x^2 + x) \, dx}{x^3 - x^2 + x - 1}$

6. $\int \dfrac{dx}{9x^4 + x^2}$

7. $\int \dfrac{dx}{x^3 + x^2 + x}$

8. $\int \dfrac{(x + 3) \, dx}{4x^4 + 4x^3 + x^2}$

9. $\displaystyle\int \frac{(2x^2 - x + 2)\,dx}{x^5 + 2x^3 + x}$

10. $\displaystyle\int \frac{(2x^3 + 9x)\,dx}{(x^2 + 3)(x^2 - 2x + 3)}$

11. $\displaystyle\int \frac{(x^2 + 2x - 1)\,dx}{27x^3 - 1}$

12. $\displaystyle\int \frac{dx}{(x^2 + 1)^3}$

13. $\displaystyle\int \frac{18\,dx}{(4x^2 + 9)^2}$

14. $\displaystyle\int \frac{(2x^2 + 3x + 2)\,dx}{x^3 + 4x^2 + 6x + 4}$

15. $\displaystyle\int \frac{(\sec^2 x + 1)\,\sec^2 x\,dx}{1 + \tan^3 x}$

16. $\displaystyle\int \frac{e^{5x}\,dx}{(e^{2x} + 1)^2}$

In Exercises 17 through 24, evaluate the definite integral.

17. $\displaystyle\int_1^4 \frac{(4 + 5x^2)\,dx}{x^3 + 4x}$

18. $\displaystyle\int_0^1 \frac{x\,dx}{x^3 + 2x^2 + x + 2}$

19. $\displaystyle\int_3^4 \frac{(5x^3 - 4x)\,dx}{x^4 - 16}$

20. $\displaystyle\int_0^1 \frac{9\,dx}{8x^3 + 1}$

21. $\displaystyle\int_{-1}^0 \frac{x^2\,dx}{(2x^2 + 2x + 1)^2}$

22. $\displaystyle\int_0^{1/2} \frac{(x + 1)\,dx}{x^3 - 1}$

23. $\displaystyle\int_0^1 \frac{(x^2 + 3x + 3)\,dx}{x^3 + x^2 + x + 1}$

24. $\displaystyle\int_{\pi/6}^{\pi/2} \frac{\cos x\,dx}{\sin x + \sin^3 x}$

25. Find the area of the region bounded by the curve $y = 4/(x^3 + 8)$, the x axis, the y axis, and the line $x = 2$.

26. Find the abscissa of the centroid of the region in Exercise 25.

27. Find the mass of a lamina in the shape of the region of Exercise 25 if the area density at any point (x, y) is kx^2 slugs/ft^2.

28. Find the volume of the solid of revolution generated by revolving the region of Exercise 25 about the y axis.

29. A particle is moving along a straight line so that if v ft/sec is the velocity of the particle at t sec, then

$$v = \frac{t^2 - t + 1}{(t + 2)^2(t^2 + 1)}$$

Find a formula for the distance traveled by the particle from the time when $t = 0$ to the time when $t = t_1$.

11.6 INTEGRATION OF RATIONAL FUNCTIONS OF SINE AND COSINE

If an integrand is a rational function of $\sin x$ and $\cos x$, it can be reduced to a rational function of z by the substitution

$$z = \tan \tfrac{1}{2}x \tag{1}$$

Using the identity $\cos 2y \equiv 2 \cos^2 y - 1$ and letting $y = \tfrac{1}{2}x$, we have

$$\cos x = 2\cos^2 \tfrac{1}{2}x - 1 = \frac{2}{\sec^2 \tfrac{1}{2}x} - 1 = \frac{2}{1 + \tan^2 \tfrac{1}{2}x} - 1 = \frac{2}{1 + z^2} - 1$$

So

$$\cos x = \frac{1 - z^2}{1 + z^2} \tag{2}$$

In a similar manner, from the identity $\sin 2y = 2 \sin y \cos y$, we have

$$\sin x = 2 \sin \tfrac{1}{2}x \cos \tfrac{1}{2}x = 2\,\frac{\sin \tfrac{1}{2}x \cos^2 \tfrac{1}{2}x}{\cos \tfrac{1}{2}x}$$

$$= 2 \tan \tfrac{1}{2}x \cdot \frac{1}{\sec^2 \tfrac{1}{2}x} = \frac{2 \tan \tfrac{1}{2}x}{1 + \tan^2 \tfrac{1}{2}x}$$

Thus,

$$\sin x = \frac{2z}{1 + z^2} \tag{3}$$

Because $z = \tan \frac{1}{2}x$,

$$dz = \tfrac{1}{2} \sec^2 \tfrac{1}{2}x \, dx = \tfrac{1}{2}(1 + \tan^2 \tfrac{1}{2}x) \, dx$$

Hence,

$$dx = \frac{2 \, dz}{1 + z^2} \tag{4}$$

EXAMPLE 1: Find

$$\int \frac{dx}{1 - \sin x + \cos x}$$

SOLUTION: Letting $z = \tan \frac{1}{2}x$ and using (2), (3), and (4), we obtain

$$\int \frac{dx}{1 - \sin x + \cos x} = \int \frac{\dfrac{2 \, dz}{1 + z^2}}{1 - \dfrac{2z}{1 + z^2} + \dfrac{1 - z^2}{1 + z^2}}$$

$$= 2 \int \frac{dz}{(1 + z^2) - 2z + (1 - z^2)}$$

$$= 2 \int \frac{dz}{2 - 2z}$$

$$= \int \frac{dz}{1 - z}$$

$$= -\ln |1 - z| + C$$

$$= -\ln |1 - \tan \tfrac{1}{2}x| + C$$

EXAMPLE 2: Find

$$\int \sec x \, dx$$

by using the substitution of this section.

SOLUTION: $\displaystyle \int \sec x \, dx = \int \frac{dx}{\cos x}$

Letting $z = \tan \frac{1}{2}x$ and using (2) and (4), we get

$$\int \frac{dx}{\cos x} = \int \frac{2 \, dz}{1 + z^2} \cdot \frac{1 + z^2}{1 - z^2} = 2 \int \frac{dz}{1 - z^2}$$

Using formula (7) from Sec. 11.4, we have

$$2 \int \frac{dz}{1 - z^2} = \ln \left| \frac{1 + z}{1 - z} \right| + C$$

Therefore,

$$\int \sec x \, dx = \ln \left| \frac{1 + \tan \tfrac{1}{2}x}{1 - \tan \tfrac{1}{2}x} \right| + C \tag{5}$$

Equation (5) can be written in another form by noting that $1 = \tan \frac{1}{4}\pi$

and using the identity $\tan(\alpha + \beta) = (\tan \alpha + \tan \beta)/(1 - \tan \alpha \tan \beta)$. So we have

$$\int \sec x \, dx = \ln \left| \frac{\tan \frac{1}{4}\pi + \tan \frac{1}{2}x}{1 - \tan \frac{1}{4}\pi \cdot \tan \frac{1}{2}x} \right| + C$$

or, equivalently,

$$\int \sec x \, dx = \ln \left| \tan(\tfrac{1}{4}\pi + \tfrac{1}{2}x) \right| + C \tag{6}$$

Formula (6) is an alternative form of the formula

$$\int \sec x \, dx = \ln |\sec x + \tan x| + C$$

which is obtained by the trick of multiplying the numerator and denominator of the integrand by $\sec x + \tan x$.

It is worth noting that still another form for $\int \sec x \, dx$ can be obtained as follows:

$$\int \sec x \, dx = \int \frac{dx}{\cos x} = \int \frac{\cos x \, dx}{\cos^2 x} = \int \frac{\cos x \, dx}{1 - \sin^2 x}$$

Substituting $u = \sin x$, $du = \cos x \, dx$, we have

$$\int \sec x \, dx = \int \frac{du}{1 - u^2} = \frac{1}{2} \ln \left| \frac{1 + u}{1 - u} \right| + C = \ln \left| \frac{1 + \sin x}{1 - \sin x} \right|^{1/2} + C$$

Because $-1 \le \sin x \le 1$ for all x, $1 + \sin x$ and $1 - \sin x$ are nonnegative; hence, the absolute-value bars can be removed and we have

$$\int \sec x \, dx = \ln \left(\frac{1 + \sin x}{1 - \sin x} \right)^{1/2} + C = \ln \sqrt{\frac{1 + \sin x}{1 - \sin x}} + C \tag{7}$$

Exercises 11.6

In Exercises 1 through 12, evaluate the indefinite integral.

1. $\displaystyle\int \frac{dx}{5 + 4 \cos x}$

2. $\displaystyle\int \frac{dx}{3 - 5 \sin x}$

3. $\displaystyle\int \frac{dx}{\cos x - \sin x + 1}$

4. $\displaystyle\int \frac{dx}{\sin x - \cos x + 2}$

5. $\displaystyle\int \frac{dx}{\sin x + \tan x}$

6. $\displaystyle\int \frac{dx}{\tan x - 1}$

7. $\displaystyle\int \frac{8 \, dx}{3 \cos 2x + 1}$

8. $\displaystyle\int \frac{\cos x \, dx}{3 \cos x - 5}$

9. $\displaystyle\int \frac{5 \, dx}{6 + 4 \sec x}$

10. $\displaystyle\int \frac{dx}{\sin x - \tan x}$

11. $\displaystyle\int \frac{dx}{2 \sin x + 2 \cos x + 3}$

12. $\displaystyle\int \frac{dx}{\cot 2x(1 - \cos 2x)}$

In Exercises 13 through 18, evaluate the definite integral.

13. $\displaystyle\int_0^{\pi/2} \frac{dx}{5 \sin x + 3}$

14. $\displaystyle\int_0^{\pi/4} \frac{8 \, dx}{\tan x + 1}$

15. $\displaystyle\int_{-\pi/3}^{\pi/2} \frac{3 \, dx}{2 \cos x + 1}$

16. $\displaystyle\int_0^{\pi/2} \frac{dx}{3 + \cos 2x}$

17. $\displaystyle\int_{\pi/6}^{\pi/3} \frac{3 \, dx}{2 \sin 2x + 1}$

18. $\displaystyle\int_0^{\pi/2} \frac{\sin 2x \, dx}{2 + \cos x}$

19. Show that formula (7) of this section is equivalent to the formula $\int \sec x \, dx = \ln|\sec x + \tan x| + C$. (HINT: Multiply the numerator and denominator under the radical sign by $(1 + \sin x)$.)

20. By using the substitution $z = \tan \frac{1}{2}x$, prove that

$$\int \csc x \, dx = \ln \sqrt{\frac{1 - \cos x}{1 + \cos x}} + C$$

21. Show that the result in Exercise 20 is equivalent to the formula $\int \csc x \, dx = \ln|\csc x - \cot x| + C$. (HINT: Use a method similar to that suggested in the hint for Exercise 19.)

11.7 MISCELLANEOUS SUBSTITUTIONS

If an integrand involves fractional powers of a variable x, the integrand can be simplified by the substitution

$$x = z^n$$

where n is the lowest common denominator of the denominators of the exponents. This is illustrated by the following example.

EXAMPLE 1:   Find

$$\int \frac{\sqrt{x} \, dx}{1 + \sqrt[3]{x}}$$

SOLUTION: We let $x = z^6$; then $dx = 6z^5 \, dz$. So

$$\int \frac{x^{1/2} \, dx}{1 + x^{1/3}} = \int \frac{z^3(6z^5 \, dz)}{1 + z^2} = 6 \int \frac{z^8}{z^2 + 1} dz$$

Dividing the numerator by the denominator, we have

$$\int \frac{x^{1/2} \, dx}{1 + x^{1/3}} = 6 \int \left(z^6 - z^4 + z^2 - 1 + \frac{1}{z^2 + 1} \right) dz$$

$$= 6 \left(\tfrac{1}{7}z^7 - \tfrac{1}{5}z^5 + \tfrac{1}{3}z^3 - z + \tan^{-1} z \right) + C$$

$$= \tfrac{6}{7}x^{7/6} - \tfrac{6}{5}x^{5/6} + 2x^{1/2} - 6x^{1/6} + 6 \tan^{-1} x^{1/6} + C$$

No general rule can be given to determine a substitution that will result in a simpler integrand. Sometimes a substitution which does not rationalize the given integrand may still result in a simpler integrand.

EXAMPLE 2:   Evaluate

$$\int x^5 \sqrt{x^2 + 4} \, dx$$

SOLUTION: Let $z = \sqrt{x^2 + 4}$. Then $z^2 = x^2 + 4$, and $2z \, dz = 2x \, dx$. So we have

$$\int x^5 \sqrt{x^2 + 4} \, dx = \int (x^2)^2 \sqrt{x^2 + 4} \ x \, dx = \int (z^2 - 4)^2 z(z \, dz)$$

$$= \int (z^6 - 8z^4 + 16z^2) \, dz = \tfrac{1}{7}z^7 - \tfrac{8}{5}z^5 + \tfrac{16}{3}z^3 + C$$

$$= \tfrac{1}{105}z^3[15z^4 - 168z^2 + 560] + C$$

$$= \tfrac{1}{105}(x^2 + 4)^{3/2}[15(x^2 + 4)^2 - 168(x^2 + 4) + 560] + C$$

$$= \tfrac{1}{105}(x^2 + 4)^{3/2}[15x^4 - 48x^2 + 128] + C$$

EXAMPLE 3:   Evaluate

$$\int \frac{dx}{x^2 \sqrt{27x^2 + 6x - 1}}$$

by using the reciprocal substitution $x = 1/z$.

SOLUTION: If $x = 1/z$, then $dx = -dz/z^2$. We have, then,

$$\int \frac{dx}{x^2 \sqrt{27x^2 + 6x - 1}} = \int \frac{\dfrac{-dz}{z^2}}{\left(\dfrac{1}{z^2}\right) \sqrt{\dfrac{27}{z^2} + \dfrac{6}{z} - 1}}$$

$$= -\int \frac{\sqrt{z^2}\, dz}{\sqrt{27 + 6z - z^2}}$$

$$= -\int \frac{|z|\, dz}{\sqrt{27 + 6z - z^2}}$$

$$= \begin{cases} -\int \dfrac{z\, dz}{\sqrt{27 + 6z - z^2}} & \text{if } z > 0 \\[3mm] \int \dfrac{z\, dz}{\sqrt{27 + 6z - z^2}} & \text{if } z < 0 \end{cases} \qquad (1)$$

We evaluate $\int z\, dz/\sqrt{27 + 6z - z^2}$.

$$\int \frac{z\, dz}{\sqrt{27 + 6z - z^2}} = -\frac{1}{2} \int \frac{(-2z + 6)\, dz}{\sqrt{27 + 6z - z^2}} + 3 \int \frac{dz}{\sqrt{27 + 6z - z^2}}$$

$$= -\frac{1}{2} \cdot 2\sqrt{27 + 6z - z^2} + 3 \int \frac{dz}{\sqrt{27 + 9 - (z^2 - 6z + 9)}}$$

$$= -\sqrt{27 + 6z - z^2} + 3 \int \frac{dz}{\sqrt{36 - (z - 3)^2}}$$

$$= -\sqrt{27 + 6z - z^2} + 3 \sin^{-1} \frac{z - 3}{6} + C$$

$$= -\sqrt{27 + \frac{6}{x} - \frac{1}{x^2}} + 3 \sin^{-1} \frac{\dfrac{1}{x} - 3}{6} + C$$

$$= -\frac{\sqrt{27x^2 + 6x - 1}}{\sqrt{x^2}} + 3 \sin^{-1} \frac{1 - 3x}{6x} + C$$

$$= -\frac{\sqrt{27x^2 + 6x - 1}}{|x|} + 3 \sin^{-1} \frac{1 - 3x}{6x} + C \qquad (2)$$

Substituting from (2) into (1) we get

$$\int \frac{dx}{x^2 \sqrt{27x^2 + 6x - 1}}$$

$$= \begin{cases} \dfrac{\sqrt{27x^2 + 6x - 1}}{|x|} - 3 \sin^{-1} \dfrac{1 - 3x}{6x} + C & \text{if } x > 0 \\[5mm] \dfrac{-\sqrt{27x^2 + 6x - 1}}{|x|} + 3 \sin^{-1} \dfrac{1 - 3x}{6x} + C & \text{if } x < 0 \end{cases}$$

$$= \begin{cases} \dfrac{\sqrt{27x^2 + 6x - 1}}{x} - 3 \sin^{-1} \dfrac{1 - 3x}{6x} + C & \text{if } x > 0 \\[3em] \dfrac{\sqrt{27x^2 + 6x - 1}}{x} + 3 \sin^{-1} \dfrac{1 - 3x}{6x} + C & \text{if } x < 0 \end{cases}$$

Exercises 11.7

In Exercises 1 through 16, evaluate the indefinite integral.

1. $\displaystyle\int \frac{x\, dx}{3 + \sqrt{x}}$

2. $\displaystyle\int \frac{dx}{\sqrt[3]{x} - x}$

3. $\displaystyle\int \frac{dx}{x\sqrt{1 + 4x}}$

4. $\displaystyle\int x(1 + x)^{2/3}\, dx$

5. $\displaystyle\int \frac{\sqrt{1 + x}}{1 - x}\, dx$

6. $\displaystyle\int \frac{dx}{3 + \sqrt{x + 2}}$

7. $\displaystyle\int \frac{dx}{1 + \sqrt[3]{x - 2}}$

8. $\displaystyle\int \frac{dx}{2\sqrt[3]{x} + \sqrt{x}}$

9. $\displaystyle\int \frac{dx}{\sqrt{2x} - \sqrt{x + 4}}$

10. $\displaystyle\int \frac{dx}{\sqrt{\sqrt{x} + 1}}$

11. $\displaystyle\int \frac{dx}{\sqrt{x}\sqrt[3]{x}(1 + \sqrt[3]{x})^2}$

12. $\displaystyle\int \frac{dx}{x\sqrt{x^2 + 2x - 1}}$

Use the reciprocal substitution $x = 1/z$.

13. Do Exercise 12 by using the substitution $\sqrt{x^2 + 2x - 1} = z - x$.

14. $\displaystyle\int \frac{dx}{x\sqrt{x^2 + 4x - 4}}$

15. $\displaystyle\int \frac{dx}{x\sqrt{1 + x + x^2}}$

16. $\displaystyle\int \frac{dx}{x^2\sqrt{1 + 2x + 3x^2}}$

In Exercises 17 through 22, evaluate the definite integral.

17. $\displaystyle\int_0^4 \frac{dx}{1 + \sqrt{x}}$

18. $\displaystyle\int_0^1 \frac{x^{3/2}}{x + 1}\, dx$

19. $\displaystyle\int_{1/2}^2 \frac{dx}{\sqrt{2x}(\sqrt{2x} + 9)}$

20. $\displaystyle\int_{16}^{18} \frac{dx}{\sqrt{x} - \sqrt[4]{x^3}}$

21. $\displaystyle\int_{1/3}^3 \frac{\sqrt[3]{x} - x^3}{x^4}\, dx$

22. $\displaystyle\int_1^2 \frac{dx}{x\sqrt{x^2 + 4x - 4}}$

11.8 THE TRAPEZOIDAL RULE

We have seen previously how many problems can be solved by evaluating definite integrals. In evaluating a definite integral by the fundamental theorem of the calculus, it is necessary to find an indefinite integral (or antiderivative). There are many functions for which there is no known method for finding an indefinite integral. However, if a function f is continuous on a closed interval $[a, b]$, the definite integral $\int_a^b f(x)\, dx$ exists and is a unique number. In this section and the next we learn two methods for computing an approximate value of a definite integral. These methods can often give us fairly good accuracy and can be used for evaluating a definite integral by electronic computers. The first method is known as the *trapezoidal rule*.

We know that if f is continuous on the closed interval $[a, b]$, the definite integral $\int_a^b f(x)\, dx$ is the limit of a Riemann sum

$$\int_a^b f(x)\, dx = \lim_{\|\Delta\| \to 0} \sum_{i=1}^n f(\xi_i)\, \Delta_i x$$

The geometric interpretation of the Riemann sum

$$\sum_{i=1}^n f(\xi_i)\, \Delta_i x$$

is that it is equal to the sum of the measures of the areas of the rectangles lying above the x axis plus the negative of the measures of the areas of the rectangles lying below the x axis (see Fig. 7.3.3).

To approximate the measure of the area of a region let us use trapezoids instead of rectangles. Let us also use regular partitions and function values at equally spaced points.

Thus, if we are considering the definite integral $\int_a^b f(x)\, dx$, we divide the interval $[a, b]$ into n subintervals, each of length $\Delta x = (b - a)/n$. This gives the following $(n + 1)$ points: $x_0 = a$, $x_1 = a + \Delta x$, $x_2 = a + 2\ \Delta x$, $\ldots$, $x_i = a + i\ \Delta x$, $\ldots$, $x_{n-1} = a + (n-1)\ \Delta x$, $x_n = b$. Then the definite integral $\int_a^b f(x)\, dx$ may be expressed as the sum of n definite integrals as follows:

$$\int_a^b f(x)\, dx = \int_a^{x_1} f(x)\, dx + \int_{x_1}^{x_2} f(x)\, dx$$

$$+ \cdots + \int_{x_{i-1}}^{x_i} f(x)\, dx + \cdots + \int_{x_{n-1}}^b f(x)\, dx \quad (1)$$

To interpret (1) geometrically, refer to Fig. 11.8.1, in which we have taken $f(x) \geq 0$ for all x in $[a, b]$; however, (1) holds for any function which is continuous on $[a, b]$.

Figure 11.8.1

Then the integral $\int_a^{x_1} f(x)\, dx$ is the measure of the area of the region bounded by the x axis, the lines $x = a$ and $x = x_1$, and the portion of the curve from P_0 to P_1. This integral may be approximated by the measure of the area of the trapezoid formed by the lines $x = a$, $x = x_1$, P_0P_1, and the x axis. By a formula from geometry, the measure of the area of this trapezoid is

$$\tfrac{1}{2}[f(x_0) + f(x_1)]\,\Delta x$$

Similarly, the other integrals on the right side of (1) may be approximated by the measure of the area of a trapezoid. Using the symbol "$\approx$" for "is approximately equal to," we have then for the ith integral

$$\int_{x_{i-1}}^{x_i} f(x)\,dx \approx \tfrac{1}{2}[f(x_{i-1}) + f(x_i)]\,\Delta x \tag{2}$$

So, using (2) for each of the integrals on the right side of (1), we have

$$\int_a^b f(x)\,dx \approx \tfrac{1}{2}[f(x_0) + f(x_1)]\,\Delta x + \tfrac{1}{2}[f(x_1) + f(x_2)]\,\Delta x + \cdots$$
$$+ \tfrac{1}{2}[f(x_{n-2}) + f(x_{n-1})]\,\Delta x + \tfrac{1}{2}[f(x_{n-1}) + f(x_n)]\,\Delta x$$

Thus,

$$\int_a^b f(x)\,dx \approx \tfrac{1}{2}\Delta x[f(x_0) + 2f(x_1) + 2f(x_2) + \cdots + 2f(x_{n-1}) + f(x_n)] \tag{3}$$

Formula (3) is known as the *trapezoidal rule*.

EXAMPLE 1: Compute
$$\int_0^3 \frac{dx}{16 + x^2}$$
by using the trapezoidal rule with $n = 6$. Express the result to three decimal places. Check by finding the exact value of the definite integral.

SOLUTION: Because $[a, b] = [0, 3]$ and $n = 6$, we have

$$\Delta x = \frac{b - a}{n} = \frac{3}{6} = 0.5$$

Therefore,

$$\int_0^3 \frac{dx}{16 + x^2} \approx \frac{0.5}{2}\,[f(x_0) + 2f(x_1) + 2f(x_2) + 2f(x_3) + 2f(x_4) + 2f(x_5) + f(x_6)]$$

where $f(x) = 1/(16 + x^2)$. The computation of the sum in brackets in the above is shown in Table 11.8.1. So,

$$\int_0^3 \frac{dx}{16 + x^2} \approx 0.25(0.6427)$$

$$\int_0^3 \frac{dx}{16 + x^2} \approx 0.1607$$

Rounding the result off to three decimal places, we get

$$\int_0^3 \frac{dx}{16 + x^2} \approx 0.161$$

We check by finding the exact value. We have

$$\int_0^3 \frac{dx}{16 + x^2} = \frac{1}{4}\tan^{-1}\frac{x}{4}\Big]_0^3$$

$$= \tfrac{1}{4} \tan^{-1} \tfrac{3}{4} - \tfrac{1}{4} \tan^{-1} 0$$

$$= \tfrac{1}{4}(0.6435) - \tfrac{1}{4}(0)$$

$$= 0.1609 \quad \text{to four decimal places}$$

Table 11.8.1

i	x_i	$f(x_i)$	k_i	$k_i \cdot f(x_i)$
0	0	0.0625	1	0.0625
1	0,5	0.0615	2	0.1230
2	1	0.0588	2	0.1176
3	1.5	0.0548	2	0.1096
4	2	0.0500	2	0.1000
5	2.5	0.0450	2	0.0900
6	3	0.0400	1	0.0400

$$\sum_{i=0}^{6} k_i f(x_i) = 0.6427$$

To consider the accuracy of the approximation of a definite integral by the trapezoidal rule, we prove first that as Δx approaches zero and n increases without bound, the limit of the approximation by the trapezoidal rule is the exact value of the definite integral. Let

$$T = \tfrac{1}{2} \Delta x [f(x_0) + 2f(x_1) + \cdots + 2f(x_{n-1}) + f(x_n)]$$

Then

$$T = [f(x_1) + f(x_2) + \cdots + f(x_n)] \Delta x + \tfrac{1}{2}[f(x_0) - f(x_n)] \Delta x$$

or, equivalently,

$$T = \sum_{i=1}^{n} f(x_i) \Delta x + \tfrac{1}{2}[f(a) - f(b)] \Delta x$$

Therefore, if $n \to +\infty$ and $\Delta x \to 0$, we have

$$\lim_{\Delta x \to 0} T = \lim_{\Delta x \to 0} \sum_{i=1}^{n} f(x_i) \Delta x + \lim_{\Delta x \to 0} \tfrac{1}{2}[f(a) - f(b)] \Delta x$$

$$= \int_a^b f(x) \, dx + 0$$

Thus, we can make the difference between T and the value of the definite integral as small as we please by taking n sufficiently large (and consequently Δx sufficiently small).

The following theorem, which is proved in advanced calculus, gives us a method for estimating the error obtained when using the trapezoidal rule. The error is denoted by ϵ_T.

11.8.1 Theorem   Let the function f be continuous on the closed interval $[a, b]$, and f' and f'' both exist on $[a, b]$. If

$$\epsilon_T = \int_a^b f(x)\ dx - T$$

where T is the approximate value of $\int_a^b f(x)\ dx$ found by the trapezoidal rule, then there is some number η in $[a, b]$ such that

$$\epsilon_T = -\tfrac{1}{12}(b - a)f''(\eta)(\Delta x)^2 \tag{4}$$

EXAMPLE 2:   Find the bounds for the error in the result of Example 1.

SOLUTION: We first find the absolute minimum and absolute maximum values of $f''(x)$ on $[0, 3]$.

$$f(x) = (16 + x^2)^{-1}$$

$$f'(x) = -2x(16 + x^2)^{-2}$$

$$f''(x) = 8x^2(16 + x^2)^{-3} - 2(16 + x^2)^{-2} = (6x^2 - 32)(16 + x^2)^{-3}$$

$$f'''(x) = -6x(6x^2 - 32)(16 + x^2)^{-4} + 12x(16 + x^2)^{-3}$$

$$= 24x(16 - x^2)(16 + x^2)^{-4}$$

Because $f'''(x) > 0$ for all x in the open interval $(0, 3)$, then f'' is increasing on the open interval $(0, 3)$. Therefore, the absolute minimum value of f'' on $[0, 3]$ is $f''(0)$, and the absolute maximum value of f'' on $[0, 3]$ is $f''(3)$.

$$f''(0) = -\frac{1}{128} \quad \text{and} \quad f''(3) = \frac{22}{15{,}625}$$

Taking $\eta = 0$ on the right side of (4), we get

$$-\frac{3}{12}\left(-\frac{1}{128}\right)\frac{1}{4} = \frac{1}{2048}$$

Taking $\eta = 3$ on the right side of (4), we have

$$-\frac{3}{12}\left(\frac{22}{15{,}625}\right)\frac{1}{4} = -\frac{11}{45{,}000}$$

Therefore, if ϵ_T is the error in the result of Example 1, we conclude

$$-\frac{11}{45{,}000} \le \epsilon_T \le \frac{1}{2048}$$

$$-0.0002 \le \epsilon_T \le 0.0005$$

Exercises 11.8

In Exercises 1 through 14, compute the approximate value of the given definite integral by the trapezoidal rule for the indicated value of n. Express the result to three decimal places. In Exercises 1 through 8, find the exact value of the definite integral and compare the result with the approximation.

1. $\int_1^2 \dfrac{dx}{x}$; $n = 5$

2. $\int_2^{10} \dfrac{dx}{1 + x}$; $n = 8$

3. $\int_0^2 x^3 \, dx$; $n = 4$

4. $\int_0^2 x\sqrt{4 - x^2} \, dx$; $n = 8$

5. $\int_0^1 \dfrac{dx}{\sqrt{1 + x^2}}$; $n = 5$

6. $\int_2^3 \sqrt{1 + x^2} \, dx$; $n = 6$

7. $\int_0^\pi \sin x \, dx$; $n = 6$

8. $\int_0^\pi x \cos x^2 \, dx$; $n = 4$

9. $\int_{\pi/2}^{3\pi/2} \dfrac{\sin x}{x} \, dx$; $n = 6$

10. $\int_2^3 \ln(1 + x^2) \, dx$; $n = 4$

11. $\int_0^1 e^{x^2} \, dx$; $n = 5$

12. $\int_0^\pi \dfrac{\sin x}{1 + x} \, dx$; $n = 6$

13. $\int_0^2 \sqrt{1 + x^4} \, dx$; $n = 6$

14. $\int_0^1 \sqrt{1 + x^3} \, dx$; $n = 4$

In Exercises 15 through 20, find the bounds for the error in the approximation of the indicated exercises.

15. Exercise 1

16. Exercise 2

17. Exercise 3

18. Exercise 6

19. Exercise 11

20. Exercise 10

21. The integral $\int_0^2 e^{-x^2} \, dx$ is very important in mathematical statistics. It is called a "probability integral" and it cannot be evaluated exactly in terms of elementary functions. Use the trapezoidal rule with $n = 6$ to find an approximate value and express the result to three decimal places.

22. The region bounded by the curve whose equation is $y = e^{-x/2}$, the x axis, the y axis, and the line $x = 2$ is revolved about the x axis. Find the volume of the solid of revolution generated. Approximate the definite integral by the trapezoidal rule to three decimal places, with $n = 5$.

23. Show that the exact value of $\int_0^2 \sqrt{4 - x^2} \, dx$ is π. Approximate the definite integral by the trapezoidal rule to three decimal places, with $n = 8$, and compare the value so obtained with the exact value.

24. Show that the exact value of $\frac{1}{2} \int_0^3 dx/(x + 1)$ is $\ln 2$. Approximate the definite integral by the trapezoidal rule with $n = 6$ to three decimal places, and compare the value so obtained with the exact value of $\ln 2$ as given in a table.

11.9 SIMPSON'S RULE

Another method for approximating the value of a definite integral is provided by *Simpson's rule* (sometimes referred to as the *parabolic rule*). For a given partition of the closed interval $[a, b]$, Simpson's rule usually gives a better approximation than the trapezoidal rule. However, Simpson's rule requires more effort to apply. In the trapezoidal rule, successive points on the graph of $y = f(x)$ are connected by segments of straight lines, whereas in Simpson's rule the points are connected by segments of parabolas. Before Simpson's rule is developed, we state and prove a theorem which will be needed.

11.9.1 Theorem If $P_0(x_0, y_0)$, $P_1(x_1, y_1)$, and $P_2(x_2, y_2)$ are three noncollinear points on the parabola having the equation $y = Ax^2 + Bx + C$, where $y_0 \geq 0$, $y_1 \geq 0$, $y_2 \geq 0$, $x_1 = x_0 + h$, and $x_2 = x_0 + 2h$, then the measure of the area of the region bounded by the parabola, the x axis, and the lines $x = x_0$ and $x = x_2$ is given by

$$\tfrac{1}{3}h(y_0 + 4y_1 + y_2) \tag{1}$$

Figure 11.9.1

PROOF: The parabola whose equation is $y = Ax^2 + Bx + C$ has a vertical axis. Refer to Fig. 11.9.1, which shows the region bounded by the parabola, the x axis, and the lines $x = x_0$ and $x = x_2$.

Because P_0, P_1, and P_2 are points on the parabola, their coordinates satisfy the equation of the parabola. So when we replace x_1 by $x_0 + h$, and x_2 by $x_0 + 2h$, we have

$$y_0 = Ax_0^2 + Bx_0 + C$$
$$y_1 = A(x_0 + h)^2 + B(x_0 + h) + C = A(x_0^2 + 2hx_0 + h^2) + B(x_0 + h) + C$$
$$y_2 = A(x_0 + 2h)^2 + B(x_0 + 2h) + C = A(x_0^2 + 4hx_0 + 4h^2) + B(x_0 + 2h) + C$$

Therefore,

$$y_0 + 4y_1 + y_2 = A(6x_0^2 + 12hx_0 + 8h^2) + B(6x_0 + 6h) + 6C \qquad (2)$$

Now if K square units is the area of the region, then K can be computed by the limit of a Riemann sum, and we have

$$K = \lim_{\Delta x \to 0} \sum_{i=1}^{n} (A\xi_i^2 + B\xi_i + C)\, \Delta x$$

$$= \int_{x_0}^{x_0 + 2h} (Ax^2 + Bx + C)\, dx$$

$$= \tfrac{1}{3}Ax^3 + \tfrac{1}{2}Bx^2 + Cx \Big]_{x_0}^{x_0 + 2h}$$

$$= \tfrac{1}{3}A(x_0 + 2h)^3 + \tfrac{1}{2}B(x_0 + 2h)^2 + C(x_0 + 2h) - (\tfrac{1}{3}Ax_0^3 + \tfrac{1}{2}Bx_0^2 + Cx_0)$$

$$= \tfrac{1}{3}h[A(6x_0^2 + 12hx_0 + 8h^2) + B(6x_0 + 6h) + 6C] \qquad (3)$$

Substituting from (2) in (3), we get

$$K = \tfrac{1}{3}h[y_0 + 4y_1 + y_2] \qquad \blacksquare$$

Let the function f be continuous on the closed interval $[a, b]$. Consider a regular partition of the interval $[a, b]$ of $2n$ subintervals ($2n$ is used instead of n because we want an even number of subintervals). The length of each subinterval is given by $\Delta x = (b - a)/2n$. Let the points on the curve $y = f(x)$ having these partitioning points as abscissas be denoted by $P_0(x_0, y_0)$, $P_1(x_1, y_1)$, . . . , $P_{2n}(x_{2n}, y_{2n})$; see Fig. 11.9.2, where $f(x) \geq 0$ for all x in $[a, b]$.

We approximate the segment of the curve $y = f(x)$ from P_0 to P_2 by the segment of the parabola with its vertical axis through P_0, P_1, and P_2. Then by Theorem 11.9.1 the measure of the area of the region bounded by this parabola, the x axis, and the lines $x = x_0$ and $x = x_2$, with $h = \Delta x$, is given by

$$\tfrac{1}{3}\Delta x(y_0 + 4y_1 + y_2) \quad \text{or} \quad \tfrac{1}{3}\Delta x[f(x_0) + 4f(x_1) + f(x_2)]$$

In a similar manner, we approximate the segment of the curve

Figure 11.9.2

$y = f(x)$ from P_2 to P_4 by the segment of the parabola with its vertical axis through P_2, P_3, and P_4. The measure of the area of the region bounded by this parabola, the x axis, and the lines $x = x_2$ and $x = x_4$ is given by

$$\tfrac{1}{3} \Delta x (y_2 + 4y_3 + y_4) \quad \text{or} \quad \tfrac{1}{3} \Delta x [f(x_2) + 4f(x_3) + f(x_4)]$$

This process is continued until we have n such regions, and the measure of the area of the last region is given by

$$\tfrac{1}{3} \Delta x (y_{2n-2} + 4y_{2n-1} + y_{2n}) \quad \text{or} \quad \tfrac{1}{3} \Delta x \, [f(x_{2n-2}) + 4f(x_{2n-1}) + f(x_{2n})]$$

The sum of the measures of the areas of these regions approximates the measure of the area of the region bounded by the curve whose equation is $y = f(x)$, the x axis, and the lines $x = a$ and $x = b$. The measure of the area of this region is given by the definite integral $\int_a^b f(x) \, dx$. So we have as an approximation to the definite integral

$$\tfrac{1}{3} \Delta x [f(x_0) + 4f(x_1) + f(x_2)] + \tfrac{1}{3} \Delta x [f(x_2) + 4f(x_3) + f(x_4)] + \cdots$$

$$+ \tfrac{1}{3} \Delta x [f(x_{2n-4}) + 4f(x_{2n-3}) + f(x_{2n-2})] + \tfrac{1}{3} \Delta x [f(x_{2n-2}) + 4f(x_{2n-1}) + f(x_{2n})]$$

Thus,

$$\int_a^b f(x) \, dx \approx \tfrac{1}{3} \Delta x [f(x_0) + 4f(x_1) + 2f(x_2) + 4f(x_3) + 2f(x_4) + \cdots$$

$$+ 2f(x_{2n-2}) + 4f(x_{2n-1}) + f(x_{2n})] \quad (4)$$

where $\Delta x = (b - a)/2n$.

Formula (4) is known as *Simpson's rule*.

EXAMPLE 1: Use Simpson's rule to approximate the value of

$$\int_0^1 \frac{dx}{x + 1}$$

SOLUTION: Applying Simpson's rule with $2n = 4$, we have $\Delta x = \tfrac{1}{4}(1 - 0) = \tfrac{1}{4}$, and

$$\int_0^1 \frac{dx}{x + 1} \approx \frac{1}{12} [f(x_0) + 4f(x_1) + 2f(x_2) + 4f(x_3) + f(x_4)] \quad (5)$$

with $2n = 4$. Give the result to four decimal places.

The computation of the expression in brackets on the right side of (5) is shown in Table 11.9.1, where $f(x) = 1/(x+1)$.

Substituting the sum from Table 11.9.1 in (5), we get

$$\int_0^1 \frac{dx}{x+1} \approx \frac{1}{12} (8.31906) \approx 0.69325^+$$

Table 11.9.1

i	x_i	$f(x_i)$	k_i	$k_i \cdot f(x_i)$
0	0	1.00000	1	1.00000
1	0.25	0.80000	4	3.20000
2	0.5	0.66667	2	1.33334
3	0.75	0.57143	4	2.28572
4	1	0.50000	1	0.50000

$$\sum_{i=0}^4 k_i f(x_i) = 8.31906$$

Rounding off the result to four decimal places gives us

$$\int_0^1 \frac{dx}{x+1} \approx 0.6933$$

The exact value of $\int_0^1 dx/(x+1)$ is found as follows:

$$\int_0^1 \frac{dx}{x+1} = \ln|x+1|\Big]_0^1 = \ln 2 - \ln 1 = \ln 2$$

From a table of natural logarithms, the value of $\ln 2$ to four decimal places is 0.6931, which agrees with our approximation in the first three places. And the error in our approximation is -0.0002.

In applying Simpson's rule, the larger we take the value of $2n$, the smaller will be the value of Δx, and so geometrically it seems evident that the greater will be the accuracy of the approximation, because a parabola passing through three points of a curve that are close to each other will be close to the curve throughout the subinterval of width $2\,\Delta x$.

The following theorem, which is proved in advanced calculus, gives a method for determining the error in applying Simpson's rule. The error is denoted by ϵ_S.

11.9.2 Theorem   Let the function f be continuous on the closed interval $[a, b]$, and f', f'', f''', and $f^{(iv)}$ all exist on $[a, b]$. If

$$\epsilon_S = \int_a^b f(x)\,dx - S$$

where S is the approximate value of $\int_a^b f(x)\,dx$ found by Simpson's rule, then there is some number η in $[a, b]$ such that

$$\epsilon_S = -\tfrac{1}{180}(b-a)f^{(iv)}(\eta)(\Delta x)^4 \tag{6}$$

EXAMPLE 2:   Find the bounds for the error in Example 1.

SOLUTION:

$$f(x) = (x+1)^{-1}$$
$$f'(x) = -1(x+1)^{-2}$$
$$f''(x) = 2(x+1)^{-3}$$
$$f'''(x) = -6(x+1)^{-4}$$
$$f^{(iv)}(x) = 24(x+1)^{-5}$$
$$f^{(v)}(x) = -120(x+1)^{-6}$$

Because $f^{(v)}(x) < 0$ for all x in $[0, 1]$, $f^{(iv)}$ is decreasing on $[0, 1]$. Thus, the absolute minimum value of $f^{(iv)}$ is at the right endpoint 1, and the absolute maximum value of $f^{(iv)}$ on $[0, 1]$ is at the left endpoint 0.

$$f^{(iv)}(0) = 24 \quad \text{and} \quad f^{(iv)}(1) = \tfrac{3}{4}$$

Substituting 0 for η in the right side of (6), we get

$$-\tfrac{1}{180}(b-a)f^{(iv)}(0)(\Delta x)^4 = -\tfrac{1}{180}(24)(\tfrac{1}{4})^4 = -\tfrac{1}{1920} = -0.00052$$

Substituting 1 for η in the right side of (6), we have

$$-\frac{1}{180}(b-a)f^{(iv)}(1)(\Delta x)^4 = -\frac{1}{180} \cdot \frac{3}{4}\left(\frac{1}{4}\right)^4 = -\frac{1}{61{,}440} = -0.00002$$

So we conclude that

$$-0.00052 \le \epsilon_S \le -0.00002 \tag{7}$$

The inequality (7) agrees with the discussion in Example 1 regarding the error in the approximation of $\int_0^1 dx/(x+1)$ by Simpson's rule because $-0.00052 < -0.0002 < -0.00002$.

If $f(x)$ is a polynomial of degree three or less, then $f^{(iv)}(x) \equiv 0$ and therefore $\epsilon_S = 0$. In other words, Simpson's rule gives an exact result for a polynomial of the third degree or lower. This statement is geometrically obvious if $f(x)$ is of the second or first degree because in the first case the graph of $y = f(x)$ is a parabola, and in the second case the graph is a straight line (a degenerate parabola).

We apply Simpson's rule to the definite integral $\int_a^b f(x)\,dx$, where $f(x)$ is a third-degree polynomial, and take $2n = 2$. Here Simpson's rule gives an exact value for the definite integral. Because $2n = 2$, $x_0 = a$, $x_1 =$

$\frac{1}{2}(a+b)$, and $x_2 = b$; and $\Delta x = \frac{1}{2}(b-a)$. So we have

$$\int_a^b f(x)\,dx = \frac{b-a}{6}\left[f(a) + 4f\left(\frac{a+b}{2}\right) + f(b)\right] \qquad (8)$$

Formula (8) is known as the *prismoidal formula*.

In Sec. 8.4, we learned that $\int_a^b f(x)\,dx$ yields the measure of the volume of a solid for which $f(x)$ represents the measure of the area of a plane section formed by a plane perpendicular to the x axis at a distance x units from the origin. Therefore, if $f(x)$ is a polynomial of the third degree or less, the prismoidal formula gives the exact measure of the volume of such a solid.

EXAMPLE 3: Find the volume of a right-circular cone of height h and base radius r by the prismoidal formula.

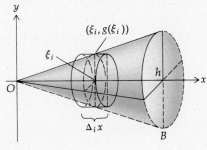

Figure 11.9.3

SOLUTION: Figure 11.9.3 illustrates a right-circular cone having its vertex at the origin and its axis along the positive side of the x axis. The area of the plane section ξ_i units from the origin is $\pi[g(\xi_i)]^2$ square units, where $g(x) = (r/h)x$, which is obtained from an equation of line OA in the xy plane. So if V cubic units is the volume of the right-circular cone, then

$$V = \lim_{\|\Delta\| \to 0} \sum_{i=1}^n \pi[g(\xi_i)]^2\,\Delta_i x$$

$$= \int_0^h \pi[g(x)]^2\,dx$$

$$= \int_0^h \pi\,\frac{r^2}{h^2}\,x^2\,dx$$

$$= \frac{\pi r^2}{h^2}\int_0^h x^2\,dx$$

Evaluating $\int_0^h x^2\,dx$ by the prismoidal formula (8) with $f(x) = x^2$, $b = h$, $a = 0$, and $\frac{1}{2}(a+b) = \frac{1}{2}h$, we have

$$V = \frac{\pi r^2}{h^2}\cdot\frac{h}{6}\,(0 + 4\cdot\frac{h^2}{4} + h^2) = \frac{\pi r^2}{6h}\,(2h^2) = \frac{1}{3}\,\pi r^2 h$$

Exercises 11.9

In Exercises 1 through 6, approximate the definite integral by Simpson's rule, using the indicated value of $2n$. Express the answers to three decimal places. Also, find the exact value of the definite integral and compare the results.

1. $\int_0^2 x^2\,dx$; $2n = 4$

2. $\int_1^2 \frac{dx}{x+1}$; $2n = 8$

3. $\int_0^1 \frac{dx}{\sqrt{1+x^2}}$; $2n = 4$

4. $\int_{-1/2}^0 \frac{dx}{\sqrt{1-x^2}}$; $2n = 4$

5. $\int_0^1 \frac{dx}{x^2+x+1}$; $2n = 4$

6. $\int_0^\pi \sin x\,dx$; $2n = 6$

In Exercises 7 through 9, find bounds for the error in the indicated exercise.

7. Exercise 1   8. Exercise 2   9. Exercise 6

Each of the definite integrals in Exercises 10 through 15 cannot be evaluated exactly in terms of elementary functions. Use Simpson's rule, with the indicated value of $2n$, to find an approximate value of the given definite integral. Express results to three decimal places.

10. $\int_0^{\pi/2} \sqrt{\sin x} \, dx; \ 2n = 6$

11. $\int_0^{\pi} \frac{\sin x}{x}; \ 2n = 6$

12. $\int_0^1 \sqrt[3]{1 - x^2} \, dx; \ 2n = 4$

13. $\int_0^2 e^{-x^2} \, dx; \ 2n = 4$

14. $\int_0^2 \sqrt{1 + x^4} \, dx; \ 2n = 6$

15. $\int_0^2 \frac{dx}{\sqrt{1 + x^3}}; \ 2n = 8$

In Exercises 16 through 19, use the prismoidal formula to find the exact volume of the given solid.

16. A sphere of radius r.

17. A right-circular cylinder of height h and base radius r.

18. A right pyramid of height h and base a square having a side of length s.

19. A frustrum of a right-circular cone of height h_1 and base radii r_1 and r_2.

20. Show that the exact value of $4 \int_0^1 \sqrt{1 - x^2} \, dx$ is π. Then use Simpson's rule with $2n = 6$ to get an approximate value of $4 \int_0^1 \sqrt{1 - x^2} \, dx$ to three decimal places. Compare the results.

21. Find an approximate value to four decimal places of the definite integral $\int_0^{\pi/3} \log_{10} \cos x \, dx$, (a) by the prismoidal formula; (b) by Simpson's rule, taking $\Delta x = \frac{1}{12}\pi$; (c) by the trapezoidal rule, taking $\Delta x = \frac{1}{12}\pi$.

22. Find the area of the region enclosed by the loop of the curve whose equation is $y^2 = 8x^2 - x^5$. Evaluate the definite integral by Simpson's rule, with $2n = 8$. Express the result to three decimal places.

Review Exercises (Chapter 11)

In Exercises 1 through 62, evaluate the indefinite integral.

1. $\int \tan^2 4x \cos^4 4x \, dx$

2. $\int \frac{5x^2 - 3}{x^3 - x} \, dx$

3. $\int \frac{e^x \, dx}{\sqrt{4 - e^x}}$

4. $\int \frac{dx}{x^2 \sqrt{a^2 + x^2}}$

5. $\int \tan^{-1} \sqrt{x} \, dx$

6. $\int \frac{dt}{t^4 + 1}$

7. $\int \cos^2 \tfrac{1}{3}x \, dx$

8. $\int \frac{\sqrt{x + 1} + 1}{\sqrt{x + 1} - 1} \, dx$

9. $\int \frac{x^2 + 1}{(x - 1)^3} \, dx$

10. $\int \frac{dy}{\sqrt{y} + 1}$

11. $\int \sin x \sin 3x \, dx$

12. $\int \cos \theta \cos 2\theta \, d\theta$

13. $\int \frac{dx}{x + x^{4/3}}$

14. $\int t \sqrt{2t - t^2} \, dt$

15. $\int (\sec 3x + \csc 3x)^2 \, dx$

16. $\int \frac{dx}{\sqrt{e^x - 1}}$

17. $\int \frac{2t^3 + 11t + 8}{t^3 + 4t^2 + 4t} \, dt$

18. $\int x^3 e^{3x} \, dx$

19. $\int \frac{x^4 + 1}{x^4 - 1} \, dx$

20. $\int \frac{\sqrt{x^2 - 4}}{x^2} \, dx$

21. $\int \sin^4 3x \cos^2 3x \, dx$

22. $\displaystyle\int t \sin^2 2t \, dt$

23. $\displaystyle\int \frac{dr}{\sqrt{3 - 4r - r^2}}$

24. $\displaystyle\int \frac{4x^2 + x - 2}{x^3 - 5x^2 + 8x - 4} \, dx$

25. $\displaystyle\int x^3 \cos x^2 \, dx$

26. $\displaystyle\int \frac{y \, dy}{9 + 16y^4}$

27. $\displaystyle\int e^{t/2} \cos 2t \, dt$

28. $\displaystyle\int \frac{du}{u^{5/8} - u^{1/8}}$

29. $\displaystyle\int \frac{\sin x \cos x}{4 + \sin^4 x} \, dx$

30. $\displaystyle\int \frac{\sqrt{w - a}}{w} \, dw, \ a > 0$

31. $\displaystyle\int \sin^5 nx \, dx$

32. $\displaystyle\int \frac{dx}{x \ln x (\ln x - 1)}$

33. $\displaystyle\int \csc^5 x \, dx$

34. $\displaystyle\int \frac{dx}{5 + 4 \sec x}$

35. $\displaystyle\int \frac{2y^2 + 1}{y^3 - 6y^2 + 12y - 8} \, dy$

36. $\displaystyle\int \frac{x^5 \, dx}{(x^2 - a^2)^3}$

37. $\displaystyle\int \frac{\sin x \, dx}{1 + \cos^2 x}$

38. $\displaystyle\int \frac{dx}{x \sqrt{x^2 + x + 1}}$

39. $\displaystyle\int \sqrt{4t - t^2} \, dt$

40. $\displaystyle\int \frac{dx}{\sqrt{1 - x + 3x^2}}$

41. $\displaystyle\int \frac{dx}{x^4 - x}$

42. $\displaystyle\int \frac{\sqrt{t} - 1}{\sqrt{t} + 1} \, dt$

43. $\displaystyle\int \frac{e^x \, dx}{\sqrt{4 - 9e^{2x}}}$

44. $\displaystyle\int \frac{dx}{5 + 4 \cos 2x}$

45. $\displaystyle\int \cot^2 3x \csc^4 3x \, dx$

46. $\displaystyle\int \frac{\cot x \, dx}{3 + 2 \sin x}$

47. $\displaystyle\int x^2 \sin^{-1} x \, dx$

48. $\displaystyle\int \frac{dx}{x \sqrt{5x - 6 - x^2}}$

49. $\displaystyle\int \frac{dx}{\sin x - 2 \csc x}$

50. $\displaystyle\int \cos x \ln(\sin x) \, dx$

51. $\displaystyle\int \frac{\cos 3t \, dt}{\sin 3t \sqrt{\sin^2 3t - \frac{1}{4}}}$

52. $\displaystyle\int \frac{dx}{(x^2 + 6x + 34)^2}$

53. $\displaystyle\int \frac{\sqrt{x^2 + a^2}}{x^4} \, dx$

54. $\displaystyle\int \tan x \sin x \, dx$

55. $\displaystyle\int \frac{\sin^{-1} \sqrt{2t}}{\sqrt{1 - 2t}} \, dt$

56. $\displaystyle\int \ln(x^2 + 1) \, dx$

57. $\displaystyle\int \frac{dx}{\sqrt{2 + \sqrt{x - 1}}}$

58. $\displaystyle\int \frac{dx}{2 + 2 \sin x + \cos x}$

59. $\displaystyle\int \sqrt{\tan x} \, dx$

60. $\displaystyle\int \frac{dx}{\sqrt{1 + \sqrt[3]{x}}}$

61. $\displaystyle\int x^n \ln x \, dx$

62. $\displaystyle\int \tan^n x \sec^4 x \, dx, \ n > 0$

In Exercises 63 through 94, evaluate the definite integral.

63. $\displaystyle\int_0^\pi \sqrt{2 + 2 \cos x} \, dx$

64. $\displaystyle\int_{1/2}^1 \sqrt{\frac{1 - x}{x}} \, dx$

65. $\displaystyle\int_1^2 \frac{2x^2 + x + 4}{x^3 + 4x^2} \, dx$

66. $\displaystyle\int_0^1 \frac{dx}{e^x + e^{-x}}$

67. $\displaystyle\int_0^2 \frac{t^3 \, dt}{\sqrt{4 + t^2}}$

68. $\displaystyle\int_0^{\pi/2} \sin^3 t \cos^3 t \, dt$

69. $\displaystyle\int_{-2}^{2\sqrt{3}} \frac{x^2 \, dx}{(16 - x^2)^{3/2}}$

70. $\displaystyle\int_0^1 \frac{xe^x \, dx}{(1 + x)^2}$

71. $\displaystyle\int_0^{\pi/4} \sec^4 x \, dx$

72. $\displaystyle\int_0^2 \frac{(1 - x) \, dx}{x^2 + 3x + 2}$

73. $\displaystyle\int_{\pi/12}^{\pi/8} \cot^3 2y \, dy$

74. $\displaystyle\int_0^2 (2^x + x^2) \, dx$

75. $\displaystyle\int_a^{a/2} \frac{\sqrt{(a^2-x^2)^3}}{x^2}\,dx$

76. $\displaystyle\int_1^2 (\ln x)^2\,dx$

77. $\displaystyle\int_{\sqrt{3}/3}^1 \frac{(2x^2-2x+1)\,dx}{x^3+x}$

78. $\displaystyle\int_{\sqrt{2}/2}^1 \frac{x^3\,dx}{\sqrt{2-x^2}}$

79. $\displaystyle\int_1^{10} \log_{10}\sqrt{ex}\,dx$

80. $\displaystyle\int_0^{2\pi} |\sin x - \cos x|\,dx$

81. $\displaystyle\int_1^2 \frac{x+2}{(x+1)^2}\,dx$

82. $\displaystyle\int_0^{\sqrt{\pi/2}} xe^{x^2}\cos x^2\,dx$

83. $\displaystyle\int_0^{\pi} |\cos^3 x|\,dx$

84. $\displaystyle\int_{-\pi/4}^{\pi/4} |\tan^5 x|\,dx$

85. $\displaystyle\int_0^{1/2} \frac{2x\,dx}{x^3-x^2-x+1}$

86. $\displaystyle\int_0^1 x^3\sqrt{1+x^2}\,dx$

87. $\displaystyle\int_0^{1/2} \frac{x\,dx}{\sqrt{1-4x^4}}$

88. $\displaystyle\int_0^{\pi/12} \frac{dx}{\cos^4 3x}$

89. $\displaystyle\int_0^1 \sqrt{2y+y^2}\,dy$

90. $\displaystyle\int_0^4 \frac{x^2\,dx}{x^3+4x^2+5x+2}$

91. $\displaystyle\int_0^{\pi/2} \frac{dt}{12+13\cos t}$

92. $\displaystyle\int_0^3 \frac{dr}{(r+2)\sqrt{r+1}}$

93. $\displaystyle\int_0^{16} \sqrt{4-\sqrt{x}}\,dx$

94. $\displaystyle\int_{2\pi/3}^{\pi} \frac{\sin\frac{1}{2}t}{1+\cos\frac{1}{2}t}\,dt$

In Exercises 95 and 96, find an approximate value for the given integral by using (a) the trapezoidal rule, and (b) Simpson's rule. Take four subintervals and express the results to three decimal places.

95. $\displaystyle\int_{1/10}^{1/2} \frac{\cos x}{x}\,dx$

96. $\displaystyle\int_1^{9/5} \sqrt{1+x^3}\,dx$

97. Find the length of the arc of the parabola $y^2 = 6x$ from $x = 6$ to $x = 12$.

98. Find the area of the region bounded by the curve $y = \sin^{-1} 2x$, the line $x = \frac{1}{4}\sqrt{3}$, and the x axis.

99. Find the centroid of the solid of revolution obtained by revolving about the x axis the region bounded by the curve $y = e^{-x}$, the coordinate axes, and the line $x = 1$.

100. Find the centroid of the solid obtained by revolving the region of Exercise 99 about the y axis.

101. The vertical end of a water trough is 3 ft wide at the top, 2 ft deep, and has the form of the region bounded by the x axis and one arch of the curve $y = 2\sin\frac{1}{3}\pi x$. If the trough is full of water, find the force due to liquid pressure on the end.

102. The linear density of a rod 3 ft long at a point x ft from one end is ke^{-3x} slugs/ft. Find the mass and center of mass of the rod.

103. Find the centroid of the region bounded by the curve $y = x \ln x$, the x axis, and the line $x = e$.

104. Find the area of the region enclosed by one loop of the curve $x^2 = y^4(1-y^2)$.

105. Two chemicals A and B react to form a chemical C and the rate of change of the amount of C is proportional to the product of the amounts of A and B remaining at any given time. Initially there are 60 lb of chemical A and 60 lb of chemical B, and to form 5 lb of C, 3 lb of A and 2 lb of B are required. After 1 hr, 15 lb of C are formed. (a) If x lb of C are formed at t hr, find an expression for x in terms of t. (b) Find the amount of C after 3 hr.

106. A tank is in the shape of the solid of revolution formed by rotating about the x axis the region bounded by the curve $y = \ln x$, the x axis, and the lines $x = e$ and $x = e^2$. If the tank is full of water, find the work done in pumping all the water to the top of the tank. Distance is measured in feet. Take the positive x axis vertically downward.

12

Hyperbolic functions

12.1 THE HYPERBOLIC FUNCTIONS

Certain combinations of e^x and e^{-x} appear so frequently in applications of mathematics that they are given special names. Two of these functions are the "hyperbolic sine function" and the "hyperbolic cosine function." The function values are related to the coordinates of the points of an equilateral hyperbola in a manner similar to that in which the values of the corresponding trigonometric functions are related to the coordinates of points of a circle (see Sec. 17.4) Following are the definitions of the hyperbolic sine function and the hyperbolic cosine function.

12.1.1 Definition

The *hyperbolic sine function* is defined by

$$\sinh x = \frac{e^x - e^{-x}}{2}$$

The domain and range are the set of all real numbers.

12.1.2 Definition

The *hyperbolic cosine function* is defined by

$$\cosh x = \frac{e^x + e^{-x}}{2}$$

The domain is the set of all real numbers and the range is the set of all numbers in the interval $[1, +\infty)$.

$y = \sinh x$ Figure 12.1.1

Sketches of the graphs of the hyperbolic sine function and the hyperbolic cosine function are shown in Figs. 12.1.1 and 12.1.2, respectively. The graphs are easily sketched by using values in the table of hyperbolic functions in the Appendix. Note that these functions are not periodic.

The remaining four hyperbolic functions may be defined in terms of the hyperbolic sine and hyperbolic cosine functions. You should note that each satisfies a relation analogous to one satisfied by corresponding trigonometric functions.

12.1.3 Definition

The *hyperbolic tangent function, hyperbolic cotangent function, hyperbolic secant function,* and *hyperbolic cosecant function* are defined, respectively, as follows:

$$\tanh x = \frac{\sinh x}{\cosh x} = \frac{e^x - e^{-x}}{e^x + e^{-x}} \qquad (1)$$

$$\coth x = \frac{\cosh x}{\sinh x} = \frac{e^x + e^{-x}}{e^x - e^{-x}} \qquad (2)$$

$$\text{sech } x = \frac{1}{\cosh x} = \frac{2}{e^x + e^{-x}} \qquad (3)$$

$$\text{csch } x = \frac{1}{\sinh x} = \frac{2}{e^x - e^{-x}} \qquad (4)$$

$y = \cosh x$

Figure 12.1.2

Figure 12.1.3

A sketch of the graph of the hyperbolic tangent function is shown in Fig. 12.1.3.

There are identities that are satisfied by the hyperbolic functions which are similar to those satisfied by the trigonometric functions. Four of the fundamental identities are given in Definition 12.1.3. The other four fundamental identities are as follows:

$$\tanh x = \frac{1}{\coth x} \tag{5}$$

$$\cosh^2 x - \sinh^2 x = 1 \tag{6}$$

$$1 - \tanh^2 x = \operatorname{sech}^2 x \tag{7}$$

$$1 - \coth^2 x = -\operatorname{csch}^2 x \tag{8}$$

Equation (5) follows immediately from (1) and (2). Following is the proof of (6).

$$\cosh^2 x - \sinh^2 x = \left(\frac{e^x + e^{-x}}{2}\right)^2 - \left(\frac{e^x - e^{-x}}{2}\right)^2$$

$$= \tfrac{1}{4}\left(e^{2x} + 2e^0 + e^{-2x} - e^{2x} + 2e^0 - e^{-2x}\right)$$

$$= 1$$

Equation (7) can be proved by using the definitions of $\tanh x$ and $\operatorname{sech} x$ in terms of e^x and e^{-x} as in the proof above, or an alternate proof is obtained by using other identities as follows:

$$1 - \tanh^2 x = 1 - \frac{\sinh^2 x}{\cosh^2 x} = \frac{\cosh^2 x - \sinh^2 x}{\cosh^2 x} = \frac{1}{\cosh^2 x} = \operatorname{sech}^2 x$$

The proof of (8) is left as an exercise (see Exercise 1). From the eight fundamental identities, it is possible to prove others. Some of these are given in the exercises that follow. Other identities, such as the hyperbolic functions of the sum or difference of two numbers and the hyperbolic functions of twice a number or one-half a number, are similar to the corresponding trigonometric identities. Sometimes it is helpful to make use of the following two relations, which follow from Definitions 12.1.1 and 12.1.2.

$$\cosh x + \sinh x = e^x \tag{9}$$

$$\cosh x - \sinh x = e^{-x} \tag{10}$$

We use them in proving the following identity:

$$\sinh(x + y) = \sinh x \cosh y + \cosh x \sinh y \tag{11}$$

From Definition 12.1.1 we have

$$\sinh(x + y) = \frac{e^{x+y} - e^{-(x+y)}}{2} = \frac{e^x e^y - e^{-x} e^{-y}}{2}$$

Applying (9) and (10) to the right side of the above equation, we obtain

$$\sinh(x+y) = \tfrac{1}{2}[(\cosh x + \sinh x)(\cosh y + \sinh y) \\ - (\cosh x - \sinh x)(\cosh y - \sinh y)]$$

Expanding the right side of the above equation and combining terms, formula (11) is obtained.

In a similar manner we can prove

$$\cosh(x+y) = \cosh x \cosh y + \sinh x \sinh y \tag{12}$$

If in (11) and (12) y is replaced by x, the following two formulas are obtained:

$$\sinh 2x = 2 \sinh x \cosh x \tag{13}$$

and

$$\cosh 2x = \cosh^2 x + \sinh^2 x \tag{14}$$

Formula (14) combined with the identity (6) gives us two alternate formulas for $\cosh 2x$, which are

$$\cosh 2x = 2 \sinh^2 x + 1 \tag{15}$$

and

$$\cosh 2x = 2 \cosh^2 x - 1 \tag{16}$$

Solving (15) and (16) for $\sinh x$ and $\cosh x$, respectively, and replacing x by $\tfrac{1}{2}x$, we get

$$\sinh \frac{x}{2} = \pm \sqrt{\frac{\cosh x - 1}{2}} \tag{17}$$

and

$$\cosh \frac{x}{2} = \sqrt{\frac{\cosh x + 1}{2}} \tag{18}$$

We do not have a $\pm$ sign on the right side of (18) since the range of the hyperbolic cosine function is $[1, +\infty)$. The details of the proofs of Eqs. (12) through (18) are left as exercises (see Exercises 2, 4, and 5).

The formulas for the derivatives of the hyperbolic sine and hyperbolic cosine functions may be obtained by applying Definitions 12.1.1 and 12.1.2 and differentiating the resulting expressions involving exponential functions. For example,

$$D_x(\cosh x) = D_x \left(\frac{e^x + e^{-x}}{2} \right) = \frac{e^x - e^{-x}}{2} = \sinh x$$

In a similar manner, we find $D_x(\sinh x) = \cosh x$ (see Exercise 15).

To find the derivative of the hyperbolic tangent function, we use some of the identities we have previously proved.

$$D_x(\tanh x) = D_x\left(\frac{\sinh x}{\cosh x}\right) = \frac{\cosh^2 x - \sinh^2 x}{\cosh^2 x} = \frac{1}{\cosh^2 x} = \text{sech}^2 x$$

The formulas for the derivatives of the remaining hyperbolic functions are as follows: $D_x(\coth x) = -\text{csch}^2 x$; $D_x(\text{sech } x) = -\text{sech } x \tanh x$; $D_x(\text{csch } x) = -\text{csch } x \coth x$. The proofs of these formulas are left as exercises (see Exercises 15 and 16).

From the above formulas and the chain rule, if u is a differentiable function of x, we have the following more general formulas:

$$D_x(\sinh u) = \cosh u \, D_x u \tag{19}$$

$$D_x(\cosh u) = \sinh u \, D_x u \tag{20}$$

$$D_x(\tanh u) = \text{sech}^2 u \, D_x u \tag{21}$$

$$D_x(\coth u) = -\text{csch}^2 u \, D_x u \tag{22}$$

$$D_x(\text{sech } u) = -\text{sech } u \tanh u \, D_x u \tag{23}$$

$$D_x(\text{csch } u) = -\text{csch } u \coth u \, D_x u \tag{24}$$

You should notice that the formulas for the derivatives of the hyperbolic sine, cosine, and tangent all have a plus sign, whereas the formulas for the derivatives of the hyperbolic cotangent, secant, and cosecant all have a minus sign. Otherwise, the formulas are similar to the corresponding formulas for the derivatives of the trigonometric functions.

EXAMPLE 1:   Find $D_x y$ if

$y = \tanh(1 - x^2)$

SOLUTION: $D_x y = -2x \, \text{sech}^2(1 - x^2)$.

EXAMPLE 2:   Find dy/dx if

$y = \ln \sinh x$

SOLUTION: $\dfrac{dy}{dx} = \dfrac{1}{\sinh x} \cdot \cosh x = \dfrac{\cosh x}{\sinh x} = \coth x.$

Formulas (19) through (24) give rise to the following indefinite integration formulas:

$$\int \sinh u \, du = \cosh u + C \tag{25}$$

$$\int \cosh u \ du = \sinh u + C \qquad (26)$$

$$\int \text{sech}^2 u \ du = \tanh u + C \qquad (27)$$

$$\int \text{csch}^2 u \ du = -\coth u + C \qquad (28)$$

$$\int \text{sech} \ u \tanh u \ du = -\text{sech} \ u + C \qquad (29)$$

$$\int \text{csch} \ u \coth u \ du = -\text{csch} \ u + C \qquad (30)$$

The methods used to integrate powers of the hyperbolic functions are similar to those used for powers of the trigonometric functions. The following two examples illustrate the method.

EXAMPLE 3:   Evaluate

$$\int \sinh^3 x \cosh^2 x \ dx$$

SOLUTION:

$$\int \sinh^3 x \cosh^2 x \ dx = \int \sinh^2 x \cosh^2 x \ (\sinh x \ dx)$$

$$= \int (\cosh^2 x - 1) \cosh^2 x \ (\sinh x \ dx)$$

$$= \int \cosh^4 x \ (\sinh x \ dx) - \int \cosh^2 x \ (\sinh x \ dx)$$

$$= \tfrac{1}{5} \cosh^5 x - \tfrac{1}{3} \cosh^3 x + C$$

EXAMPLE 4:   Evaluate

$$\int \text{sech}^4 x \ dx$$

SOLUTION:

$$\int \text{sech}^4 x \ dx = \int \text{sech}^2 x \ (\text{sech}^2 x \ dx)$$

$$= \int (1 - \tanh^2 x)(\text{sech}^2 x \ dx)$$

$$= \int \text{sech}^2 x \ dx - \int \tanh^2 x \ (\text{sech}^2 x \ dx)$$

$$= \tanh x - \tfrac{1}{3} \tanh^3 x + C$$

A *catenary* is the curve formed by a homogeneous flexible cable hanging from two points under its own weight. If the lowest point of the catenary is the point $(0, a)$, it can be shown that an equation of it is

$$y = a \cosh \left(\frac{x}{a}\right) \qquad a > 0 \qquad (31)$$

A sketch of the graph of Eq. (31) is shown in Fig. 12.1.4.

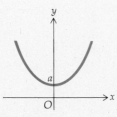

Figure 12.1.4

EXAMPLE 5:   Find the length of arc of the catenary having Eq. (31) from the point $(0, a)$ to the point (x_1, y_1) where $x_1 > 0$.

SOLUTION: If

$$f(x) = a \cosh \left(\frac{x}{a} \right)$$

then

$$f'(x) = a \sinh \left(\frac{x}{a} \right) \cdot \left(\frac{1}{a} \right) = \sinh \left(\frac{x}{a} \right)$$

and using Theorem 8.10.3, if L units is the length of the given arc, we have

$$L = \int_0^{x_1} \sqrt{1 + [f'(x)]^2} \, dx$$

$$= \int_0^{x_1} \sqrt{1 + \sinh^2 \left(\frac{x}{a} \right)} \, dx \qquad (32)$$

From formula (6), $1 + \sinh^2 x = \cosh^2 x$, and because $\cosh(x/a) \geq 1$, it follows that

$$\sqrt{1 + \sinh^2 \left(\frac{x}{a} \right)} = \sqrt{\cosh^2 \left(\frac{x}{a} \right)} = \cosh \left(\frac{x}{a} \right)$$

and substituting from the above into (32) we get

$$L = \int_0^{x_1} \cosh \left(\frac{x}{a} \right) dx$$

$$= a \sinh \left(\frac{x}{a} \right) \Big]_0^{x_1}$$

$$= a \sinh \left(\frac{x_1}{a} \right) - a \sinh 0$$

$$= a \sinh \left(\frac{x_1}{a} \right)$$

Exercises 12.1

In Exercises 1 through 10, prove the identities.

1. $1 - \coth^2 x = -\operatorname{csch}^2 x$

2. $\cosh(x + y) = \cosh x \cosh y + \sinh x \sinh y$

3. $\tanh(x + y) = \dfrac{\tanh x + \tanh y}{1 + \tanh x \tanh y}$

4. (a) $\sinh 2x = 2 \sinh x \cosh x$; (b) $\cosh 2x = \cosh^2 x + \sinh^2 x = 2 \sinh^2 x + 1 = 2 \cosh^2 x - 1$

5. (a) $\cosh \frac{1}{2}x = \sqrt{\dfrac{\cosh x + 1}{2}}$; (b) $\sinh \frac{1}{2}x = \pm \sqrt{\dfrac{\cosh x - 1}{2}}$

6. $\operatorname{csch} 2x = \frac{1}{2} \operatorname{sech} x \operatorname{csch} x$

7. (a) $\tanh(-x) = -\tanh x$; (b) $\mathrm{sech}(-x) = \mathrm{sech}\, x$

8. $\sinh 3x = 3 \sinh x + 4 \sinh^3 x$

9. $\cosh 3x = 4 \cosh^3 x - 3 \cosh x$

10. $\sinh^2 x - \sinh^2 y = \sinh(x + y) \sinh(x - y)$

11. Prove: $(\sinh x + \cosh x)^n = \cosh nx + \sinh nx$, if n is any positive integer. (HINT: Use formula (9).)

12. Prove that the hyperbolic sine function is an odd function and the hyperbolic cosine function is an even function.

13. Prove: $\tanh(\ln x) = \dfrac{x^2 - 1}{x^2 + 1}$ 14. Prove: $\dfrac{1 + \tanh x}{1 - \tanh x} = e^{2x}$

15. Prove: (a) $D_x(\sinh x) = \cosh x$; (b) $D_x(\coth x) = -\mathrm{csch}^2 x$.

16. Prove: (a) $D_x(\mathrm{sech}\, x) = -\mathrm{sech}\, x \tanh x$; (b) $D_x(\mathrm{csch}\, x) = -\mathrm{csch}\, x \coth x$.

In Exercises 17 through 26, find the derivative of the given function.

17. $f(x) = \tanh \dfrac{4x + 1}{5}$ 18. $g(x) = \ln(\sinh x^3)$ 19. $f(x) = e^x \cosh x$

20. $h(x) = \coth \dfrac{1}{x}$ 21. $h(t) = \ln(\tanh t)$ 22. $F(x) = \tan^{-1}(\sinh x^2)$

23. $G(x) = \sin^{-1}(\tanh x^2)$ 24. $f(x) = \ln(\coth 3x - \mathrm{csch}\, 3x)$ 25. $f(x) = x^{\sinh x}$

26. $g(x) = (\cosh x)^x$

27. Prove: (a) $\int \tanh u\, du = \ln |\cosh u| + C$; (b) $\int \coth u\, du = \ln |\sinh u| + C$.

28. Prove: $\int \mathrm{sech}\, u\, du = 2 \tan^{-1} e^u + C$.

29. Prove: $\int \mathrm{csch}\, u\, du = \ln |\tanh \tfrac{1}{2}u| + C$.

In Exercises 30 through 37, evaluate the indefinite integral.

30. $\displaystyle\int \sinh^4 x \cosh^3 x\, dx$ 31. $\displaystyle\int \tanh x \ln(\cosh x)\, dx$ 32. $\displaystyle\int \tanh^2 3x\, dx$ 33. $\displaystyle\int \cosh^4 7x\, dx$

34. $\displaystyle\int x \sinh^2 x^2\, dx$ 35. $\displaystyle\int \mathrm{sech}^4 3x\, dx$ 36. $\displaystyle\int \mathrm{sech}\, x \tanh^3 x\, dx$ 37. $\displaystyle\int \dfrac{\sinh \sqrt{x}}{\sqrt{x}}\, dx$

In Exercises 38 and 39, evaluate the definite integral.

38. $\displaystyle\int_{-1}^{1} \cosh^2 x\, dx$ 39. $\displaystyle\int_{0}^{2} \sinh^3 x\, dx$

40. Draw a sketch of the graph of the hyperbolic cotangent function. Find equations of the asymptotes.

41. Draw a sketch of the graph of the hyperbolic secant function. Find the relative extrema of the function, the points of inflection of the graph, the intervals on which the graph is concave upward, and the intervals on which the graph is concave downward.

42. Prove that a catenary is concave upward at each point.

43. Find the area of the region bounded by the catenary of Example 5, the y axis, the x axis, and the line $x = x_1$, where $x_1 > 0$.

44. Find the volume of the solid of revolution if the region of Exercise 43 is revolved about the x axis.

45. A particle is moving along a straight line according to the equation of motion

$$s = e^{-ct/2}(A \sinh t + B \cosh t)$$

where s ft is the directed distance of the particle from the origin at t sec. If v ft/sec and a ft/sec² are the velocity and acceleration, respectively, of the particle at t sec, find v and a. Also show that a is the sum of two numbers, one of which is proportional to s and the other is proportional to v.

46. Prove that the hyperbolic sine function is continuous and increasing on its entire domain.

47. Prove that the hyperbolic tangent function is continuous and increasing on its entire domain.

48. Prove that the hyperbolic cosine function is continuous on its entire domain but is not monotonic on its entire domain. Find the intervals on which the function is increasing and the intervals on which the function is decreasing.

12.2 THE INVERSE HYPERBOLIC FUNCTIONS

From the graph of the hyperbolic sine function (Fig. 12.1.1), we see that a horizontal line intersects the graph in one and only one point; therefore, to each number in the range of the function there corresponds one and only one number in the domain. The hyperbolic sine function is continuous and increasing on its domain (see Exercise 46 in Exercises 12.1), and so by Theorem 9.3.2 the function has an inverse function.

12.2.1 Definition

The *inverse hyperbolic sine function,* denoted by $\sinh^{-1}$, is defined as follows:

$$y = \sinh^{-1} x \quad \text{if and only if} \quad x = \sinh y$$

A sketch of the graph of the inverse hyperbolic sine function is shown in Fig. 12.2.1. Its domain is the set of all real numbers, and its range is the set of all real numbers.

It follows from Definition 12.2.1 that

$$\sinh(\sinh^{-1} x) = x \tag{1}$$

and

$$\sinh^{-1}(\sinh y) = y \tag{2}$$

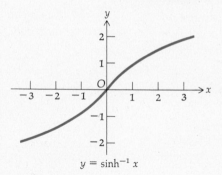

$y = \sinh^{-1} x$

Figure 12.2.1

From Fig. 12.1.2, we notice that a horizontal line $y = k$, where $k > 1$, intersects the graph of the hyperbolic cosine function in two points. Therefore, for each number greater than 1 in the range of this function, there correspond two numbers in the domain. So the hyperbolic cosine function does not have an inverse function. However, we define a function F as follows:

$$F(x) = \cosh x \quad \text{for } x \geq 0 \tag{3}$$

Figure 12.2.2

$y = \cosh x, x \geq 0$

The domain of F is the interval $[0, +\infty)$, and the range is the interval $[1, +\infty)$. A sketch of the graph of F is shown in Fig. 12.2.2. The function F is continuous and increasing on its entire domain (see Exercise 1), and so by Theorem 9.3.2, F has an inverse function, which we call the "inverse hyperbolic cosine function."

12.2.2 Definition   The *inverse hyperbolic cosine function,* denoted by $\cosh^{-1}$, is defined as follows:

$$y = \cosh^{-1} x \quad \text{if and only if} \quad x = \cosh y \quad \text{and} \quad y \geq 0$$

A sketch of the graph of the inverse hyperbolic cosine function is shown in Fig. 12.2.3. The domain of this function is the interval $[1, +\infty)$, and the range is the interval $[0, +\infty)$. From Definition 12.2.2 we conclude that

$$\cosh(\cosh^{-1} x) = x \qquad \text{if } x \geq 1 \tag{4}$$

and

$$\cosh^{-1}(\cosh y) = y \qquad \text{if } y \geq 0 \tag{5}$$

As with the hyperbolic sine function, a horizontal line intersects each of the graphs of the hyperbolic tangent function, the hyperbolic cotangent function, and the hyperbolic cosecant function at one and only one point. For the hyperbolic tangent function, this may be seen in Fig. 12.1.3. Each of the above three functions is continuous and monotonic on its domain; hence, each has an inverse function.

$y = \cosh^{-1} x$

Figure 12.2.3

12.2.3 Definition   The *inverse hyperbolic tangent function,* the *inverse hyperbolic cotangent function,* and the *inverse hyperbolic cosecant function,* denoted respectively by $\tanh^{-1}$, $\coth^{-1}$, and csch^{-1}, are defined as follows:

$$y = \tanh^{-1} x \quad \text{if and only if} \quad x = \tanh y$$
$$y = \coth^{-1} x \quad \text{if and only if} \quad x = \coth y$$
$$y = \operatorname{csch}^{-1} x \quad \text{if and only if} \quad x = \operatorname{csch} y$$

A sketch of the graph of the inverse hyperbolic tangent function is in Fig. 12.2.4.

The hyperbolic secant function does not have an inverse function. However, we proceed as we did with the hyperbolic cosine function and define a new function which has an inverse function. Let the function G be defined by

$$G(x) = \operatorname{sech} x \qquad \text{for } x \geq 0 \tag{6}$$

It can be shown that G is continuous and monotonic on its entire domain (see Exercise 2); therefore, G has an inverse function, which we call the "inverse hyperbolic secant function."

$y = \tanh^{-1} x$

Figure 12.2.4

12.2.4 Definition   The *inverse hyperbolic secant function,* denoted by sech^{-1}, is defined as follows:

$$y = \operatorname{sech}^{-1} x \quad \text{if and only if} \quad x = \operatorname{sech} y \quad \text{and} \quad y \geq 0 \tag{7}$$

The inverse hyperbolic functions can be expressed in terms of natural logarithms. This should not be surprising because the hyperbolic functions were defined in terms of the exponential function, and the natural logarithmic function is the inverse of the exponential function. Following are these expressions for $\sinh^{-1}$, $\cosh^{-1}$, $\tanh^{-1}$, and $\coth^{-1}$.

$$\sinh^{-1} x = \ln(x + \sqrt{x^2 + 1}) \qquad x \text{ any real number} \tag{8}$$

$$\cosh^{-1} x = \ln(x + \sqrt{x^2 - 1}) \qquad x \geq 1 \tag{9}$$

$$\tanh^{-1} x = \frac{1}{2} \ln \frac{1 + x}{1 - x} \qquad |x| < 1 \tag{10}$$

$$\coth^{-1} x = \frac{1}{2} \ln \frac{x + 1}{x - 1} \qquad |x| > 1 \tag{11}$$

We prove (9) and leave the proofs of the other three formulas as exercises (see Exercises 3 through 5).

To prove (9), let $y = \cosh^{-1} x$, $x \geq 1$. Then, by Definition 12.2.2, $x = \cosh y$, $y \geq 0$. Applying Definition 12.1.2 to $\cosh y$, we get

$$x = \frac{e^y + e^{-y}}{2} \qquad y \geq 0$$

from which we obtain

$$e^{2y} - 2xe^y + 1 = 0 \qquad y \geq 0$$

Solving this equation for e^y by the quadratic formula, we obtain

$$e^y = \frac{2x \pm \sqrt{4x^2 - 4}}{2} = x \pm \sqrt{x^2 - 1} \qquad y \geq 0 \tag{12}$$

We know that $y \geq 0$ and $x \geq 1$. Therefore, $e^y \geq 1$. When $x = 1$, $x + \sqrt{x^2 - 1} = x - \sqrt{x^2 - 1} = 1$. Furthermore, when $x > 1$, $0 < x - 1 < x + 1$, and so $\sqrt{x - 1} < \sqrt{x + 1}$. Therefore,

$$\sqrt{x - 1} \; \sqrt{x - 1} < \sqrt{x - 1} \; \sqrt{x + 1}$$

giving us $x - 1 < \sqrt{x^2 - 1}$. Hence, when $x > 1$, $x - \sqrt{x^2 - 1} < 1$. Consequently, we can safely reject the minus sign in (12). And since $y = \cosh^{-1} x$, we have

$$\cosh^{-1} x = \ln(x + \sqrt{x^2 - 1}) \qquad x \geq 1$$

which is (9).

EXAMPLE 1: Express each of the following in terms of a natural logarithm: (a) $\tanh^{-1}(-\frac{4}{5})$; (b) $\sinh^{-1} 2$.

SOLUTION: (a) From (10), we obtain

$$\tanh^{-1}\left(-\frac{4}{5}\right) = \frac{1}{2} \ln \frac{\frac{1}{5}}{\frac{9}{5}} = \frac{1}{2} \ln \frac{1}{9} = \ln \frac{1}{3} = -\ln 3$$

(b) From (8), we get

$$\sinh^{-1} 2 = \ln(2 + \sqrt{5})$$

To obtain a formula for the derivative of the inverse hyperbolic sine function, let $y = \sinh^{-1} x$, and then $x = \sinh y$. Thus, because $D_y x = \cosh y$ and $D_x y = 1/D_y x$, we have

$$D_x y = \frac{1}{\cosh y} \tag{13}$$

From the identity $\cosh^2 y - \sinh^2 y = 1$, it follows that $\cosh y = \sqrt{\sinh^2 y + 1}$. (NOTE: When taking the square root, the minus sign is rejected because $\cosh y \geq 1$.)

Hence, because $x = \sinh y$, $\cosh y = \sqrt{x^2 + 1}$. Substituting this in (13), we obtain

$$D_x(\sinh^{-1} x) = \frac{1}{\sqrt{x^2 + 1}} \tag{14}$$

If u is a differentiable function of x, from (14) and the chain rule it follows that

$$D_x(\sinh^{-1} u) = \frac{1}{\sqrt{u^2 + 1}} D_x u \tag{15}$$

Formula (14) can also be derived by using (8), as follows:

$$D_x(\sinh^{-1} x) = D_x \ln(x + \sqrt{x^2 + 1})$$

$$= \frac{1 + \dfrac{x}{\sqrt{x^2 + 1}}}{x + \sqrt{x^2 + 1}}$$

$$= \frac{\sqrt{x^2 + 1} + x}{\sqrt{x^2 + 1}\,(x + \sqrt{x^2 + 1})}$$

$$= \frac{1}{\sqrt{x^2 + 1}}$$

The following differentiation formulas can be obtained in analogous ways. Their proofs are left as exercises (see Exercises 6 through 10). In each formula u is a differentiable function of x.

$$D_x(\cosh^{-1} u) = \frac{1}{\sqrt{u^2 - 1}} D_x u \qquad u > 1 \tag{16}$$

$$D_x(\tanh^{-1} u) = \frac{1}{1 - u^2} D_x u \qquad |u| < 1 \tag{17}$$

$$D_x(\coth^{-1} u) = \frac{1}{1 - u^2} D_x u \qquad |u| > 1 \tag{18}$$

$$D_x(\text{sech}^{-1} u) = -\frac{1}{u\sqrt{1 - u^2}} D_x u \qquad 0 < u < 1 \tag{19}$$

$$D_x(\text{csch}^{-1} u) = -\frac{1}{|u|\sqrt{1 + u^2}} D_x u \qquad u \neq 0 \tag{20}$$

EXAMPLE 2:   Find $f'(x)$ if

$$f(x) = \tanh^{-1}(\cos 2x)$$

SOLUTION: Applying formula (17), we get

$$f'(x) = \frac{-2 \sin 2x}{1 - \cos^2 2x} = \frac{-2 \sin 2x}{\sin^2 2x} = -2 \csc 2x$$

EXAMPLE 3:   Verify that

$$D_x(x \cosh^{-1} x - \sqrt{x^2 - 1})$$

$$= \cosh^{-1} x$$

SOLUTION:

$$D_x(x \cosh^{-1} x - \sqrt{x^2 - 1}) = \cosh^{-1} x + x \cdot \frac{1}{\sqrt{x^2 - 1}} - \frac{x}{\sqrt{x^2 - 1}}$$

$$= \cosh^{-1} x$$

The main use of the inverse hyperbolic functions is in connection with integration. This topic is discussed in the next section.

Exercises 12.2

1. If $F(x) = \cosh x$ and $x \geq 0$, prove that F is continuous and increasing on its entire domain.

2. If $G(x) = \text{sech } x$ and $x \geq 0$, prove that G is continuous and monotonic on its entire domain.

In Exercises 3 through 10, prove the indicated formula of this section.

3. Formula (8)   4. Formula (10)   5. Formula (11)   6. Formula (16)

7. Formula (17)   8. Formula (18)   9. Formula (19)   10. Formula (20)

In Exercises 11 through 14, express the given quantity in terms of a natural logarithm.

11. $\sinh^{-1} \frac{1}{4}$ 12. $\cosh^{-1} 3$ 13. $\tanh^{-1} \frac{1}{2}$ 14. $\coth^{-1}(-2)$

In Exercises 15 through 28, find the derivative of the given function.

15. $f(x) = \sinh^{-1} x^2$ 16. $G(x) = \cosh^{-1} \frac{1}{3}x$ 17. $F(x) = \tanh^{-1} 4x$

18. $h(w) = \tanh^{-1} w^3$ 19. $g(x) = \coth^{-1}(3x + 1)$ 20. $f(r) = \text{csch}^{-1} \frac{1}{2}r^2$

21. $f(x) = x^2 \cosh^{-1} x^2$ 22. $h(x) = (\text{sech}^{-1} x)^2$ 23. $f(x) = \sinh^{-1}(\tan x)$

24. $g(x) = \tanh^{-1}(\sin 3x)$ 25. $h(x) = \cosh^{-1}(\csc x)$ 26. $F(x) = \coth^{-1}(\cosh x)$

27. $G(x) = x \sinh^{-1} x - \sqrt{1 + x^2}$ 28. $H(x) = \ln\sqrt{x^2 - 1} - x \tanh^{-1} x$

In Exercises 29 through 32, draw a sketch of the graph of the indicated function.

29. The inverse hyperbolic tangent function.   30. The inverse hyperbolic cotangent function.

31. The inverse hyperbolic secant function.   32. The inverse hyperbolic cosecant function.

12.3 INTEGRALS YIELDING INVERSE HYPERBOLIC FUNCTIONS

The inverse hyperbolic functions can be applied in integration, and sometimes their use shortens the computation considerably. It should be noted, however, that no new types of integrals are evaluated by their use. Only new forms of the results are obtained.

From formula (15) in Sec. 12.2 we have

$$D_x(\sinh^{-1} u) = \frac{1}{\sqrt{u^2 + 1}} D_x u$$

from which we obtain the integration formula

$$\int \frac{du}{\sqrt{u^2 + 1}} = \sinh^{-1} u + C$$

Expressing $\sinh^{-1} u$ as a natural logarithm by using formula (8) of Sec. 12.2, we get

$$\int \frac{du}{\sqrt{u^2 + 1}} = \sinh^{-1} u + C = \ln(u + \sqrt{u^2 + 1}) + C \qquad (1)$$

Formula (16) in Sec. 12.2 is

$$D_x(\cosh^{-1} u) = \frac{1}{\sqrt{u^2 - 1}} D_x u \qquad \text{where } u > 1$$

from which it follows that

$$\int \frac{du}{\sqrt{u^2 - 1}} = \cosh^{-1} u + C \qquad u > 1$$

and combining this with formula (9) in Sec. 12.2, we obtain

$$\int \frac{du}{\sqrt{u^2 - 1}} = \cosh^{-1} u + C = \ln(u + \sqrt{u^2 - 1}) + C \qquad \text{if } u > 1 \quad (2)$$

Formulas (17) and (18) of Sec. 12.2 are, respectively,

$$D_x(\tanh^{-1} u) = \frac{1}{1 - u^2} D_x u \quad \text{where } |u| < 1$$

and

$$D_x(\coth^{-1} u) = \frac{1}{1 - u^2} D_x u \quad \text{where } |u| > 1$$

From the above two formulas we get

$$\int \frac{du}{1 - u^2} = \begin{cases} \tanh^{-1} u + C & \text{if } |u| < 1 \\ \coth^{-1} u + C & \text{if } |u| > 1 \end{cases}$$

and combining this with formulas (10) and (11) of Sec. 12.2 we have

$$\int \frac{du}{1 - u^2} = \begin{cases} \tanh^{-1} u + C & \text{if } |u| < 1 \\ \coth^{-1} u + C & \text{if } |u| > 1 \end{cases} = \frac{1}{2} \ln \left| \frac{1 + u}{1 - u} \right| + C \text{ if } u \neq 1 \qquad (3)$$

We also have the following three formulas.

$$\int \frac{du}{\sqrt{u^2 + a^2}} = \sinh^{-1}\frac{u}{a} + C = \ln(u + \sqrt{u^2 + a^2}) + C \quad \text{if } a > 0 \tag{4}$$

$$\int \frac{du}{\sqrt{u^2 - a^2}} = \cosh^{-1}\frac{u}{a} + C = \ln(u + \sqrt{u^2 - a^2}) + C \quad \text{if } u > a > 0 \tag{5}$$

$$\int \frac{du}{a^2 - u^2} = \begin{cases} \frac{1}{a}\tanh^{-1}\frac{u}{a} + C & \text{if } |u| < a \\ \frac{1}{a}\coth^{-1}\frac{u}{a} + C & \text{if } |u| > a \end{cases} = \frac{1}{2a}\ln\left|\frac{a + u}{a - u}\right| + C \tag{6}$$

$$\text{if } u \neq a \text{ and } a \neq 0$$

These formulas can be proved by finding the derivative of the right side and obtaining the integrand, or else more directly by using a hyperbolic function substitution.

For example, the proof of (4) by differentiating the right side is as follows:

$$D_u\left(\sinh^{-1}\frac{u}{a}\right) = \frac{1}{\sqrt{\left(\frac{u}{a}\right)^2 + 1}} \cdot \frac{1}{a} = \frac{\sqrt{a^2}}{\sqrt{u^2 + a^2}} \cdot \frac{1}{a}$$

and because $a > 0$, $\sqrt{a^2} = a$, and we get

$$D_u\left(\sinh^{-1}\frac{u}{a}\right) = \frac{1}{\sqrt{u^2 + a^2}}$$

To obtain the natural logarithm representation we use formula (8) in Sec. 12.2 and we have

$$\sinh^{-1}\frac{u}{a} = \ln\left(\frac{u}{a} + \sqrt{\left(\frac{u}{a}\right)^2 + 1}\right)$$

$$= \ln\left(\frac{u}{a} + \frac{\sqrt{u^2 + a^2}}{a}\right)$$

$$= \ln(u + \sqrt{u^2 + a^2}) - \ln a$$

Therefore,

$$\sinh^{-1}\frac{u}{a} + C = \ln(u + \sqrt{u^2 + a^2}) - \ln a + C$$

$$= \ln(u + \sqrt{u^2 + a^2}) + C_1$$

where $C_1 = C - \ln a$.

The proof of (5) by a hyperbolic function substitution makes use of the identity $\cosh^2 x - \sinh^2 x = 1$. Letting $u = a \cosh x$, where $x > 0$, then

$du = a \sinh x \, dx$, and $x = \cosh^{-1}(u/a)$. Substituting in the integrand, we get

$$\int \frac{du}{\sqrt{u^2 - a^2}} = \int \frac{a \sinh x \, dx}{\sqrt{a^2 \cosh^2 x - a^2}}$$

$$= \int \frac{a \sinh x \, dx}{\sqrt{a^2} \sqrt{\cosh^2 x - 1}}$$

$$= \int \frac{a \sinh x \, dx}{\sqrt{a^2} \sqrt{\sinh^2 x}}$$

Because $a > 0$, $\sqrt{a^2} = a$. Furthermore, because $x > 0$, $\sinh x > 0$, and so $\sqrt{\sinh^2 x} = \sinh x$. We have, then,

$$\int \frac{du}{\sqrt{u^2 - a^2}} = \int \frac{a \sinh x \, dx}{a \sinh x}$$

$$= \int dx$$

$$= x + C$$

$$= \cosh^{-1} \frac{u}{a} + C$$

The natural logarithm representation may be obtained in a way similar to the way we obtained the one for formula (4). The proof of formula (6) is left as an exercise (see Exercise 17).

Note that formulas (1) through (6) give alternate representations of the integral in question. In evaluating a definite integral in which one of these forms occurs and a table of hyperbolic functions is available, the inverse hyperbolic function representation may be easier to use. Also the inverse hyperbolic function representation is a less cumbersome one to write for the indefinite integral. Also note that the natural logarithm form of formula (6) was obtained in Sec. 11.4 by using partial fractions.

EXAMPLE 1: Evaluate

$$\int \frac{dx}{\sqrt{x^2 - 6x + 13}}$$

SOLUTION: We apply formula (4) after rewriting the denominator.

$$\int \frac{dx}{\sqrt{x^2 - 6x + 13}} = \int \frac{dx}{\sqrt{(x^2 - 6x + 9) + 4}}$$

$$= \int \frac{dx}{\sqrt{(x - 3)^2 + 4}}$$

$$= \sinh^{-1}\left(\frac{x - 3}{2}\right) + C$$

$$= \ln(x - 3 + \sqrt{x^2 - 6x + 13}) + C$$

EXAMPLE 2: Evaluate

$$\int_6^{10} \frac{dx}{\sqrt{x^2 - 25}}$$

SOLUTION: Using formula (5), we get

$$\int_6^{10} \frac{dx}{\sqrt{x^2 - 25}} = \cosh^{-1} \frac{x}{5} \Big]_6^{10} = \cosh^{-1} 2 - \cosh^{-1} 1.2$$

Using Table 4 in the Appendix, we find

$$\cosh^{-1} 2 - \cosh^{-1}(1.2) = 1.32 - 0.62 = 0.70$$

Instead of applying the formulas, integrals of the forms of those in formulas (1) through (6) can be obtained by using a hyperbolic function substitution and proceeding in a manner similar to that using a trigonometric substitution.

EXAMPLE 3: Evaluate the integral of Example 1 without using a formula but by using a hyperbolic function substitution.

SOLUTION: In the solution of Example 1, the given integral was rewritten as

$$\int \frac{dx}{\sqrt{(x - 3)^2 + 4}}$$

If we let $x - 3 = 2 \sinh u$, then $dx = 2 \cosh u \, du$ and $u = \sinh^{-1} \frac{1}{2}(x - 3)$. We have, therefore,

$$\int \frac{dx}{\sqrt{(x - 3)^2 + 4}} = \int \frac{2 \cosh u \, du}{\sqrt{4 \sinh^2 u + 4}}$$

$$= \int \frac{2 \cosh u \, du}{2\sqrt{\sinh^2 u + 1}}$$

$$= \int \frac{\cosh u \, du}{\sqrt{\cosh^2 u}}$$

$$= \int \frac{\cosh u \, du}{\cosh u}$$

$$= \int du$$

$$= u + C$$

$$= \sinh^{-1} \left(\frac{x - 3}{2} \right) + C$$

which agrees with the result of Example 1.

Exercises 12.3

In Exercises 1 through 10, express the indefinite integral in terms of an inverse hyperbolic function and as a natural logarithm.

1. $\int \dfrac{dx}{\sqrt{4+x^2}}$

2. $\int \dfrac{dx}{\sqrt{4x^2-9}}$

3. $\int \dfrac{x\,dx}{\sqrt{x^4-1}}$

4. $\int \dfrac{dx}{25-x^2}$

5. $\int \dfrac{dx}{9x^2-16}$

6. $\int \dfrac{dx}{4e^x-e^{-x}}$

7. $\int \dfrac{\cos x\,dx}{\sqrt{4-\cos^2 x}}$

8. $\int \dfrac{dx}{\sqrt{x^2-4x+1}}$

9. $\int \dfrac{dx}{2-4x-x^2}$

10. $\int \dfrac{3x\,dx}{\sqrt{x^4+6x^2+5}}$

In Exercises 11 through 16, evaluate the definite integral and express the answer in terms of a natural logarithm.

11. $\displaystyle\int_3^5 \dfrac{dx}{\sqrt{x^2-4}}$

12. $\displaystyle\int_1^2 \dfrac{dx}{\sqrt{x^2+2x}}$

13. $\displaystyle\int_{-1/2}^{1/2} \dfrac{dx}{1-x^2}$

14. $\displaystyle\int_{-4}^{-3} \dfrac{dx}{1-x^2}$

15. $\displaystyle\int_2^3 \dfrac{dx}{\sqrt{9x^2-12x-5}}$

16. $\displaystyle\int_{-2}^2 \dfrac{dx}{\sqrt{16+x^2}}$

17. Prove formula (6) by using a hyperbolic function substitution.

18. A curve goes through the point $(0, a)$, $a > 0$, and the slope at any point is $\sqrt{y^2/a^2 - 1}$. Prove that the curve is a catenary.

19. A man wearing a parachute falls out of an airplane and when the parachute opens his velocity is 200 ft/sec. If v ft/sec is his velocity t sec after the parachute opens,

$$\frac{324}{g}\frac{dv}{dt} = 324 - v^2$$

Solve this differential equation to obtain

$$t = \frac{18}{g}\left(\coth^{-1}\frac{v}{18} - \coth^{-1}\frac{100}{9}\right)$$

Review Exercises (Chapter 12)

In Exercises 1 through 3, prove the identities.

1. (a) $\coth(-x) = -\coth x$; (b) $\operatorname{csch}(-x) = -\operatorname{csch} x$

2. $\sinh x + \sinh y = 2 \sinh \tfrac{1}{2}(x+y) \cosh \tfrac{1}{2}(x-y)$

3. $\dfrac{\cosh 2x + \cosh 4y}{\sinh 2x + \sinh 4y} = \coth(x+2y)$

4. Prove: (a) $\displaystyle\lim_{x\to+\infty} \coth x = 1$; (b) $\displaystyle\lim_{x\to+\infty} \operatorname{csch} x = 0$

In Exercises 5 through 9, find the derivative of the given function.

5. $f(x) = \cosh^3 2x$

6. $g(t) = \ln \operatorname{sech} t^2$

7. $f(u) = \dfrac{\cosh u}{1 + \operatorname{sech} u}$

8. $h(x) = e^x(\cosh x + \sinh x)$

9. $f(w) = w^2 \sinh^{-1} 2w$

10. The gudermannian is a function that occurs frequently in mathematics, and it is defined by $\operatorname{gd} x = \tan^{-1}(\sinh x)$. Show that $D_x(\operatorname{gd} x) = \operatorname{sech} x$.

In Exercises 11 through 14, evaluate the indefinite integral.

11. $\displaystyle\int x \tanh \tfrac{1}{2}x^2 \, dx$

12. $\displaystyle\int \tanh^3 x \, dx$

13. $\displaystyle\int \sinh x \sin x \, dx$

14. $\displaystyle\int x \cosh x \, dx$

In Exercises 15 and 16, evaluate the definite integral.

15. $\displaystyle\int_0^1 \operatorname{sech}^2 t \, dt$

16. $\displaystyle\int_0^1 \sqrt{1 + \cosh x} \, dx$

In Exercises 17 and 18, obtain the given result by a hyperbolic function substitution.

17. $\displaystyle\int \frac{dx}{x^2 \sqrt{a^2 + x^2}} = -\frac{1}{a^2} \coth\left(\sinh^{-1}\frac{x}{a}\right) + C$

18. $\displaystyle\int \frac{dx}{(a^2 - x^2)^{3/2}} = \frac{1}{a^2} \sinh\left(\tanh^{-1}\frac{x}{a}\right) + C$

19. Find the length of the catenary $y = \cosh x$ from $(\ln 2, \tfrac{5}{4})$ to $(\ln 3, \tfrac{5}{3})$.

20. The graph of the equation

$$x = a \sinh^{-1} \sqrt{\frac{a^2}{y^2} - 1} - \sqrt{a^2 - y^2}$$

is called a tractrix. Prove that the slope of the curve at any point (x, y) is $-y/\sqrt{a^2 - y^2}$.

13

Polar coordinates

13.1 THE POLAR COORDINATE SYSTEM

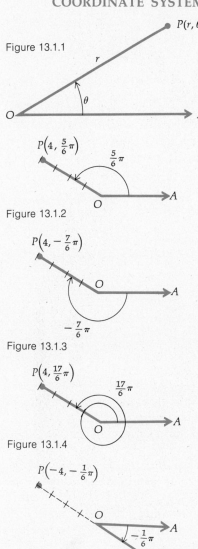

Figure 13.1.1

Figure 13.1.2

Figure 13.1.3

Figure 13.1.4

Figure 13.1.5

Figure 13.1.6

Until now we have located a point in a plane by its rectangular cartesian coordinates. There are other coordinate systems that can be used. Probably the next in importance to the cartesian coordinate system is the *polar coordinate system*. In the cartesian coordinate system, the coordinates are numbers called the abscissa and the ordinate, and these numbers are directed distances from two fixed lines. In the polar coordinate system, the coordinates consist of a distance and the measure of an angle relative to a fixed point and a fixed ray (or half line).

The fixed point is called the *pole* (or origin), and it is designated by the letter "O." The fixed ray is called the *polar axis* (or polar line), which we label OA. The ray OA is usually drawn horizontally and to the right, and it extends indefinitely (see Fig. 13.1.1).

Let P be any point in the plane distinct from O. Let θ be the radian measure of the directed angle AOP, positive when measured counterclockwise and negative when measured clockwise, having as its initial side the ray OA and as its terminal side the ray OP. Then if r is the undirected distance from O to P (i.e., $r = |\overline{OP}|$), one set of polar coordinates of P is given by r and θ, and we write these coordinates as (r, θ).

• ILLUSTRATION 1: The point $P(4, \frac{5}{6}\pi)$ is determined by first drawing the angle having radian measure $\frac{5}{6}\pi$, having its vertex at the pole and its initial side along the polar axis. Then the point on the terminal side, which is four units from the pole, is the point P (see Fig. 13.1.2). Another set of polar coordinates for this same point is $(4, -\frac{7}{6}\pi)$; see Fig. 13.1.3. Furthermore, the polar coordinates $(4, \frac{17}{6}\pi)$ would also yield the same point, as shown in Fig. 13.1.4. •

Actually the coordinates $(4, \frac{5}{6}\pi + 2n\pi)$, where n is any integer, give the same point as $(4, \frac{5}{6}\pi)$. So a given point has an unlimited number of sets of polar coordinates. This is unlike the rectangular cartesian coordinate system because there is a one-to-one correspondence between the rectangular cartesian coordinates and the position of points in the plane, whereas there is no such one-to-one correspondence between the polar coordinates and the position of points in the plane. A further example is obtained by considering sets of polar coordinates for the pole. If $r = 0$ and θ is any real number, we have the pole, which is designated by $(0, \theta)$.

We consider polar coordinates for which r is negative. In this case, instead of the point being on the terminal side of the angle, it is on the extension of the terminal side, which is the ray from the pole extending in the direction opposite to the terminal side. So if P is on the extension of the terminal side of the angle of radian measure θ, a set of polar coordinates of P is (r, θ), where $r = -|\overline{OP}|$.

• ILLUSTRATION 2: The point $(-4, -\frac{1}{6}\pi)$ shown in Fig. 13.1.5 is the same point as $(4, \frac{5}{6}\pi)$, $(4, -\frac{7}{6}\pi)$, and $(4, \frac{17}{6}\pi)$ in Illustration 1. Still another set of polar coordinates for this same point is $(-4, \frac{11}{16}\pi)$; see Fig. 13.1.6. •

The angle is usually measured in radians; thus, a set of polar coordinates of a point is an ordered pair of real numbers. For each ordered pair of real numbers there is a unique point having this set of polar coordinates. However, we have seen that a particular point can be given by an unlimited number of ordered pairs of real numbers. If the point P is not the pole, and r and θ are restricted so that $r > 0$ and $0 \leq \theta < 2\pi$, then there is a unique set of polar coordinates for P.

EXAMPLE 1: (a) Plot the point having polar coordinates $(3, -\frac{2}{3}\pi)$. Find another set of polar coordinates of this point for which (b) r is negative and $0 < \theta < 2\pi$; (c) r is positive and $0 < \theta < 2\pi$; (d) r is negative and $-2\pi < \theta < 0$.

SOLUTION: (a) The point is plotted by drawing the angle of radian measure $-\frac{2}{3}\pi$ in a clockwise direction from the polar axis. Because $r > 0$, P is on the terminal side of the angle, three units from the pole; see Fig. 13.1.7a. The answers to (b), (c), and (d) are, respectively, $(-3, \frac{1}{3}\pi)$, $(3, \frac{4}{3}\pi)$, and $(-3, -\frac{5}{3}\pi)$. They are illustrated in Fig. 13.1.7b, c, and d.

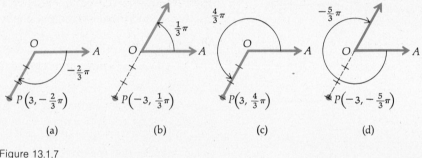

(a)   (b)   (c)   (d)

Figure 13.1.7

Often we wish to refer to both the rectangular cartesian coordinates and the polar coordinates of a point. To do this, we take the origin of the first system and the pole of the second system coincident, the polar axis as the positive side of the x axis, and the ray for which $\theta = \frac{1}{2}\pi$ as the positive side of the y axis.

Suppose that P is a point whose representation in the rectangular cartesian coordinate system is (x, y) and (r, θ) is a polar-coordinate representation of P. We distinguish two cases: $r > 0$ and $r < 0$. In the first case, if $r > 0$, then the point P is on the terminal side of the angle of θ radians, and $r = |\overline{OP}|$. Such a case is shown in Fig. 13.1.8. Then $\cos \theta = x/|\overline{OP}| = x/r$ and $\sin \theta = y/|\overline{OP}| = y/r$; and so

$$x = r \cos \theta \quad \text{and} \quad y = r \sin \theta \tag{1}$$

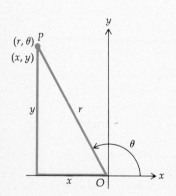

Figure 13.1.8

In the second case, if $r < 0$, then the point P is on the extension of the terminal side and $r = -|\overline{OP}|$ (see Fig. 13.1.9). Then if Q is the point $(-x, -y)$, we have

$$\cos \theta = \frac{-x}{|\overline{OQ}|} = \frac{-x}{|\overline{OP}|} = \frac{-x}{-r} = \frac{x}{r}$$

So

$$x = r \cos \theta \tag{2}$$

Figure 13.1.9

Also,

$$\sin \theta = \frac{-y}{|\overline{OQ}|} = \frac{-y}{|\overline{OP}|} = \frac{-y}{-r} = \frac{y}{r}$$

Hence,

$$y = r \sin \theta \tag{3}$$

Formulas (2) and (3) are the same as the formulas in (1); thus, the formulas (1) hold in all cases.

From formulas (1) we can obtain the rectangular cartesian coordinates of a point when its polar coordinates are known. Also, from the formulas we can obtain a polar equation of a curve if a rectangular cartesian equation is known.

To obtain formulas which give a set of polar coordinates of a point when its rectangular cartesian coordinates are known, we square on both sides of each equation in (1) and obtain

$$x^2 = r^2 \cos^2 \theta \quad \text{and} \quad y^2 = r^2 \sin^2 \theta$$

Equating the sum of the left members of the above to the sum of the right members, we have

$$x^2 + y^2 = r^2 \cos^2 \theta + r^2 \sin^2 \theta$$

or, equivalently,

$$x^2 + y^2 = r^2(\sin^2 \theta + \cos^2 \theta)$$

which gives us

$$x^2 + y^2 = r^2$$

and so

$$r = \pm\sqrt{x^2 + y^2} \tag{4}$$

From the equations in (1) and dividing, we have

$$\frac{r \sin \theta}{r \cos \theta} = \frac{y}{x}$$

or, equivalently,

$$\tan \theta = \frac{y}{x} \tag{5}$$

● ILLUSTRATION 3: The point whose polar coordinates are $(-6, \frac{7}{4}\pi)$ is plotted in Fig. 13.1.10. We find its rectangular cartesian coordinates. From (1) we have

$$x = r \cos \theta \qquad\qquad y = r \sin \theta$$

$$= -6 \cos \tfrac{7}{4}\pi \qquad\qquad = -6 \sin \tfrac{7}{4}\pi$$

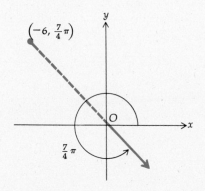

Figure 13.1.10

$$= -6 \cdot \frac{\sqrt{2}}{2} \qquad\qquad = -6 \left(-\frac{\sqrt{2}}{2} \right)$$

$$= -3\sqrt{2} \qquad\qquad = 3\sqrt{2}$$

So the point is $(-3\sqrt{2}, 3\sqrt{2})$. ●

The graph of an equation in polar coordinates r and θ consists of all those points and only those points P having at least one pair of coordinates which satisfy the equation. If an equation of a graph is given in polar coordinates, it is called a *polar equation* to distinguish it from a *cartesian equation*, which is the term used when an equation is given in rectangular cartesian coordinates.

EXAMPLE 2:   Given a polar equation of a graph is

$$r^2 = 4 \sin 2\theta$$

find a cartesian equation.

SOLUTION: Because $r^2 = x^2 + y^2$ and $\sin 2\theta = 2 \sin \theta \cos \theta = 2(y/r)(x/r)$, from (1) we have, upon substituting in the given polar equation,

$$x^2 + y^2 = 4(2) \frac{y}{r} \cdot \frac{x}{r}$$

$$x^2 + y^2 = \frac{8xy}{r^2}$$

$$x^2 + y^2 = \frac{8xy}{x^2 + y^2}$$

$$(x^2 + y^2)^2 = 8xy$$

EXAMPLE 3:   Find (r, θ) if $r > 0$ and $0 \le \theta < 2\pi$ for the point whose rectangular cartesian coordinate representation is $(-\sqrt{3}, -1)$.

SOLUTION: The point $(-\sqrt{3}, -1)$ is plotted in Fig. 13.1.11. From (4), because $r > 0$, we have

$$r = \sqrt{1 + 3} = 2$$

From (5), $\tan \theta = -1/(-\sqrt{3})$, and since $\pi < \theta < \frac{3}{2}\pi$, we have

$$\theta = \tfrac{7}{6}\pi$$

So the point is $(2, \tfrac{7}{6}\pi)$.

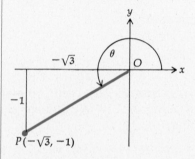

Figure 13.1.11

EXAMPLE 4:   Given a cartesian equation of a graph is

$$x^2 + y^2 - 4x = 0$$

find a polar equation.

SOLUTION: Substituting $x = r \cos \theta$ and $y = r \sin \theta$ in

$$x^2 + y^2 - 4x = 0$$

we have

$$r^2 \cos^2 \theta + r^2 \sin^2 \theta - 4r \cos \theta = 0$$

$$r^2 - 4r \cos \theta = 0$$

$$r(r - 4 \cos \theta) = 0$$

Therefore,

$$r = 0 \quad \text{or} \quad r - 4 \cos \theta = 0$$

The graph of $r = 0$ is the pole. However, the pole is a point on the graph of $r - 4 \cos \theta = 0$ because $r = 0$ when $\theta = \frac{1}{2}\pi$. Therefore, a polar equation of the graph is

$$r = 4 \cos \theta$$

The graph of $x^2 + y^2 - 4x = 0$ is a circle. The equation may be written in the form

$$(x - 2)^2 + y^2 = 4$$

which is an equation of the circle with center at (2, 0) and radius 2.

Exercises 13.1

In Exercises 1 through 6, plot the point having the given set of polar coordinates; then find another set of polar coordinates for the same point for which (a) $r < 0$ and $0 \leq \theta < 2\pi$; (b) $r > 0$ and $-2\pi < \theta \leq 0$; (c) $r < 0$ and $-2\pi < \theta \leq 0$.

1. $(4, \frac{1}{4}\pi)$

2. $(3, \frac{5}{6}\pi)$

3. $(2, \frac{1}{2}\pi)$

4. $(3, \frac{3}{2}\pi)$

5. $(\sqrt{2}, \frac{7}{4}\pi)$

6. $(2, \frac{4}{3}\pi)$

In Exercises 7 through 12, plot the point having the given set of polar coordinates; then give two other sets of polar coordinates of the same point, one with the same value of r and one with an r having opposite sign.

7. $(3, -\frac{2}{3}\pi)$

8. $(\sqrt{2}, -\frac{1}{4}\pi)$

9. $(-4, \frac{5}{6}\pi)$

10. $(-2, \frac{4}{3}\pi)$

11. $(-2, -\frac{5}{4}\pi)$

12. $(-3, -\pi)$

13. Find the rectangular cartesian coordinates of each of the following points whose polar coordinates are given: (a) $(3, \pi)$; (b) $(\sqrt{2}, -\frac{3}{4}\pi)$; (c) $(-4, \frac{2}{3}\pi)$; (d) $(-2, -\frac{1}{2}\pi)$; (e) $(-2, \frac{7}{4}\pi)$; (f) $(-1, -\frac{7}{6}\pi)$.

14. Find a set of polar coordinates for each of the following points whose rectangular cartesian coordinates are given. Take $r > 0$ and $0 \leq \theta < 2\pi$. (a) $(1, -1)$; (b) $(-\sqrt{3}, 1)$; (c) $(2, 2)$; (d) $(-5, 0)$; (e) $(0, -2)$; (f) $(-2, -2\sqrt{3})$.

In Exercises 15 through 22, find a polar equation of the graph having the given cartesian equation.

15. $x^2 + y^2 = a^2$

16. $x^3 = 4y^2$

17. $y^2 = 4(x + 1)$

18. $x^2 - y^2 = 16$

19. $(x^2 + y^2)^2 = 4(x^2 - y^2)$

20. $2xy = a^2$

21. $x^3 + y^3 - 3axy = 0$ 　　　　　　22. $y = \dfrac{2x}{x^2 + 1}$

In Exercises 23 through 30, find a cartesian equation of the graph having the given polar equation.

23. $r^2 = 2 \sin 2\theta$ 　　　　　24. $r^2 \cos 2\theta = 10$ 　　　　　25. $r^2 = \cos \theta$

26. $r^2 = \theta$ 　　　　　　　27. $r^2 = 4 \cos 2\theta$ 　　　　　28. $r = 2 \sin 3\theta$

29. $r = \dfrac{6}{2 - 3 \sin \theta}$ 　　　　30. $r = \dfrac{4}{3 - 2 \cos \theta}$

13.2 GRAPHS OF EQUATIONS IN POLAR COORDINATES

Let $r = f(\theta)$ be a polar equation of a curve. We first derive a formula for finding the slope of a tangent line to a polar curve at a point (r, θ) on the curve. Consider a rectangular cartesian coordinate system and a polar coordinate system in the same plane and having the positive side of the x axis coincident with the polar axis. In Sec. 13.1 we saw that the two sets of coordinates are related by the equations

$$x = r \cos \theta \quad \text{and} \quad y = r \sin \theta$$

x and y can be considered as functions of θ because $r = f(\theta)$. If we differentiate with respect to θ on both sides of these equations we get, by applying the chain rule,

$$\frac{dx}{d\theta} = \cos \theta \frac{dr}{d\theta} - r \sin \theta \tag{1}$$

and

$$\frac{dy}{d\theta} = \sin \theta \frac{dr}{d\theta} + r \cos \theta \tag{2}$$

If α is the radian measure of the inclination of the tangent line, then

$$\tan \alpha = \frac{dy}{dx}$$

and if $dx/d\theta \neq 0$, we have

$$\frac{dy}{dx} = \frac{\dfrac{dy}{d\theta}}{\dfrac{dx}{d\theta}} \tag{3}$$

Substituting from (1) and (2) into (3), we obtain

$$\frac{dy}{dx} = \frac{\sin \theta \dfrac{dr}{d\theta} + r \cos \theta}{\cos \theta \dfrac{dr}{d\theta} - r \sin \theta} \tag{4}$$

If $\cos \theta \neq 0$, we divide the numerator and the denominator of the right side of (4) by $\cos \theta$ and replace dy/dx by $\tan \alpha$, thereby giving us

$$\tan \alpha = \frac{\tan \theta \, \dfrac{dr}{d\theta} + r}{\dfrac{dr}{d\theta} - r \tan \theta} \tag{5}$$

EXAMPLE 1: Find the slope of the tangent line to the curve whose equation is $r = 1 - \cos \theta$ at the point $(1 - \tfrac{1}{2}\sqrt{2}, \tfrac{1}{4}\pi)$.

SOLUTION: Since $r = 1 - \cos \theta$, $dr/d\theta = \sin \theta$. So at the point $(1 - \tfrac{1}{2}\sqrt{2}, \tfrac{1}{4}\pi)$, $dr/d\theta = \tfrac{1}{2}\sqrt{2}$ and $\tan \theta = 1$; so from (5) we obtain

$$\tan \alpha = \frac{(1)\tfrac{1}{2}\sqrt{2} + (1 - \tfrac{1}{2}\sqrt{2})}{\tfrac{1}{2}\sqrt{2} - (1 - \tfrac{1}{2}\sqrt{2})(1)} = \frac{1}{\sqrt{2} - 1} = \sqrt{2} + 1$$

If we are to draw a sketch of the graph of a polar equation, it will be helpful to consider properties of symmetry of the graph. In Sec. 1.3 (Definition 1.3.4) we learned that two points P and Q are said to be symmetric with respect to a line if and only if the line is the perpendicular bisector of the line segment PQ, and that two points P and Q are said to be symmetric with respect to a third point if and only if the third point is the midpoint of the line segment PQ. Therefore, the points $(2, \tfrac{1}{3}\pi)$ and $(2, \tfrac{2}{3}\pi)$ are symmetric with respect to the $\tfrac{1}{2}\pi$ axis and the points $(2, \tfrac{1}{3}\pi)$ and $(2, -\tfrac{2}{3}\pi)$ are symmetric with respect to the pole. We also learned (Definition 1.3.5) that the graph of an equation is symmetric with respect to a line l if and only if for every point P on the graph there is a point Q, also on the graph, such that P and Q are symmetric with respect to l. Similarly, the graph of an equation is symmetric with respect to a point R if and only if for every point P on the graph there is a point S, also on the graph, such that P and S are symmetric with respect to R. We have the following rules of symmetry for graphs of polar equations.

Rule 1. If for an equation in polar coordinates an equivalent equation is obtained when (r, θ) is replaced by either $(r, -\theta + 2n\pi)$ or $(-r, \pi - \theta + 2n\pi)$, where n is any integer, the graph of the equation is symmetric with respect to the polar axis.

Rule 2. If for an equation in polar coordinates an equivalent equation is obtained when (r, θ) is replaced by either $(r, \pi - \theta + 2n\pi)$ or $(-r, -\theta + 2n\pi)$, where n is any integer, the graph of the equation is symmetric with respect to the $\tfrac{1}{2}\pi$ axis.

Rule 3. If for an equation in polar coordinates an equivalent equation is obtained when (r, θ) is replaced by either $(-r, \theta + 2n\pi)$ or $(r, \pi + \theta + 2n\pi)$, where n is any integer, the graph of the equation is symmetric with respect to the pole.

The proof of Rule 1 is as follows: If the point $P(r, \theta)$ is a point on the graph of an equation, then the graph is symmetric with respect to the polar axis if there is a point $P_1(r_1, \theta_1)$ on the graph so that the polar axis is the perpendicular bisector of the line segment P_1P (see Fig. 13.2.1). So

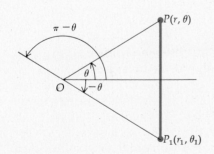

Figure 13.2.1

if $r_1 = r$, then θ_1 must equal $-\theta + 2n\pi$, where n is an integer. And if $r_1 = -r$, then θ_1 must be $\pi - \theta + 2n\pi$. The proofs of Rules 2 and 3 are similar and are omitted.

● ILLUSTRATION 1: We test for symmetry with respect to the polar axis, the $\frac{1}{2}\pi$ axis, and the pole, the graph of the equation $r = 4 \cos 2\theta$.

Using Rule 1 to test for symmetry with respect to the polar axis, we replace (r, θ) by $(r, -\theta)$ and obtain $r = 4 \cos(-2\theta)$, which is equivalent to $r = 4 \cos 2\theta$. So the graph is symmetric with respect to the polar axis.

Using Rule 2 to test for symmetry with respect to the $\frac{1}{2}\pi$ axis, we replace (r, θ) by $(r, \pi - \theta)$ and get $r = 4 \cos(2(\pi - \theta))$ or, equivalently, $r = 4 \cos(2\pi - 2\theta)$, which is equivalent to the equation $r = 4 \cos 2\theta$. Therefore, the graph is symmetric with respect to the $\frac{1}{2}\pi$ axis.

To test for symmetry with respect to the pole, we replace (r, θ) by $(-r, \theta)$ and obtain the equation $-r = 4 \cos 2\theta$, which is not equivalent to the equation. But we must also determine if the other set of coordinates works. We replace (r, θ) by $(r, \pi + \theta)$ and obtain $r = 4 \cos 2(\pi + \theta)$ or, equivalently, $r = 4 \cos(2\pi + 2\theta)$, which is equivalent to the equation $r = 4 \cos 2\theta$. Therefore, the graph is symmetric with respect to the pole.   ●

When drawing a sketch of a graph, it is desirable to determine if the pole is on the graph. This is done by substituting 0 for r and solving for θ. Also, it is advantageous to plot the points for which r has a relative maximum or relative minimum value. As a further aid in plotting, if a curve contains the pole, it is sometimes helpful to find equations of the tangent lines to the graph at the pole.

To find the slope of the tangent line at the pole we use formula (5) with $r = 0$. If $dr/d\theta \neq 0$, we have

$$\tan \alpha = \tan \theta \tag{6}$$

From (6) we conclude that the values of θ, where $0 \leq \theta < \pi$, which satisfy a polar equation of the curve when $r = 0$ are the inclinations of the tangent lines to the curve at the pole. So if $\theta_1, \theta_2, \ldots, \theta_k$ are these values of θ, then equations of the tangent lines to the curve at the pole are

$$\theta = \theta_1, \theta = \theta_2, \ldots, \theta = \theta_k$$

EXAMPLE 2:   Draw a sketch of the graph of

$$r = 1 - 2 \cos \theta$$

SOLUTION: Replacing (r, θ) by $(r, -\theta)$, we obtain an equivalent equation. Thus, the graph is symmetric with respect to the polar axis.

Table 13.2.1 gives the coordinates of some points on the graph. From these points we draw half of the graph and the remainder is drawn from its symmetry with respect to the polar axis.

If $r = 0$, we obtain $\cos \theta = \frac{1}{2}$, and if $0 \leq \theta < \pi$, $\theta = \frac{1}{3}\pi$. Therefore, the point $(0, \frac{1}{3}\pi)$ is on the graph, and an equation of the tangent line there is $\theta = \frac{1}{3}\pi$. A sketch of the graph is shown in Fig. 13.2.2. It is called a *limaçon*.

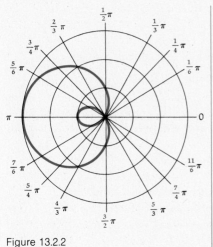

Figure 13.2.2

Table 13.2.1

θ	0	$\frac{1}{6}\pi$	$\frac{1}{3}\pi$	$\frac{1}{2}\pi$	$\frac{2}{3}\pi$	$\frac{5}{6}\pi$	π
r	-1	$1 - \sqrt{3}$	0	1	2	$1 + \sqrt{3}$	3

The graph of an equation of the form

$$r = a \pm b \cos \theta$$

or

$$r = a \pm b \sin \theta$$

is a limaçon. If $b > a$, as is the case in Example 2, the limacon has a loop. If $a = b$, the limaçon is a *cardioid*, which is heart-shaped. If $a > b$, the limaçon has a shape similar to the one in Example 3.

EXAMPLE 3:   Draw a sketch of the graph of

$$r = 3 + 2 \sin \theta$$

Figure 13.2.3

SOLUTION: The graph is symmetric with respect to the $\frac{1}{2}\pi$ axis because if (r, θ) is replaced by $(r, \pi - \theta)$, an equivalent equation is obtained.

Table 13.2.2 gives the coordinates of some of the points on the graph. A sketch of the graph is shown in Fig. 13.2.3. It is drawn by plotting the points whose coordinates are given in Table 13.2.2 and using the symmetry property.

Table 13.2.2

θ	0	$\frac{1}{6}\pi$	$\frac{1}{3}\pi$	$\frac{1}{2}\pi$	π	$\frac{7}{6}\pi$	$\frac{4}{3}\pi$	$\frac{3}{2}\pi$
r	3	4	$3 + \sqrt{3}$	5	3	2	$3 - \sqrt{3}$	1

The graph of an equation of the form

$$r = a \cos n\theta \quad \text{or} \quad r = a \sin n\theta$$

is a *rose*, having n leaves if n is odd and $2n$ leaves if n is even.

EXAMPLE 4:   Draw a sketch of the four-leafed rose

$$r = 4 \cos 2\theta$$

Figure 13.2.4

SOLUTION: In Illustration 1 we proved that the graph is symmetric with respect to the polar axis, the $\frac{1}{2}\pi$ axis, and the pole. Substituting 0 for r in the given equation, we get

$$\cos 2\theta = 0$$

from which we obtain, for $0 \le \theta < 2\pi$, $\theta = \frac{1}{4}\pi, \frac{3}{4}\pi, \frac{7}{4}\pi$, and $\frac{11}{4}\pi$.

Table 13.2.3 gives values of r for some values of θ from 0 to $\frac{1}{2}\pi$. From these values and the symmetry properties, we draw a sketch of the graph as shown in Fig. 13.2.4.

Table 13.2.3

θ	0	$\frac{1}{12}\pi$	$\frac{1}{6}\pi$	$\frac{1}{4}\pi$	$\frac{1}{3}\pi$	$\frac{5}{12}\pi$	$\frac{1}{2}\pi$
r	4	$2\sqrt{3}$	2	0	-2	$-2\sqrt{3}$	-4

The graph of the equation

$$\theta = C$$

where C is any constant, is a straight line through the pole and makes an angle of C radians with the polar axis. The same line is given by the equation

$$\theta = C \pm n\pi$$

where n is any integer.

In general, the polar form of an equation of a line is not so simple as the cartesian form. However, if the line is parallel to either the polar axis or the $\frac{1}{2}\pi$ axis, the equation is fairly simple.

If a line is parallel to the polar axis and contains the point B whose cartesian coordinates are $(0, b)$ and polar coordinates are $(b, \frac{1}{2}\pi)$, then a cartesian equation is $y = b$. If we replace y by $r \sin \theta$, we have

$$r \sin \theta = b$$

which is a polar equation of any line parallel to the polar axis. If b is posi-

Figure 13.2.5

Figure 13.2.6

Figure 13.2.7

Figure 13.2.8

Figure 13.2.9

tive, the line is above the polar axis. If b is negative, it is below the polar axis.

● ILLUSTRATION 2: In Fig. 13.2.5 we have a sketch of the graph of the equation $r \sin \theta = 3$, and in Fig. 13.2.6 we have a sketch of the graph of the equation $r \sin \theta = -3$. ●

If a line is parallel to the $\frac{1}{2}\pi$ axis or, equivalently, perpendicular to the polar axis, and goes through the point A whose cartesian coordinates are $(a, 0)$ and polar coordinates are $(a, 0)$, a cartesian equation is $x = a$. Replacing x by $r \cos \theta$, we obtain

$$r \cos \theta = a$$

which is an equation of any line perpendicular to the polar axis. If a is positive, the line is to the right of the $\frac{1}{2}\pi$ axis. If a is negative, the line is to the left of the $\frac{1}{2}\pi$ axis.

● ILLUSTRATION 3: Figure 13.2.7 shows a sketch of the graph of the equation $r \cos \theta = 3$, and Fig. 13.2.8 shows a sketch of the graph of the equation $r \cos \theta = -3$. ●

The graph of the equation

$$r = C$$

where C is any constant, is a circle whose center is at the pole and radius is $|C|$. The same circle is given by the equation

$$r = -C$$

As was the case with the straight line, the general polar equation of a circle is not so simple as the cartesian form. However, there are special cases of an equation of a circle which are worth considering in polar form.

If a circle has its center on the polar axis at the point having polar coordinates $(a, 0)$ and is tangent to the $\frac{1}{2}\pi$ axis, then its radius is $|a|$. The points of intersection of such a circle with the polar axis are the pole $(0, 0)$ and the point $(2a, 0)$ (see Fig. 13.2.9). Then if $P(r, \theta)$ is any point on the circle, the angle at P inscribed in the circle is a right angle. Therefore, $\cos \theta = r/2a$ or, equivalently,

$$r = 2a \cos \theta$$

which is a polar equation of the circle having its center on the polar axis or its extension, and tangent to the $\frac{1}{2}\pi$ axis. If a is a positive number, the circle is to the right of the pole. If a is a negative number, the circle is to the left of the pole.

In a similar manner, it may be shown that

$$r = 2b \sin \theta$$

is a polar equation of the circle having its center on the $\frac{1}{2}\pi$ axis or its extension, and tangent to the polar axis. If b is positive, the circle is above the pole. If b is negative, the circle is below the pole.

EXAMPLE 5:   Draw a sketch of the graph of

$$r = \theta \qquad \theta \geq 0$$

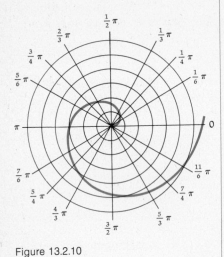

Figure 13.2.10

SOLUTION: When $\theta = n\pi$, where n is any integer, the graph intersects the polar axis or its extension, and when $\theta = \frac{1}{2}n\pi$, where n is any odd integer, the graph intersects the $\frac{1}{2}\pi$ axis or its extension. When $r = 0$, $\theta = 0$; thus, the tangent line to the curve at the pole is the polar axis. A sketch of the graph is shown in Fig. 13.2.10. The curve is called a *spiral of Archimedes*.

Exercises 13.2

In Exercises 1 through 40, draw a sketch of the graph of the given equation.

1. $r \cos \theta = 4$

2. $r \sin \theta = 2$

3. $r = 4 \cos \theta$

4. $r = 2 \sin \theta$

5. $\theta = 5$

6. $\theta = -4$

7. $r = 5$

8. $r = -4$

9. $r \sin \theta = -4$

10. $r \cos \theta = -5$

11. $r = -4 \sin \theta$

12. $r = -5 \cos \theta$

13. $r = e^{\theta}$ (logarithmic spiral)

14. $r = e^{\theta/3}$ (logarithmic spiral)

15. $r = 1/\theta$ (reciprocal spiral)

16. $r = 2\theta$ (spiral of Archimedes)

17. $r = 2 \sin 3\theta$ (three-leafed rose)

18. $r = 3 \cos 2\theta$ (four-leafed rose)

19. $r = 2 \cos 4\theta$ (eight-leafed rose)

20. $r = 4 \sin 5\theta$ (five-leafed rose)

21. $r = 4 \sin 2\theta$ (four-leafed rose)

22. $r = 3 \cos 3\theta$ (three-leafed rose)

23. $r = 2 + 2 \sin \theta$ (cardioid)

24. $r = 3 + 3 \cos \theta$ (cardioid)

25. $r = 4 - 4 \cos \theta$ (cardioid)

26. $r = 3 - 3 \sin \theta$ (cardioid)

27. $r = 4 - 3 \cos \theta$ (limaçon)

28. $r = 3 - 4 \cos \theta$ (limaçon)

29. $r = 4 + 2 \sin \theta$ (limaçon)

30. $r = 2 - 3 \sin \theta$ (limaçon)

31. $r^2 = 9 \sin 2\theta$ (lemniscate)

32. $r^2 = -4 \sin 2\theta$ (lemniscate)

33. $r^2 = -25 \cos 2\theta$ (lemniscate)

34. $r^2 = 16 \cos 2\theta$ (lemniscate)

35. $r = 2 \sin \theta \tan \theta$ (cissoid)

36. $(r - 2)^2 = 8\theta$ (parabolic spiral)

37. $r = 2 \sec \theta - 1$ (conchoid of Nicomedes)

38. $r = 2 \csc \theta + 3$ (conchoid of Nicomedes)

39. $r = |\sin 2\theta|$

40. $r = 2|\cos \theta|$

In Exercises 41 through 44, find an equation of each of the tangent lines to the given curve at the pole.

41. $r = 4 \cos \theta + 2$

42. $r = 2 \sin 3\theta$

43. $r^2 = 4 \cos 2\theta$

44. $r^2 = 9 \sin 2\theta$

45. Find the slope of the tangent line to the curve $r = 4$ at $(4, \frac{1}{4}\pi)$.

46. Find a polar equation of the tangent line to the curve $r = -6 \sin \theta$ at the point $(6, \frac{3}{2}\pi)$.

13.3 INTERSECTION OF GRAPHS IN POLAR COORDINATES

To find the points of intersection of two curves whose equations are in cartesian coordinates, we solve the two equations simultaneously. The common solutions give all the points of intersection. However, because a point has an unlimited number of sets of polar coordinates, it is possible to have as the intersection of two curves a point for which no single pair of polar coordinates satisfies both equations. This is illustrated in the following example.

EXAMPLE 1: Draw sketches of the graphs of $r = 2 \sin 2\theta$ and $r = 1$, and find the points of intersection.

Figure 13.3.1

SOLUTION: The graph of $r = 2 \sin 2\theta$ is a four-leafed rose. The graph of $r = 1$ is the circle with its center at the pole and radius 1. Sketches of the graphs are shown in Fig. 13.3.1. Solving the two equations simultaneously, we have $1 = 2 \sin 2\theta$ or $\sin 2\theta = \frac{1}{2}$. Therefore, we get

$$2\theta = \tfrac{1}{6}\pi, \tfrac{5}{6}\pi, \tfrac{13}{6}\pi, \text{ and } \tfrac{17}{6}\pi$$

$$\theta = \tfrac{1}{12}\pi, \tfrac{5}{12}\pi, \tfrac{13}{12}\pi, \text{ and } \tfrac{17}{12}\pi$$

Hence, we obtain the points of intersection $(1, \frac{1}{12}\pi)$, $(1, \frac{5}{12}\pi)$, $(1, \frac{13}{12}\pi)$, and $(1, \frac{17}{12}\pi)$. We notice in Fig. 13.3.1 that eight points of intersection are shown. The other four points are obtained if we take another form of the equation of the circle $r = 1$; that is, consider the equation $r = -1$, which is the same circle. Solving this equation simultaneously with the equation of the four-leafed rose, we have $\sin 2\theta = -\frac{1}{2}$. Then we get

$$2\theta = \tfrac{7}{6}\pi, \tfrac{11}{6}\pi, \tfrac{19}{6}\pi, \text{ and } \tfrac{23}{6}\pi$$

$$\theta = \tfrac{7}{12}\pi, \tfrac{11}{12}\pi, \tfrac{19}{12}\pi, \text{ and } \tfrac{23}{12}\pi$$

Thus, we have the four points $(-1, \frac{7}{12}\pi)$, $(-1, \frac{11}{12}\pi)$, $(-1, \frac{19}{12}\pi)$, and $(-1, \frac{23}{12}\pi)$.

Incidentally, $(-1, \frac{7}{12}\pi)$ also can be written as $(1, \frac{19}{12}\pi)$, $(-1, \frac{11}{12}\pi)$ can be written as $(1, \frac{23}{12}\pi)$, $(-1, \frac{19}{12}\pi)$ can be written as $(1, \frac{7}{12}\pi)$, and $(-1, \frac{23}{12}\pi)$ can be written as $(1, \frac{11}{12}\pi)$.

Because $(0, \theta)$ represents the pole for any θ, we determine if the pole is a point of intersection by setting $r = 0$ in each equation and solving for θ.

Often the coordinates of the points of intersection of two curves can be found directly from their graphs. However, the following is a general method.

If an equation of a curve in polar coordinates is given by

$$r = f(\theta) \tag{1}$$

then the same curve is given by

$$(-1)^n r = f(\theta + n\pi) \tag{2}$$

where n is any integer.

● ILLUSTRATION 1: Consider the curves of Example 1. The graph of $r = 2 \sin 2\theta$ also has the equation (by taking $n = 1$ in Eq. (2))

$$(-1)r = 2 \sin 2(\theta + \pi)$$

or, equivalently,

$$-r = 2 \sin 2\theta$$

If we take $n = 2$ in Eq. (2), the graph of $r = 2 \sin 2\theta$ also has the equation

$$(-1)^2 r = 2 \sin 2(\theta + 2\pi)$$

or, equivalently,

$$r = 2 \sin 2\theta$$

which is the same as the original equation. Taking n any other integer, we get either $r = 2 \sin 2\theta$ or $r = -2 \sin 2\theta$. The graph of the equation $r = 1$ also has the equation (by taking $n = 1$ in Eq. (2))

$$(-1)r = 1 \quad \text{or, equivalently,} \quad r = -1$$

Other integer values of n in (2) applied to the equation $r = 1$ give either $r = 1$ or $r = -1$. ●

If we are given the two equations $r = f(\theta)$ and $r = g(\theta)$, we obtain all the points of intersection of the graphs of the equations by doing the following.

(a) Use (2) to determine all the distinct equations of the two curves:

$$r = f_1(\theta), \; r = f_2(\theta), \; r = f_3(\theta), \; \ldots \tag{3}$$

$$r = g_1(\theta), r = g_2(\theta), r = g_3(\theta), \ldots \tag{4}$$

(b) Solve each equation in (3) simultaneously with each equation in (4).

(c) Check to see if the pole is a point of intersection by setting $r = 0$ in each equation, thereby giving

$$f(\theta) = 0 \quad \text{and} \quad g(\theta) = 0 \tag{5}$$

If Eqs. (5) each have a solution for θ, not necessarily the same, then the pole lies on both curves.

EXAMPLE 2: Find the points of intersection of the two curves $r = 2 - 2 \cos \theta$ and $r = 2 \cos \theta$. Draw sketches of their graphs.

SOLUTION: To find other equations of the curve represented by $r = 2 - 2 \cos \theta$, we have

$$(-1)r = 2 - 2 \cos(\theta + \pi)$$

or, equivalently,

$$-r = 2 + 2 \cos \theta$$

and

$$(-1)^2 r = 2 - 2 \cos(\theta + 2\pi)$$

or, equivalently,

$$r = 2 - 2 \cos \theta$$

which is the same as the original equation.

In a similar manner, we find other equations of the curve given by $r = 2 \cos \theta$:

$$(-1)r = 2 \cos(\theta + \pi)$$

$$-r = -2 \cos \theta$$

$$r = 2 \cos \theta$$

which is the same as the original equation.

So there are two possible equations for the first curve, $r = 2 - 2 \cos \theta$ and $-r = 2 + 2 \cos \theta$, and one equation for the second curve, $r = 2 \cos \theta$. Solving simultaneously $r = 2 - 2 \cos \theta$ and $r = 2 \cos \theta$ gives

$$2 \cos \theta = 2 - 2 \cos \theta$$

$$4 \cos \theta = 2$$

$$\cos \theta = \tfrac{1}{2}$$

Thus, $\theta = \tfrac{1}{3}\pi$ and $\tfrac{5}{3}\pi$, giving the points $(1, \tfrac{1}{3}\pi)$ and $(1, \tfrac{5}{3}\pi)$. Solving simultaneously $-r = 2 + 2 \cos \theta$ and $r = 2 \cos \theta$ yields

$$2 + 2 \cos \theta = -2 \cos \theta$$

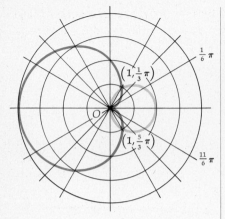

Figure 13.3.2

$$4 \cos \theta = -2$$

$$\cos \theta = -\tfrac{1}{2}$$

Hence, $\theta = \tfrac{2}{3}\pi$ and $\theta = \tfrac{4}{3}\pi$, giving the points $(-1, \tfrac{2}{3}\pi)$ and $(-1, \tfrac{4}{3}\pi)$. However, $(-1, \tfrac{2}{3}\pi)$ is the same point as $(1, \tfrac{5}{3}\pi)$, and $(-1, \tfrac{4}{3}\pi)$ is the same point as $(1, \tfrac{1}{3}\pi)$.

Checking to see if the pole is on the first curve by substituting $r = 0$ in the equation $r = 2 - 2 \cos \theta$, we have

$$0 = 2 - 2 \cos \theta$$

$$\cos \theta = 1$$

$$\theta = 0$$

Therefore, the pole lies on the first curve. In a similar fashion, by substituting $r = 0$ in $r = 2 \cos \theta$, we get

$$0 = 2 \cos \theta$$

$$\cos \theta = 0$$

$$\theta = \tfrac{1}{2}\pi \quad \text{or} \quad \tfrac{3}{2}\pi$$

So the pole lies on the second curve.

Therefore, the points of intersection of the two curves are $(1, \tfrac{1}{3}\pi)$, $(1, \tfrac{5}{3}\pi)$, and the pole. Sketches of the two curves are shown in Fig. 13.3.2.

Exercises 13.3

In Exercises 1 through 14, find the points of intersection of the graphs of the given pair of equations. Draw a sketch of each pair of graphs with the same pole and polar axis.

1. $\begin{cases} 2r = 3 \\ r = 3 \sin \theta \end{cases}$

2. $\begin{cases} 2r = 3 \\ r = 1 + \cos \theta \end{cases}$

3. $\begin{cases} r = 2 \cos \theta \\ r = 2 \sin \theta \end{cases}$

4. $\begin{cases} r = 2 \cos 2\theta \\ r = 2 \sin \theta \end{cases}$

5. $\begin{cases} r = 4\theta \\ r = \tfrac{1}{2}\pi \end{cases}$

6. $\begin{cases} \theta = \tfrac{1}{6}\pi \\ r = 2 \end{cases}$

7. $\begin{cases} r = \cos \theta - 1 \\ r = \cos 2\theta \end{cases}$

8. $\begin{cases} r = 1 - \sin \theta \\ r = \cos 2\theta \end{cases}$

9. $\begin{cases} r = \sin 2\theta \\ r = \cos 2\theta \end{cases}$

10. $\begin{cases} r^2 = 2 \cos \theta \\ r = 1 \end{cases}$

11. $\begin{cases} r = \tan \theta \\ r = 4 \sin \theta \end{cases}$

12. $\begin{cases} r = 4 \tan \theta \sin \theta \\ r = 4 \cos \theta \end{cases}$

13. $\begin{cases} r = 4(1 + \sin \theta) \\ r(1 - \sin \theta) = 3 \end{cases}$

14. $\begin{cases} r^2 \sin 2\theta = 8 \\ r \cos \theta = 2 \end{cases}$

In Exercises 15 and 16, the graph of the given equation intersects itself. Find the points at which this occurs.

15. $r = \sin \tfrac{3}{2}\theta$

16. $r = 1 + 2 \cos 2\theta$

13.4 TANGENT LINES OF POLAR CURVES

In Sec. 13.2. we derived a formula for finding the slope of a tangent line to a polar curve whose equation is $r = f(\theta)$. If α radians is the measure of the inclination of the tangent line to the curve at (r, θ), we have

$$\tan \alpha = \frac{\tan \theta \dfrac{dr}{d\theta} + r}{\dfrac{dr}{d\theta} - r \tan \theta} \tag{1}$$

Figure 13.4.1

Formula (1) is generally complicated to apply. A simpler formula is obtained by considering the angle between the line OP and the tangent line. This angle will have radian measure χ and is measured from the line OP counterclockwise to the tangent line, $0 \le \chi < \pi$.

There are two possible cases: $\alpha \ge \theta$ and $\alpha < \theta$. These two cases are illustrated in Figs. 13.4.1 and 13.4.2. In Fig. 13.4.1, $\alpha > \theta$ and $\chi = \alpha - \theta$. In Fig. 13.4.2, $\alpha < \theta$ and $\chi = \pi - (\theta - \alpha)$. In each case,

$$\tan \chi = \tan(\alpha - \theta)$$

or, equivalently,

$$\tan \chi = \frac{\tan \alpha - \tan \theta}{1 + \tan \alpha \tan \theta} \tag{2}$$

Substituting the value of $\tan \alpha$ from (1) in (2), we get

$$\tan \chi = \frac{\left(\tan \theta \dfrac{dr}{d\theta} + r\right) \Big/ \left(\dfrac{dr}{d\theta} - r \tan \theta\right) - \tan \theta}{1 + \left[\left(\tan \theta \dfrac{dr}{d\theta} + r\right) \Big/ \left(\dfrac{dr}{d\theta} - r \tan \theta\right)\right](\tan \theta)}$$

$$= \frac{\tan \theta \dfrac{dr}{d\theta} + r - \tan \theta \dfrac{dr}{d\theta} + r \tan^2 \theta}{\dfrac{dr}{d\theta} - r \tan \theta + \tan^2 \theta \dfrac{dr}{d\theta} + r \tan \theta}$$

$$= \frac{r(1 + \tan^2 \theta)}{(1 + \tan^2 \theta) \dfrac{dr}{d\theta}}$$

Hence,

$$\tan \chi = \frac{r}{\dfrac{dr}{d\theta}} \tag{3}$$

Comparing formula (3) with formula (1), you can see why it is more desirable to consider χ instead of α when working with polar coordinates.

Figure 13.4.2

EXAMPLE 1: Find χ for the cardioid $r = a + a \sin \theta$ at the point $(\frac{3}{2}a, \frac{1}{6}\pi)$.

SOLUTION: See Fig. 13.4.3. Because $r = a + a \sin \theta$, we have

$$\frac{dr}{d\theta} = a \cos \theta$$

Figure 13.4.3

Applying formula (3), we get

$$\tan \chi = \frac{a + a \sin \theta}{a \cos \theta} = \frac{1 + \sin \theta}{\cos \theta}$$

Therefore, at the point $(\frac{3}{2}a, \frac{1}{6}\pi)$,

$$\tan \chi = \frac{1 + \frac{1}{2}}{\frac{1}{2}\sqrt{3}} = \frac{3}{\sqrt{3}} = \sqrt{3}$$

So

$$\chi = \tfrac{1}{3}\pi$$

EXAMPLE 2:   Find to the nearest 10 min the measurement of the smaller angle between the tangent lines to the curves $r = 3 \cos 2\theta$ and $r = 3 \sin 2\theta$ at the point $P(\frac{3}{2}\sqrt{2}, \frac{1}{8}\pi)$.

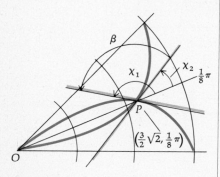

Figure 13.4.4

SOLUTION: Let χ_1 be the radian measure of the angle between the line OP and the tangent line to the curve $r = 3 \cos 2\theta$, and let χ_2 be the radian measure of the angle between the line OP and the tangent line to the curve $r = 3 \sin 2\theta$. The graph of each equation is a four-leafed rose (see Fig. 13.4.4).

If β is the radian measure of the angle between the tangent lines at $P(\frac{3}{2}\sqrt{2}, \frac{1}{8}\pi)$, then

$$\beta = \chi_1 - \chi_2$$

So

$$\tan \beta = \tan(\chi_1 - \chi_2)$$

or, equivalently,

$$\tan \beta = \frac{\tan \chi_1 - \tan \chi_2}{1 + \tan \chi_1 \tan \chi_2} \qquad (4)$$

Tan χ_1 and tan χ_2 are found from formula (3). For tan χ_1, $r = 3 \cos 2\theta$ and $dr/d\theta = -6 \sin 2\theta$. So

$$\tan \chi_1 = \frac{3 \cos 2\theta}{-6 \sin 2\theta} = -\frac{1}{2} \cot 2\theta$$

When $\theta = \frac{1}{8}\pi$, $\tan \chi_1 = -\frac{1}{2} \cot \frac{1}{4}\pi = -\frac{1}{2}$.
For tan χ_2, $r = 3 \sin 2\theta$ and $dr/d\theta = 6 \cos 2\theta$. So

$$\tan \chi_2 = \frac{3 \sin 2\theta}{6 \cos 2\theta} = \frac{1}{2} \tan 2\theta$$

When $\theta = \frac{1}{8}\pi$, $\tan \chi_2 = \frac{1}{2} \tan \frac{1}{4}\pi = \frac{1}{2}$.
Substituting $\tan \chi_1 = -\frac{1}{2}$ and $\tan \chi_2 = \frac{1}{2}$ in (4), we obtain

$$\tan \beta = \frac{-\frac{1}{2} - \frac{1}{2}}{1 + (-\frac{1}{2})(\frac{1}{2})} = \frac{-1}{1 - \frac{1}{4}} = -\frac{4}{3}$$

The angle of radian measure β has a measurement of $126°50'$ to the nearest 10 min. So the measurement of the smaller angle between the two tangent lines is $180° - 126°50' = 53°10'$.

Exercises 13.4

In Exercises 1 through 8, find χ at the point indicated.

1. $r\theta = a$; $(a, 1)$

2. $r = a\theta$; $(\frac{5}{2}\pi a, \frac{5}{2}\pi)$

3. $r = a \sec 2\theta$; $(\sqrt{2}a, -\frac{1}{8}\pi)$

4. $r = a \sin \frac{1}{2}\theta$; $(\frac{1}{2}a, \frac{1}{3}\pi)$

5. $r = \theta^2$; $(\frac{1}{4}\pi^2, \frac{1}{2}\pi)$

6. $r = a \cos 2\theta$; $(\frac{1}{2}\sqrt{3}a, \frac{1}{12}\pi)$

7. $r^2 = a^2 \cos 2\theta$; $\left(\dfrac{a}{\sqrt{2}}, \dfrac{1}{6}\pi\right)$

8. $r = a(1 - \sin \theta)$; (a, π)

In Exercises 9 through 12, find a measurement of the angle between the tangent lines of the given pair of curves at the indicated point of intersection.

9. $\begin{cases} r = a \cos \theta \\ r = a \sin \theta \end{cases}$; $(\frac{1}{2}\sqrt{2}a, \frac{1}{4}\pi)$

10. $\begin{cases} r = a \\ r = 2a \sin \theta \end{cases}$; $(a, \frac{1}{6}\pi)$

11. $\begin{cases} r = 4 \cos \theta \\ r = 4 \cos^2 \theta - 3 \end{cases}$; $(-2, \frac{2}{3}\pi)$

12. $\begin{cases} r = -a \sin \theta \\ r = a \cos 2\theta \end{cases}$; the pole

In Exercises 13 through 16, find a measurement of the angle between the tangent lines of the given pair of curves at all points of intersection.

13. $\begin{cases} r = 1 - \sin \theta \\ r = 1 + \sin \theta \end{cases}$

14. $\begin{cases} r = 3 \cos \theta \\ r = 1 + \cos \theta \end{cases}$

15. $\begin{cases} r = \cos \theta \\ r = \sin 2\theta \end{cases}$

16. $\begin{cases} r = 2 \sec \theta \\ r = \csc^2 \frac{1}{2}\theta \end{cases}$

17. Prove that $\tan \chi = \tan \frac{1}{2}\theta$ at all points of the cardioid $r = 2(1 - \cos \theta)$.

18. Prove that at each point of the logarithmic spiral $r = be^{a\theta}$, χ is the same.

19. Prove that at the points of intersection of the cardioids $r = a(1 + \sin \theta)$ and $r = b(1 - \sin \theta)$ their tangent lines are perpendicular for all values of a and b.

20. Prove that at the points of intersection of the two curves $r = a \sec^2 \frac{1}{2}\theta$ and $r = b \csc^2 \frac{1}{2}\theta$ their tangent lines are perpendicular.

13.5 AREA OF A REGION IN POLAR COORDINATES

In this section a method is developed for finding the area of a region bounded by a curve whose equation is given in polar coordinates and by two lines through the pole.

Let the function f be continuous and nonnegative on the closed interval $[\alpha, \beta]$. Let R be the region bounded by the curve whose equation is $r = f(\theta)$ and by the lines $\theta = \alpha$ and $\theta = \beta$. Then the region R is the region AOB shown in Fig. 13.5.1.

Consider a partition Δ of $[\alpha, \beta]$ defined by $\alpha = \theta_0 < \theta_1 < \theta_2 < \cdots <$

Figure 13.5.1

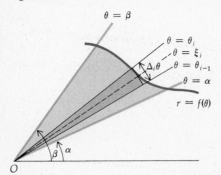

Figure 13.5.2

$\theta_{i-1} < \theta_i < \cdots < \theta_{n-1} < \theta_n = \beta$. Therefore, we have n subintervals of the form $[\theta_{i-1}, \theta_i]$, where $i = 1, 2, \ldots, n$. Let ξ_i be a value of θ in the ith subinterval $[\theta_{i-1}, \theta_i]$. See Fig. 13.5.2, where the ith subinterval is shown together with $\theta = \xi_i$. The radian measure of the angle between the lines $\theta = \theta_{i-1}$ and $\theta = \theta_i$ is denoted by $\Delta_i\theta$. The number of square units in the area of the circular sector of radius $f(\xi_i)$ units and central angle of radian measure $\Delta_i\theta$ is given by

$$\tfrac{1}{2}[f(\xi_i)]^2\,\Delta_i\theta$$

There is such a circular sector for each of the n subintervals. The sum of the measures of the areas of these n circular sectors is

$$\tfrac{1}{2}[f(\xi_1)]^2\,\Delta_1\theta + \tfrac{1}{2}[f(\xi_2)]^2\,\Delta_2\theta + \cdots + \tfrac{1}{2}[f(\xi_i)]^2\,\Delta_i\theta + \cdots + \tfrac{1}{2}[f(\xi_n)]^2\,\Delta_n\theta$$

which can be written, using sigma notation, as

$$\sum_{i=1}^{n} \tfrac{1}{2}[f(\xi_i)]^2\,\Delta_i\theta$$

Let $\|\Delta\|$ be the norm of the partition Δ; that is, $\|\Delta\|$ is the measure of the largest $\Delta_i\theta$. Then if we let A square units be the area of the region R, we define

$$A = \lim_{\|\Delta\| \to 0} \sum_{i=1}^{n} \tfrac{1}{2}[f(\xi_i)]^2\,\Delta_i\theta \qquad (1)$$

The limit in (1) is a definite integral, and we have

$$A = \tfrac{1}{2}\int_{\alpha}^{\beta} [f(\theta)]^2\,d\theta \qquad (2)$$

EXAMPLE 1: Find the area of the region bounded by the graph of $r = 2 + 2\cos\theta$.

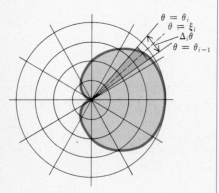

Figure 13.5.3

SOLUTION: The region together with an element of area is shown in Fig. 13.5.3. Because the curve is symmetric with respect to the polar axis, we take the θ limits from 0 to π which determine the area of the region bounded by the curve above the polar axis. Then the area of the entire region is determined by multiplying that area by 2. Thus, if A square units is the measure of the required area,

$$A = 2\lim_{\|\Delta\| \to 0} \sum_{i=1}^{n} \tfrac{1}{2}(2 + 2\cos\xi_i)^2\,\Delta_i\theta$$

$$= 2\int_{0}^{\pi} \tfrac{1}{2}(2 + 2\cos\theta)^2\,d\theta$$

$$= 4\int_{0}^{\pi} (1 + 2\cos\theta + \cos^2\theta)\,d\theta$$

$$= 4\left[\theta + 2\sin\theta + \tfrac{1}{2}\theta + \tfrac{1}{4}\sin 2\theta\right]_{0}^{\pi}$$

$$= 4(\pi + 0 + \tfrac{1}{2}\pi + 0 - 0)$$

$$= 6\pi$$

Therefore, the area is 6π square units.

EXAMPLE 2:   Find the area of the region inside the circle

$$r = 3 \sin \theta$$

and outside the limaçon

$$r = 2 - \sin \theta$$

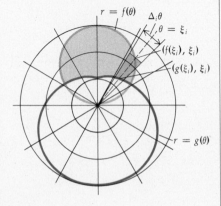

Figure 13.5.4

SOLUTION: To find the points of intersection, we set

$$3 \sin \theta = 2 - \sin \theta$$

$$\sin \theta = \tfrac{1}{2}$$

So

$$\theta = \tfrac{1}{6}\pi \quad \text{and} \quad \theta = \tfrac{5}{6}\pi$$

The curves are sketched and the region is shown together with an element of area in Fig. 13.5.4.

If we let $f(\theta) = 3 \sin \theta$ and $g(\theta) = 2 - \sin \theta$, then the equation of the circle is $r = f(\theta)$, and the equation of the limaçon is $r = g(\theta)$.

The measure of the area of the element of area is the difference of the measures of the areas of two circular sectors.

$$\tfrac{1}{2}[f(\xi_i)]^2 \, \Delta_i\theta - \tfrac{1}{2}[g(\xi_i)]^2 \, \Delta_i\theta = \tfrac{1}{2}([f(\xi_i)]^2 - [g(\xi_i)]^2) \, \Delta_i\theta$$

The sum of the measures of the areas of n such elements is given by

$$\sum_{i=1}^{n} \tfrac{1}{2}([f(\xi_i)]^2 - [g(\xi_i)]^2) \, \Delta_i\theta$$

Hence, if A square units is the area of the region desired, we have

$$A = \lim_{\|\Delta\| \to 0} \sum_{i=1}^{n} \tfrac{1}{2}([f(\xi_i)]^2 - [g(\xi_i)]^2) \, \Delta_i\theta$$

This limit is a definite integral. Instead of taking the limits $\tfrac{1}{6}\pi$ to $\tfrac{5}{6}\pi$, we use the property of symmetry with respect to the $\tfrac{1}{2}\pi$ axis and take the limits from $\tfrac{1}{6}\pi$ to $\tfrac{1}{2}\pi$ and multiply by 2. We have, then,

$$A = 2 \cdot \tfrac{1}{2} \int_{\pi/6}^{\pi/2} ([f(\theta)]^2 - [g(\theta)]^2) \, d\theta$$

$$= \int_{\pi/6}^{\pi/2} [9 \sin^2 \theta - (2 - \sin \theta)^2] \, d\theta$$

$$= 8 \int_{\pi/6}^{\pi/2} \sin^2 \theta \, d\theta + 4 \int_{\pi/6}^{\pi/2} \sin \theta \, d\theta - 4 \int_{\pi/6}^{\pi/2} d\theta$$

$$= 8 \int_{\pi/6}^{\pi/2} (1 - \cos 2\theta) \, d\theta + \Big[-4 \cos \theta - 4\theta\Big]_{\pi/6}^{\pi/2}$$

$$= 4\theta - 2 \sin 2\theta - 4 \cos \theta - 4\theta \Big]_{\pi/6}^{\pi/2}$$

$$= -2 \sin 2\theta - 4 \cos \theta \Big]_{\pi/6}^{\pi/2}$$

$$= (-2 \sin \pi - 4 \cos \tfrac{1}{2}\pi) - (-2 \sin \tfrac{1}{3}\pi - 4 \cos \tfrac{1}{6}\pi)$$

$$= 2 \cdot \tfrac{1}{2}\sqrt{3} + 4 \cdot \tfrac{1}{2}\sqrt{3}$$

$$= 3\sqrt{3}$$

Therefore, the area is $3\sqrt{3}$ square units.

Exercises 13.5

In Exercises 1 through 6, find the area of the region enclosed by the graph of the given equation.

1. $r = 3 \cos \theta$ 2. $r = 2 - \sin \theta$ 3. $r = 4 \cos 3\theta$

4. $r = 4 \sin^2 \tfrac{1}{2}\theta$ 5. $r^2 = 4 \sin 2\theta$ 6. $r = 4 \sin^2 \theta \cos \theta$

In Exercises 7 through 10, find the area of the region enclosed by one loop of the graph of the given equation.

7. $r = 3 \cos 2\theta$ 8. $r = a \sin 3\theta$

9. $r = 1 + 3 \sin \theta$ 10. $r = a(1 - 2 \cos \theta)$

In Exercises 11 through 14, find the area of the intersection of the regions enclosed by the graphs of the two given equations.

11. $\begin{cases} r = 2 \\ r = 3 - 2 \cos \theta \end{cases}$ 12. $\begin{cases} r = 4 \sin \theta \\ r = 4 \cos \theta \end{cases}$

13. $\begin{cases} r = 3 \sin 2\theta \\ r = 3 \cos 2\theta \end{cases}$ 14. $\begin{cases} r^2 = 2 \cos 2\theta \\ r = 1 \end{cases}$

In Exercises 15 through 18, find the area of the region which is inside the graph of the first equation and outside the graph of the second equation.

15. $\begin{cases} r = a \\ r = a(1 - \cos \theta) \end{cases}$ 16. $\begin{cases} r = 2a \sin \theta \\ r = a \end{cases}$

17. $\begin{cases} r = 2 \sin \theta \\ r = \sin \theta + \cos \theta \end{cases}$ 18. $\begin{cases} r^2 = 4 \sin 2\theta \\ r = \sqrt{2} \end{cases}$

19. The face of a bow tie is the region enclosed by the graph of the equation $r^2 = 4 \cos 2\theta$. How much material is necessary to cover the face of the tie?

20. Find the area of the region swept out by the radius vector of the spiral $r = a\theta$ during its second revolution which was not swept out during its first revolution.

21. Find the area of the region swept out by the radius vector of the curve of Exercise 20 during its third revolution which was not swept out during its second revolution.

Review Exercises (Chapter 13)

In Exercises 1 and 2, find a polar equation of the graph having the given cartesian equation.

1. $x^2 + y^2 - 9x + 8y = 0$ 2. $y^4 = x^2(a^2 - y^2)$

In Exercises 3 and 4, find a cartesian equation of the graph having the given polar equation.

3. $r = 9 \sin^2 \frac{1}{2}\theta$ 4. $r = a \tan^2 \theta$

5. Draw a sketch of the graph of (a) $r = 3/\theta$ (reciprocal spiral) and (b) $r = \theta/3$ (spiral of Archimedes).

6. Show that the equations $r = 1 + \sin\theta$ and $r = \sin\theta - 1$ have the same graph.

7. Draw a sketch of the graph of $r = \sqrt{|\cos\theta|}$.

8. Draw a sketch of the graph of $r = \sqrt{|\cos 2\theta|}$.

9. Find an equation of each of the tangent lines at the pole to the cardioid $r = 3 - 3\sin\theta$.

10. Find an equation of each of the tangent lines at the pole to the four-leafed rose $r = 4\cos 2\theta$.

11. Find the area of the region inside the graph of $r = 2a\sin\theta$ and outside the graph of $r = a$.

12. Find the area of the intersection of the regions enclosed by both of the graphs of the two equations $r = a\cos\theta$ and $r = a(1 - \cos\theta)$, $a > 0$.

13. Find the area of the region swept out by the radius vector of the logarithmic spiral $r = e^{k\theta}$ ($k > 0$) as θ varies from 0 to 2π.

14. Find the area of the region inside the graph of the lemniscate $r^2 = 2\sin 2\theta$ and outside the graph of the circle $r = 1$.

15. Find a polar equation of the tangent line to the curve $r = \theta$ at the point (π, π).

In Exercises 16 and 17, find all the points of intersection of the graphs of the two given equations.

16. $\begin{cases} r\cos\theta = 1 \\ r = 1 + 2\cos\theta \end{cases}$ 17. $\begin{cases} r = 2(1 + \cos\theta) \\ r^2 = 2\cos\theta \end{cases}$

18. Prove that the graphs of $r = a\theta$ and $r\theta = a$ have an unlimited number of points of intersection. Also prove that the tangent lines are perpendicular at only two of these points of intersection, and find these points.

19. Find the radian measure of the angle between the tangent lines at each point of intersection of the graphs of the equations $r = -6\cos\theta$ and $r = 2(1 - \cos\theta)$.

20. Find the slope of the tangent line to the curve $r = 6\cos\theta - 2$ at the point $(1, \frac{5}{3}\pi)$.

21. Find the area of the region enclosed by the loop of the limaçon $r = 4(1 + 2\cos\theta)$ and also the area of the region enclosed by the outer part of the limaçon.

22. Find the area enclosed by one loop of the curve $r = a\sin n\theta$, where n is a positive integer.

23. Prove that the distance between the two points $P_1(r_1, \theta_1)$ and $P_2(r_2, \theta_2)$ is

$$\sqrt{r_1^2 + r_2^2 - 2r_1 r_2 \cos(\theta_2 - \theta_1)}$$

24. Find the points of intersection of the graphs of the equations $r = \tan\theta$ and $r = \cot\theta$.

25. (a) Use the formula of Exercise 23 to find a polar equation of the parabola having its focus at $(2, \frac{1}{2}\pi)$ and the line $\theta = 0$ as its directrix. (b) Write a cartesian equation of the parabola having its focus at $(0, 2)$ and the x axis as its directrix. Compare the results of parts (a) and (b).

26. Find a polar equation of the circle having its center at (r_0, θ_0) and a radius of a units. (HINT: Apply the law of cosines to the triangle having vertices at the pole, (r_0, θ_0), and (r, θ).)

14

The conic sections

14.1 THE PARABOLA   A *conic section* is a curve of intersection of a plane with a right circular cone of two nappes. There are three types of curves that occur in this way: the parabola, the ellipse (including the circle as a special case), and the hyperbola. The resulting curve depends on the inclination of the axis of the cone to the cutting plane. In this section we study the parabola.

Following is the analytic definition of a parabola.

14.1.1 Definition   A *parabola* is the set of all points in a plane equidistant from a fixed point and a fixed line. The fixed point is called the *focus,* and the fixed line is called the *directrix.*

We now derive an equation of a parabola from the definition. In order for this equation to be as simple as possible, we choose the x axis as perpendicular to the directrix and containing the focus. The origin is taken as the point on the x axis midway between the focus and the directrix. It should be stressed that we are choosing the axes (*not* the parabola) in a special way. See Fig. 14.1.1.

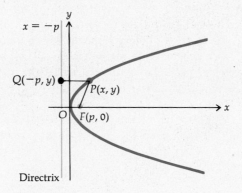

Figure 14.1.1

Let p be the directed distance $\overline{OF}$. The focus is the point $F(p, 0)$, and the directrix is the line having the equation $x = -p$. A point $P(x, y)$ is on the parabola if and only if P is equidistant from F and the directrix. That is, if $Q(-p, y)$ is the foot of the perpendicular line from P to the directrix, then P is on the parabola if and only if

$$|\overline{FP}| = |\overline{QP}|$$

Because

$$|\overline{FP}| = \sqrt{(x - p)^2 + y^2}$$

and

$$|\overline{QP}| = \sqrt{(x + p)^2 + (y - y)^2}$$

P is on the parabola if and only if

$$\sqrt{(x - p)^2 + y^2} = \sqrt{(x + p)^2}$$

By squaring on both sides of the equation, we obtain

$$x^2 - 2px + p^2 + y^2 = x^2 + 2px + p^2$$

$$y^2 = 4px$$

This result is stated as a theorem.

14.1.2 Theorem   An equation of the parabola having its focus at $(p, 0)$ and as its directrix the line $x = -p$ is

$$y^2 = 4px \tag{1}$$

Figure 14.1.2

In Fig. 14.1.1, p is positive; p may be negative, however, because it is the directed distance $\overline{OF}$. Figure 14.1.2 shows a parabola for $p < 0$.

From Figs. 14.1.1 and 14.1.2, we see that for the equation $y^2 = 4px$ the parabola opens to the right if $p > 0$ and to the left if $p < 0$. The point midway between the focus and the directrix on the parabola is called the *vertex.* The vertex of the parabolas in Figs. 14.1.1 and 14.1.2 is the origin. The line through the vertex and the focus is called the *axis* of the parabola. The axis of the parabolas in Figs. 14.1.1 and 14.1.2 is the x axis.

In the above derivation, if the x axis and the y axis are interchanged, then the focus is at the point $F(0, p)$, and the directrix is the line having the equation $y = -p$. An equation of this parabola is $x^2 = 4py$, and the result is stated as a theorem.

14.1.3 Theorem   An equation of the parabola having its focus at $(0, p)$ and as its directrix the line $y = -p$ is

$$x^2 = 4py \tag{2}$$

If $p > 0$, the parabola opens upward as shown in Fig. 14.1.3; and if $p < 0$, the parabola opens downward as shown in Fig. 14.1.4. In each case the vertex is at the origin, and the y axis is the axis of the parabola.

Figure 14.1.3

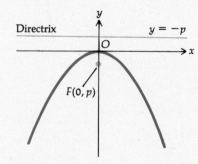

Figure 14.1.4

When we draw a sketch of the graph of a parabola, it is helpful to draw the chord through the focus, perpendicular to the axis of the parabola. This chord is called the *latus rectum* of the parabola. The length of the latus rectum is $|4p|$. (See Exercise 17.)

EXAMPLE 1: Find an equation of the parabola having its focus at $(0, -3)$ and as its directrix the line $y = 3$. Draw a sketch of the graph.

Figure 14.1.5

SOLUTION: Since the focus is on the y axis and is also below the directrix, the parabola opens downward, and $p = -3$. Hence, an equation of the parabola is

$$x^2 = -12y$$

The length of the latus rectum is

$$|4(-3)| = 12$$

A sketch of the graph is shown in Fig. 14.1.5.

Any point on the parabola is equidistant from the focus and the directrix. In Fig. 14.1.5, three such points (P_1, P_2, and P_3) are shown, and we have

$$|\overline{FP_1}| = |\overline{P_1Q_1}| \qquad |\overline{FP_2}| = |\overline{P_2Q_2}| \qquad |\overline{FP_3}| = |\overline{P_3Q_3}|$$

EXAMPLE 2: Given the parabola having the equation

$$y^2 = 7x$$

find the coordinates of the focus, an equation of the directrix, and the length of the latus rectum. Draw a sketch of the graph.

SOLUTION: The given equation is of the form of Eq. (1); so

$$4p = 7$$

$$p = \tfrac{7}{4}$$

Because $p > 0$, the parabola opens to the right. The focus is at the point $F(\tfrac{7}{4}, 0)$. An equation of the directrix is $x = -\tfrac{7}{4}$. The length of the latus rectum is 7. A sketch of the graph is shown in Fig. 14.1.6.

Figure 14.1.6

Exercises 14.1

For each of the parabolas in Exercises 1 through 8, find the coordinates of the focus, an equation of the directrix, and the length of the latus rectum. Draw a sketch of the curve.

1. $x^2 = 4y$
2. $y^2 = 6x$
3. $y^2 = -8x$
4. $x^2 = -16y$
5. $x^2 + y = 0$
6. $y^2 - 5x = 0$
7. $2y^2 - 9x = 0$
8. $3x^2 + 4y = 0$

In Exercises 9 through 16, find an equation of the parabola having the given properties.

9. Focus, $(5, 0)$; directrix, $x = -5$.

10. Focus, $(0, 4)$; directrix, $y = -4$.

11. Focus, $(0, -2)$; directrix, $y - 2 = 0$.

12. Focus, $(-\frac{5}{3}, 0)$; directrix, $5 - 3x = 0$.

13. Focus, $(\frac{1}{2}, 0)$; directrix, $2x + 1 = 0$.

14. Focus, $(0, \frac{2}{3})$; directrix, $3y + 2 = 0$.

15. Vertex, $(0, 0)$; opens to the left; length of latus rectum $= 6$.

16. Vertex, $(0, 0)$; opens upward; length of latus rectum $= 3$.

17. Prove that the length of the latus rectum of a parabola is $|4p|$.

18. Find an equation of the parabola having its vertex at the origin, the x axis as its axis, and passing through the point $(2, -4)$.

19. Find an equation of the parabola having its vertex at the origin, the y axis as its axis, and passing through the point $(-2, -4)$.

20. A parabolic arch has a height of 20 ft and a width of 36 ft at the base. If the vertex of the parabola is at the top of the arch, at what height above the base is it 18 ft wide?

21. The cable of a suspension bridge hangs in the form of a parabola when the load is uniformly distributed horizontally. The distance between two towers is 1500 ft, the points of support of the cable on the towers are 220 ft above the roadway, and the lowest point on the cable is 70 ft above the roadway. Find the vertical distance to the cable from a point in the roadway 150 ft from the foot of a tower.

22. Assume that water issuing from the end of a horizontal pipe, 25 ft above the ground, describes a parabolic curve, the vertex of the parabola being at the end of the pipe. If, at a point 8 ft below the line of the pipe, the flow of water has curved outward 10 ft beyond a vertical line through the end of the pipe, how far beyond this vertical line will the water strike the ground?

23. A reflecting telescope has a parabolic mirror for which the distance from the vertex to the focus is 30 ft. If the distance across the top of the mirror is 64 in., how deep is the mirror at the center?

24. Using Definition 14.1.1, find an equation of the parabola having as its directrix the line $y = 4$ and as its focus the point $(-3, 8)$.

25. Using Definition 14.1.1, find an equation of the parabola having as its directrix the line $x = -3$ and as its focus the point $(2, 5)$.

26. Find all points on the parabola $y^2 = 8x$ such that the foot of the perpendicular drawn from the point to the directrix, the focus, and the point itself are vertices of an equilateral triangle.

27. Find an equation of the circle passing through the vertex and the endpoints of the latus rectum of the parabola $x^2 = -8y$.

28. Prove analytically that the circle having as its diameter the latus rectum of a parabola is tangent to the directrix of the parabola.

29. A focal chord of a parabola is a line segment through the focus and with its endpoints on the parabola. If A and B are the endpoints of a focal chord of a parabola, and if C is the point of intersection of the directrix with a line through the vertex and point A, prove that the line through C and B is parallel to the axis of the parabola.

30. Prove that the distance from the midpoint of a focal chord (see Exercise 29) of a parabola to the directrix is half the length of the focal chord.

14.2 TRANSLATION OF AXES

The shape of a curve is not affected by the position of the coordinate axes; however, an equation of the curve is affected.

● ILLUSTRATION 1: If a circle with a radius of 3 has its center at the point $(4, -1)$, then an equation of this circle is

$$(x - 4)^2 + (y + 1)^2 = 9$$

$$x^2 + y^2 - 8x + 2y + 8 = 0$$

However, if the origin is at the center, the same circle has a simpler equation, namely,

$$x^2 + y^2 = 9 \qquad ●$$

If we may take the coordinate axes as we please, they are generally chosen in such a way that the equations will be as simple as possible. If the axes are given, however, we often wish to find a simpler equation of a given curve referred to another set of axes.

In general, if in the plane with given x and y axes, new coordinate axes are chosen parallel to the given ones, we say that there has been a *translation of axes* in the plane.

In particular, let the given x and y axes be translated to the x' and y' axes, having origin (h, k) with respect to the given axes. Also, assume that the positive numbers are on the same side of the origin on the x' and y' axes as they are on the x and y axes (see Fig. 14.2.1).

Figure 14.2.1

A point P in the plane, having coordinates (x, y) with respect to the given coordinate axes, will have coordinates (x', y') with respect to the new axes. To obtain relationships between these two sets of coordinates, we draw a line through P parallel to the y axis and the y' axis, and also a line through P parallel to the x axis and the x' axis. Let the first line intersect the x axis at the point A and the x' axis at the point A', and the second line intersect the y axis at the point B and the y' axis at the point B'.

With respect to the x and y axes, the coordinates of P are (x, y), the coordinates of A are $(x, 0)$, and the coordinates of A' are (x, k). Because $\overline{A'P} = \overline{AP} - \overline{AA'}$, we have

$$y' = y - k$$

or, equivalently,

$$y = y' + k$$

With respect to the x and y axes, the coordinates of B are $(0, y)$, and the coordinates of B' are (h, y). Because $\overline{B'P} = \overline{BP} - \overline{BB'}$, we have

$$x' = x - h$$

or, equivalently,

$$x = x' + h$$

These results are stated as a theorem.

14.2.1 Theorem If (x, y) represents a point P with respect to a given set of axes, and (x', y') is a representation of P after the axes are translated to a new origin having coordinates (h, k) with respect to the given axes, then

$$x = x' + h \quad \text{and} \quad y = y' + k \tag{1}$$

or, equivalently,

$$x' = x - h \quad \text{and} \quad y' = y - k \tag{2}$$

Equations (1) or (2) are called the *equations of translating the axes*.

If an equation of a curve is given in x and y, then an equation in x' and y' is obtained by replacing x by $(x' + h)$ and y by $(y' + k)$. The graph of the equation in x and y, with respect to the x and y axes, is exactly the same set of points as the graph of the corresponding equation in x' and y' with respect to the x' and y' axes.

EXAMPLE 1: Given the equation $x^2 + 10x + 6y + 19 = 0$, find an equation of the graph with respect to the x' and y' axes after a translation of axes to the new origin $(-5, 1)$.

SOLUTION: A point P, represented by (x, y) with respect to the old axes, has the representation (x', y') with respect to the new axes. Then by Eqs. (1), with $h = -5$ and $k = 1$, we have

$$x = x' - 5 \quad \text{and} \quad y = y' + 1$$

Substituting these values of x and y into the given equation, we obtain

$$(x' - 5)^2 + 10(x' - 5) + 6(y' + 1) + 19 = 0$$

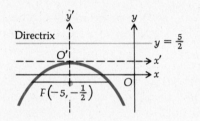

Figure 14.2.2

$$x'^2 - 10x' + 25 + 10x' - 50 + 6y' + 6 + 19 = 0$$

$$x'^2 = -6y'$$

The graph of this equation with respect to the x' and y' axes is a parabola with its vertex at the origin, opening downward, and with $4p = -6$. The graph with respect to the x and y axes is, then, a parabola having its vertex at $(-5, 1)$, its focus at $(-5, -\frac{1}{2})$, and as its directrix the line $y = \frac{5}{2}$ (see Fig. 14.2.2).

The above example illustrates how an equation can be reduced to a simpler form by a suitable translation of axes. In general, equations of the second degree which contain no term involving xy can be simplified by a translation of axes. This is illustrated in the following example.

EXAMPLE 2: Given the equation $9x^2 + 4y^2 - 18x + 32y + 37 = 0$, translate the axes so the equation of the graph with respect to the x' and y' axes contains no first-degree terms.

Figure 14.2.3

SOLUTION: We rewrite the given equation:

$$9(x^2 - 2x) + 4(y^2 + 8y) = -37$$

Completing the squares of the terms in parentheses by adding $9 \cdot 1$ and $4 \cdot 16$ on both sides of the equation, we have

$$9(x^2 - 2x + 1) + 4(y^2 + 8y + 16) = -37 + 9 + 64$$

$$9(x - 1)^2 + 4(y + 4)^2 = 36$$

Then, if we let $x' = x - 1$ and $y' = y + 4$, we obtain

$$9x'^2 + 4y'^2 = 36$$

From Eq. (2), we see that the substitutions of $x' = x - 1$ and $y' = y + 4$ result in a translation of axes to a new origin of $(1, -4)$. In Fig. 14.2.3, we have a sketch of the graph of the equation in x' and y' with respect to the x' and y' axes.

Figure 14.2.4

We shall now apply the translation of axes to finding the general equation of a parabola having its directrix parallel to a coordinate axis and its vertex at the point (h, k). In particular, let the directrix be parallel to the y axis. If the vertex is at point $V(h, k)$, then the directrix has the equation $x = h - p$, and the focus is at the point $F(h + p, k)$. Let the x' and y' axes be such that the origin O' is at $V(h, k)$ (see Fig. 14.2.4).

An equation of the parabola in Fig. 14.2.4 with respect to the x' and y' axes is

$$y'^2 = 4px'$$

To obtain an equation of this parabola with respect to the x and y axes, we replace x' by $(x - h)$ and y' by $(y - k)$ from Eq. (2), which gives us

$$(y - k)^2 = 4p(x - h)$$

The axis of this parabola is parallel to the x axis.

Similarly, if the directrix of a parabola is parallel to the x axis and the vertex is at $V(h, k)$, then its focus is at $F(h, k + p)$ and the directrix has the equation $y = k - p$, and an equation of the parabola with respect to the x and y axes is

$$(x - h)^2 = 4p(y - k)$$

The axis of this parabola is parallel to the y axis. We have proved, then, the following theorem.

14.2.2 Theorem   If p is the directed distance from the vertex to the focus, an equation of the parabola with its vertex at (h, k) and with its axis parallel to the x axis is

$$(y - k)^2 = 4p(x - h) \tag{3}$$

A parabola with the same vertex and with its axis parallel to the y axis has for an equation

$$(x - h)^2 = 4p(y - k) \tag{4}$$

EXAMPLE 3: Find an equation of the parabola having as its directrix the line $y = 1$ and as its focus the point $F(-3, 7)$.

Figure 14.2.5

SOLUTION: Since the directrix is parallel to the x axis, the axis will be parallel to the y axis, and the equation will have the form (4).

Since the vertex V is halfway between the directrix and the focus, V has coordinates $(-3, 4)$. The directed distance from the vertex to the focus is p, and so

$$p = 7 - 4 = 3$$

Therefore, an equation is

$$(x + 3)^2 = 12(y - 4)$$

Squaring and simplifying, we have

$$x^2 + 6x - 12y + 57 = 0$$

A sketch of the graph of this parabola is shown in Fig. 14.2.5.

EXAMPLE 4:   Given the parabola having the equation

$$y^2 + 6x + 8y + 1 = 0$$

SOLUTION: Rewrite the given equation as

$$y^2 + 8y = -6x - 1$$

Completing the square of the terms involving y on the left side of this find the vertex, the focus, an equation of the directrix, an equation of the axis, and the length of the latus rectum, and draw a sketch of the graph.

Figure 14.2.6

equation by adding 16 on both sides, we obtain

$$y^2 + 8y + 16 = -6x + 15$$

$$(y + 4)^2 = -6(x - \tfrac{5}{2})$$

Comparing this equation with (3), we let

$$k = -4 \qquad h = \tfrac{5}{2}$$

and

$$4p = -6 \quad \text{or} \quad p = -\tfrac{3}{2}$$

Therefore, the vertex is at $(\tfrac{5}{2}, -4)$; an equation of the axis is $y = -4$; the focus is at $(1, -4)$; an equation of the directrix is $x = 4$; and the length of the latus rectum is 6. A sketch of the graph is shown in Fig. 14.2.6.

Exercises 14.2

In Exercises 1 through 8, find a new equation of the graph of the given equation after a translation of axes to the new origin as indicated. Draw the original and the new axes and a sketch of the graph.

1. $x^2 + y^2 + 6x + 4y = 0$; $(-3, -2)$

2. $x^2 + y^2 - 10x + 4y + 13 = 0$; $(5, -2)$

3. $y^2 - 6x + 9 = 0$; $(\tfrac{3}{2}, 0)$

4. $y^2 + 3x - 2y + 7 = 0$; $(-2, 1)$

5. $x^2 + 4y^2 + 4x + 8y + 4 = 0$; $(-2, -1)$

6. $25x^2 + y^2 - 50x + 20y - 500 = 0$; $(1, -10)$

7. $y - 4 = 2(x - 1)^3$; $(1, 4)$

8. $(y + 1)^2 = 4(x - 2)^3$; $(2, -1)$

In Exercises 9 through 12, translate the axes so that an equation of the graph with respect to the new axes will contain no first-degree terms. Draw the original and the new axes and a sketch of the graph.

9. $x^2 + 4y^2 - 16x + 24y + 84 = 0$

10. $16x^2 + 25y^2 - 32x - 100y - 284 = 0$

11. $3x^2 - 2y^2 + 6x - 8y - 11 = 0$

12. $x^2 - y^2 + 14x - 8y - 35 = 0$

In Exercises 13 through 18, find the vertex, the focus, an equation of the axis, and an equation of the directrix of the given parabola. Draw a sketch of the graph.

13. $x^2 + 6x + 4y + 8 = 0$

14. $4x^2 - 8x + 3y - 2 = 0$

15. $y^2 + 6x + 10y + 19 = 0$

16. $3y^2 - 8x - 12y - 4 = 0$

17. $2y^2 = 4y - 3x$

18. $y = 3x^2 - 3x + 3$

In Exercises 19 through 28, find an equation of the parabola having the given properties. Draw a sketch of the graph.

19. Vertex at $(2, 4)$; focus at $(-3, 4)$.

20. Vertex at $(1, -3)$; directrix, $y = 1$.

21. Focus at $(-1, 7)$; directrix, $y = 3$.

22. Focus at $(-\tfrac{3}{4}, 4)$; directrix, $x = -\tfrac{5}{4}$.

23. Vertex at $(3, -2)$; axis, $x = 3$; length of the latus rectum is 6.

24. Axis parallel to the x axis; through the points $(1, 2)$, $(5, 3)$, and $(11, 4)$.

25. Vertex at $(-4, 2)$; axis, $y = 2$; through the point $(0, 6)$.

26. Directrix, $x = -2$; axis, $y = 4$; length of the latus rectum is 8.

27. Directrix, $x = 4$; axis, $y = 4$; through the point $(9, 7)$.

28. Endpoints of the latus rectum are $(1, 3)$ and $(7, 3)$.

29. Given the parabola having the equation $y = ax^2 + bx + c$, with $a \neq 0$, find the coordinates of the vertex.

30. Find the coordinates of the focus of the parabola in Exercise 29.

31. Find an equation of every parabola containing the points $A(-3, -4)$ and $B(5, -4)$, such that points A and B are each 5 units from the focus.

32. Given the equation $4x^3 - 12x^2 + 12x - 3y - 10 = 0$, translate the axes so that the equation of the graph with respect to the new axes will contain no second-degree term and no constant term. Draw a sketch of the graph and the two sets of axes. (HINT: Let $x = x' + h$ and $y = y' + k$ in the given equation.)

33. Given the equation $x^3 + 3x^2 - y^2 + 3x + 4y - 3 = 0$, translate the axes so that the equation of the graph with respect to the new axes will contain no first-degree term and no constant term. Draw a sketch of the graph and the two sets of axes (see hint for Exercise 32).

34. If a parabola has its focus at the origin and the x axis is its axis, prove that it must have an equation of the form $y^2 = 4kx + 4k^2$, $k \neq 0$.

14.3 SOME PROPERTIES OF CONICS

In Sec. 14.1 we stated that a *conic section* (or *conic*) is a curve of intersection of a plane with a right-circular cone of two nappes, and three types of curves of intersection that occur are the *parabola,* the *ellipse,* and the *hyperbola.* The Greek mathematician Apollonius studied conic sections, in terms of geometry, by using this concept. We studied the parabola in Sec. 14.1, where an analytic definition (14.1.1) of a parabola was given. In this section, an analytic definition of a conic section is given and the three types of curves are obtained as special cases of this definition.

In a consideration of the geometry of conic sections, a cone is regarded as having two nappes, extending indefinitely far in both directions. A portion of a right-circular cone of two nappes is shown in Fig. 14.3.1. A *generator* (or *element*) of the cone is a line lying in the cone, and all the generators of a cone contain the point V, called the *vertex* of the cone.

In Fig. 14.3.2 we have a cone and a cutting plane which is parallel to one and only one generator of the cone. This conic is a *parabola.* If the cutting plane is parallel to two generators, it intersects both nappes of the cone and we have a *hyperbola* (Fig. 14.3.3). An *ellipse* is obtained if the cutting plane is parallel to no generator, in which case the cutting plane intersects each generator, as in Fig. 14.3.4.

A special case of the ellipse is a *circle,* which is formed if the cutting plane, which intersects each generator, is also perpendicular to the axis of the cone. Degenerate cases of the conic sections include a point, a

Figure 14.3.1

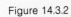

Figure 14.3.2   Figure 14.3.3   Figure 14.3.4

straight line, and two intersecting straight lines. A point is obtained if the cutting plane contains the vertex of the cone but does not contain a generator. This is a degenerate ellipse. If the cutting plane contains the vertex of the cone and only one generator, then a straight line is obtained, and this is a degenerate parabola. A degenerate hyperbola is formed when the cutting plane contains the vertex of the cone and two generators, thereby giving two intersecting straight lines.

There are many applications of conic sections to both pure and applied mathematics. We shall mention a few of them. The orbits of planets and satellites are ellipses. Ellipses are used in making machine gears. Arches of bridges are sometimes elliptical or parabolic in shape. The path of a projectile is a parabola if motion is considered to be in a plane and air resistance is neglected. Parabolas are used in the design of parabolic mirrors, searchlights, and automobile headlights. Hyperbolas are used in combat in "sound ranging" to locate the position of enemy guns by the sound of the firing of those guns. If a quantity varies inversely as another quantity, such as pressure and volume in Boyle's law for a perfect gas at a constant temperature, the graph is a hyperbola.

To discuss conics analytically as plane curves, we first state a definition which gives a property common to all conics.

14.3.1 Definition   A *conic* is the set of all points P in a plane such that the undirected distance of P from a fixed point is in a constant ratio to the undirected distance of P from a fixed line which does not contain the fixed point.

The constant ratio in the above definition is called the *eccentricity* of the conic and is denoted by e. The eccentricity e is a nonnegative number because it is the ratio of two undirected distances. Actually for nondegenerate conics, $e > 0$. (Later we see that when $e = 0$, we have a point.) If $e = 1$, we see by comparing Definitions 14.3.1 and 14.1.1 that the conic is a parabola. If $e < 1$, the conic is an ellipse, and if $e > 1$, the conic is a hyperbola.

The fixed point, referred to in Definition 14.3.1, is called a *focus* of the conic, and the fixed line is called the corresponding *directrix*. We learned in Sec. 14.1 that a parabola has one focus and one directrix. Later we see that an ellipse and a hyperbola each have two foci and two directrices, with each focus corresponding to a particular directrix.

The line through a focus of a conic perpendicular to its directrix is called the *principal axis* of the conic. The points of intersection of the conic and its principal axis are called the *vertices* of the conic. From our study of the parabola, we know that a parabola has one vertex. However, both the ellipse and the hyperbola have two vertices. This is proved in the following theorem.

14.3.2 Theorem If e is the eccentricity of a nondegenerate conic, then if $e \neq 1$, the conic has two vertices; if $e = 1$, the conic has only one vertex.

Figure 14.3.5

PROOF: Let F denote the focus of the conic and D denote the point of intersection of the directrix and the principal axis. Let d denote the undirected distance between the focus and its directrix. In Fig. 14.3.5, F is to the right of the directrix, and in Fig. 14.3.6, F is to the left of the directrix. Let V denote a vertex of the conic. We wish to show that if $e \neq 1$, there are two possible vertices V, and if $e = 1$, there is only one vertex V.

From Definition 14.3.1, we have

$$|\overline{FV}| = e|\overline{DV}|$$

Removing the absolute-value bars, we obtain

$$\overline{FV} = \pm e(\overline{DV}) \tag{1}$$

Because D, F, and V are all on the principal axis,

$$\overline{DV} = \overline{DF} + \overline{FV}$$

If F is to the right of D, $\overline{DF} = d$. Thus, we have from the above

$$\overline{DV} = d + \overline{FV} \tag{2}$$

Substituting from (1) into (2) gives

$$\overline{DV} = d \pm e(\overline{DV})$$

from which we get

$$\overline{DV} = \frac{d}{1 \pm e} \tag{3}$$

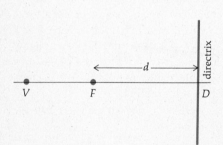

Figure 14.3.6

If $e = 1$, the minus sign in the above equations must be rejected because we would be dividing by zero. So if $e \neq 1$, two points V are obtained; if $e = 1$, we obtain only one point V.

If F is to the left of D, $\overline{DF} = -d$. Instead of (3), we get

$$\overline{DV} = \frac{-d}{1 \mp e}$$

from which the same conclusion follows. So the theorem is proved. ■

The point on the principal axis of an ellipse or a hyperbola that lies halfway between the two vertices is called the *center* of the conic. Hence, the ellipse and the hyperbola are called *central conics* in contrast to the parabola that has no center because it has only one vertex.

14.3.3 Theorem   A conic is symmetric with respect to its principal axis.

The proof of this theorem is left as an exercise (see Exercise 7).

EXAMPLE 1: Use Definition 14.3.1 to find an equation of the conic whose eccentricity is $\frac{4}{5}$ and having a focus at the point $F(1, -2)$ with the line $4y + 17 = 0$ as the corresponding directrix.

Figure 14.3.7

SOLUTION: Figure 14.3.7 shows the focus, the directrix, and the point $P(x, y)$ representing any point on the conic. Letting the point D be the foot of the perpendicular from P to the directrix, we have from Definition 14.3.1

$$\frac{|\overline{PF}|}{|\overline{PD}|} = \frac{4}{5}$$

and so

$$|\overline{PF}| = \tfrac{4}{5}|\overline{PD}|$$

Using the distance formula to find $|\overline{PF}|$ and $|\overline{PD}|$ and substituting into the above equation, we get

$$\sqrt{(x-1)^2 + (y+2)^2} = \tfrac{4}{5}|y + \tfrac{17}{4}|$$

Squaring on both sides of this equation and simplifying, we get

$$x^2 - 2x + 1 + y^2 + 4y + 4 = \tfrac{16}{25}(y^2 + \tfrac{17}{2}y + \tfrac{289}{16})$$

$$25x^2 - 50x + 25y^2 + 100y + 125 = 16y^2 + 136y + 289$$

$$25x^2 + 9y^2 - 50x - 36y = 164$$

Because $e = \tfrac{4}{5} < 1$, the equation is that of an ellipse.

Exercises 14.3

In Exercises 1 through 6, use Definition 14.3.1 and the formula of Exercise 24 of Exercises 5.3 to find an equation of the conic having the given properties.

1. Focus at $(2, 0)$; directrix: $x = -4$; $e = \frac{1}{2}$.

2. Focus at $(0, -4)$; directrix: $y = -2$; $e = \frac{3}{4}$.

3. Focus at $(-3, 2)$; directrix: $x = 1$; $e = 3$.

4. Focus at $(1, 3)$; directrix: $y = 8$; $e = \frac{3}{2}$.

5. Focus at $(4, -3)$; directrix: $2x - y - 2 = 0$; $e = \frac{1}{2}$.

6. Focus at $(-1, 4)$; directrix: $2x - y + 3 = 0$; $e = 2$.

7. Prove Theorem 14.3.3.

8. Find an equation whose graph consists of all points P in a plane such that the undirected distance of P from the point $(ae, 0)$ is in a constant ratio e to the undirected distance of P from the line $x = a/e$. Let $a^2(1 - e^2) = \pm b^2$ and consider the three cases: $e = 1$, $e < 1$, and $e > 1$.

9. Solve Exercise 8 if the point is $(-ae, 0)$ and the line is $x = -a/e$.

14.4 POLAR EQUATIONS OF THE CONICS

Figure 14.4.1

Fairly simple polar equations of conics are obtained by taking the pole at a focus and the polar axis and its extension along the principal axis. We first consider this situation when the directrix corresponding to the focus at the pole is to the left of the focus. Let D be the point of intersection of this directrix with the principal axis, and let d denote the undirected distance between a focus and its directrix (refer to Fig. 14.4.1). Let $P(r, \theta)$ be any point on the conic to the right of the directrix and on the terminal side of the angle of measure θ. Draw perpendiculars PQ and PR to the principal axis and the directrix, respectively. By Definition 14.3.1, the point P is on the conic if and only if

$$|\overline{OP}| = e|\overline{RP}| \tag{1}$$

Because P is to the right of the directrix, $\overline{RP} > 0$; thus, $|\overline{RP}| = \overline{RP}$. $|\overline{OP}| = r$ because $r > 0$. So from (1) we have

$$r = e(\overline{RP}) \tag{2}$$

However, $\overline{RP} = \overline{DQ} = \overline{DO} + \overline{OQ} = d + r \cos \theta$. Substituting this expression for $\overline{RP}$ in (2), we get

$$r = e(d + r \cos \theta)$$

from which we obtain

$$r = \frac{ed}{1 - e \cos \theta} \tag{3}$$

In a similar manner, we can derive an equation of a conic if the directrix corresponding to the focus at the pole is to the right of the focus, and we obtain

$$r = \frac{ed}{1 + e \cos \theta} \tag{4}$$

The derivation of (4) is left as an exercise (see Exercise 1).

If a focus of a conic is at the pole and the polar axis is parallel to the corresponding directrix, then the $\frac{1}{2}\pi$ axis and its extension are along the principal axis. We obtain the following equation:

$$r = \frac{ed}{1 \pm e \sin \theta} \tag{5}$$

where e and d are, respectively, the eccentricity and the undirected distance between the focus and the corresponding directrix. The plus sign is taken when the directrix corresponding to the focus at the pole is above the focus, and the minus sign is taken when it is below the focus. The derivations of Eqs. (5) are left as exercises (see Exercises 2 and 3).

We now discuss the graph of Eq. (3) for each of the three cases: $e = 1$, $e < 1$, and $e > 1$. Similar discussions apply to the graphs of Eqs. (4) and (5).

Case 1: $e = 1$. The conic is a parabola.
Equation (3) becomes

$$r = \frac{d}{1 - \cos \theta} \tag{6}$$

r is not defined when $\theta = 0$; however, r is defined for all other values of θ for which $0 < \theta < 2\pi$. Differentiating in (6), we obtain

$$D_\theta r = \frac{-d \sin \theta}{(1 - \cos \theta)^2}$$

Setting $D_\theta r = 0$, for values of θ in the interval $(0, 2\pi)$ we obtain $\theta = \pi$. Because when $0 < \theta < \pi$, $D_\theta r < 0$, and when $\pi < \theta < 2\pi$, $D_\theta r > 0$, r has an absolute minimum value at $\theta = \pi$. When $\theta = \pi$, $r = \frac{1}{2}d$, and the point $(\frac{1}{2}d, \pi)$ is the vertex. Therefore, the undirected distance from the focus to a point on the parabola is shortest when the point on the parabola is the vertex.

By Theorem 14.3.3, the parabola is symmetric with respect to its principal axis; by Theorem 14.3.2 there is one vertex. Note that the curve does not contain the pole because there is no value of θ which will give a value of 0 for r. A sketch of the parabola is shown in Fig. 14.4.2.

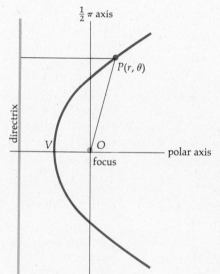

Figure 14.4.2

EXAMPLE 1:   A parabola has its focus at the pole and its vertex at $(4, \pi)$. Find an equation of the parabola and an equation of the directrix. Draw a sketch of the parabola and the directrix.

SOLUTION: Because the focus is at the pole and the vertex is at $(4, \pi)$, the polar axis and its extension are along the principal axis of the parabola. Furthermore, the vertex is to the left of the focus, and so the directrix is also to the left of the focus. Hence, an equation of the parabola is of the form of Eq. (3). Because the vertex is at $(4, \pi)$, $\frac{1}{2}d = 4$; thus, $d = 8$. The eccentricity $e = 1$, and therefore we obtain the equation

$$r = \frac{8}{1 - \cos \theta}$$

An equation of the directrix is given by $r \cos \theta = -d$, and because $d = 8$, we have $r \cos \theta = -8$. Figure 14.4.3 shows a sketch of the parabola and the directrix.

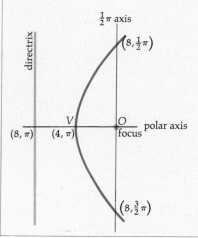

Figure 14.4.3

EXAMPLE 2: Follow the instructions of Example 1 if the parabola has its focus at the pole and its vertex at $(3, \frac{3}{2}\pi)$.

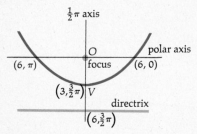

Figure 14.4.4

SOLUTION: The vertex of the parabola is below the focus, and the $\frac{1}{2}\pi$ axis and its extension are along the principal axis. Therefore, the directrix is also below the focus, and an equation of the parabola is of the form of Eq. (5) with the minus sign. The undirected distance from the focus to the vertex is $\frac{1}{2}d = 3$; thus $d = 6$. Therefore, from Eqs. (5) an equation of the parabola is

$$r = \frac{6}{1 - \sin \theta}$$

An equation of the directrix is given by $r \sin \theta = -d$. Because $d = 6$, we have $r \sin \theta = -6$. Sketches of the parabola and the directrix are shown in Fig. 14.4.4.

Case 2: $e < 1$. The conic is an ellipse.

When $e < 1$, the denominator of the fraction in Eq. (3) is never zero, and so r exists for all values of θ. To find the absolute extrema of r on the interval $[0, 2\pi)$, we find $D_\theta r$ and obtain

$$D_\theta r = \frac{-e^2 d \sin \theta}{(1 - e \cos \theta)^2} \tag{7}$$

For θ in the interval $[0, 2\pi)$, $D_\theta r = 0$ when $\theta = 0$ and π. When $-\frac{1}{2}\pi < \theta < 0$, $D_\theta r > 0$; and when $0 < \theta < \frac{1}{2}\pi$, $D_\theta r < 0$. Hence, when $\theta = 0$, r has an absolute maximum value of $ed/(1 - e)$. When $\frac{1}{2}\pi < \theta < \pi$, $D_\theta r < 0$; and when $\pi < \theta < \frac{3}{2}\pi$, $D_\theta r > 0$. Thus, r has an absolute minimum value

Figure 14.4.5

of $ed/(1 + e)$ when $\theta = \pi$. The points $(ed/(1 - e), 0)$ and $(ed/(1 + e), \pi)$ are the vertices of the ellipse. We denote them by V_1 and V_2, respectively. It follows, then, that the undirected distance from the focus $(0, 0)$ to a point on the ellipse is greatest when the point on the ellipse is V_1 and smallest when it is V_2.

By Theorem 14.3.3, the ellipse is symmetric with respect to its principal axis. There is no value of θ that will give a value of 0 for r, and so the curve does not contain the pole. A sketch of the ellipse is shown in Fig. 14.4.5.

EXAMPLE 3: Find an equation of the ellipse having a focus at the pole and vertices at $(5, 0)$ and $(2, \pi)$. Write an equation of the directrix corresponding to the focus at the pole. Draw a sketch of the ellipse.

SOLUTION: Because the vertices are at $(5, 0)$ and $(2, \pi)$, the polar axis and its extension are along the principal axis of the ellipse. The directrix corresponding to the focus at the pole is to the left of the focus because the vertex closest to this focus is at $(2, \pi)$. The required equation is therefore of the form of Eq. (3). The vertex V_1 is at $(5, 0)$ and V_2 is at $(2, \pi)$. It follows from the discussion of Case 2 that

$$\frac{ed}{1 - e} = 5 \quad \text{and} \quad \frac{ed}{1 + e} = 2$$

Solving these two equations simultaneously, we obtain $e = \frac{3}{7}$ and $d = \frac{20}{3}$. Hence, from Eq. (3) an equation of the ellipse is

$$r = \frac{\frac{3}{7} \cdot \frac{20}{3}}{1 - \frac{3}{7} \cos \theta}$$

or, equivalently,

$$r = \frac{20}{7 - 3 \cos \theta}$$

Because $d = \frac{20}{3}$, an equation of the directrix corresponding to the focus at the pole is $r \cos \theta = -\frac{20}{3}$ or, equivalently, $3r \cos \theta = -20$. A sketch of the ellipse is shown in Fig. 14.4.6.

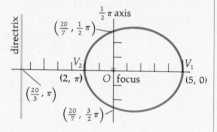

Figure 14.4.6

EXAMPLE 4: An equation of a conic is

$$r = \frac{5}{3 + 2 \sin \theta}$$

Find the eccentricity, identify the conic, write an equation of the directrix corresponding to the focus at the pole, find the vertices, and draw a sketch of the curve.

SOLUTION: Dividing the numerator and denominator of the fraction in the given equation by 3, we obtain

$$r = \frac{\frac{5}{3}}{1 + \frac{2}{3} \sin \theta}$$

which is of the form of Eqs. (5) with the plus sign. The eccentricity $e = \frac{2}{3} < 1$, and so the conic is an ellipse. Because $ed = \frac{5}{3}$, $d = \frac{5}{3} \div \frac{2}{3} = \frac{5}{2}$. The $\frac{1}{2}\pi$ axis and its extension are along the principal axis. The directrix corresponding to the focus at the pole is above the focus, and an equation of it is $r \sin \theta = \frac{5}{2}$. When $\theta = \frac{1}{2}\pi$, $r = 1$. And when $\theta = \frac{3}{2}\pi$, $r = 5$. The vertices are therefore at $(1, \frac{1}{2}\pi)$ and $(5, \frac{3}{2}\pi)$. A sketch of the ellipse is shown in Fig. 14.4.7.

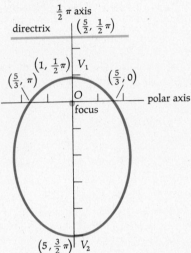

Figure 14.4.7

Case 3· $e > 1$. The conic is a hyperbola.

In the derivation of Eq. (3) we assumed that the point P on the conic is to the right of the given directrix and that P is on the terminal side of the angle of θ radians, thus making r positive. In the previous two cases, when the conic is an ellipse or a parabola, we obtain the entire curve with these assumptions. However, when $e > 1$, we shall see that we obtain only one of two branches of the hyperbola when $r > 0$, and this branch is to the right of the directrix. There is also a branch to the left of the given directrix; this is obtained by letting r assume negative as well as positive values as θ takes on values in the interval $[0, 2\pi)$.

If $e > 1$ in Eq. (3), r is undefined when $\cos \theta = 1/e$. There are two values of θ in $[0, 2\pi)$ that satisfy this equation. These values are

$$\theta_1 = \cos^{-1}\frac{1}{e} \quad \text{and} \quad \theta_2 = 2\pi - \cos^{-1}\frac{1}{e}$$

We investigate the values of r as θ increases from 0 to θ_1. When $\theta = 0$, $r = ed/(1 - e)$, and because $e > 1$, $r < 0$. So the point $(ed/(1 - e), 0)$ is the left vertex of the hyperbola. The cosine function is decreasing in the interval $(0, \theta_1)$; therefore, when $0 < \theta < \theta_1$, $\cos \theta > \cos \theta_1 = 1/e$ or, equivalently, $1 - e \cos \theta < 0$. Hence, for values of θ in the interval $(0, \theta_1)$, $r = ed/(1 - e \cos \theta) < 0$. When $\theta = \theta_1$, r is undefined; however,

$$\lim_{\theta \to \theta_1^-} r = \lim_{\theta \to \theta_1^-} \frac{ed}{1 - e \cos \theta} = -\infty$$

We conclude, then, that as θ increases from 0 to θ_1, $r < 0$ and $|r|$ increases

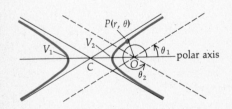

Figure 14.4.8

without bound. From these values of θ we obtain the lower half of the left branch of the curve. See Fig. 14.4.8. We show later that a hyperbola has two asymptotes. For this hyperbola one of the asymptotes is parallel to the line $\theta = \theta_1$.

Now we consider the points on the hyperbola as θ increases through values between θ_1 and θ_2. When $\theta_1 < \theta < \theta_2$, $\cos \theta < \cos \theta_1 = 1/e$ or, equivalently, $1 - e \cos \theta > 0$. Therefore, for values of θ in the interval (θ_1, θ_2), $r > 0$.

$$\lim_{\theta \to \theta_1^+} r = \lim_{\theta \to \theta_1^+} \frac{ed}{1 - e \cos \theta} = +\infty$$

When $\theta = \pi$, $r = ed/(1 + e)$; so the point $(ed/(1 + e), \pi)$ is the right vertex of the hyperbola. Finding $D_\theta r$ from Eq. (3), we get

$$D_\theta r = -\frac{e^2 d \sin \theta}{(1 - e \cos \theta)^2} \tag{8}$$

When $\theta_1 < \theta < \pi$, $\sin \theta > 0$; hence, $D_\theta r < 0$, from which we conclude that r is decreasing when θ is in the interval (θ_1, π). Therefore, for values of θ in the interval (θ_1, π) we obtain the top half of the right branch of the hyperbola shown in Fig. 14.4.8.

When $\pi < \theta < \theta_2$, $\sin \theta < 0$; so from Eq. (8), $D_\theta r > 0$. Hence, r is increasing when θ is in the interval (π, θ_2). Furthermore,

$$\lim_{\theta \to \theta_2^-} r = \lim_{\theta \to \theta_2^-} \frac{ed}{1 - e \cos \theta} = +\infty$$

Consequently, for values of θ in the interval (π, θ_2) we have the lower half of the right branch of the hyperbola. The other asymptote of the hyperbola is parallel to the line $\theta = \theta_2$.

The cosine function is increasing in the interval $(\theta_2, 2\pi)$. So when $\theta_2 < \theta < 2\pi$, $\cos \theta > \cos \theta_2 = 1/e$ or, equivalently, $1 - e \cos \theta < 0$. Thus, we see from Eq. (3) that for values of θ in the interval $(\theta_2, 2\pi)$, $r < 0$. Also,

$$\lim_{\theta \to \theta_2^+} r = \lim_{\theta \to \theta_2^+} \frac{ed}{1 - e \cos \theta} = -\infty$$

It follows from Eq. (8) that $D_\theta r > 0$; hence, r is increasing when $\theta_2 < \theta < 2\pi$. When $r < 0$ and r is increasing, $|r|$ is decreasing. Thus, for values of θ in the interval $(\theta_2, 2\pi)$ we obtain the upper half of the left branch of the hyperbola, and so the curve of Fig. 14.4.8 is complete.

EXAMPLE 5: The polar axis and its extension are along the principal axis of a hyperbola having a focus at the pole. The corresponding directrix is to the left of the focus. If the hyperbola contains the point $(1, \frac{2}{3}\pi)$ and

SOLUTION: An equation of the hyperbola is of the form of Eq. (3) with $e = 2$. We have, then,

$$r = \frac{2d}{1 - 2 \cos \theta}$$

Because the point $(1, \frac{2}{3}\pi)$ lies on the hyperbola, its coordinates satisfy the equation. Therefore,

$e = 2$, find (a) an equation of the hyperbola; (b) the vertices; (c) the center; and (d) an equation of the directrix corresponding to the focus at the pole. Draw a sketch of the hyperbola.

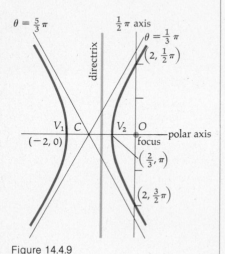

$\theta = \frac{5}{3}\pi$ $\frac{1}{2}\pi$ axis $\theta = \frac{1}{3}\pi$

directrix

$(2, \frac{1}{2}\pi)$

V_1 C V_2 O ——polar axis
$(-2, 0)$ focus

$(\frac{2}{3}, \pi)$

$(2, \frac{3}{2}\pi)$

Figure 14.4.9

$$1 = \frac{2d}{1 - 2(-\frac{1}{2})}$$

from which we obtain $d = 1$. Hence, an equation of the hyperbola is

$$r = \frac{2}{1 - 2 \cos \theta} \qquad (9)$$

The vertices are the points on the hyperbola for which $\theta = 0$ and $\theta = \pi$. From Eq. (9) we see that when $\theta = 0$, $r = -2$; and when $\theta = \pi$, $r = \frac{2}{3}$. Consequently, the left vertex V_1 is at the point $(-2, 0)$, and the right vertex V_2 is at the point $(\frac{2}{3}, \pi)$.

The center of the hyperbola is the point on the principal axis half-way between the two vertices. This is the point $(\frac{4}{3}, \pi)$.

An equation of the directrix corresponding to the focus at the pole is given by $r \cos \theta = -d$. Because $d = 1$, this equation is $r \cos \theta = -1$.

As an aid in drawing a sketch of the hyperbola, we first draw the two asymptotes. In our discussion of Case 3 we stated that these are lines through the center of the hyperbola that are parallel to the lines $\theta = \theta_1$ and $\theta = \theta_2$, where θ_1 and θ_2 are the values of θ in the interval $[0, 2\pi)$ for which r is not defined. From Eq. (9), r is not defined when $1 - 2 \cos \theta = 0$. Therefore, $\theta_1 = \frac{1}{3}\pi$ and $\theta_2 = \frac{5}{3}\pi$. Figure 14.4.9 shows a sketch of the hyperbola as well as the two asymptotes, and the directrix corresponding to the focus at the pole.

EXAMPLE 6: Find a polar equation of the hyperbola having the line $r \cos \theta = 4$ as the directrix corresponding to a focus at the pole, and $e = \frac{3}{2}$.

SOLUTION: The given directrix is perpendicular to the polar axis and is four units to the right of the focus at the pole. Therefore, an equation of the hyperbola is of the form of Eq. (4), which is

$$r = \frac{ed}{1 + e \cos \theta}$$

Because $d = 4$ and $e = \frac{3}{2}$, the equation becomes

$$r = \frac{\frac{3}{2} \cdot 4}{1 + \frac{3}{2} \cos \theta}$$

or, equivalently,

$$r = \frac{12}{2 + 3 \cos \theta}$$

Exercises 14.4

1. Show that an equation of a conic having its principal axis along the polar axis and its extension, a focus at the pole, and the corresponding directrix to the right of the focus is $r = ed/(1 + e \cos \theta)$.

2. Show that an equation of a conic having its principal axis along the $\frac{1}{2}\pi$ axis and its extension, a focus at the pole, and the corresponding directrix above the focus is $r = ed/(1 + e \sin \theta)$.

3. Show that an equation of a conic having its principal axis along the $\frac{1}{2}\pi$ axis and its extension, a focus at the pole, and the corresponding directrix below the focus is $r = ed/(1 - e \sin \theta)$.

4. Show that the equation $r = k \csc^2 \frac{1}{2}\theta$, where k is a constant, is a polar equation of a parabola.

In Exercises 5 through 14, the equation is that of a conic having a focus at the pole. In each Exercise, (a) find the eccentricity; (b) identify the conic; (c) write an equation of the directrix which corresponds to the focus at the pole; (d) draw a sketch of the curve.

5. $r = \dfrac{2}{1 - \cos \theta}$

6. $r = \dfrac{4}{1 + \cos \theta}$

7. $r = \dfrac{5}{2 + \sin \theta}$

8. $r = \dfrac{4}{1 - 3 \cos \theta}$

9. $r = \dfrac{6}{3 - 2 \cos \theta}$

10. $r = \dfrac{1}{2 + \sin \theta}$

11. $r = \dfrac{9}{5 - 6 \sin \theta}$

12. $r = \dfrac{1}{1 - 2 \sin \theta}$

13. $r = \dfrac{10}{7 - 2 \sin \theta}$

14. $r = \dfrac{7}{3 + 4 \cos \theta}$

In Exercises 15 through 18, find an equation of the conic having a focus at the pole and satisfying the given conditions.

15. Parabola; vertex at $(4, \frac{3}{2}\pi)$.

16. Ellipse; $e = \frac{1}{2}$; a vertex at $(4, \pi)$.

17. Hyperbola; vertices at $(1, \frac{1}{2}\pi)$ and $(3, \frac{1}{2}\pi)$.

18. Hyperbola; $e = \frac{4}{3}$; $r \cos \theta = 9$ is the directrix corresponding to the focus at the pole.

19. Find the area of the region inside the ellipse $r = 6/(2 - \sin \theta)$ and above the parabola $r = 3/(1 + \sin \theta)$.

20. For the ellipse and parabola of Exercise 19, find the area of the region inside the ellipse and below the parabola.

21. A comet is moving in a parabolic orbit around the sun at the focus of the parabola. When the comet is 80,000,000 miles from the sun the line segment from the sun to the comet makes an angle of $\frac{1}{3}\pi$ radians with the axis of the orbit. (a) Find an equation of the comet's orbit. (b) How close does the comet come to the sun?

22. The orbit of a planet is in the form of an ellipse having the equation $r = p/(1 + e \cos \theta)$ where the pole is at the sun. Find the average measure of the distance of the planet from the sun with respect to θ.

23. Using Definition 14.3.1 find a polar equation of a central conic for which the center is at the pole, the principal axis is along the polar axis and its extension, and the distance from the pole to a directrix is a/e.

24. Show that the tangent lines at the points of intersection of the parabolas $r = a/(1 + \cos \theta)$ and $r = b/(1 - \cos \theta)$ are perpendicular.

14.5 CARTESIAN EQUATIONS OF THE CONICS

In Sec. 14.4 we learned that a polar equation of a conic is

$$r = \frac{ed}{1 - e \cos \theta}$$

or, equivalently,

$$r = e(r \cos \theta + d) \qquad (1)$$

A cartesian representation of Eq. (1) can be obtained by replacing r by $\pm\sqrt{x^2 + y^2}$ and $r \cos \theta$ by x. Making these substitutions, we get

$$\pm\sqrt{x^2 + y^2} = e(x + d)$$

Squaring on both sides of the above equation gives

$$x^2 + y^2 = e^2x^2 + 2e^2dx + e^2d^2$$

or, equivalently,

$$y^2 + x^2(1 - e^2) = 2e^2dx + e^2d^2 \tag{2}$$

If $e = 1$, Eq. (2) becomes

$$y^2 = 2d(x + \tfrac{1}{2}d) \tag{3}$$

If we translate the origin to the point $(-\tfrac{1}{2}d, 0)$ by replacing x by $\bar{x} - \tfrac{1}{2}d$ and y by $\bar{y}$, Eq. (3) becomes

$$\bar{y}^2 = 2d\bar{x} \tag{4}$$

Equation (4) resembles Eq. (1) of Sec. 14.1

$$y^2 = 4px$$

which is an equation of the parabola having its focus at $(p, 0)$ and its directrix the line $x = -p$. Therefore, relative to the $\bar{x}$ and $\bar{y}$ axes, (4) is an equation of a parabola having its focus at $(\tfrac{1}{2}d, 0)$, which is the origin relative to the x and y axes. The parabola having its axis parallel to one of the coordinate axes was discussed in detail earlier, in Secs. 14.1 and 14.2.

If $e \neq 1$, we divide on both sides of Eq. (2) by $1 - e^2$ and obtain

$$x^2 - \frac{2e^2d}{1 - e^2}x + \frac{1}{1 - e^2}y^2 = \frac{e^2d^2}{1 - e^2}$$

Completing the square for the terms involving x by adding $e^4d^2/(1 - e^2)^2$ on both sides of the above equation, we get

$$\left(x - \frac{e^2d}{1 - e^2}\right)^2 + \frac{1}{1 - e^2}y^2 = \frac{e^2d^2}{(1 - e^2)^2} \tag{5}$$

If the origin is translated to the point $(e^2d/(1 - e^2), 0)$, Eq. (5) becomes

$$\bar{x}^2 + \frac{1}{1 - e^2}\bar{y}^2 = \frac{e^2d^2}{(1 - e^2)^2}$$

or, equivalently,

$$\frac{\bar{x}^2}{\dfrac{e^2d^2}{(1 - e^2)^2}} + \frac{\bar{y}^2}{\dfrac{e^2d^2}{1 - e^2}} = 1 \tag{6}$$

Now let $e^2d^2/(1 - e^2)^2 = a^2$, where $a > 0$. Then

$$a = \begin{cases} \dfrac{ed}{1 - e^2} & \text{if } 0 < e < 1 \\[2ex] \dfrac{ed}{e^2 - 1} & \text{if } e > 1 \end{cases} \tag{7}$$

Then Eq. (6) can be written as

$$\frac{\bar{x}^2}{a^2} + \frac{\bar{y}^2}{a^2(1-e^2)} = 1$$

Replacing $\bar{x}$ and $\bar{y}$ by x and y, we get

$$\frac{x^2}{a^2} + \frac{y^2}{a^2(1-e^2)} = 1 \qquad (8)$$

Equation (8) is a standard form of a cartesian equation of a central conic having its principal axis on the x axis. Because (5) is an equation of a conic having a focus at the origin (pole), and (8) is obtained from (5) by translating the origin to the point $(e^2d/(1-e^2), 0)$, it follows that the central conic having Eq. (8) has a focus at the point $(-e^2d/(1-e^2), 0)$. However, from (7) it follows that

$$\frac{-e^2d}{1-e^2} = \begin{cases} -ae & \text{if } 0 < e < 1 \\ ae & \text{if } e > 1 \end{cases}$$

Therefore, we conclude that if (8) is an equation of an ellipse $(0 < e < 1)$, there is a focus at the point $(-ae, 0)$. If (8) is an equation of a hyperbola $(e > 1)$, there is a focus at $(ae, 0)$. In each case the corresponding directrix is d units to the left of the focus. So if the graph of (8) is an ellipse, the directrix corresponding to the focus at $(-ae, 0)$ has as an equation

$$x = -ae - d$$

Because when $0 < e < 1$, $d = a(1 - e^2)/e$, this equation becomes

$$x = -ae - \frac{a(1-e^2)}{e}$$

$$x = -\frac{a}{e}$$

Similarly, if the graph of (8) is a hyperbola, the directrix corresponding to the focus at $(ae, 0)$ has as an equation

$$x = ae - d$$

When $e > 1$, $d = a(e^2 - 1)/e$; thus, the above equation of the directrix can be written as

$$x = \frac{a}{e}$$

Hence, we have shown that if (8) is an equation of an ellipse, a focus and its corresponding directrix are $(-ae, 0)$ and $x = -a/e$; and if (8) is an equation of a hyperbola, a focus and its corresponding directrix are $(ae, 0)$ and $x = a/e$.

Because Eq. (8) contains only even powers of x and y, its graph is symmetric with respect to both the x and y axes. Therefore, if there is a focus at $(-ae, 0)$ having a corresponding directrix of $x = -a/e$, by symmetry there is also a focus at $(ae, 0)$ having a corresponding directrix of $x = a/e$. Similarly, for a focus at $(ae, 0)$ and a corresponding directrix of $x = a/e$, there is also a focus at $(-ae, 0)$ and a corresponding directrix of $x = -a/e$. These results are summarized in the following theorem.

14.5.1 Theorem The central conic having as an equation

$$\frac{x^2}{a^2} + \frac{y^2}{a^2(1 - e^2)} = 1 \tag{9}$$

where $a > 0$, has a focus at $(-ae, 0)$, whose corresponding directrix is $x = -a/e$, and a focus at $(ae, 0)$, whose corresponding directrix is $x = a/e$.

Figures 14.5.1 and 14.5.2 show sketches of the graph of Eq. (9) together with the foci and directrices in the respective cases of an ellipse and a hyperbola.

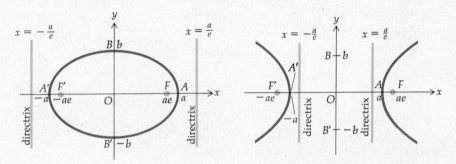

Figure 14.5.1   Figure 14.5.2

Suppose that in Eq. (9) $0 < e < 1$. Then the conic is an ellipse. Because in this case $1 - e^2 > 0$, we conclude that $\sqrt{1 - e^2}$ is a real number. Therefore, we let

$$b = a\sqrt{1 - e^2} \tag{10}$$

Because $a > 0$, it follows that $b > 0$. Substituting from (10) into (9), we obtain

$$\frac{x^2}{a^2} + \frac{y^2}{b^2} = 1 \tag{11}$$

Equation (11) is an equation of an ellipse having its principal axis on the x axis. Because the vertices are the points of intersection of the ellipse with its principal axis, they are at $(-a, 0)$ and $(a, 0)$. The center of the ellipse is at the origin because it is the point midway between the vertices. Figure 14.5.1 shows a sketch of this ellipse. Refer to this figure as you read the next two paragraphs.

If we denote the vertices $(-a, 0)$ and $(a, 0)$ by A' and A, respectively, the segment $A'A$ of the principal axis is called the *major axis* of the ellipse, and its length is $2a$ units. Then we state that a is the number of units in the length of the semimajor axis of the ellipse.

The ellipse having Eq. (11) intersects the y axis at the points $(-b, 0)$ and $(b, 0)$, which we denote by B' and B, respectively. The segment $B'B$ is called the *minor axis* of the ellipse. Its length is $2b$ units. Hence, b is the number of units in the length of the semiminor axis of the ellipse. Because a and b are positive numbers and $0 < e < 1$, it follows from Eq. (10) that $b < a$.

EXAMPLE 1: Given the ellipse having the equation

$$\frac{x^2}{25} + \frac{y^2}{16} = 1$$

find the vertices, foci, directrices, eccentricity, and extremities of the minor axis. Draw a sketch of the ellipse and show the foci and directrices.

Figure 14.5.3

SOLUTION: From the equation of the ellipse, we have $a^2 = 25$ and $b^2 = 16$; thus, $a = 5$ and $b = 4$. Therefore, the vertices are at the points $A'(-5, 0)$ and $A(5, 0)$, and the extremities of the minor axis are at the points $B'(0, -4)$ and $B(0, 4)$. From (10) we have $4 = 5\sqrt{1 - e^2}$, from which it follows that $e = \frac{3}{5}$. The foci and the directrices are obtained by applying Theorem 14.5.1. Because $ae = 3$ and $a/e = \frac{25}{3}$, we conclude that one focus F is at $(3, 0)$ and its corresponding directrix has the equation $x = \frac{25}{3}$; the other focus F' is at $(-3, 0)$ and its corresponding directrix has the equation $x = -\frac{25}{3}$. A sketch of the ellipse, the foci F and F', and the directrices are in Fig. 14.5.3. From the definition of a conic (14.3.1) it follows that if P is any point on this ellipse, the ratio of the undirected distance of P from a focus to the undirected distance of P from the corresponding directrix is equal to the eccentricity $\frac{3}{5}$.

EXAMPLE 2: An arch is in the form of a semiellipse. It is 48 ft wide at the base and has a height of 20 ft. How wide is the arch at a height of 10 ft above the base?

Figure 14.5.4

SOLUTION: Figure 14.5.4 shows a sketch of the arch and the coordinate axes which are chosen so that the x axis is along the base and the origin is at the midpoint of the base. Then the ellipse has its principal axis on the x axis, its center at the origin, $a = 24$, and $b = 20$. An equation of the ellipse is of the form of Eq. (11):

$$\frac{x^2}{576} + \frac{y^2}{400} = 1$$

Let $2\bar{x}$ be the number of feet in the width of the arch at a height of 10 ft above the base. Therefore, the point $(\bar{x}, 10)$ lies on the ellipse. Thus,

$$\frac{\bar{x}^2}{576} + \frac{100}{400} = 1$$

and so

$$\bar{x}^2 = 432$$

$$\bar{x} = 12\sqrt{3}$$

Hence, at a height of 10 ft above the base the width of the arch is $24\sqrt{3}$ ft.

Consider now the central conic of Theorem 14.5.1 when $e > 1$, that is, when the conic is a hyperbola. Because $e > 1$, $1 - e^2 < 0$; hence, $e^2 - 1 > 0$. Therefore, for a hyperbola we let

$$b = a\sqrt{e^2 - 1} \tag{12}$$

It follows from Eq. (12) that b is a positive number. Also, from (12), if $1 < e < \sqrt{2}$, $b < a$; if $e = \sqrt{2}$, $b = a$; and if $e > \sqrt{2}$, $b > a$. Substituting from (12) into (9), we get

$$\frac{x^2}{a^2} - \frac{y^2}{b^2} = 1 \tag{13}$$

Equation (13) is an equation of a hyperbola having its principal axis on the x axis, its vertices at the points $(-a, 0)$ and $(a, 0)$, and its center at the origin. A sketch of this hyperbola is in Fig. 14.5.2. If we denote the vertices $(-a, 0)$ and $(a, 0)$ by A' and A, the segment $A'A$ is called the *transverse axis* of the hyperbola. The length of the transverse axis is $2a$ units, and so a is the number of units in the length of the semitransverse axis.

Substituting 0 for x in Eq. (13), we obtain $y^2 = -b^2$, which has no real roots. Consequently, the hyperbola does not intersect the y axis. However, the line segment having extremities at the points $(0, -b)$ and $(0, b)$ is called the *conjugate axis* of the hyperbola, and its length is $2b$ units. Hence, b is the number of units in the length of the semiconjugate axis.

Solving Eq. (13) for y in terms of x, we obtain

$$y = \pm\frac{b}{a}\sqrt{x^2 - a^2} \tag{14}$$

We conclude from (14) that if $|x| < a$, there is no real value of y. Therefore, there are no points (x, y) on the hyperbola for which $-a < x < a$. We also see from (14) that if $|x| \geq a$, then y has two real values. As previously learned, the hyperbola has two branches. One branch contains the vertex $A(a, 0)$ and extends indefinitely far to the right of A. The other branch contains the vertex $A'(-a, 0)$ and extends indefinitely far to the left of A'.

EXAMPLE 3:   Given the hyperbola

$$\frac{x^2}{9} - \frac{y^2}{16} = 1$$

SOLUTION: The given equation is of the form of Eq. (13); thus, $a = 3$ and $b = 4$. The vertices are therefore at the points $A'(-3, 0)$ and $A(3, 0)$. The number of units in the length of the transverse axis is $2a = 6$, and the number of units in the length of the conjugate axis is $2b = 8$. Because find the vertices, foci, directrices, eccentricity, and lengths of the transverse and conjugate axes. Draw a sketch of the hyperbola and show the foci and the directrices.

from (12), $b = a\sqrt{e^2 - 1}$, we have $4 = 3\sqrt{e^2 - 1}$, and so $e = \frac{5}{3}$. Therefore, $ae = 5$ and $a/e = \frac{9}{5}$. Hence, the foci are at $F'(-5, 0)$ and $F(5, 0)$. The corresponding directrices have, respectively, the equations $x = -\frac{9}{5}$ and $x = \frac{9}{5}$. A sketch of the hyperbola and the foci and directrices are in Fig. 14.5.5. From Definition 14.3.1 it follows that if P is any point on this hyperbola, the ratio of the undirected distance of P from a focus to the undirected distance of P from the corresponding directrix is equal to the eccentricity $\frac{5}{3}$.

Figure 14.5.5

EXAMPLE 4: Find an equation of the hyperbola having the ends of its conjugate axis at $(0, -2)$ and $(0, 2)$ and an eccentricity equal to $\frac{3}{5}\sqrt{5}$.

SOLUTION: Because the ends of the conjugate axis are at $(0, -2)$ and $(0, 2)$, it follows that $b = 2$, the transverse axis is along the x axis, and the center is at the origin. Hence, an equation is of the form

$$\frac{x^2}{a^2} - \frac{y^2}{b^2} = 1$$

To find a we use the equation $b = a\sqrt{e^2 - 1}$ and let $b = 2$ and $e = \frac{3}{5}\sqrt{5}$, thereby yielding $2 = a\sqrt{\frac{9}{5} - 1}$. Therefore, $a = \sqrt{5}$, and an equation of the hyperbola is

$$\frac{x^2}{5} - \frac{y^2}{4} = 1$$

Exercises 14.5

In Exercises 1 through 4, find the vertices, foci, directrices, eccentricity, and ends of the minor axis of the given ellipse. Draw a sketch of the curve and show the foci and the directrices.

1. $4x^2 + 9y^2 = 36$ 2. $4x^2 + 9y^2 = 4$ 3. $2x^2 + 3y^2 = 18$ 4. $3x^2 + 4y^2 = 9$

In Exercises 5 through 9, find the vertices, foci, directrices, eccentricity, and lengths of the transverse and conjugate axes of the given hyperbola. Draw a sketch of the curve and show the foci and the directrices.

5. $9x^2 - 4y^2 = 36$ 6. $x^2 - 9y^2 = 9$ 7. $9x^2 - 16y^2 = 1$ 8. $25x^2 - 25y^2 = 1$

In Exercises 9 through 14, find an equation of the given conic satisfying the given conditions and draw a sketch of the graph.

9. Hyperbola having vertices at $(-2, 0)$ and $(2, 0)$ and a conjugate axis of length 6.

10. Ellipse having foci at $(-5, 0)$ and $(5, 0)$ and one directrix the line $x = -20$.

11. Ellipse having vertices at $(-\frac{5}{2}, 0)$ and $(\frac{5}{2}, 0)$ and one focus $(\frac{3}{2}, 0)$.

12. Hyperbola having the ends of its conjugate axis at $(0, -3)$ and $(0, 3)$ and $e = 2$.

13. Hyperbola having its center at the origin, its foci on the x axis, and passing through the points $(4, -2)$ and $(7, -6)$.

14. Ellipse having its center at the origin, its foci on the x axis, the length of the major axis equal to three times the length of the minor axis, and passing through the point $(3, 3)$.

15. Find an equation of the tangent line to the ellipse $4x^2 + 9y^2 = 72$ at the point $(3, 2)$.

16. Find an equation of the normal line to the hyperbola $4x^2 - 3y^2 = 24$ at the point $(3, 2)$.

17. Find an equation of the hyperbola whose foci are the vertices of the ellipse $7x^2 + 11y^2 = 77$ and whose vertices are the foci of this ellipse.

18. Find an equation of the ellipse whose foci are the vertices of the hyperbola $11x^2 - 7y^2 = 77$ and whose vertices are the foci of this hyperbola.

19. The ceiling in a hallway 20 ft wide is in the shape of a semiellipse and is 18 ft high in the center and 12 ft high at the side walls. Find the height of the ceiling 4 ft from either wall.

20. A football is 12 in. long, and a plane section containing a seam is an ellipse, of which the length of the minor axis is 7 in. Find the volume of the football if the leather is so stiff that every cross section is a square.

21. Solve Exercise 20 if every cross section is a circle.

22. The orbit of the earth around the sun is elliptical in shape with the sun at one focus, a semimajor axis of length 92.9 million miles, and an eccentricity of 0.017. Find (a) how close the earth gets to the sun and (b) the greatest possible distance between the earth and the sun.

23. The cost of production of a commodity is $12 less per unit at a point A than it is at a point B and the distance between A and B is 100 miles. Assuming that the route of delivery of the commodity is along a straight line, and that the delivery cost is 20 cents per unit per mile, find the curve at any point of which the commodity can be supplied from either A or B at the same total cost. (HINT: Take points A and B at $(-50, 0)$ and $(50, 0)$, respectively.)

24. Prove that there is no tangent line to the hyperbola $x^2 - y^2 = 1$ that passes through the origin.

25. Find the volume of the solid of revolution generated by revolving the region bounded by the hyperbola $x^2/a^2 - y^2/b^2 = 1$ and the line $x = 2a$ about the x axis.

26. Find the centroid of the solid of revolution of Exercise 25.

27. A tank has a horizontal axis of length 20 ft and its ends are semiellipses. The width across the top of the tank is 10 ft and the depth is 6 ft. If the tank is full of water, how much work is necessary to pump all the water to the top of the tank?

14.6 THE ELLIPSE   In Sec. 14.3 we considered ellipses for which the center is at the origin and the principal axis is on the x axis. Now more general equations of ellipses will be discussed.

  If an ellipse has its center at the origin and its principal axis on the y axis, then an equation of the ellipse is of the form

$$\frac{y^2}{a^2} + \frac{x^2}{b^2} = 1 \tag{1}$$

which is obtained from Eq. (11) of Sec. 14.5 by interchanging x and y.

● ILLUSTRATION 1: Because for an ellipse $a > b$, it follows that the ellipse having the equation

$$\frac{x^2}{16} + \frac{y^2}{25} = 1$$

has its foci on the y axis. This ellipse has the same shape as the ellipse of Example 1 in Sec. 14.5. The vertices are at $(0, -5)$ and $(0, 5)$, and the foci are at $(0, -3)$ and $(0, 3)$, and their corresponding directrices have the equations $y = -\frac{25}{3}$ and $y = \frac{25}{3}$, respectively.   ●

If the center of an ellipse is at the point (h, k) rather than at the origin, and if the principal axis is parallel to one of the coordinate axes, then by a translation of axes so that the point (h, k) is the new origin, an equation of the ellipse is $\bar{x}^2/a^2 + \bar{y}^2/b^2 = 1$ if the principal axis is horizontal, and $\bar{y}^2/a^2 + \bar{x}^2/b^2 = 1$ if the principal axis is vertical. Because $\bar{x} = x - h$ and $\bar{y} = y - k$, these equations become the following in x and y:

$$\frac{(x - h)^2}{a^2} + \frac{(y - k)^2}{b^2} = 1 \tag{2}$$

if the principal axis is horizontal, and

$$\frac{(y - k)^2}{a^2} + \frac{(x - h)^2}{b^2} = 1 \tag{3}$$

if the principal axis is vertical.

In Sec. 1.6 we discussed the general equation of the second degree in two variables:

$$Ax^2 + Bxy + Cy^2 + Dx + Ey + F = 0 \tag{4}$$

where $B = 0$ and $A = C$. In such a case, the graph of (4) is either a circle or a degenerate case of a circle, which is either a point-circle or no real locus. If we eliminate the fractions and combine terms in Eqs. (2) and (3), we obtain an equation of the form

$$Ax^2 + Cy^2 + Dx + Ey + F = 0 \tag{5}$$

where $A \neq C$ if $a \neq b$ and $AC > 0$. It can be shown by completing the squares in x and y that an equation of the form (5) can be put in the form

$$\frac{(x - h)^2}{\dfrac{1}{A}} + \frac{(y - k)^2}{\dfrac{1}{C}} = G \tag{6}$$

If $AC > 0$, then A and C have the same sign. If G has the same sign as A and C, then Eq. (6) can be written in the form of (2) or (3). Thus, the graph of (5) is an ellipse.

● ILLUSTRATION 2: Suppose we have the equation

$$6x^2 + 9y^2 - 24x - 54y + 51 = 0$$

which can be written as

$$6(x^2 - 4x) + 9(y^2 - 6y) = -51$$

Completing the squares in x and y, we get

$$6(x^2 - 4x + 4) + 9(y^2 - 6y + 9) = -51 + 24 + 81$$

or, equivalently,

$$6(x - 2)^2 + 9(y - 3)^2 = 54$$

which can be put in the form

$$\frac{(x - 2)^2}{\frac{1}{6}} + \frac{(y - 3)^2}{\frac{1}{9}} = 54$$

This is an equation of the form of Eq. (6). By dividing on both sides by 54 we have

$$\frac{(x - 2)^2}{9} + \frac{(y - 3)^2}{6} = 1$$

which has the form of Eq. (2).   ●

If in Eq. (6) G has a sign opposite to that of A and C, then (6) is not satisfied by any real values of x and y. Hence, the graph of (5) is the empty set.

● ILLUSTRATION 3: Suppose that Eq. (5) is

$$6x^2 + 9y^2 - 24x - 54y + 115 = 0$$

Then, upon completing the squares in x and y, we get

$$6(x - 2)^2 + 9(y - 3)^2 = -115 + 24 + 81$$

which can be written as

$$\frac{(x - 2)^2}{\frac{1}{6}} + \frac{(y - 3)^2}{\frac{1}{9}} = -10 \qquad (7)$$

This is of the form of Eq. (6), where $G = -10$, $A = 6$, and $C = 9$. For all values of x and y the left side of Eq. (7) is nonnegative; hence, the graph of (7) is the empty set.   ●

If $G = 0$ in (6), then the equation is satisfied by only the point (h, k).

Therefore, the graph of (5) is a single point, which we call a *point-ellipse*.

● ILLUSTRATION 4: Because the equation

$$6x^2 + 9y^2 - 24x - 54y + 105 = 0$$

can be written as

$$\frac{(x-2)^2}{\frac{1}{6}} + \frac{(y-3)^2}{\frac{1}{9}} = 0$$

its graph is the point (2, 3).   ●

If the graph of Eq. (5) is a point-ellipse or the empty set, the graph is said to be degenerate.

If $A = C$ in (5), we have either a circle or a degenerate circle, as mentioned above. A circle is a limiting form of an ellipse. This can be shown by considering the formula relating a, b, and e for an ellipse:

$$b^2 = a^2(1 - e^2)$$

From this formula, it is seen that as e approaches zero, b^2 approaches a^2. If $b^2 = a^2$, Eqs. (2) and (3) become

$$(x - h)^2 + (y - k)^2 = a^2$$

which is an equation of a circle having its center at (h, k) and radius a. We see that the results of Sec. 1.6 for a circle are the same as those obtained for Eq. (5) applied to an ellipse.

The results of the above discussion are summarized in the following theorem.

14.6.1 Theorem   If in the general second-degree Eq. (4) $B = 0$ and $AC > 0$, then the graph is either an ellipse, a point-ellipse, or the empty set. In addition, if $A = C$, then the graph is either a circle, a point-circle, or the empty set.

EXAMPLE 1: Determine the graph of the equation $25x^2 + 16y^2 + 150x - 128y - 1119 = 0$.

SOLUTION: From Theorem 14.6.1, because $B = 0$ and $AC = (25)(16) = 400 > 0$, the graph is either an ellipse or is degenerate. Completing the squares in x and y, we have

$$25(x^2 + 6x + 9) + 16(y^2 - 8y + 16) = 1119 + 225 + 256$$

$$25(x + 3)^2 + 16(y - 4)^2 = 1600$$

$$\frac{(x + 3)^2}{64} + \frac{(y - 4)^2}{100} = 1 \qquad (8)$$

Equation (8) is of the form of Eq. (3), and so the graph is an ellipse having its principal axis parallel to the y axis and its center at $(-3, 4)$.

EXAMPLE 2: For the ellipse of Example 1, find the vertices, foci, directrices, eccentricity, and extremities of the minor axis. Draw a sketch of the ellipse and show the foci and the directrices.

SOLUTION: From Eq. (8) it follows that $a = 10$ and $b = 8$. Because the center of the ellipse is at $(-3, 4)$ and the principal axis is vertical, the vertices are at the points $V'(-3, -6)$ and $V(-3, 14)$. The extremities of the minor axis are at the points $B'(-11, 4)$ and $B(5, 4)$. Because $b = a\sqrt{1 - e^2}$, we have

$$8 = 10\sqrt{1 - e^2}$$

and, solving for e, we get $e = \frac{3}{5}$. Consequently, $ae = 6$ and $a/e = \frac{50}{3}$. Therefore, the foci are at the points $F'(-3, -2)$ and $F(-3, 10)$. The corresponding directrices have, respectively, the equations $y = -\frac{38}{3}$ and $y = \frac{62}{3}$. A sketch of the ellipse, the foci, and the directrices are in Fig. 14.6.1.

Figure 14.6.1

EXAMPLE 3: Find an equation of the ellipse for which the foci are at $(-8, 2)$ and $(4, 2)$ and the eccentricity is $\frac{2}{3}$. Draw a sketch of the ellipse.

SOLUTION: The center of the ellipse which is halfway between the foci is the point $(-2, 2)$. The distance between the foci of any ellipse is $2ae$, and the distance between $(-8, 2)$ and $(4, 2)$ is 12. Therefore, we have the equation $2ae = 12$. Replacing e by $\frac{2}{3}$, we get $2a(\frac{2}{3}) = 12$, and so $a = 9$. Because $b = a\sqrt{1 - e^2}$, we have

$$b = 9\sqrt{1 - (\tfrac{2}{3})^2} = 9\sqrt{1 - \tfrac{4}{9}} = 3\sqrt{5}$$

The principal axis is parallel to the x axis; hence, an equation of the ellipse is of the form of Eq. (2). Because $(h, k) = (-2, 2)$, $a = 9$, and $b = 3\sqrt{5}$, the

required equation is

$$\frac{(x+2)^2}{81} + \frac{(y-2)^2}{45} = 1$$

A sketch of this ellipse is shown in Fig. 14.6.2.

Figure 14.6.2

We conclude this section with a theorem that gives an alternative definition of an ellipse. The theorem is based on a characteristic property of the ellipse.

14.6.2 Theorem   An ellipse can be defined as the set of points such that the sum of the distances from any point of the set to two given points (the foci) is a constant.

PROOF: The proof consists of two parts. In the first part we show that the set of points defined in the theorem is an ellipse. In the second part we prove that any ellipse is such a set of points. Refer to Fig 14.6.3 in both parts of the proof.

Let the point $P_1(x_1, y_1)$ be any point in the given set. Let the foci be the points $F'(-ae, 0)$ and $F(ae, 0)$, and let the constant sum of the distances be $2a$. Then

$$|\overline{FP_1}| + |\overline{F'P_1}| = 2a$$

Using the distance formula, we get

$$\sqrt{(x_1 - ae)^2 + y_1^2} + \sqrt{(x_1 + ae)^2 + y_1^2} = 2a$$

$$\sqrt{(x_1 - ae)^2 + y_1^2} = 2a - \sqrt{(x_1 + ae)^2 + y_1^2}$$

Squaring on both sides of the above equation, we obtain

$$x_1^2 - 2aex_1 + a^2e^2 + y_1^2 = 4a^2 - 4a\sqrt{(x_1 + ae)^2 + y_1^2}$$
$$+ x_1^2 + 2aex_1 + a^2e^2 + y_1^2$$

Figure 14.6.3

or, equivalently,

$$\sqrt{(x_1 + ae)^2 + y_1{}^2} = a + ex_1$$

Squaring on both sides again, we get

$$x_1{}^2 + 2aex_1 + a^2e^2 + y_1{}^2 = a^2 + 2aex_1 + e^2x_1{}^2$$

$$(1 - e^2)x_1{}^2 + y_1{}^2 = a^2(1 - e^2)$$

$$\frac{x_1{}^2}{a^2} + \frac{y_1{}^2}{a^2(1 - e^2)} = 1$$

Because $b^2 = a^2(1 - e^2)$, and replacing x_1 and y_1 by x and y, respectively, we obtain

$$\frac{x^2}{a^2} + \frac{y^2}{b^2} = 1$$

which is the required form of an equation of an ellipse.

Now consider the ellipse in Fig. 14.6.3; $P_1(x_1, y_1)$ is any point on the ellipse. Through P_1 draw a line that is parallel to the x axis and that intersects the directrices d and d' at the points Q and R, respectively. From Definition 14.3.1 it follows that

$$|\overline{F'P_1}| = e|\overline{RP_1}| \quad \text{and} \quad |\overline{FP_1}| = e|\overline{P_1Q}|$$

Therefore,

$$|\overline{F'P_1}| + |\overline{FP_1}| = e(|\overline{RP_1}| + |\overline{P_1Q}|) \tag{9}$$

$\overline{RP_1}$ and $\overline{P_1Q}$ are both positive because an ellipse lies between its directrices. Hence,

$$|\overline{RP_1}| + |\overline{P_1Q}| = \overline{RP_1} + \overline{P_1Q} = \overline{RQ} = \frac{a}{e} - \left(-\frac{a}{e}\right) = \frac{2a}{e} \tag{10}$$

Substituting from (10) into (9), we get

$$|\overline{F'P_1}| + |\overline{FP_1}| = 2a$$

which proves that an ellipse is a set of points as described in the theorem. ■

● ILLUSTRATION 5: The ellipse of Example 1 has foci at $(-3, -2)$ and $(-3, 10)$, and $2a = 20$. Therefore, by Theorem 14.6.2 this ellipse can be defined as the set of points such that the sum of the distances from any point of the set to the points $(-3, -2)$ and $(-3, 10)$ is equal to 20. Similarly, the ellipse of Example 3 can be defined as the set of points such that the sum of the distances from any point of the set to the points $(-8, 2)$ and $(4, 2)$ is equal to 18. ●

Exercises 14.6

In Exercises 1 through 6, find the eccentricity, center, foci, and directrices of each of the given ellipses and draw a sketch of the graph.

1. $6x^2 + 9y^2 - 24x - 54y + 51 = 0$
2. $9x^2 + 4y^2 - 18x + 16y - 11 = 0$
3. $5x^2 + 3y^2 - 3y - 12 = 0$
4. $2x^2 + 2y^2 - 2x + 18y + 33 = 0$
5. $4x^2 + 4y^2 + 20x - 32y + 89 = 0$
6. $3x^2 + 4y^2 - 30x + 16y + 100 = 0$

In Exercises 7 through 12, find an equation of the ellipse satisfying the given conditions and draw a sketch of the graph.

7. Foci at $(5, 0)$ and $(-5, 0)$; one directrix is the line $x = -20$.

8. Vertices at $(0, 5)$ and $(0, -5)$ and passing through the point $(2, -\frac{5}{3}\sqrt{5})$.

9. Center at $(4, -2)$, a vertex at $(9, -2)$, and one focus at $(0, -2)$.

10. Foci at $(2, 3)$ and $(2, -7)$ and eccentricity of $\frac{2}{3}$.

11. Foci at $(-1, -1)$ and $(-1, 7)$ and the semimajor axis of length 8 units.

12. Directrices the lines $y = 3 \pm \frac{16.9}{12}$ and a focus at $(0, -2)$.

13. The following graphical method for sketching the graph of an ellipse is based on Theorem 14.6.2. To draw a sketch of the graph of the ellipse $4x^2 + y^2 = 16$, first locate the points of intersection with the axes and then locate the foci on the y axis by use of compasses set with center at one point of intersection with the x axis and with radius of 4. Then fasten thumbtacks at each focus and tie one end of a string at one thumbtack and the other end of the string at the second thumbtack in such a way that the length of the string between the tacks is $2a = 8$. Place a pencil against the string, drawing it taut, and describe a curve with the point of the pencil by moving it against the taut string. When the curve is completed, it will necessarily be an ellipse, because the pencil point describes a locus of points whose sum of distances from the two tacks is a constant.

14. Use Theorem 14.6.2 to find an equation of the ellipse for which the sum of the distances from any point on the ellipse to $(4, -1)$ and $(4, 7)$ is equal to 12.

15. Solve Exercise 14 if the sum of the distances from $(-4, -5)$ and $(6, -5)$ is equal to 16.

16. A plate is in the shape of the region bounded by the ellipse having a semimajor axis of length 3 ft and a semiminor axis of length 2 ft. If the plate is lowered vertically in a tank of water until the minor axis lies in the surface of the water, find the force due to liquid pressure on one side of the submerged portion of the plate.

17. If the plate of Exercise 16 is lowered until the center is 3 ft below the surface of the water, find the force due to liquid pressure on one side of the plate. The minor axis is still horizontal.

14.7 THE HYPERBOLA In Sec. 14.5 we learned that an equation of a hyperbola having its center at the origin and its principal axis on the x axis is of the form $x^2/a^2 - y^2/b^2 = 1$. Interchanging x and y in this equation, we obtain

$$\frac{y^2}{a^2} - \frac{x^2}{b^2} = 1 \tag{1}$$

which is an equation of a hyperbola having its center at the origin and its principal axis on the y axis.

● ILLUSTRATION 1: The hyperbola with an equation

$$\frac{y^2}{9} - \frac{x^2}{16} = 1$$

has its foci on the y axis because the equation is of the form (1).　　●

Note that there is no general inequality involving a and b corresponding to the inequality $a > b$ for an ellipse. That is, for a hyperbola, it is possible to have $a < b$, as in Illustration 1, where $a = 3$ and $b = 4$; or it is possible to have $a > b$, as for the hyperbola having the equation $y^2/25 - x^2/16 = 1$, where $a = 5$ and $b = 4$. If, for a hyperbola, $a = b$, then the hyperbola is said to be *equilateral*.

We stated in Sec. 14.4 that a hyperbola has asymptotes, and we now show how to obtain equations of these asymptotes. In Sec. 4.2 horizontal and vertical asymptotes of the graph of a function were defined. What follows is a more general definition, of which the definitions in Sec. 4.2 are special cases.

14.7.1 Definition　The graph of the equation $y = f(x)$ has the line $y = mx + b$ as an *asymptote* if either of the following statements is true:

(i) $\displaystyle\lim_{x \to +\infty} [f(x) - (mx + b)] = 0$

(ii) $\displaystyle\lim_{x \to -\infty} [f(x) - (mx + b)] = 0$

Statement (i) indicates that for any $\epsilon > 0$ there exists a number $N > 0$ such that

$$|f(x) - (mx + b)| < \epsilon \qquad \text{whenever } x > N$$

that is, we can make the function value $f(x)$ as close to the value of $mx + b$ as we please by taking x large enough. This is consistent with our intuitive notion of an asymptote of a graph. A similar statement may be made for part (ii) of Definition 14.7.1.

For the hyperbola $x^2/a^2 - y^2/b^2 = 1$, upon solving for y, we get

$$y = \pm \frac{b}{a} \sqrt{x^2 - a^2}$$

So if

$$f(x) = \frac{b}{a} \sqrt{x^2 - a^2}$$

we have

$$\lim_{x \to +\infty} \left[f(x) - \frac{b}{a} x \right] = \lim_{x \to +\infty} \left[\frac{b}{a} \sqrt{x^2 - a^2} - \frac{b}{a} x \right]$$

$$= \frac{b}{a} \lim_{x \to +\infty} \frac{(\sqrt{x^2 - a^2} - x)(\sqrt{x^2 - a^2} + x)}{\sqrt{x^2 - a^2} + x}$$

$$= \frac{b}{a} \lim_{x \to +\infty} \frac{-a^2}{\sqrt{x^2 - a^2} + x}$$

$$= 0$$

Therefore, by Definition 14.7.1, we conclude that the line $y = bx/a$ is an asymptote of the graph of $y = b\sqrt{x^2 - a^2}/a$. Similarly, it can be shown that the line $y = bx/a$ is an asymptote of the graph of $y = -b\sqrt{x^2 - a^2}/a$. Consequently, the line $y = bx/a$ is an asymptote of the hyperbola $x^2/a^2 - y^2/b^2 = 1$. In an analogous manner, we can demonstrate that the line $y = -bx/a$ is an asymptote of this same hyperbola. We have, then, the following theorem.

14.7.2 Theorem   The lines

$$y = \frac{b}{a}x \quad \text{and} \quad y = -\frac{b}{a}x$$

are asymptotes of the hyperbola

$$\frac{x^2}{a^2} - \frac{y^2}{b^2} = 1$$

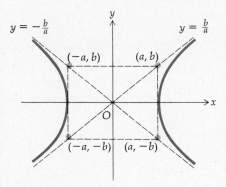

Figure 14.7.1

Figure 14.7.1 shows a sketch of the hyperbola of Theorem 14.7.2 together with its asymptotes. In the figure note that the diagonals of the rectangle having vertices at (a, b), $(a, -b)$, $(-a, b)$, and $(-a, -b)$ are on the asymptotes of the hyperbola. This rectangle is called the *auxiliary rectangle* of the hyperbola. The vertices of the hyperbola are the points of intersection of the principal axis and the auxiliary rectangle. A fairly good sketch of a hyperbola can be made by first drawing the auxiliary rectangle and then drawing the branch of the hyperbola through each vertex tangent to the side of the auxiliary rectangle there and approaching asymptotically the lines on which the diagonals of the rectangle lie.

There is a mnemonic device for obtaining equations of the asymptotes of a hyperbola. For example, for the hyperbola having the equation $x^2/a^2 - y^2/b^2 = 1$, if the right side is replaced by zero, we obtain $x^2/a^2 - y^2/b^2 = 0$. Upon factoring, this equation becomes $(x/a - y/b)(x/a + y/b) = 0$, which is equivalent to the two equations $x/a - y/b = 0$ and $x/a + y/b = 0$, which, by Theorem 14.7.2, are equations of the asymptotes of the given hyperbola. Using this device for the hyperbola having Eq. (1), we see that the asymptotes are the lines having equations $y/a - x/b = 0$ and $y/a + x/b = 0$, which are the same lines as the asymptotes of the hyperbola with the equation $x^2/b^2 - y^2/a^2 = 1$. These two hyperbolas are called *conjugate hyperbolas*.

The asymptotes of an equilateral hyperbola ($a = b$) are perpendicular to each other. The auxiliary rectangle for such a hyperbola is a square, and the transverse and conjugate axes have equal lengths.

If the center of a hyperbola is at (h, k) and its principal axis is parallel to the x axis, then if the axes are translated so that the point (h, k) is the new origin, an equation of the hyperbola relative to this new coordinate system is

$$\frac{\bar{x}^2}{a^2} - \frac{\bar{y}^2}{b^2} = 1$$

If we replace $\bar{x}$ by $x - h$ and $\bar{y}$ by $y - k$, this equation becomes

$$\frac{(x - h)^2}{a^2} - \frac{(y - k)^2}{b^2} = 1 \tag{2}$$

Similarly, an equation of a hyperbola having its center at (h, k) and its principal axis parallel to the y axis is

$$\frac{(y - k)^2}{a^2} - \frac{(x - h)^2}{b^2} = 1 \tag{3}$$

EXAMPLE 1: The vertices of a hyperbola are at $(-5, -3)$ and $(-5, -1)$, and the eccentricity is $\sqrt{5}$. Find an equation of the hyperbola and equations of the asymptotes. Draw a sketch of the hyperbola and the asymptotes.

Figure 14.7.2

SOLUTION: The distance between the vertices is $2a$, and so $a = 1$. For a hyperbola, $b = a\sqrt{e^2 - 1}$, and therefore $b = 1\sqrt{5 - 1} = 2$. Because the principal axis is parallel to the y axis, an equation of the hyperbola is of the form (3). The center (h, k) is halfway between the vertices and is therefore at the point $(-5, -2)$. We have, then, as an equation of the hyperbola

$$\frac{(y + 2)^2}{1} - \frac{(x + 5)^2}{4} = 1$$

Using the mnemonic device to obtain equations of the asymptotes, we have

$$\left(\frac{y + 2}{1} - \frac{x + 5}{2}\right)\left(\frac{y + 2}{1} + \frac{x + 5}{2}\right) = 0$$

which gives

$$y + 2 = \tfrac{1}{2}(x + 5) \quad \text{and} \quad y + 2 = -\tfrac{1}{2}(x + 5)$$

A sketch of the hyperbola and the asymptotes are in Fig. 14.7.2.

If in Eqs. (2) and (3) we eliminate fractions and combine terms, the resulting equations are of the form

$$Ax^2 + Cy^2 + Dx + Ey + F = 0 \tag{4}$$

where A and C have different signs; that is, $AC < 0$. We now wish to show that the graph of an equation of the form (4), where $AC < 0$, is either a hyperbola or it degenerates. Completing the squares in x and y in Eq. (4), where $AC < 0$, the resulting equation has the form

$$\alpha^2(x - h)^2 - \beta^2(y - k)^2 = H \tag{5}$$

If $H > 0$, Eq. (5) can be written as

$$\frac{(x-h)^2}{\dfrac{H}{\alpha^2}} - \frac{(y-k)^2}{\dfrac{H}{\beta^2}} = 1$$

which has the form of Eq. (2).

● ILLUSTRATION 2: The equation

$$4x^2 - 12y^2 + 24x + 96y - 181 = 0$$

can be written as

$$4(x^2 + 6x) - 12(y^2 - 8y) = 181$$

and upon completing the squares in x and y, we have

$$4(x^2 + 6x + 9) - 12(y^2 - 8y + 16) = 181 + 36 - 192$$

which is equivalent to

$$4(x + 3)^2 - 12(y - 4)^2 = 25$$

This has the form of Eq. (5), where $H = 25 > 0$. It may be written as

$$\frac{(x+3)^2}{\frac{25}{4}} - \frac{(y-4)^2}{\frac{25}{12}} = 1$$

which has the form of Eq. (2).

If in Eq. (5), $H < 0$, then (5) may be written as

$$\frac{(y-k)^2}{\dfrac{|H|}{\alpha^2}} - \frac{(x-h)^2}{\dfrac{|H|}{\beta^2}} = 1$$

which has the form of Eq. (3).

● ILLUSTRATION 3: Suppose that Eq. (4) is

$$4x^2 - 12y^2 + 24x + 96y - 131 = 0$$

Upon completing the squares in x and y, we get

$$4(x + 3)^2 - 12(y - 4)^2 = -25$$

This has the form of Eq. (5), where $H = -25 < 0$, and it may be written as

$$\frac{(y-4)^2}{\frac{25}{12}} - \frac{(x+3)^2}{\frac{25}{4}} = 1$$

which has the form of Eq. (3).

If $H = 0$ in Eq. (5), then (5) is equivalent to the two equations

$$\alpha(x - h) - \beta(y - k) = 0 \quad \text{and} \quad \alpha(x - h) + \beta(y - k) = 0$$

which are equations of two straight lines through the point (h, k). This is the degenerate case of the hyperbola.

The following theorem summarizes the results of the above discussion.

14.7.3 Theorem If in the general second-degree equation

$$Ax^2 + Bxy + Cy^2 + Dx + Ey + F = 0$$

$B = 0$ and $AC < 0$, then the graph is either a hyperbola or two intersecting straight lines.

EXAMPLE 2: Determine the graph of the equation

$$9x^2 - 4y^2 - 18x - 16y + 29 = 0$$

SOLUTION: From Theorem 14.7.3, because $B = 0$ and $AC = (9)(-4) = -36 < 0$, the graph is either a hyperbola or two intersecting straight lines. Completing the squares in x and y, we get

$$9(x^2 - 2x + 1) - 4(y^2 + 4y + 4) = -29 + 9 - 16$$

$$9(x - 1)^2 - 4(y + 2)^2 = -36$$

$$\frac{(y + 2)^2}{9} - \frac{(x - 1)^2}{4} = 1 \tag{6}$$

Equation (6) has the form of Eq. (3), and so the graph is a hyperbola whose principal axis is parallel to the y axis and whose center is at $(1, -2)$.

EXAMPLE 3: For the hyperbola of Example 2, find the eccentricity, the vertices, the foci, and the directrices. Draw a sketch of the hyperbola and show the foci and the directrices.

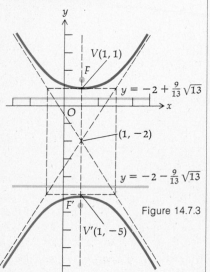

$V(1, 1)$

F

$y = -2 + \frac{9}{13}\sqrt{13}$

O

$(1, -2)$

$y = -2 - \frac{9}{13}\sqrt{13}$

F'

Figure 14.7.3

$V'(1, -5)$

SOLUTION: From Eq. (6) we see that $a = 3$ and $b = 2$. For a hyperbola, $b = a\sqrt{e^2 - 1}$; thus,

$$2 = 3\sqrt{e^2 - 1}$$

and solving for e, we obtain $e = \frac{1}{3}\sqrt{13}$. Because the center is at $(1, -2)$, the principal axis is vertical, and $a = 3$, it follows that the vertices are at the points $V'(1, -5)$ and $V(1, 1)$. Because $ae = \sqrt{13}$, the foci are at the points $F'(1, -2 - \sqrt{13})$ and $F(1, -2 + \sqrt{13})$. Furthermore, $a/e = \frac{9}{13}\sqrt{13}$; hence, the directrix corresponding to the focus at F' has as an equation $y = -2 - \frac{9}{13}\sqrt{13}$, and the directrix corresponding to the focus at F has as an equation $y = -2 + \frac{9}{13}\sqrt{13}$. Figure 14.7.3 shows a sketch of the hyperbola and the foci and the directrices.

Just as Theorem 14.6.2 gives an alternate definition of an ellipse, the following theorem gives an alternate definition of a hyperbola.

14.7.4 Theorem   A hyperbola can be defined as the set of points such that the absolute value of the difference of the distances from any point of the set to two given points (the foci) is a constant.

The proof of this theorem is similar to the proof of Theorem 14.6.2 and is left as an exercise (see Exercises 13 and 14). In the proof, take the foci at the points $F'(-ae, 0)$ and $F(ae, 0)$, and let the constant absolute value of the difference of the distances be $2a$. See Fig. 14.7.4.

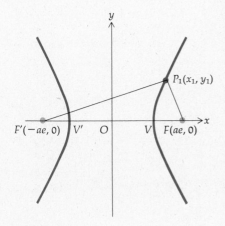

Figure 14.7.4

● ILLUSTRATION 4: Because the hyperbola of Example 2 has foci at $(1, -2 - \sqrt{13})$ and $(1, -2 + \sqrt{13})$ and $2a = 6$, it follows from Theorem 14.7.4 that this hyperbola can be defined as the set of points such that the absolute value of the difference of the distances from any point of the set to the points $(1, -2 - \sqrt{13})$ and $(1, -2 + \sqrt{13})$ is 6.   ●

The graph of the general second-degree equation

$$Ax^2 + Bxy + Cy^2 + Dx + Ey + F = 0 \tag{7}$$

where $B = 0$ and $AC > 0$, was discussed in Sec. 14.6. In this section we have so far considered the equation when $B = 0$ and $AC < 0$. Now if for Eq. (7), $B = 0$ and $AC = 0$, then either $A = 0$ or $C = 0$ (we do not consider $A = B = C = 0$ because then Eq. (7) would not be a quadratic equation). Suppose that in Eq. (7), $B = 0$, $A = 0$, and $C \neq 0$. The equation becomes

$$Cy^2 + Dx + Ey + F = 0 \tag{8}$$

If $D \neq 0$, (8) is an equation of a parabola. If $D = 0$, then the graph of (8) may be two parallel lines, one line, or the empty set. These are the degenerate cases of the parabola.

● ILLUSTRATION 5: The graph of the equation $4y^2 - 9 = 0$ is two parallel lines; $9y^2 + 6y + 1 = 0$ is an equation of one line; and $2y^2 + y + 1 = 0$ is satisfied by no real values of y.   ●

A similar discussion holds if $B = 0$, $C = 0$, and $A \neq 0$. The results are summarized in the following theorem.

14.7.5 Theorem   If in the general second-degree Eq. (7), $B = 0$ and either $A = 0$ and $C \neq 0$ or $C = 0$ and $A \neq 0$, then the graph is one of the following: a parabola, two parallel lines, one line, or the empty set.

From Theorems 14.6.1, 14.7.3, and 14.7.5, it may be concluded that the graph of the general quadratic equation in two unknowns when $B = 0$ is either a conic or a degenerate conic. The type of conic can be determined from the product of A and C. We have the following theorem.

14.7.6 Theorem   The graph of the equation $Ax^2 + Cy^2 + Dx + Ey + F = 0$, where A and C are not both zero, is either a conic or a degenerate conic; if it is a conic, then the graph is

   (i) a *parabola* if either $A = 0$ or $C = 0$, that is, if $AC = 0$;
   (ii) an *ellipse* if A and C have the same sign, that is, if $AC > 0$;
   (iii) a *hyperbola* if A and C have opposite signs, that is, if $AC < 0$.

   A discussion of the graph of the general quadratic equation, where $B \neq 0$, is given in Sec. 14.8.

Exercises 14.7

In Exercises 1 through 6, find the eccentricity, center, foci, directrices, and equations of the asymptotes of the given hyperbolas and draw a sketch of the graph.

1. $9x^2 - 18y^2 + 54x - 36y + 79 = 0$ 2. $x^2 - y^2 + 6x + 10y - 4 = 0$ 3. $3y^2 - 4x^2 - 8x - 24y - 40 = 0$

4. $4x^2 - y^2 + 56x + 2y + 195 = 0$ 5. $4y^2 - 9x^2 + 16y + 18x = 29$ 6. $y^2 - x^2 + 2y - 2x - 1 = 0$

In Exercises 7 through 12, find an equation of the hyperbola satisfying the given conditions and draw a sketch of the graph.

7. One focus at $(26, 0)$ and asymptotes the lines $12y = \pm 5x$.

8. Center at $(3, -5)$, a vertex at $(7, -5)$, and a focus at $(8, -5)$.

9. Center at $(-2, -1)$, a focus at $(-2, 14)$, and a directrix the line $5y = -53$.

10. Foci at $(3, 6)$ and $(3, 0)$ and passing through the point $(5, 3 + 6/\sqrt{5})$.

11. One focus at $(-3 - 3\sqrt{13}, 1)$, asymptotes intersecting at $(-3, 1)$, and one asymptote passing through the point $(1, 7)$.

12. Foci at $(-1, 4)$ and $(7, 4)$ and eccentricity of 3.

13. Prove that the set of points, such that the absolute value of the difference of the distances from any point of the set to two given points (the foci) is a constant, is a hyperbola.

14. Prove that any hyperbola is a set of points such that the absolute value of the difference of the distances from any point of the set to two given points (the foci) is a constant.

15. Use Theorem 14.7.4 to find an equation of the hyperbola for which the difference of the distances from any point on the hyperbola to $(2, 1)$ and $(2, 9)$ is equal to 4.

16. Solve Exercise 15 if the difference of the distances from $(-8, -4)$ and $(2, -4)$ is equal to 6.

17. Three listening posts are located at the points $A(0, 0)$, $B(0, \frac{21}{4})$, and $C(\frac{25}{3}, 0)$, the unit being 1 mile. Microphones located at these points show that a gun is $\frac{3}{8}$ mi closer to A than to C, and $\frac{7}{4}$ mi closer to B than to A. Locate the position of the gun by use of Theorem 14.7.4.

18. Prove that the eccentricity of an equilateral hyperbola is equal to $\sqrt{2}$.

14.8 ROTATION OF AXES   We have previously shown how a translation of coordinate axes can simplify the form of certain equations. A translation of axes gives a new coordinate system whose axes are parallel to the original axes. We now consider a rotation of coordinate axes which enables us to transform a second-degree equation having an xy term into one having no such term.

Suppose that we have two rectangular cartesian coordinate systems with the same origin. Let one system be the xy system and the other the $\bar{x}\bar{y}$ system. Suppose further that the $\bar{x}$ axis makes an angle of radian measure α with the x axis. Then of course the $\bar{y}$ axis makes an angle of radian measure α with the y axis. In such a case, we state that the xy system of coordinates is *rotated* through an angle of radian measure α to form the $\bar{x}\bar{y}$ system of coordinates. A point P having coordinates (x, y) with respect to the original coordinate system will have coordinates $(\bar{x}, \bar{y})$ with respect to the new one. We now obtain relationships between these two sets of coordinates. To do this, we introduce two polar coordinate systems, each system having the pole at the origin. In the first polar coordinate system the positive side of the x axis is taken as the polar axis; in the second polar coordinate system the positive side of the $\bar{x}$ axis is taken as the polar axis (see Fig. 14.8.1). Point P has two sets of polar coordinates, (r, θ) and $(\bar{r}, \bar{\theta})$, where

$$\bar{r} = r \quad \text{and} \quad \bar{\theta} = \theta - \alpha \tag{1}$$

The following equations hold:

$$\bar{x} = \bar{r} \cos \bar{\theta} \quad \text{and} \quad \bar{y} = \bar{r} \sin \bar{\theta} \tag{2}$$

Substituting from (1) into (2), we get

$$\bar{x} = r \cos(\theta - \alpha) \quad \text{and} \quad \bar{y} = r \sin(\theta - \alpha) \tag{3}$$

Using the trigonometric identities for the sine and cosine of the difference of two numbers, Eqs. (3) become

$$\bar{x} = r \cos \theta \cos \alpha + r \sin \theta \sin \alpha$$

and

$$\bar{y} = r \sin \theta \cos \alpha - r \cos \theta \sin \alpha$$

Because $r \cos \theta = x$ and $r \sin \theta = y$, we obtain from the above two equations

$$\bar{x} = x \cos \alpha + y \sin \alpha \tag{4}$$

and

$$\bar{y} = -x \sin \alpha + y \cos \alpha \tag{5}$$

Solving Eqs. (4) and (5) simultaneously for x and y in terms of $\bar{x}$ and $\bar{y}$, we obtain

$$x = \bar{x} \cos \alpha - \bar{y} \sin \alpha \tag{6}$$

and

$$y = \bar{x} \sin \alpha + \bar{y} \cos \alpha \tag{7}$$

It is left as an exercise to fill in the steps in going from (4) and (5) to (6) and (7) (see Exercise 1).

Figure 14.8.1

EXAMPLE 1: Given the equation $xy = 1$, find an equation of the graph with respect to the $\bar{x}$ and $\bar{y}$ axes after a rotation of axes through an angle of radian measure $\frac{1}{4}\pi$.

Figure 14.8.2

SOLUTION: Taking $\alpha = \frac{1}{4}\pi$ in Eqs. (6) and (7), we obtain

$$x = \frac{1}{\sqrt{2}}\bar{x} - \frac{1}{\sqrt{2}}\bar{y} \quad \text{and} \quad y = \frac{1}{\sqrt{2}}\bar{x} + \frac{1}{\sqrt{2}}\bar{y}$$

Substituting these expressions for x and y in the equation $xy = 1$, we get

$$\left(\frac{1}{\sqrt{2}}\bar{x} - \frac{1}{\sqrt{2}}\bar{y}\right)\left(\frac{1}{\sqrt{2}}\bar{x} + \frac{1}{\sqrt{2}}\bar{y}\right) = 1$$

or, equivalently,

$$\frac{\bar{x}^2}{2} - \frac{\bar{y}^2}{2} = 1$$

This is an equation of an equilateral hyperbola whose asymptotes are the bisectors of the quadrants in the $\bar{x}\bar{y}$ system. Hence, we conclude that the graph of the equation $xy = 1$ is an equilateral hyperbola lying in the first and third quadrants whose asymptotes are the x and y axes (see Fig. 14.8.2).

In Sec. 14.7 we showed that when $B = 0$ and A and C are not both zero, the graph of the general second-degree equation in two unknowns,

$$Ax^2 + Bxy + Cy^2 + Dx + Ey + F = 0 \tag{8}$$

is either a conic or a degenerate conic. We now show that if $B \neq 0$, then any equation of the form (8) can be transformed by a suitable rotation of axes into an equation of the form

$$\bar{A}\bar{x}^2 + \bar{C}\bar{y}^2 + \bar{D}\bar{x} + \bar{E}\bar{y} + \bar{F} = 0 \tag{9}$$

where $\bar{A}$ and $\bar{C}$ are not both zero.

If the xy system is rotated through an angle of radian measure α, then to obtain an equation of the graph of (8) with respect to the $\bar{x}\bar{y}$ system, we replace x by $\bar{x} \cos \alpha - \bar{y} \sin \alpha$ and y by $\bar{x} \sin \alpha + \bar{y} \cos \alpha$. We get

$$\bar{A}\bar{x}^2 + \bar{B}\bar{x}\bar{y} + \bar{C}\bar{y}^2 + \bar{D}\bar{x} + \bar{E}\bar{y} + \bar{F} = 0 \tag{10}$$

where

$$\bar{A} = A \cos^2 \alpha + B \sin \alpha \cos \alpha + C \sin^2 \alpha$$

$$\bar{B} = -2A \sin \alpha \cos \alpha + B(\cos^2 \alpha - \sin^2 \alpha) + 2C \sin \alpha \cos \alpha \tag{11}$$

$$\bar{C} = A \sin^2 \alpha - B \sin \alpha \cos \alpha + C \cos^2 \alpha$$

We wish to find an α so that the rotation transforms Eq. (8) into an equation of the form (9). Setting $\bar{B}$ from (11) equal to zero, we have

$$B(\cos^2 \alpha - \sin^2 \alpha) + (C - A)(2 \sin \alpha \cos \alpha) = 0$$

or, equivalently, with trigonometric identities,

$$B \cos 2\alpha + (C - A) \sin 2\alpha = 0$$

Because $B \neq 0$, this gives

$$\cot 2\alpha = \frac{A - C}{B} \qquad\qquad\qquad (12)$$

We have shown, then, that an equation of the form (8), where $B \neq 0$, can be transformed to an equation of the form (9) by a rotation of axes through an angle of radian measure α satisfying (12). We wish to show that $\bar{A}$ and $\bar{C}$ in (9) are not both zero. To prove this, notice that Eq. (10) is obtained from (8) by rotating the axes through the angle of radian measure α. Also, Eq. (8) can be obtained from (10) by rotating the axes back through the angle of radian measure $(-\alpha)$. If $\bar{A}$ and $\bar{C}$ in (10) are both zero, then the substitutions

$$\bar{x} = x \cos \alpha + y \sin \alpha \quad \text{and} \quad \bar{y} = -x \sin \alpha + y \cos \alpha$$

in (10) would result in the equation

$$\bar{D}(x \cos \alpha + y \sin \alpha) + \bar{E}(-x \sin \alpha + y \cos \alpha) + \bar{F} = 0$$

which is an equation of the first degree and hence different from (8) because we have assumed that at least $B \neq 0$. The following theorem has, therefore, been proved.

14.8.1 Theorem   If $B \neq 0$, the equation $Ax^2 + Bxy + Cy^2 + Dx + Ey + F = 0$ can be transformed into the equation $\bar{A}\bar{x}^2 + \bar{C}\bar{y}^2 + \bar{D}\bar{x} + \bar{E}\bar{y} + \bar{F} = 0$, where $\bar{A}$ and $\bar{C}$ are not both zero, by a rotation of axes through an angle of radian measure α for which $\cot 2\alpha = (A - C)/B$.

By Theorems 14.8.1 and 14.7.6, it follows that the graph of an equation of the form (8) is either a conic or a degenerate conic. To determine which type of conic is the graph of a particular equation, we use the fact that A, B, and C of Eq. (8) and $\bar{A}$, $\bar{B}$, and $\bar{C}$ of Eq. (10) satisfy the relation

$$B^2 - 4AC = \bar{B}^2 - 4\bar{A}\bar{C} \qquad\qquad\qquad (13)$$

which can be proved by substituting the expressions for $\bar{A}$, $\bar{B}$, and $\bar{C}$ given in Eqs. (11) in the right side of (13). This is left as an exercise (see Exercise 15).

The expression $B^2 - 4AC$ is called the *discriminant* of Eq. (8). Equation (13) states that the discriminant of the general quadratic equation in two variables is *invariant* under a rotation of axes. If the angle of rotation is chosen so that $\bar{B} = 0$, then (13) becomes

$$B^2 - 4AC = -4\bar{A}\bar{C} \tag{14}$$

From Theorem 14.7.6 it follows that if the graph of (9) is not degenerate, then it is a parabola if $\bar{A}\bar{C} = 0$, an ellipse if $\bar{A}\bar{C} > 0$, and a hyperbola if $\bar{A}\bar{C} < 0$. So we conclude that the graph of (9) is a parabola, an ellipse, or a hyperbola depending on whether $-4\bar{A}\bar{C}$ is zero, negative, or positive. Because the graph of (8) is the same as the graph of (9), it follows from (14) that if the graph of (8) is not degenerate, then it is a parabola, an ellipse, or a hyperbola depending on whether the discriminant $B^2 - 4AC$ is zero, negative, or positive. We have proved the following theorem.

14.8.2 Theorem   The graph of the equation

$$Ax^2 + Bxy + Cy^2 + Dx + Ey + F = 0$$

is either a conic or a degenerate conic. If it is a conic, then it is

(i) a *parabola* if $B^2 - 4AC = 0$;
(ii) an *ellipse* if $B^2 - 4AC < 0$;
(iii) a *hyperbola* if $B^2 - 4AC > 0$.

EXAMPLE 2:   Given the equation $17x^2 - 12xy + 8y^2 - 80 = 0$, simplify the equation by a rotation of axes. Draw a sketch of the graph of the equation showing both sets of axes.

SOLUTION: $B^2 - 4AC = (-12)^2 - 4(17)(8) = -400 < 0$. Therefore, by Theorem 14.8.2, the graph is an ellipse or else it is degenerate. To eliminate the xy term by a rotation of axes, we must choose an α such that

$$\cot 2\alpha = \frac{A - C}{B} = \frac{17 - 8}{-12} = -\frac{3}{4}$$

There is a 2α in the interval $(0, \pi)$ for which $\cot 2\alpha = -\frac{3}{4}$. Therefore, α is in the interval $(0, \frac{1}{2}\pi)$. To apply (6) and (7) it is not necessary to find α so long as we find $\cos \alpha$ and $\sin \alpha$. These functions can be found from the value of $\cot 2\alpha$ by the trigonometric identities

$$\cos \alpha = \sqrt{\frac{1 + \cos 2\alpha}{2}} \quad \text{and} \quad \sin \alpha = \sqrt{\frac{1 - \cos 2\alpha}{2}}$$

Because $\cot 2\alpha = -\frac{3}{4}$ and $0 < \alpha < \frac{1}{2}\pi$, it follows that $\cos 2\alpha = -\frac{3}{5}$. So

$$\cos \alpha = \sqrt{\frac{1 - \frac{3}{5}}{2}} = \frac{1}{\sqrt{5}}$$

and

$$\sin \alpha = \sqrt{\frac{1 + \frac{3}{5}}{2}} = \frac{2}{\sqrt{5}}$$

Substituting $x = \bar{x}/\sqrt{5} - 2\bar{y}/\sqrt{5}$ and $y = 2\bar{x}/\sqrt{5} + \bar{y}/\sqrt{5}$ in the given equa-

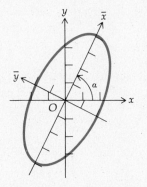

Figure 14.8.3

tion, we obtain

$$17\left(\frac{\bar{x}^2 - 4\bar{x}\bar{y} + 4\bar{y}^2}{5}\right) - 12\left(\frac{2\bar{x}^2 - 3\bar{x}\bar{y} - 2\bar{y}^2}{5}\right) + 8\left(\frac{4\bar{x}^2 + 4\bar{x}\bar{y} + \bar{y}^2}{5}\right) - 80 = 0$$

Upon simplification, this equation becomes

$$\bar{x}^2 + 4\bar{y}^2 = 16$$

or, equivalently,

$$\frac{\bar{x}^2}{16} + \frac{\bar{y}^2}{4} = 1$$

So the graph is an ellipse whose major axis is 8 units long and whose minor axis is 4 units long. A sketch of the ellipse with both sets of axes is shown in Fig. 14.8.3.

Exercises 14.8

1. Derive Eqs. (6) and (7) of this section by solving Eqs. (4) and (5) for x and y in terms of $\bar{x}$ and $\bar{y}$.

In Exercises 2 through 8, remove the xy term from the given equation by a rotation of axes. Draw a sketch of the graph and show both sets of axes.

2. $x^2 + xy + y^2 = 3$

3. $24xy - 7y^2 + 36 = 0$

4. $4xy + 3x^2 = 4$

5. $xy = 8$

6. $5x^2 + 6xy + 5y^2 = 9$

7. $31x^2 + 10\sqrt{3}xy + 21y^2 = 144$

8. $6x^2 + 20\sqrt{3}xy + 26y^2 = 324$

In Exercises 9 through 14, simplify the given equation by a rotation and translation of axes. Draw a sketch of the graph and show the three sets of axes.

9. $x^2 + xy + y^2 - 3y - 6 = 0$

10. $x^2 - 10xy + y^2 + x + y + 1 = 0$

11. $17x^2 - 12xy + 8y^2 - 68x + 24y - 12 = 0$

12. $3x^2 - 4xy + 8x - 1 = 0$

13. $11x^2 - 24xy + 4y^2 + 30x + 40y - 45 = 0$

14. $19x^2 + 6xy + 11y^2 - 26x + 38y + 31 = 0$

15. Show that for the general second-degree equation in two variables, the discriminant $B^2 - 4AC$ is invariant under a rotation of axes.

Review Exercises (Chapter 14)

In Exercises 1 through 6, find a cartesian equation of the conic satisfying the given conditions and draw a sketch of the graph.

1. Vertices at $(1, 8)$ and $(1, -4)$; $e = \frac{2}{3}$.

2. Foci at $(-5, 1)$ and $(1, 1)$; one vertex at $(-4, 1)$.

3. Center at the origin; foci on the x axis; $e = 2$; containing the point $(2, 3)$.

4. Vertex at $(4, 2)$; focus at $(4, -3)$; $e = 1$.

5. A focus at $(-5, 3)$; directrix: $x = -3$; $e = \frac{3}{4}$.

6. A focus at $(4, -2)$; directrix: $y = 2$; $e = \frac{3}{2}$.

In Exercises 7 through 10, find a polar equation of the conic satisfying the given conditions and draw a sketch of the graph.

7. A focus at the pole; vertices at $(2, \pi)$ and $(4, \pi)$.

8. A focus at the pole; a vertex at $(6, \frac{1}{2}\pi)$; $e = \frac{3}{4}$.

9. A focus at the pole; a vertex at $(3, \frac{3}{2}\pi)$; $e = 1$.

10. The line $r \sin \theta = 6$ is the directrix corresponding to the focus at the pole and $e = \frac{5}{3}$.

In Exercises 11 through 14, the equation is that of a conic having a focus at the pole. In each Exercise, (a) find the eccentricity; (b) identify the conic; (c) write an equation of the directrix which corresponds to the focus at the pole; (d) draw a sketch of the curve.

11. $r = \dfrac{2}{2 - \sin \theta}$

12. $r = \dfrac{5}{3 + 3 \sin \theta}$

13. $r = \dfrac{4}{2 + 3 \cos \theta}$

14. $r = \dfrac{4}{3 - 2 \cos \theta}$

In Exercises 15 through 18, the equation is that of either an ellipse or a hyperbola. Find the eccentricity, center, foci, and directrices, and draw a sketch of the graph. If it is a hyperbola, also find equations of the asymptotes.

15. $4x^2 + y^2 + 24x - 16y + 84 = 0$

16. $3x^2 - 2y^2 + 6x - 8y + 11 = 0$

17. $25x^2 - y^2 + 50x + 6y - 9 = 0$

18. $4x^2 + 9y^2 + 32x - 18y + 37 = 0$

In Exercises 19 and 20, simplify the given equation by a rotation and translation of axes. Draw a sketch of the graph and show the three sets of axes.

19. $3x^2 - 3xy - y^2 - 6y = 0$

20. $4x^2 + 3xy + y^2 - 6x + 12y = 0$

21. Find a polar equation of the parabola containing the point $(2, \frac{1}{3}\pi)$, whose focus is at the pole and whose vertex is on the extension of the polar axis.

22. If the distance between the two directrices of an ellipse is three times the distance between the foci, find the eccentricity.

23. Find the volume of the solid of revolution generated if the region bounded by the hyperbola $x^2/a^2 - y^2/b^2 = 1$ and the line $x = 2a$ is revolved about the y axis.

24. Show that the hyperbola $x^2 - y^2 = 4$ has the same foci as the ellipse $x^2 + 9y^2 = 9$.

25. Find an equation of the parabola having vertex at $(5, 1)$, axis parallel to the y axis, and through the point $(9, 3)$.

26. Show that any equation of the form $xy + ax + by + c = 0$ can always be written in the form $x'y' = k$ by a translation of the axes, and determine the value of k.

27. Any section of a parabolic mirror made by passing a plane through the axis of the mirror is a segment of a parabola. The altitude of the segment is 12 in. and the length of the base is 18 in. A section of the mirror made by a plane perpendicular to its axis is a circle. Find the circumference of the circular plane section if the plane perpendicular to the axis is 3 in. from the vertex.

28. The directrix of the parabola $y^2 = 4px$ is tangent to a circle having the focus of the parabola as its center. Find an equation of the circle and the points of intersection of the two curves.

29. A satellite is traveling around the earth in an elliptical orbit having the earth at one focus and an eccentricity of $\frac{1}{3}$. The

closest distance that the satellite gets to the earth is 300 mi. Find the farthest distance that the satellite gets from the earth.

30. The orbit of the planet Mercury around the sun is elliptical in shape with the sun at one focus, a semimajor axis of length 36 million miles, and an eccentricity of 0.206. Find (a) how close Mercury gets to the sun and (b) the greatest possible distance between Mercury and the sun.

31. A comet is moving in a parabolic orbit around the sun at the focus F of the parabola. An observation of the comet is made when it is at point P_1, 15 million miles from the sun, and a second observation is made when it is at point P_2, 5 million miles from the sun. The line segments FP_1 and FP_2 are perpendicular. With this information there are two possible orbits for the comet. Find how close the comet comes to the sun for each orbit.

32. The arch of a bridge is in the shape of a semiellipse having a horizontal span of 40 ft and a height of 16 ft at its center. How high is the arch 9 ft to the right or left of the center?

33. Points A and B are 1000 ft apart and it is determined from the sound of an explosion heard at these points at different times that the location of the explosion is 600 ft closer to A than to B. Show that the location of the explosion is restricted to a particular curve and find an equation of it.

34. Find the area of the region bounded by the two parabolas: $r = 2/(1 - \cos\theta)$ and $r = 2/(1 + \cos\theta)$.

35. A focal chord of a conic is a line segment passing through a focus and having its endpoints on the conic. Prove that if two focal chords of a parabola are perpendicular, the sum of the reciprocals of the measures of their lengths is a constant. (HINT: Use polar coordinates.)

36. A focal chord of a conic is divided into two segments by the focus. Prove that the sum of the reciprocals of the measures of the lengths of the two segments is the same, regardless of what chord is taken. (HINT: Use polar coordinates.)

37. Prove that the midpoints of all chords parallel to a fixed chord of a parabola lie on a line which is parallel to the axis of the parabola.

15

Indeterminate forms, improper integrals, and Taylor's formula

15.1 THE INDETERMINATE FORM 0/0

Limit theorem 9 (2.2.9) states that if $\lim\limits_{x \to a} f(x)$ and $\lim\limits_{x \to a} g(x)$ both exist, then

$$\lim_{x \to a} \frac{f(x)}{g(x)} = \frac{\lim\limits_{x \to a} f(x)}{\lim\limits_{x \to a} g(x)}$$

provided that $\lim\limits_{x \to a} g(x) \neq 0$.

There are various situations for which this theorem cannot be used. In particular, if $\lim\limits_{x \to a} g(x) = 0$ and $\lim\limits_{x \to a} f(x) = k$, where k is a constant not equal to 0, then Limit theorem 12 (2.4.4) can be applied. Consider the case when both $\lim\limits_{x \to a} f(x) = 0$ and $\lim\limits_{x \to a} g(x) = 0$. Some limits of this type have previously been considered.

● ILLUSTRATION 1: We wish to find

$$\lim_{x \to 4} \frac{x^2 - x - 12}{x^2 - 3x - 4}$$

Here, $\lim\limits_{x \to 4} (x^2 - x - 12) = 0$ and $\lim\limits_{x \to 4} (x^2 - 3x - 4) = 0$. However, the numerator and denominator can be factored, which gives

$$\lim_{x \to 4} \frac{x^2 - x - 12}{x^2 - 3x - 4} = \lim_{x \to 4} \frac{(x - 4)(x + 3)}{(x - 4)(x + 1)}$$

Because $x \neq 4$, the numerator and denominator can be divided by $(x - 4)$, and we obtain

$$\lim_{x \to 4} \frac{x^2 - x - 12}{x^2 - 3x - 4} = \lim_{x \to 4} \frac{x + 3}{x + 1} = \frac{7}{5}$$ ●

● ILLUSTRATION 2: $\lim\limits_{x \to 0} \sin x = 0$ and $\lim\limits_{x \to 0} x = 0$; and by Theorem 10.2.1,

$$\lim_{x \to 0} \frac{\sin x}{x} = 1$$ ●

15.1.1 Definition

If f and g are two functions such that $\lim\limits_{x \to a} f(x) = 0$ and $\lim\limits_{x \to a} g(x) = 0$, then the function f/g has the *indeterminate form 0/0 at a*.

● ILLUSTRATION 3: From Definition 15.1.1, $(x^2 - x - 12)/(x^2 - 3x - 4)$ has the indeterminate form 0/0 at 4; however, we saw in Illustration 1 that

$$\lim_{x \to 4} \frac{x^2 - x - 12}{x^2 - 3x - 4} = \frac{7}{5}$$

Also, $(\sin x/x)$ has the indeterminate form 0/0 at 0, while $\lim\limits_{x \to 0} (\sin x/x) = 1$, as shown in Illustration 2. ●

We now consider a general method for finding the limit, if it exists, of a function at a number where it has the indeterminate form 0/0. This method is attributed to the French mathematician Guillaume François de L'Hôpital (1661–1707), who wrote the first calculus textbook, published in 1696. It is known as *L'Hôpital's rule*.

15.1.2 Theorem
L'Hôpital's Rule

Let f and g be functions which are differentiable on an open interval I, except possibly at the number a in I. Suppose that for all $x \neq a$ in I, $g'(x) \neq 0$. Then if $\lim\limits_{x \to a} f(x) = 0$ and $\lim\limits_{x \to a} g(x) = 0$, and if

$$\lim_{x \to a} \frac{f'(x)}{g'(x)} = L$$

it follows that

$$\lim_{x \to a} \frac{f(x)}{g(x)} = L$$

The theorem is valid if all the limits are right-hand limits or all the limits are left-hand limits.

Before we prove Theorem 15.1.2, we show the use of the theorem by the following illustration and examples.

● ILLUSTRATION 4: We use L'Hôpital's rule to evaluate the limits in Illustrations 1 and 2. In Illustration 1, because $\lim\limits_{x \to 4} (x^2 - x - 12) = 0$ and $\lim\limits_{x \to 4} (x^2 - 3x - 4) = 0$, we can apply L'Hôpital's rule and obtain

$$\lim_{x \to 4} \frac{x^2 - x - 12}{x^2 - 3x - 4} = \lim_{x \to 4} \frac{2x - 1}{2x - 3} = \frac{7}{5}$$

We can apply L'Hôpital's rule in Illustration 2 because $\lim\limits_{x \to 0} \sin x = 0$ and $\lim\limits_{x \to 0} x = 0$. We have, then,

$$\lim_{x \to 0} \frac{\sin x}{x} = \lim_{x \to 0} \frac{\cos x}{1} = 1$$
●

EXAMPLE 1:   Find

$$\lim_{x \to 0} \frac{x}{1 - e^x}$$

if it exists.

SOLUTION: Because $\lim\limits_{x \to 0} x = 0$ and $\lim\limits_{x \to 0} (1 - e^x) = 0$, L'Hôpital's rule can be applied, and we have

$$\lim_{x \to 0} \frac{x}{1 - e^x} = \lim_{x \to 0} \frac{1}{-e^x} = \frac{1}{-1} = -1$$

EXAMPLE 2:   Find

$$\lim_{x \to 1} \frac{1 - x + \ln x}{x^3 - 3x + 2}$$

if it exists.

SOLUTION:

$$\lim_{x \to 1} (1 - x + \ln x) = 1 - 1 + 0 = 0$$

and

$$\lim_{x \to 1} (x^3 - 3x + 2) = 1 - 3 + 2 = 0$$

Therefore, applying L'Hôpital's rule, we have

$$\lim_{x \to 1} \frac{1 - x + \ln x}{x^3 - 3x + 2} = \lim_{x \to 1} \frac{-1 + \dfrac{1}{x}}{3x^2 - 3}$$

Now, because $\lim_{x \to 1} (-1 + 1/x) = 0$ and $\lim_{x \to 1} (3x^2 - 3) = 0$, we apply L'Hôpital's rule again giving

$$\lim_{x \to 1} \frac{-1 + \dfrac{1}{x}}{3x^2 - 3} = \lim_{x \to 1} \frac{-\dfrac{1}{x^2}}{6x} = -\frac{1}{6}$$

Therefore, we conclude

$$\lim_{x \to 1} \frac{1 - x + \ln x}{x^3 - 3x + 2} = -\frac{1}{6}$$

To prove Theorem 15.1.2 we need to use the theorem known as *Cauchy's mean-value theorem*, which extends to two functions the mean-value theorem (4.7.2) for a single function. This theorem is attributed to the French mathematician Augustin L. Cauchy (1789–1857), who was a pioneer in putting the calculus on a sound logical basis.

15.1.3 Theorem
Cauchy's Mean-Value Theorem

If f and g are two functions such that

    (i) f and g are continuous on the closed interval $[a, b]$;
    (ii) f and g are differentiable on the open interval (a, b);
    (iii) for all x in the open interval (a, b), $g'(x) \neq 0$

then there exists a number z in the open interval (a, b) such that

$$\frac{f(b) - f(a)}{g(b) - g(a)} = \frac{f'(z)}{g'(z)}$$

PROOF: We first show that $g(b) \neq g(a)$. Assume $g(b) = g(a)$. Because g satisfies the two conditions in the hypothesis of the mean-value theorem (4.7.2), there is some number c in (a, b) such that $g'(c) = [g(b) - g(a)]/(b - a)$. But if $g(b) = g(a)$, then there is some number c in (a, b) such that $g'(c) = 0$. But condition (iii) of the hypothesis of this theorem states that for all x in (a, b), $g'(x) \neq 0$. Therefore, we have a contradiction. Hence, our assumption that $g(b) = g(a)$ is false. So, $g(b) \neq g(a)$, and consequently $g(b) - g(a) \neq 0$.

Now let us consider the function h defined by

$$h(x) = f(x) - f(a) - \left[\frac{f(b) - f(a)}{g(b) - g(a)}\right] [g(x) - g(a)]$$

Then,

$$h'(x) = f'(x) - \left[\frac{f(b) - f(a)}{g(b) - g(a)} \right] g'(x) \tag{1}$$

Therefore, h is differentiable on (a, b) because f and g are differentiable there, and h is continuous on $[a, b]$ because f and g are continuous there.

$$h(a) = f(a) - f(a) - \left[\frac{f(b) - f(a)}{g(b) - g(a)} \right] [g(a) - g(a)] = 0$$

$$h(b) = f(b) - f(a) - \left[\frac{f(b) - f(a)}{g(b) - g(a)} \right] [g(b) - g(a)] = 0$$

Hence, the three conditions of the hypothesis of Rolle's theorem are satisfied by the function h. So there exists a number z in the open interval (a, b) such that $h'(z) = 0$. Thus, from (1) we have

$$f'(z) - \frac{f(b) - f(a)}{g(b) - g(a)} g'(z) = 0 \tag{2}$$

Because $g'(z) \neq 0$ on (a, b), we have from (2)

$$\frac{f(b) - f(a)}{g(b) - g(a)} = \frac{f'(z)}{g'(z)}$$

where z is some number in (a, b). This proves the theorem. ∎

We should note that if g is the function such that $g(x) = x$, then the conclusion of Cauchy's mean-value theorem becomes the conclusion of the former mean-value theorem because then $g'(z) = 1$. So the former mean-value theorem is a special case of Cauchy's mean-value theorem.

A geometric interpretation of Cauchy's mean-value theorem is given in Sec. 17.4. It is postponed until then because parametric equations are needed.

● ILLUSTRATION 5: Suppose $f(x) = 3x^2 + 3x - 1$ and $g(x) = x^3 - 4x + 2$. We find a number z in $(0, 1)$, predicted by Theorem 15.1.3.

$$f'(x) = 6x + 3 \qquad g'(x) = 3x^2 - 4$$

Thus, f and g are differentiable and continuous everywhere, and for all x in $(0, 1)$, $g'(x) \neq 0$. Hence, by Theorem 15.1.3, there exists a z in $(0, 1)$ such that

$$\frac{f(1) - f(0)}{g(1) - g(0)} = \frac{6z + 3}{3z^2 - 4}$$

Substituting $f(1) = 5$, $g(1) = -1$, $f(0) = -1$, and $g(0) = 2$, and solving for z, we have

$$\frac{5 - (-1)}{-1 - 2} = \frac{6z + 3}{3z^2 - 4}$$

$$6z^2 + 6z - 5 = 0$$

$$z = \frac{-6 \pm \sqrt{36 + 120}}{12}$$

$$= \frac{-6 \pm 2\sqrt{39}}{12}$$

$$= \frac{-3 \pm \sqrt{39}}{6}$$

Only one of these numbers is in $(0, 1)$, namely, $z = \frac{1}{6}(-3 + \sqrt{39})$.   ●

We are now in a position to prove Theorem 15.1.2. We distinguish three cases: (i) $x \to a^+$; (ii) $x \to a^-$; (iii) $x \to a$.

PROOF OF THEOREM 15.1.2(i):   Because in the hypothesis it is not assumed that f and g are defined at a, we consider two new functions F and G for which

$$\begin{aligned}
F(x) &= f(x) &&\text{if } x \neq a \quad \text{and} \quad F(a) = 0 \\
G(x) &= g(x) &&\text{if } x \neq a \quad \text{and} \quad G(a) = 0
\end{aligned} \tag{3}$$

Let b be the right endpoint of the open interval I given in the hypothesis. Because f and g are both differentiable on I, except possibly at a, we conclude that F and G are both differentiable on the interval $(a, x]$, where $a < x < b$. Therefore, F and G are both continuous on $(a, x]$. The functions F and G are also both continuous from the right at a because $\lim\limits_{x \to a^+} F(x) = \lim\limits_{x \to a^+} f(x) = 0 = F(a)$, and $\lim\limits_{x \to a^+} G(x) = \lim\limits_{x \to a^+} g(x) = 0 = G(a)$. Therefore, F and G are continuous on the closed interval $[a, x]$. So F and G satisfy the three conditions of the hypothesis of Cauchy's mean-value theorem (Theorem 15.1.3) on the interval $[a, x]$. Hence,

$$\frac{F(x) - F(a)}{G(x) - G(a)} = \frac{F'(z)}{G'(z)} \tag{4}$$

where z is some number such that $a < z < x$. From (3) and (4) we have

$$\frac{f(x)}{g(x)} = \frac{f'(z)}{g'(z)} \tag{5}$$

Because $a < z < x$, it follows that as $x \to a^+$, $z \to a^+$; therefore,

$$\lim_{x \to a^+} \frac{f(x)}{g(x)} = \lim_{x \to a^+} \frac{f'(z)}{g'(z)} = \lim_{z \to a^+} \frac{f'(z)}{g'(z)} \tag{6}$$

But by hypothesis, the limit on the right side of (6) is L. Therefore,

$$\lim_{x \to a^+} \frac{f(x)}{g(x)} = L$$ ■

The proof of case (ii) is similar to the proof of case (i) and is left as an exercise (see Exercise 27). The proof of case (iii) is based on the results of cases (i) and (ii) and is also left as an exercise (see Exercise 28).

L'Hôpital's rule also holds if either x increases without bound or x decreases without bound, as given in the next theorem.

15.1.4 Theorem
L'Hôpital's Rule

Let f and g be functions which are differentiable for all $x > N$, where N is a positive constant, and suppose that for all $x > N$, $g'(x) \neq 0$. Then if $\lim\limits_{x \to +\infty} f(x) = 0$ and $\lim\limits_{x \to +\infty} g(x) = 0$ and if

$$\lim_{x \to +\infty} \frac{f'(x)}{g'(x)} = L$$

it follows that

$$\lim_{x \to +\infty} \frac{f(x)}{g(x)} = L$$

The theorem is also valid if "$x \to +\infty$" is replaced by "$x \to -\infty$."

PROOF: We prove the theorem for $x \to +\infty$. The proof for $x \to -\infty$ is left as an exercise (see Exercise 29).

For all $x > N$, let $x = 1/t$; then $t = 1/x$. Let F and G be the functions defined by $F(t) = f(1/t)$ and $G(t) = g(1/t)$, if $t \neq 0$. Then $f(x) = F(t)$ and $g(x) = G(t)$, where $x > N$ and $0 < t < 1/N$. From Definitions 4.1.1 and 2.3.1, it may be shown that the statements

$$\lim_{x \to +\infty} f(x) = M \quad \text{and} \quad \lim_{t \to 0^+} F(t) = M$$

have the same meaning. It is left as an exercise to prove this (see Exercise 30). Because, by hypothesis, $\lim\limits_{x \to +\infty} f(x) = 0$ and $\lim\limits_{x \to +\infty} g(x) = 0$, we can conclude that

$$\lim_{t \to 0^+} F(t) = 0 \quad \text{and} \quad \lim_{t \to 0^+} G(t) = 0 \tag{7}$$

Considering the quotient $F'(t)/G'(t)$, we have, using the chain rule,

$$\frac{F'(t)}{G'(t)} = \frac{-\dfrac{1}{t^2} f'\left(\dfrac{1}{t}\right)}{-\dfrac{1}{t^2} g'\left(\dfrac{1}{t}\right)} = \frac{f'\left(\dfrac{1}{t}\right)}{g'\left(\dfrac{1}{t}\right)} = \frac{f'(x)}{g'(x)}$$

Because by hypothesis $\lim\limits_{x \to +\infty} f'(x)/g'(x) = L$, it follows from the above that

$$\lim_{t \to 0^+} \frac{F'(t)}{G'(t)} = L \tag{8}$$

Because for all $x > N$, $g'(x) \neq 0$,

$$G'(t) \neq 0 \qquad \text{for all } 0 < t < \frac{1}{N} \tag{9}$$

From (7), (8), and (9), it follows from Theorem 15.1.2 that

$$\lim_{t \to 0^+} \frac{F(t)}{G(t)} = L$$

But because $F(t)/G(t) = f(x)/g(x)$ for all $x > N$ and $t \neq 0$, we have

$$\lim_{x \to +\infty} \frac{f(x)}{g(x)} = L$$

and so the theorem is proved. ∎

Theorems 15.1.2 and 15.1.4 also hold if L is replaced by $+\infty$ or $-\infty$. The proofs for these cases are omitted.

EXAMPLE 3:   Find

$$\lim_{x \to +\infty} \frac{\sin \dfrac{1}{x}}{\tan^{-1}\left(\dfrac{1}{x}\right)}$$

if it exists.

SOLUTION: $\lim\limits_{x \to +\infty} \sin(1/x) = 0$ and $\lim\limits_{x \to +\infty} \tan^{-1}(1/x) = 0$. So applying L'Hô-pital's rule we get

$$\lim_{x \to +\infty} \frac{\sin \dfrac{1}{x}}{\tan^{-1}\left(\dfrac{1}{x}\right)} = \lim_{x \to +\infty} \frac{\cos \dfrac{1}{x} \cdot \left(-\dfrac{1}{x^2}\right)}{\dfrac{1}{1 + \dfrac{1}{x^2}} \cdot \left(-\dfrac{1}{x^2}\right)} = \lim_{x \to +\infty} \frac{\cos \dfrac{1}{x}}{\dfrac{x^2}{x^2 + 1}}$$

Because

$$\lim_{x \to +\infty} \cos \frac{1}{x} = 1 \quad \text{and} \quad \lim_{x \to +\infty} \frac{x^2}{x^2 + 1} = \lim_{x \to +\infty} \frac{1}{1 + \dfrac{1}{x^2}} = 1$$

it follows that

$$\lim_{x \to +\infty} \frac{\cos \dfrac{1}{x}}{\dfrac{x^2}{x^2 + 1}} = 1$$

Therefore, the given limit is 1.

Exercises 15.1

In Exercises 1 through 4, find all values of z in the given interval (a, b) satisfying the conclusion of Theorem 15.1.3 for the given pair of functions.

1. $f(x) = x^3$, $g(x) = x^2$; $(a, b) = (0, 2)$

2. $f(x) = \dfrac{2x}{1 + x^2}$, $g(x) = \dfrac{1 - x^2}{1 + x^2}$; $(a, b) = (0, 2)$

3. $f(x) = \sin x$, $g(x) = \cos x$; $(a, b) = (0, \pi)$ 4. $f(x) = \cos 2x$, $g(x) = \sin x$; $(a, b) = (0, \frac{1}{2}\pi)$

In Exercises 5 through 24, evaluate the limit, if it exists.

5. $\lim\limits_{x \to 0} \dfrac{x}{\tan x}$

6. $\lim\limits_{x \to 0} \dfrac{\tan x - x}{x - \sin x}$

7. $\lim\limits_{x \to +\infty} \dfrac{\sin \frac{2}{x}}{\frac{1}{x}}$

8. $\lim\limits_{x \to 2} \dfrac{\sin \pi x}{2 - x}$

9. $\lim\limits_{x \to -\infty} \dfrac{2^x}{e^x}$

10. $\lim\limits_{x \to 0} \dfrac{\sin^{-1} x}{x}$

11. $\lim\limits_{x \to \pi/2} \dfrac{\ln(\sin x)}{(\pi - 2x)^2}$

12. $\lim\limits_{x \to 0} \dfrac{e^x - \cos x}{x \sin x}$

13. $\lim\limits_{x \to 0} \dfrac{2^x - 3^x}{x}$

14. $\lim\limits_{x \to 0} \dfrac{e^{2x^2} - 1}{\sin^2 x}$

15. $\lim\limits_{\theta \to 0} \dfrac{\theta - \sin \theta}{\tan^3 \theta}$

16. $\lim\limits_{t \to 2} \dfrac{t^n - 2^n}{t - 2}$

17. $\lim\limits_{t \to 0} \dfrac{\sin^2 t}{\sin t^2}$

18. $\lim\limits_{x \to 0} \dfrac{\tanh 2x}{\tanh x}$

19. $\lim\limits_{x \to 0} \dfrac{(1 + x)^{1/5} - (1 - x)^{1/5}}{(1 + x)^{1/3} - (1 - x)^{1/3}}$

20. $\lim\limits_{x \to 0} \dfrac{e^x - 10^x}{x}$

21. $\lim\limits_{x \to \pi} \dfrac{1 + \cos 2x}{1 - \sin x}$

22. $\lim\limits_{x \to +\infty} \dfrac{\frac{1}{x^2} - 2 \tan^{-1} \frac{1}{x}}{\frac{1}{x}}$

23. $\lim\limits_{x \to 0} \dfrac{\cos x - \cosh x}{x^2}$

24. $\lim\limits_{x \to 0} \dfrac{\sinh x - \sin x}{\sin^3 x}$

25. An electrical circuit has a resistance of R ohms, an inductance of L henries, and an electromotive force of E volts, where R, L, and E are positive. If I amperes is the current flowing in the circuit t sec after a switch is turned on, then

$$I = \frac{E}{R}(1 - e^{-Rt/L})$$

For specific values of t, E, and L, find $\lim\limits_{R \to 0^+} I$.

26. In a geometric progression, if a is the first term, r is the common ratio of two successive terms, and S is the sum of the first n terms, then if $r \neq 1$,

$$S = \frac{a(r^n - 1)}{r - 1}$$

Find $\lim\limits_{r \to 1} S$. Is the result consistent with the sum of the first n terms if $r = 1$?

27. Prove Theorem 15.1.2(ii).

28. Prove Theorem 15.1.2(iii).

29. Prove Theorem 15.1.4 for $x \to -\infty$.

30. Suppose that f is a function defined for all $x > N$, where N is a positive constant. If $t = 1/x$ and $F(t) = f(1/t)$, where $t \neq 0$, prove that the statements $\lim\limits_{x \to +\infty} f(x) = M$ and $\lim\limits_{t \to 0^+} F(t) = M$ have the same meaning.

15.2 OTHER INDETERMINATE FORMS

Suppose that we wish to determine if $\lim\limits_{x \to \pi/2} (\sec^2 x/\sec^2 3x)$ exists. We cannot apply the theorem involving the limit of a quotient because

$\lim\limits_{x \to \pi/2} \sec^2 x = +\infty$ and $\lim\limits_{x \to \pi/2} \sec^2 3x = +\infty$. In this case we say that the function defined by $\sec^2 x/\sec^2 3x$ has the indeterminate form $(+\infty/+\infty)$ at $x = \frac{1}{2}\pi$. L'Hôpital's rule also applies to an indeterminate form of this type as well as to $(-\infty/-\infty)$, $(-\infty/+\infty)$ and $(+\infty/-\infty)$. This is given by the following theorems, for which the proofs are omitted because they are beyond the scope of this book.

15.2.1 Theorem
L'Hôpital's Rule

Let f and g be functions which are differentiable on an open interval I, except possibly at the number a in I, and suppose that for all $x \ne a$ in I, $g'(x) \ne 0$. Then if $\lim\limits_{x \to a} f(x) = +\infty$ or $-\infty$, and $\lim\limits_{x \to a} g(x) = +\infty$ or $-\infty$, and if

$$\lim_{x \to a} \frac{f'(x)}{g'(x)} = L$$

it follows that

$$\lim_{x \to a} \frac{f(x)}{g(x)} = L$$

The theorem is valid if all the limits are right-hand limits or if all the limits are left-hand limits.

EXAMPLE 1: Find

$$\lim_{x \to 0^+} \frac{\ln x}{\dfrac{1}{x}}$$

if it exists.

SOLUTION: Because $\lim\limits_{x \to 0^+} \ln x = -\infty$ and $\lim\limits_{x \to 0^+} (1/x) = +\infty$, we apply L'Hôpital's rule and get

$$\lim_{x \to 0^+} \frac{\ln x}{\dfrac{1}{x}} = \lim_{x \to 0^+} \frac{\dfrac{1}{x}}{-\dfrac{1}{x^2}} = \lim_{x \to 0^+} (-x) = 0$$

15.2.2 Theorem
L'Hôpital's Rule

Let f and g be functions which are differentiable for all $x > N$, where N is a positive constant, and suppose that for all $x > N$, $g'(x) \ne 0$. Then if $\lim\limits_{x \to +\infty} f(x) = +\infty$ or $-\infty$, and $\lim\limits_{x \to +\infty} g(x) = +\infty$ or $-\infty$, and if

$$\lim_{x \to +\infty} \frac{f'(x)}{g'(x)} = L$$

it follows that

$$\lim_{x \to +\infty} \frac{f(x)}{g(x)} = L$$

The theorem is also valid if "$x \to +\infty$" is replaced by "$x \to -\infty$."

Theorems 15.2.1 and 15.2.2 also hold if L is replaced by $+\infty$ or $-\infty$, and the proofs for these cases are also omitted.

EXAMPLE 2: Find

$$\lim_{x \to +\infty} \frac{\ln(2 + e^x)}{3x}$$

if it exists.

SOLUTION: Because $\lim\limits_{x \to +\infty} \ln(2 + e^x) = +\infty$ and $\lim\limits_{x \to +\infty} 3x = +\infty$, by applying L'Hôpital's rule we obtain

$$\lim_{x \to +\infty} \frac{\ln(2 + e^x)}{3x} = \lim_{x \to +\infty} \frac{\dfrac{1}{2 + e^x} \cdot e^x}{3}$$

$$= \lim_{x \to +\infty} \frac{e^x}{6 + 3e^x}$$

Now because $\lim\limits_{x \to +\infty} e^x = +\infty$ and $\lim\limits_{x \to +\infty} (6 + 3e^x) = +\infty$, we apply L'Hôpital's rule again and get

$$\lim_{x \to +\infty} \frac{e^x}{6 + 3e^x} = \lim_{x \to +\infty} \frac{e^x}{3e^x} = \lim_{x \to +\infty} \frac{1}{3} = \frac{1}{3}$$

Therefore,

$$\lim_{x \to +\infty} \frac{\ln(2 + e^x)}{3x} = \frac{1}{3}$$

EXAMPLE 3: Find

$$\lim_{x \to \pi/2^-} \frac{\sec^2 x}{\sec^2 3x}$$

if it exists.

SOLUTION: $\lim\limits_{x \to \pi/2^-} \sec^2 x = +\infty$ and $\lim\limits_{x \to \pi/2^-} \sec^2 3x = +\infty$. So by applying L'Hôpital's rule we get

$$\lim_{x \to \pi/2^-} \frac{\sec^2 x}{\sec^2 3x} = \lim_{x \to \pi/2^-} \frac{2 \sec^2 x \tan x}{6 \sec^2 3x \tan 3x}$$

$$\lim_{x \to \pi/2^-} 2 \sec^2 x \tan x = +\infty \quad \text{and} \quad \lim_{x \to \pi/2^-} 6 \sec^2 3x \tan 3x = +\infty$$

It may be seen that further applications of L'Hôpital's rule will not help us. However, the original quotient may be rewritten and we have

$$\lim_{x \to \pi/2^-} \frac{\sec^2 x}{\sec^2 3x} = \lim_{x \to \pi/2^-} \frac{\cos^2 3x}{\cos^2 x}$$

Now, because $\lim\limits_{x \to \pi/2^-} \cos^2 3x = 0$ and $\lim\limits_{x \to \pi/2^-} \cos^2 x = 0$, we may apply L'Hôpital's rule giving

$$\lim_{x \to \pi/2^-} \frac{\cos^2 3x}{\cos^2 x} = \lim_{x \to \pi/2^-} \frac{-6 \cos 3x \sin 3x}{-2 \cos x \sin x}$$

$$= \lim_{x \to \pi/2^-} \frac{3(2 \cos 3x \sin 3x)}{(2 \cos x \sin x)}$$

$$= \lim_{x \to \pi/2^-} \frac{3 \sin 6x}{\sin 2x}$$

Because $\lim\limits_{x \to \pi/2^-} 3 \sin 6x = 0$ and $\lim\limits_{x \to \pi/2^-} \sin 2x = 0$, we apply L'Hôpital's rule again and we have

$$\lim_{x \to \pi/2^-} \frac{3 \sin 6x}{\sin 2x} = \lim_{x \to \pi/2} \frac{18 \cos 6x}{2 \cos 2x} = \frac{18(-1)}{2(-1)} = 9$$

Therefore,

$$\lim_{x \to \pi/2^-} \frac{\sec^2 x}{\sec^2 3x} = 9$$

The limit in Example 3 can be evaluated without L'Hôpital's rule by using Eqs. (11) in Sec. 10.1 and Theorem 10.2.1. This is left as an exercise (see Exercise 28).

In addition to 0/0 and $\pm\infty/\pm\infty$, other indeterminate forms are $0 \cdot (+\infty)$, $+\infty - (+\infty)$, 0^0, $(\pm\infty)^0$, and $1^{\pm\infty}$. These indeterminate forms are defined analogously to the other two. For instance, if $\lim_{x \to a} f(x) = +\infty$ and $\lim_{x \to a} g(x) = 0$, then the function defined by $f(x)^{g(x)}$ has the indeterminate form $(+\infty)^0$ at a. To find the limit of a function having one of these indeterminate forms, it must be changed to either the form 0/0 or $\pm\infty/\pm\infty$ before L'Hôpital's rule can be applied. The following examples illustrate the method.

EXAMPLE 4: Find

$$\lim_{x \to 0^+} \sin^{-1} x \csc x$$

if it exists.

SOLUTION: Because $\lim_{x \to 0^+} \sin^{-1} x = 0$ and $\lim_{x \to 0^+} \csc x = +\infty$, the function defined by $\sin^{-1} x \csc x$ has the indeterminate form $0 \cdot (+\infty)$ at 0. Before we can apply L'Hôpital's rule we rewrite $\sin^{-1} x \csc x$ as $\sin^{-1} x/\sin x$, and consider $\lim_{x \to 0^+} (\sin^{-1} x/\sin x)$. Now $\lim_{x \to 0^+} \sin^{-1} x = 0$ and $\lim_{x \to 0^+} \sin x = 0$, and so we have the indeterminate form 0/0. Therefore, we apply L'Hôpital's rule and obtain

$$\lim_{x \to 0^+} \frac{\sin^{-1} x}{\sin x} = \lim_{x \to 0^+} \frac{\dfrac{1}{\sqrt{1 - x^2}}}{\cos x} = \frac{1}{1} = 1$$

EXAMPLE 5: Find

$$\lim_{x \to 0} \left(\frac{1}{x^2} - \frac{1}{x^2 \sec x} \right)$$

if it exists.

SOLUTION: Because

$$\lim_{x \to 0} \frac{1}{x^2} = +\infty \quad \text{and} \quad \lim_{x \to 0} \frac{1}{x^2 \sec x} = +\infty$$

we have the indeterminate form $+\infty - (+\infty)$. Rewriting the expression, we have

$$\lim_{x \to 0} \left(\frac{1}{x^2} - \frac{1}{x^2 \sec x} \right) = \lim_{x \to 0} \frac{\sec x - 1}{x^2 \sec x}$$

$\lim_{x \to 0} (\sec x - 1) = 0$ and $\lim_{x \to 0} (x^2 \sec x) = 0$; so we apply L'Hôpital's rule and obtain

$$\lim_{x \to 0} \frac{\sec x - 1}{x^2 \sec x} = \lim_{x \to 0} \frac{\sec x \tan x}{2x \sec x + x^2 \sec x \tan x}$$

$$= \lim_{x \to 0} \frac{\tan x}{2x + x^2 \tan x}$$

$$\lim_{x \to 0} \tan x = 0 \quad \text{and} \quad \lim_{x \to 0} (2x + x^2 \tan x) = 0$$

and so we apply the rule again and obtain

$$\lim_{x \to 0} \frac{\tan x}{2x + x^2 \tan x} = \lim_{x \to 0} \frac{\sec^2 x}{2 + 2x \tan x + x^2 \sec^2 x} = \frac{1}{2}$$

Therefore,

$$\lim_{x \to 0} \left(\frac{1}{x^2} - \frac{1}{x^2 \sec x} \right) = \frac{1}{2}$$

If we have one of the indeterminate forms, 0^0, $(\pm\infty)^0$, or $1^{\pm\infty}$, the procedure for evaluating the limit is illustrated in Example 6.

EXAMPLE 6:   Find

$$\lim_{x \to 0^+} (x + 1)^{\cot x}$$

if it exists.

SOLUTION: Because $\lim\limits_{x \to 0^+} (x + 1) = 1$ and $\lim\limits_{x \to 0^+} \cot x = +\infty$, we have the indeterminate form $1^{+\infty}$. Let

$$y = (x + 1)^{\cot x} \tag{1}$$

Then

$$\ln y = \cot x \ln(x + 1)$$

$$\ln y = \frac{\ln(x + 1)}{\tan x}$$

So

$$\lim_{x \to 0^+} \ln y = \lim_{x \to 0^+} \frac{\ln(x + 1)}{\tan x} \tag{2}$$

Because $\lim\limits_{x \to 0^+} \ln(x + 1) = 0$ and $\lim\limits_{x \to 0^+} \tan x = 0$, we may apply L'Hôpital's rule to the right side of (2) and obtain

$$\lim_{x \to 0^+} \frac{\ln(x + 1)}{\tan x} = \lim_{x \to 0^+} \frac{\dfrac{1}{x + 1}}{\sec^2 x} = 1$$

Therefore, substituting 1 on the right side of (2), we have

$$\lim_{x \to 0^+} \ln y = 1 \tag{3}$$

Because the natural logarithmic function is continuous on its entire domain, which is the set of all positive numbers, we may apply Theorem 2.6.5 and we have from (3)

$$\ln \lim_{x \to 0^+} y = 1 \tag{4}$$

Therefore (because the equation $\ln a = b$ is equivalent to the equation

$a = e^b$), it follows from Eq. (4) that

$$\lim_{x \to 0^+} y = e^1$$

But from (1), $y = (x + 1)^{\cot x}$, and so we have

$$\lim_{x \to 0^+} (x + 1)^{\cot x} = e$$

Exercises 15.2

In Exercises 1 through 27, evaluate the limit, if it exists.

1. $\displaystyle\lim_{x \to +\infty} \frac{x^2}{e^x}$

2. $\displaystyle\lim_{x \to \pi/2^-} \frac{\ln(\cos x)}{\ln(\tan x)}$

3. $\displaystyle\lim_{x \to -1/2^-} \frac{\ln(1 - 2x)}{\tan \pi x}$

4. $\displaystyle\lim_{x \to +\infty} \frac{(\ln x)^3}{x}$

5. $\displaystyle\lim_{x \to 0^+} x \csc x$

6. $\displaystyle\lim_{x \to 0^+} \sin^{-1} x \csc x$

7. $\displaystyle\lim_{x \to 1} \left(\frac{1}{\ln x} - \frac{1}{x - 1} \right)$

8. $\displaystyle\lim_{x \to 0^+} (\sinh x)^{\tan x}$

9. $\displaystyle\lim_{x \to 0^+} x^{\sin x}$

10. $\displaystyle\lim_{x \to 0} (x + e^{2x})^{1/x}$

11. $\displaystyle\lim_{x \to +\infty} (x^2 - \sqrt{x^4 - x^2 + 2})$

12. $\displaystyle\lim_{x \to 2} \left(\frac{5}{x^2 + x - 6} - \frac{1}{x - 2} \right)$

13. $\displaystyle\lim_{x \to +\infty} x^{1/x}$

14. $\displaystyle\lim_{x \to 0^+} (1 + x)^{\ln x}$

15. $\displaystyle\lim_{x \to +\infty} (e^x + x)^{2/x}$

16. $\displaystyle\lim_{x \to 0^+} x^{1/\ln x}$

17. $\displaystyle\lim_{x \to 0} (1 + ax)^{1/x}; \; a \neq 0$

18. $\displaystyle\lim_{x \to +\infty} \left(1 + \frac{1}{2x} \right)^{x^2}$

19. $\displaystyle\lim_{x \to 0} (1 + \sinh x)^{2/x}$

20. $\displaystyle\lim_{x \to 2} (x - 2) \tan \tfrac{1}{4} \pi x$

21. $\displaystyle\lim_{x \to 0} [(\cos x) e^{x^2/2}]^{4/x^4}$

22. $\displaystyle\lim_{x \to 0} (\cos x)^{1/x^2}$

23. $\displaystyle\lim_{x \to +\infty} [(x^6 + 3x^5 + 4)^{1/6} - x]$

24. $\displaystyle\lim_{x \to 0^+} x^{x^x}$

25. $\displaystyle\lim_{x \to 0^+} \frac{e^{-1/x}}{x}$

26. $\displaystyle\lim_{x \to +\infty} \frac{\ln(x + e^x)}{3x}$

27. $\displaystyle\lim_{x \to +\infty} \frac{x}{\sqrt{1 + x^2}}$

28. Evaluate the limit in Example 3 without using L'Hôpital's rule, but by using Eqs. (11) in Sec. 10.1 and Theorem 10.2.1.

29. (a) Prove that $\lim_{x \to 0} (e^{-1/x^2}/x^n) = 0$ for any positive integer n. (b) If $f(x) = e^{-1/x^2}$, use the result of (a) to prove that the limit of f and all of its derivatives, as x approaches 0, is 0.

30. If $\displaystyle\lim_{x \to +\infty} \left(\frac{nx + 1}{nx - 1} \right)^x = 9$, find n.

31. Suppose $f(x) = \displaystyle\int_1^x e^{3t} \sqrt{9t^4 + 1} \, dt$ and $g(x) = x^n e^{3x}$. If $\displaystyle\lim_{x \to +\infty} \left[\frac{f'(x)}{g'(x)} \right] = 1$, find n.

15.3 IMPROPER INTEGRALS WITH INFINITE LIMITS OF INTEGRATION   In defining the definite integral $\int_a^b f(x) \, dx$, the function f was assumed to be defined on the closed interval $[a, b]$. We now extend the definition of the definite integral to consider an infinite interval of integration and call such an integral an *improper integral*. In Sec. 15.4 we discuss another kind of improper integral.

● ILLUSTRATION 1: Consider the problem of finding the area of the region bounded by the curve $y = e^{-x}$, the x axis, the y axis, and the line $x = b$, where $b > 0$. This region is shown in Fig. 15.3.1. Letting A square units be the area of this region, we have

$$A = \lim_{||\Delta|| \to 0} \sum_{i=1}^{n} e^{-\xi_i} \Delta_i x$$

$$= \int_0^b e^{-x}\, dx$$

$$= -e^{-x} \Big]_0^b$$

$$= 1 - e^{-b}$$

If we let b increase without bound, then

$$\lim_{b \to +\infty} \int_0^b e^{-x}\, dx = \lim_{b \to +\infty} (1 - e^{-b})$$

$$\lim_{b \to +\infty} \int_0^b e^{-x}\, dx = 1 \qquad\qquad (1)$$

We conclude from Eq. (1) that no matter how large a value we take for b, the area of the region shown in Fig. 15.3.1 will always be less than 1 square unit.   ●

Equation (1) states that if $b > 0$, for any $\epsilon > 0$ there exists an $N > 0$ such that

$$\left| \int_0^b e^{-x}\, dx - 1 \right| < \epsilon \qquad \text{whenever } b > N$$

In place of (1) we write

$$\int_0^{+\infty} e^{-x}\, dx = 1$$

In general, we have the following definition.

15.3.1 Definition   If f is continuous for all $x \geq a$, then

$$\int_a^{+\infty} f(x)\, dx = \lim_{b \to +\infty} \int_a^b f(x)\, dx$$

if this limit exists.

If the lower limit of integration is infinite, we have the following definition.

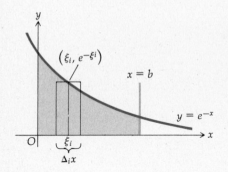

Figure 15.3.1

15.3.2 Definition If f is continuous for all $x \leq b$, then

$$\int_{-\infty}^{b} f(x)\ dx = \lim_{a \to -\infty} \int_{a}^{b} f(x)\ dx$$

if this limit exists.

Finally, we have the case when both limits of integration are infinite.

15.3.3 Definition If f is continuous for all values of x, then

$$\int_{-\infty}^{+\infty} f(x)\ dx = \lim_{a \to -\infty} \int_{a}^{0} f(x)\ dx + \lim_{b \to +\infty} \int_{0}^{b} f(x)\ dx$$

if these limits exist.

In Definitions 15.3.1, 15.3.2, and 15.3.3, if the limits exist, we say that the improper integral is *convergent*. If the limits do not exist, we say that the improper integral is *divergent*.

EXAMPLE 1:   Evaluate

$$\int_{-\infty}^{2} \frac{dx}{(4-x)^2}$$

if it converges.

SOLUTION:

$$\int_{-\infty}^{2} \frac{dx}{(4-x)^2} = \lim_{a \to -\infty} \int_{a}^{2} \frac{dx}{(4-x)^2}$$

$$= \lim_{a \to -\infty} \left[\frac{1}{4-x} \right]_{a}^{2}$$

$$= \lim_{a \to -\infty} \left(\frac{1}{2} - \frac{1}{4-a} \right)$$

$$= \tfrac{1}{2} - 0$$

$$= \tfrac{1}{2}$$

EXAMPLE 2:   Evaluate if they exist:

(a) $\displaystyle\int_{-\infty}^{+\infty} x\ dx$

and

(b) $\displaystyle\lim_{r \to +\infty} \int_{-r}^{r} x\ dx$

SOLUTION: (a) Using Definition 15.3.3, we have

$$\int_{-\infty}^{+\infty} x\ dx = \lim_{a \to -\infty} \int_{a}^{0} x\ dx + \lim_{b \to +\infty} \int_{0}^{b} x\ dx$$

$$= \lim_{a \to -\infty} \left[\tfrac{1}{2}x^2 \right]_{a}^{0} + \lim_{b \to +\infty} \left[\tfrac{1}{2}x^2 \right]_{0}^{b}$$

$$= \lim_{a \to -\infty} (-\tfrac{1}{2}a^2) + \lim_{b \to +\infty} \tfrac{1}{2}b^2$$

Because neither of these two limits exists, the improper integral diverges.

(b) $\displaystyle\lim_{r \to +\infty} \int_{-r}^{r} x\ dx = \lim_{r \to +\infty} \left[\tfrac{1}{2}x^2 \right]_{-r}^{r}$

$$= \lim_{r \to +\infty} (\tfrac{1}{2}r^2 - \tfrac{1}{2}r^2)$$

$$= \lim_{r \to +\infty} 0$$

$$= 0$$

Example 2 illustrates why we cannot use the limit in (b) as the definition of an improper integral where both limits of integration are infinite. That is, the improper integral in (a) is divergent, but the limit in (b) exists and is zero.

EXAMPLE 3: Evaluate

$$\int_{-\infty}^{+\infty} \frac{dx}{x^2 + 6x + 12}$$

if it converges.

SOLUTION:

$$\int_{-\infty}^{+\infty} \frac{dx}{x^2 + 6x + 12} = \lim_{a \to -\infty} \int_a^0 \frac{dx}{(x+3)^2 + 3} + \lim_{b \to +\infty} \int_0^b \frac{dx}{(x+3)^2 + 3}$$

$$= \lim_{a \to -\infty} \left[\frac{1}{\sqrt{3}} \tan^{-1} \frac{x+3}{\sqrt{3}} \right]_a^0 + \lim_{b \to +\infty} \left[\frac{1}{\sqrt{3}} \tan^{-1} \frac{x+3}{\sqrt{3}} \right]_0^b$$

$$= \lim_{a \to -\infty} \left(\frac{1}{\sqrt{3}} \tan^{-1} \sqrt{3} - \frac{1}{\sqrt{3}} \tan^{-1} \frac{a+3}{\sqrt{3}} \right)$$

$$+ \lim_{b \to +\infty} \left(\frac{1}{\sqrt{3}} \tan^{-1} \frac{b+3}{\sqrt{3}} - \frac{1}{\sqrt{3}} \tan^{-1} \sqrt{3} \right)$$

$$= \frac{1}{\sqrt{3}} \left[\lim_{a \to -\infty} \left(-\tan^{-1} \frac{a+3}{\sqrt{3}} \right) + \lim_{b \to +\infty} \tan^{-1} \frac{b+3}{\sqrt{3}} \right]$$

$$= \frac{1}{\sqrt{3}} \left[-\left(-\frac{\pi}{2} \right) + \frac{\pi}{2} \right]$$

$$= \frac{\pi}{\sqrt{3}}$$

EXAMPLE 4: Is it possible to assign a finite number to represent the measure of the area of the region bounded by the graphs of the equations $y = 1/x$, $y = 0$, and $x = 1$?

SOLUTION: The region is shown in Fig. 15.3.2. Let L be the number we wish to assign to the measure of the area, if possible. Let A be the measure of the area of the region bounded by the graphs of the equations $y = 1/x$, $y = 0$, $x = 1$, and $x = b$ where $b > 1$. Then

$$A = \lim_{\|\Delta\| \to 0} \sum_{i=1}^n \frac{1}{\xi_i} \Delta_i x = \int_1^b \frac{1}{x} \, dx$$

So we shall let $L = \lim_{b \to +\infty} A$ if this limit exists. But

$$\lim_{b \to +\infty} A = \lim_{b \to +\infty} \int_1^b \frac{1}{x} \, dx$$

$$= \lim_{b \to +\infty} [\ln b - \ln 1]$$

$$= +\infty$$

Therefore, it is not possible to assign a finite number to represent the measure of the area of the region.

Figure 15.3.2

EXAMPLE 5: Is it possible to assign a finite number to represent the measure of the volume of the solid formed by revolving the region in Example 4 about the x axis?

SOLUTION: The element of volume is a circular disk having a thickness of $\Delta_i x$ and a base radius of $1/\xi_i$. Let L be the number we wish to assign to the measure of the volume, and let V be the measure of the volume of the solid formed by revolving about the x axis the region bounded by the graphs of the equations $y = 1/x$, $y = 0$, $x = 1$, and $x = b$ where $b > 1$. Then

$$V = \lim_{\|\Delta\| \to 0} \sum_{i=1}^{n} \pi \left(\frac{1}{\xi_i}\right)^2 \Delta_i x = \pi \int_1^b \frac{1}{x^2}\, dx$$

We shall let $L = \lim_{b \to +\infty} V$, if the limit exists.

$$\lim_{b \to +\infty} V = \lim_{b \to +\infty} \pi \int_1^b \frac{dx}{x^2}$$

$$= \pi \lim_{b \to +\infty} \left[-\frac{1}{x}\right]_1^b$$

$$= \pi \lim_{b \to +\infty} \left(-\frac{1}{b} + 1\right)$$

$$= \pi$$

Therefore, we assign π to represent the measure of the volume of the solid.

EXAMPLE 6: Determine if

$$\int_0^{+\infty} \sin x\, dx$$

is convergent or divergent.

SOLUTION:

$$\int_0^{+\infty} \sin x\, dx = \lim_{b \to +\infty} \int_0^b \sin x\, dx$$

$$= \lim_{b \to +\infty} \left[-\cos x\right]_0^b$$

$$= \lim_{b \to +\infty} (-\cos b + 1)$$

For any integer n, as b takes on all values from $n\pi$ to $2n\pi$, $\cos b$ takes on all values from -1 to 1. Hence, $\lim_{b \to +\infty} \cos b$ does not exist. Therefore, the improper integral is divergent.

Example 6 illustrates the case for which an improper integral is divergent where the limit is not infinite.

Exercises 15.3

In Exercises 1 through 14, determine whether the improper integral is convergent or divergent. If it is convergent, evaluate it.

1. $\displaystyle\int_0^{+\infty} e^{-x}\, dx$

2. $\displaystyle\int_{-\infty}^1 e^x\, dx$

3. $\displaystyle\int_{-\infty}^0 x\, 5^{-x^2}\, dx$

4. $\displaystyle\int_1^{+\infty} 2^{-x}\, dx$

5. $\displaystyle\int_0^{+\infty} xe^{-x}\, dx$

6. $\displaystyle\int_5^{+\infty} \frac{dx}{\sqrt{x-1}}$

7. $\displaystyle\int_{-\infty}^{+\infty} x \cosh x\, dx$

8. $\displaystyle\int_{-\infty}^0 x^2 e^x\, dx$

9. $\displaystyle\int_{-\infty}^{+\infty} e^{-|x|}\, dx$

10. $\displaystyle\int_{-\infty}^{+\infty} xe^{-x^2}\, dx$

11. $\displaystyle\int_e^{+\infty} \frac{dx}{x(\ln x)^2}$

12. $\displaystyle\int_{-\infty}^{+\infty} \frac{dx}{16 + x^2}$

13. $\displaystyle\int_1^{+\infty} \ln x\, dx$

14. $\displaystyle\int_0^{+\infty} e^{-x} \cos x\, dx$

15. Evaluate if they exist: (a) $\int_{-\infty}^{+\infty} \sin x\, dx$; (b) $\lim_{r \to +\infty} \int_{-r}^r \sin x\, dx$.

16. Prove that if $\int_{-\infty}^b f(x)\, dx$ is convergent, then $\int_{-b}^{+\infty} f(-x)\, dx$ is also convergent and has the same value.

17. Show that the improper integral $\int_{-\infty}^{+\infty} x(1 + x^2)^{-2}\, dx$ is convergent and the improper integral $\int_{-\infty}^{+\infty} x(1 + x^2)^{-1}\, dx$ is divergent.

18. Prove that the improper integral $\int_1^{+\infty} dx/x^n$ is convergent if and only if $n > 1$.

19. Determine if it is possible to assign a finite number to represent the measure of the area of the region bounded by the curve whose equation is $y = 1/(e^x + e^{-x})$ and the x axis. If a finite number can be assigned, find it.

20. Determine if it is possible to assign a finite number to represent the measure of the area of the region bounded by the x axis, the line $x = 2$, and the curve whose equation is $y = 1/(x^2 - 1)$. If a finite number can be assigned, find it.

21. Determine if it is possible to assign a finite number to represent the measure of the volume of the solid formed by revolving about the x axis the region to the right of the line $x = 1$ and bounded by the curve whose equation is $y = 1/x\sqrt{x}$ and the x axis. If a finite number can be assigned, find it.

22. Determine a value of n for which the improper integral

$$\int_1^{+\infty} \left(\frac{nx^2}{x^3 + 1} - \frac{1}{3x + 1} \right) dx$$

is convergent and evaluate the integral for this value of n.

23. Determine a value of n for which the improper integral

$$\int_1^{+\infty} \left(\frac{n}{x + 1} - \frac{3x}{2x^2 + n} \right) dx$$

is convergent and evaluate the integral for this value of n.

Exercises 24, 25, and 26 show an interesting application of improper integrals in the field of economics. Suppose there is a continuous flow of income for which interest is compounded continuously at the annual rate of $100i$ percent and $f(t)$ dollars is the income per year at any time t years. If the income continues indefinitely, the present value, V dollars, of all future income is defined by

$$V = \int_0^{+\infty} f(t)e^{-it}\,dt$$

24. A continuous flow of income is decreasing with time and at t years the number of dollars in the annual income is $1000 \cdot 2^{-t}$. Find the present value of this income if it continues indefinitely using an interest rate of 8 percent compounded continuously.

25. The continuous flow of profit for a company is increasing with time, and at t years the number of dollars in the profit per year is proportional to t. Show that the present value of the company is inversely proportional to i^2, where $100i$ percent is the interest rate compounded continuously.

26. The British Consol is a bond with no maturity (i.e., it never comes due), and it affords the holder an annual lump-sum payment. By finding the present value of a flow of payments of R dollars annually and using the current interest rate of $100i$ percent, compounded continuously, show that the fair selling price of a British Consol is R/i dollars.

15.4 OTHER IMPROPER INTEGRALS

Figure 15.4.1

Figure 15.4.1 shows the region bounded by the curve whose equation is $y = 1/\sqrt{x}$, the x axis, the y axis, and the line $x = 4$. If it is possible to assign a finite number to represent the measure of the area of this region, it would be given by

$$\lim_{||\Delta||\to 0} \sum_{i=1}^n \frac{1}{\sqrt{\xi_i}}\,\Delta_i x$$

If this limit exists, it is the definite integral denoted by

$$\int_0^4 \frac{dx}{\sqrt{x}} \tag{1}$$

However, the integrand is discontinuous at the lower limit zero. Furthermore, $\lim_{x \to 0^+} 1/\sqrt{x} = +\infty$, and so we state that the integrand has an infinite discontinuity at the lower limit. Such an integral is improper, and its existence can be determined from the following definition.

15.4.1 Definition If f is continuous at all x in the interval half open on the left $(a, b]$, and if $\lim_{x \to a^+} f(x) = \pm\infty$, then

$$\int_a^b f(x)\,dx = \lim_{\epsilon \to 0^+} \int_{a+\epsilon}^b f(x)\,dx$$

if this limit exists.

● ILLUSTRATION 1: We determine if it is possible to assign a finite number to represent the measure of the area of the region shown in Fig. 15.4.1. From the discussion preceding Definition 15.4.1 the measure of the area of the given region will be the improper integral (1) if it exists. By Definition 15.4.1, we have

$$\int_0^4 \frac{dx}{\sqrt{x}} = \lim_{\epsilon \to 0^+} \int_\epsilon^4 \frac{dx}{\sqrt{x}}$$

$$= \lim_{\epsilon \to 0^+} 2x^{1/2} \Big]_\epsilon^4$$

$$= \lim_{\epsilon \to 0^+} [4 - 2\sqrt{\epsilon}]$$

$$= 4 - 0$$

$$= 4$$

Therefore, we assign 4 to the measure of the area of the given region. ●

If the integrand has an infinite discontinuity at the upper limit of integration, we use the following definition to determine the existence of the improper integral.

15.4.2 Definition If f is continuous at all x in the interval half open on the right $[a, b)$ and if $\lim\limits_{x \to b^-} f(x) = \pm\infty$, then

$$\int_a^b f(x)\ dx = \lim_{\epsilon \to 0^+} \int_a^{b-\epsilon} f(x)\ dx$$

if this limit exists.

If there is an infinite discontinuity at an interior point of the interval of integration, the existence of the improper integral is determined from the following definition.

15.4.3 Definition If f is continuous at all x in the interval $[a, b]$ except c when $a < c < b$ and if $\lim\limits_{x \to c} |f(x)| = +\infty$, then

$$\int_a^b f(x)\ dx = \lim_{\epsilon \to 0^+} \int_a^{c-\epsilon} f(x)\ dx + \lim_{\delta \to 0^+} \int_{c+\delta}^b f(x)\ dx$$

if these limits exist.

If $\int_a^b f(x)\ dx$ is an improper integral, it is convergent if the corresponding limit exists; otherwise, it is divergent.

EXAMPLE 1: Evaluate

$$\int_0^2 \frac{dx}{(x-1)^2}$$

if it is convergent.

SOLUTION: The integrand has an infinite discontinuity at 1. Applying Definition 15.4.3, we have

$$\int_0^2 \frac{dx}{(x-1)^2} = \lim_{\epsilon \to 0^+} \int_0^{1-\epsilon} \frac{dx}{(x-1)^2} + \lim_{\delta \to 0^+} \int_{1+\delta}^2 \frac{dx}{(x-1)^2}$$

$$= \lim_{\epsilon \to 0^+} \left[-\frac{1}{x-1} \right]_0^{1-\epsilon} + \lim_{\delta \to 0^+} \left[-\frac{1}{x-1} \right]_{1+\delta}^2$$

$$= \lim_{\epsilon \to 0^+} \left[\frac{1}{\epsilon} - 1 \right] + \lim_{\delta \to 0^+} \left[-1 + \frac{1}{\delta} \right]$$

Because neither of these limits exist, the improper integral is divergent.

● ILLUSTRATION 2: Suppose that in evaluating the integral in Example 1 we had failed to note the infinite discontinuity of the integrand at 1. We would have obtained

$$- \frac{1}{x - 1} \Big]_0^2 = - \frac{1}{1} + \frac{1}{-1} = -2$$

This is obviously an incorrect result. Because the integrand $1/(x-1)^2$ is never negative, the integral from 0 to 2 could not possibly be a negative number. ●

EXAMPLE 2: Evaluate

$$\int_0^1 x \ln x \, dx$$

if it is convergent.

SOLUTION: The integrand has a discontinuity at the lower limit. Applying Definition 15.4.1, we have

$$\int_0^1 x \ln x \, dx = \lim_{\epsilon \to 0^+} \int_\epsilon^1 x \ln x \, dx$$

$$= \lim_{\epsilon \to 0^+} \left[\tfrac{1}{2} x^2 \ln x - \tfrac{1}{4} x^2 \right]_\epsilon^1$$

$$= \lim_{\epsilon \to 0^+} \left[\tfrac{1}{2} \ln 1 - \tfrac{1}{4} - \tfrac{1}{2} \epsilon^2 \ln \epsilon - \tfrac{1}{4} \epsilon^2 \right]$$

Hence,

$$\int_0^1 x \ln x \, dx = 0 - \tfrac{1}{4} - \tfrac{1}{2} \lim_{\epsilon \to 0^+} \epsilon^2 \ln \epsilon - 0 \qquad (2)$$

To evaluate

$$\lim_{\epsilon \to 0^+} \epsilon^2 \ln \epsilon = \lim_{\epsilon \to 0^+} \frac{\ln \epsilon}{\dfrac{1}{\epsilon^2}}$$

we apply L'Hôpital's rule because $\lim_{\epsilon \to 0^+} \ln \epsilon = -\infty$ and $\lim_{\epsilon \to 0^+} 1/\epsilon^2 = +\infty$. We have

$$\lim_{\epsilon \to 0^+} \frac{\ln \epsilon}{\dfrac{1}{\epsilon^2}} = \lim_{\epsilon \to 0^+} \frac{\dfrac{1}{\epsilon}}{-\dfrac{2}{\epsilon^3}} = \lim_{\epsilon \to 0^+} \left[-\frac{\epsilon^2}{2} \right] = 0$$

Therefore, from (2) we have

$$\int_0^1 x \ln x \, dx = -\tfrac{1}{4}$$

EXAMPLE 3:   Evaluate

$$\int_1^{+\infty} \frac{dx}{x\sqrt{x^2-1}}$$

if it is convergent.

SOLUTION: For this integral, there is both an infinite upper limit and an infinite discontinuity of the integrand at the lower limit. We proceed as follows.

$$\int_1^{+\infty} \frac{dx}{x\sqrt{x^2-1}} = \lim_{a\to 1^+} \int_a^2 \frac{dx}{x\sqrt{x^2-1}} + \lim_{b\to +\infty} \int_2^b \frac{dx}{x\sqrt{x^2-1}}$$

$$= \lim_{a\to 1^+} \left[\sec^{-1} x \right]_a^2 + \lim_{b\to +\infty} \left[\sec^{-1} x \right]_2^b$$

$$= \lim_{a\to 1^+} (\sec^{-1} 2 - \sec^{-1} a) + \lim_{b\to +\infty} (\sec^{-1} b - \sec^{-1} 2)$$

$$= -\lim_{a\to 1^+} \sec^{-1} a + \lim_{b\to +\infty} \sec^{-1} b$$

$$= 0 + \tfrac{1}{2}\pi$$

$$= \tfrac{1}{2}\pi$$

Exercises 15.4

In Exercises 1 through 20, determine whether the improper integral is convergent or divergent. If it is convergent, evaluate it.

1. $\displaystyle\int_0^1 \frac{dx}{\sqrt{1-x}}$

2. $\displaystyle\int_0^2 \frac{dx}{\sqrt{4-x^2}}$

3. $\displaystyle\int_{\pi/4}^{\pi/2} \sec x\, dx$

4. $\displaystyle\int_0^4 \frac{x\, dx}{\sqrt{16-x^2}}$

5. $\displaystyle\int_0^{+\infty} \frac{dx}{x^3}$

6. $\displaystyle\int_0^{\pi/2} \tan\theta\, d\theta$

7. $\displaystyle\int_0^{\pi/2} \frac{dt}{1-\sin t}$

8. $\displaystyle\int_0^2 \frac{dx}{(x-1)^{2/3}}$

9. $\displaystyle\int_0^4 \frac{dx}{x^2-2x-3}$

10. $\displaystyle\int_2^{+\infty} \frac{dx}{x\sqrt{x^2-4}}$

11. $\displaystyle\int_0^{+\infty} \ln x\, dx$

12. $\displaystyle\int_{-1}^1 \frac{dx}{x^2}$

13. $\displaystyle\int_{-2}^0 \frac{dt}{(t+1)^{1/3}}$

14. $\displaystyle\int_0^2 \frac{dx}{\sqrt{2x-x^2}}$

15. $\displaystyle\int_{-2}^2 \frac{dx}{x^3}$

16. $\displaystyle\int_0^{+\infty} \frac{e^{-\sqrt{x}}}{\sqrt{x}}\, dx$

17. $\displaystyle\int_{1/2}^2 \frac{dt}{t(\ln t)^{1/5}}$

18. $\displaystyle\int_0^2 \frac{x\, dx}{1-x}$

19. $\displaystyle\int_1^2 \frac{dx}{x\sqrt{x^2-1}}$

20. $\displaystyle\int_0^1 \frac{dx}{x\sqrt{4-x^2}}$

21. Evaluate, if they exist:

(a) $\displaystyle\int_{-1}^1 \frac{dx}{x}$; (b) $\displaystyle\lim_{r\to 0^+} \left[\int_{-1}^{-r} \frac{dx}{x} + \int_r^1 \frac{dx}{x} \right]$

22. Show that it is possible to assign a finite number to represent the measure of the area of the region bounded by the curve whose equation is $y = 1/\sqrt{x}$, the line $x = 1$, and the x and y axes, but that it is not possible to assign a finite number to represent the measure of the volume of the solid of revolution generated if this region is revolved about the x axis.

In Exercises 23 through 25, find the values of n for which the improper integral converges and evaluate the integral for these values of n.

23. $\displaystyle\int_0^1 x^n \, dx$

24. $\displaystyle\int_0^1 x^n \ln x \, dx$

25. $\displaystyle\int_0^1 x^n \ln^2 x \, dx$

15.5 TAYLOR'S FORMULA   Values of polynomial functions can be found by performing a finite number of additions and multiplications. However, there are other functions, such as the logarithmic, exponential, and trigonometric functions, that cannot be evaluated as easily. We show in this section that many functions can be approximated by polynomials and that the polynomial, instead of the original function, can be used for computations when the difference between the actual function value and the polynomial approximation is sufficiently small.

There are various methods of approximating a given function by polynomials. One of the most widely used is that involving *Taylor's formula* named in honor of the English mathematician Brook Taylor (1685–1731). The following theorem, which can be considered as a generalization of the mean-value theorem (4.7.2), gives us Taylor's formula.

15.5.1 Theorem   Let f be a function such that f and its first n derivatives are continuous on the closed interval $[a, b]$. Furthermore, let $f^{(n+1)}(x)$ exist for all x in the open interval (a, b). Then there is a number ξ in the open interval (a, b) such that

$$f(b) = f(a) + \frac{f'(a)}{1!}(b-a) + \frac{f''(a)}{2!}(b-a)^2 + \cdots$$
$$+ \frac{f^{(n)}(a)}{n!}(b-a)^n + \frac{f^{(n+1)}(\xi)}{(n+1)!}(b-a)^{n+1} \qquad (1)$$

Equation (1) also holds if $b < a$; in such a case, $[a, b]$ is replaced by $[b, a]$, and (a, b) is replaced by (b, a).

Before proving this theorem, note that when $n = 0$, (1) becomes

$$f(b) = f(a) + f'(\xi)(b-a)$$

where ξ is between a and b. This is the mean-value theorem (4.7.2).

There are several known proofs of Theorem 15.5.1, although none is very well motivated. The one following makes use of Cauchy's mean-value theorem (15.1.3).

PROOF OF THEOREM 15.5.1:   Let F and G be two functions defined by

$$F(x) = f(b) - f(x) - f'(x)(b-x) - \frac{f''(x)}{2!}(b-x)^2 - \cdots$$
$$- \frac{f^{(n-1)}(x)}{(n-1)!}(b-x)^{n-1} - \frac{f^{(n)}(x)}{n!}(b-x)^n \quad (2)$$

and

$$G(x) = \frac{(b-x)^{n+1}}{(n+1)!} \tag{3}$$

It follows that $F(b) = 0$ and $G(b) = 0$. Differentiating in (2), we get

$$F'(x) = -f'(x) + f'(x) - f''(x)(b-x) + \frac{2f''(x)(b-x)}{2!}$$

$$-\frac{f'''(x)(b-x)^2}{2!} + \frac{3f'''(x)(b-x)^2}{3!} - \frac{f^{(iv)}(x)(b-x)^3}{3!} + \cdots$$

$$+ \frac{(n-1)f^{(n-1)}(x)(b-x)^{n-2}}{(n-1)!} - \frac{f^{(n)}(x)(b-x)^{n-1}}{(n-1)!}$$

$$+ \frac{nf^{(n)}(x)(b-x)^{n-1}}{n!} - \frac{f^{(n+1)}(x)(b-x)^n}{n!}$$

Combining terms, we see that the sum of every odd-numbered term with the following even-numbered term is zero, and so only the last term remains. Therefore,

$$F'(x) = -\frac{f^{(n+1)}(x)}{n!}(b-x)^n \tag{4}$$

Differentiating in (3), we obtain

$$G'(x) = -\frac{1}{n!}(b-x)^n \tag{5}$$

Checking the hypothesis of Theorem 15.1.3, we see that

(i) F and G are continuous on $[a, b]$;
(ii) F and G are differentiable on (a, b);
(iii) for all x in (a, b), $G'(x) \neq 0$.

So by the conclusion of Theorem 15.1.3 it follows that

$$\frac{F(b) - F(a)}{G(b) - G(a)} = \frac{F'(\xi)}{G'(\xi)}$$

where ξ is in (a, b). But $F(b) = 0$ and $G(b) = 0$. So

$$F(a) = \frac{F'(\xi)}{G'(\xi)}G(a) \tag{6}$$

for some ξ in (a, b).

Letting $x = a$ in (3), $x = \xi$ in (4), and $x = \xi$ in (5) and substituting into (6), we obtain

$$F(a) = -\frac{f^{(n+1)}(\xi)}{n!}(b-\xi)^n \left[-\frac{n!}{(b-\xi)^n} \right] \frac{(b-a)^{n+1}}{(n+1)!}$$

or, equivalently,

$$F(a) = \frac{f^{(n+1)}(\xi)}{(n+1)!} (b-a)^{n+1} \qquad (7)$$

Letting $x = a$ in (2), we obtain

$$F(a) = f(b) - f(a) - f'(a)(b-a) - \frac{f''(a)}{2!} (b-a)^2 - \cdots$$
$$- \frac{f^{(n-1)}(a)}{(n-1)!} (b-a)^{n-1} - \frac{f^{(n)}(a)}{n!} (b-a)^n \qquad (8)$$

Substituting from (7) into (8), we get

$$f(b) = f(a) + f'(a)(b-a) + \frac{f''(a)}{2!} (b-a)^2 + \cdots$$
$$+ \frac{f^{(n)}(a)}{n!} (b-a)^n + \frac{f^{(n+1)}(\xi)}{(n+1)!} (b-a)^{n+1}$$

which is the desired result. The theorem holds if $b < a$ because the conclusion of Theorem 15.1.3 is unaffected if a and b are interchanged. ∎

If in (1) b is replaced by x, Taylor's formula is obtained. It is

$$f(x) = f(a) + \frac{f'(a)}{1!} (x-a) + \frac{f''(a)}{2!} (x-a)^2 + \cdots$$
$$+ \frac{f^{(n)}(a)}{n!} (x-a)^n + \frac{f^{(n+1)}(\xi)}{(n+1)!} (x-a)^{n+1} \qquad (9)$$

where ξ is between a and x.

The condition under which (9) holds is that f and its first n derivatives must be continuous on a closed interval containing a and x, and the $(n+1)$st derivative of f must exist at all points of the corresponding open interval. Formula (9) may be written as

$$f(x) = P_n(x) + R_n(x) \qquad (10)$$

where

$$P_n(x) = f(a) + \frac{f'(a)}{1!} (x-a) + \frac{f''(a)}{2!} (x-a)^2 + \cdots$$
$$+ \frac{f^{(n)}(a)}{n!} (x-a)^n \qquad (11)$$

and

$$R_n(x) = \frac{f^{(n+1)}(\xi)}{(n+1)!} (x-a)^{n+1} \qquad \text{where } \xi \text{ is between } a \text{ and } x \qquad (12)$$

$P_n(x)$ is called the nth-degree *Taylor polynomial* of the function f at the number a, and $R_n(x)$ is called the *remainder*. The term $R_n(x)$ as given in (12) is called the *Lagrange form* of the remainder, named in honor of the French mathematician Joseph L. Lagrange (1736–1813).

EXAMPLE 1: Find the third-degree Taylor polynomial of the cosine function at $\frac{1}{4}\pi$ and the Lagrange form of the remainder.

SOLUTION: Letting $f(x) = \cos x$, we have from (11)

$$P_3(x) = f\left(\frac{\pi}{4}\right) + f'\left(\frac{\pi}{4}\right)\left(x - \frac{\pi}{4}\right) + \frac{f''(\frac{1}{4}\pi)}{2!}\left(x - \frac{\pi}{4}\right)^2 + \frac{f'''(\frac{1}{4}\pi)}{3!}\left(x - \frac{\pi}{4}\right)^3$$

Because $f(x) = \cos x$, $f(\frac{1}{4}\pi) = \frac{1}{2}\sqrt{2}$; $f'(x) = -\sin x$, $f'(\frac{1}{4}\pi) = -\frac{1}{2}\sqrt{2}$; $f''(x) = -\cos x$, $f''(\frac{1}{4}\pi) = -\frac{1}{2}\sqrt{2}$; $f'''(x) = \sin x$, $f'''(\frac{1}{4}\pi) = \frac{1}{2}\sqrt{2}$. Therefore,

$$P_3(x) = \frac{1}{2}\sqrt{2} - \frac{1}{2}\sqrt{2}(x - \frac{1}{4}\pi) - \frac{1}{4}\sqrt{2}(x - \frac{1}{4}\pi)^2 + \frac{1}{12}\sqrt{2}(x - \frac{1}{4}\pi)^3$$

Because $f^{(\text{iv})}(x) = \cos x$, we obtain from (12)

$$R_3(x) = \frac{1}{24}(\cos \xi)(x - \frac{1}{4}\pi)^4 \qquad \text{where } \xi \text{ is between } \frac{1}{4}\pi \text{ and } x$$

Because $|\cos \xi| \leq 1$, we may conclude that for all x, $|R_3(x)| \leq \frac{1}{24}(x - \frac{1}{4}\pi)^4$.

Taylor's formula may be used to approximate a function by means of a Taylor polynomial. From (10) we obtain

$$|R_n(x)| = |f(x) - P_n(x)| \tag{13}$$

If $P_n(x)$ is used to approximate $f(x)$, we can obtain an upper bound for the error of this approximation if we can find a number $E > 0$ such that $|R_n(x)| \leq E$ or, because of (13), such that $|f(x) - P_n(x)| \leq E$ or, equivalently,

$$P_n(x) - E \leq f(x) \leq P_n(x) + E$$

EXAMPLE 2: Use the result of Example 1 to compute an approximate value of $\cos 47°$ and determine the accuracy of the result.

SOLUTION: $47° \sim \frac{47}{180}\pi$ radians. Thus, in the solution of Example 1, we take $x = \frac{47}{180}\pi$ and $x - \frac{1}{4}\pi = \frac{1}{90}\pi$, and we have

$$\cos 47° = \frac{1}{2}\sqrt{2}[1 - \frac{1}{90}\pi - \frac{1}{2}(\frac{1}{90}\pi)^2 + \frac{1}{6}(\frac{1}{90}\pi)^3] + R_3(\frac{47}{180}\pi)$$

where

$$R_3(\tfrac{47}{180}\pi) = \frac{1}{24}\cos \xi \, (\tfrac{1}{90}\pi)^4 \qquad \text{with } \frac{1}{4}\pi < \xi < \frac{47}{180}\pi$$

Because $0 < \cos \xi < 1$,

$$0 < R_3(\tfrac{47}{180}\pi) < \tfrac{1}{24}(\tfrac{1}{90}\pi)^4 < 0.00000007$$

Taking $\frac{1}{90}\pi \approx 0.0349066$, we obtain

$$\cos 47° \approx 0.681998$$

which is accurate to six decimal places.

EXAMPLE 3: Use a Taylor polynomial at zero to find the value of $\sqrt{e}$, accurate to four decimal places.

SOLUTION: If we let $f(x) = e^x$, all the derivatives of f at x are e^x and all the derivatives evaluated at zero are 1. Therefore, from (11) we have

$$P_n(x) = 1 + x + \frac{x^2}{2!} + \frac{x^3}{3!} + \cdots + \frac{x^n}{n!}$$

and from (12) we get

$$R_n(x) = \frac{e^\xi}{(n+1)!}\, x^{n+1} \qquad \text{where } \xi \text{ is between } 0 \text{ and } x$$

We want $|R_n(\frac{1}{2})|$ to be less than 0.00005. If we take $x = \frac{1}{2}$ in the above and because $e^{1/2} < 2$, we get

$$|R_n(\tfrac{1}{2})| < \frac{e^{1/2}}{2^{n+1}(n+1)!} < \frac{2}{2^{n+1}(n+1)!} = \frac{1}{2^n(n+1)!}$$

$|R_n(\frac{1}{2})|$ will be less than 0.00005 if $1/2^n(n+1)! < 0.00005$. When $n = 5$,

$$\frac{1}{2^n(n+1)!} = \frac{1}{(32)(720)} = 0.00004 < 0.00005$$

So

$$\sqrt{e} \approx P_5(\tfrac{1}{2}) = 1 + \tfrac{1}{2} + \tfrac{1}{8} + \tfrac{1}{48} + \tfrac{1}{384} + \tfrac{1}{3840}$$

from which we obtain $\sqrt{e} \approx 1.64870$.

A special case of Taylor's formula is obtained by taking $a = 0$ in (9) and we get

$$f(x) = f(0) + \frac{f'(0)}{1!}\, x + \frac{f''(0)}{2!}\, x^2 + \cdots + \frac{f^{(n)}(0)}{n!}\, x^n + \frac{f^{(n+1)}(\xi)}{(n+1)!}\, x^{n+1} \quad (14)$$

where ξ is between 0 and x. Formula (14) is called Maclaurin's formula, named in honor of the Scottish mathematician Colin Maclaurin (1698–1746). However, the formula was obtained earlier by Taylor and by another British mathematician, James Stirling (1692–1770).

There are other forms of the remainder in Taylor's formula. Depending on the function, one form of the remainder may be more desirable to use than another. The following theorem expresses the remainder as an integral, and it is known as *Taylor's formula with integral form of the remainder.*

15.5.2 Theorem   If f is a function whose first $n + 1$ derivatives are continuous on a closed interval containing a and x, then $f(x) = P_n(x) + R_n(x)$, where $P_n(x)$ is the nth-degree Taylor polynomial of f at a and $R_n(x)$ is the remainder given by

$$R_n(x) = \frac{1}{n!} \int_a^x (x - t)^n f^{(n+1)}(t)\, dt \tag{15}$$

The proof of this theorem is left as an exercise (see Exercise 22).

Exercises 15.5

In Exercises 1 through 10, find the Taylor polynomial of degree n with the Lagrange form of the remainder at the number a for the function defined by the given equation.

1. $f(x) = \sin x; \ a = \frac{1}{6}\pi; \ n = 3$

2. $f(x) = \tan x; \ a = 0; \ n = 3$

3. $f(x) = \sinh x; \ a = 0; \ n = 4$

4. $f(x) = \cosh x; \ a = 0; \ n = 4$

5. $f(x) = \ln x; \ a = 1; \ n = 3$

6. $f(x) = \sqrt{x}; \ a = 4; \ n = 4$

7. $f(x) = \ln \cos x; \ a = \frac{1}{3}\pi; \ n = 3$

8. $f(x) = e^{-x^2}; \ a = 0; \ n = 3$

9. $f(x) = (1 + x)^{3/2}; \ a = 0; \ n = 3$

10. $f(x) = (1 - x)^{-1/2}; \ a = 0; \ n = 3$

11. Compute the value of e correct to five decimal places, and prove that your answer has the required accuracy.

12. Use the Taylor polynomial in Exercise 6 to compute $\sqrt{5}$ accurate to as many places as is justified when R_4 is neglected.

13. Compute $\sin 31°$ accurate to three decimal places by using the Taylor polynomial in Exercise 1 at $\frac{1}{6}\pi$. (Use the approximation $\frac{1}{180}\pi \approx 0.0175$.)

14. Use a Taylor polynomial at 0 for the function defined by $f(x) = \ln(1 + x)$ to compute the value of $\ln 1.2$, accurate to four decimal places.

15. Use a Taylor polynomial at 0 for the function defined by

$$f(x) = \ln \frac{1 + x}{1 - x}$$

to compute the value of $\ln 1.2$ accurate to four decimal places. Compare the computation with that of Exercise 14.

16. Show that the formula

$$(1 + x)^{3/2} \approx 1 + \tfrac{3}{2}x$$

is accurate to three decimal places if $-0.03 \le x \le 0$.

17. Show that the formula

$$(1 + x)^{-1/2} \approx 1 - \tfrac{1}{2}x$$

is accurate to two decimal places if $-0.1 \le x \le 0$.

18. Show that if $0 \le x \le \frac{1}{2}$,

$$\sin x = x - \frac{x^3}{3!} + R(x)$$

where $|R(x)| < \frac{1}{3840}$.

19. Use the result of Exercise 18 to find an approximate value of $\int_0^{1/\sqrt{2}} \sin x^2 \, dx$ and estimate the error.

20. Draw sketches of the graphs of $y = \sin x$ and $y = mx$ on the same set of axes. Note that if m is positive and close to zero, then the graphs intersect at a point whose abscissa is close to π. By finding the second-degree Taylor polynomial at π for the function f defined by $f(x) = \sin x - mx$, show that an approximate solution of the equation $\sin x = mx$, when m is positive and close to zero, is given by $x \approx \pi/(1 + m)$.

21. Use the method described in Exercise 20 to find an approximate solution of the equation $\cot x = mx$ when m is positive and close to zero.

22. Prove Theorem 15.5.2 (HINT: Let

$$\int_a^x f'(t) \, dt = f(x) - f(a)$$

Solve for $f(x)$ and integrate

$$\int_a^x f'(t)\, dt$$

by parts by letting $u = f'(t)$ and $dv = dt$. Repeat this process, and the desired result follows by mathematical induction.)

Review Exercises (Chapter 15)

In Exercises 1 through 14, evaluate the limit, if it exists.

1. $\lim\limits_{x \to 0^+} \dfrac{\tanh 2x}{\sinh^2 x}$

2. $\lim\limits_{x \to \pi/2} \left(\dfrac{1}{1 - \sin x} - \dfrac{2}{\cos^2 x} \right)$

3. $\lim\limits_{x \to 0} (\csc^2 x - x^{-2})$

4. $\lim\limits_{x \to 0} \dfrac{e - (1 + x)^{1/x}}{x}$

5. $\lim\limits_{t \to +\infty} \dfrac{\ln(1 + e^{2t}/t)}{t^{1/2}}$

6. $\lim\limits_{x \to +\infty} x \ln \dfrac{x+1}{x-1}$

7. $\lim\limits_{x \to \pi/2} (\sin^2 x)^{\tan x}$

8. $\lim\limits_{t \to +\infty} \dfrac{t^{100}}{e^t}$

9. $\lim\limits_{x \to +\infty} \dfrac{\ln(\ln x)}{\ln(x - \ln x)}$

10. $\lim\limits_{x \to 0} \dfrac{x - \tan^{-1} x}{4x^3}$

11. $\lim\limits_{\theta \to \pi/2} \dfrac{\tan \theta + 3}{\sec \theta - 1}$

12. $\lim\limits_{x \to 0} \left(\dfrac{\sin x}{x} \right)^{1/x}$

13. $\lim\limits_{x \to +\infty} (e^x - x)^{1/x}$

14. $\lim\limits_{x \to 0^+} \left(\dfrac{1}{x} \right)^{\tan x}$

In Exercises 15 through 24, determine whether the improper integral is convergent or divergent. If it is convergent, evaluate it.

15. $\displaystyle\int_{-2}^0 \dfrac{dx}{2x + 3}$

16. $\displaystyle\int_0^{+\infty} \dfrac{dx}{\sqrt{e^x}}$

17. $\displaystyle\int_{-\infty}^0 \dfrac{dx}{(x - 2)^2}$

18. $\displaystyle\int_2^4 \dfrac{x\, dx}{\sqrt{x - 2}}$

19. $\displaystyle\int_0^{\pi/4} \cot^2 \theta\, d\theta$

20. $\displaystyle\int_1^{+\infty} \dfrac{dt}{t^4 + t^2}$

21. $\displaystyle\int_{-\infty}^{+\infty} \dfrac{dx}{4x^2 + 4x + 5}$

22. $\displaystyle\int_0^1 \dfrac{\ln x}{x}\, dx$

23. $\displaystyle\int_0^1 \dfrac{dx}{x + x^3}$

24. $\displaystyle\int_{-3}^0 \dfrac{dx}{\sqrt{3 - 2x - x^2}}$

In Exercises 25 and 26, find the Taylor polynomial of degree n with the Lagrange form of the remainder at the number a for the function defined by the given equation.

25. $f(x) = \cos x$; $a = 0$; $n = 6$

26. $f(x) = (1 + x^2)^{-1}$; $a = 1$; $n = 3$

27. Given:

$$f(x) = \begin{cases} \dfrac{e^x - 1}{x} & \text{if } x \neq 0 \\ 1 & \text{if } x = 0 \end{cases}$$

(a) Prove that f is continuous at 0. (b) Prove that f is differentiable at 0 and find $f'(0)$.

28. For the function of Exercise 27, find, if they exist: (a) $\lim\limits_{x \to +\infty} f(x)$; (b) $\lim\limits_{x \to -\infty} f(x)$.

29. Given:

$$f(x) = \begin{cases} \dfrac{e^x - e^{-x}}{e^{2x} - e^{-2x}} & \text{if } x \neq 0 \\ 1 & \text{if } x = 0 \end{cases}$$

(a) Is f continuous at 0? (b) Find $\lim\limits_{x \to +\infty} f(x)$, if it exists.

30. If the normal line to the curve $y = \ln x$ at the point $(x_1, \ln x_1)$ intersects the x axis at the point having an abscissa of a, prove that $\lim\limits_{x_1 \to +\infty} (a - x_1) = 0$.

31. If the first four terms of the Taylor polynomial at 0 are used to approximate the value of $\sqrt{e}$, how accurate is the result?

32. Express both e^{x^2} and $\cos x$ as a Taylor polynomial of degree 4 at 0 and use them to evaluate

$$\lim\limits_{x \to 0} \frac{e^{x^2} - \cos x}{x^4}$$

33. Evaluate the limit in Exercise 32 by L'Hôpital's rule.

34. Apply Taylor's formula to express the polynomial

$$P(x) = 4x^3 + 5x^2 - 2x + 1$$

as a polynomial in powers of $(x + 2)$.

35. Determine if it is possible to assign a finite number to represent the measure of the area of the region to the right of the y axis bounded by the curve $4y^2 - xy^2 - x^2 = 0$ and its asymptote. If a finite number can be assigned, find it.

36. Determine if it is possible to assign a finite number to represent the measure of the area of the region in the first quadrant and below the curve having the equation $y = e^{-x}$. If a finite number can be assigned, find it.

37. Assuming a continuous flow of income for a particular business and that at t years from now the number of dollars in the income per year is given by $1000t - 300$, what is the present value of all future income if 8% is the interest rate compounded continuously? (HINT: See the paragraph preceding Exercise 24 in Sec. 15.3.)

38. Find the values of n for which the improper integral $\displaystyle\int_1^{+\infty} \frac{\ln x}{x^n}\, dx$ converges and evaluate the integral for those values of n.

39. (a) Prove that $\lim\limits_{x \to +\infty} (x^n/e^x) = 0$, for n any positive integer. (b) Find $\lim\limits_{x \to 0} (e^{-1/x}/x^n)$, where $x > 0$ and n is any positive integer, by letting $x = 1/t$ and using the result of part (a).

16

Infinite series

16.1 SEQUENCES   You have undoubtedly encountered sequences of numbers in your previous study of mathematics. For example, the numbers 5, 7, 9, 11, 13, 15 define a sequence. This sequence is said to be *finite* because there is a first and last number. If the set of numbers which defines a sequence does not have both a first and last number, the sequence is said to be *infinite*. For example, the sequence defined by

$$\tfrac{1}{3}, \tfrac{2}{5}, \tfrac{3}{7}, \tfrac{4}{9}, \; . \; . \; . \tag{1}$$

is infinite because the three dots with no number following indicate that there is no last number. We are concerned here with infinite sequences, and when we use the word "sequence" it is understood that we are referring to an infinite sequence. We define a sequence as a particular kind of function.

16.1.1 Definition   A *sequence* is a function whose domain is the set of positive integers.

The numbers in the range of the sequence, which are called the *elements* of the sequence, are restricted to real numbers in this book.

If the nth element is given by $f(n)$, then the sequence is the set of ordered pairs of the form $(n, f(n))$, where n is a positive integer.

● ILLUSTRATION 1: If $f(n) = n/(2n + 1)$, then

$$f(1) = \tfrac{1}{3} \qquad f(2) = \tfrac{2}{5} \qquad f(3) = \tfrac{3}{7} \qquad f(4) = \tfrac{4}{9}$$

and so on. We see that the range of f consists of the elements of sequence (1). Some of the ordered pairs in the sequence f are $(1, \tfrac{1}{3})$, $(2, \tfrac{2}{5})$, $(3, \tfrac{3}{7})$, $(4, \tfrac{4}{9})$, and $(5, \tfrac{5}{11})$. A sketch of the graph of this sequence is shown in Fig. 16.1.1.   ●

Figure 16.1.1

Usually the nth element $f(n)$ of the sequence is stated when the elements are listed in order. Thus, for the elements of sequence (1) we would write

$$\frac{1}{3}, \frac{2}{5}, \frac{3}{7}, \frac{4}{9}, \; . \; . \; . \; , \frac{n}{2n + 1}, \; . \; . \; .$$

Because the domain of every sequence is the same, we can use the notation $\{f(n)\}$ to denote a sequence. So the sequence (1) can be denoted by $\{n/(2n+1)\}$. We also use the subscript notation $\{a_n\}$ to denote the sequence for which $f(n) = a_n$.

You should distinguish between the elements of a sequence and the sequence itself, as shown in the following illustration.

● ILLUSTRATION 2: The sequence $\{1/n\}$ has as its elements the reciprocals of the positive integers

$$1, \frac{1}{2}, \frac{1}{3}, \frac{1}{4}, \cdots, \frac{1}{n}, \cdots \tag{2}$$

The sequence for which

$$f(n) = \begin{cases} 1 & \text{if } n \text{ is odd} \\ \dfrac{2}{n+2} & \text{if } n \text{ is even} \end{cases}$$

has as its elements

$$1, \tfrac{1}{2}, 1, \tfrac{1}{3}, 1, \tfrac{1}{4}, \cdots \tag{3}$$

The elements of sequences (2) and (3) are the same; however, the sequences are different. Sketches of the graphs of sequences (2) and (3) are shown in Figs. 16.1.2 and 16.1.3, respectively.   ●

Figure 16.1.2

Figure 16.1.3

Figure 16.1.4

We now plot on a horizontal axis the points corresponding to successive elements of a sequence. This is done in Fig. 16.1.4 for sequence (1) which is $\{n/(2n+1)\}$. We see that the successive elements of the sequence get closer and closer to $\frac{1}{2}$, even though no element in the sequence has the value $\frac{1}{2}$. Intuitively we see that the element will be as close to $\frac{1}{2}$ as we please by taking the number of the element sufficiently large. Or stating this another way, we can make $|n/(2n+1) - \frac{1}{2}|$ less than any given ϵ by taking n large enough. Because of this we state that the limit of the sequence $\{n/(2n+1)\}$ is $\frac{1}{2}$.

In general, if there is a number L such that $|a_n - L|$ is arbitrarily small for n sufficiently large, we say the sequence $\{a_n\}$ has the limit L. Following is the precise definition of the limit of a sequence.

16.1.2 Definition   A sequence $\{a_n\}$ is said to have the limit L if for every $\epsilon > 0$ there exists a number $N > 0$ such that $|a_n - L| < \epsilon$ for every integer $n > N$; and we write

$$\lim_{n \to +\infty} a_n = L$$

EXAMPLE 1: Use Definition 16.1.2 to prove that the sequence

$$\left\{ \frac{n}{2n+1} \right\}$$

has the limit $\frac{1}{2}$.

SOLUTION: We must show that for any $\epsilon > 0$ there exists a number $N > 0$ such that

$$\left| \frac{n}{2n+1} - \frac{1}{2} \right| < \epsilon \qquad \text{for every integer } n > N$$

$$\left| \frac{n}{2n+1} - \frac{1}{2} \right| = \left| \frac{2n - 2n - 1}{2(2n+1)} \right| = \left| \frac{-1}{4n+2} \right| = \frac{1}{4n+2}$$

Hence, we must find a number $N > 0$ such that

$$\frac{1}{4n+2} < \epsilon \qquad \text{for every integer } n > N$$

But

$$\frac{1}{4n+2} < \epsilon \quad \text{is equivalent to} \quad 2n+1 > \frac{1}{2\epsilon}$$

which is equivalent to

$$n > \frac{1-2\epsilon}{4\epsilon}$$

So it follows that

$$\left| \frac{n}{2n+1} - \frac{1}{2} \right| < \epsilon \qquad \text{for every integer } n > \frac{1-2\epsilon}{4\epsilon}$$

Therefore, if $N = (1-2\epsilon)/4\epsilon$, Definition 16.1.2 holds. In particular, if $\epsilon = \frac{1}{8}$, $N = (1 - \frac{1}{4})/\frac{1}{2} = \frac{3}{2}$. So

$$\left| \frac{n}{2n+1} - \frac{1}{2} \right| < \frac{1}{8} \qquad \text{for every integer } n > \frac{3}{2}$$

For instance, if $n = 4$,

$$\left| \frac{n}{2n+1} - \frac{1}{2} \right| = \left| \frac{4}{9} - \frac{1}{2} \right| = \left| \frac{-1}{18} \right| = \frac{1}{18} < \frac{1}{8}$$

● ILLUSTRATION 3: Consider the sequence $\{(-1)^{n+1}/n\}$. Note that the nth element of this sequence is $(-1)^{n+1}/n$ and $(-1)^{n+1}$ is equal to $+1$ when n is odd and to -1 when n is even. Hence, the elements of the sequence can be written

$$1, -\frac{1}{2}, \frac{1}{3}, -\frac{1}{4}, \frac{1}{5}, \cdots, \frac{(-1)^{n+1}}{n}, \cdots$$

In Fig. 16.1.5 are plotted points corresponding to successive elements of this sequence. In the figure, $a_1 = 1$, $a_2 = -\frac{1}{2}$, $a_3 = \frac{1}{3}$, $a_4 = -\frac{1}{4}$, $a_5 = \frac{1}{5}$, $a_6 = -\frac{1}{6}$, $a_7 = \frac{1}{7}$, $a_8 = -\frac{1}{8}$, $a_9 = \frac{1}{9}$, $a_{10} = -\frac{1}{10}$. The limit of the sequence is 0 and the elements oscillate about 0. ●

Figure 16.1.5

Compare Definition 16.1.2 with Definition 4.1.1 of the limit of $f(x)$ as x increases without bound. The two definitions are almost identical; however, when we state that $\lim\limits_{x \to +\infty} f(x) = L$, the function f is defined for all real numbers greater than some real number R, while when we consider $\lim\limits_{n \to +\infty} a_n$, n is restricted to positive integers. We have, however, the following theorem which follows immediately from Definition 4.1.1.

16.1.3 Theorem   If $\lim\limits_{x \to +\infty} f(x) = L$, and f is defined for every positive integer, then also $\lim\limits_{n \to +\infty} f(n) = L$ when n is any positive integer.

The proof is left as an exercise (see Exercise 20).

● ILLUSTRATION 4: We verify Theorem 16.1.3 for the sequence of Example 1. For that sequence $f(n) = n/(2n+1)$. Hence, $f(x) = x/(2x+1)$ and

$$\lim_{x \to +\infty} \frac{x}{2x+1} = \lim_{x \to +\infty} \frac{1}{2 + \dfrac{1}{x}} = \frac{1}{2}$$

It follows then from Theorem 16.1.3 that $\lim\limits_{n \to +\infty} f(n) = \frac{1}{2}$ when n is any positive integer. This agrees with the solution of Example 1. •

16.1.4 Definition If a sequence $\{a_n\}$ has a limit, the sequence is said to be *convergent,* and we say that a_n *converges* to that limit. If the sequence is not convergent, it is said to be *divergent.*

EXAMPLE 2: Determine if the sequence

$$\left\{ \frac{4n^2}{2n^2 + 1} \right\}$$

is convergent or divergent.

SOLUTION: We wish to determine if $\lim\limits_{n \to +\infty} 4n^2/(2n^2 + 1)$ exists. Let $f(x) = 4x^2/(2x^2 + 1)$ and investigate $\lim\limits_{x \to +\infty} f(x)$.

$$\lim_{x \to +\infty} \frac{4x^2}{2x^2 + 1} = \lim_{x \to +\infty} \frac{4}{2 + \dfrac{1}{x^2}} = 2$$

Therefore, by Theorem 16.1.3, $\lim\limits_{n \to +\infty} f(n) = 2$. We conclude that the given sequence is convergent and that $4n^2/(2n^2 + 1)$ converges to 2.

EXAMPLE 3: Prove that if $|r| < 1$, the sequence $\{r^n\}$ is convergent and that r^n converges to zero.

SOLUTION: First of all, if $r = 0$, the sequence is $\{0\}$ and $\lim\limits_{x \to +\infty} 0 = 0$. Hence, the sequence is convergent and the nth element converges to zero.

If $0 < |r| < 1$, we consider the function f defined by $f(x) = r^x$, where x is any positive number, and show that $\lim\limits_{x \to +\infty} r^x = 0$. Then from Theorem 16.1.3 it will follow that $\lim\limits_{n \to +\infty} r^n = 0$ when n is any positive integer.

To prove that $\lim\limits_{x \to +\infty} r^x = 0$ $(0 < |r| < 1)$, we shall show that for any $\epsilon > 0$ there exists a number $N > 0$ such that

$$|r^x - 0| < \epsilon \qquad \text{whenever } x > N \tag{4}$$

Statement (4) is equivalent to

$$|r|^x < \epsilon \qquad \text{whenever } x > N$$

which is true if and only if

$$\ln |r|^x < \ln \epsilon \qquad \text{whenever } x > N$$

or, equivalently,

$$x \ln |r| < \ln \epsilon \qquad \text{whenever } x > N \tag{5}$$

Because $0 < |r| < 1$, $\ln |r| < 0$. Thus, (5) is equivalent to

$$x > \frac{\ln \epsilon}{\ln |r|} \qquad \text{whenever } x > N$$

Therefore, if we take $N = \ln \epsilon/\ln |r|$, we may conclude (4). Consequently, $\lim\limits_{x \to +\infty} r^x = 0$, and so $\lim\limits_{n \to +\infty} r^n = 0$ if n is any positive integer. Hence, by Definitions 16.1.2 and 16.1.4, $\{r^n\}$ is convergent and r^n converges to zero.

EXAMPLE 4: Determine if the sequence $\{(-1)^n + 1\}$ is convergent or divergent.

SOLUTION: The elements of this sequence are 0, 2, 0, 2, 0, 2, . . . , $(-1)^n + 1$, ... Because $a_n = 0$ if n is odd, and $a_n = 2$ if n is even, it appears that the sequence is divergent. To prove this, let us assume that the sequence is convergent and show that this assumption leads to a contradiction. If the sequence has the limit L, then by Definition 16.1.2, for every $\epsilon > 0$ there exists a number $N > 0$ such that $|a_n - L| < \epsilon$ for every integer $n > N$. In particular, when $\epsilon = \frac{1}{2}$, there exists a number $N > 0$ such that

$$|a_n - L| < \tfrac{1}{2} \qquad \text{for every integer } n > N$$

or, equivalently,

$$-\tfrac{1}{2} < a_n - L < \tfrac{1}{2} \qquad \text{for every integer } n > N \qquad (6)$$

Because $a_n = 0$ if n is odd and $a_n = 2$ if n is even, it follows from (6) that

$$-\tfrac{1}{2} < -L < \tfrac{1}{2} \quad \text{and} \quad -\tfrac{1}{2} < 2 - L < \tfrac{1}{2}$$

But if $-L > -\frac{1}{2}$, then $2 - L > \frac{3}{2}$; hence, $2 - L$ cannot be less than $\frac{1}{2}$. So we have a contradiction, and therefore the given sequence is divergent.

EXAMPLE 5: Determine if the sequence

$$\left\{ n \sin \frac{\pi}{n} \right\}$$

is convergent or divergent.

SOLUTION: We wish to determine if $\lim\limits_{n \to +\infty} n \sin(\pi/n)$ exists. Let $f(x) = x \sin(\pi/x)$ and investigate $\lim\limits_{x \to +\infty} f(x)$. Because $f(x)$ can be written as $[\sin(\pi/x)]/(1/x)$ and $\lim\limits_{x \to +\infty} \sin(\pi/x) = 0$ and $\lim\limits_{x \to +\infty} (1/x) = 0$, we can apply L'Hôpital's rule and obtain

$$\lim_{x \to +\infty} f(x) = \lim_{x \to +\infty} \frac{-\dfrac{\pi}{x^2} \cos \dfrac{\pi}{x}}{-\dfrac{1}{x^2}} = \lim_{x \to +\infty} \pi \cos \frac{\pi}{x} = \pi$$

Therefore, $\lim\limits_{n \to +\infty} f(n) = \pi$ when n is a positive integer. So the given sequence is convergent and $n \sin(\pi/n)$ converges to π.

We have limit theorems for sequences, which are analogous to limit theorems for functions given in Chapter 2. We state these theorems by using the terminology of sequences. The proofs are omitted because they are almost identical to the proofs of the corresponding theorems given in Chapter 2.

16.1.5 Theorem If $\{a_n\}$ and $\{b_n\}$ are convergent sequences and c is a constant, then

(i) the constant sequence $\{c\}$ has c as its limit;

(ii) $\lim\limits_{n \to +\infty} ca_n = c \lim\limits_{n \to +\infty} a_n$;

(iii) $\lim\limits_{n \to +\infty} (a_n \pm b_n) = \lim\limits_{n \to +\infty} a_n \pm \lim\limits_{n \to +\infty} b_n$;

(iv) $\lim_{n \to +\infty} a_n b_n = (\lim_{n \to +\infty} a_n)(\lim_{n \to +\infty} b_n);$

(v) $\lim_{n \to +\infty} \dfrac{a_n}{b_n} = \dfrac{\lim_{n \to +\infty} a_n}{\lim_{n \to +\infty} b_n}$ if $\lim_{n \to +\infty} b_n \neq 0.$

EXAMPLE 6: Use Theorem 16.1.5 to prove that the sequence

$$\left\{ \frac{n^2}{2n+1} \sin \frac{\pi}{n} \right\}$$

is convergent and find the limit of the sequence.

SOLUTION:

$$\frac{n^2}{2n+1} \sin \frac{\pi}{n} = \frac{n}{2n+1} \cdot n \sin \frac{\pi}{n}$$

In Example 1 we showed that the sequence $\{n/(2n+1)\}$ is convergent and $\lim_{n \to +\infty} [n/(2n+1)] = \frac{1}{2}$. In Example 5 we showed that the sequence $\{n \sin(\pi/n)\}$ is convergent and $\lim_{n \to +\infty} [n \sin(\pi/n)] = \pi$. Hence, by Theorem 16.1.5(iv),

$$\lim_{n \to +\infty} \left[\frac{n}{2n+1} \cdot n \sin \frac{\pi}{n} \right] = \lim_{n \to +\infty} \frac{n}{2n+1} \cdot \lim_{n \to +\infty} n \sin \frac{\pi}{n} = \frac{1}{2} \cdot \pi$$

Thus, the given sequence is convergent, and its limit is $\frac{1}{2}\pi$.

Exercises 16.1

In Exercises 1 through 4, use Definition 16.1.2 to prove that the given sequence has the limit L.

1. $\left\{ \dfrac{3}{n-1} \right\}; L = 0$

2. $\left\{ \dfrac{1}{\sqrt{n}} \right\}; L = 0$

3. $\left\{ \dfrac{8n}{2n+3} \right\}; L = 4$

4. $\left\{ \dfrac{5-n}{2+3n} \right\}; L = -\frac{1}{3}$

In Exercises 5 through 19, determine if the sequence is convergent or divergent. If the sequence converges, find its limit.

5. $\left\{ \dfrac{n+1}{2n-1} \right\}$

6. $\left\{ \dfrac{2n^2+1}{3n^2-n} \right\}$

7. $\left\{ \dfrac{n^2+1}{n} \right\}$

8. $\left\{ \dfrac{3n^3+1}{2n^2+n} \right\}$

9. $\left\{ \dfrac{\ln n}{n^2} \right\}$

10. $\left\{ \dfrac{e^n}{n} \right\}$

11. $\{\tanh n\}$

12. $\left\{ \dfrac{\log_b n}{n} \right\}, b > 1$

13. $\left\{ \dfrac{n}{n+1} \sin \dfrac{n\pi}{2} \right\}$

14. $\left\{ \dfrac{\sinh n}{\sin n} \right\}$

15. $\left\{ \dfrac{1}{\sqrt{n^2+1}-n} \right\}$

16. $\{\sqrt{n+1} - \sqrt{n}\}$

17. $\left\{ \left(1 + \dfrac{1}{3n}\right)^n \right\}$

18. $\left\{ \left(1 + \dfrac{2}{n}\right)^n \right\}$

(HINT: Use $\lim_{x \to 0} (1+x)^{1/x} = e$.)

See Hint for Exercise 17.

19. $\{r^{1/n}\}$ and $r > 0$. (HINT: Consider two cases: $r \leq 1$ and $r > 1$.)

20. Prove Theorem 16.1.3.

21. Prove that if $|r| < 1$, the sequence $\{nr^n\}$ is convergent and nr^n converges to zero.

22. Prove that if the sequence $\{a_n\}$ is convergent and $\lim_{n \to +\infty} a_n = L$, then the sequence $\{|a_n|\}$ is also convergent and $\lim_{n \to +\infty} |a_n| = |L|$.

23. Prove that if the sequence $\{a_n\}$ is convergent and $\lim_{n \to +\infty} a_n = L$, then the sequence $\{a_n^2\}$ is also convergent and $\lim_{n \to +\infty} a_n^2 = L^2$.

24. Prove that if the sequence $\{a_n\}$ converges, then $\lim_{n \to +\infty} a_n$ is unique. (HINT: Assume that $\lim_{n \to +\infty} a_n$ has two different values, L and M, and show that this is impossible by taking $\epsilon = \frac{1}{2}|L - M|$ in Definition 16.1.2.)

| 16.2 MONOTONIC AND BOUNDED SEQUENCES | We shall be concerned with certain kinds of sequences which are given special names. |

16.2.1 Definition   A sequence $\{a_n\}$ is said to be

  (i) *increasing* if $a_n \le a_{n+1}$ for all n;
  (ii) *decreasing* if $a_n \ge a_{n+1}$ for all n.

If a sequence is increasing or if it is decreasing, it is called *monotonic*.

Note that if $a_n < a_{n+1}$ (a special case of $a_n \le a_{n+1}$), we have a *strictly increasing* sequence; if $a_n > a_{n+1}$, we have a *strictly decreasing* sequence.

EXAMPLE 1:   For each of the following sequences determine if it is increasing, decreasing, or not monotonic:

  (a) $\{n/(2n + 1)\}$
  (b) $\{1/n\}$
  (c) $\{(-1)^{n+1}/n\}$

SOLUTION: (a) The elements of the sequence can be written

$$\frac{1}{3}, \frac{2}{5}, \frac{3}{7}, \frac{4}{9}, \cdots, \frac{n}{2n + 1}, \frac{n + 1}{2n + 3}, \cdots$$

Note that a_{n+1} is obtained from a_n by replacing n by $n + 1$. Therefore, because $a_n = n/(2n + 1)$,

$$a_{n+1} = \frac{n + 1}{2(n + 1) + 1} = \frac{n + 1}{2n + 3}$$

Looking at the first four elements of the sequence, we see that the elements increase as n increases. Thus, we suspect in general that

$$\frac{n}{2n + 1} \le \frac{n + 1}{2n + 3} \tag{1}$$

Inequality (1) can be verified if we find an equivalent inequality which we know is valid. Multiplying each member of inequality (1) by $(2n + 1)(2n + 3)$, we obtain

$$n(2n + 3) \le (n + 1)(2n + 1) \tag{2}$$

Inequality (2) is equivalent to inequality (1) because (1) may be obtained from (2) by dividing each member by $(2n + 1)(2n + 3)$. Inequality (2) is equivalent to

$$2n^2 + 3n \leq 2n^2 + 3n + 1 \tag{3}$$

Inequality (3) obviously holds because the right member is 1 greater than the left member. Therefore, inequality (1) holds and so the given sequence is increasing.

(b) The elements of the sequence can be written

$$1, \frac{1}{2}, \frac{1}{3}, \frac{1}{4}, \cdots, \frac{1}{n}, \frac{1}{n+1}, \cdots$$

Because

$$\frac{1}{n} > \frac{1}{n+1}$$

for all n, the sequence is decreasing.

(c) The elements of the sequence can be written

$$1, -\frac{1}{2}, \frac{1}{3}, -\frac{1}{4}, \cdots, \frac{(-1)^{n+1}}{n}, \frac{(-1)^{n+2}}{n+1}, \cdots$$

$a_1 = 1$ and $a_2 = -\frac{1}{2}$, and so $a_1 > a_2$. But $a_3 = \frac{1}{3}$, and so $a_2 < a_3$. In a more general sense, consider three consecutive elements $a_n = (-1)^{n+1}/n$, $a_{n+1} = (-1)^{n+2}/(n+1)$, and $a_{n+2} = (-1)^{n+3}/(n+2)$. If n is odd, $a_n > a_{n+1}$ and $a_{n+1} < a_{n+2}$, and if n is even, $a_n < a_{n+1}$ and $a_{n+1} > a_{n+2}$. Hence, the sequence is neither increasing nor decreasing and so is not monotonic.

16.2.2 Definition   The number C is called a *lower bound* of the sequence $\{a_n\}$ if $C \leq a_n$ for all positive integers n, and the number D is called an *upper bound* of the sequence $\{a_n\}$ if $a_n \leq D$ for all positive integers n.

● ILLUSTRATION 1: The number zero is a lower bound of the sequence $\{n/(2n + 1)\}$ whose elements are

$$\frac{1}{3}, \frac{2}{5}, \frac{3}{7}, \frac{4}{9}, \cdots, \frac{n}{2n+1}, \cdots$$

Another lower bound of this sequence is $\frac{1}{3}$. Actually any number which is less than or equal to $\frac{1}{3}$ is a lower bound of this sequence.   ●

● ILLUSTRATION 2: For the sequence $\{1/n\}$ whose elements are

$$1, \frac{1}{2}, \frac{1}{3}, \frac{1}{4}, \cdots, \frac{1}{n}, \cdots$$

1 is an upper bound; 26 is also an upper bound. Any number which is greater than or equal to 1 is an upper bound of this sequence, and any nonpositive number will serve as a lower bound.   ●

From Illustrations 1 and 2, we see that a sequence may have many upper and lower bounds.

16.2.3 Definition   If A is a lower bound of a sequence $\{a_n\}$ and if A has the property that for every lower bound C of $\{a_n\}$, $C \leq A$, then A is called the *greatest lower bound* of the sequence. Similarly, if B is an upper bound of a sequence $\{a_n\}$ and if B has the property that for every upper bound D of $\{a_n\}$, $B \leq D$, then B is called the *least upper bound* of the sequence.

● ILLUSTRATION 3: For the sequence $\{n/(2n+1)\}$ of Illustration 1, the greatest lower bound is $\frac{1}{3}$ because every lower bound of the sequence is less than or equal to $\frac{1}{3}$. Furthermore,

$$\frac{n}{2n+1} = \frac{1}{2 + \dfrac{1}{n}} < \frac{1}{2}$$

for all n, and $\frac{1}{2}$ is the least upper bound of the sequence.

In Illustration 2, we have the sequence $\{1/n\}$ whose least upper bound is 1 because every upper bound of the sequence is greater than or equal to 1. The greatest lower bound of this sequence is 0.   ●

16.2.4 Definition   A sequence $\{a_n\}$ is said to be *bounded* if and only if it has an upper bound and a lower bound.

Because the sequence $\{1/n\}$ has an upper bound and a lower bound, it is bounded. This sequence is also a decreasing sequence and hence is a bounded monotonic sequence. There is a theorem (16.2.6) that guarantees that a bounded monotonic sequence is convergent. In particular, the sequence $\{1/n\}$ is convergent because $\lim\limits_{n \to +\infty} (1/n) = 0$. The sequence $\{n\}$ whose elements are

$$1, 2, 3, \ldots, n, \ldots$$

is monotonic (because it is increasing) but is not bounded (because there is no upper bound). It is not convergent because $\lim\limits_{n \to +\infty} n = +\infty$.

For the proof of Theorem 16.2.6 we need a very important property of the real-number system which we now state.

16.2.5 The Axiom of Completeness   Every nonempty set of real numbers which has a lower bound has a greatest lower bound. Also, every set of real numbers which has an upper bound has a least upper bound.

The axiom of completeness together with the field axioms (1.1.5 through 1.1.11) and the axiom of order (1.1.14) completely describe the real-number system. Actually, the second sentence in our statement of the axiom of completeness is unnecessary because it can be proved from the first sentence. It is included in the axiom here to expedite the discussion.

Suppose that $\{a_n\}$ is an increasing sequence that is bounded. Let D be an upper bound of the sequence. Then if the points corresponding to successive elements of the sequence are plotted on a horizontal axis, these points will all lie to the left of the point corresponding to the number D. Furthermore, because the sequence is increasing, each point will be either to the right of or coincide with the preceding point. See Fig. 16.2.1. Hence, as n increases, the elements increase toward D. Intuitively it appears that the sequence $\{a_n\}$ has a limit which is either D or some number less than D. This is indeed the case and is proved in the following theorem.

$a_1\ a_2 \quad a_3\ a_4 \quad a_5 a_6 a_7 \quad a_8\ a_9\ a_{10} \quad D$

Figure 16.2.1

16.2.6 Theorem   A bounded monotonic sequence is convergent.

PROOF: We prove the theorem for the case when the monotonic sequence is increasing. Let the sequence be $\{a_n\}$.

Because $\{a_n\}$ is bounded, there is an upper bound for the sequence. By the axiom of completeness (16.2.5), $\{a_n\}$ has a least upper bound, which we call B. Then if ϵ is a positive number, $B - \epsilon$ cannot be an upper bound of the sequence because $B - \epsilon < B$ and B is the least upper bound of the sequence. So for some positive integer N

$$B - \epsilon < a_N \tag{4}$$

Because B is the least upper bound of $\{a_n\}$, by Definition 16.2.2 it follows that

$$a_n \leq B \quad \text{for every positive integer } n \tag{5}$$

Because $\{a_n\}$ is an increasing sequence, we have from Definition 16.2.1(i)

$$a_n \leq a_{n+1} \quad \text{for every positive integer } n$$

and so

$$a_N \leq a_n \quad \text{whenever } n \geq N \tag{6}$$

From (4), (5), and (6), it follows that

$$B - \epsilon < a_N \leq a_n \leq B < B + \epsilon \quad \text{whenever } n \geq N$$

from which we get

$$B - \epsilon < a_n < B + \epsilon \quad \text{whenever } n \geq N$$

or, equivalently,

$$-\epsilon < a_n - B < \epsilon \quad \text{whenever } n \geq N$$

which can be written as

$$|a_n - B| < \epsilon \quad \text{whenever } n \geq N \tag{7}$$

But by Definition 16.1.2, (7) is the condition that $\lim\limits_{n \to +\infty} a_n = B$. Therefore, the sequence $\{a_n\}$ is convergent.

To prove the theorem when $\{a_n\}$ is a decreasing sequence, we consider the sequence $\{-a_n\}$, which will be increasing, and apply the above results. We leave it as an exercise to fill in the steps (see Exercise 13). ■

Theorem 16.2.6 states that if $\{a_n\}$ is a bounded monotonic sequence, there exists a number L such that $\lim\limits_{n \to +\infty} a_n = L$, but it does not state how to find L. For this reason, Theorem 16.2.6 is called an *existence theorem*. Many important concepts in mathematics are based on existence theorems. In particular, there are many sequences for which we cannot find the limit by direct use of the definition or by using limit theorems, but the knowledge that such a limit exists can be of great value to a mathematician.

In the proof of Theorem 16.2.6 we saw that the limit of the bounded increasing sequence is the least upper bound B of the sequence. Hence, if D is an upper bound of the sequence, $\lim\limits_{n \to +\infty} a_n = B \le D$. We have, then, the following theorem.

16.2.7 Theorem   Let $\{a_n\}$ be an increasing sequence, and suppose that D is an upper bound of this sequence. Then $\{a_n\}$ is convergent and

$$\lim_{n \to +\infty} a_n \le D$$

In proving Theorem 16.2.6 for the case when the bounded monotonic sequence is decreasing, the limit of the sequence is the greatest lower bound. The following theorem follows in a way similar to that of Theorem 16.2.7.

16.2.8 Theorem   Let $\{a_n\}$ be a decreasing sequence, and suppose that C is a lower bound of this sequence. Then $\{a_n\}$ is convergent and

$$\lim_{n \to +\infty} a_n \ge C$$

EXAMPLE 2:   Use Theorem 16.2.6 to prove that the sequence

$$\left\{ \frac{2^n}{n!} \right\}$$

is convergent.

SOLUTION: The elements of the given sequence are

$$\frac{2^1}{1!}, \frac{2^2}{2!}, \frac{2^3}{3!}, \frac{2^4}{4!}, \cdots, \frac{2^n}{n!}, \frac{2^{n+1}}{(n+1)!}, \cdots$$

$1! = 1$, $2! = 1 \cdot 2 = 2$, $3! = 1 \cdot 2 \cdot 3 = 6$, $4! = 1 \cdot 2 \cdot 3 \cdot 4 = 24$. Hence, the elements of the sequence can be written as

$$2, 2, \frac{4}{3}, \frac{2}{3}, \cdots, \frac{2^n}{n!}, \frac{2^{n+1}}{(n+1)!}, \cdots$$

We see, then, that $a_1 = a_2 > a_3 > a_4$, and so the given sequence may be decreasing. We must check to see if $a_n \geq a_{n+1}$; that is, we must determine if

$$\frac{2^n}{n!} \geq \frac{2^{n+1}}{(n+1)!} \tag{8}$$

which is equivalent to

$$2^n(n+1)! \geq 2^{n+1}n!$$

which is equivalent to

$$2^n n!(n+1) \geq 2 \cdot 2^n n!$$

which is equivalent to

$$n + 1 \geq 2 \tag{9}$$

When $n = 1$, inequality (9) becomes $2 = 2$, and (9) obviously holds when $n > 2$. Because inequality (8) is equivalent to (9), it follows that the given sequence is decreasing and hence monotonic. An upper bound for the given sequence is 2, and a lower bound is 0. Therefore, the sequence is bounded.

The sequence $\{2^n/n!\}$ is therefore a bounded monotonic sequence, and by Theorem 16.2.6 it is convergent.

Theorem 16.2.6 states that a sufficient condition for a monotonic sequence to be convergent is that it be bounded. This is also a necessary condition and is given in the following theorem.

16.2.9 Theorem   A convergent monotonic sequence is bounded.

PROOF: We prove the theorem for the case when the monotonic sequence is increasing. Let the sequence be $\{a_n\}$.

To prove that $\{a_n\}$ is bounded we must show that it has a lower bound and an upper bound. Because $\{a_n\}$ is an increasing sequence, its first element serves as a lower bound. We must now find an upper bound.

Because $\{a_n\}$ is convergent, the sequence has a limit; call this limit L. Therefore, $\lim\limits_{n \to +\infty} a_n = L$, and so by Definition 16.1.2, for any $\epsilon > 0$ there exists a number $N > 0$ such that

$$|a_n - L| < \epsilon \qquad \text{for every positive integer } n > N$$

or, equivalently,

$$-\epsilon < a_n - L < \epsilon \qquad \text{whenever } n > N$$

or, equivalently,

$$L - \epsilon < a_n < L + \epsilon \qquad \text{whenever } n > N$$

Because $\{a_n\}$ is increasing, we conclude that

$$a_n < L + \epsilon \qquad \text{for all positive integers } n$$

Therefore, $L + \epsilon$ will serve as an upper bound of the sequence $\{a_n\}$.

To prove the theorem when $\{a_n\}$ is a decreasing sequence we do as suggested in the proof of Theorem 16.2.6: Consider the sequence $\{-a_n\}$, which will be increasing, and apply the above results. You are asked to do this proof in Exercise 14. ∎

Exercises 16.2

In Exercises 1 through 12, determine if the given sequence is increasing, decreasing, or not monotonic.

1. $\left\{\dfrac{3n - 1}{4n + 5}\right\}$

2. $\{\sin n\pi\}$

3. $\left\{\dfrac{1}{n + \sin n^2}\right\}$

4. $\left\{\dfrac{2^n}{1 + 2^n}\right\}$

5. $\left\{\dfrac{5^n}{1 + 5^{2n}}\right\}$

6. $\left\{\dfrac{n^3 - 1}{n}\right\}$

7. $\left\{\dfrac{n!}{3^n}\right\}$

8. $\left\{\dfrac{n}{2^n}\right\}$

9. $\left\{\dfrac{n^n}{n!}\right\}$

10. $\{n^2 + (-1)^n n\}$

11. $\left\{\dfrac{n!}{1 \cdot 3 \cdot 5 \cdot \ldots \cdot (2n - 1)}\right\}$

12. $\left\{\dfrac{1 \cdot 3 \cdot 5 \cdot \ldots \cdot (2n - 1)}{2^n \cdot n!}\right\}$

13. Use the fact that Theorem 16.2.6 holds for an increasing sequence to prove that the theorem holds when $\{a_n\}$ is a decreasing sequence. (HINT: Consider the sequence $\{-a_n\}$.)

14. Prove Theorem 16.2.9 when $\{a_n\}$ is a decreasing sequence by a method similar to that used in Exercise 13.

In Exercises 15 through 21, prove that the given sequence is convergent by using Theorem 16.2.6.

15. The sequence of Exercise 1.

16. The sequence of Exercise 4.

17. The sequence of Exercise 5.

18. The sequence of Exercise 8.

19. The sequence of Exercise 11.

20. The sequence of Exercise 12.

21. $\left\{\dfrac{n^2}{2^n}\right\}$

16.3 INFINITE SERIES OF CONSTANT TERMS

The familiar operation of addition applies only to a finite set of numbers. We now wish to extend addition to infinitely many numbers and to define what we mean by such a sum. To carry this out we deal with a limiting process by considering sequences.

16.3.1 Definition If $\{u_n\}$ is a sequence and

$$s_n = \sum_{i=1}^{n} u_i = u_1 + u_2 + u_3 + \cdots + u_n$$

then the sequence $\{s_n\}$ is called an *infinite series.*

The numbers $u_1, u_2, u_3, \ldots$ are called the *terms* of the infinite series. We use the following symbolism to denote an infinite series:

$$\sum_{n=1}^{+\infty} u_n = u_1 + u_2 + u_3 + \cdots + u_n + \cdots \qquad (1)$$

Given the infinite series denoted by (1), $s_1 = u_1$, $s_2 = u_1 + u_2$, $s_3 = u_1 + u_2 + u_3$, and in general

$$s_k = \sum_{i=1}^{k} u_i = u_1 + u_2 + u_3 + \cdots + u_k \qquad (2)$$

where s_k, defined by (2), is called the kth *partial sum* of the given series, and the sequence $\{s_n\}$ is a sequence of partial sums.

Because $s_{n-1} = u_1 + u_2 + \cdots + u_{n-1}$ and $s_n = u_1 + u_2 + \cdots + u_{n-1} + u_n$, we have the formula

$$s_n = s_{n-1} + u_n \qquad (3)$$

EXAMPLE 1: Given the infinite series

$$\sum_{n=1}^{+\infty} u_n = \sum_{n=1}^{+\infty} \frac{1}{n(n+1)}$$

find the first four elements of the sequence of partial sums $\{s_n\}$, and find a formula for s_n in terms of n.

SOLUTION: Applying formula (3), we get

$$s_1 = u_1 = \frac{1}{1 \cdot 2} = \frac{1}{2}$$

$$s_2 = s_1 + u_2 = \frac{1}{2} + \frac{1}{2 \cdot 3} = \frac{2}{3}$$

$$s_3 = s_2 + u_3 = \frac{2}{3} + \frac{1}{3 \cdot 4} = \frac{3}{4}$$

$$s_4 = s_3 + u_4 = \frac{3}{4} + \frac{1}{4 \cdot 5} = \frac{4}{5}$$

By partial fractions, we see that

$$u_k = \frac{1}{k(k+1)} = \frac{1}{k} - \frac{1}{k+1}$$

Therefore,

$$u_1 = 1 - \frac{1}{2}, \; u_2 = \frac{1}{2} - \frac{1}{3}, \; u_3 = \frac{1}{3} - \frac{1}{4}, \; \cdots, \; u_{n-1} = \frac{1}{n-1} - \frac{1}{n}, \; u_n = \frac{1}{n} - \frac{1}{n+1}$$

Thus, because $s_n = u_1 + u_2 + \cdots + u_{n-1} + u_n$, we have

$$s_n = \left(1 - \frac{1}{2}\right) + \left(\frac{1}{2} - \frac{1}{3}\right) + \left(\frac{1}{3} - \frac{1}{4}\right) + \cdots + \left(\frac{1}{n-1} - \frac{1}{n}\right) + \left(\frac{1}{n} - \frac{1}{n+1}\right)$$

Upon removing parentheses and combining terms, we obtain

$$s_n = 1 - \frac{1}{n+1} = \frac{n}{n+1}$$

Taking $n = 1, 2, 3$, and 4, we see that our previous results agree.

Note that the method of solution of the above example applies only to a special case. In general, it is not possible to obtain such an expression for s_n.

We now define what we mean by the "sum" of an infinite series.

16.3.2 Definition   Let $\sum\limits_{n=1}^{+\infty} u_n$ be a given infinite series, and let $\{s_n\}$ be the sequence of partial sums defining this infinite series. Then if $\lim\limits_{n \to +\infty} s_n$ exists and is equal to S, we say that the given series is *convergent* and that S is the *sum* of the given infinite series. If $\lim\limits_{n \to +\infty} s_n$ does not exist, the series is said to be *divergent* and the series does not have a sum.

Essentially Definition 16.3.2 states that an infinite series is convergent if and only if the corresponding sequence of partial sums is convergent.

If an infinite series has a sum S, we also say that the series converges to S.

Observe that the sum of a convergent series is the limit of a sequence of partial sums and is not obtained by ordinary addition. For a convergent series we use the symbolism

$$\sum_{n=1}^{+\infty} a_n$$

to denote both the series and the sum of the series. The use of the same symbol should not be confusing because the correct interpretation is apparent from the context in which it is used.

EXAMPLE 2:   Determine if the infinite series of Example 1 has a sum.

SOLUTION: In the solution of Example 1, we showed that the sequence of partial sums for the given series is $\{s_n\} = \{n/(n + 1)\}$. Therefore,

$$\lim_{n \to +\infty} s_n = \lim_{n \to +\infty} \frac{n}{n + 1} = \lim_{n \to +\infty} \frac{1}{1 + \dfrac{1}{n}} = 1$$

So we conclude that the infinite series has a sum equal to 1. We can write

$$\sum_{n=1}^{+\infty} \frac{1}{n(n + 1)} = \frac{1}{2} + \frac{1}{6} + \frac{1}{12} + \frac{1}{20} + \cdots + \frac{1}{n(n + 1)} + \cdots = 1$$

As we mentioned above, in most cases it is not possible to obtain an expression for s_n in terms of n, and so we must have other methods for determining whether or not a given infinite series has a sum or, equivalently, whether a given infinite series is convergent or divergent.

16.3.3 Theorem   If the infinite series $\sum\limits_{n=1}^{+\infty} u_n$ is convergent, then $\lim\limits_{n \to +\infty} u_n = 0$.

PROOF: Letting $\{s_n\}$ be the sequence of partial sums for the given series, and denoting the sum of the series by S, we have, from Definition 16.3.2, $\lim\limits_{n \to +\infty} s_n = S$. Therefore, for any $\epsilon > 0$ there exists a number $N > 0$ such that $|S - s_n| < \frac{1}{2}\epsilon$ for every integer $n > N$. Also, for these integers $n > N$ we know that $|S - s_{n+1}| < \frac{1}{2}\epsilon$. We have, then,

$$|u_{n+1}| = |s_{n+1} - s_n| = |S - s_n + s_{n+1} - S| \le |S - s_n| + |s_{n+1} - S|$$

So

$$|u_{n+1}| < \tfrac{1}{2}\epsilon + \tfrac{1}{2}\epsilon = \epsilon \qquad \text{for every integer } n > N$$

Therefore, $\lim\limits_{n \to +\infty} u_n = 0$. ∎

The following theorem is a corollary of the preceding one.

16.3.4 Theorem   If $\lim\limits_{n \to +\infty} u_n \ne 0$, then the series $\sum\limits_{n=1}^{+\infty} u_n$ is divergent.

PROOF: Assume that $\sum\limits_{n=1}^{+\infty} u_n$ is convergent. Then by Theorem 16.3.3 $\lim\limits_{n \to +\infty} u_n = 0$. But this contradicts the hypothesis. Therefore, the series is divergent. ∎

EXAMPLE 3:   Prove that the following two series are divergent.

(a) $\displaystyle\sum_{n=1}^{+\infty} \frac{n^2 + 1}{n^2}$

$$= 2 + \frac{5}{4} + \frac{10}{9} + \frac{17}{16} + \cdots$$

(b) $\displaystyle\sum_{n=1}^{+\infty} (-1)^{n+1}3$

$$= 3 - 3 + 3 - 3 + \cdots$$

SOLUTION: (a) $\lim\limits_{n \to +\infty} u_n = \lim\limits_{n \to +\infty} \dfrac{n^2 + 1}{n^2}$

$$= \lim_{n \to +\infty} \frac{1 + \dfrac{1}{n^2}}{1}$$

$$= 1$$

$$\ne 0$$

Therefore, by Theorem 16.3.4 the series is divergent.
(b) $\lim\limits_{n \to +\infty} u_n = \lim\limits_{n \to +\infty} (-1)^{n+1}3$, which does not exist. Therefore, by Theorem 16.3.4 the series is divergent.

Note that the converse of Theorem 16.3.3 is false. That is, if $\lim\limits_{n \to +\infty} u_n = 0$, it does not follow that the series is necessarily convergent. In other words, it is possible to have a divergent series for which $\lim\limits_{n \to +\infty} u_n = 0$. An example of such a series is the one known as the *harmonic series*, which is

$$\sum_{n=1}^{+\infty} \frac{1}{n} = 1 + \frac{1}{2} + \frac{1}{3} + \frac{1}{4} + \cdots + \frac{1}{n} + \cdots \tag{4}$$

Clearly, $\lim\limits_{n \to +\infty} 1/n = 0$. In Illustration 1 we prove that the harmonic series diverges and we use the following theorem, which states that the difference between two partial sums s_R and s_T of a convergent series can be made as small as we please by taking R and T sufficiently large.

16.3.5 Theorem   Let $\{s_n\}$ be the sequence of partial sums for a given convergent series $\sum\limits_{n=1}^{+\infty} u_n$. Then for any $\epsilon > 0$ there exists a number N such that

$$|s_R - s_T| < \epsilon \qquad \text{whenever } R > N \text{ and } T > N$$

PROOF: Because the series $\sum\limits_{n=1}^{+\infty} u_n$ is convergent, call its sum S. Then for any $\epsilon > 0$ there exists an $N > 0$ such that $|S - s_n| < \frac{1}{2}\epsilon$ whenever $n > N$. Therefore, if $R > N$ and $T > N$,

$$|s_R - s_T| = |s_R - S + S - s_T| \le |s_R - S| + |S - s_T| < \tfrac{1}{2}\epsilon + \tfrac{1}{2}\epsilon$$

So

$$|s_R - s_T| < \epsilon \qquad \text{whenever } R > N \text{ and } T > N \qquad \blacksquare$$

● ILLUSTRATION 1: We prove that the harmonic series (4) is divergent. For this series,

$$s_n = 1 + \frac{1}{2} + \cdots + \frac{1}{n}$$

and

$$s_{2n} = 1 + \frac{1}{2} + \cdots + \frac{1}{n} + \frac{1}{n+1} + \cdots + \frac{1}{2n}$$

So

$$s_{2n} - s_n = \frac{1}{n+1} + \frac{1}{n+2} + \frac{1}{n+3} + \cdots + \frac{1}{2n} \qquad (5)$$

If $n > 1$,

$$\frac{1}{n+1} + \frac{1}{n+2} + \frac{1}{n+3} + \cdots + \frac{1}{2n} > \frac{1}{2n} + \frac{1}{2n} + \frac{1}{2n} + \cdots + \frac{1}{2n} \qquad (6)$$

There are n terms on each side of the inequality sign in (6); so the right side is $n(1/2n) = \frac{1}{2}$. Therefore, from (5) and (6) we have

$$s_{2n} - s_n > \tfrac{1}{2} \qquad \text{whenever } n > 1 \qquad (7)$$

But Theorem 16.3.5 states that if the given series is convergent, then $s_{2n} - s_n$ may be made as small as we please by taking n large enough; that is, if we take $\epsilon = \frac{1}{2}$, there exists an N such that $s_{2n} - s_n < \frac{1}{2}$ whenever $2n > N$ and $n > N$. But this would contradict (7). Therefore, we conclude that the harmonic series is divergent even though $\lim\limits_{n \to +\infty} 1/n = 0$. ●

A *geometric series* is a series of the form

$$\sum_{n=1}^{+\infty} ar^{n-1} = a + ar + ar^2 + \cdots + ar^{n-1} + \cdots \tag{8}$$

The nth partial sum of this series is given by

$$s_n = a(1 + r + r^2 + \cdots + r^{n-1}) \tag{9}$$

From the identity

$$1 - r^n = (1 - r)(1 + r + r^2 + \cdots + r^{n-1})$$

we can write (9) as

$$s_n = \frac{a(1 - r^n)}{1 - r} \qquad \text{if } r \neq 1 \tag{10}$$

16.3.6 Theorem The geometric series converges to the sum $a/(1-r)$ if $|r| < 1$, and the geometric series diverges if $|r| \geq 1$.

PROOF: In Example 3, Sec. 16.1, we showed that $\lim_{n \to +\infty} r^n = 0$ if $|r| < 1$. Therefore, from (10) we can conclude that if $|r| < 1$,

$$\lim_{n \to +\infty} s_n = \frac{a}{1 - r}$$

So if $|r| < 1$, the geometric series converges, and its sum is $a/(1-r)$.

If $r = 1$, $s_n = na$. Then $\lim_{n \to +\infty} s_n = +\infty$ if $a > 0$, and $\lim_{n \to +\infty} s_n = -\infty$ if $a < 0$.

If $r = -1$, the geometric series becomes $a - a + a - \cdots + (-1)^{n-1}a + \cdots$; so $s_n = 0$ if n is even, and $s_n = a$ if n is odd. Therefore, $\lim_{n \to +\infty} s_n$ does not exist. Hence, the geometric series diverges when $|r| = 1$.

If $|r| > 1$, $\lim_{n \to +\infty} ar^{n-1} = a \lim_{n \to +\infty} r^{n-1}$. Clearly, $\lim_{n \to +\infty} r^{n-1} \neq 0$ because we can make $|r^{n-1}|$ as large as we please by taking n large enough. Therefore, by Theorem 16.3.4 the series is divergent. This completes the proof. ■

● ILLUSTRATION 2:

$$\sum_{n=1}^{+\infty} \frac{1}{2^{n-1}} = 1 + \frac{1}{2} + \frac{1}{4} + \frac{1}{8} + \cdots + \frac{1}{2^{n-1}} + \cdots$$

which is the geometric series, with $a = 1$ and $r = \frac{1}{2}$. Therefore, by Theorem 16.3.6 the series is convergent. Because $a/(1-r) = 1/(1 - \frac{1}{2}) = 2$, the sum of the series is 2. ●

The following example illustrates how Theorem 16.3.6 can be used to express a nonterminating repeating decimal as a rational number.

EXAMPLE 4:   Express the decimal 0.3333. . . . as a rational number.

SOLUTION:

$$0.3333. \ . \ . = \frac{3}{10} + \frac{3}{100} + \frac{3}{1,000} + \frac{3}{10,000} + \cdot \cdot \cdot + \frac{3}{10^n} + \cdot \cdot \cdot$$

We have a geometric series in which $a = \frac{3}{10}$ and $r = \frac{1}{10}$. Because $|r| < 1$, it follows from Theorem 16.3.6 that the series converges and its sum is $a/(1-r)$. Therefore,

$$0.3333. \ . \ . = \frac{\frac{3}{10}}{1 - \frac{1}{10}} = \frac{1}{3}$$

The next theorem states that the convergence or divergence of an infinite series is not affected by changing a finite number of terms.

16.3.7 Theorem   If $\sum\limits_{n=1}^{+\infty} a_n$ and $\sum\limits_{n=1}^{+\infty} b_n$ are two infinite series, differing only in their first m terms (i.e., $a_k = b_k$ if $k > m$), then either both series converge or both series diverge.

PROOF: Let $\{s_n\}$ and $\{t_n\}$ be the sequences of partial sums of the series $\sum\limits_{n=1}^{+\infty} a_n$ and $\sum\limits_{n=1}^{+\infty} b_n$, respectively. Then

$$s_n = a_1 + a_2 + \cdot \cdot \cdot + a_m + a_{m+1} + a_{m+2} + \cdot \cdot \cdot + a_n$$

and

$$t_n = b_1 + b_2 + \cdot \cdot \cdot + b_m + b_{m+1} + b_{m+2} + \cdot \cdot \cdot + b_n$$

Because $a_k = b_k$ if $k > m$, then if $n \geq m$, we have

$$s_n - t_n = (a_1 + a_2 + \cdot \cdot \cdot + a_m) - (b_1 + b_2 + \cdot \cdot \cdot + b_m)$$

So

$$s_n - t_n = s_m - t_m \qquad \text{whenever } n \geq m \tag{11}$$

We wish to show that either both $\lim\limits_{n \to +\infty} s_n$ and $\lim\limits_{n \to +\infty} t_n$ exist or do not exist.

Suppose that $\lim\limits_{n \to +\infty} t_n$ exists. Then from Eq. (11) we have

$$s_n = t_n + (s_m - t_m) \qquad \text{whenever } n \geq m$$

and so

$$\lim_{n \to +\infty} s_n = \lim_{n \to +\infty} t_n + (s_m - t_m)$$

Hence, when $\lim\limits_{n \to +\infty} t_n$ exists, $\lim\limits_{n \to +\infty} s_n$ also exists and both series converge.

Now suppose that $\lim\limits_{n\to+\infty} t_n$ does not exist and $\lim\limits_{n\to+\infty} s_n$ exists. From Eq. (11) we have

$$t_n = s_n + (t_m - s_m) \qquad \text{whenever } n \geq m$$

Because $\lim\limits_{n\to+\infty} s_n$ exists, it follows that

$$\lim_{n\to+\infty} t_n = \lim_{n\to+\infty} s_n + (t_m - s_m)$$

and so $\lim\limits_{n\to+\infty} t_n$ has to exist, which is a contradiction. Hence, if $\lim\limits_{n\to+\infty} t_n$ does not exist, then $\lim\limits_{n\to+\infty} s_n$ does not exist, and both series diverge. ∎

EXAMPLE 5: Determine whether the infinite series

$$\sum_{n=1}^{+\infty} \frac{1}{n+4}$$

is convergent or divergent.

SOLUTION: The given series is

$$\frac{1}{5} + \frac{1}{6} + \frac{1}{7} + \cdots + \frac{1}{n+4} + \cdots$$

which can be written as

$$0 + 0 + 0 + 0 + \frac{1}{5} + \frac{1}{6} + \frac{1}{7} + \cdots + \frac{1}{n} + \cdots \qquad (12)$$

Now the harmonic series which is known to be divergent is

$$1 + \frac{1}{2} + \frac{1}{3} + \frac{1}{4} + \frac{1}{5} + \frac{1}{6} + \frac{1}{7} + \cdots + \frac{1}{n} + \cdots \qquad (13)$$

Series (12) differs from series (13) only in the first four terms. Hence, by Theorem 16.3.7, series (12) is also divergent.

EXAMPLE 6: Determine whether the following infinite series is convergent or divergent:

$$\sum_{n=1}^{+\infty} \frac{\left[\!\left[\cos \frac{3}{n}\pi + 2 \right]\!\right]}{3^n}$$

SOLUTION: The given series can be written as

$$\frac{[\![\cos 3\pi + 2]\!]}{3} + \frac{[\![\cos \frac{3}{2}\pi + 2]\!]}{3^2} + \frac{[\![\cos \pi + 2]\!]}{3^3} + \frac{[\![\cos \frac{3}{4}\pi + 2]\!]}{3^4}$$

$$+ \frac{[\![\cos \frac{3}{5}\pi + 2]\!]}{3^5} + \frac{[\![\cos \frac{1}{2}\pi + 2]\!]}{3^6} + \frac{[\![\cos \frac{3}{7}\pi + 2]\!]}{3^7} + \cdots$$

$$= \frac{1}{3} + \frac{2}{3^2} + \frac{1}{3^3} + \frac{1}{3^4} + \frac{1}{3^5} + \frac{2}{3^6} + \frac{2}{3^7} + \frac{2}{3^8} + \cdots \qquad (14)$$

Consider the geometric series with $a = \frac{2}{3}$ and $r = \frac{1}{3}$:

$$\frac{2}{3} + \frac{2}{3^2} + \frac{2}{3^3} + \frac{2}{3^4} + \frac{2}{3^5} + \frac{2}{3^6} + \frac{2}{3^7} + \frac{2}{3^8} + \cdots \qquad (15)$$

This series is convergent by Theorem 16.3.6. Because series (14) differs from series (15) only in the first five terms, it follows from Theorem 16.3.7 that series (14) is also convergent.

As a consequence of Theorem 16.3.7, for a given infinite series, we can add or subtract a finite number of terms without affecting its convergence or divergence. For instance, in Example 5 the given series may be thought of as being obtained from the harmonic series by subtracting the first four terms. And because the harmonic series is divergent, the given series is divergent. In Example 6, we could consider the convergent geometric series

$$\frac{2}{3^6} + \frac{2}{3^7} + \frac{2}{3^8} + \cdots \tag{16}$$

and obtain the given series (14) by adding five terms. Because series (16) is convergent, it follows that series (14) is convergent.

The following theorem states that if an infinite series is multiplied term by term by a nonzero constant, its convergence or divergence is not affected.

16.3.8 Theorem   Let c be any nonzero constant.

(i) If the series $\sum\limits_{n=1}^{+\infty} u_n$ is convergent and its sum is S, then the series $\sum\limits_{n=1}^{+\infty} cu_n$ is also convergent and its sum is $c \cdot S$.

(ii) If the series $\sum\limits_{n=1}^{+\infty} u_n$ is divergent, then the series $\sum\limits_{n=1}^{+\infty} cu_n$ is also divergent.

PROOF: Let the nth partial sum of the series $\sum\limits_{n=1}^{+\infty} u_n$ be s_n. Therefore, $s_n = u_1 + u_2 + \cdots + u_n$. The nth partial sum of the series $\sum\limits_{n=1}^{+\infty} cu_n$ is $c(u_1 + u_2 + \cdots + u_n) = cs_n$.

PART (i):   If the series $\sum\limits_{n=1}^{+\infty} u_n$ is convergent, then $\lim\limits_{n \to +\infty} s_n$ exists and is S. Therefore,

$$\lim_{n \to +\infty} cs_n = c \lim_{n \to +\infty} s_n = c \cdot S$$

Hence, the series $\sum\limits_{n=1}^{+\infty} cu_n$ is convergent and its sum is $c \cdot S$.

PART (ii):   If the series $\sum\limits_{n=1}^{+\infty} u_n$ is divergent, then $\lim\limits_{n \to +\infty} s_n$ does not exist. Now suppose that the series $\sum\limits_{n=1}^{+\infty} cu_n$ is convergent. Then $\lim\limits_{n \to +\infty} cs_n$ exists. But $s_n = cs_n/c$, and so

$$\lim_{n \to +\infty} s_n = \lim_{n \to +\infty} \frac{1}{c}(cs_n) = \frac{1}{c} \lim_{n \to +\infty} cs_n$$

Thus, $\lim\limits_{n \to +\infty} s_n$ must exist, which is a contradiction. Therefore, the series

$$\sum_{n=1}^{+\infty} cu_n \text{ is divergent.} \qquad \blacksquare$$

EXAMPLE 7: Determine whether the infinite series $$\sum_{n=1}^{+\infty} \frac{1}{4n}$$ is convergent or divergent.	SOLUTION: $\displaystyle\sum_{n=1}^{+\infty} \frac{1}{4n} = \frac{1}{4} + \frac{1}{8} + \frac{1}{12} + \frac{1}{16} + \cdots + \frac{1}{4n} + \cdots$ Because $\displaystyle\sum_{n=1}^{+\infty} 1/n$ is the harmonic series which is divergent, then by Theorem 16.3.8(ii) with $c = \frac{1}{4}$, the given series is divergent.

Note that Theorem 16.3.8(i) is an extension to convergent infinite series of the following property of finite sums:

$$\sum_{k=1}^{n} ca_k = c \sum_{k=1}^{n} a_k$$

Another property of finite sums is

$$\sum_{k=1}^{n} (a_k \pm b_k) = \sum_{k=1}^{n} a_k \pm \sum_{k=1}^{n} b_k$$

and its extension to convergent infinite series is given by the following theorem.

16.3.9 Theorem If $\displaystyle\sum_{n=1}^{+\infty} a_n$ and $\displaystyle\sum_{n=1}^{+\infty} b_n$ are convergent infinite series whose sums are S and R, respectively, then

(i) $\displaystyle\sum_{n=1}^{+\infty} (a_n + b_n)$ is a convergent series and its sum is $S + R$;

(ii) $\displaystyle\sum_{n=1}^{+\infty} (a_n - b_n)$ is a convergent series and its sum is $S - R$.

The proof of this theorem is left as an exercise (see Exercise 11).

The next theorem is a corollary of the above theorem and is sometimes used to prove that a series is divergent.

16.3.10 Theorem If the series $\displaystyle\sum_{n=1}^{+\infty} a_n$ is convergent and the series $\displaystyle\sum_{n=1}^{+\infty} b_n$ is divergent, then the series $\displaystyle\sum_{n=1}^{+\infty} (a_n + b_n)$ is divergent.

PROOF: Assume that $\sum_{n=1}^{+\infty} (a_n + b_n)$ is convergent and its sum is S. Let the sum of the series $\sum_{n=1}^{+\infty} a_n$ be R. Then because

$$\sum_{n=1}^{+\infty} b_n = \sum_{n=1}^{+\infty} [(a_n + b_n) - a_n]$$

it follows from Theorem 16.3.9(ii) that $\sum_{n=1}^{+\infty} b_n$ is convergent and its sum is $S - R$. But this is a contradiction to the hypothesis that $\sum_{n=1}^{+\infty} b_n$ is divergent. Hence, $\sum_{n=1}^{+\infty} (a_n + b_n)$ is divergent. ∎

EXAMPLE 8: Determine whether the infinite series

$$\sum_{n=1}^{+\infty} \left(\frac{1}{4n} + \frac{1}{4^n} \right)$$

is convergent or divergent.

SOLUTION: In Example 7 we proved that the series $\sum_{n=1}^{+\infty} 1/4n$ is divergent. Because the series $\sum_{n=1}^{+\infty} 1/4^n$ is a geometric series with $|r| = \frac{1}{4} < 1$, it is convergent. Hence, by Theorem 16.3.10 the given series is divergent.

Note that if both series $\sum_{n=1}^{+\infty} a_n$ and $\sum_{n=1}^{+\infty} b_n$ are divergent, the series $\sum_{n=1}^{+\infty} (a_n + b_n)$ may or may not be convergent. For example, if $a_n = 1/n$ and $b_n = 1/n$, then $a_n + b_n = 2/n$ and $\sum_{n=1}^{+\infty} 2/n$ is divergent. But if $a_n = 1/n$ and $b_n = -1/n$, then $a_n + b_n = 0$ and $\sum_{n=1}^{+\infty} 0$ is convergent.

Exercises 16.3

In Exercises 1 through 6, find the first four elements of the sequence of partial sums $\{s_n\}$ and find a formula for s_n in terms of n; also, determine if the infinite series is convergent or divergent, and if it is convergent, find its sum.

1. $\sum_{n=1}^{+\infty} \dfrac{1}{(2n-1)(2n+1)}$

2. $\sum_{n=1}^{+\infty} \dfrac{2}{(4n-3)(4n+1)}$

3. $\sum_{n=1}^{+\infty} \ln \dfrac{n}{n+1}$

4. $\sum_{n=1}^{+\infty} n$

5. $\sum_{n=1}^{+\infty} \dfrac{2n+1}{n^2(n+1)^2}$

6. $\sum_{n=1}^{+\infty} \dfrac{2^{n-1}}{3^n}$

In Exercises 7 through 10, find the infinite series which is the given sequence of partial sums; also determine if the infinite series is convergent or divergent, and if it is convergent, find its sum.

7. $\{s_n\} = \left\{ \dfrac{2n}{3n+1} \right\}$

8. $\{s_n\} = \left\{ \dfrac{n^2}{n+1} \right\}$

9. $\{s_n\} = \left\{ \dfrac{1}{2^n} \right\}$

10. $\{s_n\} = \{3^n\}$

11. Prove Theorem 16.3.9.

In Exercises 12 through 25, write the first four terms of the given infinite series and determine if the series is convergent or divergent. If the series is convergent, find its sum.

12. $\displaystyle\sum_{n=1}^{+\infty} \frac{n}{n+1}$ 13. $\displaystyle\sum_{n=1}^{+\infty} \frac{2n+1}{3n+2}$ 14. $\displaystyle\sum_{n=1}^{+\infty} \frac{2}{3n}$ 15. $\displaystyle\sum_{n=1}^{+\infty} \left(\frac{2}{3}\right)^n$ 16. $\displaystyle\sum_{n=1}^{+\infty} \frac{2}{3^{n-1}}$

17. $\displaystyle\sum_{n=1}^{+\infty} (-1)^{n+1} \frac{3}{2^n}$ 18. $\displaystyle\sum_{n=1}^{+\infty} \ln \frac{1}{n}$ 19. $\displaystyle\sum_{n=1}^{+\infty} e^{-n}$ 20. $\displaystyle\sum_{n=1}^{+\infty} \sin \pi n$ 21. $\displaystyle\sum_{n=1}^{+\infty} \cos \pi n$

22. $\displaystyle\sum_{n=1}^{+\infty} \frac{\sinh n}{n}$ 23. $\displaystyle\sum_{n=1}^{+\infty} (2^{-n} + 3^{-n})$ 24. $\displaystyle\sum_{n=1}^{+\infty} [1 + (-1)^n]$ 25. $\displaystyle\sum_{n=1}^{+\infty} \left(\frac{1}{2n} - \frac{1}{3n}\right)$

In Exercises 26 through 29, express the given nonterminating repeating decimal as a common fraction.

26. 0.27 27 27 . . .

27. 1.234 234 234 . . .

28. 2.045 45 45 . . .

29. 0.4653 4653 4653 . . .

30. A ball is dropped from a height of 12 ft. Each time it strikes the ground, it bounces back to a height of three-fourths the distance from which it fell. Find the total distance traveled by the ball before it comes to rest.

16.4 INFINITE SERIES OF POSITIVE TERMS

If all the terms of an infinite series are positive, the sequence of partial sums is increasing. Thus, the following theorem follows immediately from Theorems 16.2.6 and 16.2.9.

16.4.1 Theorem   An infinite series of positive terms is convergent if and only if its sequence of partial sums has an upper bound.

PROOF: For an infinite series of positive terms, the sequence of partial sums has a lower bound of 0. If the sequence of partial sums also has an upper bound, it is bounded. Furthermore, the sequence of partial sums of an infinite series of positive terms is increasing. It follows then from Theorem 16.2.6 that the sequence of partial sums is convergent, and therefore the infinite series is convergent.

Suppose now that an infinite series of positive terms is convergent. Then the sequence of partial sums is also convergent. It follows from Theorem 16.2.9 that the sequence of partial sums is bounded and so it has an upper bound.   ∎

EXAMPLE 1: Prove that the series

$$\sum_{n=1}^{+\infty} \frac{1}{n!}$$

is convergent by using Theorem 16.4.1.

SOLUTION: We must find an upper bound for the sequence of partial sums of the series $\displaystyle\sum_{n=1}^{+\infty} 1/n!$.

$$s_1 = 1, \quad s_2 = 1 + \frac{1}{1 \cdot 2}, \quad s_3 = 1 + \frac{1}{1 \cdot 2} + \frac{1}{1 \cdot 2 \cdot 3},$$

$$s_4 = 1 + \frac{1}{1 \cdot 2} + \frac{1}{1 \cdot 2 \cdot 3} + \frac{1}{1 \cdot 2 \cdot 3 \cdot 4}, \cdots,$$

$$s_n = 1 + \frac{1}{1 \cdot 2} + \frac{1}{1 \cdot 2 \cdot 3} + \frac{1}{1 \cdot 2 \cdot 3 \cdot 4} + \cdots + \frac{1}{1 \cdot 2 \cdot 3 \cdot \ldots \cdot n} \qquad (1)$$

Now consider the first n terms of the geometric series with $a = 1$ and $r = \frac{1}{2}$:

$$\sum_{k=1}^{n} \frac{1}{2^{k-1}} = 1 + \frac{1}{2} + \frac{1}{2^2} + \frac{1}{2^3} + \cdots + \frac{1}{2^{n-1}} \qquad (2)$$

By Theorem 16.3.6 the geometric series with $a = 1$ and $r = \frac{1}{2}$ has the sum $a/(1 - r) = 1/(1 - \frac{1}{2}) = 2$. Hence, summation (2) is less than 2. Observe that each term of summation (1) is less than or equal to the corresponding term of summation (2); that is,

$$\frac{1}{k!} \leq \frac{1}{2^{k-1}}$$

This is true because $k! = 1 \cdot 2 \cdot 3 \cdot \ldots \cdot k$, which in addition to the factor 1 contains $k - 1$ factors each greater than or equal to 2. Hence,

$$s_n = \sum_{k=1}^{n} \frac{1}{k!} \leq \sum_{k=1}^{n} \frac{1}{2^{k-1}} < 2$$

From the above we see that s_n has an upper bound of 2. Therefore, by Theorem 16.4.1 the given series is convergent.

In the above example the terms of the given series were compared with those of a known convergent series. This is a particular case of the following theorem known as the *comparison test*.

16.4.2 Theorem
Comparison Test

Let the series $\sum_{n=1}^{+\infty} u_n$ be a series of positive terms.

(i) If $\sum_{n=1}^{+\infty} v_n$ is a series of positive terms which is known to be convergent, and $u_n \leq v_n$ for all positive integers n, then $\sum_{n=1}^{+\infty} u_n$ is convergent.

(ii) If $\sum_{n=1}^{+\infty} w_n$ is a series of positive terms which is known to be divergent, and $u_n \geq w_n$ for all positive integers n, then $\sum_{n=1}^{+\infty} u_n$ is divergent.

PROOF OF (i): Let $\{s_n\}$ be the sequence of partial sums for the series $\sum_{n=1}^{+\infty} u_n$ and $\{t_n\}$ be the sequence of partial sums for the series $\sum_{n=1}^{+\infty} v_n$. Because $\sum\limits_{n=1}^{+\infty} v_n$ is a series of positive terms which is convergent, it follows from Theorem 16.4.1 that the sequence $\{t_n\}$ has an upper bound; call it B. Because $u_n \leq v_n$ for all positive integers n, we can conclude that $s_n \leq t_n \leq B$ for all positive integers n. Therefore, B is an upper bound of the sequence $\{s_n\}$. And because the terms of the series $\sum\limits_{n=1}^{+\infty} u_n$ are all positive, it follows from Theorem 16.4.1 that $\sum\limits_{n=1}^{+\infty} u_n$ is convergent.

PROOF OF (ii): Assume that $\sum\limits_{n=1}^{+\infty} u_n$ is convergent. Then because both $\sum\limits_{n=1}^{+\infty} u_n$ and $\sum\limits_{n=1}^{+\infty} w_n$ are infinite series of positive terms and $w_n \leq u_n$ for all positive integers n, it follows from part (i) that $\sum\limits_{n=1}^{+\infty} w_n$ is convergent. However, this contradicts the hypothesis, and so our assumption is false. Therefore, $\sum\limits_{n=1}^{+\infty} u_n$ is divergent. ∎

As we stated in Sec. 16.3, as a result of Theorem 16.3.7, the convergence or divergence of an infinite series is not affected by discarding a finite number of terms. Therefore, when applying the comparison test, if $u_i \leq v_i$ or $u_i \geq w_i$ when $i > m$, the test is valid regardless of how the first m terms of the two series compare.

EXAMPLE 2: Determine whether the infinite series

$$\sum_{n=1}^{+\infty} \frac{4}{3^n + 1}$$

is convergent or divergent.

SOLUTION: The given series is

$$\frac{4}{4} + \frac{4}{10} + \frac{4}{28} + \frac{4}{82} + \cdots + \frac{4}{3^n + 1} + \cdots$$

Comparing the nth term of this series with the nth term of the convergent geometric series

$$\frac{4}{3} + \frac{4}{9} + \frac{4}{27} + \frac{4}{81} + \cdots + \frac{4}{3^n} + \cdots \qquad r = \frac{1}{3} < 1$$

we have

$$\frac{4}{3^n + 1} < \frac{4}{3^n}$$

for every positive integer n. Therefore, by the comparison test, Theorem 16.4.2(i), the given series is convergent.

EXAMPLE 3: Determine whether the infinite series

$$\sum_{n=1}^{+\infty} \frac{1}{\sqrt{n}}$$

is convergent or divergent.

SOLUTION: The given series is

$$\sum_{n=1}^{+\infty} \frac{1}{\sqrt{n}} = \frac{1}{\sqrt{1}} + \frac{1}{\sqrt{2}} + \frac{1}{\sqrt{3}} + \cdots + \frac{1}{\sqrt{n}} + \cdots$$

Comparing the nth term of this series with the nth term of the divergent harmonic series, we have

$$\frac{1}{\sqrt{n}} \geq \frac{1}{n} \qquad \text{for every positive integer } n$$

So by Theorem 16.4.2(ii) the given series $\sum_{n=1}^{+\infty} 1/\sqrt{n}$ is divergent.

The following theorem, known as the *limit comparison test*, is a consequence of Theorem 16.4.2 and is often easier to apply.

16.4.3 Theorem
Limit Comparison Test

Let $\sum_{n=1}^{+\infty} u_n$ and $\sum_{n=1}^{+\infty} v_n$ be two series of positive terms.

(i) If $\lim_{n \to +\infty} (u_n/v_n) = c > 0$, then the two series either both converge or both diverge.

(ii) If $\lim_{n \to +\infty} (u_n/v_n) = 0$, and if $\sum_{n=1}^{+\infty} v_n$ converges, then $\sum_{n=1}^{+\infty} u_n$ converges.

(iii) If $\lim_{n \to +\infty} (u_n/v_n) = +\infty$, and if $\sum_{n=1}^{+\infty} v_n$ diverges, then $\sum_{n=1}^{+\infty} u_n$ diverges.

PROOF OF (i): Because $\lim_{n \to +\infty} (u_n/v_n) = c$, it follows that there exists an $N > 0$ such that

$$\left| \frac{u_n}{v_n} - c \right| < \frac{c}{2} \qquad \text{for all } n > N$$

or, equivalently,

$$-\frac{c}{2} < \frac{u_n}{v_n} - c < \frac{c}{2} \qquad \text{for all } n > N$$

or, equivalently,

$$\frac{c}{2} < \frac{u_n}{v_n} < \frac{3c}{2} \qquad \text{for all } n > N \qquad (3)$$

From the right-hand inequality (3) we get

$$u_n < \tfrac{3}{2} c v_n \qquad (4)$$

If $\sum\limits_{n=1}^{+\infty} v_n$ is convergent, so is $\sum\limits_{n=1}^{+\infty} \frac{3}{2}cv_n$. It follows from inequality (4) and the comparison test that $\sum\limits_{n=1}^{+\infty} u_n$ is convergent.

From the left-hand inequality (3) we get

$$v_n < \frac{2}{c} u_n \qquad (5)$$

If $\sum\limits_{n=1}^{+\infty} u_n$ is convergent, so is $\sum\limits_{n=1}^{+\infty} \frac{2}{c} u_n$. From inequality (5) and the comparison test it follows that $\sum\limits_{n=1}^{+\infty} v_n$ is convergent.

If $\sum\limits_{n=1}^{+\infty} v_n$ is divergent, we can show that $\sum\limits_{n=1}^{+\infty} u_n$ is divergent by assuming that $\sum\limits_{n=1}^{+\infty} u_n$ is convergent and getting a contradiction by applying inequality (5) and the comparison test.

In a similar manner, if $\sum\limits_{n=1}^{+\infty} u_n$ is divergent, it follows that $\sum\limits_{n=1}^{+\infty} v_n$ is divergent because a contradiction is obtained from inequality (4) and the comparison test if $\sum\limits_{n=1}^{+\infty} v_n$ is assumed to be convergent.

We have therefore proved part (i). The proofs of parts (ii) and (iii) are left as exercises (see Exercises 19 and 20).   ∎

A word of caution is in order regarding part (ii) of Theorem 16.4.3. Note that when $\lim\limits_{n \to +\infty} (u_n/v_n) = 0$, the divergence of the series $\sum\limits_{n=1}^{+\infty} v_n$ does *not* imply that the series $\sum\limits_{n=1}^{+\infty} u_n$ diverges.

EXAMPLE 4:   **Solve Example 2 by using the limit comparison test.**

SOLUTION: Let u_n be the nth term of the given series $\sum\limits_{n=1}^{+\infty} 4/(3^n + 1)$ and v_n be the nth term of the convergent geometric series $\sum\limits_{n=1}^{+\infty} 4/3^n$. Therefore,

$$\lim_{n \to +\infty} \frac{u_n}{v_n} = \lim_{n \to +\infty} \frac{\dfrac{4}{3^n + 1}}{\dfrac{4}{3^n}}$$

$$= \lim_{n \to +\infty} \frac{3^n}{3^n + 1}$$

$$= \lim_{n \to +\infty} \frac{1}{1 + 3^{-n}}$$

$$= 1$$

Hence, by part (i) of the limit comparison test, it follows that the given series is convergent.

EXAMPLE 5: Solve Example 3 by using the limit comparison test.

SOLUTION: Let u_n be the nth term of the given series $\sum_{n=1}^{+\infty} 1/\sqrt{n}$ and v_n be the nth term of the divergent harmonic series. Then

$$\lim_{n\to+\infty} \frac{u_n}{v_n} = \lim_{n\to+\infty} \frac{\dfrac{1}{\sqrt{n}}}{\dfrac{1}{n}} = \lim_{n\to+\infty} \sqrt{n} = +\infty$$

Therefore, by part (iii) of the limit comparison test, we conclude that the given series is divergent.

EXAMPLE 6: Determine whether the series

$$\sum_{n=1}^{+\infty} \frac{n^3}{n!}$$

is convergent or divergent.

SOLUTION: In Example 1, we proved that the series $\sum_{n=1}^{+\infty} 1/n!$ is convergent. Using the limit comparison test with $u_n = n^3/n!$ and $v_n = 1/n!$, we have

$$\lim_{n\to+\infty} \frac{u_n}{v_n} = \lim_{n\to+\infty} \frac{\dfrac{n^3}{n!}}{\dfrac{1}{n!}} = \lim_{n\to+\infty} n^3 = +\infty$$

Part (iii) of the limit comparison test is not applicable because $\sum_{n=1}^{+\infty} v_n$ converges. However, there is a way that we can use the limit comparison test. The given series can be written as

$$\frac{1^3}{1!} + \frac{2^3}{2!} + \frac{3^3}{3!} + \frac{4^3}{4!} + \frac{5^3}{5!} + \cdots + \frac{n^3}{n!} + \cdots$$

Because Theorem 16.3.7 allows us to subtract a finite number of terms without affecting the behavior (convergence or divergence) of a series, we discard the first three terms and obtain

$$\frac{4^3}{4!} + \frac{5^3}{5!} + \frac{6^3}{6!} + \cdots + \frac{(n+3)^3}{(n+3)!} + \cdots$$

Now letting $u_n = (n+3)^3/(n+3)!$ and, as before, letting $v_n = 1/n!$, we have

$$\lim_{n\to+\infty} \frac{u_n}{v_n} = \lim_{n\to+\infty} \frac{\dfrac{(n+3)^3}{(n+3)!}}{\dfrac{1}{n!}}$$

$$= \lim_{n\to+\infty} \frac{(n+3)^3 n!}{(n+3)!}$$

$$= \lim_{n \to +\infty} \frac{(n+3)^3 n!}{n!(n+1)(n+2)(n+3)}$$

$$= \lim_{n \to +\infty} \frac{(n+3)^2}{(n+1)(n+2)}$$

$$= \lim_{n \to +\infty} \frac{n^2 + 6n + 9}{n^2 + 3n + 2}$$

$$= \lim_{n \to +\infty} \frac{1 + \dfrac{6}{n} + \dfrac{9}{n^2}}{1 + \dfrac{3}{n} + \dfrac{2}{n^2}}$$

$$= 1$$

It follows from part (i) of the Limit Comparison Test that the given series is convergent.

● ILLUSTRATION 1: Consider the geometric series

$$1 + \frac{1}{2} + \frac{1}{4} + \frac{1}{8} + \frac{1}{16} + \frac{1}{32} + \cdots + \frac{1}{2^{n-1}} + \cdots \tag{6}$$

which converges to 2 as shown in Illustration 2 of Sec. 16.3. Regrouping the terms of this series, we have

$$\left(1 + \frac{1}{2}\right) + \left(\frac{1}{4} + \frac{1}{8}\right) + \left(\frac{1}{16} + \frac{1}{32}\right) + \cdots + \left(\frac{1}{4^{n-1}} + \frac{1}{2 \cdot 4^{n-1}}\right) + \cdots$$

which is the series

$$\frac{3}{2} + \frac{3}{8} + \frac{3}{32} + \cdots + \frac{3}{2 \cdot 4^{n-1}} + \cdots \tag{7}$$

Series (7) is the geometric series with $a = \frac{3}{2}$ and $r = \frac{1}{4}$. Thus, by Theorem 16.3.6 it is convergent, and its sum is

$$\frac{a}{1-r} = \frac{\frac{3}{2}}{1 - \frac{1}{4}} = 2$$

We see, then, that series (7), which is obtained from the convergent series (6) by regrouping the terms, is also convergent. Its sum is the same as that of series (6).   ●

Illustration 1 gives a particular case of the following theorem.

16.4.4 Theorem   If $\displaystyle\sum_{n=1}^{+\infty} u_n$ is a given convergent series of positive terms, its terms can be grouped in any manner, and the resulting series also will be convergent and will have the same sum as the given series.

PROOF: Let $\{s_n\}$ be the sequence of partial sums for the given convergent series of positive terms. Then $\lim\limits_{n \to +\infty} s_n$ exists; let this limit be S. Consider a series $\sum\limits_{n=1}^{+\infty} v_n$ whose terms are obtained by grouping the terms of $\sum\limits_{n=1}^{+\infty} u_n$ in some manner. For example, $\sum\limits_{n=1}^{+\infty} v_n$ may be the series

$$u_1 + (u_2 + u_3) + (u_4 + u_5 + u_6) + (u_7 + u_8 + u_9 + u_{10}) + \cdots$$

or it may be the series

$$(u_1 + u_2) + (u_3 + u_4) + (u_5 + u_6) + (u_7 + u_8) + \cdots$$

and so forth. Let $\{t_m\}$ be the sequence of partial sums for the series $\sum\limits_{n=1}^{+\infty} v_n$.

Each partial sum of the sequence $\{t_m\}$ is also a partial sum of the sequence $\{s_n\}$. Therefore, as m increases without bound, so does n. Because $\lim\limits_{n \to +\infty} s_n = S$, we conclude that $\lim\limits_{m \to +\infty} t_m = S$. This proves the theorem.   ∎

Theorem 16.4.4 and the next theorem state properties of the sum of a convergent series of positive terms that are similar to properties that hold for the sum of a finite number of terms.

16.4.5 Theorem   If $\sum\limits_{n=1}^{+\infty} u_n$ is a given convergent series of positive terms, the order of the terms can be rearranged, and the resulting series also will be convergent and will have the same sum as the given series.

PROOF: Let $\{s_n\}$ be the sequence of partial sums for the given convergent series of positive terms, and let $\lim\limits_{n \to +\infty} s_n = S$. Let $\sum\limits_{n=1}^{+\infty} v_n$ be a series formed by rearranging the order of the terms of $\sum\limits_{n=1}^{+\infty} u_n$. For example, $\sum\limits_{n=1}^{+\infty} v_n$ may be the series

$$u_4 + u_3 + u_7 + u_1 + u_9 + u_5 + \cdots$$

Let $\{t_n\}$ be the sequence of partial sums for the series $\sum\limits_{n=1}^{+\infty} v_n$. Each partial sum of the sequence $\{t_n\}$ will be less than S because it is the sum of n terms of the infinite series $\sum\limits_{n=1}^{+\infty} u_n$. Therefore, S is an upper bound of the sequence $\{t_n\}$. Furthermore, because all the terms of the series $\sum\limits_{n=1}^{+\infty} v_n$ are positive, $\{t_n\}$ is a monotonic increasing sequence. Hence, by Theorem 16.2.7 the sequence $\{t_n\}$ is convergent, and $\lim\limits_{n \to +\infty} t_n = T \leq S$. Now because the given series $\sum\limits_{n=1}^{+\infty} u_n$ can be obtained from the series $\sum\limits_{n=1}^{+\infty} v_n$ by rearranging the order of the terms, we can use the same argument and conclude that $S \le T$. If both inequalities, $T \le S$ and $S \le T$, must hold, it follows that $S = T$. This proves the theorem. ∎

A series which is often used in the comparison test is the one known as the *p series*, or the *hyperharmonic series*. It is

$$\frac{1}{1^p} + \frac{1}{2^p} + \frac{1}{3^p} + \cdots + \frac{1}{n^p} + \cdots \qquad \text{where } p \text{ is a constant} \qquad (8)$$

In the following illustration we prove that the p series diverges if $p \le 1$ and converges if $p > 1$.

● ILLUSTRATION 2: If $p = 1$, the p series is the harmonic series, which diverges. If $p < 1$, then $n^p \le n$, and so

$$\frac{1}{n^p} \ge \frac{1}{n} \qquad \text{for every positive integer } n$$

Hence, by Theorem 16.4.2(ii) the p series is divergent if $p < 1$.

If $p > 1$, we group the terms as follows:

$$\frac{1}{1^p} + \left(\frac{1}{2^p} + \frac{1}{3^p}\right) + \left(\frac{1}{4^p} + \frac{1}{5^p} + \frac{1}{6^p} + \frac{1}{7^p}\right) + \left(\frac{1}{8^p} + \frac{1}{9^p} + \cdots + \frac{1}{15^p}\right) + \cdots \qquad (9)$$

Consider the series

$$\frac{1}{1^p} + \frac{2}{2^p} + \frac{4}{4^p} + \frac{8}{8^p} + \cdots + \frac{2^{n-1}}{(2^{n-1})^p} + \cdots \qquad (10)$$

This is a geometric series whose ratio is $2/2^p = 1/2^{p-1}$, which is a positive number less than 1. Hence, series (10) is convergent. Rewriting the terms of series (10), we get

$$\frac{1}{1^p} + \left(\frac{1}{2^p} + \frac{1}{2^p}\right) + \left(\frac{1}{4^p} + \frac{1}{4^p} + \frac{1}{4^p} + \frac{1}{4^p}\right) + \left(\frac{1}{8^p} + \frac{1}{8^p} + \cdots + \frac{1}{8^p}\right) + \cdots \qquad (11)$$

Comparing series (9) and series (11), we see that the group of terms in each set of parentheses after the first group is less in sum for (9) than it is for (11). Therefore, by the comparison test, series (9) is convergent. Because (9) is merely a regrouping of the terms of the p series when $p > 1$, we conclude from Theorem 16.4.4 that the p series is convergent if $p > 1$. ●

Note that the series in Example 3 is the p series where $p = \frac{1}{2} < 1$; therefore, it is divergent.

EXAMPLE 7:   Determine whether the infinite series

$$\sum_{n=1}^{+\infty} \frac{1}{(n^2 + 2)^{1/3}}$$

is convergent or divergent.

SOLUTION: Because for large values of n the number $n^2 + 2$ is close to the number n^2, so is the number $1/(n^2 + 2)^{1/3}$ close to the number $1/n^{2/3}$. The series $\sum_{n=1}^{+\infty} 1/n^{2/3}$ is divergent because it is the p series with $p = \frac{2}{3} < 1$.

Using the limit comparison test with $u_n = 1/(n^2 + 2)^{1/3}$ and $v_n = 1/n^{2/3}$, we have

$$\lim_{n \to +\infty} \frac{u_n}{v_n} = \lim_{n \to +\infty} \frac{\dfrac{1}{(n^2 + 2)^{1/3}}}{\dfrac{1}{n^{2/3}}}$$

$$= \lim_{n \to +\infty} \frac{n^{2/3}}{(n^2 + 2)^{1/3}}$$

$$= \lim_{n \to +\infty} \left(\frac{n^2}{n^2 + 2}\right)^{1/3}$$

$$= \lim_{n \to +\infty} \left(\frac{1}{1 + \dfrac{2}{n^2}}\right)^{1/3}$$

$$= 1$$

Therefore, the given series is divergent.

Exercises 16.4

In Exercises 1 through 18, determine if the given series is convergent or divergent.

1. $\sum_{n=1}^{+\infty} \dfrac{1}{n2^n}$

2. $\sum_{n=1}^{+\infty} \dfrac{1}{\sqrt{2n + 1}}$

3. $\sum_{n=1}^{+\infty} \dfrac{1}{n^n}$

4. $\sum_{n=1}^{+\infty} \dfrac{n^2}{4n^3 + 1}$

5. $\sum_{n=1}^{+\infty} \dfrac{1}{\sqrt{n^2 + 4n}}$

6. $\sum_{n=1}^{+\infty} \dfrac{|\sin n|}{n^2}$

7. $\sum_{n=1}^{+\infty} \dfrac{n!}{(n + 2)!}$

8. $\sum_{n=1}^{+\infty} \dfrac{1}{\sqrt{n^3 + 1}}$

9. $\sum_{n=1}^{+\infty} \dfrac{n}{5n^2 + 3}$

10. $\sum_{n=1}^{+\infty} \sin \dfrac{1}{n}$

11. $\sum_{n=1}^{+\infty} \dfrac{n!}{(2n)!}$

12. $\sum_{n=1}^{+\infty} \dfrac{2^n}{n!}$

13. $\sum_{n=1}^{+\infty} \dfrac{|\csc n|}{\sqrt{n}}$

14. $\sum_{n=1}^{+\infty} \dfrac{1}{n + \sqrt{n}}$

15. $\sum_{n=2}^{+\infty} \dfrac{1}{n\sqrt{n^2 - 1}}$

16. $\sum_{n=1}^{+\infty} \dfrac{1}{(n + 2)(n + 4)}$

17. $\sum_{n=1}^{+\infty} \dfrac{\ln n}{n^2 + 2}$

18. $\sum_{n=1}^{+\infty} \dfrac{1}{3^n - \cos n}$

19. Prove Theorem 16.4.3(ii).

20. Prove Theorem 16.4.3(iii).

21. If $\displaystyle\sum_{n=1}^{+\infty} a_n$ and $\displaystyle\sum_{n=1}^{+\infty} b_n$ are two convergent series of positive terms, use the Limit Comparison Test to prove that the series $\displaystyle\sum_{n=1}^{+\infty} a_n b_n$ is also convergent.

22. Suppose f is a function such that $f(n) > 0$ for n any positive integer. Furthermore, suppose that if p is any positive number $\displaystyle\lim_{n \to +\infty} n^p f(n)$ exists and is positive. Prove that the series $\displaystyle\sum_{n=1}^{+\infty} f(n)$ is convergent if $p > 1$ and divergent if $0 < p \leq 1$.

16.5 THE INTEGRAL TEST The theorem known as the *integral test* makes use of the theory of improper integrals to test an infinite series of positive terms for convergence.

16.5.1 Theorem
Integral Test

Let f be a function which is continuous, decreasing, and positive valued for all $x \geq 1$. Then the infinite series

$$\sum_{n=1}^{+\infty} f(n) = f(1) + f(2) + f(3) + \cdots + f(n) + \cdots$$

is convergent if the improper integral

$$\int_{1}^{+\infty} f(x) \, dx$$

exists, and it is divergent if the improper integral increases without bound.

PROOF: If i is a positive integer, by the mean-value theorem for integrals (7.5.2) there exists a number X such that $i - 1 \leq X \leq i$ and

$$\int_{i-1}^{i} f(x) \, dx = f(X) \cdot 1 \tag{1}$$

Because f is a decreasing function,

$$f(i - 1) \geq f(X) \geq f(i)$$

and so from (1) we have

$$f(i - 1) \geq \int_{i-1}^{i} f(x) \, dx \geq f(i)$$

Therefore, if n is any positive integer,

$$\sum_{i=2}^{n} f(i - 1) \geq \sum_{i=2}^{n} \int_{i-1}^{i} f(x) \, dx \geq \sum_{i=2}^{n} f(i)$$

or, equivalently,

$$\sum_{i=1}^{n-1} f(i) \geq \int_{1}^{n} f(x) \, dx \geq \sum_{i=1}^{n} f(i) - f(1) \tag{2}$$

Figure 16.5.1

Figure 16.5.2

Figures 16.5.1 and 16.5.2 show the geometric interpretation of the above discussion for $n = 6$. In Fig. 16.5.1, we have a sketch of the graph of a function f satisfying the hypothesis. The sum of the measures of the areas of the shaded rectangles is $f(1) + f(2) + f(3) + f(4) + f(5)$, which is the left member of inequality (2) when $n = 6$. Clearly, the sum of the measures of the areas of these rectangles is greater than the measure of the area given by the definite integral when $n = 6$. In Fig. 16.5.2 the sum of the measures of the areas of the shaded rectangles is $f(2) + f(3) + f(4) + f(5) + f(6)$, which is the right member of the inequality (2) when $n = 6$. This sum is less than the value of the definite integral when $n = 6$.

If the given improper integral exists, let L be its value. Then

$$\int_1^n f(x) \, dx \le L \tag{3}$$

From the second and third members of the inequality (2) and from (3) we obtain

$$\sum_{i=1}^n f(i) \le f(1) + \int_1^n f(x) \, dx \le f(1) + L \tag{4}$$

Consider now the infinite series $\sum_{n=1}^{+\infty} f(n)$. Let the sequence of partial sums of this series be $\{s_n\}$, where $s_n = \sum_{i=1}^n f(i)$. From (4) we see that $\{s_n\}$ has an upper bound of $f(1) + L$. Hence, by Theorem 16.4.1 we conclude that $\sum_{n=1}^{+\infty} f(n)$ is convergent.

Suppose that the given improper integral increases without bound. From (2) we have

$$\sum_{i=1}^{n-1} f(i) \ge \int_1^n f(x) \, dx$$

for all positive integers n. Thus, $\sum_{i=1}^{n-1} f(i)$ must also increase without bound as $n \to +\infty$. Therefore, $\lim_{n \to +\infty} s_n = \lim_{n \to +\infty} \sum_{i=1}^n f(i) = +\infty$. Hence, $\sum_{n=1}^{+\infty} f(n)$ is divergent. ∎

EXAMPLE 1: Use the integral test to show that the p series diverges if $p \le 1$ and converges if $p > 1$.

SOLUTION: The p series is $\sum_{n=1}^{+\infty} 1/n^p$. The function f, defined by $f(x) = 1/x^p$, satisfies the hypothesis of Theorem 16.5.1. Thus, considering the improper integral, we have

$$\int_1^{+\infty} \frac{dx}{x^p} = \lim_{b \to +\infty} \int_1^b \frac{dx}{x^p}$$

If $p = 1$, the above integral gives

$$\lim_{b \to +\infty} \ln x \Big]_1^b = \lim_{b \to +\infty} \ln b = +\infty$$

If $p \neq 1$, the integral gives

$$\lim_{b \to +\infty} \frac{x^{1-p}}{1-p} \Big]_1^b = \lim_{b \to +\infty} \frac{b^{1-p} - 1}{1 - p}$$

This limit is $+\infty$ when $p < 1$; it is $-1/(1 - p)$ if $p > 1$. Therefore, by the integral test, it follows that the p series converges for $p > 1$ and diverges for $p \leq 1$.

EXAMPLE 2: Determine if the infinite series

$$\sum_{n=1}^{+\infty} n e^{-n}$$

is convergent or divergent.

SOLUTION: Letting $f(x) = xe^{-x}$, we see that f is continuous, decreasing, and positive valued for $x \geq 1$; thus, the hypothesis of the integral test is satisfied. Using integration by parts, we have $\int xe^{-x}\, dx = -e^{-x}(x + 1) + C$. Hence,

$$\int_1^{+\infty} xe^{-x}\, dx = \lim_{b \to +\infty} \left[-e^{-x}(x + 1) \right]_1^b = \lim_{b \to +\infty} \left[-\frac{b + 1}{e^b} + \frac{2}{e} \right]$$

Because $\lim_{b \to +\infty} (b + 1) = +\infty$ and $\lim_{b \to +\infty} e^b = +\infty$, we can use L'Hôpital's rule and obtain

$$\lim_{b \to +\infty} \frac{b + 1}{e^b} = \lim_{b \to +\infty} \frac{1}{e^b} = 0$$

Therefore,

$$\int_1^{+\infty} xe^{-x}\, dx = \frac{2}{e}$$

and so the given series is convergent.

EXAMPLE 3: Determine if the series

$$\sum_{n=1}^{+\infty} \frac{1}{(n + 1) \sqrt{\ln(n + 1)}}$$

is convergent or divergent.

SOLUTION: The function f defined by $f(x) = 1/(x + 1) \sqrt{\ln(x + 1)}$ is continuous, decreasing, and positive valued for $x \geq 1$; hence, the integral test can be applied.

$$\int_1^{+\infty} \frac{dx}{(x + 1) \sqrt{\ln(x + 1)}} = \lim_{b \to +\infty} \int_1^b [\ln(x + 1)]^{-1/2} \frac{dx}{x + 1}$$

$$= \lim_{b \to +\infty} \left[2\sqrt{\ln(x + 1)} \right]_1^b$$

$$= \lim_{b \to +\infty} [2\sqrt{\ln(b + 1)} - 2\sqrt{\ln 2}]$$

$$= +\infty$$

We conclude that the given series is divergent.

Exercises 16.5

In Exercises 1 through 12, determine if the given series is convergent or divergent.

1. $\displaystyle\sum_{n=1}^{+\infty} \frac{\ln n}{n}$

2. $\displaystyle\sum_{n=2}^{+\infty} \frac{1}{n \ln n}$

3. $\displaystyle\sum_{n=1}^{+\infty} \frac{\tan^{-1} n}{n^2 + 1}$

4. $\displaystyle\sum_{n=1}^{+\infty} ne^{-n^2}$

5. $\displaystyle\sum_{n=1}^{+\infty} n^2 e^{-n}$

6. $\displaystyle\sum_{n=1}^{+\infty} \cot^{-1} n$

7. $\displaystyle\sum_{n=1}^{+\infty} \operatorname{csch} n$

8. $\displaystyle\sum_{n=1}^{+\infty} \frac{e^{\tan^{-1} n}}{n^2 + 1}$

9. $\displaystyle\sum_{n=1}^{+\infty} \frac{e^{1/n}}{n^2}$

10. $\displaystyle\sum_{n=1}^{+\infty} \operatorname{sech}^2 n$

11. $\displaystyle\sum_{n=1}^{+\infty} \ln \left(\frac{n+3}{n}\right)$

12. $\displaystyle\sum_{n=2}^{+\infty} \frac{1}{n(\ln n)^3}$

13. Prove that the series $\displaystyle\sum_{n=2}^{+\infty} \frac{1}{n(\ln n)^p}$ is convergent if and only if $p > 1$.

14. Prove that the series $\displaystyle\sum_{n=3}^{+\infty} \frac{1}{n(\ln n)[\ln(\ln n)]^p}$ is convergent if and only if $p > 1$.

15. If s_k is the kth partial sum of the harmonic series, prove that

$$\ln(k + 1) < s_k < 1 + \ln k$$

(HINT: $\dfrac{1}{m+1} \leq \dfrac{1}{x} \leq \dfrac{1}{m}$ if $0 < m \leq x \leq m + 1$

Integrate each member of the inequality from m to $m + 1$; let m take on successively the values $1, 2, \ldots, n - 1$, and add the results.)

16. Use the result of Exercise 15 to estimate the sum $\displaystyle\sum_{m=50}^{100} \frac{1}{m} = \frac{1}{50} + \frac{1}{51} + \cdots + \frac{1}{100}$.

16.6 INFINITE SERIES OF POSITIVE AND NEGATIVE TERMS

In this section we consider infinite series having both positive and negative terms. The first type of such a series which we discuss is one whose terms are alternately positive and negative—an "alternating series."

16.6.1 Definition   If $a_n > 0$ for all positive integers n, then the series

$$\sum_{n=1}^{+\infty} (-1)^{n+1} a_n = a_1 - a_2 + a_3 - a_4 + \cdots + (-1)^{n+1} a_n + \cdots$$

and the series

$$\sum_{n=1}^{+\infty} (-1)^n a_n = -a_1 + a_2 - a_3 + a_4 - \cdots + (-1)^n a_n + \cdots$$

are called *alternating series*.

The following theorem gives a test for the convergence of an alternating series.

16.6.2 Theorem
Alternating-Series Test

If the numbers $u_1, u_2, u_3, \ldots, u_n, \ldots$ are alternately positive and negative, $|u_{n+1}| < |u_n|$ for all positive integers n, and $\lim_{n \to +\infty} u_n = 0$, then the alternating series $\sum_{n=1}^{+\infty} u_n$ is convergent.

PROOF: We assume that the odd-numbered terms of the given series are positive and the even-numbered terms are negative. This assumption is not a loss of generality because if this is not the case, then we consider the series whose first term is u_2 because discarding a finite number of terms does not affect the convergence of the series. So $u_{2n-1} > 0$ and $u_{2n} < 0$ for every positive integer n. Consider the partial sum

$$s_{2n} = (u_1 + u_2) + (u_3 + u_4) + \cdots + (u_{2n-1} + u_{2n}) \tag{1}$$

The first term of each quantity in parentheses in (1) is positive and the second term is negative. Because by hypothesis $|u_{n+1}| < |u_n|$, we conclude that each quantity in parentheses is positive. Therefore,

$$0 < s_2 < s_4 < s_6 < \cdots < s_{2n} < \cdots \tag{2}$$

We also can write s_{2n} as

$$s_{2n} = u_1 + (u_2 + u_3) + (u_4 + u_5) + \cdots + (u_{2n-2} + u_{2n-1}) + u_{2n} \tag{3}$$

Because $|u_{n+1}| < |u_n|$, each quantity in parentheses in (3) is negative and so also is u_{2n}. Therefore,

$$s_{2n} < u_1 \qquad \text{for every positive integer } n \tag{4}$$

From (2) and (4) we have

$$0 < s_{2n} < u_1 \qquad \text{for every positive integer } n$$

So the sequence $\{s_{2n}\}$ is bounded. Furthermore, from (2) the sequence $\{s_{2n}\}$ is monotonic. Therefore, by Theorem 16.2.6 the sequence $\{s_{2n}\}$ is convergent. Let $\lim_{n \to +\infty} s_{2n} = S$, and from Theorem 16.2.7 we know that $S \leq u_1$.

Because $s_{2n+1} = s_{2n} + u_{2n+1}$, we have

$$\lim_{n \to +\infty} s_{2n+1} = \lim_{n \to +\infty} s_{2n} + \lim_{n \to +\infty} u_{2n+1}$$

but, by hypothesis, $\lim_{n \to +\infty} u_{2n+1} = 0$, and so $\lim_{n \to +\infty} s_{2n+1} = \lim_{n \to +\infty} s_{2n}$. Therefore, the sequence of partial sums of the even-numbered terms and the sequence of partial sums of the odd-numbered terms have the same limit S.

We now show that $\lim_{n \to +\infty} s_n = S$. Because $\lim_{n \to +\infty} s_{2n} = S$, then for any $\epsilon > 0$ there exists an integer $N_1 > 0$ such that

$$|s_{2n} - S| < \epsilon \qquad \text{whenever } 2n \geq N_1$$

And because $\lim_{n \to +\infty} s_{2n+1} = S$, there exists an integer $N_2 > 0$ such that

$$|s_{2n+1} - S| < \epsilon \qquad \text{whenever } 2n + 1 \geq N_2$$

If N is the larger of the two integers N_1 and N_2, it follows that if n is any integer, either odd or even, then

$$|s_n - S| < \epsilon \qquad \text{whenever } n \geq N$$

Therefore, $\lim\limits_{n \to +\infty} s_n = S$, and so the series $\sum\limits_{n=1}^{+\infty} u_n$ is convergent.   ∎

EXAMPLE 1: Prove that the alternating series

$$\sum_{n=1}^{+\infty} \frac{(-1)^{n+1}}{n}$$

is convergent.

SOLUTION: The given series is

$$1 - \frac{1}{2} + \frac{1}{3} - \frac{1}{4} + \cdots + (-1)^{n+1} \frac{1}{n} + (-1)^{n+2} \frac{1}{n+1} + \cdots$$

Because $1/(n+1) < 1/n$ for all positive integers n, and $\lim\limits_{n \to +\infty} (1/n) = 0$, it follows from Theorem 16.6.2 that the given alternating series is convergent.

EXAMPLE 2: Determine if the series

$$\sum_{n=1}^{+\infty} (-1)^n \frac{n+2}{n(n+1)}$$

is convergent or divergent.

SOLUTION: The given series is an alternating series, with

$$u_n = (-1)^n \frac{n+2}{n(n+1)} \quad \text{and} \quad u_{n+1} = (-1)^{n+1} \frac{n+3}{(n+1)(n+2)}$$

$$\lim_{n \to +\infty} \frac{n+2}{n(n+1)} = \lim_{n \to +\infty} \frac{\dfrac{1}{n} + \dfrac{2}{n^2}}{1 + \dfrac{1}{n}} = 0$$

Before we can apply the alternating-series test we must also show that $|u_{n+1}| < |u_n|$ or, equivalently, $|u_{n+1}|/|u_n| < 1$.

$$\frac{|u_{n+1}|}{|u_n|} = \frac{n+3}{(n+1)(n+2)} \cdot \frac{n(n+1)}{n+2} = \frac{n(n+3)}{(n+2)^2} = \frac{n^2 + 3n}{n^2 + 4n + 4} < 1$$

Then it follows from Theorem 16.6.2 that the given series is convergent.

16.6.3 Definition If an infinite series $\sum\limits_{n=1}^{+\infty} u_n$ is convergent and its sum is S, then the *remainder* obtained by approximating the sum of the series by the kth partial sum s_k is denoted by R_k and

$$R_k = S - s_k$$

16.6.4 Theorem Suppose $\sum\limits_{n=1}^{+\infty} u_n$ is an alternating series, $|u_{n+1}| < |u_n|$, and $\lim\limits_{n \to +\infty} u_n = 0$. Then, if R_k is the remainder obtained by approximating the sum of the series by the sum of the first k terms, $|R_k| < |u_{k+1}|$.

PROOF: Assume that the odd-numbered terms of the given series are positive and the even-numbered terms are negative. Then, from (2) in the proof of Theorem 16.6.2, we see that the sequence $\{s_{2n}\}$ is increasing. So if S is the sum of the given series, we have

$$s_{2k} < s_{2k+2} < S \qquad \text{for all } k \geq 1 \tag{5}$$

To show that the sequence $\{s_{2n-1}\}$ is decreasing, we write

$$s_{2n-1} = u_1 + (u_2 + u_3) + (u_4 + u_5) + \cdots + (u_{2n-2} + u_{2n-1}) \tag{6}$$

The first term of each quantity in parentheses in (6) is negative and the second term is positive, and because $|u_{n+1}| < |u_n|$, it follows that each quantity in parentheses is negative. Therefore, because $u_1 > 0$, we conclude that $s_1 > s_3 > s_5 > \cdots > s_{2n-1} > \cdots$; and so the sequence $\{s_{2n-1}\}$ is decreasing. Thus,

$$S < s_{2k+1} < s_{2k-1} \qquad \text{for all } k \geq 1 \tag{7}$$

From (7) we have $S - s_{2k} < s_{2k+1} - s_{2k} = u_{2k+1}$, and from (5) we have $0 < S - s_{2k}$. Therefore,

$$0 < S - s_{2k} < u_{2k+1} \qquad \text{for all } k \geq 1 \tag{8}$$

From (5) we have $-S < -s_{2k}$; hence, $s_{2k-1} - S < s_{2k-1} - s_{2k} = -u_{2k}$. Because from (7) it follows that $0 < s_{2k-1} - S$, we have

$$0 < s_{2k-1} - S < -u_{2k} \qquad \text{for all } k \geq 1 \tag{9}$$

Because from Definition 16.6.3, $R_k = S - s_k$, (8) can be written as $0 < |R_{2k}| < |u_{2k+1}|$ and (9) can be written as $0 < |R_{2k-1}| < |u_{2k}|$. Hence, we have $|R_k| < |u_{k+1}|$ for all $k \geq 1$, and the theorem is proved. ■

EXAMPLE 3:   A series for computing $\ln(1 - x)$ if x is in the open interval $(-1, 1)$ is

$$\ln(1 - x) = \sum_{n=1}^{+\infty} -\frac{x^n}{n}$$

Find an estimate of the error when the first three terms of this series are used to approximate the value of $\ln 1.1$.

SOLUTION: Using the given series with $x = -0.1$, we get

$$\ln 1.1 = 0.1 - \frac{(0.1)^2}{2} + \frac{(0.1)^3}{3} - \frac{(0.1)^4}{4} + \cdots$$

This series satisfies the conditions of Theorem 16.6.4; so if R_3 is the difference between the actual value of $\ln 1.1$ and the sum of the first three terms, then

$$|R_3| < |u_4| = 0.000025$$

Thus, we know that the sum of the first three terms will yield a value of $\ln 1.1$ accurate at least to four decimal places. Using the first three terms, we get

$$\ln 1.1 \approx 0.0953$$

Associated with each infinite series is the series whose terms are the absolute values of the terms of that series.

16.6.5 Definition   The infinite series $\sum\limits_{n=1}^{+\infty} u_n$ is said to be *absolutely convergent* if the series $\sum\limits_{n=1}^{+\infty} |u_n|$ is convergent.

• ILLUSTRATION 1: Consider the series

$$\sum_{n=1}^{+\infty} (-1)^{n+1} \frac{2}{3^n} = \frac{2}{3} - \frac{2}{3^2} + \frac{2}{3^3} - \frac{2}{3^4} + \cdots + (-1)^{n+1} \frac{2}{3^n} + \cdots \qquad (10)$$

This series will be absolutely convergent if the series

$$\sum_{n=1}^{+\infty} \frac{2}{3^n} = \frac{2}{3} + \frac{2}{3^2} + \frac{2}{3^3} + \frac{2}{3^4} + \cdots + \frac{2}{3^n} + \cdots$$

is convergent. Because this is the geometric series with $r = \frac{1}{3} < 1$, it is convergent. Therefore, series (10) is absolutely convergent.   •

• ILLUSTRATION 2: A convergent series which is not absolutely convergent is the series

$$\sum_{n=1}^{+\infty} \frac{(-1)^{n+1}}{n}$$

In Example 1 we proved that this series is convergent. The series is not absolutely convergent because the series of absolute values is the harmonic series which is divergent.   •

The series of Illustration 2 is an example of a "conditionally convergent" series.

16.6.6 Definition   A series which is convergent, but not absolutely convergent, is said to be *conditionally convergent*.

It is possible, then, for a series to be convergent but not absolutely convergent. If a series is absolutely convergent, it must be convergent, however, and this is given by the next theorem.

16.6.7 Theorem   If the infinite series $\sum\limits_{n=1}^{+\infty} u_n$ is absolutely convergent, it is convergent and

$$\left| \sum_{n=1}^{+\infty} u_n \right| \leq \sum_{n=1}^{+\infty} |u_n|$$

PROOF: Consider the three infinite series $\sum\limits_{n=1}^{+\infty} u_n$, $\sum\limits_{n=1}^{+\infty} |u_n|$, and $\sum\limits_{n=1}^{+\infty} (u_n + |u_n|)$, and let their sequences of partial sums be $\{s_n\}$, $\{t_n\}$, and $\{r_n\}$, respectively. For every positive integer n, $u_n + |u_n|$ is either 0 or $2|u_n|$; so we have the inequality

$$0 \leq u_n + |u_n| \leq 2|u_n| \qquad (11)$$

Because $\sum\limits_{n=1}^{+\infty} |u_n|$ is convergent, it has a sum, which we denote by T.

$\{t_n\}$ is an increasing sequence of positive numbers, and so $t_n \leq T$ for all positive integers n. From (11), it follows that

$$0 \leq r_n \leq 2t_n \leq 2T$$

Therefore, the sequence $\{r_n\}$ has an upper bound of $2T$. Thus, by Theorem 16.4.1 the series $\sum\limits_{n=1}^{+\infty} (u_n + |u_n|)$ is convergent, and we call its sum R. Because from (11), $\{r_n\}$ is an increasing sequence, it may be concluded from Theorem 16.2.7 that $R \leq 2T$.

Each of the series $\sum\limits_{n=1}^{+\infty} (u_n + |u_n|)$ and $\sum\limits_{n=1}^{+\infty} |u_n|$ is convergent; hence, from Theorem 16.3.9 the series

$$\sum_{n=1}^{+\infty} [(u_n + |u_n|) - |u_n|] = \sum_{n=1}^{+\infty} u_n$$

is also convergent.

Let the sum of the series $\sum\limits_{n=1}^{+\infty} u_n$ be S. Then, also from Theorem 16.3.9, $S = R - T$. And because $R \leq 2T$, $S \leq 2T - T = T$.

Because $\sum\limits_{n=1}^{+\infty} u_n$ is convergent and has the sum S, it follows from Theorem 16.3.8 that $\sum\limits_{n=1}^{+\infty} (-u_n)$ is convergent and has the sum $-S$. Because $\sum\limits_{n=1}^{+\infty} |-u_n| = \sum\limits_{n=1}^{+\infty} |u_n| = T$, we can replace $\sum\limits_{n=1}^{+\infty} u_n$ by $\sum\limits_{n=1}^{+\infty} (-u_n)$ in the above discussion and show that $-S \leq T$. Because $S \leq T$ and $-S \leq T$, we have $|S| \leq T$; therefore, $\left| \sum\limits_{n=1}^{+\infty} u_n \right| \leq \sum\limits_{n=1}^{+\infty} |u_n|$, and the theorem is proved. ∎

EXAMPLE 4: Determine if the series

$$\sum_{n=1}^{+\infty} \frac{\cos \frac{1}{3} n\pi}{n^2}$$

is convergent or divergent.

SOLUTION: Denote the given series by $\sum\limits_{n=1}^{+\infty} u_n$. Therefore,

$$\sum_{n=1}^{+\infty} u_n = \frac{\frac{1}{2}}{1^2} - \frac{\frac{1}{2}}{2^2} - \frac{1}{3^2} - \frac{\frac{1}{2}}{4^2} + \frac{\frac{1}{2}}{5^2} + \frac{1}{6^2} + \frac{\frac{1}{2}}{7^2} - \cdots + \frac{\cos \frac{1}{3} n\pi}{n^2} + \cdots$$

$$= \tfrac{1}{2} - \tfrac{1}{8} - \tfrac{1}{9} - \tfrac{1}{32} + \tfrac{1}{50} + \tfrac{1}{36} + \tfrac{1}{98} - \cdots$$

We have a series of positive and negative terms. We can prove this series is convergent if we can show that it is absolutely convergent.

$$\sum_{n=1}^{+\infty} |u_n| = \sum_{n=1}^{+\infty} \frac{|\cos \frac{1}{3} n\pi|}{n^2}$$

Because

$$|\cos \tfrac{1}{3}n\pi| \leq 1 \qquad \text{for all } n$$

$$\frac{|\cos \tfrac{1}{3}n\pi|}{n^2} \leq \frac{1}{n^2} \qquad \text{for all positive integers } n$$

The series $\sum_{n=1}^{+\infty} 1/n^2$ is the p series, with $p = 2$, and is therefore convergent.

So by the comparison test $\sum_{n=1}^{+\infty} |u_n|$ is convergent. The given series is there-fore absolutely convergent; hence, by Theorem 16.6.7 it is convergent.

You will note that the terms of the series $\sum_{n=1}^{+\infty} |u_n|$ neither increase monotonically nor decrease monotonically. For example, $|u_4| = \tfrac{1}{32}$, $|u_5| = \tfrac{1}{50}$, $|u_6| = \tfrac{1}{36}$; and so $|u_5| < |u_4|$, but $|u_6| > |u_5|$.

The *ratio test*, given in the next theorem, is used frequently to determine whether a given series is absolutely convergent.

16.6.8 Theorem
Ratio Test

Let $\sum_{n=1}^{+\infty} u_n$ be a given infinite series for which every u_n is nonzero. Then

(i) if $\lim_{n \to +\infty} |u_{n+1}/u_n| = L < 1$, the given series is absolutely convergent;

(ii) if $\lim_{n \to +\infty} |u_{n+1}/u_n| = L > 1$ or if $\lim_{n \to +\infty} |u_{n+1}/u_n| = +\infty$, the series is divergent;

(iii) if $\lim_{n \to +\infty} |u_{n+1}/u_n| = 1$, no conclusion regarding convergence may be made.

PROOF OF (i): We are given that $L < 1$, and let R be a number such that $L < R < 1$. Let $R - L = \epsilon < 1$. Because $\lim_{n \to +\infty} |u_{n+1}/u_n| = L$, there exists an integer $N > 0$ such that

$$\left| \left| \frac{u_{n+1}}{u_n} \right| - L \right| < \epsilon \qquad \text{whenever } n \geq N$$

or, equivalently,

$$0 < \left| \frac{u_{n+1}}{u_n} \right| < L + \epsilon = R \qquad \text{whenever } n \geq N \tag{12}$$

Letting n take on the successive values $N, N+1, N+2, \ldots$, and so forth, we obtain from (12)

$$|u_{N+1}| < R|u_N|$$

$$|u_{N+2}| < R|u_{N+1}| < R^2|u_N|$$

$$|u_{N+3}| < R|u_{N+2}| < R^3|u_N|$$

. . .

In general, we have

$$|u_{N+k}| < R^k|u_N| \qquad \text{for every positive integer } k \tag{13}$$

The series

$$\sum_{k=1}^{+\infty} |u_N|R^k = |u_N|R + |u_N|R^2 + \cdots + |u_N|R^n + \cdots$$

is convergent because it is a geometric series whose ratio is less than 1.

So from (13) and the comparison test, it follows that the series $\sum_{k=1}^{+\infty} |u_{N+k}|$ is convergent. The series $\sum_{k=1}^{+\infty} |u_{N+k}|$ differs from the series $\sum_{n=1}^{+\infty} |u_n|$ in only the first N terms. Therefore, $\sum_{n=1}^{+\infty} |u_n|$ is convergent, and so the given series is absolutely convergent.

PROOF OF (ii): If $\lim\limits_{n \to +\infty} |u_{n+1}/u_n| = L > 1$ or $\lim\limits_{n \to +\infty} |u_{n+1}/u_n| = +\infty$, then in either case there is an integer $N > 0$ such that $|u_{n+1}/u_n| > 1$ for all $n \geq N$. Letting n take on the successive values $N, N+1, N+2, \ldots$, and so on, we obtain

$$|u_{N+1}| > |u_N|$$

$$|u_{N+2}| > |u_{N+1}| > |u_N|$$

$$|u_{N+3}| > |u_{N+2}| > |u_N|$$

. . .

So we may conclude that $|u_n| > |u_N|$ for all $n > N$. Hence, $\lim\limits_{n \to +\infty} u_n \neq 0$, and so the given series is divergent.

PROOF OF (iii): If we apply the ratio test to the p series, we have

$$\lim_{n \to +\infty} \left| \frac{u_{n+1}}{u_n} \right| = \lim_{n \to +\infty} \left| \frac{\dfrac{1}{(n+1)^p}}{\dfrac{1}{n^p}} \right| = \lim_{n \to +\infty} \left| \left(\frac{n}{n+1} \right)^p \right| = 1$$

Because the p series diverges if $p \leq 1$ and converges if $p > 1$, we have shown that it is possible to have both convergent and divergent series for which we have $\lim\limits_{n \to +\infty} |u_{n+1}/u_n| = 1$. This proves part (iii). ∎

EXAMPLE 5:   Determine if the series

$$\sum_{n=1}^{+\infty} \frac{(-1)^{n+1}n}{2^n}$$

is convergent or divergent.

SOLUTION: $u_n = (-1)^{n+1}n/2^n$ and $u_{n+1} = (-1)^{n+2}(n+1)/2^{n+1}$.

Therefore,

$$\left| \frac{u_{n+1}}{u_n} \right| = \frac{n+1}{2^{n+1}} \cdot \frac{2^n}{n} = \frac{n+1}{2n}$$

So

$$\lim_{n \to +\infty} \left| \frac{u_{n+1}}{u_n} \right| = \lim_{n \to +\infty} \frac{1 + \dfrac{1}{n}}{2} = \frac{1}{2} < 1$$

Therefore, by the ratio test, the given series is absolutely convergent and hence, by Theorem 16.6.7, it is convergent.

EXAMPLE 6:   In Example 2, the series

$$\sum_{n=1}^{+\infty} (-1)^n \frac{n+2}{n(n+1)}$$

was shown to be convergent. Is this series absolutely convergent or conditionally convergent?

SOLUTION: To test for absolute convergence we apply the ratio test. In the solution of Example 2 we showed that $|u_{n+1}|/|u_n| = (n^2 + 3n)/(n^2 + 4n + 4)$. Hence,

$$\lim_{n \to +\infty} \left| \frac{u_{n+1}}{u_n} \right| = \lim_{n \to +\infty} \frac{1 + \dfrac{3}{n}}{1 + \dfrac{4}{n} + \dfrac{4}{n^2}} = 1$$

So the ratio test fails. Because

$$|u_n| = \frac{n+2}{n(n+1)} = \frac{n+2}{n+1} \cdot \frac{1}{n} > \frac{1}{n}$$

we can apply the comparison test. And because the series $\displaystyle\sum_{n=1}^{+\infty} 1/n$ is the harmonic series, which diverges, we conclude that the series $\displaystyle\sum_{n=1}^{+\infty} |u_n|$ is divergent and hence $\displaystyle\sum_{n=1}^{+\infty} u_n$ is not absolutely convergent. Therefore, the series is conditionally convergent.

It should be noted that the ratio test does not include all possibilities for $\displaystyle\lim_{n \to +\infty} |u_{n+1}/u_n|$ because it is possible that the limit does not exist and is not $+\infty$. The discussion of such cases is beyond the scope of this book.

To conclude the discussion of infinite series of constant terms, we suggest a possible procedure to follow for determining the convergence or divergence of a given series. First of all, if $\displaystyle\lim_{n \to +\infty} u_n \neq 0$, we may conclude that the series is divergent. If $\displaystyle\lim_{n \to +\infty} u_n = 0$ and the series is an alternating series, then try the alternating-series test. If this test is not applicable, try the ratio test. If in applying the ratio test, $L = 1$, then another test must be used. The integral test may work when the ratio test does not; this was shown for the p series. Also, the comparison test can be tried.

Exercises 16.6

In Exercises 1 through 8, determine if the given alternating series is convergent or divergent.

1. $\sum_{n=2}^{+\infty} (-1)^n \dfrac{1}{\ln n}$

2. $\sum_{n=1}^{+\infty} (-1)^{n+1} \sin \dfrac{\pi}{n}$

3. $\sum_{n=1}^{+\infty} (-1)^{n+1} \dfrac{n^2}{n^3 + 2}$

4. $\sum_{n=1}^{+\infty} (-1)^{n+1} \dfrac{\ln n}{n}$

5. $\sum_{n=1}^{+\infty} (-1)^{n+1} \dfrac{\ln n}{n^2}$

6. $\sum_{n=1}^{+\infty} (-1)^n \dfrac{e^n}{n}$

7. $\sum_{n=1}^{+\infty} (-1)^n \dfrac{n}{2^n}$

8. $\sum_{n=1}^{+\infty} (-1)^n \dfrac{\sqrt{n}}{3n - 1}$

In Exercises 9 through 12, find the error if the sum of the first four terms is used as an approximation to the sum of the given infinite series.

9. $\sum_{n=1}^{+\infty} (-1)^{n+1} \dfrac{1}{n}$

10. $\sum_{n=1}^{+\infty} (-1)^n \dfrac{1}{n!}$

11. $\sum_{n=1}^{+\infty} (-1)^{n+1} \dfrac{1}{(2n-1)^2}$

12. $\sum_{n=1}^{+\infty} (-1)^{n+1} \dfrac{1}{n^n}$

In Exercises 13 through 16, find the sum of the given infinite series, accurate to three decimal places.

13. $\sum_{n=1}^{+\infty} (-1)^{n+1} \dfrac{1}{(2n)^3}$

14. $\sum_{n=1}^{+\infty} (-1)^{n+1} \dfrac{1}{(2n)!}$

15. $\sum_{n=1}^{+\infty} (-1)^{n+1} \dfrac{1}{n2^n}$

16. $\sum_{n=1}^{+\infty} (-1)^n \dfrac{1}{(2n+1)^3}$

In Exercises 17 through 28, determine if the given series is absolutely convergent, conditionally convergent, or divergent. Prove your answer.

17. $\sum_{n=1}^{+\infty} (-1)^{n+1} \dfrac{2^n}{n!}$

18. $\sum_{n=1}^{+\infty} (-1)^{n+1} \dfrac{1}{(2n-1)!}$

19. $\sum_{n=1}^{+\infty} \dfrac{n^2}{n!}$

20. $\sum_{n=1}^{+\infty} n \left(\dfrac{2}{3} \right)^n$

21. $\sum_{n=1}^{+\infty} (-1)^n \dfrac{n!}{2^{n+1}}$

22. $\sum_{n=1}^{+\infty} (-1)^{n+1} \dfrac{1}{n(n+2)}$

23. $\sum_{n=1}^{+\infty} (-1)^{n+1} \dfrac{3^n}{n!}$

24. $\sum_{n=1}^{+\infty} (-1)^n \dfrac{n^2 + 1}{n^3}$

25. $\sum_{n=2}^{+\infty} (-1)^{n+1} \dfrac{1}{n(\ln n)^2}$

26. $\sum_{n=1}^{+\infty} (-1)^n \dfrac{\cos n}{n^2}$

27. $\sum_{n=1}^{+\infty} \dfrac{n^n}{n!}$

28. $\sum_{n=1}^{+\infty} \dfrac{1 \cdot 3 \cdot 5 \cdot \ldots \cdot (2n-1)}{1 \cdot 4 \cdot 7 \cdot \ldots \cdot (3n-2)}$

29. Prove by mathematical induction that $1/n! \le 1/2^{n-1}$.

30. Prove that if $\sum_{n=1}^{+\infty} u_n$ is absolutely convergent and $u_n \neq 0$ for all n, then $\sum_{n=1}^{+\infty} 1/|u_n|$ is divergent.

31. Prove that if $\sum\limits_{n=1}^{+\infty} u_n$ is absolutely convergent, then $\sum\limits_{n=1}^{+\infty} u_n{}^2$ is convergent.

32. Show by means of an example that the converse of Exercise 31 is not true.

16.7 POWER SERIES

We now study an important type of series of variable terms called "power series."

16.7.1 Definition

A *power series* in $(x - a)$ is a series of the form

$$c_0 + c_1(x - a) + c_2(x - a)^2 + \cdots + c_n(x - a)^n + \cdots \tag{1}$$

We use the notation $\sum\limits_{n=0}^{+\infty} c_n(x - a)^n$ to represent series (1). (Note that we take $(x - a)^0 = 1$, even when $x = a$, for convenience in writing the general term.) If x is a particular number, the power series (1) becomes an infinite series of constant terms, as was discussed in previous sections. A special case of (1) is obtained when $a = 0$ and the series becomes a power series in x, which is

$$\sum\limits_{n=0}^{+\infty} c_n x^n = c_0 + c_1 x + c_2 x^2 + \cdots + c_n x^n + \cdots \tag{2}$$

In addition to power series in $(x - a)$ and x, there are power series of the form

$$\sum\limits_{n=0}^{+\infty} c_n[\phi(x)]^n = c_0 + c_1\phi(x) + c_2[\phi(x)]^2 + \cdots + c_n[\phi(x)]^n + \cdots$$

where ϕ is a function of x. Such a series is called a power series in $\phi(x)$. In this book, we are concerned exclusively with power series of the forms (1) and (2), and when we use the term "power series," we mean either of these forms. In discussing the theory of power series, we confine ourselves to series (2). The more general power series (1) can be obtained from (2) by the translation $x = \bar{x} - a$; therefore, our results can be applied to series (1) as well.

In dealing with an infinite series of constant terms, we were concerned with the question of convergence or divergence of the series. In considering a power series, we ask, For what values of x, if any, does the power series converge? For each value of x for which the power series converges, the series represents the number which is the sum of the series. Therefore, we can think of a power series as defining a function. The function f, with function values

$$f(x) = \sum\limits_{n=0}^{+\infty} c_n x^n \tag{3}$$

has as its domain all values of x for which the power series in (3) converges. It is apparent that every power series (2) is convergent for $x = 0$. There are some series (see Example 3) which are convergent for no other value of x, and there are also series which converge for every value of x (see Example 2).

The following three examples illustrate how the ratio test can be used to determine the values of x for which a power series is convergent. Note that when $n!$ is used in representing the nth term of a power series (as in Example 2), we take $0! = 1$ so that the expression for the nth term will hold when $n = 0$.

EXAMPLE 1: Find the values of x for which the power series

$$\sum_{n=1}^{+\infty} (-1)^{n+1} \frac{2^n x^n}{n3^n}$$

is convergent.

SOLUTION: For the given series,

$$u_n = (-1)^{n+1} \frac{2^n x^n}{n3^n} \quad \text{and} \quad u_{n+1} = (-1)^{n+2} \frac{2^{n+1} x^{n+1}}{(n+1)3^{n+1}}$$

So

$$\lim_{n \to +\infty} \left| \frac{u_{n+1}}{u_n} \right| = \lim_{n \to +\infty} \left| \frac{2^{n+1} x^{n+1}}{(n+1)3^{n+1}} \cdot \frac{n3^n}{2^n x^n} \right| = \lim_{n \to +\infty} \frac{2}{3} |x| \frac{n}{n+1} = \frac{2}{3} |x|$$

Therefore, the power series is absolutely convergent when $\frac{2}{3}|x| < 1$ or, equivalently, when $|x| < \frac{3}{2}$. The series is divergent when $\frac{2}{3}|x| > 1$ or, equivalently, when $|x| > \frac{3}{2}$. When $\frac{2}{3}|x| = 1$ (i.e., when $x = \pm\frac{3}{2}$), the ratio test fails. When $x = \frac{3}{2}$, the given power series becomes

$$\frac{1}{1} - \frac{1}{2} + \frac{1}{3} - \frac{1}{4} + \cdots + (-1)^{n+1} \frac{1}{n} + \cdots$$

which is convergent, as was shown in Example 1 of Sec. 16.6. When $x = -\frac{3}{2}$, we have

$$-\frac{1}{1} - \frac{1}{2} - \frac{1}{3} - \frac{1}{4} - \cdots - \frac{1}{n} - \cdots$$

which by Theorem 16.3.8 is divergent. We conclude, then, that the given power series is convergent when $-\frac{3}{2} < x \le \frac{3}{2}$. The series is absolutely convergent when $-\frac{3}{2} < x < \frac{3}{2}$ and is conditionally convergent when $x = \frac{3}{2}$. If $x \le -\frac{3}{2}$ or $x > \frac{3}{2}$, the series is divergent.

EXAMPLE 2: Find the values of x for which the power series

$$\sum_{n=0}^{+\infty} \frac{x^n}{n!}$$

is convergent.

SOLUTION: For the given series, $u_n = x^n/n!$ and $u_{n+1} = x^{n+1}/(n+1)!$. So by applying the ratio test, we have

$$\lim_{n \to +\infty} \left| \frac{u_{n+1}}{u_n} \right| = \lim_{n \to +\infty} \left| \frac{x^{n+1}}{(n+1)!} \cdot \frac{n!}{x^n} \right| = |x| \lim_{n \to +\infty} \frac{1}{n+1} = 0 < 1$$

We conclude that the given power series is absolutely convergent for all values of x.

EXAMPLE 3:   Find the values of x for which the power series

$$\sum_{n=0}^{+\infty} n!x^n$$

is convergent.

SOLUTION: For the given series $u_n = n!x^n$ and $u_{n+1} = (n+1)!x^{n+1}$. Applying the ratio test, we have

$$\lim_{n\to+\infty} \left| \frac{u_{n+1}}{u_n} \right| = \lim_{n\to+\infty} \left| \frac{(n+1)!x^{n+1}}{n!x^n} \right|$$

$$= \lim_{n\to+\infty} |(n+1)x|$$

$$= \begin{cases} 0 & \text{if } x = 0 \\ +\infty & \text{if } x \neq 0 \end{cases}$$

It follows that the series is divergent for all values of x except 0.

16.7.2 Theorem   If the power series $\sum_{n=0}^{+\infty} c_n x^n$ is convergent for $x = x_1$ ($x_1 \neq 0$), then it is absolutely convergent for all values of x for which $|x| < |x_1|$.

PROOF: If $\sum_{n=0}^{+\infty} c_n x_1^n$ is convergent, then $\lim_{n\to+\infty} c_n x_1^n = 0$. Therefore, if we take $\epsilon = 1$ in Definition 4.1.1, there exists an integer $N > 0$ such that

$$|c_n x_1^n| < 1 \qquad \text{whenever } n \geq N$$

Now if x is any number such that $|x| < |x_1|$, we have

$$|c_n x^n| = \left| c_n x_1^n \frac{x^n}{x_1^n} \right| = |c_n x_1^n| \left| \frac{x}{x_1} \right|^n < \left| \frac{x}{x_1} \right|^n \qquad \text{whenever } n \geq N \qquad (4)$$

The series

$$\sum_{n=N}^{+\infty} \left| \frac{x}{x_1} \right|^n \qquad\qquad (5)$$

is convergent because it is a geometric series with $r = |x/x_1| < 1$ (because $|x| < |x_1|$). Comparing the series $\sum_{n=N}^{+\infty} |c_n x^n|$, where $|x| < |x_1|$, with series (5), we see from (4) and the comparison test that $\sum_{n=N}^{+\infty} |c_n x^n|$ is convergent for $|x| < |x_1|$. So the given power series is absolutely convergent for all values of x for which $|x| < |x_1|$.   ∎

● ILLUSTRATION 1:   An illustration of Theorem 16.7.2 is given in Example 1. The power series is convergent for $x = \frac{3}{2}$ and is absolutely convergent for all values of x for which $|x| < \frac{3}{2}$.   ●

The following theorem is a corollary of Theorem 16.7.2.

16.7.3 Theorem   If the power series $\sum_{n=0}^{+\infty} c_n x^n$ is divergent for $x = x_2$, it is divergent for all values of x for which $|x| > |x_2|$.

PROOF: Suppose that the given power series is convergent for some number x for which $|x| > |x_2|$. Then by Theorem 16.7.2 the series must converge when $x = x_2$. However, this contradicts the hypothesis. Therefore, the given power series is divergent for all values of x for which $|x| > |x_2|$. ∎

● ILLUSTRATION 2: To illustrate Theorem 16.7.3 we consider again the power series of Example 1. It is divergent for $x = -\frac{3}{2}$ and is also divergent for all values of x for which $|x| > |-\frac{3}{2}|$. ●

From Theorems 16.7.2 and 16.7.3, we can prove the following important theorem.

16.7.4 Theorem   Let $\sum\limits_{n=0}^{+\infty} c_n x^n$ be a given power series. Then exactly one of the following conditions holds:

(i) the series converges only when $x = 0$;

(ii) the series is absolutely convergent for all values of x;

(iii) there exists a number $R > 0$ such that the series is absolutely convergent for all values of x for which $|x| < R$ and is divergent for all values of x for which $|x| > R$.

PROOF: If we replace x by zero in the given power series, we have $c_0 + 0 + 0 + \cdots$, which is obviously convergent. Therefore, every power series of the form $\sum\limits_{n=0}^{+\infty} c_n x^n$ is convergent when $x = 0$. If this is the only value of x for which the series converges, then condition (i) holds.

Suppose that the given series is convergent for $x = x_1$ where $x_1 \neq 0$. Then it follows from Theorem 16.7.2 that the series is absolutely convergent for all values of x for which $|x| < |x_1|$. Now if in addition there is no value of x for which the given series is divergent, we can conclude that the series is absolutely convergent for all values of x. This is condition (ii).

If the given series is convergent for $x = x_1$, where $x_1 \neq 0$, and is divergent for $x = x_2$, where $|x_2| > |x_1|$, it follows from Theorem 16.7.3 that the series is divergent for all values of x for which $|x| > |x_2|$. Hence, $|x_2|$ is an upper bound of the set of values of $|x|$ for which the series is absolutely convergent. Therefore, by the axiom of completeness (16.2.5), this set of numbers has a least upper bound, which is the number R of condition (iii). This proves that exactly one of the three conditions holds. ∎

Theorem 16.7.4(iii) can be illustrated on the number line. See Fig. 16.7.1.

If instead of the power series $\sum\limits_{n=0}^{+\infty} c_n x^n$ we have the series $\sum\limits_{n=0}^{+\infty} c_n (x-a)^n$,

series convergent
for $|x| < R$

series divergent for $|x| > R$

Figure 16.7.1

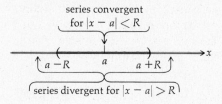

series convergent for $|x - a| < R$

series divergent for $|x - a| > R$

Figure 16.7.2

in conditions (i) and (iii) of Theorem 16.7.4, x is replaced by $x - a$. The conditions become

(i) the series converges only when $x = a$;

(iii) there exists a number $R > 0$ such that the series is absolutely convergent for all values of x for which $|x - a| < R$ and is divergent for all values of x for which $|x - a| > R$. (See Fig. 16.7.2 for an illustration of this on the number line.)

The set of all values of x for which a given power series is convergent is called the *interval of convergence* of the power series. The number R of condition (iii) of Theorem 16.7.4 is called the *radius of convergence* of the power series. If condition (i) holds, we take $R = 0$; if condition (ii) holds, we write $R = +\infty$.

● ILLUSTRATION 3: For the power series of Example 1, $R = \frac{3}{2}$ and the interval of convergence is $(-\frac{3}{2}, \frac{3}{2}]$. In Example 2, $R = +\infty$, and we write the interval of convergence as $(-\infty, +\infty)$. ●

If R is the radius of convergence of the power series $\sum\limits_{n=0}^{+\infty} c_n x^n$, the interval of convergence is one of the following intervals: $(-R, R)$, $[-R, R]$, $(-R, R]$, or $[-R, R)$. For the more general power series $\sum\limits_{n=0}^{+\infty} c_n (x - a)^n$, the interval of convergence is one of the following: $(a - R, a + R)$, $[a - R, a + R]$, $(a - R, a + R]$, or $[a - R, a + R)$.

A given power series defines a function having the interval of convergence as its domain. The most useful method at our disposal for determining the interval of convergence of a power series is the ratio test. However, the ratio test will not reveal anything about the convergence or divergence of the power series at the endpoints of the interval of convergence. At an endpoint, a power series may be either absolutely convergent, conditionally convergent, or divergent. If a power series converges absolutely at one endpoint, it follows from the definition of absolute convergence that the series is absolutely convergent at each endpoint (see Exercise 21). If a power series converges at one endpoint and diverges at the other, the series is conditionally convergent at the endpoint at which it converges (see Exercise 22). There are cases for which the convergence or divergence of a power series at the endpoints cannot be determined by the methods of elementary calculus.

EXAMPLE 4: Determine the interval of convergence of the power series

$$\sum_{n=1}^{+\infty} n(x - 2)^n$$

SOLUTION: The given series is

$$(x - 2) + 2(x - 2)^2 + \cdots + n(x - 2)^n + (n + 1)(x - 2)^{n+1} + \cdots$$

Applying the ratio test, we have

$$\lim_{n \to +\infty} \left| \frac{u_{n+1}}{u_n} \right| = \lim_{n \to +\infty} \left| \frac{(n + 1)(x - 2)^{n+1}}{n(x - 2)^n} \right| = |x - 2| \lim_{n \to +\infty} \frac{n + 1}{n} = |x - 2|$$

The given series then will be absolutely convergent if $|x - 2| < 1$ or, equivalently, $-1 < x - 2 < 1$ or, equivalently, $1 < x < 3$.

When $x = 1$, the series is $\sum\limits_{n=1}^{+\infty} (-1)^n n$, which is divergent because $\lim\limits_{n \to +\infty} u_n \neq 0$. When $x = 3$, the series is $\sum\limits_{n=1}^{+\infty} n$, which is also divergent because $\lim\limits_{n \to +\infty} u_n \neq 0$. Therefore, the interval of convergence is $(1, 3)$. So the given power series defines a function having the interval $(1, 3)$ as its domain.

EXAMPLE 5: Determine the interval of convergence of the power series

$$\sum_{n=1}^{+\infty} \frac{x^n}{2 + n^2}$$

SOLUTION: The given series is

$$\frac{x}{2 + 1^2} + \frac{x^2}{2 + 2^2} + \frac{x^3}{2 + 3^2} + \cdots + \frac{x^n}{2 + n^2} + \frac{x^{n+1}}{2 + (n+1)^2} + \cdots$$

Applying the ratio test, we have

$$\lim_{n \to +\infty} \left| \frac{u_{n+1}}{u_n} \right| = \lim_{n \to +\infty} \left| \frac{x^{n+1}}{2 + (n+1)^2} \cdot \frac{2 + n^2}{x^n} \right| = |x| \lim_{n \to +\infty} \frac{2 + n^2}{2 + n^2 + 2n + 1} = |x|$$

So the given series will be absolutely convergent if $|x| < 1$ or, equivalently, $-1 < x < 1$. When $x = 1$, we have the series

$$\frac{1}{2 + 1^2} + \frac{1}{2 + 2^2} + \frac{1}{2 + 3^2} + \cdots + \frac{1}{2 + n^2} + \cdots$$

Because $1/(2 + n^2) < 1/n^2$ for all positive integers n, and because $\sum\limits_{n=1}^{+\infty} 1/n^2$ is a convergent p series, it follows from the comparison test that the given power series is convergent when $x = 1$. When $x = -1$, we have the series $\sum\limits_{n=1}^{+\infty} (-1)^n/(2 + n^2)$, which is convergent because we have just seen that it is absolutely convergent. Hence, the interval of convergence of the given power series is $[-1, 1]$.

Exercises 16.7

In Exercises 1 through 20, find the interval of convergence of the given power series.

1. $\sum\limits_{n=1}^{+\infty} (-1)^{n+1} \dfrac{x^{2n-1}}{(2n-1)!}$

2. $\sum\limits_{n=0}^{+\infty} \dfrac{x^n}{n+1}$

3. $\sum\limits_{n=1}^{+\infty} \dfrac{2^n x^n}{n^2}$

4. $\sum\limits_{n=1}^{+\infty} (-1)^n \dfrac{x^{2n}}{(2n)!}$

5. $\sum\limits_{n=1}^{+\infty} n! x^n$

6. $\sum\limits_{n=0}^{+\infty} \dfrac{x^n}{(n+1)5^n}$

7. $\sum\limits_{n=1}^{+\infty} (-1)^n \dfrac{x^n}{(2n-1)3^{2n-1}}$

8. $\sum\limits_{n=1}^{+\infty} (-1)^{n+1} \dfrac{(n+1)x}{n!}$

9. $\displaystyle\sum_{n=1}^{+\infty} (-1)^{n+1} \frac{(x-1)^n}{n}$

10. $\displaystyle\sum_{n=1}^{+\infty} \frac{(x+2)^n}{(n+1)2^n}$

11. $\displaystyle\sum_{n=0}^{+\infty} (\sinh 2n)x^n$

12. $\displaystyle\sum_{n=1}^{+\infty} \frac{x^n}{\ln(n+1)}$

13. $\displaystyle\sum_{n=2}^{+\infty} (-1)^{n+1} \frac{x^n}{n(\ln n)^2}$

14. $\displaystyle\sum_{n=1}^{+\infty} \frac{(x+5)^{n-1}}{n^2}$

15. $\displaystyle\sum_{n=1}^{+\infty} \frac{n!x^n}{n^n}$

16. $\displaystyle\sum_{n=1}^{+\infty} \frac{x^n}{n^n} x^n$

17. $\displaystyle\sum_{n=1}^{+\infty} \frac{\ln n(x-5)^n}{n+1}$

18. $\displaystyle\sum_{n=1}^{+\infty} x^n(x-3)^n$

19. $\displaystyle\sum_{n=1}^{+\infty} (-1)^n \frac{1 \cdot 3 \cdot 5 \cdot \ldots \cdot (2n-1)}{2 \cdot 4 \cdot 6 \cdot \ldots \cdot 2n} x^{2n+1}$

20. $\displaystyle\sum_{n=1}^{+\infty} \frac{(-1)^{n+1} 1 \cdot 3 \cdot 5 \cdot \ldots \cdot (2n-1)}{2 \cdot 4 \cdot 6 \cdot \ldots \cdot 2n} x^n$

21. Prove that if a power series converges absolutely at one endpoint of its interval of convergence, then the power series is absolutely convergent at each endpoint.

22. Prove that if a power series converges at one endpoint of its interval of convergence and diverges at the other endpoint, then the power series is conditionally convergent at the endpoint at which it converges.

23. Prove that if the radius of convergence of the power series $\displaystyle\sum_{n=1}^{+\infty} u_n x^n$ is r, then the radius of convergence of the series $\displaystyle\sum_{n=1}^{+\infty} u_n x^{2n}$ is $\sqrt{r}$.

24. Prove that if $\displaystyle\lim_{n \to +\infty} \sqrt[n]{|u_n|} = L$ $(L \neq 0)$, then the radius of convergence of the power series $\displaystyle\sum_{n=1}^{+\infty} u_n x^n$ is $1/L$.

16.8 DIFFERENTIATION OF POWER SERIES

A power series $\displaystyle\sum_{n=0}^{+\infty} c_n x^n$ defines a function whose domain is the interval of convergence of the series.

● ILLUSTRATION 1: Consider the geometric series with $a = 1$ and $r = x$, which is $\displaystyle\sum_{n=0}^{+\infty} x^n$. By Theorem 16.3.6 this series converges to the sum $1/(1-x)$ if $|x| < 1$. Therefore, the power series $\displaystyle\sum_{n=0}^{+\infty} x^n$ defines the function f for which $f(x) = 1/(1-x)$ and $|x| < 1$. Hence, we can write

$$1 + x + x^2 + x^3 + \cdots + x^n + \cdots = \frac{1}{1-x} \qquad \text{if } |x| < 1 \qquad (1) \ ●$$

The series in (1) can be used to form other power series whose sums can be determined.

● ILLUSTRATION 2: If in (1) we replace x by $-x$, we have

$$1 - x + x^2 - x^3 + \cdots + (-1)^n x^n + \cdots = \frac{1}{1+x} \qquad \text{if } |x| < 1 \qquad (2)$$

Letting $x = x^2$ in (1), we get

$$1 + x^2 + x^4 + x^6 + \cdots + x^{2n} + \cdots = \frac{1}{1 - x^2} \qquad \text{if } |x| < 1 \qquad (3)$$

If x is replaced by $-x^2$ in (1) we obtain

$$1 - x^2 + x^4 - x^6 + \cdots + (-1)^n x^{2n} + \cdots = \frac{1}{1 + x^2} \quad \text{if } |x| < 1 \quad (4) \quad \bullet$$

In this section and the next we learn that other interesting series can be obtained from those like the above by differentiation and integration. We prove that if $R \neq 0$ is the radius of convergence of a power series which defines a function f, then f is differentiable on the open interval $(-R, R)$ and the derivative of f can be obtained by differentiating the power series term by term. Furthermore, we show that f is integrable on every closed subinterval of $(-R, R)$, and the integral of f is evaluated by integrating the power series term by term. We first need some preliminary theorems.

16.8.1 Theorem If $\displaystyle\sum_{n=0}^{+\infty} c_n x^n$ is a power series having a radius of convergence of $R > 0$, then the series $\displaystyle\sum_{n=1}^{+\infty} n c_n x^{n-1}$ also has R as its radius of convergence.

This theorem states that the series, obtained by differentiating term by term each term of a given power series, will have the same radius of convergence as the given series.

PROOF: Let x be any number in the open interval $(-R, R)$. Then $|x| < R$. Choose a number x_1 so that $|x| < |x_1| < R$. Because $|x_1| < R$, $\displaystyle\sum_{n=0}^{+\infty} c_n x_1{}^n$ is convergent. Hence, $\displaystyle\lim_{n \to +\infty} c_n x_1{}^n = 0$. So if we take $\epsilon = 1$ in Definition 4.1.1, there exists a number $N > 0$ such that

$$|c_n x_1{}^n| < 1 \qquad \text{whenever } n > N$$

Let M be the largest of the numbers $|c_1 x_1|, |c_2 x_1{}^2|, |c_3 x_1{}^3|, \ldots, |c_N x_1{}^N|, 1$. Then

$$|c_n x_1{}^n| \leq M \qquad \text{for all positive integers } n \qquad (5)$$

Now

$$|n c_n x^{n-1}| = \left| n c_n \cdot \frac{x^{n-1}}{x_1{}^n} \cdot x_1{}^n \right| = n \frac{|c_n x_1{}^n|}{|x_1|} \left| \frac{x}{x_1} \right|^{n-1}$$

From (5) and the above equation, we get

$$|n c_n x^{n-1}| \leq n \frac{M}{|x_1|} \left| \frac{x}{x_1} \right|^{n-1} \qquad (6)$$

Applying the ratio test to the series

$$\frac{M}{|x_1|} \sum_{n=1}^{+\infty} n \left|\frac{x}{x_1}\right|^{n-1} \tag{7}$$

we have

$$\lim_{n \to +\infty} \left|\frac{u_{n+1}}{u_n}\right| = \lim_{n \to +\infty} \left|\frac{(n+1)|x|^n}{|x_1|^n} \cdot \frac{|x_1|^{n-1}}{n|x|^{n-1}}\right|$$

$$= \left|\frac{x}{x_1}\right| \lim_{n \to +\infty} \frac{n+1}{n}$$

$$= \left|\frac{x}{x_1}\right| < 1$$

Therefore, series (7) is absolutely convergent; so from (6) and the comparison test, the series $\sum_{n=1}^{+\infty} nc_n x^{n-1}$ is also absolutely convergent. Because x is any number in $(-R, R)$, it follows that if the radius of convergence of $\sum_{n=1}^{+\infty} nc_n x^{n-1}$ is R', then $R' \geq R$.

To complete the proof we must show that R' cannot be greater than R. Assume that $R' > R$ and let x_2 be a number such that $R < |x_2| < R'$. Because $|x_2| > R$, it follows that

$$\sum_{n=0}^{+\infty} c_n x_2^{n} \quad \text{is divergent} \tag{8}$$

Because $|x_2| < R'$, it follows that $\sum_{n=1}^{+\infty} nc_n x_2^{n-1}$ is absolutely convergent. Furthermore,

$$|x_2| \sum_{n=1}^{+\infty} |nc_n x_2^{n-1}| = \sum_{n=1}^{+\infty} |nc_n x_2^{n}|$$

and so from Theorem 16.3.8 we may conclude that

$$\sum_{n=1}^{+\infty} |nc_n x_2^{n}| \quad \text{is convergent} \tag{9}$$

If n is any positive integer

$$|c_n x_2^{n}| \leq n|c_n x_2^{n}| = |nc_n x_2^{n}| \tag{10}$$

From statement (9), inequality (10), and the comparison test it follows that $\sum_{n=1}^{+\infty} |c_n x_2^{n}|$ is convergent. Therefore, the series $\sum_{n=0}^{+\infty} c_n x_2^{n}$ is convergent, which contradicts statement (8). Hence, the assumption that $R' > R$ is false. Therefore, R' cannot be greater than R; and because we showed that $R' \geq R$, it follows that $R' = R$, which proves the theorem. ∎

● ILLUSTRATION 3: We verify Theorem 16.8.1 for the power series

$$\sum_{n=0}^{+\infty} \frac{x^{n+1}}{(n+1)^2} = x + \frac{x^2}{4} + \frac{x^3}{9} + \cdots + \frac{x^{n+1}}{(n+1)^2} + \frac{x^{n+2}}{(n+2)^2} + \cdots$$

To find the radius of convergence, we apply the ratio test.

$$\lim_{n \to +\infty} \left| \frac{u_{n+1}}{u_n} \right| = \lim_{n \to +\infty} \left| \frac{(n+1)^2 x^{n+2}}{(n+2)^2 x^{n+1}} \right| = |x| \lim_{n \to +\infty} \left| \frac{n^2 + 2n + 1}{n^2 + 4n + 4} \right| = |x|$$

Hence, the power series is convergent when $|x| < 1$, and so its radius of convergence $R = 1$.

The power series obtained from the given series by differentiating term by term is

$$\sum_{n=0}^{+\infty} \frac{(n+1)x^n}{(n+1)^2} = \sum_{n=0}^{+\infty} \frac{x^n}{n+1} = 1 + \frac{x}{2} + \frac{x^2}{3} + \frac{x^3}{4} + \cdots + \frac{x^n}{n+1} + \frac{x^{n+1}}{n+2} + \cdots$$

Applying the ratio test for this power series, we have

$$\lim_{n \to +\infty} \left| \frac{u_{n+1}}{u_n} \right| = \lim_{n \to +\infty} \left| \frac{(n+1)x^{n+1}}{(n+2)x^n} \right| = |x| \lim_{n \to +\infty} \left| \frac{n+1}{n+2} \right| = |x|$$

This power series is convergent when $|x| < 1$; thus, its radius of convergence $R' = 1$. Because $R = R'$, Theorem 16.8.1 is verified. ●

16.8.2 Theorem If the radius of convergence of the power series $\sum_{n=0}^{+\infty} c_n x^n$ is $R > 0$, then R is also the radius of convergence of the series $\sum_{n=2}^{+\infty} n(n-1)c_n x^{n-2}$.

PROOF: If we apply Theorem 16.8.1 to the series $\sum_{n=1}^{+\infty} nc_n x^{n-1}$, we have the desired result. ∎

We are now in a position to prove the theorem regarding term-by-term differentiation of a power series.

16.8.3 Theorem Let $\sum_{n=0}^{+\infty} c_n x^n$ be a power series whose radius of convergence is $R > 0$. Then if f is the function defined by

$$f(x) = \sum_{n=0}^{+\infty} c_n x^n \tag{11}$$

$f'(x)$ exists for every x in the open interval $(-R, R)$, and it is given by

$$f'(x) = \sum_{n=1}^{+\infty} nc_n x^{n-1}$$

PROOF: Let x and a be two distinct numbers in the open interval $(-R, R)$. Taylor's formula (formula (9) in Sec. 15.5), with $n = 1$, is

$$f(x) = f(a) + \frac{f'(a)}{1!}(x - a) + \frac{f''(\xi)}{2!}(x - a)^2$$

Using this formula with $f(x) = x^n$, we have for every positive integer n

$$x^n = a^n + na^{n-1}(x - a) + \tfrac{1}{2}n(n - 1)(\xi_n)^{n-2}(x - a)^2 \tag{12}$$

where ξ_n is between a and x for every positive integer n. From (11) we have

$$f(x) - f(a) = \sum_{n=0}^{+\infty} c_n x^n - \sum_{n=0}^{+\infty} c_n a^n$$

$$= c_0 + \sum_{n=1}^{+\infty} c_n x^n - c_0 - \sum_{n=1}^{+\infty} c_n a^n$$

$$= \sum_{n=1}^{+\infty} c_n (x^n - a^n)$$

Dividing by $x - a$ (because $x \neq a$) and using (12), we have from the above equation

$$\frac{f(x) - f(a)}{x - a} = \frac{1}{x - a} \sum_{n=1}^{+\infty} c_n [na^{n-1}(x - a) + \tfrac{1}{2}n(n - 1)(\xi_n)^{n-2}(x - a)^2]$$

So

$$\frac{f(x) - f(a)}{x - a} = \sum_{n=1}^{+\infty} nc_n a^{n-1} + \tfrac{1}{2}(x - a) \sum_{n=2}^{+\infty} n(n - 1)c_n(\xi_n)^{n-2} \tag{13}$$

Because a is in $(-R, R)$, it follows from Theorem 16.8.1 that $\sum_{n=1}^{+\infty} nc_n a^{n-1}$ is absolutely convergent.

Because both a and x are in $(-R, R)$, there is some number $K > 0$ such that $|a| < K < R$ and $|x| < K < R$. It follows from Theorem 16.8.2 that

$$\sum_{n=2}^{+\infty} n(n - 1)c_n K^{n-2}$$

is absolutely convergent. Then because

$$|n(n - 1)c_n(\xi_n)^{n-2}| < |n(n - 1)c_n K^{n-2}| \tag{14}$$

for each ξ_n, we can conclude from the comparison test that

$$\sum_{n=2}^{+\infty} n(n - 1)c_n(\xi_n)^{n-2}$$

is absolutely convergent.

It follows from (13) that

$$\left| \frac{f(x) - f(a)}{x - a} - \sum_{n=1}^{+\infty} n c_n a^{n-1} \right| = \left| \frac{1}{2}(x - a) \sum_{n=2}^{+\infty} n(n-1) c_n (\xi_n)^{n-2} \right| \qquad (15)$$

However, from Theorem 16.6.7 we know that if $\sum_{n=1}^{+\infty} u_n$ is absolutely convergent, then

$$\left| \sum_{n=1}^{+\infty} u_n \right| \leq \sum_{n=1}^{+\infty} |u_n|$$

Applying this to the right side of (15), we obtain

$$\left| \frac{f(x) - f(a)}{x - a} - \sum_{n=1}^{+\infty} n c_n a^{n-1} \right| \leq \frac{1}{2}|x - a| \sum_{n=2}^{+\infty} n(n-1)|c_n||\xi_n|^{n-2} \qquad (16)$$

From (14) and (16) we get

$$\left| \frac{f(x) - f(a)}{x - a} - \sum_{n=1}^{+\infty} n c_n a^{n-1} \right| \leq \frac{1}{2}|x - a| \sum_{n=2}^{+\infty} n(n-1)|c_n|K^{n-2} \qquad (17)$$

where $0 < K < R$. Because the series on the right side of (17) is absolutely convergent, the limit of the right side, as x approaches a, is zero. Therefore, from (17) and Theorem 4.3.3 it follows that

$$\lim_{x \to a} \frac{f(x) - f(a)}{x - a} = \sum_{n=1}^{+\infty} n c_n a^{n-1}$$

or, equivalently,

$$f'(a) = \sum_{n=1}^{+\infty} n c_n a^{n-1}$$

and because a may be any number in the open interval $(-R, R)$, the theorem is proved. ∎

EXAMPLE 1: Let f be the function defined by the power series of Illustration 3. (a) Find the domain of f; (b) write the power series which defines the function f' and find the domain of f'.

SOLUTION:

(a) $f(x) = \sum_{n=0}^{+\infty} \frac{x^{n+1}}{(n+1)^2}$

The domain of f is the interval of convergence of the power series. In Illustration 3 we showed that the radius of convergence of the power series is 1; that is, the series converges when $|x| < 1$. We now consider the power series when $|x| = 1$. When $x = 1$, the series is

$$1 + \frac{1}{4} + \frac{1}{9} + \cdots + \frac{1}{(n+1)^2} + \cdots$$

which is convergent because it is the p series with $p = 2$. When $x = -1$, we have the series $\sum_{n=0}^{+\infty} (-1)^{n+1}/(n + 2)^2$, which is convergent because it is absolutely convergent. Hence, the domain of f is the interval $[-1, 1]$.

(b) From Theorem 16.8.3 it follows that f' is defined by

$$f'(x) = \sum_{n=0}^{+\infty} \frac{x^n}{n + 1} \tag{18}$$

and that $f'(x)$ exists for every x in the open interval $(-1, 1)$. In Illustration 3 we showed that the radius of convergence of the power series in (18) is 1. We now consider the power series in (18) when $x = \pm 1$. When $x = 1$, the series is

$$1 + \frac{1}{2} + \frac{1}{3} + \frac{1}{4} + \cdots + \frac{1}{n + 1} + \cdots$$

which is the harmonic series and hence is divergent. When $x = -1$, the series is

$$1 - \frac{1}{2} + \frac{1}{3} - \frac{1}{4} + \cdots + (-1)^n \frac{1}{n + 1} + \cdots$$

which is a convergent alternating series. Therefore, the domain of f' is the interval $[-1, 1)$.

Example 1 illustrates the fact that if a function f is defined by a power series and this power series is differentiated term by term, the resulting power series, which defines f', has the same radius of convergence but not necessarily the same interval of convergence.

EXAMPLE 2: Obtain a power-series representation of

$$\frac{1}{(1 - x)^2}$$

SOLUTION: From (1) we have

$$\frac{1}{1 - x} = 1 + x + x^2 + x^3 + \cdots + x^n + \cdots \qquad \text{if } |x| < 1$$

Using Theorem 16.8.3, differentiating on both sides of the above, we get

$$\frac{1}{(1 - x)^2} = 1 + 2x + 3x^2 + \cdots + nx^{n-1} + \cdots \qquad \text{if } |x| < 1$$

EXAMPLE 3: Show that

$$e^x = \sum_{n=0}^{+\infty} \frac{x^n}{n!}$$

$$= 1 + x + \frac{x^2}{2!} + \frac{x^3}{3!} + \cdots$$

for all real values of x.

SOLUTION: In Example 2 of Sec. 16.7 we showed that the power series $\sum_{n=0}^{+\infty} x^n/n!$ is absolutely convergent for all real values of x. Therefore, if f is the function defined by

$$f(x) = \sum_{n=0}^{+\infty} \frac{x^n}{n!} \tag{19}$$

the domain of f is the set of all real numbers; that is, the interval of convergence is $(-\infty, +\infty)$. It follows from Theorem 16.8.3 that for all real values of x

$$f'(x) = \sum_{n=1}^{+\infty} \frac{nx^{n-1}}{n!} \tag{20}$$

Because $n/n! = 1/(n-1)!$, (20) can be written as

$$f'(x) = \sum_{n=1}^{+\infty} \frac{x^{n-1}}{(n-1)!}$$

or, equivalently,

$$f'(x) = \sum_{n=0}^{+\infty} \frac{x^n}{n!} \tag{21}$$

Comparing (19) and (21), we see that $f'(x) = f(x)$ for all real values of x. Therefore, the function f satisfies the differential equation

$$\frac{dy}{dx} = y$$

for which the general solution is $y = Ce^x$. Hence, for some constant C, $f(x) = Ce^x$. From (19) we see that $f(0) = 1$. (Remember that we take $x^0 = 1$ even when $x = 0$ for convenience in writing the general term.) Therefore, $C = 1$, and so $f(x) = e^x$, and we have the desired result.

EXAMPLE 4: Use the result of Example 3 to find a power-series representation of e^{-x}.

SOLUTION: If we replace x by $-x$ in the series for e^x, it follows that

$$e^{-x} = 1 - x + \frac{x^2}{2!} - \frac{x^3}{3!} + \cdots + (-1)^n \frac{x^n}{n!} + \cdots$$

for all real values of x.

EXAMPLE 5: Use the series of Example 4 to find the value of e^{-1} correct to five decimal places.

SOLUTION: Taking $x = 1$ in the series for e^{-x}, we have

$$e^{-1} = 1 - 1 + \frac{1}{2!} - \frac{1}{3!} + \frac{1}{4!} - \frac{1}{5!} + \frac{1}{6!} - \frac{1}{7!} + \frac{1}{8!} - \frac{1}{9!} + \frac{1}{10!} - \cdots$$

$$= 1 - 1 + \frac{1}{2} - \frac{1}{6} + \frac{1}{24} - \frac{1}{120} + \frac{1}{720} - \frac{1}{5,040} + \frac{1}{40,320} - \frac{1}{362,880}$$

$$+ \frac{1}{3,628,800} - \cdots$$

$$\approx 1 - 1 + 0.5 - 0.166667 + 0.041667 - 0.008333 + 0.001389$$

$$- 0.000198 + 0.000025 - 0.000003 + 0.0000003 - \cdots$$

We have a convergent alternating series for which $|u_{n+1}| < |u_n|$. So if we use the first ten terms to approximate the sum, by Theorem 16.6.4 the error is less than the absolute value of the eleventh term. Adding the first ten terms, we obtain 0.367880. Rounding off to five decimal places gives

$$e^{-1} \approx 0.36788$$

In computation with infinite series two kinds of errors occur. One is the error given by the remainder after the first n terms. The other is the round-off error which occurs when each term of the series is approximated by a decimal with a finite number of places. In particular, in Example 5 we wanted the result accurate to five decimal places so we rounded off each term to six decimal places. After computing the sum, we rounded off this result to five decimal places. Of course, the error given by the remainder can be reduced by considering additional terms of the series, whereas the round-off error can be reduced by using more decimal places.

Exercises 16.8

In Exercises 1 through 8, a function f is defined by a power series. In each exercise do the following: (a) Find the radius of convergence of the given power series and the domain of f; (b) write the power series which defines the function f' and find its radius of convergence by using methods of Sec. 16.7 (thus verifying Theorem 16.8.1); (c) find the domain of f'.

1. $f(x) = \sum\limits_{n=1}^{+\infty} \dfrac{x^n}{n^2}$

2. $f(x) = \sum\limits_{n=1}^{+\infty} (-1)^{n-1} \dfrac{x^n}{n}$

3. $f(x) = \sum\limits_{n=1}^{+\infty} \dfrac{x^n}{\sqrt{n}}$

4. $f(x) = \sum\limits_{n=2}^{+\infty} \dfrac{(x-2)^n}{\sqrt{n-1}}$

5. $f(x) = \sum\limits_{n=1}^{+\infty} (-1)^{n-1} \dfrac{x^{2n-1}}{(2n-1)!}$

6. $f(x) = \sum\limits_{n=1}^{+\infty} \dfrac{x^{2n-2}}{(2n-2)!}$

7. $f(x) = \sum\limits_{n=1}^{+\infty} \dfrac{(x-1)^n}{n3^n}$

8. $f(x) = \sum\limits_{n=2}^{+\infty} (-1)^n \dfrac{(x-3)^n}{n(n-1)}$

9. Use the result of Example 2 to find a power-series representation of $1/(1-x)^3$.

10. Use the result of Example 3 to find a power-series representation of $e^{\sqrt{x}}$.

11. Obtain a power-series representation of $1/(1+x)^2$ if $|x| < 1$ by differentiating series (2) term by term.

12. Obtain a power-series representation of $x/(1+x^2)^2$ if $|x| < 1$ by differentiating series (4) term by term.

13. Use the result of Example 4 to find the value of $1/\sqrt{e}$ correct to five decimal places.

14. If $f(x) = \sum\limits_{n=0}^{+\infty} (-1)^n \dfrac{x^{2n}}{3^n}$, find $f'(\frac{1}{2})$ correct to four decimal places.

15. Use the results of Examples 3 and 4 to find a power-series representation of (a) $\sinh x$ and (b) $\cosh x$.

16. Show that each of the power series in parts (a) and (b) of Exercise 15 can be obtained from the other by term-by-term differentiation.

17. Use the result of Example 2 to find the sum of the series $\sum\limits_{n=1}^{+\infty} \dfrac{n}{2^n}$.

18. (a) Find a power-series representation for $(e^x - 1)/x$.

(b) By differentiating term by term the power series in part (a), show that $\sum\limits_{n=1}^{+\infty} \dfrac{n}{(n+1)!} = 1$.

19. (a) Find a power-series representation for $x^2 e^{-x}$. (b) By differentiating term by term the power series in part (a), show that $\displaystyle\sum_{n=1}^{+\infty} (-2)^{n+1} \frac{n+2}{n!} = 4.$

20. Assume that the constant 0 has a power-series representation $\displaystyle\sum_{n=0}^{+\infty} c_n x^n$, where the radius of convergence $R > 0$. Prove that $c_n = 0$ for all n.

21. Suppose a function f has the power-series representation $\displaystyle\sum_{n=0}^{+\infty} c_n x^n$, where the radius of convergence $R > 0$. If $f'(x) = f(x)$ and $f(0) = 1$, find the power series by using only properties of power series and nothing about the exponential function.

22. (a) Using only properties of power series, find a power-series representation of the function f for which $f(x) > 0$ and $f'(x) = 2xf(x)$ for all x, and $f(0) = 1$. (b) Verify your result in part (a) by solving the differential equation $D_x y = 2xy$ having the boundary condition $y = 1$ when $x = 0$.

16.9 INTEGRATION OF POWER SERIES	The theorem regarding the term-by-term integration of a power series is a consequence of Theorem 16.8.3.

16.9.1 Theorem   Let $\displaystyle\sum_{n=0}^{+\infty} c_n x^n$ be a power series whose radius of convergence is $R > 0$. Then if f is the function defined by

$$f(x) = \sum_{n=0}^{+\infty} c_n x^n$$

f is integrable on every closed subinterval of $(-R, R)$, and we evaluate the integral of f by integrating the given power series term by term; that is, if x is in $(-R, R)$, then

$$\int_0^x f(t)\, dt = \sum_{n=0}^{+\infty} \frac{c_n}{n+1} x^{n+1}$$

Furthermore, R is the radius of convergence of the resulting series.

PROOF: Let g be the function defined by

$$g(x) = \sum_{n=0}^{+\infty} \frac{c_n}{n+1} x^{n+1}$$

Because the terms of the power-series representation of $f(x)$ are the derivatives of the terms of the power-series representation of $g(x)$, the two series have, by Theorem 16.8.1, the same radius of convergence. By Theorem 16.8.3 it follows that

$$g'(x) = f(x) \qquad \text{for every } x \text{ in } (-R, R)$$

By Theorem 16.8.2, it follows that $f'(x) = g''(x)$ for every x in $(-R, R)$. Because f is differentiable on $(-R, R)$, f is continuous there; consequently, f is continuous on every closed subinterval of $(-R, R)$. From Theorem

7.6.2 it follows that if x is in $(-R, R)$, then

$$\int_0^x f(t) \; dt = g(x) - g(0) = g(x)$$

or, equivalently,

$$\int_0^x f(t) \; dt = \sum_{n=0}^{+\infty} \frac{c_n}{n+1} x^{n+1}$$

■

Theorem 16.9.1 often is used to compute a definite integral which cannot be evaluated directly by finding an antiderivative of the integrand. Examples 1 and 2 illustrate the technique. The definite integral $\int_0^x e^{-t^2} \, dt$ appearing in these two examples represents the measure of the area of a region under the "normal probability curve."

EXAMPLE 1: Find a power-series representation of

$$\int_0^x e^{-t^2} \, dt$$

SOLUTION: In Example 4 of Sec. 16.8 we showed that

$$e^{-x} = \sum_{n=0}^{+\infty} \frac{(-1)^n x^n}{n!}$$

for all values of x. Replacing x by t^2, we get

$$e^{-t^2} = 1 - t^2 + \frac{t^4}{2!} - \frac{t^6}{3!} + \cdots + (-1)^n \frac{t^{2n}}{n!} + \cdots \qquad \text{for all values of } t$$

Applying Theorem 16.9.1, we integrate term by term and obtain

$$\int_0^x e^{-t^2} \, dt = \sum_{n=0}^{+\infty} \int_0^x (-1)^n \frac{t^{2n}}{n!} \, dt$$

$$= x - \frac{x^3}{3} + \frac{x^5}{2! \cdot 5} - \frac{x^7}{3! \cdot 7} + \cdots + (-1)^n \frac{x^{2n+1}}{n!(2n+1)} + \cdots$$

The power series represents the integral for all values of x.

EXAMPLE 2: Using the result of Example 1, compute accurate to three decimal places the value of

$$\int_0^{1/2} e^{-t^2} \, dt$$

SOLUTION: Replacing x by $\frac{1}{2}$ in the power series obtained in Example 1, we have

$$\int_0^{1/2} e^{-t^2} \, dt = \frac{1}{2} - \frac{1}{24} + \frac{1}{320} - \frac{1}{5376} + \cdots$$

$$\approx 0.5 - 0.0417 + 0.0031 - 0.0002 + \cdots$$

We have a convergent alternating series with $|u_{n+1}| < |u_n|$. Thus, if we use the first three terms to approximate the sum, by Theorem 16.6.4 the error is less than the absolute value of the fourth term. From the first three terms we get

$$\int_0^{1/2} e^{-t^2} \, dt \approx 0.461$$

EXAMPLE 3: Obtain a power-series representation of $\ln(1 + x)$.

SOLUTION: Consider the function f defined by $f(t) = 1/(1 + t)$. A power-series representation of this function is given by series (2) in Sec. 16.8, which is

$$\frac{1}{1 + t} = 1 - t + t^2 - t^3 + \cdots + (-1)^n t^n + \cdots \qquad \text{if } |t| < 1$$

Applying Theorem 16.9.1, we integrate term by term and obtain

$$\int_0^x \frac{dt}{1 + t} = \sum_{n=0}^{+\infty} \int_0^x (-1)^n t^n \, dt \qquad \text{if } |x| < 1$$

and so

$$\ln(1 + x) = x - \frac{x^2}{2} + \frac{x^3}{3} - \frac{x^4}{4} + \cdots + (-1)^n \frac{x^{n+1}}{n + 1} + \cdots \qquad \text{if } |x| < 1$$

or, equivalently,

$$\ln(1 + x) = \sum_{n=1}^{+\infty} (-1)^{n-1} \frac{x^n}{n} \qquad \text{if } |x| < 1 \tag{1}$$

Note that because $|x| < 1$, $|1 + x| = (1 + x)$. Thus, the absolute-value bars are not needed when writing $\ln(1 + x)$.

In Example 3, Theorem 16.9.1 allows us to conclude that the power series in (1) represents the function only for values of x in the open interval $(-1, 1)$. However, the power series is convergent at the right endpoint 1, as was shown in Example 1 of Sec. 16.6. When $x = -1$, the power series becomes the negative of the harmonic series and is divergent. Hence, the interval of convergence of the power series in (1) is $(-1, 1]$.

In the following illustration we show that the power series in (1) represents $\ln(1 + x)$ at $x = 1$ by proving that the sum of the series $\sum_{n=1}^{+\infty} (-1)^{n-1}/n$ is $\ln 2$.

● ILLUSTRATION 1: For the infinite series $\sum_{n=1}^{+\infty} (-1)^{n-1}/n$, the nth partial sum is

$$s_n = 1 - \frac{1}{2} + \frac{1}{3} - \frac{1}{4} + \cdots + (-1)^{n-1} \frac{1}{n} \tag{2}$$

It follows from Definition 16.3.2 that if we show $\lim_{n \to +\infty} s_n = \ln 2$, we will have proved that the sum of the series is $\ln 2$.

From algebra we have the following formula for the sum of a geometric progression:

$$a + ar + ar^2 + ar^3 + \cdots + ar^{n-1} = \frac{a - ar^n}{1 - r}$$

Using this formula with $a = 1$ and $r = -t$, we have

$$1 - t + t^2 - t^3 + \cdots + (-t)^{n-1} = \frac{1 - (-t)^n}{1 + t}$$

which we can write as

$$1 - t + t^2 - t^3 + \cdots + (-1)^{n-1}t^{n-1} = \frac{1}{1 + t} + (-1)^{n+1}\frac{t^n}{1 + t}$$

Integrating from 0 to 1, we get

$$\int_0^1 [1 - t + t^2 - t^3 + \cdots + (-1)^{n-1}t^{n-1}] \, dt = \int_0^1 \frac{dt}{1 + t} + (-1)^{n+1} \int_0^1 \frac{t^n}{1 + t} \, dt$$

which gives

$$1 - \frac{1}{2} + \frac{1}{3} - \frac{1}{4} + \cdots + (-1)^{n-1}\frac{1}{n} = \ln 2 + (-1)^{n+1} \int_0^1 \frac{t^n}{1 + t} \, dt \qquad (3)$$

Referring to Eq. (2), we see that the left side of Eq. (3) is s_n. Letting

$$R_n = (-1)^{n+1} \int_0^1 \frac{t^n}{1 + t} \, dt$$

Eq. (3) may be written as

$$s_n = \ln 2 + R_n \qquad (4)$$

Because $t^n/(1 + t) \leq t^n$ for all t in $[0, 1]$ it follows from Theorem 7.4.8 that

$$\int_0^1 \frac{t^n}{1 + t} \, dt \leq \int_0^1 t^n \, dt$$

Hence,

$$0 \leq |R_n| = \int_0^1 \frac{t^n}{1 + t} \, dt \leq \int_0^1 t^n \, dt = \frac{1}{n + 1}$$

Because $\lim_{n \to +\infty} 1/(n + 1) = 0$, it follows from the above inequality and the squeeze theorem (4.3.3) that $\lim_{n \to +\infty} R_n = 0$. So from Eq. (4) we get

$$\lim_{n \to +\infty} s_n = \ln 2 + \lim_{n \to +\infty} R_n$$

$$= \ln 2$$

Therefore,

$$\sum_{n=1}^{+\infty} (-1)^{n-1}\frac{1}{n} = 1 - \frac{1}{2} + \frac{1}{3} - \frac{1}{4} + \cdots = \ln 2 \qquad (5) \quad \bullet$$

The solution of Example 3 showed that the power series in (1) represents $\ln(x + 1)$ if $|x| < 1$. Hence, with the result of Illustration 1 we can conclude that the power series in (1) represents $\ln(x + 1)$ for all x in its interval of convergence $(-1, 1]$.

Although it is interesting that the sum of the series in (5) is $\ln 2$, this series converges too slowly to use it to calculate $\ln 2$. We now proceed to obtain a power series for computation of natural logarithms.

From (1) we have

$$\ln(1 + x) = x - \frac{x^2}{2} + \frac{x^3}{3} - \cdots + (-1)^{n-1}\frac{x^n}{n} + \cdots \quad \text{for } x \text{ in } (-1, 1] \quad (6)$$

Replacing x by $-x$ in this series, we get

$$\ln(1 - x) = -x - \frac{x^2}{2} - \frac{x^3}{3} - \frac{x^4}{4} - \cdots - \frac{x^n}{n} - \cdots \quad \text{for } x \text{ in } [-1, 1) \quad (7)$$

Subtracting term by term (7) from (6), we obtain

$$\ln\frac{1 + x}{1 - x} = 2\left(x + \frac{x^3}{3} + \frac{x^5}{5} + \cdots + \frac{x^{2n-1}}{2n - 1} + \cdots\right) \qquad \text{if } |x| < 1 \quad (8)$$

The series in (8) can be used to compute the value of the natural logarithm of any positive number.

• ILLUSTRATION 2: If y is any positive number, let

$$y = \frac{1 + x}{1 - x} \quad \text{and then} \quad x = \frac{y - 1}{y + 1} \quad \text{and } |x| < 1$$

For instance, if $y = 2$, then $x = \frac{1}{3}$. We have from (8)

$$\ln 2 = 2\left(\frac{1}{3} + \frac{1}{3^4} + \frac{1}{5 \cdot 3^5} + \frac{1}{7 \cdot 3^7} + \frac{1}{9 \cdot 3^9} + \frac{1}{11 \cdot 3^{11}} + \cdots\right)$$

$$= 2\left(\frac{1}{3} + \frac{1}{81} + \frac{1}{1,215} + \frac{1}{15,309} + \frac{1}{177,147} + \frac{1}{1,948,617} + \cdots\right)$$

$$\approx 2(0.333333 + 0.012346 + 0.000823 + 0.000065 + 0.000006$$

$$+ 0.000001 + \cdots)$$

Using the first six terms in parentheses, multiplying by 2, and rounding off to five decimal places, we get

$$\ln 2 \approx 0.69315$$

•

EXAMPLE 4: Obtain a power-series representation of $\tan^{-1} x$.

SOLUTION: From series (4) in Sec. 16.8 we have

$$\frac{1}{1 + x^2} = 1 - x^2 + x^4 - x^6 + \cdots + (-1)^n x^{2n} + \cdots \qquad \text{if } |x| < 1$$

Applying Theorem 16.9.1 and integrating term by term, we get

$$\int_0^x \frac{1}{1+t^2}\, dt = x - \frac{x^3}{3} + \frac{x^5}{5} - \cdots + (-1)^n \frac{x^{2n+1}}{2n+1} + \cdots$$

Therefore,

$$\tan^{-1} x = \sum_{n=0}^{+\infty} (-1)^n \frac{x^{2n+1}}{2n+1} \qquad \text{if } |x| < 1 \tag{9}$$

Although Theorem 16.9.1 allows us to conclude that the power series in (9) represents $\tan^{-1} x$ only for values of x such that $|x| < 1$, it can be shown that the interval of convergence of the power series is $[-1, 1]$ and that the power series is a representation of $\tan^{-1} x$ for all x in its interval of convergence. (You are asked to do this in Exercise 16.) We therefore have

$$\tan^{-1} x = \sum_{n=0}^{+\infty} (-1)^n \frac{x^{2n+1}}{2n+1} = x - \frac{x^3}{3} + \frac{x^5}{5} - \cdots \qquad \text{if } |x| \le 1 \tag{10}$$

- ILLUSTRATION 3: Taking $x = 1$ in (10), we get

$$\frac{\pi}{4} = 1 - \frac{1}{3} + \frac{1}{5} - \frac{1}{7} + \cdots + (-1)^n \frac{1}{2n+1} + \cdots \qquad \bullet$$

The series in Illustration 3 is not suitable for computing π because it converges too slowly. The following example gives a better method.

EXAMPLE 5:   Prove that

$$\tfrac{1}{4}\pi = \tan^{-1}\tfrac{1}{2} + \tan^{-1}\tfrac{1}{3}$$

Use this formula and the power series for $\tan^{-1} x$ of Example 4 to compute the value of π accurate to four decimal places.

SOLUTION: Let $\alpha = \tan^{-1}\tfrac{1}{2}$ and $\beta = \tan^{-1}\tfrac{1}{3}$. Then

$$\tan(\alpha + \beta) = \frac{\tan \alpha + \tan \beta}{1 - \tan \alpha \tan \beta}$$

$$= \frac{\tfrac{1}{2} + \tfrac{1}{3}}{1 - \tfrac{1}{2} \cdot \tfrac{1}{3}}$$

$$= \frac{3 + 2}{6 - 1}$$

$$= 1$$

$$= \tan \tfrac{1}{4}\pi$$

Therefore,

$$\tfrac{1}{4}\pi = \alpha + \beta = \tan^{-1}\tfrac{1}{2} + \tan^{-1}\tfrac{1}{3} \tag{11}$$

From formula (10) with $x = \tfrac{1}{2}$ we get

$$\tan^{-1}\frac{1}{2} = \frac{1}{2} - \frac{1}{3}\left(\frac{1}{2}\right)^3 + \frac{1}{5}\left(\frac{1}{2}\right)^5 - \frac{1}{7}\left(\frac{1}{2}\right)^7 + \frac{1}{9}\left(\frac{1}{2}\right)^9 - \frac{1}{11}\left(\frac{1}{2}\right)^{11} + \frac{1}{13}\left(\frac{1}{2}\right)^{13}$$

$$-\frac{1}{15}\left(\frac{1}{2}\right)^{15}+\cdots$$

$$=\frac{1}{2}-\frac{1}{24}+\frac{1}{160}-\frac{1}{896}+\frac{1}{4{,}608}-\frac{1}{22{,}528}+\frac{1}{106{,}492}-\frac{1}{491{,}520}+\cdots$$

$$\approx 0.5-0.04167+0.00625-0.00112+0.00022-0.00004$$
$$+0.00001-0.000002+\cdots$$

Because the series is alternating and $|u_{n+1}| < |u_n|$, we know by Theorem 16.6.4 that if the first seven terms are used to approximate the sum of the series, the error is less than the absolute value of the eighth term. Therefore,

$$\tan^{-1}\tfrac{1}{2}\approx 0.46365 \qquad (12)$$

Using formula (10) with $x=\tfrac{1}{3}$, we have

$$\tan^{-1}\frac{1}{3}=\frac{1}{3}-\frac{1}{3}\left(\frac{1}{3}\right)^{3}+\frac{1}{5}\left(\frac{1}{3}\right)^{5}-\frac{1}{7}\left(\frac{1}{3}\right)^{7}+\frac{1}{9}\left(\frac{1}{3}\right)^{9}-\frac{1}{11}\left(\frac{1}{3}\right)^{11}+\cdots$$

$$=\frac{1}{3}-\frac{1}{81}+\frac{1}{1{,}215}-\frac{1}{15{,}309}+\frac{1}{177{,}147}-\frac{1}{1{,}948{,}617}+\cdots$$

$$\approx 0.33333-0.01235+0.00082-0.00007+0.00001$$
$$-0.000001+\cdots$$

Using the first five terms to approximate the sum, we get

$$\tan^{-1}\tfrac{1}{3}\approx 0.32174 \qquad (13)$$

Substituting from (12) and (13) into (11), we get

$$\tfrac{1}{4}\pi\approx 0.46365+0.32174=0.78539$$

Multiplying by 4 and rounding off to four decimal places gives $\pi \approx 3.1416$.

Exercises 16.9

In Exercises 1 through 7, compute the value of the given integral, accurate to four decimal places, by using series.

1. $\displaystyle\int_0^{1/2}\frac{dx}{1+x^3}$

2. $\displaystyle\int_0^{1/3}\frac{dx}{1+x^4}$

3. $\displaystyle\int_0^1 e^{-x^2}\,dx$

4. $\displaystyle\int_0^{1/2} f(x)\,dx$, where $f(x)=\begin{cases}\dfrac{\ln(1+x)}{x} & \text{if } x \neq 0 \\ 1 & \text{if } x = 0\end{cases}$

5. $\displaystyle\int_0^{1/4} g(x)\,dx$, where $g(x)=\begin{cases}\dfrac{\tan^{-1}x}{x} & \text{if } x \neq 0 \\ 1 & \text{if } x = 0\end{cases}$

6. $\displaystyle\int_0^1 h(x)\,dx$, where $h(x)=\begin{cases}\dfrac{\sinh x}{x} & \text{if } x \neq 0 \\ 1 & \text{if } x = 0\end{cases}$

7. $\displaystyle\int_0^1 f(x)\,dx$, where $f(x)=\begin{cases}\dfrac{e^x-1}{x} & \text{if } x \neq 0 \\ 1 & \text{if } x = 0\end{cases}$

8. Use the power series in Eq. (8) to compute ln 3 accurate to four decimal places.

9. Use the power series in Eq. (9) to compute $\tan^{-1} \frac{1}{4}$ accurate to four decimal places.

10. Integrate term by term from 0 to x a power-series representation for $(1 - t^2)^{-1}$ to obtain the power series in Eq. (8) for $\ln[(1 + x)/(1 - x)]$.

11. Find a power-series representation for $\tanh^{-1} x$ by integrating term by term from 0 to x a power-series representation for $(1 - t^2)^{-1}$.

12. Find a power series for xe^x by multiplying the series for e^x by x, and then integrate the resulting series term by term from 0 to 1 and show that $\displaystyle\sum_{n=1}^{+\infty} \frac{1}{n!(n + 2)} = \frac{1}{2}$.

13. By integrating term by term from 0 to x a power-series representation for $\ln(1 - t)$, show that

$$\sum_{n=2}^{+\infty} \frac{x^n}{(n - 1)n} = x + (1 - x) \ln(1 - x)$$

14. By integrating term by term from 0 to x a power-series representation for $t \tan^{-1} t$, show that

$$\sum_{n=1}^{+\infty} (-1)^{n+1} \frac{x^{2n+1}}{(2n - 1)(2n + 1)} = \frac{1}{2}[(x^2 + 1) \tan^{-1} x - x]$$

15. Find the power series in x of $f(x)$ if $f''(x) = -f(x)$, $f(0) = 0$, and $f'(0) = 1$. Also, find the radius of convergence of the resulting series.

16. Show that the interval of convergence of the power series in Eq. (9) is $[-1, 1]$ and that the power series is a representation of $\tan^{-1} x$ for all x in its interval of convergence.

16.10 TAYLOR SERIES

If f is the function defined by

$$f(x) = \sum_{n=0}^{+\infty} c_n x^n = c_0 + c_1 x + c_2 x^2 + c_3 x^3 + \cdots + c_n x^n + \cdots \tag{1}$$

whose radius of convergence is $R > 0$, it follows from successive applications of Theorem 16.8.3 that f has derivatives of all orders on $(-R, R)$. We say such a function is *infinitely differentiable* on $(-R, R)$. Successive differentiations of the function in (1) give

$$f'(x) = c_1 + 2c_2 x + 3c_3 x^2 + 4c_4 x^3 + \cdots + nc_n x^{n-1} + \cdots \tag{2}$$

$$f''(x) = 2c_2 + 2 \cdot 3c_3 x + 3 \cdot 4c_4 x^2 + \cdots + (n - 1)nc_n x^{n-2} + \cdots \tag{3}$$

$$f'''(x) = 2 \cdot 3c_3 + 2 \cdot 3 \cdot 4c_4 x + \cdots + (n - 2)(n - 1)nc_n x^{n-3} + \cdots \tag{4}$$

$$f^{(\mathrm{iv})}(x) = 2 \cdot 3 \cdot 4c_4 + \cdots + (n - 3)(n - 2)(n - 1)nc_n x^{n-4} + \cdots \tag{5}$$

etc. Letting $x = 0$ in (1), we get

$$f(0) = c_0$$

For $x = 0$ in (2) we see that

$$f'(0) = c_1$$

If in (3) we take $x = 0$, we have

$$f''(0) = 2c_2 \quad \text{and so} \quad c_2 = \frac{f''(0)}{2!}$$

From (4), taking $x = 0$, we get

$$f'''(0) = 2 \cdot 3c_3 \quad \text{and so} \quad c_3 = \frac{f'''(0)}{3!}$$

In a similar manner from (5), if $x = 0$, we obtain

$$f^{(iv)}(0) = 2 \cdot 3 \cdot 4c_4 \quad \text{and so} \quad c_4 = \frac{f^{(iv)}(0)}{4!}$$

In general, we have

$$c_n = \frac{f^{(n)}(0)}{n!} \qquad \text{for every positive integer } n \tag{6}$$

Formula (6) also holds when $n = 0$ if we take $f^{(0)}(0)$ to be $f(0)$ and $0! = 1$. So from (1) and (6) we can write the power series of f in x as

$$\sum_{n=0}^{+\infty} \frac{f^{(n)}(0)}{n!} x^n = f(0) + f'(0)x + \frac{f''(0)}{2!} x^2 + \cdots + \frac{f^{(n)}(0)}{n!} x^n + \cdots \tag{7}$$

In a more general sense, consider the function f as a power series in $(x - a)$; that is,

$$f(x) = \sum_{n=0}^{+\infty} c_n(x - a)^n$$

$$= c_0 + c_1(x - a) + c_2(x - a)^2 + \cdots + c_n(x - a)^n + \cdots \tag{8}$$

If the radius of convergence of this series is R, then f is infinitely differentiable on $(a - R, a + R)$. Successive differentiations of the function in (8) give

$$f'(x) = c_1 + 2c_2(x - a) + 3c_3(x - a)^2 + 4c_4(x - a)^3 + \cdots$$
$$+ nc_n(x - a)^{n-1} + \cdots$$

$$f''(x) = 2c_2 + 2 \cdot 3c_3(x - a) + 3 \cdot 4c_4(x - a)^2 + \cdots$$
$$+ (n - 1)nc_n(x - a)^{n-2} + \cdots$$

$$f'''(x) = 2 \cdot 3c_3 + 2 \cdot 3 \cdot 4c_4(x - a) + \cdots$$
$$+ (n - 2)(n - 1)nc_n(x - a)^{n-3} + \cdots$$

etc. Letting $x = a$ in the power-series representations of f and its derivatives, we get

$$c_0 = f(a) \qquad c_1 = f'(a) \qquad c_2 = \frac{f''(a)}{2!} \qquad c_3 = \frac{f'''(a)}{3!}$$

and in general

$$c_n = \frac{f^{(n)}(a)}{n!} \tag{9}$$

From (8) and (9) we can write the power series of f in $(x - a)$ as

$$\sum_{n=0}^{+\infty} \frac{f^{(n)}(a)}{n!} (x - a)^n = f(a) + f'(a)(x - a) + \frac{f''(a)}{2!} (x - a)^2$$

$$+ \cdots + \frac{f^{(n)}(a)}{n!} (x - a)^n + \cdots \tag{10}$$

The series in (10) is called the *Taylor series* of f at a. The special case of (10), when $a = 0$, is Eq. (7), which is called the *Maclaurin series*.

EXAMPLE 1: Find the Maclaurin series for e^x.

SOLUTION: If $f(x) = e^x$, $f^{(n)}(x) = e^x$ for all x; therefore, $f^{(n)}(0) = 1$ for all n. So from (7) we have the Maclaurin series for e^x:

$$1 + x + \frac{x^2}{2!} + \frac{x^3}{3!} + \cdots + \frac{x^n}{n!} + \cdots \tag{11}$$

Note that series (11) is the same as the series for e^x obtained in Example 3 of Sec. 16.8.

EXAMPLE 2: Find the Taylor series for $\sin x$ at a.

SOLUTION: If $f(x) = \sin x$, $f'(x) = \cos x$, $f''(x) = -\sin x$, $f'''(x) = -\cos x$, $f^{(iv)}(x) = \sin x$, and so forth. Thus, from formula (9) we have $c_0 = \sin a$, $c_1 = \cos a$, $c_2 = (-\sin a)/2!$, $c_3 = (-\cos a)/3!$, $c_4 = (\sin a)/4!$, and so on. The required Taylor series is obtained from (10), and it is

$$\sin a + \cos a(x - a) - \sin a \frac{(x - a)^2}{2!} - \cos a \frac{(x - a)^3}{3!}$$

$$+ \sin a \frac{(x - a)^4}{4!} + \cdots \tag{12}$$

We can deduce that a power-series representation of a function is unique. That is, if two functions have the same function values in some interval containing the number a, and if both functions have a power-series representation in $(x - a)$, then these series must be the same because the coefficients in the series are obtained from the values of the functions and their derivatives at a. Therefore, if a function has a power-series representation in $(x - a)$, this series must be its Taylor series at a. Hence, the Taylor series for a given function does not have to be obtained by using formula (10). Any method that gives a power series in $(x - a)$ representing the function will be the Taylor series of the function at a.

● ILLUSTRATION 1: To find the Taylor series for e^x at a, we can write $e^x = e^a e^{x-a}$ and then use series (11), where x is replaced by $(x - a)$. We then have

$$e^x = e^a \left[1 + (x - a) + \frac{(x - a)^2}{2!} + \frac{(x - a)^3}{3!} + \cdots + \frac{(x - a)^n}{n!} + \cdots \right] \quad ●$$

● ILLUSTRATION 2: We can use the series for $\ln(1 + x)$ found in Example 3 of Sec. 16.9 to find the Taylor series for $\ln x$ at a ($a > 0$) by writing

$$\ln x = \ln[a + (x - a)] = \ln a + \ln\left(1 + \frac{x - a}{a}\right)$$

Then because

$$\ln(1 + x) = \sum_{n=1}^{+\infty} (-1)^{n-1} \frac{x^n}{n} \qquad \text{if } -1 < x \le 1$$

we have

$$\ln x = \ln a + \frac{x - a}{a} - \frac{(x - a)^2}{2a^2} + \frac{(x - a)^3}{3a^3} - \cdots$$

and the series represents $\ln x$ if $-1 < (x - a)/a \le 1$ or, equivalently, $0 < x \le 2a$.   ●

A natural question that arises is: If a function has a Taylor series in $(x - a)$ having radius of convergence $R > 0$, does this series represent the function for all values of x in the interval $(a - R, a + R)$? For most elementary functions the answer is yes. However, there are functions for which the answer is no. The following example shows this.

EXAMPLE 3:   Let f be the function defined by

$$f(x) = \begin{cases} e^{-1/x^2} & \text{if } x \ne 0 \\ 0 & \text{if } x = 0 \end{cases}$$

Find the Maclaurin series for f and show that it converges for all values of x but that it represents $f(x)$ only when $x = 0$.

SOLUTION: To find $f'(0)$ we use the definition of a derivative. We have

$$f'(0) = \lim_{x \to 0} \frac{e^{-1/x^2} - 0}{x - 0} = \lim_{x \to 0} \frac{\dfrac{1}{x}}{e^{1/x^2}}$$

Because $\lim_{x \to 0} (1/x) = +\infty$ and $\lim_{x \to 0} e^{1/x^2} = +\infty$, we use L'Hôpital's rule and get

$$f'(0) = \lim_{x \to 0} \frac{-\dfrac{1}{x^2}}{e^{1/x^2}\left(-\dfrac{2}{x^3}\right)} = \lim_{x \to 0} \frac{x}{2e^{1/x^2}} = 0$$

By a similar method, using the definition of a derivative and L'Hôpital's rule, we get 0 for every derivative. So $f^{(n)}(0) = 0$ for all n. Therefore, the Maclaurin series for the given function is $0 + 0 + 0 + \cdots + 0 + \cdots$. This series converges to 0 for all x; however, if $x \ne 0$, $f(x) = e^{-1/x^2} \ne 0$.

A theorem that gives a test for determining whether a function is represented by its Taylor series is the following.

16.10.1 Theorem   Let f be a function such that f and all of its derivatives exist in some interval $(a - r, a + r)$. Then the function is represented by its Taylor series

$$\sum_{n=0}^{+\infty} \frac{f^{(n)}(a)}{n!} (x - a)^n$$

for all x such that $|x - a| < r$ if and only if

$$\lim_{n \to +\infty} R_n(x) = \lim_{n \to +\infty} \frac{f^{(n+1)}(\xi_n)}{(n+1)!} (x - a)^{n+1} = 0$$

where each ξ_n is between x and a.

PROOF: In the interval $(a - r, a + r)$, the function f satisfies the hypothesis of Theorem 15.5.1 for which

$$f(x) = P_n(x) + R_n(x) \tag{13}$$

where $P_n(x)$ is the nth-degree Taylor polynomial of f at a and $R_n(x)$ is the remainder, given by

$$R_n(x) = \frac{f^{(n+1)}(\xi_n)}{(n+1)!} (x - a)^{n+1} \tag{14}$$

where each ξ_n is between x and a.

Now $P_n(x)$ is the nth partial sum of the Taylor series of f at a. So if we show that $\lim_{n \to +\infty} P_n(x)$ exists and equals $f(x)$ if and only if $\lim_{n \to +\infty} R_n(x) = 0$, the theorem will be proved. From Eq. (13) we have

$$P_n(x) = f(x) - R_n(x) \tag{15}$$

If $\lim_{n \to +\infty} R_n(x) = 0$, it follows from Eq. (15) that

$$\lim_{n \to +\infty} P_n(x) = f(x) - \lim_{n \to +\infty} R_n(x)$$

$$= f(x) - 0$$

$$= f(x)$$

Now under the hypothesis that $\lim_{n \to +\infty} P_n(x) = f(x)$ we wish to show that $\lim_{n \to +\infty} R_n(x) = 0$. From Eq. (13) we have

$$R_n(x) = f(x) - P_n(x)$$

and so

$$\lim_{n \to +\infty} R_n(x) = f(x) - \lim_{n \to +\infty} P_n(x)$$

$$= f(x) - f(x)$$

$$= 0$$

This proves the theorem.   ∎

Theorem 16.10.1 also holds for other forms of the remainder $R_n(x)$ besides the Lagrange form.

It is often difficult to apply Theorem 16.10.1 in practice because the values of ξ_n are arbitrary. However, sometimes an upper bound for $R_n(x)$ can be found, and we may be able to prove that the limit of the upper bound is zero as $n \to +\infty$. The following limit is helpful in some cases:

$$\lim_{n \to +\infty} \frac{x^n}{n!} = 0 \qquad \text{for all } x \tag{16}$$

This follows from Example 2 of Sec. 16.7, where we showed that the power series $\sum\limits_{n=0}^{+\infty} x^n/n!$ is convergent for all values of x and hence the limit of its nth term must be zero. In a similar manner, because $\sum\limits_{n=0}^{+\infty} (x-a)^n/n!$ is convergent for all values of x, we have

$$\lim_{n \to +\infty} \frac{(x-a)^n}{n!} = 0 \qquad \text{for all } x \tag{17}$$

EXAMPLE 4: Use Theorem 16.10.1 to show that the Maclaurin series for e^x, found in Example 1, represents the function for all values of x.

SOLUTION: The Maclaurin series for e^x is series (11) and

$$R_n(x) = \frac{e^{\xi_n}}{(n+1)!} x^{n+1}$$

where each ξ_n is between 0 and x.

We must show that $\lim\limits_{n \to +\infty} R_n = 0$ for all x. We distinguish three cases: $x > 0$, $x < 0$, and $x = 0$.

If $x > 0$, then $0 < \xi_n < x$; hence, $e^{\xi_n} < e^x$. So

$$0 < \frac{e^{\xi_n}}{(n+1)!} x^{n+1} < e^x \frac{x^{n+1}}{(n+1)!} \tag{18}$$

From (16) it follows that $\lim\limits_{n \to +\infty} x^{n+1}/(n+1)! = 0$, and so

$$\lim_{n \to +\infty} e^x \frac{x^{n+1}}{(n+1)!} = 0$$

Therefore, from (18) and the squeeze theorem (4.3.3) we can conclude that $\lim\limits_{n \to +\infty} R_n(x) = 0$.

If $x < 0$, then $x < \xi_n < 0$ and $0 < e^{\xi_n} < 1$. Therefore, if $x^{n+1} > 0$,

$$0 < \frac{e^{\xi_n}}{(n+1)!} x^{n+1} < \frac{x^{n+1}}{(n+1)!}$$

and if $x^{n+1} < 0$,

$$\frac{x^{n+1}}{(n+1)!} < \frac{e^{\xi_n}}{(n+1)!} x^{n+1} < 0$$

In either case, because $\lim\limits_{n \to +\infty} x^{n+1}/(n+1)! = 0$, it follows that $\lim\limits_{n \to +\infty} R_n = 0$.

Finally, if $x = 0$, the series has the sum of 1 which is e^0. Hence, we can conclude that the series (11) represents e^x for all values of x.

From the results of the above example we can write

$$e^x = \sum_{n=0}^{+\infty} \frac{x^n}{n!} = 1 + x + \frac{x^2}{2!} + \frac{x^3}{3!} + \cdots \qquad \text{for all } x \qquad (19)$$

and this agrees with Example 3 of Sec. 16.8.

EXAMPLE 5: Show that the Taylor series for $\sin x$ at a, found in Example 2, represents the function for all values of x.

SOLUTION: We use Theorem 16.10.1; so we must show that

$$\lim_{n \to +\infty} R_n(x) = \lim_{n \to +\infty} \frac{f^{(n+1)}(\xi_n)}{(n+1)!} (x - a)^{n+1} = 0$$

Because $f(x) = \sin x$, $f^{(n+1)}(\xi_n)$ will be one of the following numbers: $\cos \xi_n$, $\sin \xi_n$, $-\cos \xi_n$, or $-\sin \xi_n$. In any case, $|f^{(n+1)}(\xi_n)| \leq 1$. Hence,

$$0 < |R_n(x)| \leq \frac{|x - a|^{n+1}}{(n+1)!} \qquad (20)$$

From (17) we know that $\lim\limits_{n \to +\infty} |x - a|^{n+1}/(n+1)! = 0$. Thus, by the squeeze theorem (4.3.3) and (20) it follows that $\lim\limits_{n \to +\infty} R_n(x) = 0$.

EXAMPLE 6: Compute the value of $\sin 47°$ accurate to four decimal places.

SOLUTION: In Examples 2 and 5 we obtained the Taylor series for $\sin x$ at a which represents the function for all values of x. It is

$$\sin x = \sin a + \cos a (x - a) - \sin a \frac{(x - a)^2}{2!} - \cos a \frac{(x - a)^3}{3!} + \cdots$$

To make $(x - a)$ small we choose a value of a near the value of x for which we are computing the function value. We also need to know the sine and cosine of a. We therefore choose $a = \frac{1}{4}\pi$ and have

$$\sin x = \sin \tfrac{1}{4}\pi + \cos \tfrac{1}{4}\pi (x - \tfrac{1}{4}\pi) - \sin \tfrac{1}{4}\pi \frac{(x - \tfrac{1}{4}\pi)^2}{2!}$$
$$- \cos \tfrac{1}{4}\pi \frac{(x - \tfrac{1}{4}\pi)^3}{3!} + \cdots \qquad (21)$$

Because $47°$ is equivalent to $\frac{47}{180}\pi$ radians $= (\frac{1}{4}\pi + \frac{1}{90}\pi)$ radians, from Eq. (21) we have

$$\sin \tfrac{47}{180}\pi = \tfrac{1}{2}\sqrt{2} + \tfrac{1}{2}\sqrt{2} \cdot \tfrac{1}{90}\pi - \tfrac{1}{2}\sqrt{2} \cdot \tfrac{1}{2}(\tfrac{1}{90}\pi)^2 - \tfrac{1}{2}\sqrt{2} \cdot \tfrac{1}{6}(\tfrac{1}{90}\pi)^3 + \cdots$$
$$\approx \tfrac{1}{2}\sqrt{2}(1 + 0.03490 - 0.00061 - 0.000002 + \cdots)$$

Taking $\sqrt{2} = 1.41421$ and using the first three terms of the series, we get

$$\sin \tfrac{47}{180}\pi \approx (0.70711)(1.03429) = 0.73136$$

Rounding off to four decimal places gives $\sin 47° \approx 0.7314$. The error introduced by using the first three terms is $R_2(\frac{47}{180}\pi)$, and from (20) we have

$$\left| R_2\left(\frac{47}{180}\,\pi\right) \right| \leq \frac{(\frac{1}{90}\pi)^3}{3!} \approx 0.00001$$

Our result, then, is accurate to four decimal places.

The following Maclaurin series represent the function for all values of x:

$$\sin x = \sum_{n=0}^{+\infty} \frac{(-1)^n x^{2n+1}}{(2n+1)!} = x - \frac{x^3}{3!} + \frac{x^5}{5!} - \frac{x^7}{7!} + \cdots \tag{22}$$

$$\cos x = \sum_{n=0}^{+\infty} \frac{(-1)^n x^{2n}}{(2n)!} = 1 - \frac{x^2}{2!} + \frac{x^4}{4!} - \frac{x^6}{6!} + \cdots \tag{23}$$

$$\sinh x = \sum_{n=0}^{+\infty} \frac{x^{2n+1}}{(2n+1)!} = x + \frac{x^3}{3!} + \frac{x^5}{5!} + \frac{x^7}{7!} + \cdots \tag{24}$$

$$\cosh x = \sum_{n=0}^{+\infty} \frac{x^{2n}}{(2n)!} = 1 + \frac{x^2}{2!} + \frac{x^4}{4!} + \frac{x^6}{6!} + \cdots \tag{25}$$

Series (22) is a direct result of Examples 2 and 5 with $a = 0$. You are asked to verify series (23), (24), and (25) in Exercises 1, 2, and 3.

EXAMPLE 7: Evaluate

$$\int_{1/2}^{1} \frac{\sin x}{x}\, dx$$

accurate to six decimal places.

SOLUTION: We cannot find an antiderivative of the integrand in terms of elementary functions. However, using series (22) we have

$$\frac{\sin x}{x} = \frac{1}{x} \cdot \sin x$$

$$= \frac{1}{x}\left(x - \frac{x^3}{3!} + \frac{x^5}{5!} - \frac{x^7}{7!} + \frac{x^9}{9!} - \cdots \right)$$

$$= 1 - \frac{x^2}{3!} + \frac{x^4}{5!} - \frac{x^6}{7!} + \frac{x^8}{9!} - \cdots$$

which is true for all $x \neq 0$. Using term-by-term integration we get

$$\int_{1/2}^{1} \frac{\sin x}{x}\, dx = x - \frac{x^3}{3 \cdot 3!} + \frac{x^5}{5 \cdot 5!} - \frac{x^7}{7 \cdot 7!} + \frac{x^9}{9 \cdot 9!} - \cdots \Big]_{1/2}^{1}$$

$$\approx (1 - 0.0555555 + 0.0016667 - 0.0000283 + 0.0000003 - \cdots)$$

$$- (0.5 - 0.0069444 + 0.0000521 - 0.0000002 + \cdots)$$

In each set of parentheses we have a convergent alternating series with $|u_{n+1}| < |u_n|$. In the first set of parentheses we use the first four terms because the error obtained is less than 0.0000003. In the second set of parentheses we use the first three terms where the error obtained is less than 0.0000002. Doing the arithmetic and rounding off to six decimal places, we get

$$\int_{1/2}^{1} \frac{\sin x}{x} \, dx \approx 0.452975$$

Exercises 16.10

1. Prove that the series

$$\sum_{n=0}^{+\infty} \frac{(-1)^n x^{2n}}{(2n)!}$$

represents cos x for all values of x.

2. Prove that the series

$$\sum_{n=0}^{+\infty} \frac{x^{2n+1}}{(2n+1)!}$$

represents sinh x for all values of x.

3. Prove that the series

$$\sum_{n=0}^{+\infty} \frac{x^{2n}}{(2n)!}$$

represents cosh x for all values of x.

4. Obtain the Maclaurin series for the cosine function by differentiating the Maclaurin series for the sine function. Also obtain the Maclaurin series for the sine function by differentiating the one for the cosine function.

5. Obtain the Maclaurin series for the hyperbolic sine function by differentiating the Maclaurin series for the hyperbolic cosine function. Also differentiate the Maclaurin series for the hyperbolic sine function to obtain the one for the hyperbolic cosine function.

6. Find the Taylor series for e^x at 3 by using the Maclaurin series for e^x.

7. Use the Maclaurin series for $\ln(1 + x)$ to find the Taylor series for $\ln x$ at 2.

8. Given $\ln 2 = 0.6931$, use the series obtained in Exercise 7 to find $\ln 3$ accurate to four decimal places.

In Exercises 9 through 14, find a power-series representation for the given function at the number a and determine its radius of convergence.

9. $f(x) = \ln(1 + x); a = 1$

10. $f(x) = \dfrac{1}{x}; a = 1$

11. $f(x) = \sqrt{x}; a = 4$

12. $f(x) = 2^x; a = 0$

13. $f(x) = \cos x; a = \frac{1}{3}\pi$

14. $f(x) = \ln |x|; a = -1$

15. Find the Maclaurin series for $\sin^2 x$. (HINT: Use $\sin^2 x = \frac{1}{2}(1 - \cos 2x)$.)

16. Find the Maclaurin series for $\cos^2 x$. (HINT: Use $\cos^2 x = \frac{1}{2}(1 + \cos 2x)$.)

17. (a) Find the first three nonzero terms of the Maclaurin series for tan x. (b) Use the result of part (a) and term-by-term differentiation to find the first three nonzero terms of the Maclaurin series for sec² x. (c) Use the result of part (a) and term-by-term integration to find the first three nonzero terms of the Maclaurin series for ln cos x.

In Exercises 18 through 23, use a power series to compute the value of the given quantity to the indicated accuracy.

18. sinh $\frac{1}{2}$; five decimal places.

19. cos 58°; four decimal places.

20. $\sqrt[5]{e}$; four decimal places.

21. $\sqrt[5]{30}$; five decimal places.

22. $\sqrt[3]{29}$; three decimal places.

23. $\ln(0.8)$; four decimal places.

24. Compute the value of e correct to seven decimal places, and prove that your answer has the required accuracy.

In Exercises 25 through 29, compute the value of the definite integral accurate to four decimal places.

25. $\displaystyle\int_{0}^{1/2} \sin x^2 \, dx$

26. $\displaystyle\int_{0}^{1} \cos \sqrt{x} \, dx$

27. $\displaystyle\int_{0}^{0.1} \ln(1 + \sin x) \, dx$

28. $\int_0^{1/3} f(x)\,dx$, where $f(x) = \begin{cases} \dfrac{\sin x}{x} & \text{if } x \neq 0 \\ 1 & \text{if } x = 0 \end{cases}$

29. $\int_0^1 g(x)\,dx$, where $g(x) = \begin{cases} \dfrac{1 - \cos x}{x} & \text{if } x \neq 0 \\ 0 & \text{if } x = 0 \end{cases}$

30. The function E defined by

$$E(x) = \frac{2}{\sqrt{\pi}} \int_0^x e^{-t^2}\,dt$$

is called the *error function,* and it is important in mathematical statistics. Find the Maclaurin series for the error function.

31. Determine a_n ($n = 0, 1, 2, 3, 4$) so that the polynomial

$$f(x) = 3x^4 - 17x^3 + 35x^2 - 32x + 17$$

is written in the form

$$f(x) = a_4(x-1)^4 + a_3(x-1)^3 + a_2(x-1)^2 + a_1(x-1) + a_0$$

16.11 THE BINOMIAL SERIES

In elementary algebra you learned that the binomial theorem expresses $(a + b)^m$ as a sum of powers of a and b, where m is a positive integer, as follows:

$$(a + b)^m = a^m + ma^{m-1}b + \frac{m(m-1)}{2!}a^{m-2}b^2 + \cdots$$

$$+ \frac{m(m-1) \cdot \ldots \cdot (m-k+1)}{k!} a^{m-k}b^k + \cdots + b^m$$

We now take $a = 1$ and $b = x$, and apply the binomial theorem to the expression $(1 + x)^m$, where m is not a positive integer. We obtain the power series

$$1 + mx + \frac{m(m-1)}{2!}x^2 + \frac{m(m-1)(m-2)}{3!}x^3 + \cdots$$

$$+ \frac{m(m-1)(m-2) \cdot \ldots \cdot (m-n+1)}{n!}x^n + \cdots \tag{1}$$

Series (1) is the Maclaurin series for $(1 + x)^m$. It is called a *binomial series.* To find the radius of convergence of series (1), we apply the ratio test and get

$$\lim_{n \to +\infty} \left| \frac{u_{n+1}}{u_n} \right|$$

$$= \lim_{n \to +\infty} \left| \frac{\dfrac{m(m-1) \cdot \ldots \cdot (m-n+1)(m-n)}{(n+1)!} x^{n+1}}{\dfrac{m(m-1) \cdot \ldots \cdot (m-n+1)}{n!} x^n} \right|$$

$$= \lim_{n \to +\infty} \left| \frac{m-n}{n+1} \right| |x|$$

$$= \lim_{n \to +\infty} \left| \frac{\frac{m}{n} - 1}{1 + \frac{1}{n}} \right| |x|$$

$$= |x|$$

So the series is convergent if $|x| < 1$. We now prove that series (1) represents $(1 + x)^m$ for all real numbers m if x is in the open interval $(-1, 1)$. We do not do this by calculating $R_n(x)$ and showing that its limit is zero because this is quite difficult, as you will soon see if you attempt to do so. Instead, we use the following method. Let

$$f(x) = 1 + \sum_{n=1}^{+\infty} \frac{m(m-1) \cdot \ldots \cdot (m-n+1)}{n!} x^n \qquad |x| < 1 \qquad (2)$$

We wish to show that $f(x) = (1 + x)^m$, where $|x| < 1$. By Theorem 16.8.3 we have

$$f'(x) = \sum_{n=1}^{+\infty} \frac{m(m-1) \cdot \ldots \cdot (m-n+1)}{(n-1)!} x^{n-1} \qquad |x| < 1 \qquad (3)$$

Multiplying on both sides of Eq. (3) by x, we get from Theorem 16.3.8

$$xf'(x) = \sum_{n=1}^{+\infty} \frac{m(m-1) \cdot \ldots \cdot (m-n+1)}{(n-1)!} x^n \qquad (4)$$

Rewriting the right side of (3), we have

$$f'(x) = m + \sum_{n=2}^{+\infty} \frac{m(m-1) \cdot \ldots \cdot (m-n+1)}{(n-1)!} x^{n-1} \qquad (5)$$

Rewriting the summation in (5) by decreasing the lower limit by 1 and replacing n by $n + 1$, we get

$$f'(x) = m + \sum_{n=1}^{+\infty} (m-n) \frac{m(m-1) \cdot \ldots \cdot (m-n+1)}{n!} x^n \qquad (6)$$

If in (4) we multiply the numerator and the denominator by n, we get

$$xf'(x) = \sum_{n=1}^{+\infty} n \frac{m(m-1) \cdot \ldots \cdot (m-n+1)}{n!} x^n \qquad (7)$$

Because the series in (6) and (7) are absolutely convergent for $|x| < 1$, then by Theorem 16.3.9 we can add them term by term, and the resulting series will be absolutely convergent for $|x| < 1$. When we add we get

$$(1+x)f'(x) = m \left[1 + \sum_{n=1}^{+\infty} \frac{m(m-1) \cdot \ldots \cdot (m-n+1)}{n!} x^n \right]$$

Because by (2) the expression in brackets is $f(x)$, we have

$$(1+x)f'(x) = mf(x)$$

or, equivalently,

$$\frac{f'(x)}{f(x)} = \frac{m}{1+x}$$

The left side of the above equation is $D_x[\ln f(x)]$; so we can write

$$D_x[\ln f(x)] = \frac{m}{1+x}$$

However, we also know that

$$D_x[\ln(1+x)^m] = \frac{m}{1+x}$$

Because $\ln f(x)$ and $\ln(1+x)^m$ have the same derivative, they differ by a constant. Hence,

$$\ln f(x) = \ln(1+x)^m + C$$

We see from (2) that $f(0) = 1$. Therefore, $C = 0$ and we get

$$f(x) = (1+x)^m$$

We have proved the general binomial theorem, which we now state.

16.11.1 Theorem   If m is any real number, then
Binomial Theorem

$$(1+x)^m = 1 + \sum_{n=1}^{+\infty} \frac{m(m-1)(m-2) \cdot \ldots \cdot (m-n+1)}{n!} x^n \qquad (8)$$

for all values of x such that $|x| < 1$.

If m is a positive integer, the binomial series will terminate after a finite number of terms.

EXAMPLE 1:   Express

$$\frac{1}{\sqrt{1+x}}$$

as a power series in x.

SOLUTION: From Theorem 16.11.1 we have, when $|x| < 1$,

$$(1+x)^{-1/2} = 1 - \frac{1}{2}x + \frac{(-\frac{1}{2})(-\frac{1}{2}-1)}{2!}x^2 + \frac{(-\frac{1}{2})(-\frac{1}{2}-1)(-\frac{1}{2}-2)}{3!}x^3$$

$$+ \cdots + \frac{(-\frac{1}{2})(-\frac{3}{2})(-\frac{5}{2}) \cdot \ldots \cdot (-\frac{1}{2}-n+1)}{n!}x^n + \cdots$$

$$= 1 - \frac{1}{2}x + \frac{1 \cdot 3}{2^2 \cdot 2!}x^2 - \frac{1 \cdot 3 \cdot 5}{2^3 \cdot 3!}x^3 + \cdots$$

$$+ (-1)^n \frac{1 \cdot 3 \cdot 5 \cdot \ldots \cdot (2n-1)}{2^n n!}x^n + \cdots$$

EXAMPLE 2:   From the result of Example 1 obtain a binomial

SOLUTION: Replacing x by $-x^2$ in the series for $(1+x)^{-1/2}$, we get for $|x| < 1$

series for $(1 - x^2)^{-1/2}$ and use it to find a power series for $\sin^{-1} x$.

$$(1 - x^2)^{-1/2} = 1 + \frac{1}{2} x^2 + \frac{1 \cdot 3}{2^2 \cdot 2!} x^4 + \frac{1 \cdot 3 \cdot 5}{2^3 \cdot 3!} x^6 + \cdots$$

$$+ \frac{1 \cdot 3 \cdot 5 \cdot \ldots \cdot (2n - 1)}{2^n n!} x^{2n} + \cdots$$

Applying Theorem 16.9.1, we integrate term by term and obtain

$$\int_0^x \frac{dt}{\sqrt{1 - t^2}} = x + \frac{1}{2} \cdot \frac{x^3}{3} + \frac{1 \cdot 3}{2^2 \cdot 2!} \cdot \frac{x^5}{5} + \frac{1 \cdot 3 \cdot 5}{2^3 \cdot 3!} \cdot \frac{x^7}{7} + \cdots$$

$$+ \frac{1 \cdot 3 \cdot 5 \cdot \ldots \cdot (2n - 1)}{2^n n!} \cdot \frac{x^{2n+1}}{2n + 1} + \cdots$$

and so

$$\sin^{-1} x = x + \sum_{n=1}^{+\infty} \frac{1 \cdot 3 \cdot 5 \cdot \ldots \cdot (2n - 1)}{2^n n!} \cdot \frac{x^{2n+1}}{2n + 1} \qquad \text{for } |x| < 1$$

EXAMPLE 3: Compute the value of $\sqrt[3]{25}$ accurate to three decimal places by using the binomial series for $(1 + x)^{1/3}$.

SOLUTION: From Eq. (8) we have

$$(1 + x)^{1/3} = 1 + \frac{1}{3} x + \left(\frac{1}{3}\right)\left(-\frac{2}{3}\right)\frac{x^2}{2!} + \left(\frac{1}{3}\right)\left(-\frac{2}{3}\right)\left(-\frac{5}{3}\right)\frac{x^3}{3!} + \cdots \qquad (9)$$

$$\text{if } |x| < 1$$

We can write

$$\sqrt[3]{25} = \sqrt[3]{27} \; \sqrt[3]{\tfrac{25}{27}} = 3\sqrt[3]{1 - \tfrac{2}{27}} = 3\left(1 - \tfrac{2}{27}\right)^{1/3} \qquad (10)$$

Using Eq. (9) with $x = -\frac{2}{27}$, we get

$$\left(1 - \frac{2}{27}\right)^{1/3} = 1 + \frac{1}{3}\left(-\frac{2}{27}\right) - \frac{2}{3^2 \cdot 2!}\left(-\frac{2}{27}\right)^2 + \frac{2 \cdot 5}{3^3 \cdot 3!}\left(-\frac{2}{27}\right)^3 + \cdots$$

$$\approx 1 - 0.0247 - 0.0006 - 0.00003 - \cdots \qquad (11)$$

If the first three terms of the above series are used, we see from Eq. (14) of Sec. 16.10 that the remainder is

$$R_2\left(-\frac{2}{27}\right) = \frac{f'''(\xi_2)}{3!}\left(-\frac{2}{27}\right)^3$$

$$= \left(\frac{1}{3}\right)\left(-\frac{2}{3}\right)\left(-\frac{5}{3}\right)\left(\frac{1}{3!}\right)(1 + \xi_2)^{(1/3)-3}\left(-\frac{2}{27}\right)^3$$

where $-\frac{2}{27} < \xi_2 < 0$. Therefore,

$$\left|R_2\left(-\frac{2}{27}\right)\right| = \left(\frac{2 \cdot 5}{3^3 \cdot 3!}\right)\frac{(1 + \xi_2)^{1/3}}{(1 + \xi_2)^3}\left(\frac{2}{27}\right)^3 \qquad (12)$$

Because $-\frac{2}{27} < \xi_2 < 0$, it follows that

$$(1 + \xi_2)^{1/3} < 1^{1/3} = 1 \quad \text{and} \quad \frac{1}{(1 + \xi_2)^3} < \frac{1}{\left(\frac{25}{27}\right)^3} \qquad (13)$$

Furthermore,

$$\frac{2 \cdot 5}{3^3 \cdot 3!} = \frac{2 \cdot 5}{3 \cdot 3 \cdot 3 \cdot 1 \cdot 2 \cdot 3} = \frac{2}{3} \cdot \frac{5}{6} \cdot \frac{1}{9} < \frac{1}{9} \qquad (14)$$

and so using inequalities (13) and (14) in (12) we see that

$$\left| R_2\left(-\frac{2}{27}\right) \right| < \frac{1}{9} \cdot \frac{1}{(\frac{25}{27})^3} \cdot \left(\frac{2}{27}\right)^3 = \frac{8}{140,625} < 0.00006$$

Using, then, the first three terms of series (11) gives

$$\left(1 - \frac{2}{27}\right)^{1/3} \approx 0.9747$$

with an error less than 0.00006. From (10) we obtain

$$\sqrt[3]{25} \approx 3(0.9747) = 2.9241$$

with an error less than $3(0.00006) = 0.00018$. Rounding off to three decimal places gives $\sqrt[3]{25} \approx 2.924$.

Exercises 16.11

In Exercises 1 through 6, use a binomial series to find the Maclaurin series for the given function. Determine the radius of convergence of the resulting series.

1. $f(x) = \sqrt{1 + x}$

2. $f(x) = (9 + x^4)^{-1/2}$

3. $f(x) = (4 + x^2)^{-1}$

4. $f(x) = \sqrt[3]{8 + x}$

5. $f(x) = \dfrac{x^2}{\sqrt{1 + x}}$

6. $f(x) = \dfrac{x}{\sqrt[3]{1 + x^2}}$

7. Integrate term by term from 0 to x the binomial series for $(1 + t^2)^{-1/2}$ to obtain the Maclaurin series for $\sinh^{-1} x$. Determine the radius of convergence.

8. Use a method similar to that of Exercise 7 to find the Maclaurin series for $\tanh^{-1} x$. Determine the radius of convergence.

In Exercises 9 through 12, compute the value of the given quantity accurate to three decimal places by using a binomial series.

9. $\sqrt{24}$

10. $\sqrt[3]{66}$

11. $\sqrt[4]{630}$

12. $\dfrac{1}{\sqrt[5]{31}}$

In Exercises 13 through 16, compute the value of the definite integral accurate to four decimal places.

13. $\displaystyle\int_0^{1/3} \frac{dx}{\sqrt[3]{x^2 + 1}}$

14. $\displaystyle\int_0^{1/2} \sqrt{1 - x^3}\, dx$

15. $\displaystyle\int_0^{1/2} \frac{dx}{\sqrt{1 - x^3}}$

16. $\displaystyle\int_0^{1/2} f(x)\, dx$, where $f(x) = \begin{cases} \dfrac{\sin^{-1} x}{x} & \text{if } x \neq 0 \\ 1 & \text{if } x = 0 \end{cases}$

Review Exercises (Chapter 16)

In Exercises 1 through 6, write the first four numbers of the sequence and find the limit of the sequence, if it exists.

1. $\left\{\dfrac{3n}{n + 2}\right\}$

2. $\left\{\dfrac{(-1)^{n-1}}{(n + 1)^2}\right\}$

3. $\left\{\dfrac{n^2 - 1}{n^2 + 1}\right\}$

4. $\left\{\dfrac{n + 3n^2}{4 + 2n^3}\right\}$

5. $\{2 + (-1)^n\}$

6. $\left\{\dfrac{n^2}{n + 2} - \dfrac{n^2}{n - 2}\right\}$

In Exercises 7 through 13, determine if the series is convergent or divergent. If the series is convergent, find its sum.

7. $\displaystyle\sum_{n=1}^{+\infty} \left(\frac{3}{4}\right)^n$

8. $\displaystyle\sum_{n=1}^{+\infty} e^{-2n}$

9. $\displaystyle\sum_{n=1}^{+\infty} \frac{n-1}{n+1}$

10. $\displaystyle\sum_{n=0}^{+\infty} [(-1)^n + (-1)^{n+1}]$

11. $\displaystyle\sum_{n=0}^{+\infty} \sin^n \tfrac{1}{3}\pi$

12. $\displaystyle\sum_{n=0}^{+\infty} \cos^n \tfrac{1}{3}\pi$

13. $\displaystyle\sum_{n=1}^{+\infty} \frac{1}{(3n-1)(3n+2)}$ (HINT: To find the sum, first find the sequence of partial sums.)

In Exercises 14 through 25, determine if the series is convergent or divergent.

14. $\displaystyle\sum_{n=1}^{+\infty} \frac{1}{(2n+1)^3}$

15. $\displaystyle\sum_{n=1}^{+\infty} \frac{2}{n^2+6n}$

16. $\displaystyle\sum_{n=1}^{+\infty} \frac{3+\sin n}{n^2}$

17. $\displaystyle\sum_{n=1}^{+\infty} \cos\left(\frac{\pi}{2n^2-1}\right)$

18. $\displaystyle\sum_{n=1}^{+\infty} \frac{n}{\sqrt{3n+2}}$

19. $\displaystyle\sum_{n=1}^{+\infty} \frac{(n!)^2}{(2n)!}$

20. $\displaystyle\sum_{n=1}^{+\infty} \frac{(-1)^{n+1}}{1+\sqrt{n}}$

21. $\displaystyle\sum_{n=1}^{+\infty} (-1)^n \ln \frac{1}{n}$

22. $\displaystyle\sum_{n=1}^{+\infty} \frac{\ln n}{n^2}$

23. $\displaystyle\sum_{n=2}^{+\infty} \frac{1}{n(\ln n)^2}$

24. $\displaystyle\sum_{n=0}^{+\infty} \frac{n!}{10^n}$

25. $\displaystyle\sum_{n=1}^{+\infty} \frac{1}{1+2\ln n}$

In Exercises 26 through 33, determine if the given series is absolutely convergent, conditionally convergent, or divergent. Prove your answer.

26. $\displaystyle\sum_{n=0}^{+\infty} (-1)^n \frac{5^{2n+1}}{(2n+1)!}$

27. $\displaystyle\sum_{n=0}^{+\infty} (-1)^n \frac{n^2}{3^n}$

28. $\displaystyle\sum_{n=1}^{+\infty} (-1)^{n-1} \frac{6^n}{5^{n+1}}$

29. $\displaystyle\sum_{n=1}^{+\infty} (-1)^{n-1} \frac{1}{(n+1)^{3/4}}$

30. $\displaystyle\sum_{n=1}^{+\infty} (-1)^n \frac{\sqrt{2n-1}}{n}$

31. $\displaystyle\sum_{n=1}^{+\infty} (-1)^n \frac{n!}{10n}$

32. $\displaystyle\sum_{n=1}^{+\infty} c_n$, where $c_n = \begin{cases} -\dfrac{1}{n} & \text{if } \tfrac{1}{4}n \text{ is an integer} \\[2mm] \dfrac{1}{n^2} & \text{if } \tfrac{1}{4}n \text{ is not an integer} \end{cases}$

33. $\displaystyle\sum_{n=1}^{+\infty} c_n$, where $c_n = \begin{cases} -\dfrac{1}{n} & \text{if } n \text{ is a perfect square} \\[2mm] \dfrac{1}{n^2} & \text{if } n \text{ is not a perfect square} \end{cases}$

In Exercises 34 through 42, find the interval of convergence of the given power series.

34. $\displaystyle\sum_{n=0}^{+\infty} \frac{x^n}{2^n}$

35. $\displaystyle\sum_{n=1}^{+\infty} \frac{x^n}{\sqrt{n}}$

36. $\displaystyle\sum_{n=1}^{+\infty} \frac{(x-2)^n}{n}$

37. $\displaystyle\sum_{n=1}^{+\infty} \frac{x^n}{3^n(n^2+n)}$

38. $\displaystyle\sum_{n=1}^{+\infty} n(2x-1)^n$

39. $\displaystyle\sum_{n=0}^{+\infty} \frac{n!}{2^n}(x-3)^n$

40. $\displaystyle\sum_{n=1}^{+\infty} \frac{(-1)^{n-1}x^{2n-1}}{(2n-1)!}$

41. $\displaystyle\sum_{n=1}^{+\infty} \frac{n^2}{6^n}(x+1)^n$

42. $\displaystyle\sum_{n=1}^{+\infty} n^n x^n$

In Exercises 43 through 50, use a power series to compute the value of the given quantity accurate to four decimal places.

43. $\tan^{-1} \frac{1}{5}$

44. $\sin 0.3$

45. $\sqrt[3]{130}$

46. $\sin^{-1} 1$

47. $\cos 3°$

48. $\sqrt[4]{e}$

49. $\displaystyle\int_0^{1/4} \sqrt{x} \sin x \, dx$

50. $\displaystyle\int_0^1 \cos x^3 \, dx$

In Exercises 51 through 53, find the Maclaurin series for the given function and find its interval of convergence.

51. $f(x) = a^x (a > 0)$

52. $f(x) = \dfrac{1}{2 - x}$

53. $f(x) = \sin^3 x$

In Exercises 54 through 56, find the Taylor series for the given function at the given number.

54. $f(x) = e^{x-2}$; at 2

55. $f(x) = \sin 3x$; at $-\frac{1}{3}\pi$

56. $f(x) = \dfrac{1}{x}$; at 2

Exercises 57 through 61 pertain to the functions J_0 and J_1 defined by power series as follows:

$$J_0(x) = \sum_{n=0}^{+\infty} (-1)^n \frac{x^{2n}}{n!n!2^{2n}} \qquad J_1(x) = \sum_{n=0}^{+\infty} (-1)^n \frac{x^{2n+1}}{n!(n+1)!2^{2n+1}}$$

The functions J_0 and J_1 are called *Bessel functions of the first kind* of orders zero and one, respectively.

57. Show that both J_0 and J_1 converge for all real values of x.

58. Show that $J_0'(x) = -J_1(x)$.

59. Show that $D_x(xJ_1(x)) = xJ_0(x)$.

60. Show that $y = J_0(x)$ is a solution of the differential equation

$$x\frac{d^2y}{dx^2} + \frac{dy}{dx} + xy = 0$$

61. Show that $y = J_1(x)$ is a solution of the differential equation

$$x^2\frac{d^2y}{dx^2} + x\frac{dy}{dx} + (x^2 - 1)y = 0$$

Appendix

Table 1 Powers and roots

n	n^2	$\sqrt{n}$	n^3	$\sqrt[3]{n}$	n	n^2	$\sqrt{n}$	n^3	$\sqrt[3]{n}$
1	1	1.000	1	1.000	51	2,601	7.141	132,651	3.708
2	4	1.414	8	1.260	52	2,704	7.211	140,608	3.732
3	9	1.732	27	1.442	53	2,809	7.280	148,877	3.756
4	16	2.000	64	1.587	54	2,916	7.348	157,464	3.780
5	25	2.236	125	1.710	55	3,025	7.416	166,375	3.803
6	36	2.449	216	1.817	56	3,136	7.483	175,616	3.826
7	49	2.646	343	1.913	57	3,249	7.550	185,193	3.848
8	64	2.828	512	2.000	58	3,364	7.616	195,112	3.871
9	81	3.000	729	2.080	59	3,481	7.681	205,379	3.893
10	100	3.162	1,000	2.154	60	3,600	7.746	216,000	3.915
11	121	3.317	1,331	2.224	61	3,721	7.810	226,981	3.936
12	144	3.464	1,728	2.289	62	3,844	7.874	238,328	3.958
13	169	3.606	2,197	2.351	63	3,969	7.937	250,047	3.979
14	196	3.742	2,744	2.410	64	4,096	8.000	262,144	4.000
15	225	3.873	3,375	2.466	65	4,225	8.062	274,625	4.021
16	256	4.000	4,096	2.520	66	4,356	8.124	287,496	4.041
17	289	4.123	4,913	2.571	67	4,489	8.185	300,763	4.062
18	324	4.243	5,832	2.621	68	4,624	8.246	314,432	4.082
19	361	4.359	6,859	2.668	69	4,761	8.307	328,509	4.102
20	400	4.472	8,000	2.714	70	4,900	8.367	343,000	4.121
21	441	4.583	9,261	2.759	71	5,041	8.426	357,911	4.141
22	484	4.690	10,648	2.802	72	5,184	8.485	373,248	4.160
23	529	4.796	12,167	2.844	73	5,329	8.544	389,017	4.179
24	576	4.899	13,824	2.884	74	5,476	8.602	405,224	4.198
25	625	5.000	15,625	2.924	75	5,625	8.660	421,875	4.217
26	676	5.099	17,576	2.962	76	5,776	8.718	438,976	4.236
27	729	5.196	19,683	3.000	77	5,929	8.775	456,533	4.254
28	784	5.291	21,952	3.037	78	6,084	8.832	474,552	4.273
29	841	5.385	24,389	3.072	79	6,241	8.888	493,039	4.291
30	900	5.477	27,000	3.107	80	6,400	8.944	512,000	4.309
31	961	5.568	29,791	3.141	81	6,561	9.000	531,441	4.327
32	1,024	5.657	32,768	3.175	82	6,724	9.055	551,368	4.344
33	1,089	5.745	35,937	3.208	83	6,889	9.110	571,787	4.362
34	1,156	5.831	39,304	3.240	84	7,056	9.165	592,704	4.380
35	1,225	5.916	42,875	3.271	85	7,225	9.220	614,125	4.397
36	1,296	6.000	46,656	3.302	86	7,396	9.274	636,056	4.414
37	1,369	6.083	50,653	3.332	87	7,569	9.327	658,503	4.431
38	1,444	6.164	54,872	3.362	88	7,744	9.381	681,472	4.448
39	1,521	6.245	59,319	3.391	89	7,921	9.434	704,969	4.465
40	1,600	6.325	64,000	3.420	90	8,100	9.487	729,000	4.481
41	1,681	6.403	68,921	3.448	91	8,281	9.539	753,571	4.498
42	1,764	6.481	74,088	3.476	92	8,464	9.592	778,688	4.514
43	1,849	6.557	79,507	3.503	93	8,649	9.643	804,357	4.531
44	1,936	6.633	85,184	3.530	94	8,836	9.695	830,584	4.547
45	2,025	6.708	91,125	3.557	95	9,025	9.747	857,375	4.563
46	2,116	6.782	97,336	3.583	96	9,216	9.798	884,736	4.579
47	2,209	6.856	103,823	3.609	97	9,409	9.849	912,673	4.595
48	2,304	6.928	110,592	3.634	98	9,604	9.899	941,192	4.610
49	2,401	7.000	117,649	3.659	99	9,801	9.950	970,299	4.626
50	2,500	7.071	125,000	3.684	100	10,000	10.000	1,000,000	4.642

Table 2   Natural logarithms

N	0	1	2	3	4	5	6	7	8	9
1.0	0000	0100	0198	0296	0392	0488	0583	0677	0770	0862
1.1	0953	1044	1133	1222	1310	1398	1484	1570	1655	1740
1.2	1823	1906	1989	2070	2151	2231	2311	2390	2469	2546
1.3	2624	2700	2776	2852	2927	3001	3075	3148	3221	3293
1.4	3365	3436	3507	3577	3646	3716	3784	3853	3920	3988
1.5	4055	4121	4187	4253	4318	4383	4447	4511	4574	4637
1.6	4700	4762	4824	4886	4947	5008	5068	5128	5188	5247
1.7	5306	5365	5423	5481	5539	5596	5653	5710	5766	5822
1.8	5878	5933	5988	6043	6098	6152	6206	6259	6313	6366
1.9	6419	6471	6523	6575	6627	6678	6729	6780	6831	6881
2.0	6931	6981	7031	7080	7129	7178	7227	7275	7324	7372
2.1	7419	7467	7514	7561	7608	7655	7701	7747	7793	7839
2.2	7885	7930	7975	8020	8065	8109	8154	8198	8242	8286
2.3	8329	8372	8416	8459	8502	8544	8587	8629	8671	8713
2.4	8755	8796	8838	8879	8920	8961	9002	9042	9083	9123
2.5	9163	9203	9243	9282	9322	9361	9400	9439	9478	9517
2.6	9555	9594	9632	9670	9708	9746	9783	9821	9858	9895
2.7	9933	9969	*0006	*0043	*0080	*0116	*0152	*0188	*0225	*0260
2.8	1.0296	0332	0367	0403	0438	0473	0508	0543	0578	0613
2.9	0647	0682	0716	0750	0784	0818	0852	0886	0919	0953
3.0	1.0986	1019	1053	1086	1119	1151	1184	1217	1249	1282
3.1	1314	1346	1378	1410	1442	1474	1506	1537	1569	1600
3.2	1632	1663	1694	1725	1756	1787	1817	1848	1878	1909
3.3	1939	1969	2000	2030	2060	2090	2119	2149	2179	2208
3.4	2238	2267	2296	2326	2355	2384	2413	2442	2470	2499
3.5	1.2528	2556	2585	2613	2641	2669	2698	2726	2754	2782
3.6	2809	2837	2865	2892	2920	2947	2975	3002	3029	3056
3.7	3083	3110	3137	3164	3191	3218	3244	3271	3297	3324
3.8	3350	3376	3403	3429	3455	3481	3507	3533	3558	3584
3.9	3610	3635	3661	3686	3712	3737	3762	3788	3813	3838
4.0	1.3863	3888	3913	3938	3962	3987	4012	4036	4061	4085
4.1	4110	4134	4159	4183	4207	4231	4255	4279	4303	4327
4.2	4351	4375	4398	4422	4446	4469	4493	4516	4540	4563
4.3	4586	4609	4633	4656	4679	4702	4725	4748	4770	4793
4.4	4816	4839	4861	4884	4907	4929	4951	4974	4996	5019
4.5	1.5041	5063	5085	5107	5129	5151	5173	5195	5217	5239
4.6	5261	5282	5304	5326	5347	5369	5390	5412	5433	5454
4.7	5476	5497	5518	5539	5560	5581	5602	5623	5644	5665
4.8	5686	5707	5728	5748	5769	5790	5810	5831	5851	5872
4.9	5892	5913	5933	5953	5974	5994	6014	6034	6054	6074
5.0	1.6094	6114	6134	6154	6174	6194	6214	6233	6253	6273
5.1	6292	6312	6332	6351	6371	6390	6409	6429	6448	6467
5.2	6487	6506	6525	6544	6563	6582	6601	6620	6639	6658
5.3	6677	6696	6715	6734	6752	6771	6790	6808	6827	6845
5.4	6864	6882	6901	6919	6938	6956	6974	6993	7011	7029

Table 2 (Continued)

N	0	1	2	3	4	5	6	7	8	9
5.5	1.7047	7066	7084	7102	7120	7138	7156	7174	7192	7210
5.6	7228	7246	7263	7281	7299	7317	7334	7352	7370	7387
5.7	7405	7422	7440	7457	7475	7492	7509	7527	7544	7561
5.8	7579	7596	7613	7630	7647	7664	7681	7699	7716	7733
5.9	7750	7766	7783	7800	7817	7834	7851	7867	7884	7901
6.0	1.7918	7934	7951	7967	7984	8001	8017	8034	8050	8066
6.1	8083	8099	8116	8132	8148	8165	8181	8197	8213	8229
6.2	8245	8262	8278	8294	8310	8326	8342	8358	8374	8390
6.3	8405	8421	8437	8453	8469	8485	8500	8516	8532	8547
6.4	8563	8579	8594	8610	8625	8641	8656	8672	8687	8703
6.5	1.8718	8733	8749	8764	8779	8795	8810	8825	8840	8856
6.6	8871	8886	8901	8916	8931	8946	8961	8976	8991	9006
6.7	9021	9036	9051	9066	9081	9095	9110	9125	9140	9155
6.8	9169	9184	9199	9213	9228	9242	9257	9272	9286	9301
6.9	9315	9330	9344	9359	9373	9387	9402	9416	9430	9445
7.0	1.9459	9473	9488	9502	9516	9530	9544	9559	9573	9587
7.1	9601	9615	9629	9643	9657	9671	9685	9699	9713	9727
7.2	9741	9755	9769	9782	9796	9810	9824	9838	9851	9865
7.3	9879	9892	9906	9920	9933	9947	9961	9974	9988	*0001
7.4	2.0015	0028	0042	0055	0069	0082	0096	0109	0122	0136
7.5	2.0149	0162	0176	0189	0202	0215	0229	0242	0255	0268
7.6	0281	0295	0308	0321	0334	0347	0360	0373	0386	0399
7.7	0412	0425	0438	0451	0464	0477	0490	0503	0516	0528
7.8	0541	0554	0567	0580	0592	0605	0618	0630	0643	0656
7.9	0669	0681	0694	0707	0719	0732	0744	0757	0769	0782
8.0	2.0794	0807	0819	0832	0844	0857	0869	0882	0894	0906
8.1	0919	0931	0943	0956	0968	0980	0992	1005	1017	1029
8.2	1041	1054	1066	1078	1090	1102	1114	1126	1138	1150
8.3	1163	1175	1187	1199	1211	1223	1235	1247	1258	1270
8.4	1282	1294	1306	1318	1330	1342	1353	1365	1377	1389
8.5	2.1401	1412	1424	1436	1448	1459	1471	1483	1494	1506
8.6	1518	1529	1541	1552	1564	1576	1587	1599	1610	1622
8.7	1633	1645	1656	1668	1679	1691	1702	1713	1725	1736
8.8	1748	1759	1770	1782	1793	1804	1815	1827	1838	1849
8.9	1861	1872	1883	1894	1905	1917	1928	1939	1950	1961
9.0	2.1972	1983	1994	2006	2017	2028	2039	2050	2061	2072
9.1	2083	2094	2105	2116	2127	2138	2148	2159	2170	2181
9.2	2192	2203	2214	2225	2235	2246	2257	2268	2279	2289
9.3	2300	2311	2322	2332	2343	2354	2364	2375	2386	2396
9.4	2407	2418	2428	2439	2450	2460	2471	2481	2492	2502
9.5	2.2513	2523	2534	2544	2555	2565	2576	2586	2597	2607
9.6	2618	2628	2638	2649	2659	2670	2680	2690	2701	2711
9.7	2721	2732	2742	2752	2762	2773	2783	2793	2803	2814
9.8	2824	2834	2844	2854	2865	2875	2885	2895	2905	2915
9.9	2925	2935	2946	2956	2966	2976	2986	2996	3006	3016

Use ln 10 = 2.30259 to find logarithms of numbers greater than 10 or less than 1. *Example:* ln 220 = ln 2.2 + 2 ln 10 = 0.7885 + 2(2.30259) = 5.3937.

Table 3 *Exponential functions*

x	e^x	$\log_{10}(e^x)$	e^{-x}	x	e^x	$\log_{10}(e^x)$	e^{-x}
0.00	1.0000	0.00000	1.000000	**0.50**	1.6487	0.21715	0.606531
0.01	1.0101	.00434	0.990050	0.51	1.6653	.22149	.600496
0.02	1.0202	.00869	.980199	0.52	1.6820	.22583	.594521
0.03	1.0305	.01303	.970446	0.53	1.6989	.23018	.588605
0.04	1.0408	.01737	.960789	0.54	1.7160	.23452	.582748
0.05	1.0513	0.02171	0.951229	**0.55**	1.7333	0.23886	0.576950
0.06	1.0618	.02606	.941765	0.56	1.7507	.24320	.571209
0.07	1.0725	.03040	.932394	0.57	1.7683	.24755	.565525
0.08	1.0833	.03474	.923116	0.58	1.7860	.25189	.559898
0.09	1.0942	.03909	.913931	0.59	1.8040	.35623	.554327
0.10	1.1052	0.04343	0.904837	**0.60**	1.8221	0.26058	0.548812
0.11	1.1163	.04777	.895834	0.61	1.8404	.26492	.543351
0.12	1.1275	.05212	.886920	0.62	1.8589	.26926	.537944
0.13	1.1388	.05646	.878095	0.63	1.8776	.27361	.532592
0.14	1.1503	.06080	.869358	0.64	1.8965	.27795	.527292
0.15	1.1618	0.06514	0.860708	**0.65**	1.9155	0.28229	0.522046
0.16	1.1735	.06949	.852144	0.66	1.9348	.28663	.516851
0.17	1.1853	.07383	.843665	0.67	1.9542	.29098	.511709
0.18	1.1972	.07817	.835270	0.68	1.9739	.29532	.506617
0.19	1.2092	.08252	.826959	0.69	1.9937	.29966	.501576
0.20	1.2214	0.08686	0.818731	**0.70**	2.0138	0.30401	0.496585
0.21	1.2337	.09120	.810584	0.71	2.0340	.30835	.491644
0.22	1.2461	.09554	.802519	0.72	2.0544	.31269	.486752
0.23	1.2586	.09989	.794534	0.73	2.0751	.31703	.481909
0.24	1.2712	.10423	.786628	0.74	2.0959	.32138	.477114
0.25	1.2840	0.10857	0.778801	**0.75**	2.1170	0.32572	0.472367
0.26	1.2969	.11292	.771052	0.76	2.1383	.33006	.467666
0.27	1.3100	.11726	.763379	0.77	2.1598	.33441	.463013
0.28	1.3231	.12160	.755784	0.78	2.1815	.33875	.458406
0.29	1.3364	.12595	.748264	0.79	2.2034	.34309	.453845
0.30	1.3499	0.13029	0.740818	**0.80**	2.2255	0.34744	0.449329
0.31	1.3634	.13463	.733447	0.81	2.2479	.35178	.444858
0.32	1.3771	.13897	.726149	0.82	2.2705	.35612	.440432
0.33	1.3910	.14332	.718924	0.83	2.2933	.36046	.436049
0.34	1.4049	.14766	.711770	0.84	2.3164	.36481	.431711
0.35	1.4191	0.15200	0.704688	**0.85**	2.3396	0.36915	0.427415
0.36	1.4333	.15635	.697676	0.86	2.3632	.37349	.423162
0.37	1.4477	.16069	.690734	0.87	2.3869	.37784	.418952
0.38	1.4623	.16503	.683861	0.88	2.4109	.38218	.414783
0.39	1.4770	.16937	.677057	0.89	2.4351	.38652	.410656
0.40	1.4918	0.17372	0.670320	**0.90**	2.4596	0.39087	0.406570
0.41	1.5068	.17806	.663650	0.91	2.4843	.39521	.402524
0.42	1.5220	.18240	.657047	0.92	2.5093	.39955	.398519
0.43	1.5373	.18675	.650509	0.93	2.5345	.40389	.394554
0.44	1.5527	.19109	.644036	0.94	2.5600	.40824	.390628
0.45	1.5683	0.19543	0.637628	**0.95**	2.5857	0.41258	0.386741
0.46	1.5841	.19978	.631284	0.96	2.6117	.41692	.382893
0.47	1.6000	.20412	.625002	0.97	2.6379	.42127	.379083
0.48	1.6161	.20846	.618783	0.98	2.6645	.42561	.375311
0.49	1.6323	.21280	.612626	0.99	2.6912	.42995	.371577
0.50	1.6487	0.21715	0.606531	**1.00**	2.7183	0.43429	0.367879

Table 3 (*Continued*)

x	e^x	$\log_{10}(e^x)$	e^{-x}	x	e^x	$\log_{10}(e^x)$	e^{-x}
1.00	2.7183	0.43429	0.367879	**1.50**	4.4817	0.65144	0.223130
1.01	2.7456	.43864	.364219	1.51	4.5267	.65578	.220910
1.02	2.7732	.44298	.360595	1.52	4.5722	.66013	.218712
1.03	2.8011	.44732	.357007	1.53	4.6182	.66447	.216536
1.04	2.8292	.45167	.353455	1.54	4.6646	.66881	.214381
1.05	2.8577	0.45601	0.349938	**1.55**	4.7115	0.67316	0.212248
1.06	2.8864	.46035	.346456	1.56	4.7588	.67750	.210136
1.07	2.9154	.46470	.343009	1.57	4.8066	.68184	.208045
1.08	2.9447	.46904	.339596	1.58	4.8550	.68619	.205975
1.09	2.9743	.47338	.336216	1.59	4.9037	.69053	.203926
1.10	3.0042	0.47772	0.332871	**1.60**	4.9530	0.69487	0.201897
1.11	3.0344	.48207	.329559	1.61	5.0028	.69921	.199888
1.12	3.0649	.48641	.326280	1.62	5.0531	.70356	.197899
1.13	3.0957	.49075	.323033	1.63	5.1039	.70790	.195930
1.14	3.1268	.49510	.319819	1.64	5.1552	.71224	.193980
1.15	3.1582	0.49944	0.316637	**1.65**	5.2070	0.71659	0.192050
1.16	3.1899	.50378	.313486	1.66	5.2593	.72093	.190139
1.17	3.2220	.50812	.310367	1.67	5.3122	.72527	.188247
1.18	3.2544	.51247	.307279	1.68	5.3656	.72961	.186374
1.19	3.2871	.51681	.304221	1.69	5.4195	.73396	.184520
1.20	3.3201	0.52115	0.301194	**1.70**	5.4739	0.73830	0.182684
1.21	3.3535	.52550	.298197	1.71	5.5290	.74264	.180866
1.22	3.3872	.52984	.295230	1.72	5.5845	.74699	.179066
1.23	3.4212	.53418	.292293	1.73	5.6407	.75133	.177284
1.24	3.4556	.53853	.289384	1.74	5.6973	.75567	.175520
1.25	3.4903	0.54287	0.286505	**1.75**	5.7546	0.76002	0.173774
1.26	3.5254	.54721	.283654	1.76	5.8124	.76436	.172045
1.27	3.5609	.55155	.280832	1.77	5.8709	.76870	.170333
1.28	3.5966	.55590	.278037	1.78	5.9299	.77304	.168638
1.29	3.6328	.56024	.275271	1.79	5.9895	.77739	.166960
1.30	3.6693	0.56458	0.272532	**1.80**	6.0496	0.78173	0.165299
1.31	3.7062	.56893	.269820	1.81	6.1104	.78607	.163654
1.32	3.7434	.57327	.267135	1.82	6.1719	.79042	.162026
1.33	3.7810	.57761	.264477	1.83	6.2339	.79476	.160414
1.34	3.8190	.58195	.261846	1.84	6.2965	.79910	.158817
1.35	3.8574	0.58630	0.259240	**1.85**	6.3598	0.80344	0.157237
1.36	3.8962	.59064	.256661	1.86	6.4237	.80779	.155673
1.37	3.9354	.59498	.254107	1.87	6.4483	.81213	.154124
1.38	3.9749	.59933	.251579	1.88	6.5535	.81647	.152590
1.39	4.0149	.60367	.249075	1.89	6.6194	.82082	.151072
1.40	4.0552	0.60801	0.246597	**1.90**	6.6859	0.82516	0.149569
1.41	4.0960	.61236	.244143	1.91	6.7531	.82950	.148080
1.42	4.1371	.61670	.241714	1.92	6.8210	.83385	.146607
1.43	4.1787	.62104	.239309	1.93	6.8895	.83819	.145148
1.44	4.2207	.62538	.236928	1.94	6.9588	.84253	.143704
1.45	4.2631	0.62973	0.234570	**1.95**	7.0287	0.84687	0.142274
1.46	4.3060	.63407	.232236	1.96	7.0993	.85122	.140858
1.47	4.3492	.63841	.229925	1.97	7.1707	.85556	.139457
1.48	4.3929	.64276	.227638	1.98	7.2427	.85990	.138069
1.49	4.4371	.64710	.225373	1.99	7.3155	.86425	.136695
1.50	4.4817	0.65144	0.223130	**2.00**	7.3891	0.86859	0.135335

Table 3 (*Continued*)

x	e^x	$\log_{10}(e^x)$	e^{-x}	x	e^x	$\log_{10}(e^x)$	e^{-x}
2.00	7.3891	0.86859	0.135335	**2.50**	12.182	1.08574	0.082085
2.01	7.4633	.87293	.133989	2.51	12.305	1.09008	.081268
2.02	7.5383	.87727	.132655	2.52	12.429	1.09442	.080460
2.03	7.6141	.88162	.131336	2.53	12.554	1.09877	.079659
2.04	7.6906	.88596	.130029	2.54	12.680	1.10311	.078866
2.05	7.7679	0.89030	0.128735	**2.55**	12.807	1.10745	0.078082
2.06	7.8460	.89465	.127454	2.56	12.936	1.11179	.077305
2.07	7.9248	.89899	.126186	2.57	13.066	1.11614	.076536
2.08	8.0045	.90333	.124930	2.58	13.197	1.12048	.075774
2.09	8.0849	.90756	.123687	2.59	13.330	1.12482	.075020
2.10	8.1662	0.91202	0.122456	**2.60**	13.464	1.12917	0.074274
2.11	8.2482	.91636	.121238	2.61	13.599	1.13351	.073535
2.12	8.3311	.92070	.120032	2.62	13.736	1.13785	.072803
2.13	8.4149	.92505	.118837	2.63	13.874	1.14219	.072078
2.14	8.4994	.92939	.117655	2.64	14.013	1.14654	.071361
2.15	8.5849	0.93373	0.116484	**2.65**	14.154	1.15088	0.070651
2.16	8.6711	.93808	.115325	2.66	14.296	1.15522	.069948
2.17	8.7583	.94242	.114178	2.67	14.440	1.15957	.069252
2.18	8.8463	.94676	.113042	2.68	14.585	1.16391	.068563
2.19	8.9352	.95110	.111917	2.69	14.732	1.16825	.067881
2.20	9.0250	0.95545	0.110803	**2.70**	14.880	1.17260	0.067206
2.21	9.1157	.95979	.109701	2.71	15.029	1.17694	.066537
2.22	9.2073	.96413	.108609	2.72	15.180	1.18128	.065875
2.23	9.2999	.96848	.107528	2.73	15.333	1.18562	.065219
2.24	9.3933	.97282	.106459	2.74	15.487	1.18997	.064570
2.25	9.4877	0.97716	0.105399	**2.75**	15.643	1.19431	0.063928
2.26	9.5831	.98151	.104350	2.76	15.800	1.19865	.063292
2.27	9.6794	.98585	.103312	2.77	15.959	1.20300	.062662
2.28	9.7767	.99019	.102284	2.78	16.119	1.20734	.062039
2.29	9.8749	.99453	.101266	2.79	16.281	1.21168	.061421
2.30	9.9742	0.99888	0.100259	**2.80**	16.445	1.21602	0.060810
2.31	10.074	1.00322	.099261	2.81	16.610	1.22037	.060205
2.32	10.176	1.00756	.098274	2.82	16.777	1.22471	.059606
2.33	10.278	1.01191	.097296	2.83	16.945	1.22905	.059013
2.34	10.381	1.01625	.096328	2.84	17.116	1.23340	.058426
2.35	10.486	1.02059	0.095369	**2.85**	17.288	1.23774	0.057844
2.36	10.591	1.02493	.094420	2.86	17.462	1.24208	.057269
2.37	10.697	1.02928	.093481	2.87	17.637	1.24643	.056699
2.38	10.805	1.03362	.092551	2.88	17.814	1.25077	.056135
2.39	10.913	1.03796	.091630	2.89	17.993	1.25511	.055576
2.40	11.023	1.04231	0.090718	**2.90**	18.174	1.25945	0.055023
2.41	11.134	1.04665	.089815	2.91	18.357	1.26380	.054476
2.42	11.246	1.05099	.088922	2.92	18.541	1.26814	.053934
2.43	11.359	1.05534	.088037	2.93	18.728	1.27248	.053397
2.44	11.473	1.05968	.087161	2.94	18.916	1.27683	.052866
2.45	11.588	1.06402	0.086294	**2.95**	19.106	1.28117	0.052340
2.46	11.705	1.06836	.085435	2.96	19.298	1.28551	.051819
2.47	11.822	1.07271	.084585	2.97	19.492	1.28985	.051303
2.48	11.941	1.07705	.083743	2.98	19.688	1.29420	.050793
2.49	12.061	1.08139	.082910	2.99	19.886	1.29854	.050287
2.50	12.182	1.08574	0.082085	**3.00**	20.086	1.30288	0.049787

Table 3 (*Continued*)

x	e^x	$\log_{10}(e^x)$	e^{-x}	x	e^x	$\log_{10}(e^x)$	e^{-x}
3.00	20.086	1.30288	0.049787	**3.50**	33.115	1.52003	0.030197
3.01	20.287	1.30723	.049292	3.51	33.448	1.52437	.029897
3.02	20.491	1.31157	.048801	3.52	33.784	1.52872	.029599
3.03	20.697	1.31591	.048316	3.53	34.124	1.53306	.029305
3.04	20.905	1.32026	.047835	3.54	34.467	1.53740	.029013
3.05	21.115	1.32460	0.047359	**3.55**	34.813	1.54175	0.028725
3.06	21.328	1.32894	.046888	3.56	35.163	1.54609	.028439
3.07	21.542	1.33328	.046421	3.57	35.517	1.55043	.028156
3.08	21.758	1.33763	.045959	3.58	35.874	1.55477	.027876
3.09	21.977	1.34197	.045502	3.59	36.234	1.55912	.027598
3.10	22.198	1.34631	0.045049	**3.60**	36.598	1.56346	0.027324
3.11	22.421	1.35066	.044601	3.61	36.966	1.56780	.027052
3.12	22.646	1.35500	.044157	3.62	37.338	1.57215	.026783
3.13	22.874	1.35934	.043718	3.63	37.713	1.57649	.026516
3.14	23.104	1.36368	.043283	3.64	38.092	1.58083	.026252
3.15	23.336	1.36803	0.042852	**3.65**	38.475	1.58517	0.025991
3.16	23.571	1.37237	.042426	3.66	38.861	1.58952	.025733
3.17	23.807	1.36671	.042004	3.67	39.252	1.59386	.025476
3.18	24.047	1.38106	.041586	3.68	39.646	1.59820	.025223
3.19	24.288	1.38540	.041172	3.69	40.045	1.60255	.024972
3.20	24.533	1.38974	0.040764	**3.70**	40.447	1.60689	0.024724
3.21	24.779	1.39409	.040357	3.71	40.854	1.61123	.024478
3.22	25.028	1.39843	.039955	3.72	41.264	1.61558	.024234
3.23	25.280	1.40277	.039557	3.73	41.679	1.61992	.023993
3.24	25.534	1.40711	.039164	3.74	42.098	1.62426	.023754
3.25	25.790	1.41146	0.038774	**3.75**	42.521	1.62860	0.023518
3.26	26.050	1.41580	.038388	3.76	42.948	1.63295	.023284
3.27	26.311	1.42014	.038006	3.77	43.380	1.63729	.023052
3.28	26.576	1.42449	.037628	3.78	43.816	1.64163	.022823
3.29	26.843	1.42883	.037254	3.79	44.256	1.64598	.022596
3.30	27.113	1.44317	0.036883	**3.80**	44.701	1.65032	0.022371
3.31	27.385	1.43751	.036516	3.81	45.150	1.65466	.022148
3.32	27.660	1.44186	.036153	3.82	45.604	1.65900	.021928
3.33	27.938	1.44620	.035793	3.83	46.063	1.66335	.021710
3.34	28.219	1.45054	.035437	3.84	46.525	1.66769	.021494
3.35	28.503	1.45489	0.035084	**3.85**	46.993	1.67203	0.021280
3.36	28.789	1.45923	.034735	3.86	47.465	1.67638	.021068
3.37	29.079	1.46357	.034390	3.87	47.942	1.68072	.020858
3.38	29.371	1.46792	.034047	3.88	48.424	1.68506	.020651
3.39	29.666	1.47226	.033709	3.89	48.911	1.68941	.020445
3.40	29.964	1.47660	0.033373	**3.90**	49.402	1.69375	0.020242
3.41	30.265	1.48094	.033041	3.91	49.899	1.69809	.020041
3.42	30.569	1.48529	.032712	3.92	50.400	1.70243	.019840
3.43	30.877	1.48963	.032387	3.93	50.907	1.70678	.019644
3.44	31.187	1.49397	.032065	3.94	51.419	1.71112	.019448
3.45	31.500	1.49832	0.031746	**3.95**	51.935	1.71546	0.019255
3.46	31.817	1.50266	.031430	3.96	52.457	1.71981	.019063
3.47	32.137	1.50700	.031117	3.97	52.985	1.72415	.018873
3.48	32.460	1.51134	.030807	3.98	53.517	1.72849	.018686
3.49	32.786	1.51569	.030501	3.99	54.055	1.73283	.018500
3.50	33.115	1.52003	0.030197	**4.00**	54.598	1.73718	0.018316

Table 3 (*Continued*)

x	e^x	$\log_{10}(e^x)$	e^{-x}	x	e^x	$\log_{10}(e^x)$	e^{-x}
4.00	54.598	1.73718	0.018316	**4.50**	90.017	1.95433	0.011109
4.01	55.147	1.74152	.018133	4.51	90.922	1.95867	.010998
4.02	55.701	1.74586	.017953	4.52	91.836	1.96301	.010889
4.03	56.261	1.75021	.017774	4.53	92.759	1.96735	.010781
4.04	56.826	1.75455	.017597	4.54	93.691	1.97170	.010673
4.05	57.397	1.75889	0.017422	**4.55**	94.632	1.97604	0.010567
4.06	57.974	1.76324	.017249	4.56	95.583	1.98038	.010462
4.07	58.577	1.76758	.017077	4.57	96.544	1.98473	.010358
4.08	59.145	1.77192	.016907	4.58	97.514	1.98907	.010255
4.09	59.740	1.77626	.016739	4.59	98.494	1.99341	.010153
4.10	60.340	1.78061	0.016573	**4.60**	99.484	1.99775	0.010052
4.11	60.947	1.78495	.016408	4.61	100.48	2.00210	.009952
4.12	61.559	1.78929	.016245	4.62	101.49	2.00644	.009853
4.13	62.178	1.79364	.016083	4.63	102.51	2.01078	.009755
4.14	62.803	1.79798	.015923	4.64	103.54	2.01513	.009658
4.15	63.434	1.80232	0.015764	**4.65**	104.58	2.01947	0.009562
4.16	64.072	1.80667	.015608	4.66	105.64	2.02381	.009466
4.17	64.715	1.81101	.015452	4.67	106.70	2.02816	.009372
4.18	65.366	1.81535	.015299	4.68	107.77	2.03250	.009279
4.19	66.023	1.81969	.015146	4.69	108.85	2.03684	.009187
4.20	66.686	1.82404	0.014996	**4.70**	109.95	2.04118	0.009095
4.21	67.357	1.82838	.014846	4.71	111.05	2.04553	.009005
4.22	68.033	1.83272	.014699	4.72	112.17	2.04987	.008915
4.23	68.717	1.83707	.014552	4.73	113.30	2.05421	.008826
4.24	69.408	1.84141	.014408	4.74	114.43	2.05856	.008739
4.25	70.105	1.84575	0.014264	**4.75**	115.58	2.06290	0.008652
4.26	70.810	1.85009	.014122	4.76	116.75	2.06724	.008566
4.27	71.522	1.85444	.013982	4.77	117.92	2.07158	.008480
4.28	72.240	1.85878	.013843	4.78	119.10	2.07593	.008396
4.29	72.966	1.86312	.013705	4.79	120.30	2.08027	.008312
4.30	73.700	1.86747	0.013569	**4.80**	121.51	2.08461	0.008230
4.31	74.440	1.87181	.013434	4.81	122.73	2.08896	.008148
4.32	75.189	1.87615	.013300	4.82	123.97	2.09330	.008067
4.33	75.944	1.88050	.013168	4.83	125.21	2.09764	.007987
4.34	76.708	1.88484	.013037	4.84	126.47	2.10199	.007907
4.35	77.478	1.88918	0.012907	**4.85**	127.74	2.10633	0.007828
4.36	78.257	1.89352	.012778	4.86	129.02	2.11067	.007750
4.37	79.044	1.89787	.012651	4.87	130.32	2.11501	.007673
4.38	79.838	1.90221	.012525	4.88	131.63	2.11936	.007597
4.39	80.640	1.90655	.012401	4.89	132.95	2.12370	.007521
4.40	81.451	1.91090	0.012277	**4.90**	134.29	2.12804	0.007477
4.41	82.269	1.91524	.012155	4.91	135.64	2.13239	.007372
4.42	83.096	1.91958	.012034	4.92	137.00	2.13673	.007299
4.43	83.931	1.92392	.011914	4.93	138.38	2.14107	.007227
4.44	84.775	1.92827	.011796	4.94	139.77	2.14541	.007155
4.45	85.627	1.93261	0.011679	**4.95**	141.17	2.14976	0.007083
4.46	86.488	1.93695	.011562	4.96	142.59	2.15410	.007013
4.47	87.357	1.94130	.011447	4.97	144.03	2.15844	.006943
4.48	88.235	1.94564	.011333	4.98	145.47	2.16279	.006874
4.49	89.121	1.94998	.011221	4.99	146.94	2.16713	.006806
4.50	90.017	1.95433	0.011109	**5.00**	148.41	2.17147	0.006738

Table 3 (Continued)

x	e^x	$\log_{10}(e^x)$	e^{-x}	x	e^x	$\log_{10}(e^x)$	e^{-x}
5.00	148.41	2.17147	0.006738	**5.50**	244.69	2.38862	0.0040868
5.01	149.90	2.17582	.006671	5.55	257.24	2.41033	.0038875
5.02	151.41	2.18016	.006605	5.60	270.43	2.43205	.0036979
5.03	152.93	2.18450	.006539	5.65	284.29	2.45376	.0035175
5.04	154.47	2.18884	.006474	5.70	298.87	2.47548	.0033460
5.05	156.02	2.19319	0.006409	**5.75**	314.19	2.49719	0.0031828
5.06	157.59	2.19753	.006346	5.80	330.30	2.51891	.0030276
5.07	159.17	2.20187	.006282	5.85	347.23	2.54062	.0028799
5.08	160.77	2.20622	.006220	5.90	365.04	2.56234	.0027394
5.09	162.39	2.21056	.006158	5.95	383.75	2.58405	.0026058
5.10	164.02	2.21490	0.006097	**6.00**	403.43	2.60577	0.0024788
5.11	165.67	2.21924	.006036	6.05	424.11	2.62748	.0023579
5.12	167.34	2.22359	.005976	6.10	445.86	2.64920	.0022429
5.13	169.02	2.22793	.005917	6.15	468.72	2.67091	.0021335
5.14	170.72	2.23227	.005858	6.20	492.75	2.69263	.0020294
5.15	172.43	2.23662	0.005799	**6.25**	518.01	2.71434	0.0019305
5.16	174.16	2.24096	.005742	6.30	544.57	2.73606	.0018363
5.17	175.91	2.24530	.005685	6.35	572.49	2.75777	.0017467
5.18	177.68	2.24965	.005628	6.40	601.85	2.77948	.0016616
5.19	179.47	2.25399	.005572	6.45	632.70	2.80120	.0015805
5.20	181.27	2.25833	0.005517	**6.50**	665.14	2.82291	0.0015034
5.21	183.09	2.26267	.005462	6.55	699.24	2.84463	.0014301
5.22	184.93	2.26702	.005407	6.60	735.10	2.86634	.0013604
5.23	186.79	2.27136	.005354	6.65	772.78	2.88806	.0012940
5.24	188.67	2.27570	.005300	6.70	812.41	2.90977	.0012309
5.25	190.57	2.28005	0.005248	**6.75**	854.06	2.93149	0.0011709
5.26	192.48	2.28439	.005195	6.80	897.85	2.95320	.0011138
5.27	194.42	2.28873	.005144	6.85	943.88	2.97492	.0010595
5.28	196.37	2.29307	.005092	6.90	992.27	2.99663	.0010078
5.29	198.34	2.29742	.005042	6.95	1043.1	3.01835	.0009586
5.30	200.34	2.30176	0.004992	**7.00**	1096.6	3.04006	0.0009119
5.31	202.35	2.30610	.004942	7.05	1152.9	3.06178	.0008674
5.32	204.38	2.31045	.004893	7.10	1212.0	3.08349	.0008251
5.33	206.44	2.31479	.004844	7.15	1274.1	3.10521	.0007849
5.34	208.51	2.31913	.004796	7.20	1339.4	3.12692	.0007466
5.35	210.61	2.32348	0.004748	**7.25**	1408.1	3.14863	0.0007102
5.36	212.72	2.32782	.004701	7.30	1480.3	3.17035	.0006755
5.37	214.86	2.33216	.004654	7.35	1556.2	3.19206	.0006426
5.38	217.02	2.33650	.004608	7.40	1636.0	3.21378	.0006113
5.39	219.20	2.34085	.004562	7.45	1719.9	3.23549	.0005814
5.40	221.41	2.34519	0.004517	**7.50**	1808.0	3.25721	0.0005531
5.41	223.63	2.34953	.004472	7.55	1900.7	3.27892	.0005261
5.42	225.88	2.35388	.004427	7.60	1998.2	3.30064	.0005005
5.43	228.15	2.35822	.004383	7.65	2100.6	3.32235	.0004760
5.44	230.44	2.36256	.004339	7.70	2208.3	3.34407	.0004528
5.45	232.76	2.36690	0.004296	**7.75**	2321.6	3.36578	0.0004307
5.46	235.10	2.37125	.004254	7.80	2440.6	3.38750	.0004097
5.47	237.46	2.37559	.004211	7.85	2565.7	3.40921	.0003898
5.48	239.85	2.37993	.004169	7.90	2697.3	3.43093	.0003707
5.49	242.26	2.38428	.004128	7.95	2835.6	3.45264	.0003527
5.50	244.69	2.38862	0.004087	**8.00**	2981.0	3.47436	0.0003355

Table 3 (Continued)

x	e^x	$\log_{10}(e^x)$	e^{-x}	x	e^x	$\log_{10}(e^x)$	e^{-x}
8.00	2981.0	3.47436	0.0003355	**9.00**	8103.1	3.90865	0.0001234
8.05	3133.8	3.49607	.0003191	9.05	8518.5	3.93037	.0001174
8.10	3294.5	3.51779	.0003035	9.10	8955.3	3.95208	.0001117
8.15	3463.4	3.53950	.0002887	9.15	9414.4	3.97379	.0001062
8.20	3641.0	3.56121	.0002747	9.20	9897.1	3.99551	.0001010
8.25	3827.6	3.58293	0.0002613	**9.25**	10405	4.01722	0.0000961
8.30	4023.9	3.60464	.0002485	9.30	10938	4.03894	.0000914
8.35	4230.2	3.62636	.0002364	9.35	11499	4.06065	.0000870
8.40	4447.1	3.64807	.0002249	9.40	12088	4.08237	.0000827
8.45	4675.1	3.66979	.0002139	9.45	12708	4.10408	.0000787
8.50	4914.8	3.69150	0.0002036	**9.50**	13360	4.12580	0.0000749
8.55	5166.8	3.71322	.0001935	9.55	14045	4.14751	.0000712
8.60	5431.7	3.73493	.0001841	9.60	14765	4.16923	.0000677
8.65	5710.0	3.75665	.0001751	9.65	15522	4.19094	.0000644
8.70	6002.9	3.77836	.0001666	9.70	16318	4.21266	.0000613
8.75	6310.7	3.80008	0.0001585	**9.75**	17154	4.23437	0.0000583
8.80	6634.2	3.82179	.0001507	9.80	18034	4.25609	.0000555
8.85	6974.4	3.84351	.0001434	9.85	18958	4.27780	.0000527
8.90	7332.0	3.86522	.0001364	9.90	19930	4.29952	.0000502
8.95	7707.9	3.88694	.0001297	9.95	20952	4.32123	0.0000477
9.00	8103.1	3.90865	0.0001234	**10.00**	22026	4.34294	0.0000454

Table 4 Hyperbolic functions

x	sinh x	cosh x	tanh x
0	.00000	1.0000	.00000
0.1	.10017	1.0050	.09967
0.2	.20134	1.0201	.19738
0.3	.30452	1.0453	.29131
0.4	.41075	1.0811	.37995
0.5	.52110	1.1276	.46212
0.6	.63665	1.1855	.53705
0.7	.75858	1.2552	.60437
0.8	.88811	1.3374	.66404
0.9	1.0265	1.4331	.71630
1.0	1.1752	1.5431	.76159
1.1	1.3356	1.6685	.80050
1.2	1.5095	1.8107	.83365
1.3	1.6984	1.9709	.86172
1.4	1.9043	2.1509	.88535
1.5	2.1293	2.3524	.90515
1.6	2.3756	2.5775	.92167
1.7	2.6456	2.8283	.93541
1.8	2.9422	3.1075	.94681
1.9	3.2682	3.4177	.95624
2.0	3.6269	3.7622	.96403
2.1	4.0219	4.1443	.97045
2.2	4.4571	4.5679	.97574
2.3	4.9370	5.0372	.98010
2.4	5.4662	5.5569	.98367
2.5	6.0502	6.1323	.98661
2.6	6.6947	6.7690	.98903
2.7	7.4063	7.4735	.99101
2.8	8.1919	8.2527	.99263
2.9	9.0596	9.1146	.99396
3.0	10.018	10.068	.99505
3.1	11.076	11.122	.99595
3.2	12.246	12.287	.99668
3.3	13.538	13.575	.99728
3.4	14.965	14.999	.99777
3.5	16.543	16.573	.99818
3.6	18.285	18.313	.99851
3.7	20.211	20.236	.99878
3.8	22.339	22.362	.99900
3.9	24.691	24.711	.99918
4.0	27.290	27.308	.99933
4.1	30.162	30.178	.99945
4.2	33.336	33.351	.99955
4.3	36.843	36.857	.99963
4.4	40.719	40.732	.99970
4.5	45.003	45.014	.99975
4.6	49.737	49.747	.99980
4.7	54.969	54.978	.99983
4.8	60.751	60.759	.99986
4.9	67.141	67.149	.99989
5.0	74.203	74.210	.99991

Table 5   *Trigonometric functions*

Degrees	Radians	Sin	Cos	Tan	Cot		
0	0.0000	0.0000	1.0000	0.0000		1.5708	90
1	0.0175	0.0175	0.9998	0.0175	57.290	1.5533	89
2	0.0349	0.0349	0.9994	0.0349	28.636	1.5359	88
3	0.0524	0.0523	0.9986	0.0524	19.081	1.5184	87
4	0.0698	0.0698	0.9976	0.0699	14.301	1.5010	86
5	0.0873	0.0872	0.9962	0.0875	11.430	1.4835	85
6	0.1047	0.1045	0.9945	0.1051	9.5144	1.4661	84
7	0.1222	0.1219	0.9925	0.1228	8.1443	1.4486	83
8	0.1396	0.1392	0.9903	0.1405	7.1154	1.4312	82
9	0.1571	0.1564	0.9877	0.1584	6.3138	1.4137	81
10	0.1745	0.1736	0.9848	0.1763	5.6713	1.3963	80
11	0.1920	0.1908	0.9816	0.1944	5.1446	1.3788	79
12	0.2094	0.2079	0.9781	0.2126	4.7046	1.3614	78
13	0.2269	0.2250	0.9744	0.2309	4.3315	1.3439	77
14	0.2443	0.2419	0.9703	0.2493	4.0108	1.3265	76
15	0.2618	0.2588	0.9659	0.2679	3.7321	1.3090	75
16	0.2793	0.2756	0.9613	0.2867	3.4874	1.2915	74
17	0.2967	0.2924	0.9563	0.3057	3.2709	1.2741	73
18	0.3142	0.3090	0.9511	0.3249	3.0777	1.2566	72
19	0.3316	0.3256	0.9455	0.3443	2.9042	1.2392	71
20	0.3491	0.3420	0.9397	0.3640	2.7475	1.2217	70
21	0.3665	0.3584	0.9336	0.3839	2.6051	1.2043	69
22	0.3840	0.3746	0.9272	0.4040	2.4751	1.1868	68
23	0.4014	0.3907	0.9205	0.4245	2.3559	1.1694	67
24	0.4189	0.4067	0.9135	0.4452	2.2460	1.1519	66
25	0.4363	0.4226	0.9063	0.4663	2.1445	1.1345	65
26	0.4538	0.4384	0.8988	0.4877	2.0503	1.1170	64
27	0.4712	0.4540	0.8910	0.5095	1.9626	1.0996	63
28	0.4887	0.4695	0.8829	0.5317	1.8807	1.0821	62
29	0.5061	0.4848	0.8746	0.5543	1.8040	1.0647	61
30	0.5236	0.5000	0.8660	0.5774	1.7321	1.0472	60
31	0.5411	0.5150	0.8572	0.6009	1.6643	1.0297	59
32	0.5585	0.5299	0.8480	0.6249	1.6003	1.0123	58
33	0.5760	0.5446	0.8387	0.6494	1.5399	0.9948	57
34	0.5934	0.5592	0.8290	0.6745	1.4826	0.9774	56
35	0.6109	0.5736	0.8192	0.7002	1.4281	0.9599	55
36	0.6283	0.5878	0.8090	0.7265	1.3764	0.9425	54
37	0.6458	0.6018	0.7986	0.7536	1.3270	0.9250	53
38	0.6632	0.6157	0.7880	0.7813	1.2799	0.9076	52
39	0.6807	0.6293	0.7771	0.8098	1.2349	0.8901	51
40	0.6981	0.6428	0.7660	0.8391	1.1918	0.8727	50
41	0.7156	0.6561	0.7547	0.8693	1.1504	0.8552	49
42	0.7330	0.6691	0.7431	0.9004	1.1106	0.8378	48
43	0.7505	0.6820	0.7314	0.9325	1.0724	0.8203	47
44	0.7679	0.6947	0.7193	0.9657	1.0355	0.8029	46
45	0.7854	0.7071	0.7071	1.0000	1.0000	0.7854	45
		Cos	Sin	Cot	Tan	Radians	Degrees

Table 6 *Common logarithms*

N	0	1	2	3	4	5	6	7	8	9
10	0000	0043	0086	0128	0170	0212	0253	0294	0334	0374
11	0414	0453	0492	0531	0569	0607	0645	0682	0719	0755
12	0792	0828	0864	0899	0934	0969	1004	1038	1072	1106
13	1139	1173	1206	1239	1271	1303	1335	1367	1399	1430
14	1461	1492	1523	1553	1584	1614	1644	1673	1703	1732
15	1761	1790	1818	1847	1875	1903	1931	1959	1987	2014
16	2041	2068	2095	2122	2148	2175	2201	2227	2253	2279
17	2304	2330	2355	2380	2405	2430	2455	2480	2504	2529
18	2553	2577	2601	2625	2648	2672	2695	2718	2742	2765
19	2788	2810	2833	2856	2878	2900	2923	2945	2967	2989
20	3010	3032	3054	3075	3096	3118	3139	3160	3181	3201
21	3222	3243	3263	3284	3304	3324	3345	3365	3385	3404
22	3424	3444	3464	3483	3502	3522	3541	3560	3579	3598
23	3617	3636	3655	3674	3692	3711	3729	3747	3766	3784
24	3802	3820	3838	3856	3874	3892	3909	3927	3945	3962
25	3979	3997	4014	4031	4048	4065	4082	4099	4116	4133
26	4150	4166	4183	4200	4216	4232	4249	4265	4281	4298
27	4314	4330	4346	4362	4378	4393	4409	4425	4440	4456
28	4472	4487	4502	4518	4533	4548	4564	4579	4594	4609
29	4624	4639	4654	4669	4683	4698	4713	4728	4742	4757
30	4771	4786	4800	4814	4829	4843	4857	4871	4886	4900
31	4914	4928	4942	4955	4969	4983	4997	5011	5024	5038
32	5051	5065	5079	5092	5105	5119	5132	5145	5159	5172
33	5185	5198	5211	5224	5237	5250	5263	5276	5289	5302
34	5315	5328	5340	5353	5366	5378	5391	5403	5416	5428
35	5441	5453	5465	5478	5490	5502	5514	5527	5539	5551
36	5563	5575	5587	5599	5611	5623	5635	5647	5658	5670
37	5682	5694	5705	5717	5729	5740	5752	5763	5775	5786
38	5798	5809	5821	5832	5843	5855	5866	5877	5888	5899
39	5911	5922	5933	5944	5955	5966	5977	5988	5999	6010
40	6021	6031	6042	6053	6064	6075	6085	6096	6107	6117
41	6128	6138	6149	6160	6170	6180	6191	6201	6212	6222
42	6232	6243	6253	6263	6274	6284	6294	6304	6314	6325
43	6335	6345	6355	6365	6375	6385	6395	6405	6415	6425
44	6435	6444	6454	6464	6474	6484	6493	6503	6513	6522
45	6532	6542	6551	6561	6571	6580	6590	6599	6609	6618
46	6628	6637	6646	6656	6665	6675	6684	6693	6702	6712
47	6721	6730	6739	6749	6758	6767	6776	6785	6794	6803
48	6812	6821	6830	6839	6848	6857	6866	6875	6884	6893
49	6902	6911	6920	6928	6937	6946	6955	6964	6972	6981
50	6990	6998	7007	7016	7024	7033	7042	7050	7059	7067
51	7076	7084	7093	7101	7110	7118	7126	7135	7143	7152
52	7160	7168	7177	7185	7193	7202	7210	7218	7226	7235
53	7243	7251	7259	7267	7275	7284	7292	7300	7308	7316
54	7324	7332	7340	7348	7356	7364	7372	7380	7388	7396

Table 6 (*Continued*)

N	0	1	2	3	4	5	6	7	8	9
55	7404	7412	7419	7427	7435	7443	7451	7459	7466	7474
56	7482	7490	7497	7505	7513	7520	7528	7536	7543	7551
57	7559	7566	7574	7582	7589	7597	7604	7612	7619	7627
58	7634	7642	7649	7657	7664	7672	7679	7686	7694	7701
59	7709	7716	7723	7731	7738	7745	7752	7760	7767	7774
60	7782	7789	7796	7803	7810	7818	7825	7832	7839	7846
61	7853	7860	7868	7875	7882	7889	7896	7903	7910	7917
62	7924	7931	7938	7945	7952	7959	7966	7973	7980	7987
63	7993	8000	8007	8014	8021	8028	8035	8041	8048	8055
64	8062	8069	8075	8082	8089	8096	8102	8109	8116	8122
65	8129	8136	8142	8149	8156	8162	8169	8176	8182	8189
66	8195	8202	8209	8215	8222	8228	8235	8241	8248	8254
67	8261	8267	8274	8280	8287	8293	8299	8306	8312	8319
68	8325	8331	8338	8344	8351	8357	8363	8370	8376	8382
69	8388	8395	8401	8407	8414	8420	8426	8432	8439	8445
70	8451	8457	8463	8470	8476	8482	8488	8494	8500	8506
71	8513	8519	8525	8531	8537	8543	8549	8555	8561	8567
72	8573	8579	8585	8591	8597	8603	8609	8615	8621	8627
73	8633	8639	8645	8651	8657	8663	8669	8675	8681	8686
74	8692	8698	8704	·8710	8716	8722	8727	8733	8739	8745
75	8751	8756	8762	8768	8774	8779	8785	8791	8797	8802
76	8808	8814	8820	8825	8831	8837	8842	8848	8854	8859
77	8865	8871	8876	8882	8887	8893	8899	8904	8910	8915
78	8921	8927	8932	8938	8943	8949	8954	8960	8965	8971
79	8976	8982	8987	8993	8998	9004	9009	9015	9020	9025
80	9031	9036	9042	9047	9053	9058	9063	9069	9074	9079
81	9085	9090	9096	9101	9106	9112	9117	9122	9128	9133
82	9138	9143	9149	9154	9159	9165	9170	9175	9180	9186
83	9191	9196	9201	9206	9212	9217	9222	9227	9232	9238
84	9243	9248	9253	9258	9263	9269	9274	9279	9284	9289
85	9294	9299	9304	9309	9315	9320	9325	9330	9335	9340
86	9345	9350	9355	9360	9365	9370	9375	9380	9385	9390
87	9395	9400	9405	9410	9415	9420	9425	9430	9435	9440
88	9445	9450	9455	9460	9465	9469	9474	9479	9484	9489
89	9494	9499	9504	9509	9513	9518	9523	9528	9533	9538
90	9542	9547	9552	9557	9562	9566	9571	9576	9581	9586
91	9590	9595	9600	9605	9609	9614	9619	9624	9628	9633
92	9638	9643	9647	9652	9657	9661	9666	9671	9675	9680
93	9685	9689	9694	9699	9703	9708	9713	9717	9722	9727
94	9731	9736	9741	9745	9750	9754	9759	9763	9768	9773
95	9777	9782	9786	9791	9795	9800	9805	9809	9814	9818
96	9823	9827	9832	9836	9841	9845	9850	9854	9859	9863
97	9868	9872	9877	9881	9886	9890	9894	9899	9903	9908
98	9912	9917	9921	9926	9930	9934	9939	9943	9948	9952
99	9956	9961	9965	9969	9974	9978	9983	9987	9991	9996

Table 7   The Greek alphabet

α	alpha	ν	nu
β	beta	ξ	xi
γ	gamma	o	omicron
δ	delta	π	pi
ϵ	epsilon	ρ	rho
ζ	zeta	σ	sigma
η	eta	τ	tau
θ	theta	υ	upsilon
ι	iota	ϕ	phi
κ	kappa	χ	chi
λ	lambda	ψ	psi
μ	mu	ω	omega

Answers to odd-numbered exercises

Exercises 1.1   (*Page 14*)

1. $\{0, 1, 2, 4, 6, 8\}$ 3. $\{2, 4, 8\}$ 5. $\{0, 1, 2, 3, 4, 6, 8, 9\}$ 7. $\varnothing$ 9. $\{0, 1, 6\}$ 11. $(-2, +\infty)$ 13. $(-\infty, \frac{3}{4}]$ 15. $[4, 8]$
17. $(-\frac{5}{3}, \frac{4}{3}]$ 19. $(-\infty, -\frac{1}{2}) \cup (0, +\infty)$ 21. $(-\infty, -2) \cup (2, +\infty)$ 23. $(-\infty, -5) \cup (3, +\infty)$ 25. $[-1, \frac{1}{2}]$ 27. $(-3, \frac{3}{4})$
29. $(-\infty, -1) \cup (\frac{1}{3}, 3)$ 31. $(\frac{3}{2}, \frac{31}{14}) \cup (\frac{7}{3}, +\infty)$

Exercises 1.2   (*Page 20*)

1. $1, -\frac{5}{2}$ 3. $-3, 8$ 5. $-\frac{1}{4}, 4$ 7. $-\frac{2}{3}, \frac{1}{2}$ 9. $\frac{4}{3}, 3$ 11. $[\frac{5}{8}, +\infty)$ 13. $(-\infty, 1] \cup [4, +\infty)$ 15. $(-11, 3)$ 17. $[\frac{2}{3}, 2]$
19. $(-\infty, 1) \cup (4, +\infty)$ 21. $(-\infty, \frac{2}{3}] \cup [10, +\infty)$ 23. $[-\frac{9}{2}, \frac{3}{2}]$ 25. $(-\infty, \frac{10}{9}) \cup (2, +\infty)$ 29. $|x| > |a|$ 31. $|x - 2| > 2$
35. $|c| < a - b$

Exercises 1.3   (*Page 27*)

1. (a) $(1, 2)$; (b) $(-1, -2)$; (c) $(-1, 2)$; (d) $(-2, 1)$ 3. (a) $(2, -2)$; (b) $(-2, 2)$; (c) $(-2, -2)$; (d) does not apply   5. (a) $(-2, 1)$;
(b) $(1, -3)$; (c) $(1, 3)$; (d) $(-3, -1)$

Exercises 1.4   (*Page 32*)

5. $\frac{1}{2}\sqrt{53}$; $\frac{1}{2}\sqrt{89}$; $\sqrt{26}$ 7. $\frac{41}{2}$ 11. $-2, 8$ 13. $(-2 + \frac{3}{2}\sqrt{3}, \frac{3}{2} + 2\sqrt{3})$ and $(-2 - \frac{3}{2}\sqrt{3}, \frac{3}{2} - 2\sqrt{3})$ 15. $77x^2 + 90xy + 21y^2 - 122x$
$- 66y - 55 = 0$ 17. $(-\frac{9}{4}, \frac{17}{4})$; $(\frac{1}{2}, \frac{11}{2})$; $(\frac{13}{4}, \frac{27}{4})$ 19. $(\frac{9}{4}, \frac{11}{4})$ 21. $(-\frac{3}{2}, \frac{7}{2})$ 23. $(5, -7)$ 25. (a) $2x + y = 5$

Exercises 1.5   (*Page 41*)

1. -1 3. $-\frac{1}{7}$ 5. $4x - y - 11 = 0$ 7. $x = -3$ 9. $4x - 3y + 12 = 0$ 11. $\sqrt{3}x - y + (2\sqrt{3} - 5) = 0$ 13. $x + y = 0$
15. $\frac{x}{\frac{8}{5}} + \frac{y}{8} = 1$ 19. (a) yes; (b) yes; (c) no; (d) no   21. $2x + 3y + 7 = 0$; $\sqrt{13}$ 23. (a) $-\dfrac{A}{B}$; (b) $-\dfrac{C}{B}$; (c) $-\dfrac{C}{A}$; (d) $Bx - Ay = 0$
25. $y = 1$; $9x - 4y - 11 = 0$; $9x + 4y - 19 = 0$ 27. $2x + 3y - 12 = 0$; $(2 + 2\sqrt{2})x + (3 - 3\sqrt{2})y - 12 = 0$; $(2 - 2\sqrt{2})x + (3 + 3\sqrt{2})y$
$- 12 = 0$ 29. (a) $x = 1$; (b) $y = 1$; (c) $x = 1$; (d) $2x + y - 3 = 0$; (e) $x - 2y + 1 = 0$; (f) $x + y - 2 = 0$

Exercises 1.6   (*Page 47*)

1. $(x - 4)^2 + (y + 3)^2 = 25$; $x^2 + y^2 - 8x + 6y = 0$ 3. $(x + 5)^2 + (y + 12)^2 = 9$; $x^2 + y^2 + 10x + 24y + 160 = 0$ 5. $x^2 + y^2 - 2x - 4y$
$- 8 = 0$ 7. $x^2 + y^2 + 6x + 10y + 9 = 0$ 9. $x^2 + y^2 - 4x - 4y - 2 = 0$ 11. $(3, 4)$; 4 13. $(0, -\frac{2}{3})$; $\frac{5}{3}$ 15. circle   17. the
empty set   19. circle   21. $x + y + 5 = 0$ 23. $3x + 4y - 19 = 0$

Exercises 1.7 *(Page 55)*

1. domain: $(-\infty, +\infty)$; range: $(-\infty, +\infty)$ 3. domain: $(-\infty, +\infty)$; range: $[-6, +\infty)$ 5. domain: $[\frac{4}{3}, +\infty)$; range: $[0, +\infty)$
7. domain: all x not in $(-2, 2)$; range: $[0, +\infty)$ 9. domain: $(-\infty, +\infty)$; range: $[0, +\infty)$ 11. domain: $(-\infty, +\infty)$; range: -2 and 2
13. domain: $(-\infty, +\infty)$; range: all real numbers except 3   15. domain: $(-\infty, +\infty)$; range: $[-4, +\infty)$ 17. domain: all real numbers
except -5 and -1; range: all real numbers except -7 and -3 19. domain: all x not in $(-1, 4)$; range: $[0, +\infty)$ 21. domain: all real
numbers except 2; range: $[0, +\infty)$ 23. domain: all real numbers except -5; range: $[1, +\infty)$ 25. domain: $(-\infty, +\infty)$; range: $[1, +\infty)$
(see Fig. EX1.7-25)   27. domain: $(-\infty, +\infty)$; $[0, 1)$ (see Fig. EX1.7-27)   29. domain: $(-\infty, +\infty)$; range: the nonnegative
integers (see Fig. EX1.7-29)   31. domain: all real numbers except 0; range: $(-\infty, -1] \cup \{0\} \cup (\frac{1}{2}, 1]$ (see Fig. EX1.7-31)
33. domain: $(-\infty, +\infty)$; range: $\{1, 3\}$ (see Fig. EX1.7-33)

Figure EX1.7-25

Figure EX1.7-27

Figure EX1.7-29

Figure EX1.7-31

Figure EX1.7-33

Exercises 1.8 *(Page 61)*

1. (a) -5; (b) -6; (c) -3; (d) 30; (e) $2h^2 + 9h + 4$; (f) $8x^4 + 10x^2 - 3$; (g) $2x^4 - 7x^2$; (h) $2x^2 + 4hx + 5x + 2h^2 + 5h - 3$; (i) $2x^2 + 5x + 2h^2$
$+ 5h - 6$; (j) $4x + 2h + 5$ 3. (a) 1; (b) $\sqrt{11}$; (c) 2; (d) $3\sqrt{7}$; (e) $\sqrt{4x + 9}$; (f) $\dfrac{2}{(\sqrt{2x + 2h + 3} + \sqrt{2x + 3})}$ 5. (a) 1; (b) -1; (c) 1; (d) -1;
(e) -1 if $x > 0$, 1 if $x \le 0$; (f) 1 if $x \ge -1$, -1 if $x < -1$; (g) 1; (h) -1 7. (a) $x^2 + x - 6$, domain: $(-\infty, +\infty)$; (b) $-x^2 + x - 4$, domain:
$(-\infty, +\infty)$; (c) $x^3 - 5x^2 - x + 5$, domain: $(-\infty, +\infty)$; (d) $(x - 5)/(x^2 - 1)$, domain: all real numbers except -1 and 1; (e) $(x^2 - 1)/(x - 5)$,
domain: all real numbers except 5; (f) $x^2 - 6$, domain: $(-\infty, +\infty)$; (g) $x^2 - 10x + 24$, domain: $(-\infty, +\infty)$ 9. (a) $\dfrac{x^2 + 2x - 1}{x^2 - x}$, domain: all
real numbers except 0 and 1; (b) $\dfrac{x^2 + 1}{x^2 - x}$, domain: all real numbers except 0 and 1; (c) $\dfrac{x + 1}{x^2 - x}$, domain: all real numbers except 0 and 1;
(d) $\dfrac{x^2 + x}{x - 1}$, domain: all real numbers except 0 and 1; (e) $\dfrac{x - 1}{x^2 + x}$, domain: all real numbers except -1, 0, and 1; (f) $\dfrac{1 + x}{1 - x}$, domain: all real
numbers except 0 and 1; (g) $\dfrac{x - 1}{x + 1}$, domain: all real numbers except -1 and 1   11. (a) $\sqrt{x^2 - 1} + \sqrt{x - 1}$, domain: $[1, +\infty)$;
(b) $\sqrt{x^2 - 1} - \sqrt{x - 1}$, domain: $[1, +\infty)$; (c) $(x - 1)\sqrt{x + 1}$, domain: $[1, +\infty)$; (d) $\sqrt{x + 1}$, domain: $(1, +\infty)$; (e) $\dfrac{1}{\sqrt{x + 1}}$, domain: $(1, +\infty)$;
(f) $\sqrt{x - 2}$, domain: $[2, +\infty)$; (g) $\sqrt{\sqrt{x^2 - 1} - 1}$, domain: $(-\infty, -\sqrt{2}]$ and $[\sqrt{2}, +\infty)$
13. (a) even; (b) odd; (c) neither; (d) even; (e) neither; (f) even; (g) odd; (h) neither   17. (a) $[x^2 + 2] + [0]$;
(b) $[-1] + [x^3]$; (c) $[x^4 + 3] + [x^3 - x]$; (d) $[0] + \left[\dfrac{1}{x}\right]$; (e) $\left[\dfrac{x^2 + 1}{x^2 - 1}\right] + \left[\dfrac{-2x}{x^2 - 1}\right]$; (f) $\frac{1}{2}[|2x| + |x - 1| + |x + 1|] + \frac{1}{2}[|x - 1| - |x + 1|]$

19. (a) even; (b) odd; (c) even; (d) even   21. domain: $(-\infty, +\infty)$; range $\{0, 1\}$ (Sketches of the graphs for Exercises 23–33 appear in Figs. EX1.8-23 through EX1.8-33.)

Figure EX1.8-23

Figure EX1.8-25

Figure EX1.8-27

Figure EX1.8-29

Figure EX1.8-31

Figure EX1.8-33

35. $(f \circ g)(x) = \begin{cases} 2 & \text{if } x < 0 \\ x & \text{if } 0 \le x \le 1 \\ 2 & \text{if } x > 1 \end{cases}$

37. $(f \circ g)(x) = \begin{cases} 1 & \text{if } x < 0 \\ 4x^2 & \text{if } 0 \le x \le \frac{1}{2} \\ 0 & \text{if } \frac{1}{2} < x \le 1 \\ 1 & \text{if } x > 1 \end{cases}$ 39. $g(x) = x - 3$; $g(x) = 1 - x$

Review Exercises for Chapter 1 (Page 63)

1. $(\frac{4}{5}, \frac{6}{5}]$ 3. $(-\frac{3}{2}, 1)$ 5. $[-\frac{12}{5}, \frac{6}{5}]$ 7. (a) $(x - 3)^2 + (y + 5)^2 = 0$; (b) $(x - 3)^2 + (y + 5)^2 < 16$; (c) $(x - 3)^2 + (y + 5)^2 \ge 25$
9. $x = 0, 3x + 4y = 0$ 11. $k = -\frac{3}{8}; h = \frac{10}{3}$ 13. $(3, -6); (-2, -5)$ 15. $0 \le k \le 2$.   17. $7x^2 + 7y^2 + 11x - 19y - 6 = 0$ 19. $12x + 3y - 2 = 0$
21. domain: $[-\frac{5}{2}, +\infty)$; range: $[0, +\infty)$ 23. domain: all real numbers except $-\frac{5}{2}$ and 2; range: all real numbers except $\frac{1}{2}$ and 5

25. (a) $x^2 + 4x - 7$, domain: $(-\infty, +\infty)$; (b) $x^2 - 4x - 1$, domain: $(-\infty, +\infty)$; (c) $(x^2 - 4)(4x - 3)$, domain: $(-\infty, +\infty)$; (d) $\dfrac{x^2 - 4}{4x - 3}$, domain:

all real numbers except $\frac{3}{4}$; (e) $\dfrac{4x - 3}{x^2 - 4}$, domain: all real numbers except -2 and 2; (f) $16x^2 - 24x + 5$, domain: $(-\infty, +\infty)$; (g) $4x^2 - 19$,

domain: $(-\infty, +\infty)$ 27. (a) $\dfrac{x^2 - 2x + 1}{(x - 3)(x + 1)}$, domain: all real numbers except -1 and 3; (b) $\dfrac{-x^2 + 4x + 1}{(x - 3)(x + 1)}$, domain: all real numbers

except -1 and 3; (c) $\dfrac{x}{(x - 3)(x + 1)}$, domain: all real numbers except -1 and 3; (d) $\dfrac{x + 1}{x^2 - 3x}$, domain: all real numbers except $0, -1$, and 3;

(e) $\dfrac{x^2 - 3x}{x + 1}$, domain: all real numbers except -1 and 3; (f) $-\dfrac{x + 1}{2x + 3}$, domain: all real numbers except $-\dfrac{3}{2}$ and -1; (g) $\dfrac{1}{x - 2}$, domain: all real

numbers except 2 and 3   35. $(\frac{13}{3}, \frac{13}{3}); (9, 7); (2, 3)$

Exercise 2.1 (Page 73)

1. 0.005   3. 0.005   5. $\frac{1}{1400}$ 7. 0.01   9. $\delta = \dfrac{\epsilon}{5}$ 11. $\delta = \epsilon$ 13. $\delta = \min(1, \frac{1}{5}\epsilon)$ 15. $\delta = \min(1, \frac{1}{2}\epsilon)$ 17. $\delta = \min(\frac{1}{2}, \frac{1}{4}\epsilon)$
19. $\delta = \min(1, \frac{1}{8}\epsilon)$ 21. $\delta = \min(1, \frac{1}{6}\epsilon)$ 23. $\delta = \min(1, (2\sqrt{2} + 3)\epsilon)$

Exercises 2.2 (*Page 83*)

1. 7 3. $-\frac{1}{22}$ 5. 12 7. $\frac{1}{7}$ 9. $\frac{3}{2}$ 11. $\frac{1}{5}\sqrt{30}$ 13. $\frac{1}{4}\sqrt{2}$ 15. $\frac{1}{3}$ 17. $\frac{11}{7}$ 23. (a) 0

Exercises 2.3 (*Page 87*)

1. (a) -3; (b) 2; (c) does not exist 3. (a) 7; (b) 7; (c) 7 5. (a) 5; (b) 5; (c) 5 7. (a) 0; (b) 0; (c) 0 9. (a) 1; (b) -1; (c) does not exist 11. (a) -2; (b) 2; (c) does not exist 13. (a) 2; (b) 1; (c) does not exist

Exercises 2.4 (*Page 96*)

1. $+\infty$ 3. $+\infty$ 5. $-\infty$ 7. $-\infty$ 9. $+\infty$ 11. $-\infty$ 13. $-\infty$ 15. $+\infty$

Exercises 2.5 (*Page 100*)

1. 4; $\lim\limits_{x\to 4} f(x)$ does not exist. 3. -3; $F(-3)$ does not exist. 5. -3; $\lim\limits_{x\to-3} g(x) \neq g(-3)$ 7. $-3, 2$; $h(-3)$ and $h(2)$ do not exist. 9. 0; $\lim\limits_{x\to 0} f(x)$ does not exist. 11. continuous everywhere 13. 3; $f(3)$ does not exist. 15. 2; $\lim\limits_{x\to 2} g(x)$ does not exist. 17. all integers; $\lim\limits_{x\to n} f(x)$ does not exist if n is any integer. 19. 0; $\lim\limits_{x\to 0} f(x)$ does not exist. 21. $-1, 0$; $\lim\limits_{x\to-1} f(x)$ does not exist, $\lim\limits_{x\to 0} f(x)$ does not exist. 23. removable; 4 25. removable; 0 27. removable; $\frac{1}{48}$ 29. essential 31. f is continuous everywhere.

Exercises 2.6 (*Page 107*)

5. $\frac{1}{5}$ 7. -2 9. 15 11. all real numbers 13. all real numbers except 2 and -2 15. all real numbers except 1, -3, and -4 17. all x not in $[-4, 4]$ 19. all x not in $[-4, 4]$ 21. all real numbers 23. all x in $(0, +\infty)$ 25. all x in $(-1, 0)$ and $(0, 1)$

Review Exercises for Chapter 2 (*Page 108*)

1. 9 3. $-\frac{1}{6}$ 5. continuous on $(-\infty, -\frac{3}{2}]$ and $[\frac{3}{2}, +\infty)$ 7. continuous on $[3, 4]$ 9. $\delta = \frac{1}{3}\epsilon$ 11. $\delta = \min(1, \epsilon)$

13. $\delta = \min(1, 5\epsilon)$ 17. $\frac{1}{3}$ 19. $-\infty$ 21. $\dfrac{2}{3\sqrt[3]{a}}$ 23. $-\frac{1}{2}$ 25. (a) yes; (b) no 27. $f(x) = \text{sgn } x$ 29. (b) all real numbers; (c) any number that is not an integer

Exercises 3.1 (*Page 114*)

1. $-2x_1$ 3. $-6 - 2x_1$ 5. $3x_1^2 - 3$ 7. $12x_1^2 - 26x_1 + 4$ 9. $8x + y + 9 = 0$; $x - 8y + 58 = 0$ 11. $6x - y - 16 = 0$; $x + 6y - 52 = 0$ 13. $2x + 5y - 17 = 0$; $5x - 2y + 30 = 0$ 15. $2x + 3y - 12 = 0$; $3x - 2y - 5 = 0$ 17. $x - 12y + 16 = 0$; $12x + y - 98 = 0$ 19. $8x - y - 5 = 0$ 21. $2x - y - 2 = 0$ 23. $(12 - 2\sqrt{30})x - y - 30 + 4\sqrt{30} = 0$; $(12 + 2\sqrt{30})x - y - 30 - 4\sqrt{30} = 0$

Exercises 3.2 (*Page 120*)

1. $6t_1^2 - 8t_1 + 2$ 3. $6t_1$; 18 5. $\dfrac{1}{2\sqrt{t_1 + 1}}; \dfrac{1}{4}$ 7. $\dfrac{-5}{(5t_1 + 6)^{3/2}}; -\dfrac{5}{64}$ 9. $t < -3$, moving to right; $-3 < t < 1$, moving to left; $t > 1$, moving to right; changes direction when $t = -3$ and $t = 1$ 11. $t < -1 - \sqrt{5}$, moving to left; $-1 - \sqrt{5} < t < -1 + \sqrt{5}$, moving to right; $t > -1 + \sqrt{5}$, moving to left; changes direction when $t = -1 \pm \sqrt{5}$ 13. (a) -32 ft/sec; (b) -64 ft/sec; (c) 4 sec; (d) -128 ft/sec 15. (a) $(20t_1 + 24)$ ft/sec; (b) $\frac{6}{5}$ sec

Exercises 3.3 (*Page 125*)

1. $8x + 5$ 3. $\dfrac{1}{2\sqrt{x}}$ 5. $-\dfrac{1}{(x + 1)^2}$ 7. $-\dfrac{2}{x^3} - 1$ 9. $-\dfrac{1}{2\sqrt{(x + 1)^3}}$ 11. -6 13. $-\frac{1}{216}$ 15. $\frac{5}{4}$ 17. 3 19. -12

21. $-\frac{1}{27}$ 23. $\dfrac{1}{3\sqrt[3]{(x - 1)^2}}$; no 25. $g(a)$

Exercises 3.4 (*Page 129*)

1. (b) yes; (c) $+1, -1$; (d) no 3. (b) yes; (c) $-1, +1$; (d) no 5. (b) yes; (c) 0, 1; (d) no 7. (b) yes; (c) 0, 0; (d) yes 9. (b) yes;

(c) does not exist, 0; (d) no   11. (b) yes; (c) neither exist; (d) no   13. (b) yes; (c) $-6, -6$; (d) yes   17. $f'_+(0) = 0$ 19. $a = 2$ and $b = -1$ 21. (a) 0; (b) 1; (c) does not exist

Exercises 3.5   (Page 137)

1. $3x^2 - 6x + 5$ 3. $x^7 - 4x^3$ 5. $t^3 - t$ 7. $4\pi r^2$ 9. $2x + 3 - \dfrac{2}{x^3}$ 11. $-\dfrac{6}{x^3} - \dfrac{20}{x^5}$ 13. $3\sqrt{3}s^2 - 2\sqrt{3}s$ 15. $70x^6 + 60x^4$

$- 15x^2 - 6$ 17. $-\dfrac{4(x+1)}{(x-1)^3}$ 19. $-\dfrac{1}{(x-1)^2}$ 21. $\dfrac{5(1-2x^2)}{(1+2x^2)^2}$ 23. $\dfrac{48x^2}{(x^3+8)^2}$ 25. $\dfrac{6(x^2+10x+1)}{(x+5)^2}$ 29. $2(3x+2)(6x^2+2x-3)$

31. $3(2x^2+x+1)^2(4x+1)$ 33. $x + (4\sqrt{6} - 10)y - 8\sqrt{6} + 21 = 0$; $x - (4\sqrt{6} + 10)y + 8\sqrt{6} + 21 = 0$ 35. $x + 8y + 2 = 0$; $x + 8y - 2 = 0$

Exercises 3.6   (Page 141)

1. $6(x+2)(x^2+4x+5)^2$ 3. $2(8t^3 - 21t^2 + 2)(2t^4 - 7t^3 + 2t - 1)$ 5. $-2(x+4)^{-3}$ 7. $6(3u-1)(3u^2+5)^2(12u^2 - 3u + 5)$
9. $2(-12x+17)(2x-5)^{-2}(4x+3)^{-3}$ 11. $18(y-7)(y+2)^{-3}$ 13. $-2(14x+3)(7x^2+3x-1)^{-2}$
15. $2(r^2+1)^2(2r+5)(8r^2+15r+2)$ 17. $2z(z^2-5)^2(z^2+22)(z^2+4)^{-3}$

19. $4(4x-1)^2(x^2+2)^3(21x^4 - 3x^3 + 49x^2 - 4x + 30)(3x^2+5)^{-3}$ 21. $\dfrac{8t_1(t_1^2 - 1)}{(t_1^2+1)^3}$ ft/sec; 0 ft/sec; $\dfrac{960}{2197}$ ft/sec   23. $x + 16y - 35 = 0$

25. (a) $3x^4$; (b) $6x^5$

Exercises 3.7   (Page 145)

1. $2(3x+5)^{-1/3}$ 3. $\dfrac{17}{2\sqrt{2x-5}\sqrt{(3x+1)^3}}$ 5. $2x^{-1/2} - \frac{5}{2}x^{-3/2}$ 7. $\dfrac{6x^2 - 10x + 1}{3\sqrt[3]{(2x^3 - 5x^2 + x)^2}}$ 9. $\dfrac{1}{\sqrt{2t}}\left(1 - \dfrac{1}{t}\right)$ 11. $\dfrac{1}{x^2\sqrt{x^2-1}}$

13. $\dfrac{x+5}{6\sqrt{x-1}\sqrt[3]{(x+1)^4}}$ 15. $\dfrac{x(5x^2-1)}{3\sqrt{x^2-5}\sqrt[3]{(x^2+3)^2}}$ 17. $-\dfrac{1}{4\sqrt{9+\sqrt{9-x}}\sqrt{9-x}}$ 19. $4x - 5y + 9 = 0$ 21. $x + 4y = 0$

23. (a) 0; (b) $\frac{1}{2}$; (c) no value of t 25. $2x\left(\dfrac{x^2-4}{|x^2-4|}\right)$ 27. $3x|x|$ 33. $\frac{4}{3}(3x+2)^3(x^2-1)^{-1/3}(12x^2+2x-9)$

35. $\frac{1}{8}(t^3 - 2t + 1)^{1/2}(t^2 + t + 5)^{-2/3}(31t^4 + 29t^3 + 109t^2 - 18t - 88)$

Exercises 3.8   (Page 150)

1. $-\dfrac{x}{y}$ 3. $\dfrac{8y - 3x^2}{3y^2 - 8x}$ 5. $-\dfrac{y^2}{x^2}$ 7. $-y^{1/2}x^{-1/2}$ 9. $\dfrac{x - xy^2}{x^2y - y}$ 11. $\dfrac{3x^2 - 4y}{4x - 3y^2}$ 13. $\dfrac{y + 2x(x-y)^2}{x}$ 15. $\dfrac{y + 4\sqrt{xy}}{\sqrt{x} - x}$ 17. $\dfrac{3x^2 - y^3}{x^3 - 6xy}$

19. $-\dfrac{x^3 + 8y^3}{3x^2y - 4x^3}$ 21. $2x + y = 4$ 25. (a) $f_1(x) = 2\sqrt{x-2}$, domain: $x \ge 2$; $f_2(x) = -2\sqrt{x-2}$, domain: $x \ge 2$; (d) $f'_1(x) = (x-2)^{-1/2}$,

domain: $x > 2$; $f'_2(x) = -(x-2)^{-1/2}$, domain: $x > 2$; (e) $\dfrac{2}{y'}$; (f) $x - y - 1 = 0$; $x + y - 1 = 0$ 27. (a) $f_1(x) = \sqrt{x^2 - 9}$, domain: $|x| \ge 3$;

$f_2(x) = -\sqrt{x^2 - 9}$, domain: $|x| \ge 3$; (d) $f'_1(x) = x(x^2 - 9)^{-1/2}$, domain: $|x| > 3$; $f'_2(x) = -x(x^2 - 9)^{-1/2}$, domain: $|x| > 3$; (e) $\dfrac{x}{y'}$;

(f) $5x + 4y + 9 = 0$; $5x - 4y + 9 = 0$ 29. (a) $f_1(x) = \sqrt{8 - x^2 + 2x} + 2$, domain: $-2 \le x \le 4$; $f_2(x) = -\sqrt{8 - x^2 + 2x} + 2$, domain:

$-2 \le x \le 4$; (d) $(1-x)(8 - x^2 + 2x)^{-1/2}$, domain: $-2 < x < 4$; $(x-1)(8 - x^2 + 2x)^{-1/2}$, domain: $-2 < x < 4$; (e) $\dfrac{1-x}{y-2}$; (f) $y - 5 = 0$,

$y + 1 = 0$

Exercises 3.9   (Page 153)

1. (a) 8.6; (b) 8.3; (c) 8.1; (d) 8   3. (a) $-\frac{1}{16}, -\frac{1}{4}$; (b) $-\frac{1}{100}, -\frac{1}{10}$ 5. (a) 18,750 gal/min; (b) 17,500 gal/min   7. (a) profitable;

(b) not profitable   9. $D_I R = -\dfrac{E}{I^2}$ 11. 2.7 mi/min

Exercises 3.10   (Page 156)

1. $\dfrac{9}{5}$ ft/sec   3. $\dfrac{1}{2\pi}$ ft/min   5. $\dfrac{5}{8\pi}$ ft/min   7. $\dfrac{25}{3}$ ft/sec   9. $\dfrac{6}{25\pi}$ ft/min   11. 1800 lb/ft^2 per min   13. 14 ft/sec

15. $\frac{1}{164}(3\sqrt{97} + 97)$ ft/sec ≈ 0.65 ft/sec   17. 22 ft^3/min

Exercises 3.11   *(Page 160)*

1. $f'(x) = 5x^4 - 6x^2 + 1$; $f''(x) = 20x^3 - 12x$ 3. $g'(s) = 8s^3 - 12s^2 + 7$; $g''(s) = 24s^2 - 24s$ 5. $f'(x) = x(x^2 + 1)^{-1/2}$; $f''(x) = (x^2 + 1)^{-3/2}$ 7. $F'(x) = \frac{5}{2}x^{3/2} - 5$; $F''(x) = \frac{15}{4}x^{1/2}$ 9. $G'(x) = -2x(3 + 2x^2)^{-3/2}$; $G''(x) = (8x^2 - 6)(3 + 2x^2)^{-5/2}$
11. $D_x^3 y = 24x$ 13. $D_x^3 f(x) = 6(3 + x)(1 - x)^{-5}$ 15. $D_x^4 y = \frac{5}{8}(\frac{21}{2}x^{-1/2} + 3x^{-3/2} - \frac{3}{2}x^{-7/2})$ 19. $D_x^2 y = -3a^4 x^2 y^{-7}$ 21. $-\frac{7}{4}$; 5
23. $v = t^3 - 6t^2 + 8t$; $a = 3t^2 - 12t + 8$; $a = 0$ when $t = 0$ and $t = 4$; toward the origin: $2 < t < 4$; away from the origin: $0 < t < 2$
and $t > 4$ 25. $\frac{1}{2}$; $\frac{249}{80}$; $-\frac{11}{8}$ 27. $\frac{3}{2}$; $\frac{4}{3}\sqrt{6}$; $\frac{2}{3}\sqrt{6}$ 29. $f'(x) = 2|x|$, domain: $(-\infty, +\infty)$; $f''(x) = 2\frac{|x|}{x}$; domain: $(-\infty, 0) \cup (0, +\infty)$
31. $f'(x) = 4|x^3|$, domain: $(-\infty, +\infty)$; $f''(x) = 12x|x|$, domain: $(-\infty, +\infty)$ 33. $f'''(x) = 24|x|$ 35. $h''(x) = (f'' \circ g)(x)(g'(x))^2$
$+ (f' \circ g)(x)g''(x)$

Review Exercises for Chapter 3   *(Page 161)*

1. $\frac{x(2a^3 - x^3)}{(x^3 + a^3)^2}$ 3. $\frac{8x}{y(3y - 8)}$ 5. $\frac{3}{2}\left(\sqrt{x} + \frac{1}{\sqrt{x}}\right)^2\left(\frac{x - 1}{x\sqrt{x}}\right)$ 7. $\frac{1 - 2x^3}{3x^{2/3}(x^3 + 1)^{4/3}}$ 9. $\frac{1}{\sqrt{x^2 - 1}(x - \sqrt{x^2 - 1})}$ 11. $\frac{x(4x^2 - 13)\sqrt{x^2 - 1}}{\sqrt{x^2 - 4}}$
13. $2x + 3[x^3 + (x^4 + x)^2]^2[3x^2 + 2(x^4 + x)(4x^3 + 1)]$ 15. (a) $t = 3$ and $t = 8$; (b) when $t = 3$, $v = -15$, and particle is moving to the
left; when $t = 8$, $v = 40$, and particle is moving to the right   17. $5x - 4y - 6 = 0$; $4x + 5y - 13 = 0$ 19. $\frac{2}{\sqrt{4x - 3}}$
21. $2(|x + 1| - |x|)\left(\frac{x + 1}{|x + 1|} - \frac{x}{|x|}\right)$ 23. (b) 0; (c) 0   25. -1 27. $(-1, 0)$ 29. (a) 32 ft/sec; (b) 256 ft; (c) 7 sec; (d) -128 ft/sec
31. $a = -\frac{1}{2}$; $b = \frac{3}{2}$ 33. $\frac{445 - 180\sqrt{2}}{\sqrt{409} - 60\sqrt{2}}$ knots ≈ 10.6 knots   35. $\frac{512}{625\pi}$in./sec   37. $-\frac{12}{5}$ units/sec   39. decreasing at a rate of
$\frac{864}{175}$ lb/ft² per min   41. $(f \circ g)'(0) = 2$ 43. $f(x) = |x|$, $g(x) = x^2$ 47. $p'(r)$

Exercises 4.1   *(Page 170)*

1. $\frac{2}{5}$ 3. 0   5. 1   7. $\frac{1}{2}$ 9. 0   11. 0   13. $+\infty$ 23. f is discontinuous at 0

Exercises 4.2   *(Page 173)*

1. $x = 5$; $y = 0$ 3. $x = -2$; $y = 0$ 5. $x = -6$, $x = 1$; $y = 0$ 7. $x = 3$, $x = -3$; $y = 4$ 9. $x = -2$, $x = 2$; $y = 0$
11. $y = -3$, $y = 3$ 13. $x = -\sqrt{2}$, $x = \sqrt{2}$ 15. $x = \frac{4}{3}$; $y = \frac{2}{3}$ 17. $y = -1$, $y = 1$ 19. $x = 3$; $y = -1$, $y = 1$ 21. $x = -3$; $y = 1$

Exercises 4.4   *(Page 180)*

1. continuous; discontinuous; discontinuous; continuous; discontinuous; continuous   3. continuous; continuous; continuous;
continuous; discontinuous   5. continuous; discontinuous; discontinuous; discontinuous; continuous   7. continuous; continuous;
continuous; continuous; discontinuous; discontinuous   9. continuous; discontinuous; discontinuous; discontinuous
11. discontinuous; continuous; continuous; continuous; discontinuous; discontinuous; discontinuous; continuous   13. $(-\infty, -2)$;
$(-2, 2)$; $(2, +\infty)$ 15. $(-\infty, -3]$; $[4, +\infty)$ 17. $(-\infty, -1)$; $(-1, 1)$; $(1, +\infty)$ 19. continuous on $(0, 1)$ and all intervals $[n, n + 1)$
where n is any integer except zero   21. $\sqrt{x^3}$; continuous at all x in $(0, +\infty)$ 23. $\frac{1}{\sqrt{x - 2}}$; continuous at all x in $(2, +\infty)$ 25. $\frac{1}{\sqrt{x - 2}}$;
continuous at all x in $(0, 4)$ and $(4, +\infty)$ 27. $\frac{\sqrt{x} + 1}{\sqrt{x} - 1}$; continuous at all x in $(0, 1)$ and $(1, +\infty)$ 29. 5   31. $c = -3$ and $k = 4$
33. no; f will be continuous on $[a, c]$ if $\lim\limits_{x \to b^-} g(x)$ exists and is equal to $h(b)$.

Exercises 4.5   *(Page 188)*

1. $-5, \frac{1}{3}$ 3. $-3, -1, 1$ 5. $0, 2$ 7. $-2, 0, 2$ 9. no critical numbers   11. abs min: $f(2) = -2$ 13. no absolute extrema
15. abs min: $f(-3) = 0$ 17. abs min: $f(5) = 1$ 19. abs min: $f(4) = 1$ 21. abs max: $f(5) = 2$ 23. abs min: $f(2) = 0$
25. abs min: $f(-3) = -46$; abs max: $f(-1) = -10$ 27. abs min: $f(-2) = 0$; abs max: $f(-4) = 144$ 29. abs min: $f(2) = 0$; abs max:
$f(3) = 25$ 31. abs min: $f(-1) = -1$; abs max: $f(2) = \frac{1}{2}$ 33. abs min: $f(-1) = 0$; abs max: $f(1) = \sqrt[3]{4}$ 35. abs min: $f(-3) = -13$;
abs max: $f(3) = 7$

Exercises 4.6 (*Page 194*)

1. 2500 ft² 3. $\frac{5}{3}$ in. 5. From A to P to C, where P is 4 miles down the river from B. 7. 8 mi 9. radius $= 3\sqrt{2}$ in., height $= 6\sqrt{2}$ in. 11. (a) 3.4 units; (b) 9.4 units 13. 225 15. 400 17. (a) radius of circle $= \dfrac{5}{(\pi + 4)}$ ft and length of side of square $= \dfrac{10}{(\pi + 4)}$ ft; (b) radius of circle $= \dfrac{5}{\pi}$ ft and there is no square.

Exercises 4.7 (*Page 200*)

1. 2 3. $\frac{1}{3}(2 + \sqrt{7})$ or $\frac{1}{3}(2 - \sqrt{7})$ 5. $(-3, -\frac{1}{2})$, $c = -1 - \frac{1}{6}\sqrt{39}$; $(-3, \frac{1}{2})$, $c = -1 + \frac{1}{6}\sqrt{39}$ or $c = -1 - \frac{1}{6}\sqrt{39}$; $(-\frac{1}{2}, \frac{1}{2})$, $c = -1 + \frac{1}{6}\sqrt{39}$
7. $\frac{1}{2}$ 9. $\frac{8}{27}$ 11. $\frac{1}{2}(3 + 4\sqrt{3})$ 13. 1 15. (i), (ii), (iii) satisfied; (c) $(\frac{3}{4}, -\frac{9}{8}\sqrt[3]{6})$ 17. (b) (ii) not satisfied 19. (b) (i) not satisfied 21. (b) (ii) not satisfied 23. (b) (i), (ii), (iii) satisfied; (c) $(0, 9)$ 25. 4 27. $3 + \frac{1}{10}\sqrt{2}$ 29. $\pm\frac{1}{3}\sqrt{39}$ 31. (i) not satisfied 33. (ii) not satisfied

Review Exercises for Chapter 4 (*Page 202*)

1. 4 3. $-\frac{1}{2}$ 5. $y = 5$; $x = 2$, $x = -2$ 7. $(f \circ g)(x) = \sqrt{x - 1}$; continuous at all x in $(1, +\infty)$; continuous on the closed interval $[1, +\infty)$ 9. $(f \circ g)(x) = \operatorname{sgn}(x^2 - 1)$; continuous at all real numbers except -1 and 1 11. abs min: $f(-5) = 0$ 13. abs max: $f(0) = 9$; abs min: $f(3) = 0$ 15. abs max: $f(5) = 361$; abs min: $f(\sqrt{6}) = 0$ 17. 6 and 6 19. length $= \frac{100}{3}$ in.; width $=$ depth $= \frac{50}{3}$ in. 25. $y = 2$, $y = -2$; $x = 7$, $x = -1$ 27. 12 mi from point on bank nearest A 29. (a) $f(x) = \operatorname{sgn} x$;

(b) $f(x) = \begin{cases} x & \text{if } x < 0 \\ \frac{1}{2} & \text{if } 0 \le x \le 1 \\ x & \text{if } 1 < x \end{cases}$; (c) $f(x) = \begin{cases} x & \text{if } x \le 1 \\ x + 1 & \text{if } 1 < x \end{cases}$

Exercises 5.1 (*Page 210*)

1. (a) and (b) $f(2) = -5$, rel min; (c) $[2, +\infty)$; (d) $(-\infty, 2]$ 3. (a) and (b) no relative extrema; (c) $(-\infty, +\infty)$; (d) nowhere 5. (a) and (b) $f(2) = -50$, rel min; $f(-2) = 46$, rel max; (c) $(-\infty, -2]$, $[2, +\infty)$; (d) $[-2, 2]$ 7. (a) and (b) no relative extrema; (c) $(0, +\infty)$; (d) nowhere 9. (a) and (b) $f(2) = 4$, rel max; (c) $(-\infty, 2]$; (d) $[2, 3]$ 11. (a) and (b) $f(\frac{1}{5}) = \frac{3456}{3125}$, rel max; $f(1) = 0$, rel min; (c) $(-\infty, \frac{1}{5}]$, $[1, +\infty)$; (d) $[\frac{1}{5}, 1]$ 13. (a) and (b) $f(4) = 2$, rel max; (c) $(-\infty, 4]$; (d) $[4, +\infty)$ 15. (a) and (b) $f(4) = 9$, rel max; (c) $(-\infty, 4]$; (d) $[4, +\infty)$ 17. (a) and (b) $f(-2) = 5$, rel max; $f(0) = 1$, rel min; (c) $(-\infty, -2]$, $[0, +\infty)$; (d) $[-2, 0]$ 19. (a) and (b) $f(2) = -3$, rel min; (c) $[2, +\infty)$; (d) $(-\infty, 2]$ 21. (a) and (b) $f(-1) = 2$, rel max; $f(0) = 1$, rel min; $f(2) = 5$, rel max; (c) $(-\infty, -1]$, $[0, 2]$; (d) $[-1, 0]$, $[2, +\infty)$ 23. (a) and (b) $f(-9) = -8$, rel min; $f(-4) = -5$, rel min; $f(2) = -7$, rel min; $f(-7) = -4$, rel max; $f(0) = -3$, rel max; (c) $[-9, -7]$, $[-4, 0]$, $[2, +\infty)$; (d) $(-\infty, -9]$, $[-7, -4]$, $[0, 2]$ 25. (a) and (b) no relative extrema; (c) $[0, +\infty)$; (d) nowhere 27. (a) and (b) $f(-1) = 0$, rel max; $f(1) = -\sqrt[3]{4}$, rel min; (c) $(-\infty, -1]$, $[1, +\infty)$; (d) $[-1, 1]$ 29. (a) and (b) $f(4) = \frac{1}{4}\sqrt[3]{4}$, rel max; (c) $(-4, 4]$; (d) $(-\infty, -4)$, $[4, +\infty)$ 31. $a = -3$, $b = 7$ 33. $a = -2$, $b = 9$, $c = -12$, $d = 7$

Exercises 5.2 (*Page 213*)

1. $f(\frac{1}{3}) = \frac{2}{3}$, rel min 3. $f(\frac{3}{2}) = \frac{81}{4}$, rel max; $f(-1) = -11$, rel min 5. $f(4) = 0$, rel min 7. $G(3) = 0$, rel min 9. $h(-2) = -2$, rel min 11. $f(1) = 8$, rel min 13. $F(27) = 9$, rel max

Exercises 5.3 (*Page 219*)

1. $f(0) = 0$, abs min 3. no absolute extrema 5. $g(\frac{1}{4}) = \frac{3}{4}$, abs min 7. $f(0) = 0$, abs min; $f(\sqrt{2}) = \frac{1}{18}\sqrt{3}$, abs max 9. 45 yd by 60 yd 11. Depth is one-half the length of the base. 13. $\sqrt{2}$ 15. Ratio of height of rectangle to radius of semicircle is $\frac{1}{4}(4 + \pi)$. 17. If R is the radius of the cylinder, breadth $= R$; depth $= \sqrt{3}R$. 19. $30(\sqrt{10} + 1)$ ft by $44(\sqrt{10} + 1)$ ft 21. $R = r$ 23. $2\sqrt{2}$

Exercises 5.4 (*Page 226*)

1. concave downward for $x < 0$; concave upward for $x > 0$; $(0, 0)$ pt. of infl. 3. concave upward everywhere 5. concave downward for $x < -1$ and $0 < x < 1$; concave upward for $-1 < x < 0$ and $x > 1$; $(0, 0)$ pt. of infl. 7. concave upward for $x < 2$; concave downward for $x > 2$; $(2, 0)$, pt. of infl. 9. concave upward for $x < 0$; concave downward for $x > 0$; $(0, 0)$ pt. of infl. 11. $a = -1$, $b = 3$ 13. $a = 2$, $b = -6$, $c = 0$, $d = 3$ (Sketches of the graphs for Exercises 15–25 appear in Figs. EX5.4-15 through EX5.4-25.)

Figure EX5.4-15 Figure EX5.4-17 Figure EX5.4-19 Figure EX5.4-21 Figure EX5.4-23 Figure EX5.4-25

Exercises 5.5 (Page 229)

(Sketches of the graphs appear in Figs. EX5.5-1 through EX5.5-33.)

1. $f(-1) = 5$, rel max; $f(1) = -3$, rel min; $(0, 1)$, pt. of infl; f increasing on $(-\infty, -1]$ and $[1, +\infty)$; f decreasing on $[-1, 1]$; graph concave downward for $x < 0$; graph concave upward for $x > 0$. 3. $f(\frac{3}{2}) = -\frac{27}{16}$, rel min; $(0, 0)$, $(1, -1)$, pts. of infl.; f increasing on $[\frac{3}{2}, +\infty)$; f decreasing on $(-\infty, \frac{3}{2}]$; graph concave upward for $x < 0$ and $x > 1$; graph concave downward for $0 < x < 1$ 5. $f(-3) = 5$, rel max; $f(-\frac{1}{3}) = -\frac{121}{27}$, rel min; $(-\frac{5}{3}, \frac{7}{27})$, pt. of infl.; f increasing on $(-\infty, -3]$ and $[-\frac{1}{3}, +\infty)$; f decreasing on $[-3, -\frac{1}{3}]$; graph concave downward for $x < -\frac{5}{3}$; graph concave upward for $x > -\frac{5}{3}$ 7. $f(0) = 1$, rel min; $(\frac{1}{2}, \frac{23}{16})$, $(1, 2)$, pts. of infl.; f decreasing on $(-\infty, 0]$; f increasing on $[0, +\infty)$; graph concave upward for $x < \frac{1}{2}$ and $x > 1$; graph concave downward for $\frac{1}{2} < x < 1$ 9. $f(-1) = \frac{7}{12}$, rel min; $f(0) = 1$, rel max; $f(2) = -\frac{5}{3}$, rel min; pts. of infl. at $x = \frac{1}{3}(1 \pm \sqrt{7})$; f decreasing on $(-\infty, -1]$ and $[0, 2]$; f increasing on $[-1, 0]$ and $[2, +\infty)$; graph concave upward for $x < \frac{1}{3}(1 - \sqrt{7})$ and $x > \frac{1}{3}(1 + \sqrt{7})$; graph concave downward for $\frac{1}{3}(1 - \sqrt{7}) < x < \frac{1}{3}(1 + \sqrt{7})$ 11. $f(0) = 0$, rel min; no pts. of infl.; f decreasing on $(-\infty, 0]$; f increasing on $[0, +\infty)$; graph concave upward everywhere 13. no relative extrema; $(0, 0)$ pt. of infl. with horizontal tangent; f increasing on $(-\infty, +\infty)$; graph concave downward on $(-\infty, 0)$; graph concave upward on $(0, +\infty)$ 15. $f\left(\frac{4}{5}\right) = \frac{26{,}244}{3{,}125}$, rel max; $f(2) = 0$, rel min; pts. of infl. at $(-1, 0)$ and $x = \frac{1}{10}(8 \pm 3\sqrt{6})$; f increasing on $(-\infty, \frac{4}{5}]$ and $[2, +\infty)$; f decreasing on $[\frac{4}{5}, 2]$; graph concave downward for $x < -1$ and $\frac{1}{10}(8 - 3\sqrt{6}) < x < \frac{1}{10}(8 + 3\sqrt{6})$; graph concave upward for $-1 < x < \frac{1}{10}(8 - 3\sqrt{6})$ and $x > \frac{1}{10}(8 + 3\sqrt{6})$ 17. $f(-\frac{4}{3}) = \frac{256}{81}$, rel max; $f(0) = 0$, rel. min; $(-1, 2)$, pt. of infl.; f increasing on $(-\infty, -\frac{4}{3}]$ and $[0, +\infty)$; f decreasing on $[-\frac{4}{3}, 0]$; graph concave downward for $x < -1$; graph concave upward for $x > -1$ 19. $f(0) = 0$, rel min; $f(1) = 1$, rel max; f decreasing on $(-\infty, 0)$ and $[1, +\infty)$; f increasing on $(0, 1]$; graph concave downward for $x < 0$ and $x > 0$ 21. $f(-\frac{1}{4}) = -\frac{3}{8}$, rel min; $(0, 0)$, $(\frac{1}{4}, \frac{3}{4}\sqrt[3]{2})$, pts. of infl.; f decreasing on $(-\infty, -\frac{1}{4}]$; f increasing on $[-\frac{1}{4}, +\infty)$; graph concave upward for $x < 0$ and $x > \frac{1}{4}$; graph concave downward for $0 < x < \frac{1}{4}$ 23. no relative extrema; $(3, 2)$, pt. of infl.; f increasing on $(-\infty, +\infty)$; graph concave downward for $x > 3$; graph concave upward for $x < 3$ 25. no relative extrema; $(3, 2)$, pt. of infl. with horizontal tangent; f increasing on $(-\infty, +\infty)$; graph concave downward for $x < 3$; graph concave upward for $x > 3$ 27. $f(-1) = 3$, rel min; f decreasing on $(-\infty, -1]$; f increasing on $[-1, +\infty)$; graph concave upward for all x 29. $f(0) = 0$, rel min; $f(\frac{16}{5}) = \frac{512}{125}\sqrt{5}$, rel max; pt. of infl. at $x = \frac{1}{15}(48 - 8\sqrt{6})$; f decreasing on $(-\infty, 0]$ and $[\frac{16}{5}, 4]$; f increasing on $[0, \frac{16}{5}]$; graph concave upward for $x < \frac{1}{15}(48 - 8\sqrt{6})$; graph concave downward for $\frac{1}{15}(48 - 8\sqrt{6}) < x < 4$ 31. $f(-1) = 0$, rel min; $f(1) = 2$, rel max; pts. of infl. at $x = 0$ and $x = \pm\sqrt{3}$; f decreasing on $(-\infty, -1]$ and $[1, +\infty)$; f increasing on $[-1, 1]$; graph concave upward for $-\sqrt{3} < x < 0$ and $x > \sqrt{3}$; graph concave downward for $x < -\sqrt{3}$ and $0 < x < \sqrt{3}$ 33. $f(-\frac{2}{3}) = \frac{4}{9}\sqrt{6}$, rel max; f increasing on $(-\infty, -\frac{2}{3}]$; f decreasing on $[-\frac{2}{3}, 0]$; graph concave downward for $x < 0$

Figure EX5.5-1

Figure EX5.5-3

Figure EX5.5-5

Figure EX5.5-7

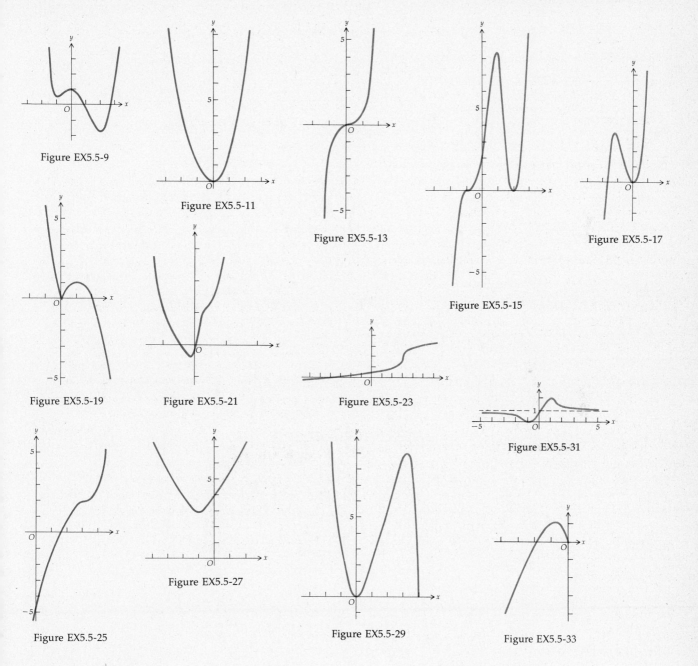

Figure EX5.5-9

Figure EX5.5-11

Figure EX5.5-13

Figure EX5.5-17

Figure EX5.5-15

Figure EX5.5-19

Figure EX5.5-21

Figure EX5.5-23

Figure EX5.5-31

Figure EX5.5-25

Figure EX5.5-27

Figure EX5.5-29

Figure EX5.5-33

Exercises 5.6   (*Page 238*)

1. (a) $30 - \dfrac{20}{x^2}$; (b) \$29.99; (c) \$29.9878   3. (a) 50 cents per gallon; (b) 25   5. (a) $Q(x) = x + 4 + \dfrac{8}{x}$; (b) $C'(x) = 2x + 4$; (c) $Q'(x) = 1 - \dfrac{8}{x^2}$;

(d) \$9.66   7. (a) $[2, +\infty)$; (b) $C'(x) = x^2 - 4x + 5$; (c) decreasing on $[0, 2]$ and increasing on $[2, +\infty)$; (d) graph concave downward for $0 < x < 2$, graph concave upward for $x > 2$, pt. of infl. at $(2, \frac{20}{3})$, infl. tangent: $3x - 3y + 14 = 0$ 9. (a) $C(x) = 3x + 400$;

(b) $Q(x) = 3 + \dfrac{400}{x}$; (c) $C'(x) = 3$; (e) 953   11. (a) $3 - \frac{3}{4}x$; (b) $3x - \frac{3}{8}x^2$; (c) $3 - \frac{3}{4}x$ 13. (a) $P(x) = \sqrt{36 - x^2}$; (b) $R(x) = 100x\sqrt{36 - x^2}$;

(c) $R'(x) = \dfrac{3600 - 200x^2}{\sqrt{36 - x^2}}$; (d) \$1800   15. (a) $S(x) = -2x^2 + 16x - 2$; (c) \$3000; (d) $R'(x) = 14 - 2x$, $C'(x) = 2x - 2$ 17. (a) $[0, 8]$;

(b) $R'(x) = 3x^2 - 32x + 64$; $C'(x) = 18 - 2x$; (c) $\frac{1}{3}(15 - \sqrt{87}) \approx 1.89$ 19. (a) 1625; (b) 67.5 cents; (c) \$328.12   21. 37.5 cents

Review Exercises for Chapter 5   (Page 240)

1. $\dfrac{\sqrt{17}}{2}$ 5. $\frac{3}{2}$ sec; velocity of horizontal particle = 1 ft/sec; velocity of vertical particle = 3 ft/sec   7. $f\left(\dfrac{8}{5}\right) = \dfrac{839,808}{3125}$, rel max;

$f(4) = 0$, rel min; pts. of infl. at $x = -2$ and $x = \frac{1}{5}(8 \pm 3\sqrt{6})$; f increasing on $(-\infty, \frac{8}{5}]$ and $[4, +\infty)$; f decreasing on $[\frac{8}{5}, 4]$; graph concave upward for $-2 < x < \frac{1}{5}(8 - 3\sqrt{6})$ and $\frac{1}{5}(8 + 3\sqrt{6}) < x < +\infty$; graph concave downward for $-\infty < x < -2$ and $\frac{1}{5}(8 - 3\sqrt{6}) < x < \frac{1}{5}(8 + 3\sqrt{6})$ 9. no relative extrema; pt. of infl. at $x = 3$; f increasing on $(-\infty, +\infty)$; graph concave upward for $3 < x < +\infty$; graph concave downward for $-\infty < x < 3$ 15. (a) increasing at a rate of \$10,400 per year; (b) increasing at a rate of \$800 per year   17. radius $= \frac{3}{2}r$ in.; altitude $= 3h$ in.   19. (a) $P(x) = \dfrac{36 - 4x}{x + 3}$; (b) $R(x) = \dfrac{3600x - 400x^2}{x + 3}$;

(c) $R'(x) = -\dfrac{400(x + 9)(x - 3)}{(x + 3)^2}$; (d) 1200   21. 1000, \$11   23. $(h^{2/3} + w^{2/3})^{3/2}$ ft

Exercises 6.1   (Page 248)

1. (a) $3x^2 \Delta x + 3x(\Delta x)^2 + (\Delta x)^3$; (b) $3x^2 \Delta x$; (c) $3x(\Delta x)^2 + (\Delta x)^3$ 3. (a) $\sqrt{x + \Delta x} - \sqrt{x}$; (b) $\dfrac{\Delta x}{2\sqrt{x}}$; (c) $-(2\sqrt{x})^{-1}(\sqrt{x} - \sqrt{x + \Delta x})^2$

5. (a) $(6x^2 + 6x) \Delta x + (6x + 3)(\Delta x)^2 + 2(\Delta x)^3$; (b) $(6x^2 + 6x) \Delta x$; (c) $(6x + 3)(\Delta x)^2 + 2(\Delta x)^3$ 7. (a) 0.0309; (b) 0.03; (c) 0.0009

9. (a) -0.875; (b) -1.5; (c) 0.625   11. (a) -0.00248; (b) -0.00250; (c) 0.00002   13. 6.125   15. 3.009   17. 0.0993   19. $\frac{76}{375}$

21. (a) 6.75 in.^{3}; (b) 0.3 in.^{2} 23. $\frac{5}{4}\pi$ ft^3 25. 10 ft^3 27. 4%

Exercises 6.2   (Page 252)

1. $6(3x - 1)(3x^2 - 2x + 1)^2\,dx$ 3. $\frac{2}{3}(7x^2 + 9x)(2x + 3)^{-2/3}\,dx$ 5. $(x - 1)^{-1/2}(x + 1)^{-3/2}\,dx$ 7. $2(x^2 + 1)^{-3/2}\,dx$ 9. $\dfrac{-9x^2}{8y}$

11. $-y^{1/2}x^{-1/2}$ 13. $\dfrac{4x^3 - 9x^2y + 4y^3}{3x^3 - 12xy^2 - 4y^3}$ 15. $\dfrac{9x^2 - 2xy + 2y^2 - 6x}{x^2 - 4xy + 3y^2 - 2y}$ 17. $18t^5 - 56t^3 + 38t$ 19. $(2t - 1)[1 - \frac{3}{2}(t^2 - t + 4)^{-1/2}]$

21. $6t^5 - 4t^3 - 2t - 9t(t^2 + 1)^{1/2} + 6t(t^2 + 1)^{-1/2}$ 23. $\dfrac{8t(16t^4 - 8t^2y + 8t^2 - 2y + 1)}{16t^4 + 8t^2 - y^2 + 1}$

Exercises 6.3   (Page 260)

1. $\frac{3}{5}x^5 + C$ 3. $\frac{1}{3}t^3 - t^2 + 3t + C$ 5. $5x - \dfrac{1}{x^2} - \dfrac{3}{x} + C$ 7. $\frac{2}{3}\sqrt{2x^3} - \sqrt{2x} + C$ 9. $\frac{2}{9}(x^3 - 1)^{3/2} + C$ 11. $\frac{1}{9}\sqrt{3s^2 + 1} + C$

13. $-\dfrac{1}{2}\left(1 + \dfrac{1}{3x}\right)^{3/2} + C$ 15. $-\frac{1}{9}x^9 + \frac{12}{7}x^7 - \frac{48}{5}x^5 + \frac{64}{3}x^3 + C$ 17. $2[\frac{1}{3}(t + 3)^{3/2} - 3(t + 3)^{1/2}] + C$ 19. $-\frac{2}{7}(3 - x)^{7/2}$

$+ \frac{12}{5}(3 - x)^{5/2} - 6(3 - x)^{3/2} + C$ 21. $\frac{2}{3}(x^3 + 3x^2 + 1)^{1/2} + C$ 23. $\frac{3}{4}(3 - y)^{4/3} - 18(3 - y)^{1/3} + C$ 25. $\frac{3}{5}(r^{1/3} + 2)^5 + C$

27. (a) $2x^4 + 4x^3 + 3x^2 + x + C$; (b) $\frac{1}{8}(2x + 1)^4 + C$ 29. g is not differentiable on $(-1, 1)$

Exercises 6.4   (Page 264)

1. $y = x^3 + x^2 - 7x + C$ 3. $3x^2y + Cy + 2 = 0$ 5. $2\sqrt{1 + y^2} = 3x^2 + C$ 7. $12y = 5x^4 + 6x^2 + C_1x + C_2$ 9. $3y = x^3 - 3x^2 - 12x + 18$

11. $x^2 = 4y^2$ 13. $y = 3x^4 + 4x^3 + 2x^2 + 2x$ 15. $y = x^2 - 3x + 2$ 17. $3y = -2x^3 + 3x^2 + 2x + 6$ 19. $12y = -x^4 + 6x^2 - 20x + 27$

21. $x^2 + 2y^2 = C$

Exercises 6.5   (Page 268)

1. $v = 2 + 5t - t^2$; $s = 2t + \frac{5}{2}t^2 - \frac{1}{3}t^3$ 3. $1600s = v^2 + 1200$ 5. $\frac{5}{4}$ sec; 20 ft/sec; $\frac{5}{8}$ sec; $\frac{25}{4}$ ft   7. 3.4 sec; 99 ft/sec

9. $v^2 = -64s + 1600$; 24 ft/sec   11. $\frac{77}{16}$ ft/sec^2 13. $\frac{11}{3}$ sec; $\frac{1210}{9}$ ft   15. $\dfrac{300\sqrt{2}}{11}$ mi/hr

Exercises 6.6   (Page 272)

1. $R(x) = 12x - \frac{3}{2}x^2$ 3. $px(x + 5) = -18x - 4x^2$ 5. x in $[0, 4]$; $R(x) = 16x - x^3$; $p = 16 - x^2$ 7. $C(x) = x^3 + 4x^2 + 4x + 6$ 9. \$325

Review Exercises for Chapter 6   (Page 272)

1. $-\frac{4}{3}x^{-1/4} + C$ 3. $\frac{5}{9}(2 + 3x^2)^{3/2} + C$ 5. $\frac{1}{420}(4x + 3)^{3/2}(30x^2 - 18x + 79) + C$ 7. $\frac{1}{2}(y^2 - 1)^{-1} = x^{-1} + C$ 9. $y + y^{-1} = -x + C$

11. (a) -0.16; (b) -0.64 13. $y = 10x - 2x^2 - 9$ 15. 0 17. $\dfrac{dx}{dt} = \left(\dfrac{4y - 24x^2}{81y^2 - 4x}\right)\left(\dfrac{3t^2 + 2tx}{3x^2 - t^2}\right)$ 19. (a) $\dfrac{(x^3 + 1)^3}{9} + C$;

(b) $\dfrac{x^9}{9} + \dfrac{x^6}{3} + \dfrac{x^3}{3} + C$ 21. $y = \frac{4}{15}(x + 4)^{5/2} + \frac{1}{3}(6 - 32\sqrt{2})x - \frac{1}{15}(75 - 128\sqrt{2})$ 23. 1 sec; 80 ft/sec   25. $25\sqrt{3}$ sec ≈ 43.3 sec

27. an error of $\frac{5}{24}$ in. allowed   29. an error of approximately $\pi^2/1610t$ sec   33. $R(x) = -\dfrac{ab}{x + b} + a$; $(p + c)x^2 + (pb + bc - a)x = 0$

Exercises 7.1   (Page 280)

1. 51   3. $\frac{73}{12}$ 5. $\frac{63}{4}$ 7. $\frac{7}{12}$ 17. 10,400   19. $10(10^n - 1)$ 21. $\frac{100}{101}$ 23. $n^4 - \frac{2}{3}n^3 - 3n^2 - \frac{4}{3}n$ 25. $3^{2n} - \frac{1}{9}(3^{-2n}) - \frac{20}{9}n - \frac{8}{9}$

Exercises 7.2   (Page 287)

1. $\frac{8}{3}$ sq units   3. 15 sq units   5. $\frac{5}{3}$ sq units   7. 9 sq units   9. $\frac{3}{5}$ sq units   11. $\frac{17}{4}$ sq units   13. $\frac{1}{2}m(b^2 - a^2)$ sq units
15. $\frac{1}{2}h(b_1 + b_2)$ sq units

Exercises 7.3   (Page 295)

1. $\frac{247}{32}$ 3. $\frac{1469}{1320}$ 5. 0.835   7. $\frac{8}{3}$ 9. $\frac{15}{4}$ 11. 66   13. 4   15. 20 sq units   17. $\frac{5}{3}$ sq units   19. $\frac{305}{6}$ sq units
21. $\displaystyle\int_0^2 x^2\, dx$ 23. $\displaystyle\int_0^1 \frac{1}{x^2}\, dx$

Exercises 7.4   (Page 305)

9. 0; 64   11. 0; 27   13. 0; 576   15. $-3; \frac{3}{2}$ 17. 0; 6

Exercises 7.5   (Page 310)

1. $c = \frac{1}{2}(1 + \sqrt{5})$ 3. $c = -4$ 5. f discontinuous at -2 7. f discontinuous at 1   9. $\frac{1}{2}\sqrt[3]{30}$ 11. $-2 + \sqrt{21}$ 13. 0
15. $32t$; 32   17. π

Exercises 7.6   (Page 319)

1. $\frac{200}{3}$ 3. $\frac{140}{3}$ 5. -8 7. $2 - \sqrt[3]{2}$ 9. $\frac{104}{5}$ 11. $\frac{29}{2}$ 13. $\frac{2}{3}\sqrt{2}$ 15. $\frac{41}{6}$ 17. $\frac{6215}{12}$ 19. $\sqrt{4 + x^6}$ 21. $\dfrac{2}{3 + x^2}$
23. $\frac{22}{3}$ sq units   25. $\frac{52}{3}$ sq units   27. $\frac{1}{3}(40\sqrt{5} - 20)$ sq units   29. $\frac{32}{3}$; $\frac{4}{3}(3 - \sqrt{3})$ 31. $\dfrac{42,304}{175}$ 35. $\$4,933\ 33$

Review Exercises for Chapter 7   (Page 320)

1. $-\frac{27}{4}$ 3. 4,100,656,560   7. $\frac{4374}{7}$ 9. $\frac{2}{3}(\sqrt{14} - \sqrt{2})$ 11. $\frac{2}{27}(20\sqrt{10} + \frac{64}{5})$ 13. $\frac{652}{15}$ 15. $\frac{313}{2}$
19. $4\sqrt{5} \leq \displaystyle\int_1^4 \sqrt{5 + 4x - x^2}\, dx \leq 9$ 21. 18 sq units   23. $\frac{224}{3}$ sq units   25. $\dfrac{22,304}{175}$ 29. $\$1196.67$

Exercises 8.1   (Page 329)

1. $\frac{32}{3}$ sq units   3. $\frac{32}{3}$ sq units   5. $\frac{1}{2}$ sq units   7. $\frac{9}{2}$ sq units   9. $\frac{8}{3}\sqrt{2}$ sq units   11. $\frac{5}{12}$ sq units   13. $\frac{27}{10}$ sq units
15. $\frac{64}{3}$ sq units   17. $\frac{253}{12}$ sq units   19. $\frac{7}{3}$ sq units   21. 12 sq units   23. $\frac{128}{5}$ sq units   25. 64 sq units   27. (a) $\frac{16}{3}p^2$ sq units;
(b) 32   29. $-\dfrac{8}{m^4}$

Exercises 8.2   (Page 335)

1. 64π cu units   3. $\frac{704}{5}\pi$ cu units   5. $\frac{384}{7}\pi$ cu units   7. $\frac{3456}{35}\pi$ cu units   9. $\frac{4}{3}\pi r^3$ cu units   11. $\frac{128}{7}\pi$ cu units
13. $\frac{1250}{3}\pi$ cu units   15. $\frac{64}{5}\pi$ cu units   17. 180π cu units   19. $\frac{16}{3}\pi$ cu units

Exercises 8.3   (Page 340)

9. $\frac{1}{2}\pi$ cu units   11. $\frac{3}{10}\pi$ cu units   13. $\frac{5}{8}\pi$ cu units   15. $\frac{49}{30}\pi$ cu units   17. $\frac{32}{15}\pi a^3$ cu units   19. $\frac{7}{2}\pi$ cu units   21. $\frac{224}{3}\pi$ cu units

Exercises 8.4   *(Page 344)*

1. $\frac{4}{3}\sqrt{3}r^3$ cu units   3. $\frac{8}{3}r^3$ cu units   5. $\frac{1}{6}abc$ cu units   7. 1944 in.^{3} 9. $\frac{2}{3}r^3$ in.^{3}

Exercises 8.5   *(Page 347)*

1. 180 in.-lb   3. 12,000 in.-lb   5. 6562.5w ft-lb   7. 256πw ft-lb   9. 100,000 ft-lb   11. 5500 ft-lb   13. 2$\sqrt{3}$ ft   15. $\frac{144}{55}w$ sec

Exercises 8.6   *(Page 350)*

1. 320w lb   3. 64w lb   5. 2.25w lb   7. $\frac{1250}{3}w$ lb   9. 96w lb   11. 11,250$\sqrt{3}w$ lb   13. 250$\sqrt{409}w$ lb

Exercises 8.7   *(Page 356)*

1. 4   3. 6   5. 171 slugs; 5.92 in. from one end   7. 25 slugs; 5.33 ft from left end   9. 16 slugs; $\frac{16}{5}$ ft from one end

11. $\dfrac{20}{L^2}x^2$ slugs/ft

Exercises 8.8   *(Page 365)*

1. $(2,\frac{1}{3})$ 5. $(0,\frac{8}{5})$ 7. $(0,\frac{12}{5})$ 9. $(\frac{16}{15},\frac{64}{21})$ 11. $(\frac{1}{2},-\frac{2}{5})$ 13. $\frac{5}{3}p$ 15. 2.25w lb   17. 100,000w ft-lb   19. $(2,0)$
23. The point on the bisecting radial line whose distance from the center of the circle is $4/3\pi$ times the radius.   25. $\frac{1}{2}r^3(\pi+\frac{4}{3})$

Exercises 8.9   *(Page 371)*

1. $(0,\frac{8}{5},0)$ 3. $(\frac{1}{2},0,0)$ 5. $(\frac{16}{5},0,0)$ 7. $(2,\frac{10}{7},0)$ 9. $(0,\frac{7}{3},0)$ 11. $(0,\frac{12}{5},0)$ 13. $(\frac{5}{16},4,0)$ 15. $(2,\frac{5}{8}p,0)$
17. on axis, $\frac{3}{4}h$ units from vertex   19. $(\frac{10}{3},0,0)$

Exercises 8.10   *(Page 378)*

1. $\frac{14}{3}$ 3. $\frac{33}{16}$ 5. $\frac{1}{27}(97^{3/2}-125)$ 7. 12   9. $\dfrac{8a^3-(a^2+3b^2)^{3/2}}{8(a^2-b^2)}$ 11. $4\sqrt{3}+\frac{4}{3}$

Review Exercises for Chapter 8   *(Page 379)*

1. $\frac{256}{15}$ sq units   3. 1024 in.^{3} 5. $\dfrac{13,600}{3}w\pi$ ft-lb   7. $\frac{7}{3}$ sq units   9. 3π cu units   11. $\frac{16}{3}\sqrt{3}$ 13. $(\frac{39}{13},\frac{29}{15})$ 15. $(\frac{8}{5},\frac{1}{2})$
17. 28 slugs; $\bar{x}=\frac{18}{7}$ 19. $\frac{25}{6}\pi$ cu units   21. 90 ft^3 23. $\frac{2752}{3}w\pi$ ft-lb   25. 400 ft-lb   27. $\frac{1}{5320}[(2251)^{3/2}-\frac{1}{8}(10999)^{3/2}]$
29. 756 lb   31. $\frac{1}{3}\pi r^2h$ cu units   33. $(0,\frac{4}{3})$

Exercises 9.1   *(Page 390)*

1. $\dfrac{8x}{1+4x^2}$ 3. $\dfrac{-x}{4-x^2}$ 5. $\dfrac{1+\ln x^2}{x\ln x}$ 7. $\dfrac{3x^2}{x^3+1}$ 9. $\frac{1}{2}(1+\sqrt{x+1})^{-1}$ 11. $\frac{1}{5}(x^7+1)^{-6/5}(8x^9-4x^7+15x^2+10)$

13. $\frac{3}{2}(3x+4)[(x+1)(x+2)]^{-3/2}$ 15. $\dfrac{x\ln(x^2-1)}{\sqrt{x^2+1}}+\dfrac{2x\sqrt{x^2+1}}{x^2-1}$ 17. $-\dfrac{xy+y}{xy+x}$ 19. $\ln|3-2x|^{-1/2}+C$ 21. $\ln|\ln x|+C$

23. $\frac{1}{3}\ln^3 3x+C$ 25. $x^2+4\ln|x^2-4|+C$ 27. $\ln 5$ 29. $\frac{1}{2}\ln\frac{7}{4}$

Exercises 9.2   *(Page 395)*

11. $2-2\ln 2=x-2y$ 13. $\ln 4$ sq units   15. 2000 $\ln 2$ lb/ft^2 17. $\ln x=-\frac{1}{2}$ 19. $\ln 16$ slugs; $\bar{x}=\dfrac{6}{\ln 16}-1$

Exercises 9.3   *(Page 404)*

1. $f^{-1}(x)=\sqrt[3]{x}$; domain: $(-\infty,+\infty)$ 3. no inverse   5. $f^{-1}(x)=\dfrac{1}{2-x}$; domain: $(-\infty,2)\cup(2,+\infty)$ 7. no inverse

9. (a) $f_1(x)=\sqrt{9-x^2}$; $f_2(x)=-\sqrt{9-x^2}$; (b) neither has an inverse; (c) $D_xy=-\dfrac{x}{y}$, $D_yx=-\dfrac{y}{x}$ 11. (a) $f(x)=\dfrac{4}{x}$; (b) $f^{-1}(x)=\dfrac{4}{x}$; domain:

$(-\infty,0)\cup(0,+\infty)$; (c) $D_xy=-\dfrac{y}{x}$, $D_yx=-\dfrac{x}{y}$ 13. (a) $f(x)=\dfrac{2x^2+1}{3x}$; (b) no inverse; (c) $D_xy=\dfrac{4x-3y}{3x}$, $D_yx=\dfrac{3x}{4x-3y}$

15. domain: $[0, +\infty)$; range: $[4, +\infty)$ 17. domain: $(-\infty, +\infty)$; range: $(0, +\infty)$ 19. domain: $(-\infty, +\infty)$; range: $(-\infty, +\infty)$

21. $f^{(-1)\prime}(x) = \dfrac{1}{\sqrt{1 - (f^{-1}(x))^4}}$ 23. $f'(x) = \begin{cases} x & \text{if } x < 1 \\ \sqrt{x} & \text{if } 1 \le x \le 81 \\ \dfrac{x^2}{729} & \text{if } x > 81 \end{cases}$

Exercises 9.4   (Page 412)

5. $-6xe^{-3x^2}$ 7. $\dfrac{2e^{2x}(x-1)}{x^3}$ 9. $\dfrac{4}{(e^x + e^{-x})^2}$ 11. $2x$ 13. $x^x(\ln x + 1)$ 15. $\dfrac{e^x(1-e^y)}{e^y(e^x-1)}$ 17. $-\dfrac{y^2 + 2ye^{2x}}{2e^{2x} + 3xy}$ 19. $-\frac{1}{5}e^{(2-5x)} + C$

21. $e^x - e^{-x} + C$ 23. $\dfrac{1}{6(1 - 2e^{3x})} + C$ 25. $e^x - 3\ln(e^x + 3) + C$ 27. e^2 29. $\frac{1}{2}(e^4 - 1)$ 33. $2y + x = 1 + \ln 2$

35. $\frac{1}{2}(e^2 - e^{-2} - 4)$ cu units ≈ 1.627 cu units   37. -9.17 lb/ft^2 per sec   39. $\dfrac{6}{10^3}$ 41. $(e^3 + \frac{1}{2})$ ft ≈ 20.586 ft
43. $\frac{1}{2}\pi w(e^{-2} - e^{-8})$ ft-lb

Exercises 9.5   (Page 419)

9. $(5\ln 3)3^{5x}$ 11. $2^{5x}3^{4x^2}(5\ln 2 + 8x \ln 3)$ 13. $\dfrac{\log_{10} \frac{e}{x}}{x^2}$ 15. $\dfrac{\log_a e}{2x\sqrt{\log_a x}}$ 17. $\dfrac{(\log_{10} e)^2}{(x+1)\log_{10}(x+1)}$ 19. $x^{\sqrt{x} - (1/2)}(1 + \frac{1}{2}\ln|x|)$

21. $x^e e^x\left(\ln|x| + \dfrac{1}{x}\right)$ 23. $4^{3x}e^{3x^2}(6x + 6\ln 2)$ 25. $\dfrac{3^{2x}}{2\ln 3} + C$ 27. $\dfrac{a^x e^x}{1 + \ln a} + C$ 29. $\dfrac{10^{x^3}}{3\ln 10} + C$ 31. $\dfrac{2^{e^x}3^{e^x}}{\ln 6} + C$

33. $(4\ln 2 + 1)x - (8\ln 2 + 4)y + 4 = 0$ 35. (a) 61 sales per day; (b) 2.26 sales per day   37. 2.999

Exercises 9.6   (Page 426)

1. $8000\sqrt{2} \approx 11,300$ 3. 43.9 g   5. 68.4 years   7. 69.9   9. 102 sec; (b) 42.1°   11. (a) 96%; (b) 66%   13. 118.7
15. 15.9 years   17. 15,000 years

Review Exercises for Chapter 9   (Page 427)

1. $\dfrac{4\ln x^2}{x}$ 3. $\dfrac{\log_{10} e}{\sqrt{\log_{10}\frac{1+x}{1-x}}\,(1-x^2)}$ 5. 0   7. $(x)^{x^{(e^x)} + e^x}\left[\dfrac{1}{x} + e^x \ln^2|x| + \dfrac{1}{x}e^x \ln|x|\right]$ 9. $\frac{3}{2}\ln(1 + e^{2x}) + C$

11. $\dfrac{1}{3}\left(e^{3x} + \dfrac{a^{3x}}{\ln a}\right) + C$ 13. $\dfrac{2}{3\ln 2}(3 \cdot 2^x + 4)^{1/2} + C$ 15. $\frac{1}{3}(e^8 - 1)$ 17. $\frac{3}{4}\ln 4$ 19. $-\dfrac{ye^x + e^y + 1}{e^x + xe^y + 1}$ 21. ln 5 slugs;

$\dfrac{4 - \ln 5}{\ln 5}$ ft from one end   23. $v = e^t - e^{-t} + 1$; $s = e^t + e^{-t} + t$ 25. $\frac{1}{2}\pi(1 - e^{-2b})$; $\frac{1}{2}\pi$ 27. 8212 years   29. $g(x) = -e^x$; domain:

$(-\infty, +\infty)$ 31. $f^{-1}(x) = \sqrt[3]{\dfrac{x+2}{8x}}$; domain: $(-\infty, 0) \cup (0, +\infty)$ 35. $3000\ln\frac{3}{2}$ in.-lb   37. 8.66 years   39. $\operatorname{sgn} t \,(1 - e^{-|t|})$

Exercises 10.1   (Page 437)

7. $\sin 3t = 3\sin t - 4\sin^3 t$ 9. (a) $\frac{1}{2}\sqrt{2 - \sqrt{3}}$; (b) $\frac{1}{2}\sqrt{2 + \sqrt{3}}$ 11. (a) $\frac{1}{2}\sqrt{2 + \sqrt{3}}$; (b) $\frac{1}{2}\sqrt{2 - \sqrt{3}}$ 13. (a) $-\cos t$; (b) $-\cos(\frac{1}{2}\pi - t)$;
(c) $-\cos t$; (d) $\cos(\frac{1}{2}\pi - t)$ 15. (a) $\cos(\frac{1}{2}\pi - t)$; (b) $-\cos t$; (c) $-\cos(\frac{1}{2}\pi - t)$; (d) $-\cos t$ 17. (a) $t = (2n + \frac{1}{2})\pi$, where n is any
integer; (b) $t = 2n\pi$, where n is any integer   19. (a) $t = (2n + \frac{1}{6})\pi$ or $(2n + \frac{5}{6})\pi$, where n is any integer; (b) $t = (2n \pm \frac{1}{3})\pi$, where n is
any integer

Exercises 10.2   (Page 446)

1. 4   3. $\frac{9}{7}$ 5. $\frac{1}{2}$ 7. 12   9. $6\cos 2x$ 11. $3\cos 6x$ 13. $-\dfrac{\sin\sqrt{t}}{\sqrt{t}}$ 15. $5\dfrac{\cos 5x}{\sin 5x}$ 17. $\dfrac{1 + 2\cos x}{(2 + \cos x)^2}$ 19. $3\cos x \cos 2x$

21. $(\sin x^2)^{4x}\left(4\ln|\sin x^2| + 8x^2\dfrac{\cos x^2}{\sin x^2}\right)$ 23. $(\cos x)^{\sin x}\left(-\dfrac{\sin^2 x}{\cos x} + \cos x \ln|\cos x|\right)$ 25. $\dfrac{\cos^4 x + 2\sin^2 x \cos^2 x + 2\sin^2 x + 1}{\cos^4 x\sqrt{1 + \cos^2 x}}$

27. $\dfrac{\sin(x - y)}{\sin(x - y) - 1}$ 35. decreasing at the rate of $\frac{1}{48}$ rad/sec   37. $1/\sqrt{1 + k^2}$

Exercises 10.3 (*Page 451*)

1. $2 \sin x - 3 \cos x + C$ 3. $-e^{\cos x} + C$ 5. $\cos(\cos x) + C$ 7. $\frac{1}{3} \cos^3 x - \cos x + C$ 9. $\frac{3}{8}x - \frac{1}{4} \sin 2x + \frac{1}{32} \sin 4x + C$

11. $\frac{1}{2}x + \frac{1}{2} \sin x + C$ 13. $-\frac{1}{3} \cos^3 x + \frac{2}{5} \cos^5 x - \frac{1}{7} \cos^7 x + C$ 15. $\frac{1}{8}t - \frac{1}{96} \sin 12t + C$ 17. $\frac{1}{2} \sin^{2/3} 3x - \frac{1}{8} \sin^{8/3} 3x + C$

19. $\frac{1}{14} \sin 7x + \frac{1}{2} \sin x + C$ 21. $x - \sin x - \frac{1}{8} \sin 4x + \frac{1}{5} \sin 5x - \frac{1}{12} \sin 6x + C$ 23. 1   25. $\frac{2}{3}$ 27. $\frac{1}{8}$ 35. $\frac{4}{\pi}$ volts

37. 2 sq units   39. $\frac{5}{8}\pi^2$ cu units

Exercises 10.4 (*Page 460*)

3. $2x \sec x^2 \tan x^2$ 5. $2 \tan 2x$ 7. $-\dfrac{3 \csc^2 3r}{2\sqrt{\cot 3r}}$ 9. $2 \sec^3 x - \sec x$ 11. $-3t^2 \csc(t^3 + 1) \cot(t^3 + 1)$ 13. $4 \cot t \csc^2 t$

15. $5 \sec 5x$ 17. $3^x \sec x (\ln 3 + \tan x)$ 19. $(\sin x)^{\tan x}(\sec^2 x \ln |\sin x| + 1)$ 21. $\dfrac{1}{\sqrt{1 - \cot^2 x}} (\sec^2 x + \sin^2 x - 3 \cos^2 x)$

23. $-\csc^2(x + y)$ 25. $\sec^2 x \tan x \sin^2 y \tan y$ 31. $y = \sqrt{2}(x + 1 - \frac{1}{4}\pi)$ 33. $5\sqrt{5}$ ft

Exercises 10.5 (*Page 465*)

1. (a) $\frac{1}{2}$; (b) $\frac{10}{11}$; (c) $-\frac{7}{4}$; (d) $\frac{7}{31}$; (e) $\frac{7}{26}$ 3. $27°, 45°, 108°$ 5. $3x - y + 7 = 0$; $x + 3y - 11 = 0$ 9. $-\frac{19}{3} - \frac{1}{3}\sqrt{370}$

13. $(\frac{1}{4}(1 + 4n)\pi, \frac{1}{2}\sqrt{2})$, where n is any even integer; $(\frac{1}{4}(1 + 4n)\pi, -\frac{1}{2}\sqrt{2})$, where n is any odd integer; $109° \, 30'$

Exercises 10.6 (*Page 470*)

1. $\frac{1}{2} \ln |\sec 2x| + C$ 3. $\frac{1}{10} \ln |\csc 5x^2 - \cot 5x^2| + C$ 5. $-\frac{1}{2} \csc^2 x - \ln |\sin x| + C$ 7. $-\frac{1}{6} \cot 6x + C$ 9. $\frac{1}{7} \tan^7 x + \frac{1}{9} \tan^9 x + C$

11. $-\frac{1}{9} \cot^3 3x - \frac{1}{15} \cot^5 3x + C$ 13. $\frac{1}{3}(\tan 3x - \cot 3x) + C$ 15. $x - 2 \tan \frac{1}{2}x + \frac{2}{3} \tan^3 \frac{1}{2}x + C$ 17. $-\frac{1}{10} \cot^5 2t + \frac{1}{6} \cot^3 2t - \frac{1}{2} \cot 2t$

$- t + C$ 19. $u - 2 \tan \frac{1}{4}u + C$ 21. $-\frac{1}{3} \csc^3 x + C$ 23. $\frac{1}{8} \ln 2$ 25. $\frac{56}{15}$ 27. $\frac{1}{5}$ 31. $\ln(2 + \sqrt{3})$ 33. $\frac{1}{4}\pi$ cu units

Exercises 10.7 (*Page 477*)

1. (a) $-\frac{1}{2}\pi$; (b) π; (c) $-\frac{1}{4}\pi$; (d) $\frac{3}{4}\pi$; (e) π; (f) $-\frac{1}{2}\pi$ 3. (a) $\frac{2}{3}\sqrt{2}$; (b) $\frac{1}{4}\sqrt{2}$; (c) $2\sqrt{2}$; (d) $\frac{3}{4}\sqrt{2}$; (e) 3   5. (a) $-\frac{2}{5}\sqrt{5}$; (b) $\frac{1}{5}\sqrt{5}$; (c) $-\frac{1}{2}$; (d) $\sqrt{5}$;

(e) $-\frac{1}{2}\sqrt{5}$ 7. (a) $\sqrt{3}$; (b) $\frac{1}{7}\sqrt{21}$ 9. (a) $\frac{1}{2}\pi$; (b) $-\frac{1}{4}\pi$; (c) π; (d) $\frac{3}{4}\pi$ 11. $\frac{140}{169}$ 13. $\frac{3}{8}(1 + \sqrt{10})$ 15. $\frac{1}{39}(48 - 25\sqrt{3})$

17. $\frac{1}{15}(4\sqrt{10} + \sqrt{5})$

Exercises 10.8 (*Page 482*)

3. $\dfrac{1}{\sqrt{4 - x^2}}$ 5. $\dfrac{1}{|t| \sqrt{25t^2 - 1}}$ 7. $\dfrac{4}{4 + x^2}$ 9. $\sin^{-1} 2y + \dfrac{2y}{\sqrt{1 - 4y^2}}$ 11. $\csc^{-1} \dfrac{1}{x} + \dfrac{x}{\sqrt{1 - x^2}}$ 13. $2\sqrt{4 - x^2}$ 15. $\dfrac{|a| - t}{\sqrt{a^2 - t^2}}$

17. $-\dfrac{\cos x}{|\cos x|}$ 19. 0   21. $\cot^{-1} x$ 23. $-e^x - \dfrac{1}{\sqrt{1 - x^2}}$ 25. $\dfrac{(1 + y^2)(3x^2 + \sin y)}{1 - x \cos y(1 + y^2)}$ 27. $\frac{52}{3}\pi$ mi/min   29. 0.078 rad/sec

31. 8 ft/sec   33. $\dfrac{6}{x\sqrt{x^2 - 64}}$

Exercises 10.9 (*Page 486*)

7. $\dfrac{1}{5} \tan^{-1} \dfrac{x}{5} + C$ 9. $\dfrac{\sqrt{5}}{5} \sin^{-1} \dfrac{\sqrt{10}}{2} x + C$ 11. $\frac{1}{8} \sin^{-1}(\frac{3}{4}r^2) + C$ 13. $\dfrac{1}{\sqrt{7}} \tan^{-1} \left(\dfrac{e^x}{\sqrt{7}}\right) + C$ 15. $2 \tan^{-1} \sqrt{x} + C$

17. $\dfrac{2}{\sqrt{7}} \tan^{-1} \left(\dfrac{2x - 1}{\sqrt{7}}\right) + C$ 19. $\cos^{-1} \left(\dfrac{1 - x}{4}\right) + C$ 21. $\cos^{-1} \left(\dfrac{1 + x}{2}\right) - \sqrt{3 - 2x - x^2} + C$ 23. $\sin^{-1} \left(\dfrac{1 + x}{\sqrt{5}}\right) - \sqrt{4 - 2x - x^2} + C$

25. $\frac{1}{2}(x + 2)^2 + \frac{5}{4} \ln(2x^2 - 4x + 3) - \frac{1}{2}\sqrt{2} \tan^{-1} \sqrt{2}(x - 1) + C$ 27. $\frac{1}{4}\pi + \frac{1}{2} \ln 2$ 29. $\frac{1}{3}\pi$ 31. $\tan^{-1} e - \frac{1}{4}\pi$ 33. $\frac{1}{4}\pi$

35. $\bar{x} = \dfrac{4 \ln 2}{\pi}$ 37. $2\pi r$ 39. $s = 5 \cos 4t$; amplitude $= 5$, period $= \frac{1}{2}\pi$

Review Exercises for Chapter 10 (*Page 488*)

1. $\frac{1}{3}$ 3. 4   7. $\dfrac{\cos 4x}{(\sin 4x)^{3/4}}$ 9. $\cos \dfrac{1}{x} + \dfrac{1}{x} \sin \dfrac{1}{x}$ 11. $\dfrac{2^x \ln 2}{1 + 2^{2x}}$ 13. $\dfrac{(\tan x)^{1/x^2}(x \sec^2 x - 2 \tan x \ln |\tan x|)}{x^3 \tan x}$

15. $\dfrac{6xy - 9y^4 - x^4y^2}{3x^2 + 18xy^3 + 2x^5y}$ 17. $\frac{1}{16}x - \frac{1}{24} \sin^3 x - \frac{1}{32} \sin 2x + C$ 19. $\dfrac{2}{\sqrt{31}} \tan^{-1} \dfrac{4x + 3}{\sqrt{31}} + C$ 21. $t - \frac{1}{3} \tan \frac{3}{2}t + C$

23. $\frac{1}{4}\cos 2x - \frac{1}{16}\cos 8x + C$ 25. $\frac{856}{105}$ 27. $\frac{2}{3}\pi + \sqrt{3} - 2$ 29. $\ln(2+\sqrt{3})$ 31. $106°, 90°, 112°, 52°$ 33. $\frac{1}{10}\pi$ hr; he walks all the way   37. $\sqrt{3} - \frac{1}{6}\pi$ 39. $\frac{1}{2}\pi - 1$ 41. $v^2 = 4(5-s)(s-3); a = 4(4-s)$ 43. (a) 120 rad/hr; (b) 60 rad/hr
45. $T = 2\pi, P = 200$ 47. $\sqrt{A^2 + B^2}$

Exercises 11.2   (Page 497)

1. $x(\ln x - 1) + C$ 3. $x\tan x + \ln|\cos x| + C$ 5. $x\sin^{-1}x + \sqrt{1-x^2} + C$ 7. $\frac{1}{2}\tan^{-1}x(x^2+1) - \frac{1}{2}x + C$
9. $\frac{1}{2}e^x(\cos x + \sin x) + C$ 11. $-x^2\sqrt{1-x^2} - \frac{2}{3}(1-x^2)^{3/2} + C$ 13. $(2-x^2)\cos x + 2x\sin x + C$ 15. $\frac{1}{4}\sec^3 x\tan x$
$+\frac{3}{8}[\sec x\tan x + \ln|\sec x + \tan x|] + C$ 17. $\frac{9}{16}$ 19. $\frac{1}{4}(3e^4 + 1)$ 21. $\frac{4}{25}(e^{3\pi/4} + 1)$ 23. $\frac{4}{3}\pi - \sqrt{3}$ 25. $(e^2 + 1)$ sq units
27. $\frac{1}{2}\pi(3e^4 + 1)$ cu units   29. $2(1 - e^{-6})$ slugs; $\frac{e^6 - 7}{e^6 - 1}$ ft from one end   31. $(4 - \frac{1}{4}\pi)w$ lb   33. $\frac{1}{4}(1 - 9e^{-8})w\pi$ ft-lb   35. \$6320

Exercises 11.3   (Page 503)

1. $-\frac{(4-x^2)^{1/2}}{4x} + C$ 3. $-\frac{(9-x^2)^{1/2}}{x} - \sin^{-1}\frac{x}{3} + C$ 5. $\frac{1}{5}\ln\left|\frac{5-\sqrt{25-x^2}}{x}\right| + C$ 7. $\frac{1}{2}(\sin^{-1}u + u\sqrt{1-u^2}) + C$
9. $32\sin^{-1}(\frac{1}{4}x) - \frac{1}{4}(16-x^2)^{1/2}(8x - x^3) + C$ 11. $-\frac{1}{9}x(4x^2 - 9)^{-1/2} + C$ 13. $\ln|x + 2 + \sqrt{4x + x^2}| + C$ 15. $\frac{x+2}{9\sqrt{5-4x-x^2}} + C$
17. $\frac{\tan x}{4\sqrt{4-\tan^2 x}} + C$ 19. $\frac{128}{3} - 24\sqrt{3}$ 21. $\frac{6-2\sqrt{3}}{27}$ 23. $\frac{1}{2}\cos^{-1}\frac{1}{3} - \frac{1}{6}\pi$ 25. $\frac{625}{16}\pi$ 27. $(\ln 3 - \frac{4}{5})$ sq units
29. $\ln\frac{1}{3}(2\sqrt{5} + \sqrt{10} - \sqrt{2} - 1) + \sqrt{10} - \sqrt{2}$ 31. $\left(0, \frac{\ln\frac{5}{3} - \frac{8}{25}}{6(\frac{4}{3} - \sec^{-1}\frac{5}{3})}, 0\right)$ 33. $s = \frac{c}{k}\sin kt$ 35. $(\frac{8}{3}\pi + 3\sqrt{3})w$ lb

Exercises 11.4   (Page 511)

1. $\frac{1}{4}\ln\left|\frac{x-2}{x+2}\right| + C$ 3. $\ln|C(x-2)^2(x+2)^3|$ 5. $\frac{1}{4}\ln\left|\frac{Cx^4(2x+1)^3}{(2x-1)}\right|$ 7. $\frac{1}{9}\ln\left|\frac{x+3}{x}\right| - \frac{1}{3x} + C$ 9. $-\frac{1}{2}(x+2)^{-2} + C$
11. $\frac{3}{x+1} + \ln|x+1| - \frac{1}{2}\ln|2x+3| + C$ 13. $\frac{x^2}{2} + 2x - \frac{3}{x-1} - \ln|(x-1)(x+3)| + C$ 15. $-\ln(3x+2)^{2/3}(x-1)^2$
$-\frac{1}{3(3x+2)} - \frac{3}{x-1} + C$ 17. $4\ln\frac{4}{3} - \frac{3}{2}$ 19. $-2 + \ln\frac{27}{4}$ 21. $-4\ln 5 + 13\ln 2$ 23. $\ln\frac{7}{2} - \frac{5}{3}$ 25. $\ln 4.5$ sq units
27. $2\pi(2 + 6\ln 3 - 2\ln 2)$ cu units   29. $\left(\frac{8\ln 3 - 8}{2 - \ln 3}, \frac{2}{9(2 - \ln 3)}\right)$ 31. $\frac{31}{18}$ 33. 7.4 lb

Exercises 11.5   (Page 515)

1. $\frac{1}{2}\ln\left(\frac{Cx^2}{2x^2+1}\right)$ 3. $\frac{1}{8}\ln\left|\frac{2x-1}{2x+1}\right| - \frac{1}{4}\tan^{-1}2x + C$ 5. $\ln|x-1| + \tan^{-1}x + C$ 7. $\frac{1}{2}\left(\ln\frac{Cx^2}{x^2+x+1}\right) - \frac{1}{\sqrt{3}}\tan^{-1}\left(\frac{2x+1}{\sqrt{3}}\right)$
9. $\ln\left(\frac{Cx^2}{x^2+1}\right) - \frac{1}{2}\tan^{-1}x - \frac{1}{2}x(x^2+1)^{-1}$ 11. $\frac{5}{162}\ln|9x^2 + 3x + 1| - \frac{2}{81}\ln|3x-1| + \frac{5}{9\sqrt{35}}\tan^{-1}\left(\frac{6x+1}{\sqrt{35}}\right) + C$ 13. $\frac{1}{6}\tan^{-1}\frac{2}{3}x$
$+ x(4x^2 + 9)^{-1} + C$ 15. $\ln|1 + \tan x| + \frac{2}{\sqrt{3}}\tan^{-1}\left(\frac{2\tan x - 1}{\sqrt{3}}\right) + C$ 17. $6\ln 2$ 19. $\ln\frac{12}{5} + \frac{3}{2}\ln\frac{20}{13}$ 21. $\frac{1}{4}\pi$ 23. $\frac{3}{4}\ln 2 + \frac{5}{8}\pi$
25. $(\frac{1}{3}\ln 2 + \frac{1}{9}\sqrt{3}\pi)$ sq units   27. $\frac{4}{3}k\ln 2$ slugs   29. $\frac{3}{50}\ln\frac{(t_1+2)^2}{4(t_1^2+1)} - \frac{7}{5}(t_1+2)^{-1} - \frac{4}{25}\tan^{-1}t_1 + \frac{7}{10}$

Exercises 11.6   (Page 518)

1. $\frac{2}{3}\tan^{-1}(\frac{1}{3}\tan\frac{1}{2}x) + C$ 3. $-\ln|1 - \tan\frac{1}{2}x| + C$ 5. $\frac{1}{2}\ln|\tan\frac{1}{2}x| - \frac{1}{4}\tan^2\frac{1}{2}x + C$ 7. $2\sqrt{2}\ln\left|\frac{\sqrt{2} + \tan x}{\sqrt{2} - \tan^2 x}\right| + C$
9. $\frac{5}{3}\tan^{-1}\left(\tan\frac{1}{2}x\right) - \frac{\sqrt{5}}{3}\ln\left(\frac{\sqrt{5} + \tan\frac{1}{2}x}{\sqrt{5} - \tan\frac{1}{2}x}\right) + C$ 11. $2\tan^{-1}(2 + \tan\frac{1}{2}x) + C$ 13. $\frac{1}{4}\ln 3$ 15. $2\sqrt{3}\ln(1 + \sqrt{3})$
17. $\frac{1}{2}\sqrt{3}\ln(1 + \frac{1}{2}\sqrt{3})$

Exercises 11.7   (Page 521)

1. $\frac{2}{3}x^{3/2} - 3x + 18\sqrt{x} - 54\ln(3 + \sqrt{x}) + C$ 3. $\ln\left|\frac{\sqrt{1+4x} - 1}{\sqrt{1+4x} + 1}\right| + C$ 5. $-2\sqrt{1+x} + \sqrt{2}\ln\left|\frac{\sqrt{1+x} + \sqrt{2}}{\sqrt{1+x} - \sqrt{2}}\right| + C$

$-3(x-2)^{1/3}+3\ln|1+(x-2)^{1/3}|+C$ 9. $2\sqrt{2x}+2\sqrt{x+4}+4\sqrt{2}\ln\left|\dfrac{(2\sqrt{2}-\sqrt{x+4})(\sqrt{x}-2)}{x-4}\right|+C$

11. $3\tan^{-1}\sqrt[6]{x}+\dfrac{3\sqrt[6]{x}}{1+\sqrt[3]{x}}+C$ 13. $2\tan^{-1}(x+\sqrt{x^2+2x-1})+C$ 15. $\begin{cases}\ln\left|\dfrac{Cx}{x+2+2\sqrt{1+x+x^2}}\right| & \text{if } x>0 \\[2mm] -\ln\left|\dfrac{Cx}{x+2-2\sqrt{1+x+x^2}}\right| & \text{if } x<0\end{cases}$ 17. $4-2\ln 3$

19. $\ln\frac{11}{10}$ 21. $\frac{1}{9}(54-2\sqrt[3]{3})$

Exercises 11.8   *(Page 525)*

1. approx: 0.695; exact: $\ln 2\approx 0.693$ 3. approx: 4.250; exact: 4   5. approx: 0.880; exact: $\ln(1+\sqrt{2})\approx 0.881$ 7. approx: 1.954;

exact: 2   9. 0.248   11. 1.481   13. 3.694   15. $-0.007\le\epsilon_T\le-0.001$ 17. $-0.5\le\epsilon_T\le 0$ 19. $-\frac{1}{50}e\le\epsilon_T\le-\frac{1}{150}$

21. 0.882   23. 3.090

Exercises 11.9   *(Page 531)*

1. by Simpson's rule: $\frac{8}{3}$; exact: $\frac{8}{3}$ 3. by Simpson's rule: 0.881; exact: $\ln(1+\sqrt{2})\approx 0.881$ 5. by Simpson's rule: 0.6045; exact:

$\frac{1}{9}\pi\sqrt{3}\approx 0.6044$ 7. $\epsilon_s=0$ 9. $-\dfrac{\pi^5}{233{,}280}\le\epsilon_s\le 0$ 11. 1.677   13. 0.883   15. 1.402   17. $\pi r^2 h$ 19. $\frac{1}{3}\pi h_1(r_1{}^2+r_2{}^2+r_1 r_2)$

21. (a) -0.0962; (b) -0.0950; (c) -0.0991

Review Exercises for Chapter 11   *(Page 532)*

1. $\frac{1}{8}x-\frac{1}{128}\sin 16x+C$ 3. $-2\sqrt{4-e^x}+C$ 5. $(x+1)\tan^{-1}\sqrt{x}-\sqrt{x}+C$ 7. $\frac{1}{2}x+\frac{3}{4}\sin\frac{2}{3}x+C$ 9. $\ln|x-1|-2(x-1)^{-1}$

$-(x-1)^{-2}+C$ 11. $\frac{1}{4}\sin 2x-\frac{1}{8}\sin 4x+C$ 13. $3\ln\left|\dfrac{x^{1/3}}{1+x^{1/3}}\right|+C$ 15. $\frac{1}{3}\tan 3x-\frac{1}{3}\cot 3x+\frac{2}{3}\ln|\tan 3x|+C$

17. $2t+\ln\dfrac{t^2}{(t+2)^{10}}-\dfrac{15}{t+2}+C$ 19. $x-\tan^{-1}x+\frac{1}{2}\ln\left|\dfrac{x-1}{x+1}\right|+C$ 21. $\frac{1}{16}x-\frac{1}{192}\sin 12x-\frac{1}{144}\sin^3 6x+C$ 23. $\sin^{-1}\left(\dfrac{r+2}{\sqrt{7}}\right)+C$

25. $\frac{1}{2}x^2\sin x^2+\frac{1}{2}\cos x^2+C$ 27. $\frac{2}{17}e^{t/2}(4\sin 2t+\cos 2t)+C$ 29. $\frac{1}{4}\tan^{-1}(\frac{1}{2}\sin^2 x)+C$

31. $\begin{cases}\dfrac{1}{n}\left(-\cos nx+\dfrac{2}{3}\cos^3 nx-\dfrac{1}{5}\cos^5 nx\right)+C & \text{if } n\ne 0 \\[2mm] C & \text{if } n=0\end{cases}$ 33. $-\frac{1}{4}\csc^3 x\cot x-\frac{3}{8}\csc x\cot x+\frac{3}{8}\ln|\csc x-\cot x|+C$

35. $2\ln|y-2|-8(y-2)^{-1}-\frac{9}{2}(y-2)^{-2}+C$ 37. $-\tan^{-1}(\cos x)+C$ 39. $2\sin^{-1}\left(\dfrac{t-2}{2}\right)+\dfrac{1}{2}(t-2)(4t-t^2)^{1/2}+C$

41. $\dfrac{1}{3}\ln\left|1-\dfrac{1}{x^3}\right|+C$ 43. $\frac{1}{3}\sin^{-1}(\frac{3}{2}e^x)+C$ 45. $-\frac{1}{15}\cot^5 3x-\frac{1}{9}\cot^3 3x+C$ 47. $\frac{1}{4}x^3\sin^{-1}x+\frac{1}{8}(x^2+2)\sqrt{1-x^2}+C$

49. $\tan^{-1}(\cos x)+C$ 51. $\frac{2}{3}\sec^{-1}|2\sin 3t|+C$ 53. $-\dfrac{(x^2+a^2)^{3/2}}{3a^2x^3}+C$ 55. $\sqrt{2t}-\sqrt{1-2t}\sin^{-1}\sqrt{2t}+C$

57. $\frac{4}{3}\sqrt{2+\sqrt{x-1}}(\sqrt{x-1}-4)+C$ 59. $\dfrac{\sqrt{2}}{4}\ln\left|\dfrac{\tan x-\sqrt{2}\tan x+1}{\tan x+\sqrt{2}\tan x+1}\right|+\dfrac{\sqrt{2}}{2}\tan^{-1}(\sqrt{2}\tan x-1)+\dfrac{\sqrt{2}}{2}\tan^{-1}(\sqrt{2}\tan x+1)+C$

61. $\begin{cases}\dfrac{x^{n+1}\ln x}{n+1}-\dfrac{x^{n+1}}{(n+1)^2}+C & \text{if } n\ne -1 \\[2mm] \frac{1}{2}\ln^2 x+C & \text{if } n=-1\end{cases}$ 63. 4   65. $\frac{1}{2}+2\ln\frac{6}{5}$ 67. $\frac{16}{3}-\frac{8}{3}\sqrt{2}$ 69. $\frac{4}{9}\sqrt{3}-\frac{1}{2}\pi$ 71. $\frac{4}{3}$ 73. $\frac{1}{2}-\frac{1}{4}\ln 2$

75. $a^2(\frac{1}{2}\pi-\frac{3}{8}\sqrt{3})$ 77. $\frac{1}{2}\ln\frac{9}{2}-\frac{1}{8}\pi$ 79. 5   81. $\frac{1}{8}+\ln\frac{3}{2}$ 83. $\frac{4}{3}$ 85. $1-\frac{1}{2}\ln 3$ 87. $\frac{1}{24}\pi$ 89. $\sqrt{3}-\frac{1}{2}\ln(2+\sqrt{3})$

91. $\frac{1}{8}\ln\frac{3}{2}$ 93. $\frac{256}{15}$ 95. (a) 1.624; (b) 1.563   97. $9\sqrt{2}-3\sqrt{5}+\frac{3}{2}\ln(2\sqrt{10}+3\sqrt{5}-4\sqrt{2}-6)$ 99. $\left(\dfrac{e^2-3}{2e^2-2},0,0\right)$ 101. $3w$ lb

103. $\bar{x}=\dfrac{4}{9}\left(\dfrac{2e^3+1}{e^2+1}\right);\ \bar{y}=\dfrac{2}{27}\left(\dfrac{5e^3-2}{e^2+1}\right)$ 105. (a) $x=300\left(\dfrac{18^t-17^t}{3\cdot 18^t-2\cdot 17^t}\right)$; (b) 35.94 lb

Exercises 12.1   *(Page 541)*

17. $\dfrac{4}{5}\operatorname{sech}^2\dfrac{4x+1}{5}$ 19. $e^x(\cosh x+\sinh x)$ 21. $2\operatorname{csch} 2t$ 23. $2x\operatorname{sech} x^2$ 25. $x^{\sinh x-1}(x\cosh x\ln|x|+\sinh x)$

31. $\frac{1}{2}\ln^2\cosh x+C$ 33. $\frac{1}{224}\sinh 28x+\frac{1}{28}\sinh 14x+\frac{3}{8}x+C$ 35. $\frac{1}{3}\tanh 3x-\frac{1}{9}\tanh^3 3x+C$ 37. $2\cosh\sqrt{x}+C$

39. $\frac{1}{3}\cosh^3 2-\cosh 2+\frac{2}{3}$ 43. $a^2\sinh\dfrac{x_1}{a}$ sq units   45. $v=e^{-ct/2}[(B-\frac{1}{2}cA)\sinh t+(A-\frac{1}{2}cB)\cosh t]$;

$a = e^{-ct/2}[(A - cB + \frac{1}{4}c^2A)\sinh t + (B - cA + \frac{1}{4}c^2B)\cosh t]$; $a = K_1 s + K_2 v$, where $K_1 = 1 - \frac{1}{4}c^2$ and $K_2 = -c$

Exercises 12.2 (Page 547)

11. $\ln(\frac{1}{4} + \frac{1}{4}\sqrt{17})$ 13. $\frac{1}{2}\ln 3$ 15. $\dfrac{2x}{\sqrt{x^4 + 1}}$ 17. $\dfrac{4}{1 - 16x^2}$ 19. $-\dfrac{1}{2x + 3x^2}$ 21. $2x\left(\cosh^{-1}x^2 + \dfrac{x^2}{\sqrt{x^4 - 1}}\right)$ 23. $|\sec x|$

25. $-\csc x \cot x/|\cot x|$

Exercises 12.3 (Page 551)

1. $\sinh^{-1}\frac{1}{2}x + C = \ln\frac{1}{2}(x + \sqrt{x^2 + 4}) + C$ 3. $\frac{1}{2}\cosh^{-1}x^2 + C = \frac{1}{2}\ln(x^2 + \sqrt{x^4 - 1}) + C$

5. $\left.\begin{cases} -\frac{1}{12}\tanh^{-1}(\frac{3}{4}x) + C & \text{if } |x| < \frac{4}{3} \\ -\frac{1}{12}\coth^{-1}(\frac{3}{4}x) + C & \text{if } |x| > \frac{4}{3} \end{cases}\right\} = \dfrac{1}{24}\ln\left|\dfrac{4 - 3x}{4 + 3x}\right| + C$ 7. $\sinh^{-1}\dfrac{\sin x}{\sqrt{3}} + C = \ln(\sin x + \sqrt{4 - \cos^2 x}) + C$

9. $\left.\begin{cases} \dfrac{1}{\sqrt{6}}\tanh^{-1}\left(\dfrac{x+2}{\sqrt{6}}\right) + C & \text{if } |x + 2| < \sqrt{6} \\ \dfrac{1}{\sqrt{6}}\coth^{-1}\left(\dfrac{x+2}{\sqrt{6}}\right) + C & \text{if } |x + 2| > \sqrt{6} \end{cases}\right\} = \dfrac{1}{2\sqrt{6}}\ln\left|\dfrac{\sqrt{6} + 2 + x}{\sqrt{6} - 2 - x}\right| + C$ 11. $\ln\left(\dfrac{5 + \sqrt{21}}{3 + \sqrt{5}}\right)$ 13. $\ln 3$ 15. $\dfrac{1}{3}\ln\dfrac{7 + \sqrt{40}}{4 + \sqrt{7}}$

Review Exercises for Chapter 12 (Page 552)

5. $6\cosh^2 2x \sinh 2x$ 7. $\dfrac{\sinh u + 2\tanh w}{(1 + \operatorname{sech} u)^2}$ 9. $2w \sin h^{-1}2w + \dfrac{2w^2}{\sqrt{4w^2 + 1}}$ 11. $\ln\cosh\frac{1}{2}x^2 + C$

13. $\frac{1}{2}\cosh x \sin x - \frac{1}{2}\sinh x \cos x + C$ 15. $\tanh 1$ 19. $\frac{7}{12}$

Exercises 13.1 (Page 559)

1. (a) $(-4, \frac{5}{4}\pi)$; (b) $(4, -\frac{7}{4}\pi)$; (c) $(-4, -\frac{3}{4}\pi)$ 3. (a) $(-2, \frac{3}{2}\pi)$; (b) $(2, -\frac{3}{2}\pi)$; (c) $(-2, -\frac{1}{2}\pi)$ 5. (a) $(-\sqrt{2}, \frac{3}{4}\pi)$; (b) $(\sqrt{2}, -\frac{1}{4}\pi)$;

(c) $(-\sqrt{2}, -\frac{5}{4}\pi)$ 7. $(3, \frac{4}{3}\pi)$; $(-3, \frac{1}{3}\pi)$ 9. $(-4, -\frac{7}{6}\pi)$; $(4, -\frac{1}{6}\pi)$ 11. $(-2, \frac{3}{4}\pi)$; $(2, \frac{7}{4}\pi)$ 13. (a) $(-3, 0)$; (b) $(-1, -1)$;

(c) $(2, -2\sqrt{3})$; (d) $(0, 2)$; (e) $(-\sqrt{2}, \sqrt{2})$; (f) $(\frac{1}{2}\sqrt{3}, -\frac{1}{2})$ 15. $r = |a|$ 17. $r = \dfrac{2}{1 - \cos\theta}$ 19. $r^2 = 4\cos 2\theta$

21. $r = \dfrac{3a \sin 2\theta}{2(\sin^3\theta + \cos^3\theta)}$ 23. $(x^2 + y^2)^2 = 4xy$ 25. $(x^2 + y^2)^3 = x^2$ 27. $(x^2 + y^2)^2 = 4(x^2 - y^2)$ 29. $4x^2 - 5y^2 - 36y - 36 = 0$

Exercises 13.2 (Page 566)

41. $\theta = \frac{2}{3}\pi$, $\theta = \frac{4}{3}\pi$ 43. $\theta = \frac{1}{4}\pi$, $\theta = \frac{3}{4}\pi$ 45. -1

Exercises 13.3 (Page 570)

1. $(\frac{3}{2}, \frac{1}{6}\pi)$; $(\frac{3}{2}, \frac{5}{6}\pi)$ 3. pole; $(\sqrt{2}, \frac{1}{4}\pi)$ 5. $(\frac{1}{2}\pi, \frac{1}{6}\pi)$; $(-\frac{1}{2}\pi, -\frac{1}{6}\pi)$ 7. $(1, \frac{3}{2}\pi)$; $(1, \frac{1}{2}\pi)$; $(\frac{1}{2}, \frac{1}{3}\pi)$; $(\frac{1}{2}, \frac{2}{3}\pi)$; pole; $(0.22, 2.47)$;

$(0.22, 3.82)$ 9. pole; $(\frac{1}{2}\sqrt{2}, \frac{1}{8}(2n + 1)\pi)$, where $n = 0, 1, \dots, 7$ 11. pole; $(\sqrt{15}, \cos^{-1}\frac{1}{4})$; $(\sqrt{15}, \pi - \cos^{-1}\frac{1}{4})$

13. $(6, \frac{1}{6}\pi)$; $(6, \frac{5}{6}\pi)$; $(2, \frac{7}{6}\pi)$; $(2, \frac{11}{6}\pi)$ 15. pole; $(\frac{1}{2}\sqrt{2}, \frac{1}{6}(2n + 1)\pi)$, where $n = 0, 1, 2, 3, 4, 5$

Exercises 13.4 (Page 573)

1. $\frac{3}{4}\pi$ 3. $153° \, 26'$ 5. $38° \, 9'$ 7. $\frac{5}{8}\pi$ 9. $\frac{1}{2}\pi$ 11. $\frac{1}{3}\pi$ 13. 0 at pole; $\frac{1}{2}\pi$ at $(1, \pi)$; $\frac{1}{2}\pi$ at $(1, 0)$ 15. $0°$ at $(0, \frac{1}{2}\pi)$; $79° \, 6'$ at

$(\frac{1}{2}\sqrt{3}, \frac{1}{6}\pi)$; $79° \, 6'$ at $(-\frac{1}{2}\sqrt{3}, \frac{5}{6}\pi)$

Exercises 13.5 (Page 576)

1. $\frac{9}{4}\pi$ 3. 4π 5. 4 7. $\frac{3}{8}\pi$ 9. $\frac{11}{4}\pi - \frac{11}{2}\sin^{-1}\frac{1}{3} - 3\sqrt{2}$ 11. $\frac{19}{3}\pi - \frac{11}{2}\sqrt{3}$ 13. $\frac{9}{2}\pi - 9$ 15. $a^2(2 - \frac{1}{4}\pi)$ 17. $\frac{1}{2}(\pi + 1)$

19. 4 21. $16a^2\pi^3$

Review Exercises for Chapter 13 (Page 576)

1. $r = 9\cos\theta - 8\sin\theta$ 3. $4x^4 + 8x^2y^2 + 4y^4 + 36x^3 + 36xy^2 - 81y^2 = 0$ 9. $\theta = \frac{1}{2}\pi$ 11. $a^2(\frac{1}{3}\pi + \frac{1}{2}\sqrt{3})$ 13. $\dfrac{e^{4k\pi} - 1}{4k}$

15. $r = \dfrac{\pi^2}{\sin\theta - \pi\cos\theta}$ 17. no points of intersection   19. $\frac{1}{6}\pi, \frac{5}{6}\pi, \frac{1}{2}\pi$ 21. $16\pi - 24\sqrt{3}$; $32\pi + 24\sqrt{3}$

25. (a) $4r\sin\theta - r^2\cos^2\theta = 4$; (b) $x^2 = 4y - 4$

Exercises 14.1 (Page 582)

1. $(0, 1)$; $y = -1$; 4 3. $(-2, 0)$; $x = 2$; 8 5. $(0, -\frac{1}{4})$; $y = \frac{1}{4}$; 1 7. $(\frac{9}{8}, 0)$; $x = -\frac{9}{8}$; $\frac{9}{2}$ 9. $y^2 = 20x$ 11. $x^2 = -8y$ 13. $y^2 = 2x$
15. $y^2 = -6x$ 19. $x^2 = -y$ 21. 166 ft 23. $\frac{32}{45}$ in. 25. $y^2 - 10x - 10y + 20 = 0$ 27. $x^2 + y^2 + 10y = 0$

Exercises 14.2 (Page 587)

1. $x'^2 + y'^2 = 13$ 3. $y'^2 = 6x'$ 5. $x'^2 + 4y'^2 = 4$ 7. $y' = 2x'^3$ 9. $x'^2 + 4y'^2 = 16$ 11. $3x'^2 - 2y'^2 = 6$ 13. $(-3, \frac{1}{4})$;
$(-3, -\frac{3}{4})$; $x = -3$; $y = \frac{5}{4}$ 15. $(1, -5)$; $(-\frac{1}{2}, -5)$; $y = -5$; $x = \frac{5}{2}$ 17. $(\frac{2}{3}, 1)$; $(\frac{7}{24}, 1)$; $y = 1$; $x = \frac{25}{24}$ 19. $y^2 + 20x - 8y - 24 = 0$
21. $x^2 + 2x - 8y + 41 = 0$ 23. $x^2 - 6x - 6y - 3 = 0$; $x^2 - 6x + 6y + 21 = 0$ 25. $y^2 - 4x - 4y - 12 = 0$ 27. $y^2 - 2x - 8y + 25 = 0$;
$y^2 - 18x - 8y + 169 = 0$ 29. $\left(-\dfrac{b}{2a}, \dfrac{4ac - b^2}{4a}\right)$ 31. $x^2 - 2x + 4y + 1 = 0$; $x^2 - 2x - 16y - 79 = 0$; $x^2 - 2x - 4y - 31 = 0$; $x^2 - 2x + 16y$
$+ 49 = 0$ 33. $x'^3 - y'^2 = 0$

Exercises 14.3 (Page 591)

1. $3x^2 - 24x + 4y^2 = 0$ 3. $8x^2 - 24x - y^2 + 4y - 4 = 0$ 5. $16x^2 + 4xy + 19y^2 - 152x + 116y + 496 = 0$ 9. $e = 1$: $y = 0$; $e < 1$:
$\dfrac{x^2}{a^2} + \dfrac{y^2}{b^2} = 1$; $e > 1$: $\dfrac{x^2}{a^2} - \dfrac{y^2}{b^2} = 1$

Exercises 14.4 (Page 598)

5. (a) 1; (b) parabola; (c) $r \cos \theta = -2$ 7. (a) $\frac{1}{2}$; (b) ellipse; (c) $r \sin \theta = 5$ 9. (a) $\frac{2}{3}$; (b) ellipse; (c) $r \cos \theta = -3$ 11. (a) $\frac{6}{5}$;
(b) hyperbola; (c) $2r \sin \theta = -3$ 13. (a) $\frac{2}{7}$; (b) ellipse; (c) $r \sin \theta = -5$ 15. $r = \dfrac{8}{1 - \sin \theta}$ 17. $r = \dfrac{3}{1 + 2 \sin \theta}$
19. $\frac{16}{3}\sqrt{3}\pi$ sq units 21. (a) $r = \dfrac{40{,}000{,}000}{1 - \cos \theta}$; (b) 20,000,000 miles 23. $r^2 = \dfrac{a^2(1 - e^2)}{1 - e^2 \cos^2 \theta}$

Exercises 14.5 (Page 605)

1. vertices: $(\pm 3, 0)$; foci: $(\pm\sqrt{5}, 0)$; directrices: $x = \pm\frac{9}{5}\sqrt{5}$; $e = \frac{1}{3}\sqrt{5}$; ends of minor axis: $(0, \pm 2)$ 3. vertices: $(\pm 3, 0)$; foci: $(\pm\sqrt{3}, 0)$;
directrices: $x = \pm 3\sqrt{3}$; $e = \frac{1}{3}\sqrt{3}$; ends of minor axis: $(0, \pm\sqrt{6})$ 5. vertices: $(\pm 2, 0)$; foci: $(\pm\sqrt{13}, 0)$; directrices: $x = \pm\frac{4}{13}\sqrt{13}$;
$e = \frac{1}{2}\sqrt{13}$; $2a = 4$; $2b = 6$ 7. vertices: $(\pm\frac{1}{3}, 0)$; foci: $(\pm\frac{5}{12}, 0)$; directrices: $x = \pm\frac{4}{15}$; $e = \frac{5}{4}$; $2a = \frac{2}{3}$; $2b = \frac{1}{2}$ 9. $9x^2 - 4y^2 = 36$
11. $16x^2 + 25y^2 = 100$ 13. $32x^2 - 33y^2 - 380 = 0$ 15. $2x + 3y - 12 = 0$ 17. $7x^2 - 4y^2 = 28$ 19. $16\frac{4}{5}$ ft 21. 98π in.^{3}
23. the right branch of the hyperbola $16x^2 - 9y^2 = 14400$ 25. $\frac{4}{3}\pi ab^2$ 27. $2400w$ ft-lb

Exercises 14.6 (Page 613)

1. $e = \frac{1}{3}\sqrt{3}$; center: $(2, 3)$; foci: $(2 \pm \sqrt{3}, 3)$; directrices: $x = 2 \pm 3\sqrt{3}$ 3. $e = \frac{1}{5}\sqrt{10}$; center: $(0, \frac{1}{2})$; foci: $(0, \frac{1}{2} \pm \frac{1}{10}\sqrt{170})$; directrices:
$y = \frac{1}{2} \pm \frac{1}{4}\sqrt{170}$ 5. point-circle $(-\frac{5}{2}, 4)$ 7. $3x^2 + 4y^2 = 300$ 9. $\dfrac{(x - 4)^2}{25} + \dfrac{(y + 2)^2}{9} = 1$ 11. $\dfrac{(y - 3)^2}{64} + \dfrac{(x + 1)^2}{48} = 1$
15. $\dfrac{(x - 1)^2}{64} + \dfrac{(y + 5)^2}{39} = 1$ 17. $18\pi w$ lb

Exercises 14.7 (Page 620)

1. $e = \sqrt{3}$; center: $(-3, -1)$; foci: $(-3, -1 \pm \frac{2}{3}\sqrt{6})$; directrices: $y = -1 \pm \frac{2}{9}\sqrt{6}$; asymptotes: $\pm x + \sqrt{2}y + \sqrt{2} \pm 3 = 0$ 3. $e = \frac{1}{2}\sqrt{7}$; center:
$(-1, 4)$; foci: $(-1, -3)$, $(-1, 11)$; directrices: $y = 0$, $y = 8$; asymptotes: $\pm 2x + \sqrt{3}y \pm 2 - 4\sqrt{3} = 0$ 5. $e = \frac{1}{3}\sqrt{13}$; center: $(1, -2)$; foci:
$(1, -2 \pm \sqrt{13})$; directrices: $y = -2 \pm \frac{9}{13}\sqrt{13}$; asymptotes: $3x + 2y + 1 = 0$, $3x - 2y - 7 = 0$ 7. $25x^2 - 144y^2 = 14{,}400$
9. $\dfrac{(y + 1)^2}{144} - \dfrac{(x + 2)^2}{81} = 1$ 11. $\dfrac{(x + 3)^2}{36} - \dfrac{(y - 1)^2}{81} = 1$ 15. $\dfrac{(y - 5)^2}{4} - \dfrac{(x - 2)^2}{12} = 1$ 17. $(3, 4)$

Exercises 14.8 (Page 625)

3. $16\bar{y}^2 - 9\bar{x}^2 = 36$ 5. $\bar{x}^2 - \bar{y}^2 = 16$ 7. $9\bar{x}^2 + 4\bar{y}^2 = 36$ 9. $3\bar{x}'^2 + \bar{y}'^2 = 18$ 11. $\bar{x}'^2 + 4\bar{y}'^2 = 16$ 13. $\bar{x}'^2 - 4\bar{y}'^2 = 16$

Review Exercises for Chapter 14 (Page 625)

1. $9(x - 1)^2 + 5(y - 2)^2 = 180$ 3. $3x^2 - y^2 - 3 = 0$ 5. $49(x + \frac{5}{7})^2 + 16(y - 3)^2 = 576$ 7. $r = \dfrac{8}{1 - 3 \cos \theta}$ 9. $r = \dfrac{6}{1 - \sin \theta}$

11. (a) $e = \frac{1}{2}$; (b) ellipse; (c) $r \sin \theta = -2$ 13. (a) $e = \frac{3}{2}$; (b) hyperbola; (c) $3r \cos \theta = 4$ 15. $e = \frac{1}{2}\sqrt{3}$; center: $(-3, 8)$; foci:
$(-3, 8 \pm 2\sqrt{3})$; directrices: $y = 8 \pm \frac{8}{3}\sqrt{3}$ 17. $e = \sqrt{26}$; center: $(-1, 3)$; foci: $(-1 \pm \sqrt{26}, 3)$; directrices: $x = -1 \pm \frac{1}{26}\sqrt{26}$; asymptotes:

$5x + y + 2 = 0, 5x - y + 8 = 0$ 19. $21\bar{x}'^2 - 49\bar{y}'^2 = 72$ 21. $r = \dfrac{1}{1 - \cos \theta}$ 23. $4\sqrt{3}\pi a^2 b$ 25. $(x - 5)^2 = 8(y - 1)$ 27. 9π in.

29. 600 miles   31. $(3 \pm \frac{3}{4}\sqrt{6})$ million miles   33. the left branch of the hyperbola $16x^2 - 9y^2 = 1{,}440{,}000$

Exercises 15.1 *(Page 635)*

1. $\frac{4}{3}$ 3. $\frac{1}{2}\pi$ 5. 1   7. 2   9. $+\infty$ 11. $-\frac{1}{8}$ 13. $\ln \frac{2}{3}$ 15. $\frac{1}{6}$ 17. 1   19. $\frac{3}{5}$ 21. 2   23. -1 25. $\dfrac{Et}{L}$

Exercises 15.2 *(Page 641)*

1. 0   3. 0   5. 1   7. $\frac{1}{2}$ 9. 1   11. $\frac{1}{2}$ 13. 1   15. e^2 17. e^a 19. e^2 21. $e^{-1/3}$ 23. $\frac{1}{2}$ 25. 0   27. 1   31. 2

Exercises 15.3 *(Page 646)*

1. 1   3. $-\dfrac{1}{\ln 25}$ 5. 1   7. divergent   9. 2   11. 1   13. divergent   15. (a) divergent; (b) 0   17. (a) 0   19. $\frac{1}{2}\pi$

21. $\frac{1}{2}\pi$ 23. $n = \frac{3}{2}; \frac{3}{4}\ln \frac{7}{16}$

Exercises 15.4 *(Page 650)*

1. 2   3. divergent   5. divergent   7. divergent   9. divergent   11. divergent   13. 0   15. divergent   17. 0   19. $\frac{1}{3}\pi$

21. (a) divergent; (b) 0   23. $n > -1; \dfrac{1}{n + 1}$ 25. $n > -1; \dfrac{2}{(n + 1)^3}$

Exercises 15.5 *(Page 656)*

1. $P_3(x) = \frac{1}{2} + \frac{1}{2}\sqrt{3}(x - \frac{1}{6}\pi) - \frac{1}{4}(x - \frac{1}{6}\pi)^2 - \frac{1}{12}\sqrt{3}(x - \frac{1}{6}\pi)^3$; $R_3(x) = \frac{1}{24}\sin \xi (x - \frac{1}{6}\pi)^4$, ξ between $\frac{1}{6}\pi$ and x 3. $P_4(x) = x + \frac{1}{6}x^3$;
$R_4(x) = \frac{1}{120}\cosh \xi x^5$, ξ between 0 and x 5. $P_3(x) = x - 1 - \frac{1}{2}(x - 1)^2 + \frac{1}{3}(x - 1)^3$; $R_3(x) = -\frac{1}{4}\xi^{-4}(x - 1)^4$, ξ between 1 and x
7. $P_3(x) = -\ln 2 - \sqrt{3}(x - \frac{1}{3}\pi) - 2(x - \frac{1}{3}\pi)^2 - \frac{4}{3}\sqrt{3}(x - \frac{1}{3}\pi)^3$; $R_3(x) = -\frac{1}{12}(2 \sec^2 \xi \tan^2 \xi + \sec^4 \xi)(x - \frac{1}{3}\pi)^4$, ξ between $\frac{1}{3}\pi$ and x

9. $P_3(x) = 1 + \frac{3}{2}x + \frac{3}{8}x^2 - \frac{1}{16}x^3$; $R_3(x) = \frac{3}{128}(1 + \xi)^{-5/2}x^4$, ξ between 0 and x 11. 2.71828   13. 0.515   15. 0.1823   19. $\dfrac{55\sqrt{2}}{672}$

$|\text{error}| < \frac{1}{7680}\sqrt{2}$ 21. $x \approx \dfrac{\pi}{2(1 + m)}$

Review Exercises for Chapter 15 *(Page 657)*

1. $+\infty$ 3. $\frac{1}{3}$ 5. $+\infty$ 7. 1   9. 0   11. 1   13. e 15. divergent   17. $\frac{1}{2}$ 19. divergent   21. $\frac{1}{4}\pi$ 23. divergent

25. $P_6(x) = 1 - \frac{1}{2}x^2 + \frac{1}{24}x^4 - \frac{1}{720}x^6$; $R_6(x) = \frac{1}{5040}\sin \xi x^7$ 27. $f'(0) = \frac{1}{2}$ 29. (a) no; (b) 0   31. $|R_3(\frac{1}{2})| < \frac{1}{192} \approx 0.005$ 33. $+\infty$

35. $\frac{64}{3}$ sq units   37. \$152,500   39. (b) 0

Exercises 16.1 *(Page 666)*

5. $\frac{1}{2}$ 7. divergent   9. 0   11. 1   13. divergent   15. divergent   17. $e^{1/3}$ 19. 1

Exercises 16.2 *(Page 673)*

1. increasing   3. not monotonic   5. decreasing   7. not monotonic   9. increasing   11. decreasing

Exercises 16.3 *(Page 683)*

1. $s_n = \dfrac{n}{2n + 1}; \frac{1}{2}$ 3. $s_n = \ln \left(\dfrac{1}{n + 1}\right)$; divergent   5. $s_n = \dfrac{n(n + 2)}{(n + 1)^2}; 1$ 7. $\displaystyle\sum_{n=1}^{+\infty} \dfrac{2}{(3n - 2)(3n + 1)}; \frac{2}{3}$ 9. $\dfrac{1}{2} - \displaystyle\sum_{n=2}^{+\infty} \dfrac{1}{2^n}; 0$

13. divergent   15. 2   17. 1   19. $\dfrac{1}{e - 1}$ 21. divergent   23. $\frac{3}{2}$ 25. divergent   27. $\frac{137}{111}$ 29. $\frac{47}{101}$

Exercises 16.4 *(Page 693)*

1. convergent   3. convergent   5. divergent   7. convergent   9. divergent   11. convergent   13. divergent
15. convergent   17. convergent

Exercises 16.5 (Page 697)

1. divergent 3. convergent 5. convergent 7. convergent 9. convergent 11. divergent

Exercises 16.6 (Page 706)

1. convergent 3. convergent 5. convergent 7. convergent 9. $|R_4| < \frac{1}{5}$ 11. $|R_4| < \frac{1}{81}$ 13. 0.113 15. 0.406
17. absolutely convergent 19. absolutely convergent 21. divergent 23. absolutely convergent 25. absolutely convergent
27. divergent

Exercises 16.7 (Page 712)

1. $(-\infty, +\infty)$ 3. $[-\frac{1}{2}, \frac{1}{2}]$ 5. 0 7. $(-9, 9]$ 9. $(0, 2]$ 11. $\left(-\frac{1}{e^2}, \frac{1}{e^2}\right)$ 13. $[-1, 1]$ 15. $(-e, e)$ 17. $[4, 6]$

19. $[-1, 1]$

Exercises 16.8 (Page 721)

1. (a) $r = 1$; $[-1, 1]$; (b) $\sum_{n=1}^{+\infty} \frac{x^{n-1}}{n}$; $r = 1$; (c) $[-1, 1)$ 3. (a) $r = 1$; $[-1, 1)$; (b) $\sum_{n=1}^{+\infty} \sqrt{n} x^{n-1}$; $r = 1$; (c) $(-1, 1)$ 5. (a) $r = +\infty$; $(-\infty, +\infty)$;

(b) $\sum_{n=1}^{+\infty} (-1)^{n-1} \frac{x^{2n-2}}{(2n-2)!}$; (c) $(-\infty, +\infty)$ 7. (a) $r = 3$; $[-2, 4)$; (b) $\sum_{n=1}^{+\infty} \frac{(x-1)^{n-1}}{3^n}$; $r = 3$; (c) $(-2, 4)$ 9. $\frac{1}{2} \sum_{n=2}^{+\infty} n(n-1) x^{n-2}$

11. $\sum_{n=0}^{+\infty} (-1)^n (n+1) x^n$ 13. 0.60653 15. (a) $\sum_{n=0}^{+\infty} \frac{x^{2n+1}}{(2n+1)!}$; (b) $\sum_{n=0}^{+\infty} \frac{x^{2n}}{(2n)!}$ 17. 2 19. (a) $\sum_{n=0}^{+\infty} (-1)^n \frac{x^{n+2}}{n!}$ 21. $\sum_{n=0}^{+\infty} \frac{x^n}{n!}$

Exercises 16.9 (Page 728)

1. 0.4854 3. 0.7468 5. 0.2483 7. 1.3179 9. 0.2450 11. $\sum_{n=0}^{+\infty} \frac{x^{2n+1}}{2n+1}$ 15. $\sum_{n=0}^{+\infty} \frac{(-1)^n x^{2n+1}}{(2n+1)!}$; $+\infty$

Exercises 16.10 (Page 737)

7. $\ln 2 + \sum_{n=1}^{+\infty} (-1)^{n-1} \frac{(x-2)^n}{n2^n}$ 9. $\sum_{n=1}^{+\infty} (-1)^{n-1} \frac{(x-1)^n}{n}$; $R = 1$ 11. $2 + \frac{1}{4}(x-4) + 2 \sum_{n=2}^{+\infty} (-1)^{n-1} \frac{1 \cdot 3 \cdot 5 \cdot \ldots \cdot (2n-3)(x-4)^n}{2 \cdot 4 \cdot 6 \cdot \ldots \cdot (2n) \cdot 4^n}$;

$R = 4$ 13. $\frac{1}{2} - \frac{1}{2}\sqrt{3}(x - \frac{1}{3}\pi) - \frac{1}{4}(x - \frac{1}{3}\pi)^2 + \frac{1}{12}\sqrt{3}(x - \frac{1}{3}\pi)^3 + \frac{1}{48}(x - \frac{1}{3}\pi)^4 - \cdots$; $R = +\infty$ 15. $\frac{1}{2} \sum_{n=1}^{+\infty} \frac{(-1)^{n-1}(2x)^{2n}}{(2n)!}$

17. (a) $x + \frac{1}{3}x^3 + \frac{2}{15}x^5$; (b) $1 + x^2 + \frac{2}{3}x^4$; (c) $\frac{1}{2}x^2 + \frac{1}{12}x^4 + \frac{1}{45}x^6$ 19. 0.5299 21. 1.97435 23. -0.2231 25. 0.0415 27. 0.0048
29. 0.2398 31. $a_4 = 3$; $a_3 = -5$; $a_2 = 2$; $a_1 = -1$; $a_0 = 6$

Exercises 16.11 (Page 742)

1. $1 + \sum_{n=1}^{+\infty} \frac{(-1)^n(-1) \cdot 1 \cdot 3 \cdot \ldots \cdot (2n-3)}{2^n n!} x^n$; 1 3. $\sum_{n=0}^{+\infty} \frac{(-1)^n x^{2n}}{2^{2n+2}}$; 2 5. $1 + \sum_{n=1}^{+\infty} \frac{(-1)^n \cdot 1 \cdot 3 \cdot 5 \cdot \ldots \cdot (2n-1)}{2^n n!} x^{n+2}$; 1

7. $x + \sum_{n=1}^{+\infty} \frac{(-1)^n \cdot 1 \cdot 3 \cdot 5 \cdot \ldots \cdot (2n-1)}{2^n n!(2n+1)} x^{2n+1}$ 9. 4.8989 11. 5.010 13. 0.3361 15. 0.5082

Review Exercises for Chapter 16 (Page 742)

1. 1, $\frac{3}{2}$, $\frac{9}{5}$, 2; 3 3. 0, $\frac{1}{3}$, $\frac{4}{5}$, $\frac{15}{17}$; 1 5. 1, 3, 1, 3; no limit 7. convergent; 3 9. divergent 11. convergent; $4 + 2\sqrt{3}$
13. convergent; $\frac{1}{6}$ 15. convergent 17. divergent 19. convergent 21. divergent 23. convergent 25. divergent
27. absolutely convergent 29. conditionally convergent 31. divergent 33. absolutely convergent 35. $[-1, 1)$
37. $[-3, 3]$ 39. $x = 3$ 41. $(-7, 5)$ 43. 0.1973 45. 5.0658 47. 0.9986 49. 0.0124 51. $\sum_{n=0}^{+\infty} \frac{(\ln a)^n}{n!} x^n$; $(-\infty, +\infty)$

53. $\frac{3}{4} \sum_{n=1}^{+\infty} (-1)^{n-1} \frac{(3^{2n}-1)}{(2n+1)!} x^{2n+1}$; $(-\infty, +\infty)$ 55. $\sum_{n=1}^{+\infty} (-1)^n \frac{(3x+\pi)^{2n-1}}{(2n-1)!}$

Index

44. $\int \dfrac{u^2\,du}{\sqrt{a^2-u^2}} = -\dfrac{u}{2}\sqrt{a^2-u^2} + \dfrac{a^2}{2}\sin^{-1}\dfrac{u}{a} + C$

45. $\int \dfrac{du}{u\sqrt{a^2-u^2}} = -\dfrac{1}{a}\ln\left|\dfrac{a+\sqrt{a^2-u^2}}{u}\right| + C$

$\qquad = -\dfrac{1}{a}\cosh^{-1}\dfrac{a}{u} + C$

46. $\int \dfrac{du}{u^2\sqrt{a^2-u^2}} = -\dfrac{\sqrt{a^2-u^2}}{a^2 u} + C$

47. $\int (a^2-u^2)^{3/2}\,du = -\dfrac{u}{8}(2u^2-5a^2)\sqrt{a^2-u^2} + \dfrac{3a^4}{8}\sin^{-1}\dfrac{u}{a} + C$

48. $\int \dfrac{du}{(a^2-u^2)^{3/2}} = \dfrac{u}{a^2\sqrt{a^2-u^2}} + C$

Forms Containing $2au-u^2$

49. $\int \sqrt{2au-u^2}\,du = \dfrac{u-a}{2}\sqrt{2au-u^2} + \dfrac{a^2}{2}\cos^{-1}\left(1-\dfrac{u}{a}\right) + C$

50. $\int u\sqrt{2au-u^2}\,du = \dfrac{2u^2-au-3a^2}{6}\sqrt{2au-u^2}$

$\qquad\qquad + \dfrac{a^3}{2}\cos^{-1}\left(1-\dfrac{u}{a}\right) + C$

51. $\int \dfrac{\sqrt{2au-u^2}\,du}{u} = \sqrt{2au-u^2} + a\cos^{-1}\left(1-\dfrac{u}{a}\right) + C$

52. $\int \dfrac{\sqrt{2au-u^2}\,du}{u^2} = -\dfrac{2\sqrt{2au-u^2}}{u} - \cos^{-1}\left(1-\dfrac{u}{a}\right) + C$

53. $\int \dfrac{du}{\sqrt{2au-u^2}} = \cos^{-1}\left(1-\dfrac{u}{a}\right) + C$

54. $\int \dfrac{u\,du}{\sqrt{2au-u^2}} = -\sqrt{2au-u^2} + a\cos^{-1}\left(1-\dfrac{u}{a}\right) + C$

55. $\int \dfrac{u^2\,du}{\sqrt{2au-u^2}} = -\dfrac{(u+3a)}{2}\sqrt{2au-u^2} + \dfrac{3a^2}{2}\cos^{-1}\left(1-\dfrac{u}{a}\right) + C$

56. $\int \dfrac{du}{u\sqrt{2au-u^2}} = -\dfrac{\sqrt{2au-u^2}}{au} + C$

57. $\int \dfrac{du}{(2au-u^2)^{3/2}} = \dfrac{u-a}{a^2\sqrt{2au-u^2}} + C$

58. $\int \dfrac{u\,du}{(2au-u^2)^{3/2}} = \dfrac{u}{a\sqrt{2au-u^2}} + C$

Forms Containing Trigonometric Functions

59. $\int \sin u\,du = -\cos u + C$

60. $\int \cos u\,du = \sin u + C$

61. $\int \tan u\,du = \ln|\sec u| + C$

62. $\int \cot u\,du = \ln|\sin u| + C$

63. $\int \sec u\,du = \ln|\sec u + \tan u| + C$

$\qquad = \ln|\tan(\tfrac{1}{4}\pi + \tfrac{1}{2}u)| + C$

64. $\int \csc u\,du = \ln|\csc u - \cot u| + C$

$\qquad = \ln|\tan \tfrac{1}{2}u| + C$

65. $\int \sec^2 u\,du = \tan u + C$

66. $\int \csc^2 u\,du = -\cot u + C$

67. $\int \sec u \tan u\,du = \sec u + C$

68. $\int \csc u \cot u\,du = -\csc u + C$

69. $\int \sin^2 u\,du = \tfrac{1}{2}u - \tfrac{1}{4}\sin 2u + C$

70. $\int \cos^2 u\,du = \tfrac{1}{2}u + \tfrac{1}{4}\sin 2u + C$

71. $\int \tan^2 u\,du = \tan u - u + C$

72. $\int \cot^2 u\,du = -\cot u - u + C$

73. $\int \sin^n u\,du = -\dfrac{1}{n}\sin^{n-1} u \cos u + \dfrac{n-1}{n}\int \sin^{n-2} u\,du$

74. $\int \cos^n u\,du = \dfrac{1}{n}\cos^{n-1} u \sin u + \dfrac{n-1}{n}\int \cos^{n-2} u\,du$

75. $\int \tan^n u\,du = \dfrac{1}{n-1}\tan^{n-1} u - \int \tan^{n-2} u\,du$

76. $\int \cot^n u\,du = -\dfrac{1}{n-1}\cot^{n-1} u - \int \cot^{n-2} u\,du$

77. $\int \sec^n u\,du = \dfrac{1}{n-1}\sec^{n-2} u \tan u + \dfrac{n-2}{n-1}\int \sec^{n-2} u\,du$

78. $\int \csc^n u\,du = -\dfrac{1}{n-1}\csc^{n-2} u \cot u + \dfrac{n-2}{n-1}\int \csc^{n-2} u\,du$

79. $\int \sin mu \sin nu\,du = -\dfrac{\sin(m+n)u}{2(m+n)} + \dfrac{\sin(m-n)u}{2(m-n)} + C$

80. $\int \cos mu \cos nu\,du = \dfrac{\sin(m+n)u}{2(m+n)} + \dfrac{\sin(m-n)u}{2(m-n)} + C$

81. $\int \sin mu \cos nu\,du = -\dfrac{\cos(m+n)u}{2(m+n)} - \dfrac{\cos(m-n)u}{2(m-n)} + C$

82. $\int u \sin u\,du = \sin u - u \cos u + C$

83. $\int u \cos u\,du = \cos u + u \sin u + C$

84. $\int u^2 \sin u\,du = 2u \sin u + (2-u^2)\cos u + C$